NOOTAN

According to the Latest Syllabus for ICSE Class IX

AF809304

# ICSE MATHEMATICS

## Class IX

Madhur Gupta
Ex. PGT
CJ DAV Centenary School, Meerut

NP

Nageen Prakashan Pvt. Ltd.

Published by :

**Nageen Prakashan Pvt. Ltd.**

Registered Office :
310, Western Kutchery Road,
**Meerut**-250 002, U.P. (INDIA)
Ph. : +91-121-2792600

Corporate Office :
Vill. Salarpur, P.O. Rajpura
Mawana Road,
**Meerut**-250 001, U.P. (INDIA)
Ph. : +91-121-2793401

**E-mail :** info@nageenprakashan.com
nageenprakashan@yahoo.com
**Visit us :** www.nageenprakashan.in

Latest Edition

ISBN : **978-81-19514-78-6**

This edition can be exported from India only by the publisher.

Price : **₹ 600.00 (In India)**
**$ 20.00 (Outside India)**

Printed at :
**Nageen Print-Pack Pvt. Ltd.**
Vill. Salarpur, P.O. Rajpura
Mawana Road,
Meerut-250 001, U.P. (INDIA)
info@nageenprintpack.com
Ph. : +91-121-2793401, 7060405175



Disclaimer :
Every effort has been made to avoid errors or omissions in this publication. In spite of this, some errors might have crept in. Any mistake, error or discrepancy noted may be brought to our notice which shall be taken care of in the next edition. It is notified that neither the publisher nor the author(s) nor the seller will be responsible for any damage or loss of action to any one, of any kind, in any manner, therefrom.
All disputes are subject to Meerut jurisdiction only.



## What's Inside?

- **Chapter Explanation**
  Definitions, concepts and theorems in simple and lucid language
- **Illustrative Examples**
  Numerous solved examples based on the topic covered
- **Remark**
  Amazing facts related to the concept taught
- **Note**
  Important points to notice for knowledge gain
- **Conclusion**
  Simple clarification to conclude the concept
- **Topic-wise Exercises**
  Different types of exercises (with answers) to assess the learners' alertness and their learning
- **Chapter Exercise**
  MCQs, Assertion-Reason type and Valid Statement type questions as per the latest pattern
- **Summary of the Chapter**
  All concepts of the chapter in a nutshell for quick revision
- **Chapter Test**
  Various questions based on the chapter for self-evaluation

# PREFACE

I am very happy to present the latest edition of the book **"NOOTAN ICSE MATHEMATICS"** for class IX. This book is strictly prepared as per the guidelines prescribed by the "Council for the Indian School Certificate Examinations" for class IX. Every chapter of this book is enriched with the definitions, concepts and theorems followed by exercises based on these concepts.

This book covers a variety of exercises including Multiple Choice Questions (MCQs), Assertion-Reason Type Questions and Valid Statement Questions. At the end of each chapter all concepts dealt in the chapter are given under **"Summary of the Chapter"** for a quick revision. Finally, a **"Chapter Test"** is also given which gives the proper revision of the chapter.

The sweet memories of **Late Shri Nageen Chand Jain,** the founder of **Nageen Prakashan Pvt. Ltd., Meerut,** will always remain alive in my heart. His soothing voice, inspiring attitude, and friendly behaviour always gave me strength. I am thankful to Shri Mohit Jain, Managing Director, Nageen Prakashan Pvt. Ltd., Meerut, for taking great pains in bringing out the revised edition of the book in attractive getup in a very short span of time. I am also thankful to DTP Department of the Press Unit.

The efforts of the author and the publisher will be fruitful only if this book benefits students and teachers for whom it is primarily meant.

We welcome all the suggestions for further improvement of the book. All suggestions will be acknowledged and taken care of in the next edition.

**Madhur Gupta**
Ex. PGT
CJ DAV Centenary School, Meerut

# Latest ICSE Syllabus

## MATHEMATICS (51)

### Aims

1. To acquire knowledge and understanding of the terms, symbols, concepts, principles, processes, proofs, etc., of mathematics.
2. To develop an understanding of mathematical concepts and their application to further studies in mathematics and science.
3. To develop skills to apply mathematical knowledge to solve real life problems.
4. To develop the necessary skills to work with modern technological devices such as calculators and computers in real life situations.
5. To develop drawing skills, skills of reading tables, charts and graphs.
6. To develop an interest in mathematics.

## CLASS IX

*There will be* ***one*** *paper of* ***three*** *hours duration carrying 80 marks and Internal Assessment of 20 marks.*

*Certain questions may require the use of Mathematical tables (Logarithmic and Trigonometric tables).*

*The solution of a question may require the knowledge of more than one branch of the syllabus.*

### 1. Pure Arithmetic

Rational and Irrational Numbers

*Rational, irrational numbers as real numbers, their place in the number system. Surds and rationalization of surds. Simplifying an expression by rationalizing the denominator. Representation of rational and irrational numbers on the number line.*

Proofs of irrationality of $\sqrt{2}, \sqrt{3}, \sqrt{5}$

### 2. Commercial Mathematics

Compound Interest

(a) *Compound interest as a repeated Simple Interest computation with a growing Principal. Use of this in computing Amount over a period of 2 or 3 years.*

(b) *Use of formula* $A = P\left(1 + \frac{r}{100}\right)^n$. *Finding CI from the relation* $CI = A - P$.

- *Interest compounded half-yearly included.*
- *Using the formula to find one quantity given different combinations of A, P, r, n, CI and SI; difference between CI and SI* type included. Rate of growth and depreciation.

**Note:** Paying back in equal installments, being given rate of interest and installment amount, not included.

### 3. Algebra

(i) Expansions

*Recall of concepts learned in earlier classes.*

$(a \pm b)^2$

$(a \pm b)^3$

$(x \pm a)(x \pm b)$

$(a \pm b \pm c)^2$

(ii) Factorisation

$a^2 - b^2$

$a^3 \pm b^3$

$ax^2 + bx + c$, *by splitting the middle term.*

(iii) Simultaneous linear equations in two variables. (With numerical coefficients only)

- *Solving algebraically by:*
  - *Elimination*
  - *Substitution and*
  - *Cross Multiplication Method*
- *Solving simple problems by framing appropriate equations.*

(iv) Indices/Exponents

*Handling positive, fractional, negative and "zero" indices.*

*Simplification of expressions involving various exponents.*

$a^m \times a^n = a^{m+n}$, $a^m \div a^n = a^{m-n}$, $(a^m)^n = a^{mn}$, etc. Use of laws of exponents.

(v) Logarithms

*(a) Logarithmic form vis-à-vis exponential form : interchanging.*

*(b) Laws of Logarithms and their uses.*

*Expansion of expression with the help of laws of logarithms*

*e.g.,* $y = \frac{a^4 \times b^2}{c^3}$

$\log y = 4 \log a + 2 \log b - 3 \log c$ etc.

### 4. Geometry

(i) Triangles

(a) Congruency: four cases: SSS, SAS, AAS, and RHS. Illustration through cutouts. Simple applications.

(b) Problems based on:

- *Angles opposite equal sides are equal and converse.*
- *If two sides of a triangle are unequal, then the greater angle is opposite the greater side and converse.*
- *Sum of any two sides of a triangle is greater than the third side.*
- *Of all straight lines that can be drawn to a given line from a point outside it, the perpendicular is the shortest.*

***Proofs not required.***

(c) Mid-Point Theorem and its converse, equal intercept theorem

*(i) Proof and simple applications of mid-point theorem and its converse.*

*(ii) Equal intercept theorem: proof and simple application.*

(d) Pythagoras Theorem

*Area based proof and simple applications of Pythagoras Theorem and its converse.*

(ii) Rectilinear Figures

(a) Proof and use of theorems on parallelogram.

- *Both pairs of opposite sides equal (without proof).*
- *Both pairs of opposite angles equal.*
- *One pair of opposite sides equal and parallel (without proof).*
- *Diagonals bisect each other and bisect the parallelogram.*
- *Rhombus as a special parallelogram whose diagonals meet at right angles.*
- *In a rectangle, diagonals are equal, in a square they are equal and meet at right angles.*

(b) Constructions of polygons

*Construction of quadrilaterals (including parallelograms and rhombus) and regular hexagon using ruler and compasses only.*

(c) Proof and use of area theorems on parallelograms:

- *Parallelograms on the same base and between the same parallels are equal in area.*
- *The area of a triangle is half that of a parallelogram on the same base and between the same parallels.*
- *Triangles between the same base and between the same parallels are equal in area (without proof).*
- *Triangles with equal areas on the same bases have equal corresponding altitudes.*

(iii) Circle:

(a) Chord properties

- *A straight line drawn from the centre of a circle to bisect a chord which is not a diameter is at right angles to the chord.*
- *The perpendicular to a chord from the centre bisects the chord (without proof).*
- *Equal chords are equidistant from the centre.*
- *Chords equidistant from the centre are equal (without proof).*
- *There is one and only one circle that passes through three given points not in a straight line.*

(b) Arc and chord properties:

- *If two arcs subtend equal angles at the centre, they are equal, and its converse.*
- *If two chords are equal, they cut off equal arcs, and its converse (without proof).*

**Note:** Proofs of the theorems given above are to be taught unless specified otherwise.

## 5. Statistics

Introduction, collection of data, presentation of data, graphical representation of data, mean, median of ungrouped data.

(i) Understanding and recognition of raw, arrayed and grouped data.

(ii) Tabulation of raw data using tally-marks.

(iii) Understanding and recognition of discrete and continuous variables.

(iv) Mean, median of ungrouped data.

(v) Class intervals, class boundaries and limits, frequency, frequency table, class size for grouped data.

(vi) Grouped frequency distributions: the need to and how to convert discontinuous intervals to continuous intervals.

(vii) Drawing a frequency polygon.

## 6. Mensuration

Area and perimeter of a triangle and a quadrilateral. Area and circumference of circle. Surface area and volume of cube and cuboids.

*(a) Area and perimeter of triangle (including Heron's formula), all types of quadrilaterals.*

*(b) Circle: Area and circumference. Direct application problems including inner and outer area.*

*Areas of sectors of circles other than quarter-circle and semicircle are not included.*

*(c) Surface area and volume of 3-D solids: Cube and cuboid including problems of type involving:*

- *Different internal and external dimensions of the solid.*
- *Cost.*
- *Concept of volume being equal to area of cross-section x height.*
- *Open/closed cubes/cuboids.*

## 7. Trigonometry

*(a) Trigonometric Ratios: sine, cosine, tangent of an angle and their reciprocals.*

*(b) Trigonometric ratios of standard angles—0, 30, 45, 60, 90 degrees. Evaluation of an expression involving these ratios.*

*(c) Simple 2-D problems involving one right-angled triangle.*

*(d) Concept of trigonometric ratios of complementary angles and their direct application:*

- $\sin A = \cos (90 - A)$, $\cos A = \sin (90 - A)$
- $\tan A = \cot (90 - A)$, $\cot A = \tan (90 - A)$
- $\sec A = \operatorname{cosec} (90 - A)$, $\operatorname{cosec} A = \sec (90 - A)$

## 8. Coordinate Geometry

Cartesian system, plotting of points in the plane for given coordinates, solving simultaneous linear equations in 2 variables graphically and finding the distance between two points using distance formula.

(a) Dependent and independent variables.

(b) Ordered pairs, coordinates of points and plotting them in the Cartesian plane.

(c) Solution of simultaneous linear equations graphically.

(d) Distance formula.

# INTERNAL ASSESSMENT

A minimum of two assignments are to be done during the year as prescribed by the teacher.

**Suggested Assignments**

- Conduct a survey of a group of students and represent it graphically—height, weight, number of family members, pocket money, etc.
- Planning delivery routes for a postman/milkman.
- Running a tuck shop/canteen.
- Study ways of raising a loan to buy a car or house, *e.g.*, bank loan or purchase a refrigerator or a television set through hire purchase.
- Cutting a circle into equal sections of a small central angle to find the area of a circle by using the formula $A = \pi r^2$.
- To use flat cutouts to form cube, cuboids and pyramids to obtain formulae for volume and total surface area.
- Draw a circle of radius $r$ on a 1/2 cm graph paper, and then on a 2 mm graph paper. Estimate the area enclosed in each case by actually counting the squares. Now try out with circles of different radii. Establish the pattern, if any, between the two observed values and the theoretical value (area $= \pi r^2$). Any modifications?

# CONTENTS

UNIT I : PURE ARITHMETIC

Chapter 1

# RATIONAL AND IRRATIONAL NUMBERS

## Syllabus

- Rational, irrational numbers as real numbers, their place in the number system. Surds and rationalization of surds. Simplifying an expression by rationalizing the denominator. Representation of rational and irrational numbers on the number line.
- Proofs of irrationality of $\sqrt{2}, \sqrt{3}, \sqrt{5}$.

## INTRODUCTION

We have studied about natural numbers, whole numbers, integers, etc. We are also familiar with the operations—addition, subtraction, multiplication and division on these numbers and the representation of these numbers on the number line. Now, we shall study about the rational and irrational numbers, their decimal expansions, terminating and non-terminating decimal expansions, surds and problems containing surds.

## Rational Numbers

A number which can be written in the form of $\frac{a}{b}$, where $a$ and $b$ are integers and $b \neq 0$, is called a rational number. The set of rational numbers is represented by $Q$.

$$Q = \left\{\frac{a}{b} : a, b \in Z \text{ and } b \neq 0\right\}$$

*For example :* (i) $\frac{2}{5}, \frac{1}{3}, \frac{-3}{7}$, etc.

(ii) 7 is also a rational number since 7 can be written as $\frac{7}{1}$ which is of the form $\frac{a}{b}$ and $b = 1 \neq 0$.

(iii) 0 is also a rational number since 0 can be written as $\frac{0}{5}$ which is of the form $\frac{a}{b}$ and $b = 5 \neq 0$.

## Simplest Form of a Rational Number

A rational number $\frac{a}{b}$ is called in the simplest form if $a$ and $b$ have no common factor except 1.

*For example :*

(i) $\frac{3}{5}$ is the rational number in the simplest form as 3 and 5 have no common factor except 1.

(ii) $\frac{6}{9}$ is the rational number but it is not in the simplest form as 6 and 9 have a common factor 3.

$$\therefore \quad \frac{6}{9} = \frac{3 \times 2}{3 \times 3} = \frac{2}{3}$$

Thus, $\frac{2}{3}$ is its simplest form.

**Remark**

Here, $\frac{2}{3}$ and $\frac{6}{9}$ are called **equivalent rational numbers.**

- Simplest form of a rational number is also called the lowest form or irreducible form of the rational number.

## Properties of Rational Numbers

1. The sum of two rational numbers is also a rational number. If $p$ and $q$ are two rational numbers, then the sum $(p + q)$ is also a rational number.

   *For example :* Consider two rational numbers $\frac{1}{3}$ and $\frac{2}{7}$.

   Now, their sum $= \frac{1}{3} + \frac{2}{7} = \frac{7+6}{21} = \frac{13}{21}$

   which is a rational number.

2. The difference of two rational numbers is also a rational number. If $p$ and $q$ are two rational numbers, then the difference $(p - q)$ is also a rational number.

   *For example :* Consider two rational numbers $\frac{1}{2}$ and $\frac{5}{7}$.

Now, their difference $= \frac{1}{2} - \frac{5}{7} = \frac{7-10}{14} = \frac{-3}{14}$

which is a rational number.

3. The multiplication of two rational numbers is also a rational number. If $p$ and $q$ are two rational numbers, then the multiplication $(p \times q)$ is also a rational number.

   *For example :* Consider two rational numbers $\frac{1}{5}$ and $\frac{3}{11}$,

   Now, their multiplication $= \frac{1}{5} \times \frac{3}{11} = \frac{3}{55}$

   which is a rational number.

4. The division of a rational number by a non-zero rational number is also a rational number. If $p$ and $q$ are two rational numbers and $q \neq 0$ then the division $(p \div q)$ is also a rational number.

   *For example :* Consider two rational numbers $\frac{5}{6}$ and $\frac{1}{2}$,

   Now, their division $= \frac{5}{6} \div \frac{1}{2} = \frac{5}{6} \times \frac{2}{1} = \frac{5}{3}$

   which is a rational number.

5. The set of rational numbers is ordered. If $p$ and $q$ are two rational numbers, then $p < q$ or $p = q$ or $p > q$.

## To Determine a Rational Number between Two Rational Numbers

### First Method

If $a$ and $b$ are two rational numbers and $a < b$, then $\frac{a+b}{2}$ is a rational number, lying between $a$ and $b$.

*i.e.,*
$$a < \frac{a+b}{2} < b.$$

### Second Method

If $\frac{a}{b}$ and $\frac{c}{d}$ are two rational numbers then $\frac{a+c}{b+d}$ is a rational number, lying between $\frac{a}{b}$ and $\frac{c}{d}$.

## To Determine 'n' Rational Numbers between Two Rational Numbers

Let $a$ and $b$ be two rational numbers and $a < b$.
Let $a < a_1 < a_2 < a_3 ... < a_n < b$,
*i.e.*, $a_1, a_2, a_3, \ldots, a_n$ be $n$ rational numbers between $a$ and $b$.

To determine these number,

first, we find $\frac{b-a}{n+1}$

then multiply it by 1, 2, 3, ... , $n$ and add '$a$' in each to determine the values of $a_1, a_2, a_3, \ldots, a_n$, respectively.

Thus,
$$a_1 = a + \frac{b-a}{n+1}$$
$$a_2 = a + \frac{2 \cdot (b-a)}{n+1}$$
$$a_3 = a + \frac{3 \cdot (b-a)}{n+1}$$
$$\vdots$$
$$a_n = a + \frac{n \cdot (b-a)}{n+1}.$$

# Illustrative Examples

**Example 1.** Find a rational number between $\frac{1}{2}$ and $\frac{2}{3}$.

**Solution.** Here, $\frac{1}{2} < \frac{2}{3}$

$\therefore \quad \frac{1}{2} < \frac{1}{2}\left(\frac{1}{2}+\frac{2}{3}\right) < \frac{2}{3} \quad \Rightarrow \quad \frac{1}{2} < \frac{1}{2}\left(\frac{3+4}{6}\right) < \frac{2}{3} \quad \Rightarrow \quad \frac{1}{2} < \frac{7}{12} < \frac{2}{3}$

Hence, a rational number between two given rational numbers is $\frac{7}{12}$. Ans.

**Alternate Method**

A rational number between $\frac{1}{2}$ and $\frac{2}{3}$ is $\frac{1+2}{2+3} = \frac{3}{5}$. Ans.

**Remark**

There exists infinitely many rational numbers between two rational numbers, so different answers may be occurred in different methods.

**Example 2.** Find a rational number between $\frac{-1}{3}$ and $\frac{3}{7}$.

**Solution.** Here, $-\frac{1}{3} < \frac{3}{7}$

$\therefore \quad -\frac{1}{3} < \frac{1}{2}\left(-\frac{1}{3}+\frac{3}{7}\right) < \frac{3}{7} \quad \Rightarrow \quad -\frac{1}{3} < \frac{1}{2}\left(\frac{-7+9}{21}\right) < \frac{3}{7} \quad \Rightarrow \quad -\frac{1}{3} < \frac{1}{21} < \frac{3}{7}$

Hence, a rational number between two given rational numbers is $\frac{1}{21}$. Ans.

**Example 3.** Insert 3 rational numbers between –5 and 7.

**Solution.** Here, $-5 < 7$

A rational number between – 5 and 7 $= \frac{-5+7}{2} = 1$

$\therefore \quad -5 < 1 < 7$

Again, a rational number between $-5$ and $1 = \frac{-5+1}{2} = -2$

and a rational number between $1$ and $7 = \frac{1+7}{2} = 4$

$\therefore \quad -5 < -2 < 1 < 4 < 7$

Hence, 3 rational numbers between two given rational numbers are –2, 1, 4. Ans.

**Example 4.** Find five rational numbers between $\frac{1}{2}$ and $\frac{13}{5}$.

**Solution.** Here, $\frac{1}{2} < \frac{13}{5}$

First, we find the L.C.M. of 2 and 5.

L.C.M (2, 5) = 10

$\therefore \quad \frac{1}{2} = \frac{1}{2} \times \frac{10}{10} = \frac{5}{10}$ and $\frac{13}{5} = \frac{13}{5} \times \frac{10}{10} = \frac{26}{10}$

Now, $\frac{1}{2} < \frac{13}{5}$

$\Rightarrow \frac{5}{10} < \frac{26}{10} \Rightarrow \frac{5}{10} < \frac{6}{10} < \frac{7}{10} < \frac{8}{10} < \frac{9}{10} < \frac{10}{10} < \frac{26}{10} \Rightarrow \frac{1}{2} < \frac{3}{5} < \frac{7}{10} < \frac{4}{5} < \frac{9}{10} < 1 < \frac{13}{5}$

Hence, 5 rational numbers between two given rational numbers are

$$\frac{3}{5}, \frac{7}{10}, \frac{4}{5}, \frac{9}{10}, 1.$$ Ans.

**Example 5.** Insert two rational numbers between $\frac{3}{4}$ and $\frac{11}{3}$.

**Solution.** Here, $\frac{3}{4} < \frac{11}{3}$

A rational number between $\frac{3}{4}$ and $\frac{11}{3} = \frac{3+11}{4+3} = \frac{14}{7} = 2$

$\therefore \quad \frac{3}{4} < 2 < \frac{11}{3}$

Again, a rational number between $\frac{3}{4}$ and $2 = \frac{3+2}{4+1} = \frac{5}{5} = 1$

$\therefore \quad \frac{3}{4} < 1 < 2 < \frac{11}{3}$

Hence, two rational numbers between two given rational numbers are 1, 2. Ans.

**Example 6.** Insert three rational numbers between $\frac{1}{2}$ and $\frac{24}{7}$ and arrange them in descending order.

**Solution.** First, we find the L.C.M. of 2 and 7.

L.C.M. (2, 7) =14

$\therefore \quad \frac{1}{2} = \frac{1}{2} \times \frac{14}{14} = \frac{7}{14}$ and $\frac{24}{7} = \frac{24}{7} \times \frac{14}{14} = \frac{48}{14}$

Now, $\frac{1}{2} < \frac{24}{7}$

$\Rightarrow \frac{7}{14} < \frac{48}{14} \Rightarrow \frac{7}{14} < \frac{10}{14} < \frac{14}{14} < \frac{18}{14} < \frac{48}{14}$

$\Rightarrow \frac{1}{2} < \frac{5}{7} < 1 < \frac{9}{7} < \frac{24}{7} \Rightarrow \frac{24}{7} > \frac{9}{7} > 1 > \frac{5}{7} > \frac{1}{2}$

Hence, three rational numbers between two given rational numbers are $\frac{5}{7}, 1, \frac{9}{7}$ Ans.

and their descending order is $\frac{9}{7} > 1 > \frac{5}{7}$. Ans.

**Example 7.** Find 9 rational numbers between $\frac{1}{5}$ and $\frac{13}{3}$.

**Solution.** Here, $\frac{1}{5} < \frac{13}{3}$

Let $a = \frac{1}{5}, b = \frac{13}{3}, n = 9$

Now, $\frac{b-a}{n+1} = \frac{\frac{13}{3} - \frac{1}{5}}{9+1} = \frac{1}{10}\left(\frac{65-3}{15}\right) = \frac{31}{75}$

$\therefore$ First rational number $= a + \frac{b-a}{n+1} = \frac{1}{5} + \frac{31}{75} = \frac{15+31}{75} = \frac{46}{75}$

Second rational number $= a + \frac{2(b-a)}{n+1} = \frac{1}{5} + \frac{2 \times 31}{75} = \frac{15+62}{75} = \frac{77}{75}$

Third rational number $= a + \frac{3(b-a)}{n+1} = \frac{1}{5} + \frac{3 \times 31}{75} = \frac{5+31}{25} = \frac{36}{25}$

Fourth rational number $= a + \frac{4(b-a)}{n+1} = \frac{1}{5} + \frac{4 \times 31}{75} = \frac{15+124}{75} = \frac{139}{75}$

Fifth rational number $= a + \frac{5(b-a)}{n+1} = \frac{1}{5} + \frac{5 \times 31}{75} = \frac{3+31}{15} = \frac{34}{15}$

Sixth rational number $= a + \frac{6(b-a)}{n+1} = \frac{1}{5} + \frac{6 \times 31}{75} = \frac{5+62}{25} = \frac{67}{25}$

Seventh rational number $= a + \frac{7(b-a)}{n+1} = \frac{1}{5} + \frac{7 \times 31}{75} = \frac{15+217}{75} = \frac{232}{75}$

Eighth rational number $= a + \frac{8(b-a)}{n+1} = \frac{1}{5} + \frac{8 \times 31}{75} = \frac{15+248}{75} = \frac{263}{75}$

Ninth rational number $= a + \frac{9(b-a)}{n+1} = \frac{1}{5} + \frac{9 \times 31}{75} = \frac{5+93}{25} = \frac{98}{25}$

Hence, 9 rational numbers, between two given rational numbers are

$$\frac{46}{75}, \frac{77}{75}, \frac{36}{25}, \frac{139}{75}, \frac{34}{15}, \frac{67}{25}, \frac{232}{75}, \frac{263}{75}, \frac{98}{25}$$ Ans.

**Alternate Method**

Here, $\frac{1}{5} < \frac{13}{3}$

First, we find the L.C.M. of 5 and 3.

L.C.M. (5, 3) = 15

$\therefore \quad \frac{1}{5} = \frac{1}{5} \times \frac{15}{15} = \frac{3}{15}$ and $\frac{13}{3} = \frac{13}{3} \times \frac{15}{15} = \frac{65}{15}$

Now, $\frac{1}{5} < \frac{13}{3}$

$\Rightarrow \quad \frac{3}{15} < \frac{65}{15}$

$\Rightarrow \quad \frac{3}{15} < \frac{4}{15} < \frac{5}{15} < \frac{6}{15} < \frac{7}{15} < \frac{8}{15} < \frac{9}{15} < \frac{10}{15} < \frac{11}{15} < \frac{12}{15} < \frac{65}{15}$

$\Rightarrow \quad \frac{1}{5} < \frac{4}{15} < \frac{1}{3} < \frac{2}{5} < \frac{7}{15} < \frac{8}{15} < \frac{3}{5} < \frac{2}{3} < \frac{11}{15} < \frac{4}{5} < \frac{13}{3}$

Hence, 9 rational numbers between two given rational numbers are

$$\frac{4}{15}, \frac{1}{3}, \frac{2}{5}, \frac{7}{15}, \frac{8}{15}, \frac{3}{5}, \frac{2}{3}, \frac{11}{15}, \frac{4}{5}$$ Ans.

# Exercise 1A

**1.** Insert one rational number between the following rational numbers :

(i) 3 and 8 (ii) −2 and 5 (iii) $\frac{1}{4}$ and $\frac{3}{5}$ (iv) $-\frac{2}{5}$ and $-\frac{3}{2}$

**2.** Insert three rational numbers between the following rational numbers and write them in descending order :

(i) $\frac{3}{8}$ and $-\frac{1}{4}$ (ii) $\frac{6}{11}$ and $\frac{8}{5}$

**3.** Insert five rational numbers between the following rational numbers :

(i) $\frac{1}{2}$ and $\frac{5}{14}$ (ii) $\frac{3}{4}$ and $\frac{17}{8}$

**4.** Insert two rational numbers between the following rational numbers :

(i) $\frac{3}{5}$ and $\frac{5}{6}$ (ii) $-\frac{1}{3}$ and $-\frac{1}{4}$

**5.** Insert four rational numbers between the following rational numbers :

(i) $-\frac{2}{5}$ and $\frac{1}{3}$ (ii) $\frac{1}{2}$ and $\frac{4}{9}$

**6.** Insert 9 rational numbers between the following rational numbers :

(i) $\frac{3}{10}$ and $\frac{7}{5}$ (ii) $\frac{3}{2}$ and 2

## *Answers*

**1.** (i) $\frac{11}{2}$ (ii) $\frac{3}{2}$ (iii) $\frac{17}{40}$ (iv) $\frac{-19}{20}$

**2.** (i) $\frac{-1}{16}, \frac{1}{16}, \frac{7}{32}$ (ii) $\frac{89}{110}, \frac{59}{55}, \frac{147}{110}$

**3.** (i) $\frac{51}{140}, \frac{13}{35}, \frac{53}{140}, \frac{27}{70}, \frac{11}{28}$ (ii) $\frac{7}{8}, 1, \frac{9}{8}, \frac{5}{4}, \frac{11}{8}$

**4.** (i) $\frac{43}{60}, \frac{93}{120}$ (ii) $\frac{-5}{16}, \frac{-7}{24}$

**5.** (i) $\frac{1}{15}, \frac{2}{15}, \frac{1}{5}, \frac{4}{15}$ (ii) $\frac{9}{20}, \frac{41}{90}, \frac{83}{180}, \frac{7}{15}$

**6.** (i) $\frac{2}{5}, \frac{1}{2}, \frac{3}{5}, \frac{7}{10}, \frac{4}{5}, \frac{9}{10}, 1, \frac{11}{10}, \frac{6}{5}$ (ii) $\frac{31}{20}, \frac{8}{5}, \frac{33}{20}, \frac{17}{10}, \frac{7}{4}, \frac{9}{5}, \frac{37}{20}, \frac{19}{10}, \frac{39}{20}$

## Irrational Numbers

A number which cannot be expressed in the form $\frac{p}{q}$, where $p$ and $q$ are integers and $q \neq 0$, is called an irrational number.

**or**

A number which is not a rational number, is said to be an irrational number.

*For example :* $\sqrt{2}, \sqrt{5}, \sqrt{7}, -\sqrt{3}, \frac{1}{\sqrt{3}}$, etc., are irrational numbers.

**NOTE**

There are infinitely many irrational numbers. Irrational numbers can be represented on the number line by using Pythagoras Theorem.

### Pythagoras Theorem

In a right-angled triangle, the square of the hypotenuse is equal to the sum of the squares of the other two sides.

## Representation of $\sqrt{2}$, $\sqrt{3}$ and $\sqrt{5}$ on a Number Line

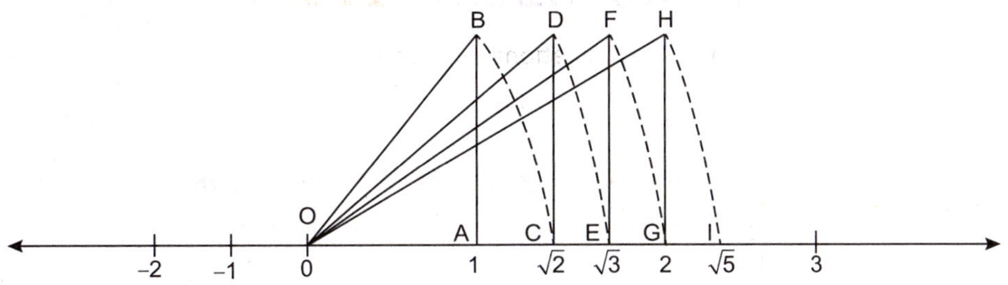


Construct a right-angled triangle $OAB$, right-angled at $A$. Here, $O$ is the zero of the number line and $OA = AB = 1$ unit.
In $\Delta OAB$,
Using Pythagoras theorem, we get

$$OB^2 = OA^2 + AB^2 = 1^2 + 1^2 = 2 \quad \Rightarrow \quad OB = \sqrt{2}$$

Draw an arc with centre $O$ and radius $OB$, which intersects the number line at $C$.

$$\therefore \qquad OC = OB = \sqrt{2}.$$

$\Rightarrow$ $C$ represents the irrational number $\sqrt{2}$ on the number line.

Construct a right-angled triangle $OCD$, right-angled at $C$. Here, $OC = \sqrt{2}$ unit and $CD = 1$ unit.

In $\Delta OCD$,

Using Pythagoras theorem, we get

$$OD^2 = OC^2 + CD^2 = (\sqrt{2})^2 + (1)^2 = 2 + 1 = 3 \quad \Rightarrow \quad OD = \sqrt{3}$$

Draw an arc with centre $O$ and radius $OD$, which intersects the number line at $E$.

$$\therefore \qquad OE = OD = \sqrt{3}$$

$\Rightarrow$ $E$ represents the irrational number $\sqrt{3}$ on the number line.
Construct a right-angled triangle $OGH$, right-angled at $G$.
Here, $OG = 2$ unit and $GH = 1$ unit.
In $\Delta OGH$,
Using Pythagoras theorem, we get

$$OH^2 = OG^2 + GH^2 = 2^2 + 1^2 = 5 \quad \Rightarrow \quad OH = \sqrt{5}$$

Draw an arc with centre $O$ and radius $OH$, which intersects the number line at $I$.

$$\therefore \qquad OI = OH = \sqrt{5}$$

$\Rightarrow$ $H$ represents the irrational number $\sqrt{5}$ on the number line.

**Remark**

$\pi$ is an irrational number.

**Conclusion**

There exists one and only one point on the number line corresponding to every irrational number.

## Real Numbers

The set of all rational and irrational numbers, together, is called the set of real numbers.

We know that all rational numbers can be represented on a number line, so we can conclude that :

There exists one and only one point on the number line corresponding to every real (rational or irrational) number and conversely, corresponding to every point on the number line, there exists one and only one real number.

## Some Theorems

1. If $a$ is any natural number and $p$ is a prime number such that $p$ divides $a^2$, then $p$ divides $a$.
   In general, if $a$, $n$ are natural numbers and $p$ is a prime number such that $p$ divides $a^n$, then $p$ divides $a$.
2. If $a$ and $b$ are natural numbers and $p$ is a prime number such that $p$ divides $ab$ then $p$ divides $a$ or $p$ divides $b$ or $p$ divides $a$ and $b$ both.

# Illustrative Examples

**Example 1.** Prove that $\sqrt{2}$ is an irrational number.

**Solution.** Let $\sqrt{2}$ be a rational number. We know that every rational number can be written in the form $\frac{a}{b}$, where $a$ and $b$ are integers and $b \neq 0$.

Let $\sqrt{2} = \frac{a}{b}$, where $a$ and $b$ are integers, $b \neq 0$ and $a$ and $b$ have no common factor except 1.

$\Rightarrow \quad a = b\sqrt{2}$

$\Rightarrow \quad a^2 = 2b^2 \quad \ldots(i)$

Now, 2 divides $2b^2$.

$\Rightarrow$ 2 divides $a^2$.

$\Rightarrow$ 2 divides $a$. ($\because$ 2 is a prime number.)

Let $a = 2c$

$\Rightarrow \quad a^2 = 4c^2$

$\Rightarrow \quad 2b^2 = 4c^2 \quad$ [From $(ii)$]

$\Rightarrow \quad b^2 = 2c^2$

Now, 2 divides $2c^2$.

$\Rightarrow$ 2 divides $b^2$.

$\Rightarrow$ 2 divides $b$ ($\because$ 2 is a prime number.)

So, $a$ and $b$ have a common factor 2 which contradicts the fact that $a$ and $b$ have no common factor except 1. Thus, our assumption is wrong.

So, $\sqrt{2}$ is not a rational number.

Hence, $\sqrt{2}$ is an irrational number. Hence Proved.

**Example 2.** Prove that $\sqrt{7}$ is an irrational number.

**Solution.** Let $\sqrt{7}$ be a rational number.

We know that every rational number can be written in the form $\frac{a}{b}$, where $a$ and $b$ are integers, and $b \neq 0$

Let $\sqrt{7} = \frac{a}{b}$, where $a$ and $b$ are integers, $b \neq 0$ and $a$ and $b$ have no common factor except 1.

$\Rightarrow \quad a = b\sqrt{7}$

$\Rightarrow \quad a^2 = 7b^2 \quad \ldots(i)$

Now, 7 divides $7b^2$.

$\Rightarrow$ 7 divides $a^2$.

$\Rightarrow$ 7 divides $a$. ($\because$ 7 is a prime number.)

Let $a = 7c$

$\Rightarrow \quad a^2 = 49c^2$

$\Rightarrow \quad 7b^2 = 49c^2 \quad$ [From $(i)$]

$\Rightarrow \quad b^2 = 7c^2$

Now, 7 divides $7c^2$.

$\Rightarrow$ 7 divides $b^2$.

$\Rightarrow$ 7 divides $b$. ($\because$ 7 is a prime number.)

So, $a$ and $b$ have a common factor 7 which contradicts the fact that $a$ and $b$ have no common factor except 1.

Thus, our assumption is wrong.

So, $\sqrt{7}$ is not a rational number.

Hence, $\sqrt{7}$ is an irrational number. Hence Proved.

**Example 3.** Prove that $\sqrt{m}$ is an irrational number, where $m$ is prime.

**Solution.** Let $\sqrt{m}$ be a rational number.

We know that every rational number can be written in the form $\frac{a}{b}$, where $a$ and $b$ are integers and $b \neq 0$.

Let $\sqrt{m} = \frac{a}{b}$, where $a$ and $b$ are integers, $b \neq 0$ and $a$ and $b$ have no common factor except 1.

$$\Rightarrow \quad a = b\sqrt{m}$$

$$\Rightarrow \quad a^2 = mb^2 \quad \ldots(i)$$

Now, $m$ divides $mb^2$.

$\Rightarrow$ $m$ divides $a^2$.

$\Rightarrow$ $m$ divides $a$. ($\because$ $m$ is a prime number.)

Let $a = mc$

$$\Rightarrow \quad a^2 = m^2c^2$$

$$\Rightarrow \quad mb^2 = m^2c^2 \quad \text{[From (i)]}$$

$$\Rightarrow \quad b^2 = mc^2$$

Now, $m$ divides $mc^2$.

$\Rightarrow$ $m$ divides $b^2$.

$\Rightarrow$ $m$ divides $b$. ($\because$ $m$ is a prime number.)

So, $a$ and $b$ have a common factor $m$ which contradicts the fact that $a$ and $b$ have no common factor except 1.

Thus, our assumption is wrong.

So, $\sqrt{m}$ is not a rational number.

Hence, $\sqrt{m}$ is an irrational number. Hence Proved.

**Example 4.** Prove that $\frac{1}{\sqrt{3}}$ is an irrational number.

**Solution.** Let $\frac{1}{\sqrt{3}}$ be a rational number.

Let $\frac{1}{\sqrt{3}} = \frac{a}{b}$, where $a$ and $b$ are integers, $b \neq 0$ and $a$ and $b$ have no common factor except 1.

$$\Rightarrow \quad b = a\sqrt{3}$$

$$\Rightarrow \quad b^2 = 3a^2. \quad \ldots(i)$$

Now, 3 divides $3a^2$.

$\Rightarrow$ 3 divides $b^2$.

$\Rightarrow$ 3 divides $b$. ($\because$ 3 is a prime number.)

Let $b = 3c$

$$\Rightarrow \quad b^2 = 9c^2$$

$$\Rightarrow \quad 3a^2 = 9c^2 \quad \text{[From (i)]}$$

$$\Rightarrow \quad a^2 = 3c^2$$

Now, 3 divides $3c^2$.

$\Rightarrow$ 3 divides $a^2$.

$\Rightarrow$ 3 divides $a$. ($\because$ 3 is a prime number.)

So, $a$ and $b$ have a common factor 3 which contradicts the fact that $a$ and $b$ have no common factor except 1.

Thus, our assumption is wrong.

So, $\frac{1}{\sqrt{3}}$ is not a rational number.

Hence, $\frac{1}{\sqrt{3}}$ is an irrational number. Hence Proved.

**Example 5.** Prove that $(3+\sqrt{2})$ is an irrational number.

**Solution.** Let $(3+\sqrt{2})$ is a rational number.

Let $3+\sqrt{2} = \frac{a}{b}$

where $a$ and $b$ are integers and $b \neq 0$

$$\Rightarrow \quad \sqrt{2} = \frac{a}{b} - 3 \quad \Rightarrow \quad \sqrt{2} = \frac{a-3b}{b}$$

$\because$ $a$ and $b$ are integers.

$\therefore$ $a - 3b$ is also an integer.

$\Rightarrow$ $\frac{a-3b}{b}$ is a rational number.

$\Rightarrow$ $\sqrt{2}$ is a rational number, but it is a contradiction, because $\sqrt{2}$ is an irrational number.

So, our assumption is wrong.

$\Rightarrow$ $(3+\sqrt{2})$ is not a rational number.

$\Rightarrow$ $(3+\sqrt{2})$ is an irrational number. Hence Proved.

**Example 6.** Show that $(5+2\sqrt{3})$ is an irrational number.

**Solution.** Let $(5+2\sqrt{3})$ be a rational number.

Let $5+2\sqrt{3} = \frac{a}{b}$

where $a$ and $b$ are integers and $b \neq 0$.

$$\Rightarrow \quad 2\sqrt{3} = \frac{a}{b} - 5 \quad \Rightarrow \quad 2\sqrt{3} = \frac{a-5b}{b} \quad \Rightarrow \quad \sqrt{3} = \frac{a-5b}{2b}$$

$\because$ $a$ and $b$ are integers.

$\therefore$ $a - 5b$ is also an integer.

$\Rightarrow$ $\frac{a-5b}{2b}$ is a rational number.

$\Rightarrow$ $\sqrt{3}$ is a rational number, but it is a contradiction, because $\sqrt{3}$ is an irrational number. So, our assumption is wrong.

$\Rightarrow$ $(5+2\sqrt{3})$ is not a rational number.

$\Rightarrow$ $(5+2\sqrt{3})$ is an irrational number. Hence Proved.

**Example 7.** Show that $2\sqrt{5}$ is an irrational number.

**Solution.** Let $2\sqrt{5}$ be a rational number.

Let $2\sqrt{5} = \frac{a}{b}$

where $a$ and $b$ are integers and $b \neq 0$.

$\Rightarrow \quad \sqrt{5} = \dfrac{a}{2b}$

$\because$ $a$ and $b$ are integers.

$\therefore$ $\dfrac{a}{2b}$ is a rational number.

$\Rightarrow$ $\sqrt{5}$ is a rational number but it is a contradiction, because $\sqrt{5}$ is an irrational number.

So, our assumption is wrong.

$\Rightarrow$ $2\sqrt{5}$ is not a rational number.

$\Rightarrow$ $2\sqrt{5}$ is an irrational number. Hence Proved.

**Example 8.** Prove that $(\sqrt{2} + \sqrt{3})$ is an irrational number.

**Solution.** Let $(\sqrt{2} + \sqrt{3})$ be a rational number.

Let $\sqrt{2} + \sqrt{3} = k$, where $k \neq 0$ is rational.

$\Rightarrow \quad \sqrt{3} = k - \sqrt{2} \quad \Rightarrow \quad (\sqrt{3})^2 = (k - \sqrt{2})^2$

$\Rightarrow \quad 3 = k^2 + 2 - 2\sqrt{2}k \quad \Rightarrow \quad k \cdot 2\sqrt{2} = k^2 - 1$

$\Rightarrow \quad \sqrt{2} = \dfrac{k^2 - 1}{2k}$

$\because$ $k$ is a rational number.

$\therefore$ $\dfrac{k^2 - 1}{2k}$ is also a rational number.

$\Rightarrow$ $\sqrt{2}$ is a rational number.

but it is a contradiction, because $\sqrt{2}$ is an irrational number.

So, our assumption is wrong.

$\Rightarrow$ $(\sqrt{2} + \sqrt{3})$ is not a rational number.

$\Rightarrow$ $(\sqrt{2} + \sqrt{3})$ is an irrational number. Hence Proved.

**Example 9.** Prove that the negative of an irrational number is irrational.

**Solution.** Let $m$ be an irrational number.

and $(-m)$ be rational.

We know that negative of a rational number is always rational.

So, $-(-m)$ is rational.

$\Rightarrow$ $m$ is rational.

which contradicts our assumption that $m$ is an irrational number.

So, our assumption is wrong.

$\Rightarrow$ $(-m)$ is not a rational number.

$\Rightarrow$ $(-m)$ is an irrational number.

Hence, negative of an irrational number is irrational. Hence Proved.

**Example 10.** Prove that the sum of a rational and an irrational number is irrational.

**Solution.** Let $m$ and $n$ be rational and irrational numbers, respectively.

Let $(m + n)$ be rational.

We know that the difference of two rational numbers is rational.

$\because$ $(m + n)$ and $m$ are rational numbers.

$\therefore$ $(m + n) - m$ is also rational.

$n$ is rational which contradicts our assumption that $n$ is an irrational number.

So, our assumption is wrong.

$\Rightarrow$ $(m + n)$ is not a rational number.

$\Rightarrow$ $(m + n)$ is an irrational number.

Hence, the sum of a rational and an irrational numbers is irrational. Hence Proved.

**Example 11.** Prove that the product of a non-zero rational number and an irrational number is an irrational number.

**Solution.** Let $m$ be a non-zero rational number and $n$ be an irrational number.

Let $mn$ be a rational number.

We know that the division of a rational number by a non-zero rational number is rational.

$\because$ $mn$ is a rational number and $m$ is a non-zero rational number.

$\therefore$ $\frac{mn}{m}$ is a rational number.

$\Rightarrow$ $n$ is a rational number which contradicts our assumption that $n$ is an irrational number.

So, our assumption is wrong.

$\Rightarrow$ $mn$ is not a rational number.

$\Rightarrow$ $mn$ is an irrational number. Hence Proved.

**Example 12.** Using by suitable examples, show that :

(i) the sum of two irrational numbers may be rational.

(ii) the difference of two irrational numbers may be rational.

(iii) the product of two irrational numbers may be rational.

(iv) the quotient of two irrational numbers may be rational.

**Solution.** (i) Let $m = 3 + 5\sqrt{2}$ and $n = 6 - 5\sqrt{2}$ be two irrational numbers, then $m + n = 3 + 5\sqrt{2} + 6 - 5\sqrt{2} = 9$ which is rational.

So, the sum of two irrational numbers may be rational. Hence Proved.

(ii) Let $m = 3 + 2\sqrt{5}$ and $n = 6 + 2\sqrt{5}$ be two irrational numbers, then $m - n = (3 + 2\sqrt{5}) - (6 + 2\sqrt{5}) = -3$ which is rational.

So, the difference of two irrational numbers may be rational. Hence Proved.

(iii) Let $m = 5 + \sqrt{2}$ and $n = 5 - \sqrt{2}$ be two irrational numbers then

$$mn = (5 + \sqrt{2})(5 - \sqrt{2}) = (5)^2 - (\sqrt{2})^2 = 25 - 2 = 23$$

which is rational.

So, the product of two irrational numbers may be rational. Hence Proved.

(iv) Let $m = 5\sqrt{3}$ and $n = 2\sqrt{3}$ be two irrational numbers, then

$$\frac{m}{n} = \frac{5\sqrt{3}}{2\sqrt{3}} = \frac{5}{2}$$

which in rational.

So, the quotient of two irrational numbers may be rational. Hence Proved.

## Exercise 1B

1. Prove that $\sqrt{3}$ is an irrational number.
2. Prove that $\sqrt{5}$ is an irrational number.
3. Prove that $\sqrt{11}$ is an irrational number.

4. Prove that $\frac{1}{\sqrt{2}}$ is an irrational number.

5. Prove that $(5+\sqrt{3})$ is an irrational number.

6. Prove that $6\sqrt{2}$ is an irrational number.

7. Prove that $3+2\sqrt{5}$ is an irrational number.

8. Prove that $4-3\sqrt{5}$ is an irrational number.

9. Prove that $\sqrt{3}+\sqrt{5}$ is an irrational number.

10. Using suitable examples, show that the
(i) sum (ii) difference (iii) product (iv) quotient, of two irrational numbers may be rational.

## Real Numbers

We have already studied that the set of all rational numbers and irrational numbers, together is called the set of real numbers.

Thus, we can say that every real number is either rational or irrational. Now, the different number systems are given below in the following table :

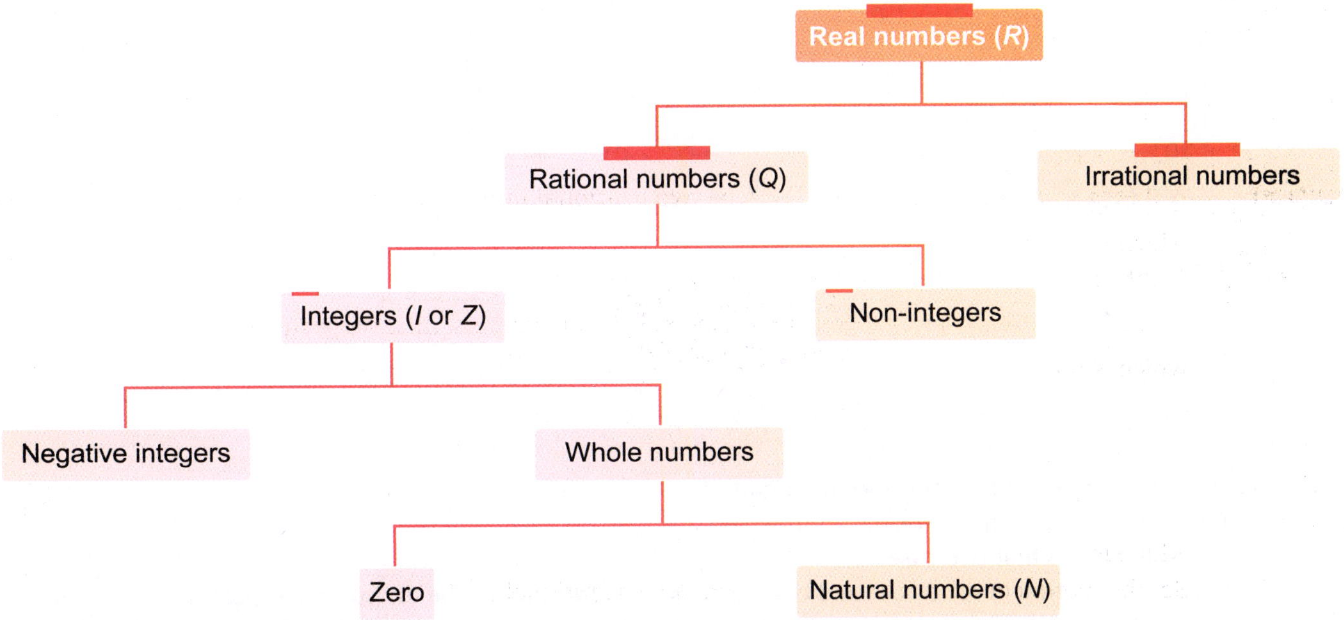


### Properties of Real Numbers

1. The sum of two real numbers is always a real number.
2. The difference of two real numbers is always a real number.
3. The product of two real numbers is always a real number.
4. The division of a real number by a non-zero real number is always a real number.
5. The set of real numbers is ordered, *i.e.*, for two real numbers $a$ and $b$,
   $a > b$ or $a = b$ or $a < b$
   It is tricotomy law.
6. There are infinitely many real numbers between any two real numbers.
7. If $a$ and $b$ are two real numbers such that $a < b$, then

$$a < \frac{a+b}{2} < b.$$

## Decimal Expansions of Real Numbers

First, we shall discuss the decimal expansion of rational numbers. Consider the following examples :

1. $\frac{23}{4}$

```
    5.75
 4)23.0
   20
    30
    28
     20
     20
      0   Complete
```

$\therefore \frac{23}{4} = 5.75$

2. $\frac{93}{5}$

```
   18.6
 5)93.0
   5
   43
   40
    30
    30
     0   Complete
```

$\therefore \frac{93}{5} = 18.6$

3. $\frac{17}{6}$

```
    2.8333......
 6)17.0
   12
    50
    48
     20
     18
      20
      18
       20
       18
        2   Repeatition
```

$\therefore \frac{17}{6} = 2.8333......$

4. $\frac{10}{7}$

```
    1.428571......
 7) 10.0
     7
     30
     28
      20
      14
       60
       56
        40
        35
         50
         49
          10
           7
           3   Repeatition
```

$\therefore \frac{10}{7} = 1.428571......$

We observe the following from the above four examples :

1. Remainder is smaller than divisor.
2. Remainder is zero in first two cases.
3. Remainder is repeating in third case and only one digit is repeating in the divisor. So, repeating block is 3.
4. Remainder is repeating in fourth case and six digits are repeating in the divisor. So, repeating block is 428571.

Now, the following cases arise :

1. **When the remainder is zero :**
   In example 1 and 2, the remainder becomes zero after finite steps, such decimal expansions are called terminating decimal expansions.
2. **When the remainder is never zero :**
   In examples 3 and 4, the remainder never becomes zero and repeats after some steps. Such decimal expansions are called non-terminating recurring decimals or non-terminating repeating decimals.

**Remark**

1. If there is only one digit in recurring decimal, we put a dot or a line, called vinculum above this digit. In example 3.

   $\therefore \frac{17}{6} = 2.8333...... = 2.8\dot{3}$ or $2.8\overline{3}$

2. If more than one digit are there in recurring decimal, we put a dot above on each repeating digit or a line above all repeating digits. In example 4.

   $\therefore \frac{10}{7} = 1.428571....... = 1.\dot{4}\dot{2}\dot{8}\dot{5}\dot{7}\dot{1}$ or $1.\overline{428571}$

**Conclusion**

From the above discussion, we conclude that a rational number has either a terminating or non-terminating repeating decimal expansion and conversely, every terminating decimal or a non-terminating repeating decimal is a rational number.

**Remark**

Consider the rational number $\frac{p}{q}$, where $p$, $q$ are integers and $q \neq 0$ and $p$ and $q$ are co-prime, *i.e.*, have no common factor except 1. Then,

1. this rational number is terminating if $q$ is of the form $2^m.5^n$ where $m$, $n$ are whole numbers.
2. this rational number is non-terminating repeating if $q$ has a prime factor other than 2 or 5.

Now, we can say the decimal expansion of an irrational number is non-terminating non-repeating and conversely, every non-terminating non-repeating decimal number is an irrational number.

We know that $\sqrt{2}$ is an irrational number. Let us see the decimal expansion of $\sqrt{2}$.

| | 1.414213 |
|---|---|
| 1 | $2.\overline{00}\ \overline{00}\ \overline{00}\ \overline{00}\ \overline{00}\ \overline{00}$ |
| | 1 |
| 24 | 100 |
| | 96 |
| 281 | 400 |
| | 281 |
| 2824 | 11900 |
| | 11296 |
| 28282 | 60400 |
| | 56564 |
| 282841 | 383600 |
| | 282841 |
| 2828423 | 10075900 |
| | 8485269 |
| | 1590631 |

$\therefore \quad \sqrt{2} = 1.414213......$

which is non-terminating and non-repeating.

So, $\sqrt{2}$ is an irrational number.

# Illustrative Examples

**Example 1.** Represent the following terminating decimals in the form of a rational number $\left(\text{in fraction form } \frac{p}{q}\right)$:

(i) 0.15 (ii) 1.125 (iii) 12.16 (iv) 2.325

**Solution.** (i) $0.15 = \frac{15}{100} = \frac{3}{20}$ **Ans.**

(ii) $1.125 = \frac{1125}{1000} = \frac{9}{8}$ **Ans.**

(iii) $12.16 = \frac{1216}{100} = \frac{304}{25}$ **Ans.**

(iv) $2.325 = \frac{2325}{1000} = \frac{97}{40}$ **Ans.**

**Example 2.** Express the following recurring decimals in the form of a rational number $\left(\text{in fraction form } \frac{p}{q}\right)$:

(i) $0.\dot{5}$ (ii) $1.\overline{18}$ (iii) $0.3\overline{14}$ (iv) $0.2\dot{3}$ (v) $0.\overline{013}$ (vi) $12.\overline{143}$

**Solution.** (i) Let $x = 0.\dot{5}$

$\Rightarrow \quad x = 0.555......$ ...(i)

Here, one digit is repeating after decimal place,
so, multiply both sides by 10,

$10x = 5.555......$ ...(ii)

Subtracting equation *(i)* from equation *(ii)*,

$\Rightarrow \quad 9x = 5$

$\Rightarrow \quad x = \frac{5}{9} \Rightarrow 0.\dot{5} = \frac{5}{9}$ **Ans.**

(ii) Let $x = 1.\overline{18}$

$\Rightarrow \quad x = 1.181818......$ ...(i)

Here, two digits are repeating after decimal place,
so, multiply both sides by 100,

$100x = 118.1818......$ ...(ii)

$\Rightarrow \quad 99x = 117$

Subtracting equation *(i)* from equation *(ii)*,

$99x = 117$

$\Rightarrow \quad x = \frac{117}{99} \Rightarrow 1.\overline{18} = \frac{13}{11}$ **Ans.**

(iii) Let $x = 0.3\overline{14} \Rightarrow x = 0.3141414......$

Here, one digit is not repeating after decimal place,
so, multiply both sides by 10,

$10x = 3.141414......$ ...(i)

Here, two digits are repeating after decimal place,
so, multiply both sides by 100,

$1000x = 314.141414......$ ...(ii)

Subtracting equation *(i)* from equation *(ii)*,

$990x = 311$

$\Rightarrow \quad x = \dfrac{311}{990} \quad \Rightarrow \quad 0.\overline{314} = \dfrac{311}{990}$ Ans.

(iv) Let $x = 0.2\dot{3}$

$\Rightarrow x = 0.2333......$

Here, one digit is not repeating after decimal place,
so, multiply both sides by 10,

$10x = 2.333......$ ...(i)

Here, two digits are repeating after decimal place,
so, multiply both sides by 100,

$1000x = 233.333......$ ...(ii)

Subtracting equation (i) from equation (ii)

$990x = 231$

$\Rightarrow \quad x = \dfrac{231}{990} \quad \Rightarrow \quad 0.2\dot{3} = \dfrac{7}{30}$ Ans.

(v) Let $x = 0.0\overline{13}$

$\Rightarrow \quad x = 0.0\,131313......$

Here, one digit is not repeating after decimal place,
so, multiply both sides by 10,

$10x = 0.131313......$ ...(i)

Here, two digits are repeating after decimal place,
so, multiply both sides by 100,

$1000x = 13.131313......$ ...(ii)

Subtracting equation (i) by equation (ii)

$990x = 13$

$\Rightarrow \quad x = \dfrac{13}{990} \quad \Rightarrow \quad 0.0\overline{13} = \dfrac{13}{990}$ Ans.

(vi) Let $x = 12.1\overline{43}$

$\Rightarrow \quad x = 12.1434343......$

Here, one digit is not repeating after decimal place,
so, multiply both sides by 10,

$10x = 121.434343......$ ...(i)

Here, two digits are repeating after decimal place,
so, multiply both sides by 100,

$1000x = 12143.434343......$ ...(ii)

Subtracting equation (i) from equation (ii)

$990x = 12122$

$\Rightarrow \quad x = \dfrac{12122}{990} \quad \Rightarrow \quad 12.1\overline{43} = \dfrac{551}{45}$ Ans.

**Example 3.** Write $1.4\dot{3} + 0.\overline{15}$ in the form of a rational number $\left(\text{in fraction form } \dfrac{p}{q}\right)$.

**Solution.** Let $x = 1.4\dot{3}$

$\Rightarrow \quad x = 1.4333......$

Here, one digit is not repeating after decimal place,
so, multiply both sides by 10,

$$10x = 14.3333...... \quad ...(i)$$

Here, one digit is repeating after decimal place,
so, multiply both sides by 10,

$$100x = 143.3333...... \quad ...(ii)$$

Subtracting equation *(i)* from equation *(ii)*,

$$90x = 129$$

$$\Rightarrow \quad x = \frac{129}{90} \Rightarrow 1.4\dot{3} = \frac{43}{30} \quad ...(iii)$$

Let $y = 0.\overline{15}$

$$\Rightarrow \quad y = 0.151515...... \quad ...(iv)$$

Here, two digits are repeating after decimal place,
so, multiply both sides by 100,

$$100y = 15.151515...... \quad ...(v)$$

Subtracting equation *(iv)* from equation *(v)*,

$$99y = 15$$

$$\Rightarrow \quad y = \frac{15}{99} \Rightarrow 0.\overline{15} = \frac{5}{33} \quad ...(vi)$$

Adding equation *(iii)* and equation *(vi)*,

$$1.4\dot{3} + 0.\overline{15} = \frac{43}{30} + \frac{5}{33} = \frac{473+50}{330} = \frac{523}{330}$$ Ans.

**Example 4.** Without performing long division process, determine whether the following rational numbers have a terminating decimal expansion or a non-terminating recurring decimal expansion. Also write the decimal expansion of those rational numbers which have terminating decimal expansions.

(i) $\frac{5}{16}$ (ii) $\frac{7}{24}$ (iii) $\frac{11}{400}$ (iv) $\frac{19}{500}$ (v) $\frac{15}{800}$

(vi) $\frac{14}{375}$ (vii) $\frac{311}{340}$ (viii) $\frac{75}{3500}$ (ix) $\frac{47}{1250}$ (x) $\frac{18}{525}$

**Solution.** (i) Given rational number $= \frac{5}{16}$

which is in the simplest form.

Its denominator $= 16 = 2^4 = 2^4 \times 5^0$

which is in the form $2^m \times 5^n$, where $m = 4$ and $n = 0$ are whole numbers.

$\therefore \quad \frac{5}{16}$ has a terminating decimal. Ans.

Now, $\frac{5}{16} = \frac{5}{2^4} = \frac{5 \times 5^4}{2^4 \times 5^4} = \frac{3125}{10^4} = 0.3125$ Ans.

which is the required decimal expansion.

(ii) Given rational number $= \frac{7}{24}$

which is in the simplest form.

Its denominator $= 24 = 2^3 \times 3$

which contains 3 other than 2.

$\therefore \quad \frac{7}{24}$ has a non-terminating recurring decimal expansion. Ans.

(iii) Given rational number $= \frac{11}{400}$

which is in the simplest form.
Its denominator $= 400 = 2^4 \times 5^2$
which is in the form $2^m \times 5^n$, where $m = 4$ and $n = 2$ are whole numbers.

$\therefore \quad \frac{11}{400}$ has a terminating decimal. Ans.

Now, $\frac{11}{400} = \frac{11}{2^4 \times 5^2} = \frac{11 \times 5^2}{2^4 \times 5^4} = \frac{275}{10^4} = 0.0275$ Ans.

which is the required decimal expansion.

(iv) Given rational number $= \frac{19}{500}$

which is in the simplest form.
Its denominator $= 500 = 2^2 \times 5^3$
which is in the form $2^m \times 5^n$, where $m = 2$ and $n = 3$ are whole numbers.

$\therefore \quad \frac{19}{500}$ has a terminating decimal. Ans.

Now, $\frac{19}{500} = \frac{19}{2^2 \times 5^3} = \frac{19 \times 2}{2^3 \times 5^3} = \frac{38}{10^3} = 0.038$ Ans.

which is the required decimal expansion.

(v) Given rational number $= \frac{15}{800} = \frac{3 \times 5}{2^5 \times 5^2} = \frac{3}{2^5 \times 5^1}$

Now, it is the simplest form of given rational number.
Its denominator is $2^5 \times 5^1$.
which is in the form $2^m \times 5^n$, where $m = 5$ and $n = 1$ are whole numbers.

$\therefore \quad \frac{15}{800}$ has a terminating decimal. Ans.

Now, $\frac{15}{800} = \frac{3}{2^5 \times 5^1} = \frac{3 \times 5^4}{2^5 \times 5^5} = \frac{1875}{10^5} = 0.01875$ Ans.

which is the required decimal expansion.

(vi) Given rational number $= \frac{14}{375}$

which is in the simplest form.
Its denominator $= 375$
$= 3 \times 5^3$
which contains 3 other than 5.

$\therefore \quad \frac{14}{375}$ has a non-terminating recurring decimal expansion. Ans.

(vii) Given rational number $= \frac{311}{340}$

which is in the simplest form.
Its denominator $= 340 = 2^2 \times 5 \times 17$
which contains 17 other than 2 and 5.

$\therefore \quad \frac{311}{340}$ has a non-terminating recurring decimal expansion. Ans.

(viii) Given rational number $= \dfrac{75}{3500}$

$$= \frac{3 \times 5 \times 5}{2 \times 2 \times 5 \times 5 \times 5 \times 7}$$

$$= \frac{3}{2^2 \times 5 \times 7}$$

which is the simplest form of the given rational number. Now, the denominator $2^2 \times 5 \times 7$ **contains 7 other** than 2 and 5.

$\therefore \dfrac{75}{3500}$ has a non-terminating recurring decimal expansion. Ans.

(ix) Given rational number $= \dfrac{47}{1250}$

which is in the simplest form.

Its denominator $= 1250 = 2^1 \times 5^4$

which is in the form $2^m \times 5^n$ where $m = 1$ and $n = 4$ are whole numbers.

$\therefore \dfrac{47}{1250}$ has a terminating decimal. Ans.

Now, $\dfrac{47}{1250} = \dfrac{47}{2^1 \times 5^4} = \dfrac{47 \times 2^3}{2^4 \times 5^4} = \dfrac{376}{10^4} = 0.0376$ Ans.

which is the required decimal expansion.

(x) Given rational number $= \dfrac{18}{525} = \dfrac{2 \times 3 \times 3}{3 \times 5 \times 5 \times 7} = \dfrac{6}{5^2 \times 7}$

Now, the denominator $5^2 \times 7$ contains 7 other than 5.

$\therefore \dfrac{18}{525}$ has a non-terminating recurring decimal expansion. Ans.

**Example 5.** The following real numbers have decimal expansions as given below. In each case, state whether they are rational or irrational. If they are rational, express them in the form $\dfrac{p}{q}$, where $p$ and $q$ are co-prime integers and $q \neq 0$, then what can you say about the prime factors of $q$?.

(i) 2.024 (ii) 29.1385 (iii) 3.141441444... (iv) $0.\overline{52}$ (v) 3.16

**Solution.** (i) 2.024

It is a terminating decimal number,

so, it is a rational number. Ans.

$$\therefore \quad 2.024 = \frac{2024}{1000} = \frac{253}{125}$$ Ans.

which is in the form of $\dfrac{p}{q}$.

Here, $q = 125 = 5^3$

Prime factor of $q = 5$. Ans.

(ii) 29.1385

It is a terminating decimal number,

so, it is a rational number. Ans.

$$\therefore \quad 29.1385 = \frac{291385}{10000} = \frac{58277}{5000}$$ Ans.

which is in the form of $\frac{p}{q}$.

Here, $q = 5000 = 2 \times 2 \times 2 \times 5 \times 5 \times 5 \times 5 = 2^3 \times 5^4$

Prime factors of $q$ are 2 and 5. Ans.

(iii) 3.141441444 ...

It is non-terminating non-recurring decimal,
so, it is irrational number. Ans.

(iv) $0.\overline{52}\cdots$

It is non-terminating recurring decimal,
so, it is a rational number. Ans.

Let $x = 0.\overline{52}$

$\Rightarrow \quad x = 0.525252\ldots\ldots \quad \ldots(i)$

Here, two digits are repeating after decimal place,
so, multiply both sides by 100,

$$100x = 52.5252\ldots\ldots \quad \ldots(ii)$$

Subtracting equation *(i)* from equation *(ii)*,

$$99x = 52$$

$\Rightarrow \quad x = \frac{52}{99} \quad \Rightarrow \quad 0.\overline{52} = \frac{52}{99}$ Ans.

which is in the form of $\frac{p}{q}$.

Here, $q = 99 = 3^2 \times 11$

Prime factors of $q$ are 3 and 11. Ans.

(v) 3.16

It is a terminating decimal number,
so, it is a rational number.

$\therefore \quad 3.16 = \frac{316}{100} = \frac{79}{25}$ Ans.

which is in the form of $\frac{p}{q}$.

Here, $q = 25 = 5^2$

Prime factor of $q = 5$. Ans.

**Example 6.** Insert two irrational numbers between 3 and 5.

**Solution.** Here, $3^2 = 9$ and $5^2 = 25$

Now, $\quad 9 < 11 < 13 < 25$

$\Rightarrow \quad \sqrt{9} < \sqrt{11} < \sqrt{13} < \sqrt{25} \quad \Rightarrow \quad 3 < \sqrt{11} < \sqrt{13} < 5$

Thus, two irrational numbers between 3 and 5 are $\sqrt{11}$ and $\sqrt{13}$. Ans.

**Example 7.** Insert an irrational number between $\frac{1}{4}$ and $\frac{1}{2}$.

**Solution.** The decimal expansion of $\frac{1}{4} = 0.25$

$$\frac{1}{2} = 0.5$$

Now, we can write many non-terminating, non-recurring decimal numbers lying between 0.25 and 0.5.
One such irrational number = 0.323223222... . Ans.

**Example 8.** Find a rational number between $\sqrt{5}$ and $\sqrt{6}$.

**Solution.** We know that $5<5.76<6$

$\Rightarrow \quad \sqrt{5} < \sqrt{5.76} < \sqrt{6} \quad \Rightarrow \quad \sqrt{5} < 2.4 < \sqrt{6}$

and 2.4 is rational because it is terminating decimal.

$\therefore$ A rational number between $\sqrt{5}$ and $\sqrt{6}$ is 2.4. **Ans.**

**Remark**

We can take a rational number in decimal form between two given numbers which is a perfect square.

**Example 9.** Insert two irrational numbers between $\sqrt{5}$ and 4.

**Solution.** Here, $(\sqrt{5})^2 = 5$ and $4^2 = 16$

We know that $5 < 6 < 8 < 16$

$\Rightarrow \sqrt{5} < \sqrt{6} < \sqrt{8} < \sqrt{16} \quad \Rightarrow \quad \sqrt{5} < \sqrt{6} < \sqrt{8} < 4$

So, two irrational numbers between $\sqrt{5}$ and 4 are $\sqrt{6}$ and $\sqrt{8}$. **Ans.**

**Example 10.** Insert three irrational numbers between $2\sqrt{3}$ and $3\sqrt{2}$.

**Solution.** Here, $(2\sqrt{3})^2 = 12$ and $(3\sqrt{2})^2 = 18$

We know that $12 < 13 < 14 < 15 < 18$

$\Rightarrow \sqrt{12} < \sqrt{13} < \sqrt{14} < \sqrt{15} < \sqrt{18} \quad \Rightarrow \quad 2\sqrt{3} < \sqrt{13} < \sqrt{14} < \sqrt{15} < 3\sqrt{2}$

So, three irrational numbers between $2\sqrt{3}$ and $3\sqrt{2}$ are $\sqrt{13}, \sqrt{14}, \sqrt{15}$. **Ans.**

**Example 11.** Represent $\sqrt{2}$ on the number line.

**Solution.** Draw a number line $l$ at which $O$ represents the number zero and $OA = 1$ unit.

Construct $\Delta OAB$ in which $\angle OAB = 90°$ and $AB = 1$ unit.

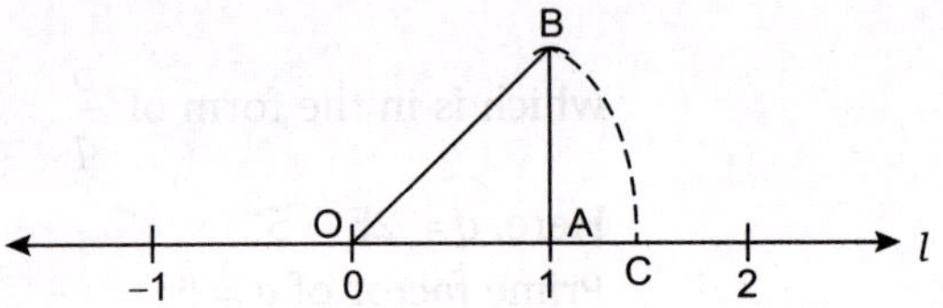


In $\Delta OAB$,

Using Pythagoras theorem,

$$OB^2 = OA^2 + AB^2 = 1^2 + 1^2 = 2$$

$$\Rightarrow \quad OB = \sqrt{2}$$

With centre $O$ and radius $OB$, draw an arc intersecting the number line $l$ at $C$.

$$\therefore \quad OC = OB = \sqrt{2}$$

So, $C$ represents $\sqrt{2}$ on the number line.

**Example 12.** Represent $\sqrt{5}$ on the number line.

**Solution.** Draw a number line $l$ at which $O$ represents the number zero and $OA = 2$ units.

Construct $\Delta OAB$ in which $\angle OAB = 90°$ and $AB = 1$ unit.

In $\Delta OAB$,

Using Pythagoras theorem,

$$OB^2 = OA^2 + AB^2 = 2^2 + 1^2 = 5 \quad \Rightarrow \quad OB = \sqrt{5}$$

With centre $O$ and radius $OB$, draw an arc intersecting the number line $l$ at $M$.

$$\therefore \quad OM = OB = \sqrt{5}$$

So, $M$ represents $\sqrt{5}$ on the number line.

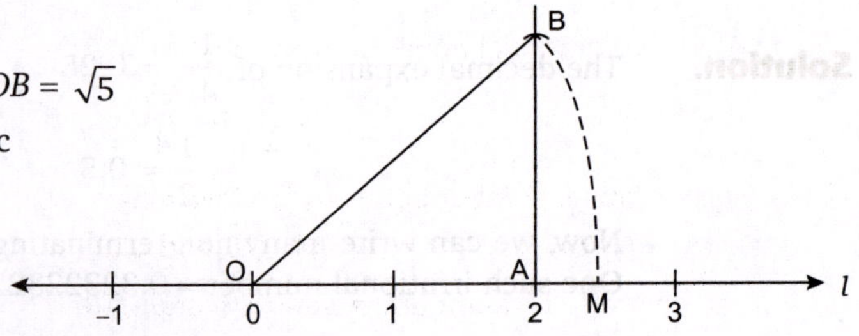

# Exercise 1C

1. Represent the following terminating decimals in the form of a rational number $\left(\text{in fraction form } \frac{p}{q}\right)$:

(i) 0.36 (ii) 0.875 (iii) 3.125 (iv) 42.75

2. Write the decimal expansions of the following rational numbers and state which type of decimal expansion each has?

(i) $\frac{21}{50}$ (ii) $\frac{3}{11}$ (iii) $2\frac{1}{5}$ (iv) $\frac{1}{7}$

(v) $12\frac{5}{6}$ (vi) $\frac{17}{400}$

3. Without actually preforming the long division, state whether the following rational numbers will have a terminating decimal expansion or a non-terminating recurring decimal expansion.

(i) $\frac{3}{8}$ (ii) $\frac{11}{48}$ (iii) $\frac{7}{200}$ (iv) $\frac{13}{350}$

(v) $\frac{19}{3750}$ (vi) $\frac{47}{225}$

4. Write the decimal expansions of those numbers from the following which have terminating decimals.

(i) $\frac{17}{343}$ (ii) $\frac{11}{4000}$ (iii) $\frac{37}{400}$ (iv) $\frac{15}{160}$

(v) $\frac{77}{175}$ (vi) $\frac{7}{375}$

5. Write the decimal expansion of $\frac{1}{7}$. Hence, write the decimal expansions of $\frac{2}{7}, \frac{3}{7}, \frac{4}{7}, \frac{5}{7}$ and $\frac{6}{7}$.

6. Express the following recurring decimals in the form of a rational number $\left(\text{in fraction form } \frac{p}{q}\right)$:

(i) $0.\overline{6}$ (ii) $0.\overline{24}$ (iii) $1.4\dot{6}$ (iv) $0.2\overline{73}$

(v) $3.2\overline{35}$ (vi) $11.\overline{53}$

7. Express $1.2\dot{6} + 0.\overline{35}$ in the form of a rational number $\left(\text{in fraction form } \frac{p}{q}\right)$.

8. The following real numbers have decimal expansions as given below. In each case, state whether they are rational or irrational. If they are rational, express them in the form $\frac{p}{q}$, where $p$ and $q$ are co-prime integers and $q \neq 0$ and then what can you say about the prime factors of $q$ ?

(i) 15.764 (ii) $18.\overline{32}$ (iii) 1.585585558... (iv) 1.636363

9. Insert an irrational number between the following :

(i) 4 and 5 (ii) $\frac{1}{3}$ and $\frac{1}{2}$ (iii) 0.3 and 0.5 (iv) $-\frac{1}{3}$ and $-\frac{4}{5}$ .

10. Insert two irrational numbers between :

(i) 4 and 6 (ii) $\frac{1}{2}$ and $\frac{13}{4}$

11. Find a rational number between the following :

(i) $\sqrt{2}$ and $\sqrt{3}$ (ii) $\sqrt{18}$ and $\sqrt{19}$

12. Find an irrational number between $\sqrt{6}$ and $\sqrt{10}$.

13. Find an irrational number between 3 and $\sqrt{15}$.

14. Find two irrational numbers between $4\sqrt{2}$ and $3\sqrt{3}$.

15. Represent $\sqrt{10}$ on the number line.

16. Represent $\sqrt{3}$ on the number line.

17. Represent $\sqrt{6}$ on the number line.

## Answers

**1.** (i) $\frac{9}{25}$ (ii) $\frac{7}{8}$ (iii) $\frac{25}{8}$ (iv) $\frac{171}{4}$

**2.** (i) 0.42, terminating decimal (ii) $0.\dot{2}\dot{7}$, non-terminating repeating decimal (iii) 2.2, terminating decimal
(iv) $0.\overline{142857}$, non-terminating repeating decimal (v) $12.8\dot{3}$, non-terminating repeating decimal
(vi) 0.0425, terminating decimal

**3.** (i) terminating (ii) non-terminating recurring (iii) terminating (iv) non-terminating recurring
(v) non-terminating recurring (vi) non-terminating recurring

**4.** (ii) 0.00275 (iii) 0.0925 (iv) 0.09375 (v) 0.44

**5.** $\frac{1}{7} = 0.\overline{142857}$, $\frac{2}{7} = 0.\overline{285714}$, $\frac{3}{7} = 0.\overline{428571}$, $\frac{4}{7} = 0.\overline{571428}$, $\frac{5}{7} = 0.\overline{714285}$, $\frac{6}{7} = 0.\overline{857142}$

**6.** (i) $\frac{2}{3}$ (ii) $\frac{8}{33}$ (iii) $\frac{22}{15}$ (iv) $\frac{271}{990}$ (v) $\frac{3203}{990}$ (vi) $\frac{1142}{99}$ **7.** $\frac{802}{495}$

**8.** (i) rational, $\frac{3941}{250}$, prime factors = 2, 5 (ii) rational, $\frac{1814}{99}$, prime factors = 3, 11
(iii) irrational (iv) rational, $\frac{1636363}{1000000}$, prime factors = 2, 5

**9.** (i) $\sqrt{20}$ (ii) $\sqrt{0.17}$ (iii) $\sqrt{0.15}$ (iv) $-\sqrt{0.2}$ **10.** (i) $\sqrt{17}, \sqrt{18}$ (ii) $\sqrt{2}, \sqrt{3}$

**11.** (i) 1.5 (ii) 4.3 **12.** $\sqrt{7}$ **13.** $\sqrt{10}$ **14.** $\sqrt{28}, \sqrt{29}$

## Surds

We are familiar to the irrational numbers $\sqrt{2}, \sqrt{3}, \sqrt{5}$,..... . All of these are the square roots of some positive rational numbers, and these rational numbers are not the perfect squares.

Similarly, we can take the cube roots of some positive rational numbers like $\sqrt[3]{2}$, $\sqrt[3]{3}$, $\sqrt[3]{4}$...

Such numbers are called the surds or radicals.

If '$a$' is any positive rational number and $n > 1$ is a positive integer then

$\sqrt[n]{a} = a^{1/n}$ is called a surd of order '$n$'.

**Remark**

All surds are irrational numbers.

**Note that :**

(i) '$a$' is a positive integer. (ii) $n > 1$ is a positive integer. (iii) $\sqrt[n]{a}$ is not a rational number.

## Laws of Surds

1. $(\sqrt[n]{a})^n = a$
2. $\sqrt[n]{a} . \sqrt[n]{b} = \sqrt[n]{ab}$
3. $\frac{\sqrt[n]{a}}{\sqrt[n]{b}} = \sqrt[n]{\frac{a}{b}}$

where $a$ and $b$ are positive rational numbers and $n > 1$ is a positive integer.

**Remember**

1. $\sqrt{3}+\sqrt{5} \neq \sqrt{8}$ 2. $\sqrt{5}-\sqrt{3} \neq \sqrt{2}$ 3. $\sqrt{3}+\sqrt{3} = 2\sqrt{3}$ 4. $5\sqrt{2}-2\sqrt{2} = 3\sqrt{2}$
5. (i) $(\sqrt{a}+\sqrt{b})^2 = a + 2\sqrt{ab} + b$ (ii) $(\sqrt{a}-\sqrt{b})^2 = a - 2\sqrt{ab} + b$
   (iii) $(\sqrt{a}+\sqrt{b})(\sqrt{a}-\sqrt{b}) = a - b$ (iv) $(a+\sqrt{b})(a-\sqrt{b}) = a^2 - b$
   where $a$ and $b$ are positive rational numbers.
6. (i) $\sqrt{a} < \sqrt{b}$ if $a < b$ (ii) $\sqrt{a} > \sqrt{b}$ if $a > b$

where $\sqrt{a}$ and $\sqrt{b}$ are positive irrational numbers.

## Illustrative Examples

**Example 1.** State with reason, which of the following are surds and which are not?

(i) $\sqrt{72}$ (ii) $\sqrt{2} \times \sqrt{18}$ (iii) $\sqrt[3]{3} \times \sqrt[3]{243}$ (iv) $\sqrt{243} \times \sqrt{9}$ (v) $\sqrt[3]{16} \times \sqrt[3]{48}$

**Solution.** (i) $\sqrt{72} = \sqrt{2 \times 2 \times 2 \times 3 \times 3} = 2 \times 3 \times \sqrt{2} = 6\sqrt{2}$

which is not a rational number.

$\therefore$ $\sqrt{72}$ is a surd. Ans.

(ii) $\sqrt{2} \times \sqrt{18} = \sqrt{2 \times 18} = \sqrt{2 \times 2 \times 3 \times 3} = 2 \times 3 = 6$

which is a rational number.

$\therefore$ $\sqrt{2} \times \sqrt{18}$ is not a surd. Ans.

(iii) $\sqrt[3]{3} \times \sqrt[3]{243} = \sqrt[3]{3 \times 243} = \sqrt[3]{3 \times 3 \times 3 \times 3 \times 3 \times 3} = 3 \times 3 = 9$

which is a rational number.

$\therefore$ $\sqrt[3]{3} \times \sqrt[3]{243}$ is not a surd. Ans.

(iv) $\sqrt{243} \times \sqrt{9} = \sqrt{243 \times 9} = \sqrt{3 \times 3 \times 3 \times 3 \times 3 \times 3 \times 3} = 3 \times 3 \times 3 \times \sqrt{3} = 27\sqrt{3}$

which is not a rational number.

$\therefore$ $\sqrt{243} \times \sqrt{9}$ is a surd. Ans.

(v) $\sqrt[3]{16} \times \sqrt[3]{48} = \sqrt[3]{16 \times 48} = \sqrt[3]{2 \times 2 \times 2 \times 2 \times 2 \times 2 \times 2 \times 2 \times 3} = 2 \times 2 \times \sqrt[3]{2 \times 2 \times 3} = 4 \times \sqrt[3]{12}$

which is not a rational number.

$\therefore$ $\sqrt[3]{16} \times \sqrt[3]{48}$ is a surd. Ans.

**Example 2.** Simplify :

(i) $(\sqrt{3}+\sqrt{5})^2$ (ii) $(\sqrt{7}-\sqrt{2})^2$ (iii) $(\sqrt{5}+2)(\sqrt{5}-2)$ (iv) $(\sqrt{8}+\sqrt{6})(\sqrt{8}-\sqrt{6})$

(v) $(3+\sqrt{5})(\sqrt{2}+1)$

**Solution.** (i) $(\sqrt{3}+\sqrt{5})^2 = (\sqrt{3})^2 + 2(\sqrt{3})(\sqrt{5}) + (\sqrt{5})^2 = 3 + 2\sqrt{15} + 5 = 8 + 2\sqrt{15}$ Ans.

(ii) $(\sqrt{7}-\sqrt{2})^2 = (\sqrt{7})^2 - 2(\sqrt{7})(\sqrt{2}) + (\sqrt{2})^2 = 7 - 2\sqrt{14} + 2 = 9 - 2\sqrt{14}$ Ans.

(iii) $(\sqrt{5}+2)(\sqrt{5}-2) = (\sqrt{5})^2 - (2)^2 = 5 - 4 = 1$ Ans.

(iv) $(\sqrt{8}+\sqrt{6})(\sqrt{8}-\sqrt{6}) = (\sqrt{8})^2 - (\sqrt{6})^2 = 8 - 6 = 2$ Ans.

(v) $(3+\sqrt{5})(\sqrt{2}+1) = 3(\sqrt{2}+1) + \sqrt{5}(\sqrt{2}+1) = 3\sqrt{2} + 3 + \sqrt{10} + \sqrt{5}$ Ans.

**Example 3.** Show that $\sqrt[3]{3}$ is an irrational number.

**Solution.** Let $\sqrt[3]{3}$ be a rational number.

Let $\sqrt[3]{3} = \frac{a}{b}$, where $a$ and $b$ are integers, $b \neq 0$ and $a$ and $b$ have no common factor except 1.

$\Rightarrow \quad 3 = \frac{a^3}{b^3} \Rightarrow a^3 = 3b^3$ ...(i)

Now, 3 divides $3b^3$

$\Rightarrow$ 3 divides $a^3$.

$\Rightarrow$ 3 divides $a$. ($\because$ 3 in a prime number.)

Let $a = 3c \Rightarrow a^3 = 27c^3 \Rightarrow 3b^3 = 27c^3$ [From (i)]

$\Rightarrow b^3 = 9c^3$

Now, 3 divides $9c^3$.

$\Rightarrow$ 3 divides $b^3$.

$\Rightarrow$ 3 divides $b$. ($\because$ 3 is a prime number.)

So, $a$ and $b$ have a common factor 3,

which contradicts the fact that $a$ and $b$ have no common factor except 1.

Thus, our assumption is wrong.

So, $\sqrt[3]{3}$ is not a rational number.

Hence, $\sqrt[3]{3}$ is an irrational number. Hence Proved.

**Example 4.** Prove that $\sqrt[3]{6}$ is an irrational number.

**Solution.** Let $\sqrt[3]{6}$ be a rational number.

Let, $\sqrt[3]{6} = \frac{a}{b}$, where $a$ and $b$ are integers, $b \neq 0$ and $a$ and $b$ have no common factor except 1.

$\Rightarrow \quad 6 = \frac{a^3}{b^3} \Rightarrow a^3 = 6b^3$ ...(i)

Now, 3 divides $6b^3$.

$\Rightarrow$ 3 divides $a^3$.

$\Rightarrow$ 3 divides $a$. ($\because$ 3 is a prime number.)

Let $a = 3c \Rightarrow a^3 = 27c^3 \Rightarrow 6b^3 = 27c^3$ [From (i)]

$\Rightarrow 2b^3 = 9c^3$

Now, 3 divides $9c^3$.

$\Rightarrow$ 3 divides $2b^3$.

$\Rightarrow$ 3 divides $b^3$.

$\Rightarrow$ 3 divides b. ($\because$ 3 is a prime number.)

So, $a$ and $b$ have a common factor 3,

which contradicts the fact that $a$ and $b$ have no common factor except 1.

Thus, our assumption is wrong.

So, $\sqrt[3]{6}$ is not a rational number.

Hence, $\sqrt[3]{6}$ is an irrational number. Hence Proved.

**Example 5.** If $\sqrt{2} = 1.414$, then find the value of $\sqrt{8} + 3\sqrt{50}$.

**Solution.** $\sqrt{8} + 3\sqrt{50} = \sqrt{2 \times 2 \times 2} + 3\sqrt{5 \times 5 \times 2} = 2\sqrt{2} + 3 \times 5\sqrt{2}$

$= 2\sqrt{2} + 15\sqrt{2} = 17\sqrt{2} = 17 \times 1.414 = 24.038$ Ans.

**Example 6.** If $\sqrt{2} = 1.414$ and $\sqrt{3} = 1.732$, then find the value of $\sqrt{32} + 2\sqrt{48} - \sqrt{75}$.

**Solution.**

$$\sqrt{32} + 2\sqrt{48} - \sqrt{75} = \sqrt{2 \times 2 \times 2 \times 2 \times 2} + 2\sqrt{2 \times 2 \times 2 \times 2 \times 3} - \sqrt{5 \times 5 \times 3}$$
$$= 2 \times 2 \times \sqrt{2} + 2 \times 2 \times 2 \times \sqrt{3} - 5\sqrt{3} = 4\sqrt{2} + 8\sqrt{3} - 5\sqrt{3}$$
$$= 4\sqrt{2} + 3\sqrt{3} = 4 \times 1.414 + 3 \times 1.732 = 5.656 + 5.196 = 10.852$$
Ans.

**Example 7.** Simplify the following :

(i) $\sqrt{4 + 2\sqrt{3}}$ (ii) $\sqrt{8 - 2\sqrt{15}}$

**Solution.**

(i) $\sqrt{4 + 2\sqrt{3}} = \sqrt{3 + 1 + 2\sqrt{3}} = \sqrt{(\sqrt{3})^2 + (1)^2 + 2(\sqrt{3})(1)} = \sqrt{(\sqrt{3} + 1)^2} = \sqrt{3} + 1$ Ans.

(ii) $\sqrt{8 - 2\sqrt{15}} = \sqrt{5 + 3 - 2\sqrt{5}\sqrt{3}} = \sqrt{(\sqrt{5})^2 + (\sqrt{3})^2 - 2\sqrt{5}\sqrt{3}} = \sqrt{(\sqrt{5} - \sqrt{3})^2} = \sqrt{5} - \sqrt{3}$ Ans.

**Example 8.** Which is smaller : $2\sqrt{3}$ or $3\sqrt{2}$ ?

**Solution.**

$$2\sqrt{3} = \sqrt{2 \times 2 \times 3} = \sqrt{12}$$
$$3\sqrt{2} = \sqrt{3 \times 3 \times 2} = \sqrt{18}$$

Now, $\sqrt{12} < \sqrt{18} \Rightarrow 2\sqrt{3} < 3\sqrt{2}$

$\therefore 2\sqrt{3}$ is smaller. Ans.

**Example 9.** Arrange the following in ascending order :

$$\sqrt{45},\ 2\sqrt{5},\ 3\sqrt{3}$$

**Solution.**

$$2\sqrt{5} = \sqrt{2 \times 2 \times 5} = \sqrt{20}$$
$$3\sqrt{3} = \sqrt{3 \times 3 \times 3} = \sqrt{27}$$

Now, $\sqrt{20} < \sqrt{27} < \sqrt{45} \Rightarrow 2\sqrt{5} < 3\sqrt{3} < \sqrt{45}$ Ans.

**Example 10.** Compare $\sqrt[3]{4}$ and $\sqrt[4]{3}$.

**Solution.**

$$\sqrt[3]{4} = 4^{\frac{1}{3}} \text{ and } \sqrt[4]{3} = 3^{\frac{1}{4}}$$

Powers are $\frac{1}{3}$ and $\frac{1}{4}$.

L.C.M. (3, 4) = 12

$\therefore$
$$\sqrt[3]{4} = 4^{\frac{1}{3}} = 4^{\frac{3}{12}} = (4^3)^{\frac{1}{12}} = \sqrt[12]{64}$$
$$\sqrt[4]{3} = 3^{\frac{1}{4}} = 3^{\frac{4}{12}} = (3^4)^{\frac{1}{12}} = \sqrt[12]{81}$$

Now, $\sqrt[12]{64} < \sqrt[12]{81} \Rightarrow \sqrt[3]{4} < \sqrt[4]{3}$ Ans.

## Exercise 1D

**1.** State with reason, which of the following are surds and which are not ?

(i) $\sqrt{12}$ (ii) $6\sqrt{16}$ (iii) $2\sqrt{3} \times 6\sqrt{27}$ (iv) $\sqrt[3]{8} \times \sqrt[3]{32}$

(v) $3\sqrt{2} - 7$

**2.** Simplify :

(i) $(\sqrt{2} + 1)^2$ (ii) $(\sqrt{3} - \sqrt{2})^2$ (iii) $(\sqrt{7} - \sqrt{3})(\sqrt{7} + \sqrt{3})$ (iv) $(4 + \sqrt{3})(4 - \sqrt{3})$

(v) $(1 + \sqrt{3})(\sqrt{2} - 1)$ (vi) $(6 - \sqrt{5})^2$

3. Show that $\sqrt[3]{2}$ is an irrational number.
4. Show that $\sqrt[3]{5}$ is an irrational number.
5. Show that $\sqrt[3]{4}$ is an irrational number.
6. Show that $\sqrt[3]{12}$ is an irrational number.
7. If $\sqrt{2} = 1.414$, find the value of the following :
   (i) $\sqrt{200} + \sqrt{50} - 5\sqrt{32}$ (ii) $3\sqrt{72} + 6\sqrt{128} - \sqrt{288}$
8. If $\sqrt{2} = 1.414, \sqrt{3} = 1.732$, find the value of the following :
   (i) $5\sqrt{12} + \sqrt{98} - \sqrt{108}$ (ii) $3\sqrt{243} + 6\sqrt{72} - 3\sqrt{8}$
9. Simplify the following :
   (i) $\sqrt{7 + 4\sqrt{3}}$ (ii) $\sqrt{3 - 2\sqrt{2}}$ (iii) $\sqrt{10 + 2\sqrt{21}}$ (iv) $\sqrt{7 - 2\sqrt{10}}$
10. Which is greater ?
   (i) $3\sqrt{5}$ and $6\sqrt{2}$ (ii) $6\sqrt{5}$ and $5\sqrt{6}$
11. Arrange in ascending order.
   (i) $2\sqrt{7}, 3\sqrt{2}, 4\sqrt{3}$ (ii) $7\sqrt{2}, 3\sqrt{11}, 5\sqrt{3}$
12. Compare.
   (i) $\sqrt[3]{3}$ and $\sqrt[4]{5}$ (ii) $\sqrt[4]{7}$ and $\sqrt[3]{6}$

## Answers

**1.** (i), (iv), (v) are surds. **2.** (i) $3 + 2\sqrt{2}$ (ii) $5 - 2\sqrt{6}$ (iii) 4 (iv) 13 (v) $\sqrt{2} - 1 + \sqrt{6} - \sqrt{3}$ (vi) $41 - 12\sqrt{5}$
**7.** (i) –7.07 (ii) 76.356 **8.** (i) 16.826 (ii) 89.184 **9.** (i) $2 + \sqrt{3}$ (ii) $\sqrt{2} - 1$ (iii) $\sqrt{7} + \sqrt{3}$ (iv) $\sqrt{5} - \sqrt{2}$
**10.** (i) $6\sqrt{2} > 3\sqrt{5}$ (ii) $6\sqrt{5} > 5\sqrt{6}$ **11.** (i) $3\sqrt{2} < 2\sqrt{7} < 4\sqrt{3}$ (ii) $5\sqrt{3} < 7\sqrt{2} < 3\sqrt{11}$ **12.** (i) $\sqrt[3]{3} < \sqrt[4]{5}$ (ii) $\sqrt[4]{7} < \sqrt[3]{6}$

## Rationalising Factor of a Surd

When the product of two irrational numbers is a rational number, then each irrational number is called the rationalising factor of the other irrational number.

*For example :*

1. $\sqrt{2} \times \sqrt{2} = 2$.

   So, $\sqrt{2}$ is the rationalising factor of $\sqrt{2}$.

2. $(3)^{\frac{1}{3}} \times (3)^{\frac{2}{3}} = 3$

   So, $(3)^{\frac{1}{3}}$ and $(3)^{\frac{2}{3}}$ are the rationalising factors of each other.

3. $(3 + \sqrt{2})(3 - \sqrt{2}) = (3)^2 - (\sqrt{2})^2 = 9 - 2 = 7$

So, $3 + \sqrt{2}$ and $3 - \sqrt{2}$ are the rationalising factors of each other.

Thus, we conclude that :

1. The rationalising factor of $a + \sqrt{b}$ is $a - \sqrt{b}$
2. The rationalising factor of $a - \sqrt{b}$ is $a + \sqrt{b}$
3. The rationalising factor of $\sqrt{a} + \sqrt{b}$ is $\sqrt{a} - \sqrt{b}$
4. The rationalising factor of $\sqrt{a} - \sqrt{b}$ is $\sqrt{a} + \sqrt{b}$

**NOTE**

If we have to rationalise the denominator of an expression, we multiply the numerator and denominator by the rationalising factor of the denominator.

# Illustrative Examples

**Example 1.** Rationalise the denominators of the following :

(i) $\frac{1}{\sqrt{3}}$ (ii) $\frac{\sqrt{2}}{\sqrt{5}}$ (iii) $\frac{1}{\sqrt{2}+1}$ (iv) $\frac{3}{\sqrt{5}-\sqrt{2}}$

**Solution.** (i) $\frac{1}{\sqrt{3}} = \frac{1}{\sqrt{3}} \times \frac{\sqrt{3}}{\sqrt{3}}$ ($\because$ Rationalising factor of $\sqrt{3}$ is $\sqrt{3}$.)

$= \frac{\sqrt{3}}{3}$ Ans.

(ii) $\frac{\sqrt{2}}{\sqrt{5}} = \frac{\sqrt{2}}{\sqrt{5}} \times \frac{\sqrt{5}}{\sqrt{5}}$ ($\because$ Rationalising factor of $\sqrt{5}$ is $\sqrt{5}$.)

$= \frac{\sqrt{10}}{5}$ Ans.

(iii) $\frac{1}{\sqrt{2}+1} = \frac{1}{\sqrt{2}+1} \times \frac{\sqrt{2}-1}{\sqrt{2}-1}$ ($\because$ Rationalising factor of $\sqrt{2}+1$ is $\sqrt{2}-1$.)

$= \frac{\sqrt{2}-1}{(\sqrt{2})^2-(1)^2} = \frac{\sqrt{2}-1}{2-1} = \sqrt{2}-1$ Ans.

(iv) $\frac{3}{\sqrt{5}-\sqrt{2}} = \frac{3}{\sqrt{5}-\sqrt{2}} \times \frac{\sqrt{5}+\sqrt{2}}{\sqrt{5}+\sqrt{2}}$ ($\because$ Rationalising factor of $\sqrt{5}-\sqrt{2}$ is $\sqrt{5}+\sqrt{2}$.)

$= \frac{3(\sqrt{5}+\sqrt{2})}{(\sqrt{5})^2-(\sqrt{2})^2} = \frac{3(\sqrt{5}+\sqrt{2})}{5-2} = \sqrt{5}+\sqrt{2}$ Ans.

**Example 2.** Rationalise the denominators of the following :

(i) $\frac{6}{3\sqrt{2}-2\sqrt{3}}$ (ii) $\frac{30}{5\sqrt{2}+2\sqrt{5}}$

**Solution.** (i) $\frac{6}{3\sqrt{2}-2\sqrt{3}} = \frac{6}{3\sqrt{2}-2\sqrt{3}} \times \frac{3\sqrt{2}+2\sqrt{3}}{3\sqrt{2}+2\sqrt{3}}$ ($\because$ Rationalising factor of $3\sqrt{2}-2\sqrt{3}$ is $3\sqrt{2}+2\sqrt{3}$.)

$= \frac{6(3\sqrt{2}+2\sqrt{3})}{(3\sqrt{2})^2-(2\sqrt{3})^2} = \frac{6(3\sqrt{2}+2\sqrt{3})}{18-12} = 3\sqrt{2}+2\sqrt{3}$ Ans.

(ii) $\frac{30}{5\sqrt{2}+2\sqrt{5}} = \frac{30}{5\sqrt{2}+2\sqrt{5}} \times \frac{5\sqrt{2}-2\sqrt{5}}{5\sqrt{2}-2\sqrt{5}}$ ($\because$ Rationalising factor of $5\sqrt{2}+2\sqrt{5}$ is $5\sqrt{2}-2\sqrt{5}$.)

$= \frac{30(5\sqrt{2}-2\sqrt{5})}{(5\sqrt{2})^2-(2\sqrt{5})^2} = \frac{30(5\sqrt{2}-2\sqrt{5})}{50-20} = 5\sqrt{2}-2\sqrt{5}$ Ans.

**Example 3.** Simplify : $\frac{1}{\sqrt{2}+1} + \frac{1}{\sqrt{3}+\sqrt{2}} + \frac{1}{\sqrt{4}+\sqrt{3}}$

**Solution.** $\frac{1}{\sqrt{2}+1} + \frac{1}{\sqrt{3}+\sqrt{2}} + \frac{1}{\sqrt{4}+\sqrt{3}} = \frac{1}{\sqrt{2}+1} \times \frac{\sqrt{2}-1}{\sqrt{2}-1} + \frac{1}{\sqrt{3}+\sqrt{2}} \times \frac{\sqrt{3}-\sqrt{2}}{\sqrt{3}-\sqrt{2}} + \frac{1}{2+\sqrt{3}} \times \frac{2-\sqrt{3}}{2-\sqrt{3}}$

$= \frac{\sqrt{2}-1}{(\sqrt{2})^2-(1)^2} + \frac{\sqrt{3}-\sqrt{2}}{(\sqrt{3})^2-(\sqrt{2})^2} + \frac{2-\sqrt{3}}{(2)^2-(\sqrt{3})^2}$

$$= \frac{\sqrt{2}-1}{2-1} + \frac{\sqrt{3}-\sqrt{2}}{3-2} + \frac{2-\sqrt{3}}{4-3} = \sqrt{2} - 1 + \sqrt{3} - \sqrt{2} + 2 - \sqrt{3} = 1$$ Ans.

**Example 4.** Simplify : $\frac{\sqrt{6}}{\sqrt{3}+\sqrt{2}} + \frac{\sqrt{6}}{\sqrt{2}+1} - \frac{2\sqrt{6}}{\sqrt{3}+1}$

**Solution.**
$$\frac{\sqrt{6}}{\sqrt{3}+\sqrt{2}} + \frac{\sqrt{6}}{\sqrt{2}+1} - \frac{2\sqrt{6}}{\sqrt{3}+1} = \frac{\sqrt{6}}{\sqrt{3}+\sqrt{2}} \times \frac{\sqrt{3}-\sqrt{2}}{\sqrt{3}-\sqrt{2}} + \frac{\sqrt{6}}{\sqrt{2}+1} \times \frac{\sqrt{2}-1}{\sqrt{2}-1} - \frac{2\sqrt{6}}{\sqrt{3}+1} \times \frac{\sqrt{3}-1}{\sqrt{3}-1}$$
$$= \frac{\sqrt{18}-\sqrt{12}}{(\sqrt{3})^2-(\sqrt{2})^2} + \frac{\sqrt{12}-\sqrt{6}}{(\sqrt{2})^2-(1)^2} - \frac{2\sqrt{18}-2\sqrt{6}}{(\sqrt{3})^2-(1)^2}$$
$$= (3\sqrt{2} - 2\sqrt{3}) + (2\sqrt{3} - \sqrt{6}) - (3\sqrt{2} - \sqrt{6})$$
$$= 3\sqrt{2} - 2\sqrt{3} + 2\sqrt{3} - \sqrt{6} - 3\sqrt{2} + \sqrt{6} = 0$$ Ans.

**Example 5.** If $\sqrt{2} = 1.414$ and $\sqrt{3} = 1.732$, then evaluate the following after rationalising the denominator :

(i) $\frac{7}{3-\sqrt{2}}$ (ii) $\frac{19}{2\sqrt{3}+5\sqrt{2}}$

**Solution.** (i) $\frac{7}{3-\sqrt{2}} = \frac{7}{3-\sqrt{2}} \times \frac{3+\sqrt{2}}{3+\sqrt{2}} = \frac{7(3+\sqrt{2})}{(3)^2-(\sqrt{2})^2} = \frac{7\left(3+\sqrt{2}\right)}{9-2} = 3 + \sqrt{2} = 3 + 1.414 = 4.414$ Ans.

(ii) $\frac{19}{2\sqrt{3}+5\sqrt{2}} = \frac{19}{5\sqrt{2}+2\sqrt{3}} \times \frac{5\sqrt{2}-2\sqrt{3}}{5\sqrt{2}-2\sqrt{3}} = \frac{19\left(5\sqrt{2}-2\sqrt{3}\right)}{\left(5\sqrt{2}\right)^2-\left(2\sqrt{3}\right)^2} = \frac{19\left(5\sqrt{2}-2\sqrt{3}\right)}{50-12}$

$$= \frac{5\sqrt{2}-2\sqrt{3}}{2} = \frac{5 \times 1.414 - 2 \times 1.732}{2} = \frac{7.070 - 3.464}{2} = \frac{3.606}{2} = 1.803$$ Ans.

**Example 6.** If $a$ and $b$ are rational numbers, find the values of $a$ and $b$.

(i) $a + b\sqrt{3} = \frac{4-\sqrt{3}}{4+\sqrt{3}}$ (ii) $a + b\sqrt{2} = \frac{3+2\sqrt{2}}{3-2\sqrt{2}}$ (iii) $a + b\sqrt{6} = \frac{7+2\sqrt{6}}{5+\sqrt{6}} - \frac{7-2\sqrt{6}}{5-\sqrt{6}}$

**Solution.** (i) $a + b\sqrt{3} = \frac{4-\sqrt{3}}{4+\sqrt{3}} = \frac{4-\sqrt{3}}{4+\sqrt{3}} \times \frac{4-\sqrt{3}}{4-\sqrt{3}} = \frac{(4)^2+(\sqrt{3})^2-2(4)(\sqrt{3})}{(4)^2-(\sqrt{3})^2} = \frac{16+3-8\sqrt{3}}{16-3} = \frac{19}{13} - \frac{8}{13}\sqrt{3}$

On comparing, we get

$$a = \frac{19}{13},\ b = \frac{-8}{13}$$ Ans.

(ii) $a + b\sqrt{2} = \frac{3+2\sqrt{2}}{3-2\sqrt{2}} = \frac{3+2\sqrt{2}}{3-2\sqrt{2}} \times \frac{3+2\sqrt{2}}{3+2\sqrt{2}} = \frac{(3)^2+(2\sqrt{2})^2+2(3)(2\sqrt{2})}{(3)^2-(2\sqrt{2})^2}$

$$= \frac{9+8+12\sqrt{2}}{9-8} = 17 + 12\sqrt{2}$$

On comparing, we get

$$a = 17, b = 12$$ Ans.

(iii) $a + b\sqrt{6} = \frac{7+2\sqrt{6}}{5+\sqrt{6}} - \frac{7-2\sqrt{6}}{5-\sqrt{6}} = \frac{\left(7+2\sqrt{6}\right)\left(5-\sqrt{6}\right)-\left(7-2\sqrt{6}\right)\left(5+\sqrt{6}\right)}{\left(5+\sqrt{6}\right)\left(5-\sqrt{6}\right)}$

$$= \frac{\left(35-7\sqrt{6}+10\sqrt{6}-12\right)-\left(35+7\sqrt{6}-10\sqrt{6}-12\right)}{(5)^2-\left(\sqrt{6}\right)^2}$$

$$= \frac{6\sqrt{6}}{25-6} = \frac{6}{19}\sqrt{6} = 0 + \frac{6}{19}\sqrt{6}$$

On comparing, we get $a = 0,\ b = \dfrac{6}{19}$ **Ans.**

**Example 7.** If $x = 3 + 2\sqrt{2}$, find :

(i) $\dfrac{1}{x}$ (ii) $x + \dfrac{1}{x}$ (iii) $x^2 + \dfrac{1}{x^2}$

**Solution.** (i) $\dfrac{1}{x} = \dfrac{1}{3+2\sqrt{2}} = \dfrac{1}{3+2\sqrt{2}} \times \dfrac{3-2\sqrt{2}}{3-2\sqrt{2}} = \dfrac{3-2\sqrt{2}}{(3)^2-(2\sqrt{2})^2} = \dfrac{3-2\sqrt{2}}{9-8} = 3-2\sqrt{2}$ **Ans.**

(ii) $x + \dfrac{1}{x} = (3+2\sqrt{2}) + (3-2\sqrt{2}) = 6$ **Ans.**

(iii) $x^2 + \dfrac{1}{x^2} = \left(x^2 + \dfrac{1}{x^2} + 2\right) - 2 = \left(x + \dfrac{1}{x}\right)^2 - 2 = 6^2 - 2 = 34$ **Ans.**

**Example 8.** If $x = \dfrac{\sqrt{2}+1}{\sqrt{2}-1}$ and $y = \dfrac{\sqrt{2}-1}{\sqrt{2}+1}$, find :

(i) $x^2$ (ii) $y^2$ (iii) $xy$ (iv) $x^2+y^2+xy$

**Solution.** (i) $x = \dfrac{\sqrt{2}+1}{\sqrt{2}-1} = \dfrac{\sqrt{2}+1}{\sqrt{2}-1} \times \dfrac{\sqrt{2}+1}{\sqrt{2}+1} = \dfrac{(\sqrt{2})^2 + 1^2 + 2(\sqrt{2})(1)}{(\sqrt{2})^2 - (1)^2} = \dfrac{2+1+2\sqrt{2}}{2-1} = 3+2\sqrt{2}$

$\Rightarrow\quad x^2 = (3+2\sqrt{2})^2 = (3)^2 + (2\sqrt{2})^2 + 2(3)(2\sqrt{2}) = 9 + 8 + 12\sqrt{2} = 17 + 12\sqrt{2}$ **Ans.**

(ii) $y = \dfrac{\sqrt{2}-1}{\sqrt{2}+1} = \dfrac{\sqrt{2}-1}{\sqrt{2}+1} \times \dfrac{\sqrt{2}-1}{\sqrt{2}-1} = \dfrac{(\sqrt{2})^2 + 1^2 - 2(\sqrt{2})(1)}{(\sqrt{2})^2 - 1^2} = \dfrac{2+1-2\sqrt{2}}{2-1} = 3-2\sqrt{2}$

$\Rightarrow\quad y^2 = (3-2\sqrt{2})^2 = 3^2 + (2\sqrt{2})^2 - 2(3)(2\sqrt{2}) = 9 + 8 - 12\sqrt{2} = 17 - 2\sqrt{2}$ **Ans.**

(iii) $xy = \dfrac{\sqrt{2}+1}{\sqrt{2}-1} \times \dfrac{\sqrt{2}-1}{\sqrt{2}+1} = 1$ **Ans.**

(iv) $x^2 + y^2 + xy = (17 + 2\sqrt{2}) + (17 - 2\sqrt{2}) + 1 = 35$ **Ans.**

**Example 9.** If $x = 12 + 6\sqrt{3}$ then find the value of $\sqrt{x} + \dfrac{6}{\sqrt{x}}$

**Solution.**

$x = 12 + 6\sqrt{3} = 9 + 3 + 6\sqrt{3} = 3^2 + (\sqrt{3})^2 + 2(3)(\sqrt{3}) = (3+\sqrt{3})^2$

$\Rightarrow\quad \sqrt{x} = 3 + \sqrt{3}$

$\Rightarrow\quad \dfrac{1}{\sqrt{x}} = \dfrac{1}{3+\sqrt{3}} = \dfrac{1}{3+\sqrt{3}} \times \dfrac{3-\sqrt{3}}{3-\sqrt{3}} = \dfrac{3-\sqrt{3}}{3^2-(\sqrt{3})^2} = \dfrac{3-\sqrt{3}}{9-3} = \dfrac{3-\sqrt{3}}{6}$

$\Rightarrow\quad \dfrac{6}{\sqrt{x}} = 3 - \sqrt{3}$

Now, $\sqrt{x} + \dfrac{6}{\sqrt{x}} = (3+\sqrt{3}) + (3-\sqrt{3}) = 6$ **Ans.**

**Example 10.** Prove that $\dfrac{1}{\sqrt{2}+1}$ is an irrational number.

**Solution.** $\dfrac{1}{\sqrt{2}+1} = \dfrac{1}{\sqrt{2}+1} \times \dfrac{\sqrt{2}-1}{\sqrt{2}-1} = \dfrac{\sqrt{2}-1}{(\sqrt{2})^2 - 1^2} = \dfrac{\sqrt{2}-1}{2-1} = \sqrt{2}-1$

Let $\sqrt{2} - 1$ be rational.

and $\sqrt{2} - 1 = \frac{a}{b}$

where $a$, $b$ are integers and $b \neq 0$

$\Rightarrow \quad \sqrt{2} = \frac{a}{b} + 1 \quad \Rightarrow \quad \sqrt{2} = \frac{a+b}{b}$

$\because$ $a$, $b$ are integers.

$\therefore$ $a + b$ is also an integer.

$\Rightarrow$ $\frac{a+b}{b}$ is a rational number.

$\Rightarrow$ $\sqrt{2}$ is a rational number,

which contradicts that $\sqrt{2}$ is an irrational number.

So, our assumption that $\sqrt{2} - 1$ be a rational number, is wrong.

So, $\sqrt{2} - 1$ is not a rational number.

Hence, $\sqrt{2} - 1$ is an irrational number. Hence Proved.

## Exercise 1E

**1.** Rationalise the denominators of the following :

(i) $\frac{1}{\sqrt{2}}$ (ii) $\frac{\sqrt{3}}{\sqrt{7}}$ (iii) $\frac{3}{4+\sqrt{7}}$ (iv) $\frac{1}{\sqrt{6}-\sqrt{5}}$

(v) $\frac{\sqrt{2}+1}{\sqrt{2}-1}$ (vi) $\frac{3+\sqrt{2}}{3-\sqrt{2}}$

**2.** Rationalise the denominators of the following :

(i) $\frac{7-4\sqrt{3}}{7+4\sqrt{3}}$ (ii) $\frac{3\sqrt{5}-4\sqrt{2}}{3\sqrt{5}+4\sqrt{2}}$

**3.** Simplify the following :

(i) $\frac{1}{\sqrt{2}+1} + \frac{1}{\sqrt{3}+\sqrt{2}} + \frac{3}{\sqrt{6}+\sqrt{3}} - \frac{2}{\sqrt{6}+2}$ (ii) $\frac{1}{\sqrt{2}+\sqrt{3}} + \frac{1}{\sqrt{3}+\sqrt{4}} + \frac{1}{\sqrt{5}+\sqrt{6}} + \frac{1}{\sqrt{6}+\sqrt{7}}$

**4.** Rationalise the denominators of the following and hence find their values by using $\sqrt{2} = 1.414$ and $\sqrt{3} = 1.732$ :

(i) $\frac{7}{3-\sqrt{2}}$ (ii) $\frac{13}{4+\sqrt{3}}$ (iii) $\frac{5}{3\sqrt{3}-4\sqrt{2}}$

**5.** If $a$ and $b$ are rational numbers, find the values of $a$ and $b$ :

(i) $a + b\sqrt{2} = \frac{4+3\sqrt{2}}{4-3\sqrt{2}}$ (ii) $a + b\sqrt{6} = \frac{2\sqrt{3}-\sqrt{2}}{2\sqrt{3}+\sqrt{2}}$ (iii) $a - b\sqrt{3} = \frac{4\sqrt{3}-7}{4\sqrt{3}+7}$ (iv) $a + b\sqrt{5} = \frac{4+2\sqrt{5}}{\sqrt{5}+1} - \frac{4-2\sqrt{5}}{\sqrt{5}-1}$

**6.** If $x = \sqrt{2} + 1$, find :

(i) $\frac{1}{x}$ (ii) $x + \frac{1}{x}$ (iii) $x - \frac{1}{x}$ (iv) $x^2 + \frac{1}{x^2}$

**7.** If $x = 2 + \sqrt{3}$, find :

(i) $\frac{1}{x}$ (ii) $x + \frac{1}{x}$ (iii) $x - \frac{1}{x}$ (iv) $x^2 + \frac{1}{x^2}$

**8.** If $x = \frac{3+\sqrt{2}}{3-\sqrt{2}}$, $y = \frac{3-\sqrt{2}}{3+\sqrt{2}}$, find :

(i) $x^2$ (ii) $y^2$ (iii) $xy$ (iv) $x^2 + y^2 + xy$

9. If $x = 7 + 4\sqrt{3}$, find the value of $\sqrt{x} - \frac{1}{\sqrt{x}}$.

10. Prove that $\frac{1}{\sqrt{3}+1}$ is an irrational number.

## Answers

**1.** (i) $\frac{\sqrt{2}}{2}$ (ii) $\frac{\sqrt{21}}{7}$ (iii) $\frac{4-\sqrt{7}}{3}$ (iv) $\sqrt{6}+\sqrt{5}$ (v) $3+2\sqrt{2}$ (vi) $\frac{11+6\sqrt{2}}{7}$ **2.** (i) $97-56\sqrt{3}$ (ii) $\frac{77-24\sqrt{10}}{13}$

**3.** (i) 1 (ii) $2-\sqrt{2}-\sqrt{5}+\sqrt{7}$ **4.** (i) $3+\sqrt{2}, 4.414$ (ii) $4-\sqrt{3}$, 2.268 (iii) $-(3\sqrt{3}+4\sqrt{2}), -10.852$

**5.** (i) $a=-17$, $b=-12$ (ii) $a=\frac{7}{5}, b=-\frac{2}{5}$ (iii) $a=-97$, $b=-56$ (iv) $a=3, b=0$

**6.** (i) $\sqrt{2}-1$ (ii) $2\sqrt{2}$ (iii) 2 (iv) 6 **7.** (i) $2-\sqrt{3}$ (ii) 4 (iii) $2\sqrt{3}$ (iv) 14

**8.** (i) $\frac{193+132\sqrt{2}}{49}$ (ii) $\frac{193-132\sqrt{2}}{49}$ (iii) 1 (iv) $\frac{435}{49}$ **9.** $2\sqrt{3}$

# Exercise 1F

## Multiple Choice Questions

Choose the correct answer from the given four options in each of the following questions :

1. $\pi$ is :
(a) a rational number (b) an irrational number (c) an integer (d) a whole number

2. The rationalising factor of $\sqrt{5}$ is :
(a) $\sqrt{5}$ (b) 1 (c) $\sqrt{2}$ (d) $\sqrt{3}$

3. The decimal representation of an irrational number is :
(a) terminating (b) non-terminating
(c) non-terminating repeating (d) non-terminating non-repeating.

4. Which of the following is an irrational number ?
(a) $3.\overline{73}$ (b) 1.626262...... (c) 1.323223222....... (d) $1.\dot{8}$

5. The rationalising factor of $\sqrt{2}+1$ is :
(a) 1 (b) $\sqrt{2}$ (c) $\frac{1}{\sqrt{2}-1}$ (d) $\sqrt{2}-1$

6. A rational number between $\sqrt{2}$ and $\sqrt{3}$ is :
(a) 1.4 (b) 1.35 (c) 1.5 (d) 1.8

7. Which of the following numbers has non-terminating repeating decimal expansion ?
(a) $\frac{11}{640}$ (b) $\frac{7}{120}$ (c) $\frac{1}{125}$ (d) $\frac{3}{250}$

8. The decimal expansion of the rational number $\frac{17}{160}$ will terminate after ____ decimal places.
(a) 1 (b) 2 (c) 4 (d) 5

9. The decimal expansion of $\frac{15}{32}$ is :
(a) terminating (b) non-terminating
(c) non-terminating repeating (d) non-terminating non-repeating.

10. $(\sqrt{3}+\sqrt{5})(\sqrt{5}-\sqrt{3})$ is equal to :

(a) 1 (b) 2 (c) 3 (d) 8

11. If $x=\sqrt{2}+1$ then $x+\frac{1}{x}$ is equal to :

(a) 2 (b) $2\sqrt{2}$ (c) $\sqrt{2}-1$ (d) 4

12. $\sqrt{8}\times\sqrt{64}$ is equal to :

(a) 16 (b) 32 (c) $16\sqrt{2}$ (d) $32\sqrt{2}$

13. Which of the following is an irrational number ?

(a) $\sqrt{\frac{4}{9}}$ (b) $\frac{\sqrt{12}}{\sqrt{3}}$ (c) $\sqrt{5}$ (d) $\sqrt{81}$

14. The simplest form of the rational number $\frac{63}{84}$ is :

(a) $\frac{3}{4}$ (b) $\frac{21}{28}$ (c) $\frac{9}{12}$ (d) $\frac{42}{63}$

15. $\sqrt{32}+\sqrt{50}$ is equal to :

(a) $3\sqrt{2}$ (b) $5\sqrt{2}$ (c) $7\sqrt{2}$ (d) $9\sqrt{2}$

16. Every irrational number is :

(a) a natural number (b) an integer (c) a rational number (d) a real number.

## Answers

| | | | | | | | | | |
|---|---|---|---|---|---|---|---|---|---|
| 1. (b) | 2. (a) | 3. (d) | 4. (c) | 5. (d) | 6. (c) | 7. (b) | 8. (d) | 9. (a) | 10. (b) |
| 11. (b) | 12. (c) | 13. (c) | 14. (a) | 15. (d) | 16. (d) | | | | |

## Assertion-Reason Type *Questions*

In the following questions, a statement of Assertion (A) and a statement of Reason (R) are given:

(a) Both Assertion (A) and Reason (R) are true and Reason (R) is the correct explanation of Assertion (A).
(b) Both Assertion (A) and Reason (R) are true and Reason (R) is not the correct explanation of Assertion (A).
(c) Assertion (A) is true but Reason (R) is false.
(d) Assertion (A) is false but Reason (R) is true.

1. **Assertion :** $\sqrt{2}$ is an irrational number.

   **Reason :** The sum of a rational and an irrational number is irrational.

2. **Assertion :** $\frac{3}{\sqrt{6}+\sqrt{3}}=\sqrt{6}-\sqrt{3}$

   **Reason :** The rationalising factor of $\sqrt{6}+\sqrt{3}$ is $\sqrt{6}-\sqrt{3}$.

3. **Assertion :** $\frac{7}{120}$ is terminating repeating decimal expansion.

   **Reason :** $\pi$ is an irrational number.

4. **Assertion :** 0.7 is a rational number between 0.5 and 0.9.

   **Reason :** A rational number between $a$ and $b$ is $\frac{a+b}{3}$.

## Answers

| | | | |
|---|---|---|---|
| 1. (b) | 2. (a) | 3. (d) | 4. (c) |

## Valid Statements *Questions*

In the following questions, two statements (i) and (ii) are given. Choose the valid statement.

(a) Only (i) (b) Only (ii) (c) Both (i) and (ii) (d) Neither (i) nor (ii)

**1.** (i) $\sqrt{3}$ is a rational number.

(ii) The rationalising factor of $\sqrt{3}+1$ is $\sqrt{3}-1$.

**2.** (i) $\dfrac{\sqrt{3}+1}{\sqrt{3}-1} = 2+\sqrt{3}$.

(ii) $\dfrac{22}{7}$ is an irrational number.

**3.** (i) A rational number between $\dfrac{1}{2}$ and $\dfrac{1}{5}$ is $\dfrac{1}{10}$.

(ii) $\dfrac{\sqrt{7}+1}{\sqrt{7}-1}$ can be written as $\left(\sqrt{7}+1\right)^2$.

**4.** (i) If $m$ is prime then $\sqrt{m}$ is an irrational number.

(ii) There are infinitely many irrational numbers between any two rational numbers.

### *Answers*

**1.** (b) **2.** (a) **3.** (d) **4.** (c)

## SUMMARY *of the Chapter*

- A number which can be written in the form of $a/b$, where $a$ and $b$ are integers and $b \neq 0$, is called a rational number.
- A rational number $a/b$ is called in the simplest form if $a$ and $b$ have no common factor except 1.
- There are infinitely many rational numbers between any two rational numbers.
- A number which is not a rational number is called an irrational number.
- The decimal expansion of a rational number is either terminating or non-terminating repeating.
- The decimal expansion of an irrational number is non-terminating non-repeating.
- The decimal expansion of a rational number $a/b$ which is in its simplest form, where $a$, $b$ are integers and $b \neq 0$, is
  (i) terminating if the prime factors of $b$ are 2 or 5 or both.
  (ii) non-terminating repeating if $b$ has a prime factor other than 2 and 5.
- All rational and irrational numbers together are called real numbers.
- Every real number can be represented by a unique point on the number line and conversely every point on the number line represents a unique real number.
- If $a$ is a positive rational number and $n$ is a positive integer, then $\sqrt[n]{a} = a^{1/n}$ is an irrational number, called a surd of order $n$.
- If the product of two surds is rational, then each surd is called the rationalising factor of other surd.
- $\sqrt{a}$ is the rationalising surd of $\sqrt{a}$.
- $a-\sqrt{b}$ and $a+\sqrt{b}$ are the rationalising surds of each other.
- $\sqrt{a}-\sqrt{b}$ and $\sqrt{a}+\sqrt{b}$ are the rationalising surds of each other.

# CHAPTER TEST

1. Insert 2 rational numbers between $\frac{2}{5}$ and $\frac{13}{4}$.

2. Insert 3 irrational numbers between $\frac{1}{3}$ and $\frac{1}{2}$.

3. Insert 2 rational numbers between $\sqrt{2}$ and $\sqrt{5}$.

4. Prove that $\sqrt{3}$ is an irrational number.

5. Express $3.1\overline{64}$ in the form of rational number.

6. Compare $\sqrt[3]{12}$ and $\sqrt[4]{20}$.

7. Write in ascending order : $2\sqrt{7}, 3\sqrt{5}, 4\sqrt{2}$.

8. If $a + b\sqrt{3} = \frac{7 + 4\sqrt{3}}{7 - 4\sqrt{3}}$, find the values of $a$ and $b$.

9. If $x = 3 + 2\sqrt{2}$, find

   (i) $\frac{1}{x}$ (ii) $x + \frac{1}{x}$ (iii) $x^2 + \frac{1}{x^2}$

10. Represent $\sqrt{2}$ on the number line.

## Answers

**1.** 0.6, 0.8 **2.** $\sqrt{0.41}, \sqrt{0.42}, \sqrt{0.43}$ **3.** 1.5, 2 **5.** $\frac{3133}{990}$ **6.** $\sqrt[3]{12} > \sqrt[4]{20}$

**7.** $2\sqrt{7} < 4\sqrt{2} < 3\sqrt{5}$ **8.** $a = 97, b = 56$ **9.** (i) $3 - \sqrt{2}$ (ii) 6 (iii) 34

UNIT II : COMMERCIAL MATHEMATICS

Chapter 2

# COMPOUND INTEREST

## Syllabus

**Compound Interest**

**(a)** Compound interest as a repeated simple interest computation with a growing principal. Use of this in computing amount over a period of 2 or 3 years.

**(b)** Use of formula $A = P\left(1+\frac{r}{100}\right)^n$. Finding CI from the relation $CI = A - P$.

- Interest compounded half-yearly included.
- Using the formula to find one quantity given different combinations of $A$, $P$, $r$, $n$, CI and SI; difference between CI and SI type included. Rate of growth and depreciation.

**Note :** Paying back in equal installments, being given rate of interest and installment amount, not included.

## INTRODUCTION

In earlier classes, we have studied about the simple interest and their applications. Now, we shall study about compound interest, difference between simple and compound interest, compound interest as a repeating simple interest with increasing principal, formula for compound interest and their uses in depreciation and growth.

## Some Terms Related to Interest

1. Principal : The money borrowed is called the principal.
2. Rate : It is the interest paid on ₹ 100 for a specific period.
3. Time : It is the time for which the money is borrowed.
4. Simple Interest : It is the extra money paid on the principal at the given rate and time. We use the following formula to calculate the simple interest.

Simple Interest (S.I.)

$$= \frac{\text{Principal} \times \text{Rate} \times \text{Time}}{100}$$

5. Amount : It is the sum of the principal and the interest paid.

$\therefore$ Amount = Principal + Interest.

## Compound Interest

When the interest accured after the specific period is not paid, but added to the principal, then this amount becomes the principal for the next specified period. This process is repeated for the given periods. The difference between the final amount and given principal is called the compound interest.

**Remember**

If the interest is compounded half yearly (semi-annually), the principal changes after every six months.

**NOTE**

The principal remains same for the whole time while calculating the simple interest but it changes after every specific period while calculating the compound interest.

## Illustrative Examples

**Example 1.** Find the amount and compound interest on ₹ 10000 at 8% per annum for 2 years.

**Solution.** **For first year,**

Principal = ₹ 10000, Rate = 8%, Time = 1 year.

$$\therefore \quad \text{Simple Interest} = \frac{\text{Principal} \times \text{Rate} \times \text{Time}}{100}$$

$$= ₹\,\frac{10000 \times 8 \times 1}{100} = ₹\,800$$

$\therefore$ Amount = Principal + Simple Interest

= ₹ 10000 + ₹ 800 = ₹ 10,800

**For second year,**

Principal = ₹ 10,800, Rate = 8%, Time = 1 year.

$\therefore$ Simple Interest $= \dfrac{\text{Principal} \times \text{Rate} \times \text{Time}}{100} = ₹\ \dfrac{10800 \times 8 \times 1}{100} = ₹\ 864$

$\therefore$ Amount = Principal + Simple Interest = ₹ 10800 + ₹ 864 = ₹ 11664

Now, Compound Interest = Final amount – given principal = ₹ 11664 – ₹ 10000 = ₹ 1664

Hence, amount = ₹ 11664 and compound interest = ₹ 1664 **Ans.**

**Example 2.** Shiv invests ₹ 51,200 for three years at the rate of 10% per annum compound interest. Find :

(i) the amount at the end of first year.
(ii) the interest earned for the second year.
(iii) the compound interest earned for three years.

**Solution.** (i) **For first year,**

Principal = ₹ 51200, Rate = 10%, Time = 1 year

$\therefore$ Simple Interest $= \dfrac{\text{Principal} \times \text{Rate} \times \text{Time}}{100} = ₹\ \dfrac{51200 \times 10 \times 1}{100} = ₹\ 5120$

$\therefore$ Amount = Principal + Simple Interest = ₹ 51200 + ₹ 5120 = ₹ 56320 **Ans.**

(ii) **For second year,**

Principal = ₹ 56320, Rate = 10%, Time = 1 year

$\therefore$ Simple Interest $= \dfrac{\text{Principal} \times \text{Rate} \times \text{Time}}{100} = ₹\ \dfrac{56320 \times 10 \times 1}{100} = ₹\ 5632$ **Ans.**

(iii) Amount for 2nd year = Principal + Simple Interest = ₹ 56320 + ₹ 5632 = ₹ 61952

**For third year,**

Principal = ₹ 61952, Rate = 10%, Time = 1 year

$\therefore$ Simple Interest $= \dfrac{\text{Principal} \times \text{Rate} \times \text{Time}}{100} = ₹\ \dfrac{61952 \times 10 \times 1}{100} = ₹\ 6195.20$

$\therefore$ Amount = Principal + Simple Interest = ₹ 61952 + ₹ 6195.20 = ₹ 68147.20

Now, compound interest for three years = Final amount – given principal

= ₹ 68147.20 – ₹ 51200 = ₹ 16947.20 **Ans.**

**Example 3.** Find the amount and compound interest on ₹ 40000 at 8% per annum for 1 year, interest being compounded half yearly.

**Solution.** For first six months,

$P$ = ₹ 40000, $R$ = 8%, $T$ = 1/2 year

S.I. $= \dfrac{P \times R \times T}{100} = ₹\ \dfrac{40000 \times 8 \times 1}{100 \times 2} = ₹\ 1600$

and $A = P +$ S.I. = ₹ 40000 + ₹ 1600 = ₹ 41600

For second six months,

$P$ = ₹ 41600, $R$ = 8%, $T$ = 1/2 year

S.I. $= \dfrac{P \times R \times T}{100} = ₹\ \dfrac{41600 \times 8 \times 1}{100 \times 2} = ₹\ 1664$

and $A = P +$ S.I. = ₹ 41600 + ₹ 1664 = ₹ 43264

and C.I. = Final amount – given principal = ₹ 43264 – ₹ 40000 = ₹ 3264 **Ans.**

**Example 4.** Find the compound interest and amount on ₹ 20000 for 2 years 4 months at 5% per annum compounded annually.

**Solution.** **For first year,**

$P$ = ₹ 20000, $R$ = 5%, $T$ = 1 year

S.I. $= \dfrac{P \times R \times T}{100} = ₹\ \dfrac{20000 \times 5 \times 1}{100} = ₹\ 1000$

and $A = P + \text{S.I.} = ₹\ 20000 + ₹\ 1000 = ₹\ 21000$

**For second year,**

$P = ₹\ 21000, R = 5\%, T = 1$ year

$$\therefore \quad \text{S.I.} = \frac{P \times R \times T}{100} = ₹\ \frac{21000 \times 5 \times 1}{100} = ₹\ 1050$$

and $A = P + \text{S.I.} = ₹\ 21000 + ₹\ 1050 = ₹\ 22050$

For last 4 months

$$P = ₹\ 22050, R = 5\%, \text{T} = 4 \text{ months} = \frac{4}{12} \text{ years} = \frac{1}{3} \text{ years}$$

$$\text{S.I.} = \frac{P \times T \times T}{100} = ₹\ \frac{22050 \times 5 \times 1}{100 \times 3} = ₹\ 367.50$$

and $A = P + \text{S.I.} = ₹\ 22050 + ₹\ 367.50 = ₹\ 22417.50$ Ans.

Now, C.I. = Final amount – given principal = ₹ 22417.50 – ₹ 20000 = ₹ 2417.50 Ans.

**Example 5.** Hanif invests ₹ 12000 for two years at a certain rate of interest compounded annually. After one year it amounts to ₹ 13200. Find

(i) the rate of interest.

(ii) the compound interest after two years.

**Solution.** (i) $P = ₹\ 12000, A = ₹\ 13200$

$$\therefore \quad \text{S.I.} = A - P = ₹\ 13200 - ₹\ 12000 = ₹\ 1200$$

Now, $$\frac{P \times R \times T}{100} = \text{S.I.}$$

$$\Rightarrow \quad \frac{12000 \times R \times 1}{100} = 1200 \Rightarrow \quad R = 10$$

$\therefore$ Rate = 10% Ans.

(ii) **For second year,**

$P = ₹\ 13200, R = 10\%, T = 1$ year

$$\therefore \quad \text{S.I.} = \frac{P \times R \times T}{100} = ₹\ \frac{13200 \times 10 \times 1}{100} = ₹\ 1320$$

and $A = P + \text{S.I.} = ₹\ 13200 - ₹\ 1320 = ₹\ 14520$

Now, C.I. = Final amount – given principal = ₹ 14520 – ₹ 12000 = ₹ 2520 Ans.

**Example 6.** Find the compound interest on ₹ 40000 for 3 years if the rates of interest for 3 successive years are 5%, 6% and 10%, respectively.

**Solution.** **For first year,**

$P = ₹\ 40000, R = 5\%, T = 1$ year

$$\text{S.I.} = \frac{P \times R \times T}{100} = ₹\ \frac{40000 \times 5 \times 1}{100} = ₹\ 2000$$

and $A = P + \text{S.I.} = ₹\ 40000 + ₹\ 2000 = ₹\ 42000$

**For second year,**

$P = ₹\ 42000, R = 6\%, T = 1$ year

$$\text{S.I.} = \frac{P \times R \times T}{100} = ₹\ \frac{42000 \times 6 \times 1}{100} = ₹\ 2520$$

and $A = P + \text{S.I.} = ₹\ 42000 + ₹\ 2520 = ₹\ 44520$

**For third year,**

$P = ₹\ 44520, R = 10\%, T = 1$ year

$$\text{S.I.} = \frac{P \times R \times T}{100} = ₹\ \frac{44520 \times 10 \times 1}{100} = ₹\ 4452$$

and $A = P + \text{S.I.} = ₹\ 44520 + ₹\ 4452 = ₹\ 48972$

Now, $\text{C.I.} = \text{Final amount} - \text{given principal} = ₹\ 48972 - ₹\ 40000 = ₹\ 8972$ Ans.

**Example 7.** A man borrows ₹ 16000 at 8% per annum compounded interest. If he repays ₹ 7280 at the end of first year, find the amount paid by him at the end of second year to clear the debt.

**Solution.** **For first year,**

$P = ₹\ 16000, R = 8\%, T = 1$ year

$$\text{S.I.} = \frac{P \times R \times T}{100} = ₹\ \frac{16000 \times 8 \times 1}{100} = ₹\ 1280$$

and $A = P + \text{S.I.} = ₹\ 16000 + ₹\ 1280 = ₹\ 17280$

Sum paid after one year = ₹ 7280

**For second year,**

$P = ₹\ 17280 - ₹\ 7280 = ₹\ 10000, R = 8\%, T = 1$ year

$$\text{S.I.} = \frac{P \times R \times T}{100} = ₹\ \frac{10000 \times 8 \times 1}{100} = ₹\ 800$$

and $A = P + \text{S.I.} = ₹\ 10000 + ₹\ 800 = ₹\ 10800$

$\therefore$ Required sum paid to clear the debt = ₹ 10800 Ans.

**Example 8.** Find the difference between the compound interest and simple interest on ₹ 8000 at 5% per annum in 2 years.

**Solution.** Calculation of simple interest

$P = ₹\ 8000, R = 5\%, T = 2$ years

$$\text{S.I.} = \frac{P \times R \times T}{100} = ₹\ \frac{8000 \times 5 \times 2}{100} = ₹\ 800$$

Calculation of compound interest

**For first year,**

$P = ₹\ 8000, R = 5\%, T = 1$ year

$$\text{S.I.} = \frac{P \times R \times T}{100} = ₹\ \frac{8000 \times 5 \times 1}{100} = ₹\ 400$$

and $A = P + \text{S.I.} = ₹\ 8000 + ₹\ 400 = ₹\ 8400$

**For second year**

$P = ₹\ 8400, R = 5\%, T = 1$ year

$$\text{S.I.} = \frac{P \times R \times T}{100} = ₹\ \frac{8400 \times 5 \times 1}{100} = ₹\ 420$$

and $A = P + \text{S.I.} = ₹\ 8400 + ₹\ 420 = ₹\ 8820$

Now, $\text{C.I.} = \text{Final amount} - \text{original principal} = ₹\ 8820 - ₹\ 8000 = ₹\ 820$

Difference between C.I. and S.I. = ₹ 820 − ₹ 800 = ₹ 20 Ans.

**Example 9.** For a certain sum of money invested at the rate of 5% per annum compounded annually, the difference between the interest of the third year and first year is ₹ 61.50. Find the sum.

**Solution.** Let principal be ₹ 100

**For first year,**

$P = ₹\ 100, R = 5\%, T = 1$ year

$$\text{S.I.} = \frac{P \times R \times T}{100} = ₹\ \frac{100 \times 5 \times 1}{100} = ₹\ 5$$

and $\quad A = P + \text{S.I.} = ₹\ 100 + ₹\ 5 = ₹\ 105$

**For second year,**

$P = ₹\ 105, R = 5\%, T = 1$ year

$$\text{S.I.} = \frac{P \times R \times T}{100} = ₹\ \frac{105 \times 5 \times 1}{100} = ₹\ 5.25$$

and $\quad A = P + \text{S.I.} = ₹\ 105 + ₹\ 5.25 = ₹\ 110.25$

**For third year,**

$P = ₹\ 110.25, R = 5\%, T = 1$ year

$$\text{S.I.} = \frac{P \times R \times T}{100} = ₹\ \frac{110.25 \times 5 \times 1}{100} = ₹\ 5.5125$$

Difference of interest between third year and first year

$$= ₹\ 5.5125 - ₹\ 5 = ₹\ 0.5125$$

If difference is ₹ 0.5125, then principal = ₹ 100

If difference is ₹ 61.50, then principal $= ₹\ \frac{100 \times 61.50}{0.5125} = ₹\ 12000$ **Ans.**

**Example 10.** A sum of money becomes ₹ 6615 in 2 years and ₹ 6945.75 in 3 years on compound interest. Find the sum.

**Solution.** **For third year,**

$P = ₹\ 6615, A = ₹\ 6945.75, T = 1$ year

$$\text{S.I.} = A - P = ₹\ 6945.75 - ₹\ 6615 = ₹\ 330.75$$

Now, $\quad \frac{P \times R \times T}{100} = \text{S.I.} \Rightarrow \frac{6615 \times R \times 1}{100} = 330.75 \Rightarrow R = 5\%$

Let principal be ₹ 100.

**For first year,**

$P = ₹\ 100, R = 5\%, T = 1$ year

$$\text{S.I.} = \frac{P \times R \times T}{100} = ₹\ \frac{100 \times 5 \times 1}{100} = ₹\ 5$$

and $\quad A = P + \text{S.I.} = ₹\ 100 + ₹\ 5 = ₹\ 105$

**For second year,**

$P = ₹\ 105, R = 5\%, T = 1$ year

$$\text{S.I.} = \frac{P \times R \times T}{100} = ₹\ \frac{105 \times 5 \times 1}{100} = ₹\ 5.25$$

and $\quad A = P + \text{S.I.} = ₹\ 105 + ₹\ 5.25 = ₹\ 110.25$

If amount is ₹ 110.25, then principal = ₹ 100

If amount is ₹ 6615, then principal $= ₹\ \frac{100 \times 6615}{110.25} = ₹\ 6000$ **Ans.**

**Example 11.** The simple interest on a certain sum of money for 5 years at 8% per annum is ₹ 2100. Find

(i) the sum of money.

(ii) the compound interest on this sum for 2 years at 10% per annum.

**Solution.** (i) Simple interest for 5 years = ₹ 2100

Now, $\quad \frac{P \times R \times T}{100} = \text{S.I.} \Rightarrow \frac{P \times 8 \times 5}{100} = 2100 \Rightarrow P = ₹\ 5250$

$\therefore$ Sum of money = ₹ 5250 **Ans.**

(ii) **For first year,**

$$\text{S.I.} = ₹\,\frac{2100}{5} = ₹\,420$$

and $A = P + \text{S.I.} = ₹\,5250 + ₹\,420 = ₹\,5690$

**For second year,**

$P = ₹\,5690, R = 8\%, T = 1$ year

$$\text{S.I.} = \frac{P \times R \times T}{100} = ₹\,\frac{5690 \times 8 \times 1}{100} = ₹\,455.20$$

and $A = P + \text{S.I.} = ₹\,5690 + ₹\,455.20 = ₹\,6145.20$

Now, $\text{C.I.} = \text{Final amount} - \text{original principal} = ₹\,6145.20 - ₹\,5250 = ₹\,495.20$ **Ans.**

**Example 12.** Ravish borrows ₹ 50000 at 8% simple interest and gives it to Kamal at 8% compounded half yearly. Find his gain in one year.

**Solution.** For Ravish,

$P = ₹\,50000, R = 8\%, T = 1$ year

$$\text{S.I.} = \frac{P \times R \times T}{100} = ₹\,\frac{50000 \times 8 \times 1}{100} = ₹\,4000$$

For Kamal,

For first half yearly,

$P = ₹\,50000, R = 8\%, T = 1/2$ year

$$\text{S.I.} = \frac{P \times R \times T}{100} = ₹\,\frac{50000 \times 8 \times 1}{100 \times 2} = ₹\,2000$$

and $A = P + \text{S.I.} = ₹\,50000 + ₹\,2000 = ₹\,52000$

For second half yearly

$P = ₹\,52000, R = 8\%, T = 1/2$ year

$$\text{S.I.} = \frac{P \times R \times T}{100} = ₹\,\frac{52000 \times 8 \times 1}{100 \times 2} = ₹\,2080$$

and $A = P + \text{S.I.} = ₹\,52000 + ₹\,2080 = ₹\,54080$

$\text{C.I.} = \text{Final amount} - \text{original principal} = ₹\,54080 - ₹\,50000 = ₹\,4080$

$\text{Gain} = \text{C.I.} - \text{S.I.} = ₹\,4080 - ₹\,4000 = ₹\,80$ **Ans.**

## Exercise 2A

1. Find the amount and compound interest of ₹ 24000 at 10% per annum for 2 years.
2. Find the amount and compound interest of ₹ 12500 at 8% per annum for 3 years.
3. Find the amount and compound interest of ₹ 64000 at 5% per annum for $1\frac{1}{2}$ years, interest being compounded half-yearly.
4. Find the amount and compound interest of ₹ 6250 at 16% per annum for 6 months, interest being compounded quarterly.
5. Ruhi invests ₹ 12800 for 3 years at the rate of 10% per annum compound interest. Find
   (i) the sum due at the end of first year. (ii) the interest for the second year.
   (iii) the compound interest after 3 years.
6. Shanker invests ₹ 48000 for 3 years at 5% per annum compound interest. Find
   (i) the interest for the first year. (ii) the amount at the end of second year.
   (iii) the interest for third year.
7. David invests ₹ 25000 for 3 years at 6% per annum compound interest. Find
   (i) the interest for the first year. (ii) the amount at the end of second year.
   (iii) the compound interest for 3 years.

8. A man invests ₹ 12500 at 12% per annum compound interest for 3 years. Find
   (i) the interest for the first year. (ii) the interest for third year.
   (iii) the compound interest for 3 years.
9. A man invests ₹ 8000 for 2 years at a certain rate of interest compound annually. At the end of first year, this sum amounts to ₹ 8640. Find
   (i) the rate of interest. (ii) the amount at the end of second year.
10. A man invests ₹ 10000 for 3 years at a certain rate of interest compounded annually. At the end of first year, this sum amounts to ₹ 11000. Find
    (i) the rate of interest. (ii) the compound interest for 3 years.
11. A man invests ₹ 50000 for 18 months at a certain rate of interest compounded half-yearly. At the end of 6 months, it amounts to ₹ 53000. Find
    (i) the rate of interest per annum. (ii) the amount after 18 months.
12. Kanti borrows ₹ 100000 from a bank at 8% per annum compounded yearly. He repays ₹ 38000 at the end of first year and ₹ 35600 at the end of second year. Find the remaining amount at the end of third year.
13. Shantanu borrows ₹ 65000 from a bank at 10% per annum compounded yearly. He repays ₹ 21500 at the end of first year and ₹ 25000 at the end of second year. Find the remaining amount at the beginning of third year.
14. Find the amount and compound interest on ₹ 20000 for 2 years if the rate of interest for successive years are 8% and 9%.
15. Find the amount and compound interest on ₹ 40000 for 3 years if the rates of interest for successive years are 10%, 6% and 5%.
16. Rahul borrows ₹ 25000 for 2 years and the rates of interest for two successive years are 10% and 8% respectively. If he repays ₹ 7500 at the end of first year, find the amount due at the end of second year.
17. Find the difference between C.I. and S.I. on ₹ 7500 for 2 years at 10% per annum.
18. On a certain sum of money invested at the rate of 11% per annum compounded annually, the difference between the interest of the third year and first year is ₹ 255.31. Find the sum.
19. Find the difference between the C.I. and S.I. on ₹ 15000 at 6% per annum in 2 years.
20. On a certain sum of money invested at the rate of 4% per annum compounded annually, the difference between the interest of third year and first year is ₹ 81.60. Find the sum.
21. A sum of money becomes ₹ 5832 in 2 years and ₹ 6298.56 in 3 years, invested compounded annually. Find the rate of interest and the sum of money.
22. A sum of money becomes ₹ 8427 in 2 years and ₹ 8932.62 in 3 years, invested compounded annually. Find the rate of interest and the sum of money.
23. The simple interest on a sum of money for 3 years at 4% per annum is ₹ 510. Find
    (i) the sum of money. (ii) the C.I. on this sum for one year payable half-yearly at the same rate.
24. A sum of money is invested at C.I. payable annually. The amounts of interest in two successive years are ₹ 960 and ₹ 1036.80 Find the rate of interest.
25. A man borrows ₹ 90000 for 2 years at 5% per annum simple interest and immediately invests for 2 years at 5% compounded interest annually. Find his profit.

## *Answers*

| | | | |
|---|---|---|---|
| **1.** ₹ 29040, ₹ 5040 | **2.** ₹ 15746.40, ₹ 3246.40 | **3.** ₹ 68921, ₹ 4921 | **4.** ₹ 6760, ₹ 510 |
| **5.** (i) ₹ 14080 (ii) ₹ 1408 (iii) ₹ 4236.80 | **6.** (i) ₹ 2400 (ii) ₹ 52920 (iii) ₹ 2646 | | |
| **7.** (i) ₹ 1500 (ii) ₹ 28090 (iii) ₹ 4775.40 | **8.** (i) ₹ 1500 (ii) ₹ 1881.60 (iii) ₹ 5061.60 | | |
| **9.** (i) 8% (ii) ₹ 9331.20 | **10.** (i) 10% (ii) ₹ 3310 | **11.** (i) 12% (ii) ₹ 59550.80 | **12.** ₹ 43200 |
| **13.** ₹ 30000 | **14.** ₹ 23544, ₹ 3544 | **15.** ₹ 48972, ₹ 8972 | **16.** ₹ 21600 |
| **17.** ₹ 75 | **18.** ₹ 1000 | **19.** ₹ 54 | **20.** ₹ 25000 |
| **21.** ₹ 5000, 8% | **22.** ₹ 7500, 6% | **23.** (i) ₹ 4250 (ii) ₹ 171.70 | **24.** 8% |
| **25.** ₹ 225 | | | |

## Compound Interest Using Formulae

If $P$ = principal
$r$ = rate of interest
$n$ = number of years

then

Amount $A = P\left(1+\frac{r}{100}\right)^n$

and Compound interest, C.I. $= A - P$

$$\text{C.I.} = P\left(1+\frac{r}{100}\right)^n - P = P\left\{\left(1+\frac{r}{100}\right)^n - 1\right\}$$

**NOTE**

If the rates of interest for successive years are $r_1$, $r_2$ and $r_3$, then

$$A = P\left(1+\frac{r_1}{100}\right)\left(1+\frac{r_2}{100}\right)\left(1+\frac{r_3}{100}\right)$$

**Remark**

1. If the rate of interest is compounded half-yearly, then rate is divided by 2 and number of years is multiplied by 2.
2. If the rate of interest is compounded qurterly, then rate is divided by 4 and number of years is multiplied by 4.

## Illustrative Examples

**Example 1.** Find the amount and compound interest of ₹ 24000 at 10% per annum for 2 years.

**Solution.** Here, $P =$ ₹ 24000, $r = 10\%$, $n = 2$ years

$\therefore$ Amount, $A = P\left(1+\frac{r}{100}\right)^2$

$= ₹\ 24000\left(1+\frac{10}{100}\right)^2 = ₹\ 24000 \times \left(\frac{110}{100}\right)^2 = ₹\ 24000 \times \frac{11}{10} \times \frac{11}{10} = ₹\ 29040$ Ans.

and C.I. $= A - P =$ ₹ 29040 − ₹ 24000 = ₹ 5040 Ans.

**Example 2.** Find the amount and compound interest of ₹ 37500 at 8% per annum for 3 years.

**Solution.** Here, $P =$ ₹ 37500, $r = 8\%$, $n = 3$ years

$\therefore$ Amount, $A = P\left(1+\frac{r}{100}\right)^n = ₹\ 37500\left(1+\frac{8}{100}\right)^3 = ₹\ 37500 \times \left(\frac{108}{100}\right)^3$

$= ₹\ 37500 \times \frac{108}{100} \times \frac{108}{100} \times \frac{108}{100} = ₹\ 47239.20$ Ans.

and C.I. $= A - P =$ ₹ 47239.20 − ₹ 37500 = ₹ 9739.20 Ans.

**Example 3.** Find the amount and compound interest of ₹ 36000 in two years if the rates of interest for successive years are 10% and 12%.

**Solution.** Here, $P =$ ₹ 36000, $r_1 = 10\%$, $r_2 = 12\%$,

$\therefore$ Amount, $A = P\left(1+\frac{r_1}{100}\right)^1\left(1+\frac{r_2}{100}\right)^1 = ₹\ 36000\left(1+\frac{10}{100}\right)^1\left(1+\frac{12}{100}\right)^1$

$$= ₹\ 36000 \times \frac{110}{100} \times \frac{112}{100} = ₹\ 44352$$ Ans.

and $\quad$ C.I. $= A - P = ₹\ 44352 - ₹\ 36000 = ₹\ 8352$ Ans.

**Example 4.** Find the compound interest on ₹ 12500 for 3 years if the rates of interest for first year is 10% and for next 2 years is 4%.

**Solution.** Here, $P = ₹\ 12500$, $r_1 = 10\%$ for 1 year

and $\quad r_2 = 4\%$ for next 2 years.

$\therefore$ Amount, $$A = P\left(1+\frac{r_1}{100}\right)^1\left(1+\frac{r_2}{100}\right)^2 = ₹\ 12500\left(1+\frac{10}{100}\right)^1\left(1+\frac{4}{100}\right)^2$$

$$= ₹\ 12500 \times \frac{110}{100} \times \frac{104}{100} \times \frac{104}{100} = ₹\ 14872$$

and $\quad$ C.I. $= A - P = ₹\ 14872 - ₹\ 12500 = ₹\ 2372$ Ans.

**Example 5.** Find the compound interest on ₹ 32000 in $1\frac{1}{2}$ years at 10% per annum compounded half-yearly.

**Solution.** Here, $\quad P = ₹\ 32000$

$$r = \frac{10}{2}\% \text{ per half-yearly} = 5\% \text{ per half-yearly}$$

$$n = 1\frac{1}{2} \text{ years} = \frac{3}{2} \times 2 \text{ half-years} = 3 \text{ half-years}$$

$\therefore$ Amount, $$A = P\left(1+\frac{r}{100}\right)^n = ₹\ 32000\left(1+\frac{5}{100}\right)^3 = ₹\ 32000 \times \left(\frac{105}{100}\right)^3$$

$$= ₹\ 32000 \times \frac{105}{100} \times \frac{105}{100} \times \frac{105}{100} = ₹\ 37044$$

and $\quad$ C.I. $= A - P = ₹\ 37044 - ₹\ 32000 = ₹\ 5044$ Ans.

**Example 6.** Find the compound interest of ₹ 16000 for $2\frac{1}{2}$ years at 10% per annum compounded yearly.

**Solution.** For first 2 years,

$P = ₹\ 16000$, $n = 2$ years, $r = 10\%$

$\therefore$ Amount, $$A = P\left(1+\frac{r}{100}\right)^n = ₹\ 16000\left(1+\frac{10}{100}\right)^2 = ₹\ 16000 \times \frac{110}{100} \times \frac{110}{100} = ₹\ 19360$$

For last half year,

$P = ₹\ 19360$, $R = \frac{10}{2}\% = 5\%$, $n = 1$ half year

$\therefore$ Amount, $$A = P\left(1+\frac{r}{100}\right)^n = ₹\ 19360\left(1+\frac{5}{100}\right)^1 = ₹\ 19360 \times \frac{105}{100} = ₹\ 20328$$

and $\quad$ C.I. $= A - P = ₹\ 20328 - ₹\ 16000 = ₹\ 4328$ Ans.

**Example 7.** What sum of money will amount to ₹ 15435 in 2 years at 5% per annum compounded annually?

**Solution.** Here, $\quad A = ₹\ 15435$, $n = 2$ years, $r = 5\%$

$$\therefore \quad P\left(1+\frac{r}{100}\right)^n = A \quad \Rightarrow \quad P\left(1+\frac{5}{100}\right)^2 = 15435$$

$\Rightarrow \quad P \times \frac{105}{100} \times \frac{105}{100} = ₹\ 15435 \quad \Rightarrow \quad P = ₹\ 15435 \times \frac{100}{105} \times \frac{100}{105} = ₹\ 14000$ Ans.

**Example 8.** On a certain sum, the compound interest in 2 years at 10% per annum is ₹ 2520. Find the sum.

**Solution.** Here, C.I. = ₹ 2520, $n = 2$ years, $r = 10\%$

$\therefore \quad P\left[\left(1+\frac{r}{100}\right)^n - 1\right] = \text{C.I.} \quad \Rightarrow \quad P\left[\left(1+\frac{10}{100}\right)^2 - 1\right] = ₹\ 2520$

$\Rightarrow \quad P\left[\left(\frac{110}{100}\right)^2 - 1\right] = ₹\ 2520 \quad \Rightarrow \quad P\left(\frac{121}{100} - 1\right) = ₹\ 2520$

$\Rightarrow \quad P \times \frac{21}{100} = ₹\ 2520 \quad \Rightarrow \quad P = ₹\ 12000$

$\therefore$ Sum is ₹ 12000. Ans.

**Example 9.** In how many years will ₹ 17000 amount to ₹ 22482.50 at 15% per annum compound interest?

**Solution.** Here, $P = ₹\ 17000$, $A = ₹\ 22482.50$, $r = 15\%$

Now, $\quad P\left(1+\frac{r}{100}\right)^n = A$

$\Rightarrow \quad 17000\left(1+\frac{15}{100}\right)^n = 22482.50$

$\Rightarrow \quad \left(\frac{115}{100}\right)^n = \frac{22482.50}{17000} = \frac{224825}{170000} = \frac{13225}{10000} \quad \Rightarrow \quad \left(\frac{115}{100}\right)^n = \left(\frac{115}{100}\right)^2$

$\Rightarrow \quad n = 2$

$\therefore$ Required time = 2 years Ans.

**Example 10.** At what rate percent will ₹ 16000 amounts to ₹ 20070.40 as compound interest in 2 years?

**Solution.** Here, $P = ₹\ 16000$, $A = ₹\ 20070.40$, $n = 2$ years

Now, $\quad P\left(1+\frac{r}{100}\right)^n = A$

$\Rightarrow \quad 16000\left(1+\frac{r}{100}\right)^2 = 20070.40$

$\Rightarrow \quad \left(1+\frac{r}{100}\right)^2 = \frac{20070.40}{16000} = \frac{2007040}{1600000} = 1.2544$

$\Rightarrow \quad \left(1+\frac{r}{100}\right)^2 = (1.12)^2 \quad \Rightarrow \quad 1+\frac{r}{100} = 1.12 \quad \Rightarrow \quad \frac{r}{100} = 0.12 \quad \Rightarrow \quad r = 12$

$\therefore$ Required rate = 12% Ans.

**Example 11.** A sum of ₹ 8000 earns a compound interest of ₹ 1261 in $1\frac{1}{2}$ years while the interest is reckoned half-yearly. Find the rate of interest.

**Solution.** Here, $P = ₹\ 8000$, C.I. = ₹ 1261, $n = 1\frac{1}{2}$ years $= \frac{3}{2} \times 2$ half-years = 3 half-years

Let $R$ be the rate of interest per annum.

Now, $A = P + \text{C.I.}$

$= ₹\ 8000 + ₹\ 1261 = ₹\ 9261$

and $$P\left(1+\frac{r}{100}\right)^n = A$$

$$\Rightarrow \quad 8000\left(1+\frac{R}{2\times 100}\right)^3 = 9261 \qquad (\because \text{Interest is reckoned half-yearly})$$

$$\Rightarrow \quad \left(1+\frac{R}{200}\right)^3 = \frac{9261}{8000} = \left(\frac{21}{20}\right)^3 \quad \Rightarrow \quad 1+\frac{R}{200} = \frac{21}{20}$$

$$\Rightarrow \quad \frac{R}{200} = \frac{21}{20} - 1 = \frac{1}{20} \quad \Rightarrow \quad R = 10$$

$\therefore$ Rate is 10%. **Ans.**

**Example 12.** The simple interest on a sum of money for 5 years is ₹ 850 at 4% per annum. Find :

(i) the sum of money.

(ii) the compound interest on this sum for one year payable half-yearly at the same rate.

**Solution.** (i) Here, S.I. = ₹ 850, $T = 5$ years, $R = 4\%$

$$\therefore \quad \frac{P\times R\times T}{100} = \text{S.I.} \quad \Rightarrow \quad \frac{P\times 4\times 5}{100} = ₹\ 850 \quad \Rightarrow \quad P = ₹\ 4250$$

(ii) For compound interest,

$P = ₹\ 4250$, $n = 1$ year = 2 half-years, $R = 4\%$ per annum

$$\therefore \quad A = P\left(1+\frac{r}{100}\right)^n = ₹\ 4250\left(1+\frac{4}{2\times 100}\right)^2 \qquad \left(\because r = \frac{4}{2}\%\ \text{due to half-yearly}\right)$$

$$= ₹\ 4250 \times \frac{51}{50}\times\frac{51}{50} = ₹\ 4421.70$$

$$\therefore \quad \text{C.I.} = A - P = ₹\ 4421.70 - ₹\ 4250 = ₹\ 171.70$$ **Ans.**

**Example 13.** The compound interest on a certain sum of money at 8% per annum for 2 years is ₹ 2496. Find the simple interest on the same sum for 5 years at 6% per annum.

**Solution.** For compound interest,

$r = 8\%$, $n = 2$ years, C.I. = ₹ 2496

Now, $$P\left[\left(1+\frac{r}{100}\right)^n - 1\right] = \text{C.I.}$$

$$\Rightarrow \quad P\left[\left(1+\frac{8}{100}\right)^2 - 1\right] = ₹\ 2496 \quad \Rightarrow \quad P\left[\left(\frac{108}{100}\right)^2 - 1\right] = ₹\ 2496$$

$$\Rightarrow \quad P\left[\frac{11664}{10000} - 1\right] = ₹\ 2496 \quad \Rightarrow \quad P\times\frac{1664}{10000} = ₹\ 2496$$

$$\Rightarrow \quad P = \frac{₹\ 2496\times 10000}{1664} = ₹\ 15000$$

For simple interest,

$P = ₹\ 15000$, $T = 5$ years, $R = 6\%$

$$\therefore \quad \text{S.I.} = \frac{P\times R\times T}{100} = ₹\ \frac{15000\times 6\times 5}{100} = ₹\ 4500$$ **Ans.**

**Example 14.** A sum of money becomes ₹ 5832 in 2 years and ₹ 6298.56 in 3 years, invested compounded annually. Find the rate of interest and the sum of money.

**Solution.** Let $P$ be the sum and $r$ be the rate of interest per annum.

$$\therefore \quad P\left(1+\frac{r}{100}\right)^2 = 5832 \qquad \text{...}(i)$$

and $$P\left(1+\frac{r}{100}\right)^3 = 6298.56 \Rightarrow P\left(1+\frac{r}{100}\right)^2\left(1+\frac{r}{100}\right) = 6298.56$$

$$\Rightarrow \quad 5832\left(1+\frac{r}{100}\right) = 6298.56 \Rightarrow 1+\frac{r}{100} = \frac{6298.56}{5832} = 1.08 \Rightarrow \frac{r}{100} = 0.08 \Rightarrow r = 8$$

From $(i)$,

$$P\left(1+\frac{8}{100}\right)^2 = ₹\ 5832 \Rightarrow P\times\frac{108\times108}{100\times100} = ₹\ 5832$$

$$\Rightarrow \quad P = ₹\ \frac{5832\times100\times100}{108\times108} = ₹\ 5000$$

$\therefore$ Rate of interest = 8% and sum of money = ₹ 5000 **Ans.**

**Example 15.** Divide ₹ 4420 between $A$ and $B$ so that when their shares are invested at 10% compound interest per year, the amount that $A$ receives in 5 years is the same as that $B$ receives in 3 years.

**Solution.** Let $A$'s share = ₹ $x$

$\therefore$ $B$'s share = ₹ $(4420 - x)$

Amount of $A$'s share in 5 years $= x\left(1+\frac{10}{100}\right)^5$

and amount of $B$'s share in 3 years $= (4420-x)\left(1+\frac{10}{100}\right)^3$

Given that their amounts are equal.

$$\therefore \quad x\left(1+\frac{10}{100}\right)^5 = (4420-x)\left(1+\frac{10}{100}\right)^3$$

$$\Rightarrow \quad x\left(1+\frac{10}{100}\right)^2 = (4420-x) \Rightarrow \frac{121x}{100} = 4420 - x$$

$$\Rightarrow \quad 121x = 442000 - 100x \Rightarrow 221x = 442000 \Rightarrow x = 2000$$

So, $4420 - x = 4420 - 2000 = 2420$

Hence, $A$'s share = ₹ 2000 and $B$'s share = ₹ 2420 **Ans.**

**Example 16.** The difference between the compound interest and simple interest on ₹ 8000 for 2 years is ₹ 20 at the same rate of interest. Find the rate of interest.

**Solution.** Here, $P$ = ₹ 8000, $n$ = 2 years

Let rate of interest = $r$%

$$\text{S.I.} = ₹\ \frac{8000\times2\times r}{100} = ₹\ 160r$$

For compound interest,

$$A = P\left(1+\frac{r}{100}\right)^n = ₹\ 8000\left(1+\frac{r}{100}\right)^2$$

and $\quad \text{C.I.} = A - P = ₹\, 8000\left(1+\frac{r}{100}\right)^2 - ₹\, 8000$

$$= ₹\, 8000\left(1+\frac{r}{50}+\frac{r^2}{10000}\right) - ₹\, 8000 = ₹\left(160r+\frac{4r^2}{5}\right)$$

Given that C.I. – S.I. = ₹ 20

$\Rightarrow \quad 160r+\frac{4r^2}{5}-160r = 20 \quad \Rightarrow \quad \frac{4r^2}{5} = 20 \quad \Rightarrow \quad r^2 = 25 \quad \Rightarrow \quad r = 5$

$\therefore$ Rate of interest = 5% **Ans.**

**Example 17.** On what sum of money will the difference between C.I. and S.I. for 2 years at 10% per annum be equal to ₹ 120?

**Solution.** Let principal = $P$
Given, $n = 2$ years, $r = 10\%$

$$\text{S.I.} = \frac{P\times 2\times 10}{100} = \frac{P}{5}$$

$$\text{C.I.} = P\left[\left(1+\frac{r}{100}\right)^n - 1\right] = P\left[\left(1+\frac{r}{100}\right)^2 - 1\right] = P\left(\frac{121}{100}-1\right) = \frac{21P}{100}$$

Given, $\quad$ C.I. – S.I. = ₹ 120

$\Rightarrow \quad \frac{21P}{100}-\frac{P}{5} = ₹\,120 \quad \Rightarrow \quad \frac{P}{100} = ₹\,120 \quad \Rightarrow \quad P = ₹\,12000$

$\therefore$ Principal = ₹ 12000 **Ans.**

**Example 18.** A sum of money lent out at compound interest at certain rate of interest becomes 2 times of itself in 5 years. In how many years, it will become 8 times of itself?

**Solution.** Let principal = $P$ and rate of interest = $r\%$
Given, it becomes 2 times in 5 years.

$\therefore \quad P\left(1+\frac{r}{100}\right)^5 = 2P \quad \Rightarrow \quad \left(1+\frac{r}{100}\right)^5 = 2 \quad$ ...(*i*)

Let it becomes 8 times in $n$ years.

$\therefore \quad P\left(1+\frac{r}{100}\right)^n = 8P$

$\Rightarrow \quad \left(1+\frac{r}{100}\right)^n = 8 = 2^3 = \left\{\left(1+\frac{r}{100}\right)^5\right\}^3 = \left(1+\frac{r}{100}\right)^{15} \quad$ from (*i*)

$\Rightarrow \quad n = 15$

$\therefore$ Required time = 15 years **Ans.**

## Exercise 2B

1. Find the amount and compound interest on ₹ 50000 in 2 years at 8% compounded annually.
2. Find the amount and compound interest on ₹ 36000 in 3 years at 10% compounded annually.
3. Find the compound interest on ₹ 7000 in 2 years at 12% compounded annually.
4. Find the amount and compound interest on ₹ 10000 in 2 years when the rates of interest for the successive years are 6% and 7% respectively.

5. Find the amount and compound interest on ₹ 20000 in 3 years when the rates of interest for three successive years are 10%, 5% and 8% respectively.
6. What sum of money will amount to ₹ 5618 in 2 years at 6% per annum compounded yearly?
7. What sum of money will amount to ₹ 3515.20 in 3 years at 4% per annum compounded yearly?
8. What sum of money will amount to ₹ 9240 in 2 years if the rates of interest for two successive years are 5% and 10%, respectively?
9. On a certain sum, the compound interest in 2 years at 15% per annum is ₹ 11610. Find the sum.
10. On a certain sum, the compound interest in 3 years at 5% per annum is ₹ 1261. Find the sum.
11. At what rate percent per annum compound interest will ₹ 8000 amount to ₹ 10125 in 2 years?
12. At what rate percent will ₹ 30000 yield ₹ 2448 as compound interest in 2 years?
13. In how many years will ₹ 8500 amount to ₹ 11313.50 at 10% per annum compound interest?
14. In how many years will ₹ 18000 amount to ₹ 23805 at 15% per annum compound interest?
15. In what period will ₹ 24000 yield ₹ 7944 as compound interest at 10% per annum compounded yearly.
16. Divide ₹ 8400 between *A* and *B* so that when their shares are invested at 10% compounded yearly, the amount that *A* receives in 4 years is the same as *B* receives in 5 years.
17. Divide ₹ 39030 between *A* and *B* so that when their shares are invested at 4% per annum compounded yearly, the amount that A receives in 5 years is same as *B* receives in 3 years.
18. Find the amount when ₹ 6000 is invested for $2\frac{1}{2}$ years at 10% per annum compounded yearly.
19. Find the amount when ₹ 40000 is invested for $2\frac{1}{2}$ years at 8% per annum compounded yearly.
20. Find the amount and compound interest of ₹ 16000 in 1 year at 10% per annum compounded half yearly.
21. Find the compound interest of ₹ 96000 in $1\frac{1}{2}$ year at 5% per annum compounded half-yearly.
22. A sum of ₹ 48000 amount to ₹ 55566 in 18 months when the interest is reckoned half-yearly. Find the rate of interest per annum.
23. A sum of ₹ 8192 becomes ₹ 9826 at 12.5% per annum compounded half-yearly. Find the time period.
24. The compound interest on a certain sum of money at 6% per annum for 2 years is ₹ 306. Find the simple interest on the same sum for 3 years at 10% per annum.
25. The compound interest on a certain sum of money at 5% per annum for 2 years is ₹ 4100. Find the simple interest on the same sum for 3 years at 8% per annum.
26. The simple interest on a sum of money for 3 years at 10% per annum is ₹ 1200. Find
    (i) the sum of money.
    (ii) the compound interest on this sum for one year payable half-yearly at the same rate.
27. The simple interest on a certain sum of money at a certain rate is ₹ 900 in 2 years while the compound interest is ₹ 927. Find the sum and the rate of interest.
28. On a certain sum and at a certain rate of interest, the simple interest for first year is ₹ 300 and the compound interest for first 2 years is ₹ 630. Find the sum and the rate of interest.
29. A certain sum of money amounts to ₹ 4840 in 2 years and ₹ 5856.40 in 4 years at compound interest. Find the sum and the rate of interest.
30. A certain sum of money amounts to ₹ 26460 in 2 years and ₹ 29172.15 in 4 years at compound interest. Find the sum and the rate of interest.
31. On what sum of money will the difference between compound and simple interest for 2 years at 6% per annum be equal to ₹ 72?
32. On what sum of money will the difference between compound and simple interest for 2 years at 5% per annum be equal to ₹ 30?
33. The difference between the compound interest and simple interest on ₹ 7500 for 2 years is ₹ 27 at the same rate of interest per year. Find the rate of interest.
34. The difference between the compound interest and simple interest on ₹ 20000 for 2 years is ₹ 32 at the same rate of interest. Find the rate of interest.
35. A sum of money lent out at compound interest at certain rate of interest becomes 2 times of itself in 3 years. In how many years, it will become 16 times of itself?

## Answers

| | | | | | | | | | | | |
|---|---|---|---|---|---|---|---|---|---|---|---|
| **1.** | ₹ 58320, ₹ 8320 | **2.** | ₹ 47916, ₹ 11916 | | | **3.** | ₹ 1780.80 | **4.** | ₹ 11342, ₹ 1342 | | |
| **5.** | ₹ 24948, ₹ 4948 | **6.** | ₹ 5000 | **7.** | ₹ 3125 | **8.** | ₹ 8000 | **9.** | ₹ 36000 | **10.** | ₹ 8000 |
| **11.** | 12.5% **12.** 4% | **13.** | 3 years | **14.** | 2 years | **15.** | 3 years | **16.** | ₹ 4400, ₹ 4000 | | |
| **17.** | ₹ 18750, ₹ 20280 | **18.** | ₹ 7623 | **19.** | ₹ 48522.24 | **20.** | ₹ 17640, ₹ 1640 | | | **21.** | ₹ 7381.50 |
| **22.** | 10% **23.** 18 months | **24.** | ₹ 750 | **25.** | ₹ 600 | **26.** | (i) ₹ 4000 (ii) ₹ 410 | | | **27.** | ₹ 7500, 6% |
| **28.** | ₹ 3000, 10% **29.** ₹ 4000, 10% | **30.** | ₹ 24000, 5% | **31.** | ₹ 20000 | **32.** | ₹ 12000 | **33.** | 6% | **34.** | 4% |
| **35.** | 12 years. | | | | | | | | | | |

# Growth and Depreciation

## Growth

The growth per unit time is called the rate of growth.

*For example :* Population increase, height of plant, etc.

If the rate of growth is constant, then $V = V_0\left(1+\frac{r}{100}\right)^n$

where $V_0$ = present value, $V$ = value after $n$ years, $r\%$ = rate of growth.

**NOTE**

If $V_0$ = Value $n$ years ago and $V$ = present value, then $V = V_0\left(1+\frac{r}{100}\right)^n$

## Depreciation

The decrease of the value per unit time is called the rate of depreciation.

*For example :* Cost of machinery or vehicles decreases with time.

If rate of depreciation is constant, then $V = V_0\left(1-\frac{r}{100}\right)^n$

where $V_0$ = present value, $V$ = value after $n$ years, $r\%$ = rate of depreciation

**NOTE**

If $V_0$ = Value $n$ years ago and $V$ = present value, then $V = V_0\left(1-\frac{r}{100}\right)^n$

# Illustrative Examples

**Example 1.** The value of a machine depreciates 10% every year. If the original value of the machine is ₹ 20000, find its value after 2 years.

**Solution.** For first year,

$$\text{Depreciation} = 10\% \text{ of ₹ } 20000 = ₹\ \frac{10}{100}\times 20000 = ₹\ 2000$$

Value of machine after one year = ₹ 20000 – ₹ 2000 = ₹ 18000

For second year,

$$\text{Depreciation} = 10\% \text{ of } 18000 = ₹\ \frac{10}{100}\times 18000 = ₹\ 1800$$

Value of machine after two years = ₹ (18000 – 1800) = ₹ 16200 Ans.

**Example 2.** The cost of a machine is supposed to depreciate each year at 8% of its value at the beginning of the year. If the cost of machine is ₹ 40000 at the beginning of 2004, find its value
(i) at the end of 2005.
(ii) at the beginning of 2003.

**Solution.** Here, $V$ = ₹ 40000 (value at the beginning of 2004)

(i) Value of machine at the end of 2005 $= V\left(1-\frac{r}{100}\right)^2 = ₹\ 40000\left(1-\frac{8}{100}\right)^2 = ₹\ 33856$ Ans.

(ii) $V$ = (Value of the machine at the beginning of 2003) $\left(1-\frac{r}{100}\right)^1$

$$\Rightarrow \quad 40000 = V_0 \times 0.92 \quad \Rightarrow \quad V_0 = ₹\ \frac{40000}{0.92} = ₹\ 43478.26$$ Ans.

**Example 3.** The population of a town is 101000. If it is decreasing at a rate of 10% every year, find its population after 2 years.

**Solution.** Here, present population ($P_0$) = 101000
Rate of decreasing ($r$) = 10%, time ($n$) = 2 years
Let the population after 2 years = $P$

$$\therefore \quad P = P_0\left(1-\frac{r}{100}\right)^n = 101000\left(1-\frac{10}{100}\right)^2 = 101000\times\frac{9}{10}\times\frac{9}{10} = 81810$$ Ans.

**Example 4.** The present population of a city is 653184. It is increasing 8% every year. Find its population 2 years ago.

**Solution.** Here present population = 653184
$n$ = 2 years
$r$ = 8% (increasing)
Let the population 2 years ago = $P$

$$\therefore \quad P_0 = P\left(1+\frac{r}{100}\right)^n \quad \Rightarrow \quad 653184 = P\left(1+\frac{8}{100}\right)^2$$

$$\Rightarrow \quad P = \frac{653184}{(1.08)^2} = 560000$$

∴ Population of the city 2 years ago = 560000 Ans.

**Example 5.** The population of a village increases 10% in the first year and 6% in the second year. If the population of the village was 60000 in two years ago find its present population.

**Solution.** Here, $r_1 = 10\%$, $r_2 = 6\%$, $V_0 = 60000$

$$\therefore \quad V = V_0\left(1+\frac{r_1}{100}\right)\left(1+\frac{r_2}{100}\right) = 60000\left(1+\frac{10}{100}\right)\left(1+\frac{6}{100}\right)$$

$$= 60000\times\frac{110}{100}\times\frac{106}{100} = 69960$$

∴ Present population is 69960. Ans.

## Exercise 2C

1. The present price of a T.V. is ₹ 72900. If its value decreases 10% every year then what was its value 2 years ago?
2. The present value of a machine is ₹ 24000. If its value decreases 20% every year, find its value :
(i) 2 years ago (ii) after 2 years

3. The present value of a car is ₹ 525000. Its value depreciates at the rate of 10% in the first year and then 6% every year. Find its value after 3 years.
4. The present value of a plot is ₹ 960000. Its value increases 6% every year. Find its value after 2 years.
5. The value of a machine depreciates 15% in the first year and increases by 10% in the second year. If its present value is ₹ 60000, find its value after 2 years.
6. The population of a village increases 5% every year. If the present population of the village is 8820, find its population 2 years ago.
7. The population of a town decreases 5% every year. If its present population is ₹ 216600. Find its population 2 years ago.
8. The population of a town increases 10% in the first year and decreases 12% in the second year. If its present population is 118000, find its population after 2 years.
9. The present population of a town is 48400. It is increasing 10% every year. Find the population of the town :
   (i) 2 years ago, (ii) after 2 years.
10. The cost of a machine depreciated by ₹ 900 during the second year and by ₹ 810 during the third year. Find :
   (i) the rate of depreciation (ii) the original cost of the machine.
11. The population of a village increases 10% every year. If its present population is 12,100, find its population :
   (i) 2 years ago, (ii) after 2 years.

### Answers

**1.** ₹ 90000 **2.** (i) ₹ 37500 (ii) ₹ 15360 **3.** ₹ 417501 **4.** ₹ 1078656 **5.** ₹ 56100 **6.** 8000
**7.** 240000 **8.** 114224 **9.** (i) 40000 (ii) 58564 **10.** (i) 10% (ii) ₹ 10000
**11.** (i) 100000 (ii) 146410

# Exercise 2D

## Multiple Choice *Questions*

Choose the correct answer from the given four options in each of the following questions :

1. The cost of a machine is ₹ 50000. It depreciates 10% every year. The cost of machine after 1 year will be :
   (a) ₹ 55000 (b) ₹ 40000 (c) ₹ 45000 (d) ₹ 48000
2. The present population of a town is 20000, it increases 2% every year. The population of the town after 2 years will be :
   (a) 20808 (b) 20804 (c) 20800 (d) 20400
3. If the number of conversion period is greater than or equal to 2 then the correct relation is :
   (a) C.I. > S.I. (b) C.I. = S.I. (c) C.I. < S.I. (d) none of these
4. The amount of ₹ 6000 for 2 years at the rate of 10% per annum compounded annually is :
   (a) ₹ 7200 (b) ₹ 7260 (c) ₹ 7500 (d) ₹ 7810
5. The time period in which the sum of money ₹ 12000 becomes ₹ 15870 at the rate of 15% per annum compounded annually, is :
   (a) 6 months (b) 1 year (c) $1\frac{1}{2}$ year (d) 2 years
6. The rate of interest at which the sum of money ₹ 2000 yields ₹ 420 as compound interest compounded annually in 2 years is :
   (a) 8% (b) 10% (c) 11% (d) 12%
7. The compound interest of ₹ 28000 for 1 year at 10% per annum compounded half-yearly is :
   (a) ₹ 2680 (b) ₹ 2870 (c) ₹ 2920 (d) ₹ 3050

### Answers

**1.** (c) **2.** (a) **3.** (a) **4.** (b) **5.** (d) **6.** (b) **7.** (b)

## SUMMARY *of the Chapter*

- S.I. $= \dfrac{P \times R \times T}{100}$
- Amount = Principal + Interest
- When the interest is compounded yearly, the principal changes every year.
- When the interest is compounded yearly.
  (i) the C.I. of 2nd year is always more than the C.I. of the 1st year.
  (ii) the C.I. of 3rd year is always more than the C.I. of the 2nd year.
- $$A = P\left(1 + \frac{R}{100}\right)^n$$
- If the rates of interest for successive years are different then
$$A = P\left(1 + \frac{R_1}{100}\right)\left(1 + \frac{R_2}{100}\right)\left(1 + \frac{R_3}{100}\right)\ldots$$
- If the interest is compounded half-yearly then the rate percent is divided by 2 and the number of years is multiplied by 2.
- When the value of a machine depreciates by $r$ % every year then value of machine after '$n$' years = Present value $\times \left(1 - \dfrac{r}{100}\right)^n$
- When the population of a town or city, etc., increases at a rate $r$ % per year then
  (i) Population after '$n$' years = Present population $\times \left(1 + \dfrac{r}{100}\right)^n$
  (ii) Present population = Population '$n$' years ago $\times \left(1 + \dfrac{r}{100}\right)^n$

# CHAPTER TEST

1. Find the amount and compound interest of ₹ 25000 at 10% per annum for 2 years.
2. Find the amount and compound interest of ₹ 40000 at 8% per annum compounded half-yearly for 1 year.
3. Find the compound interest of ₹ 40000 for $2\frac{1}{2}$ years at 10% per annum compounded annually.
4. Samit invests ₹ 20000 for 3 years at 6% per annum compound interest. Find :
   (i) the interest for first year
   (ii) the amount of the end of second year.
   (iii) the compound interest for 3 years.
5. A sum of money is invested at compound interest payable annually. The interest in the successive years are ₹ 225 and ₹ 240. Find the rate of interest.
6. Find the difference between compound interest and simple interest on ₹ 12750 for 2 years at 10% per annum.
7. What sum of money will amount to ₹ 1815 in 2 years at 10% per annum compounded annually?
8. At what rate percent will ₹ 30000 yield ₹ 2448 as compound interest in 2 years?
9. Divide ₹ 3903 between A and B so that when their shares are lent out at 4% per annum compounded yearly, the amount that A receives in 3 years is the same as B receives in 1 year.
10. On what sum of money will the difference between compound interest and simple interest for 2 years at 5% per annum is ₹ 600?

## *Answers*

**1.** ₹ 30250, ₹ 5250 **2.** ₹ 43264, ₹ 3264 **3.** ₹ 10820

**4.** (i) ₹ 1200 (ii) ₹ 22472 (iii) ₹ 3820.32 **5.** $6\frac{2}{3}\%$ **6.** ₹ 127.50 **7.** ₹ 1500 **8.** 4%

**9.** ₹ 1875, ₹ 2028 **10.** ₹ 240000

UNIT III : ALGEBRA

# Chapter 3

# EXPANSIONS

## Syllabus

Recall of concepts learned in earlier classes.

$(a \pm b)^2$

$(a \pm b)^3$

$(x \pm a)\,(x \pm b)$

$(a \pm b \pm c)^2$

## INTRODUCTION

In previous classes, we have learnt about algebraic expressions. We are also familiar with the basic operations, *i.e.*, addition, subtraction, multiplication, division on these algebraic expressions. Now, we shall study the product and expansions of algebraic expressions.

## Product of Algebraic Expressions

1. $$(x+a)(x+b) = x(x+b) + a(x+b) = x^2 + bx + ax + ab = x^2 + ax + bx + ab = x^2 + x(a+b) + ab$$
$$\therefore\ (x+a)(x+b) = x^2 + x(a+b) + ab$$

2. $$(x+a)(x-b) = x(x-b) + a(x-b) = x^2 - bx + ax - ab = x^2 + ax - bx - ab = x^2 + x(a-b) - ab$$
$$\therefore\ (x+a)(x-b) = x^2 + x(a-b) - ab$$

3. $$(x-a)(x+b) = x(x+b) - a(x+b) = x^2 + bx - ax - ab = x^2 - ax + bx - ab = x^2 + x(-a+b) - ab$$
$$\therefore\ (x-a)(x+b) = x^2 + x(-a+b) - ab$$

4. $$(x-a)(x-b) = x(x-b) - a(x-b) = x^2 - bx - ax + ab = x^2 - ax - bx + ab = x^2 - x(a+b) + ab$$
$$\therefore\ (x-a)(x-b) = x^2 - x(a+b) + ab$$

5. Put $a = b = y$ in product (1),
$$(x+y)(x+y) = x^2 + x(y+y) + y \cdot y$$
$$\Rightarrow\ (x+y)^2 = x^2 + 2xy + y^2$$

6. Put $a = b = y$ in product (4),
$$(x-y)(x-y) = x^2 - x(y+y) + y \cdot y$$
$$\Rightarrow\ (x-y)^2 = x^2 - 2xy + y^2$$

7. Put $a = b = y$ in product (2),
$$(x+y)(x-y) = x^2 + x(y-y) - y \cdot y$$
$$\Rightarrow\ (x+y)\,(x-y) = x^2 - y^2$$

8. Put $x = a,\ y = \frac{1}{a}$ in product (5),
$$\left(a+\frac{1}{a}\right)^2 = a^2 + 2\cdot a\cdot\frac{1}{a} + \frac{1}{a^2}$$
$$\Rightarrow\ \left(a+\frac{1}{a}\right)^2 = a^2 + \frac{1}{a^2} + 2,\ a \neq 0$$

9. Put $x = a,\ y = \frac{1}{a}$ in product (6),
$$\left(a-\frac{1}{a}\right)^2 = a^2 - 2\cdot a\cdot\frac{1}{a} + \frac{1}{a^2}$$
$$\Rightarrow\ \left(a-\frac{1}{a}\right)^2 = a^2 + \frac{1}{a^2} - 2,\ a \neq 0$$

10. Put $x = a,\ y = \frac{1}{a}$ in product (7),
$$\left(a+\frac{1}{a}\right)\left(a-\frac{1}{a}\right) = a^2 - \frac{1}{a^2},\ a \neq 0$$

11. $(x+y+z)^2 = (x+a)^2$ where $y+z=a$
$= x^2 + a^2 + 2xa$ [From product (5)]
$= x^2 + (y+z)^2 + 2x(y+z)$
$= x^2 + y^2 + z^2 + 2yz + 2xy + 2zx$ [From product (5)]
$$\therefore\ (x+y+z)^2 = x^2 + y^2 + z^2 + 2(xy + yz + zx)$$

12. $(x+y)^3 = (x+y)(x+y)^2$
$= (x+y)(x^2 + 2xy + y^2)$ [From product (5)]
$= x(x^2 + 2xy + y^2) + y(x^2 + 2xy + y^2)$

$$= x^3 + 2x^2y + xy^2 + x^2y + 2xy^2 + y^3$$
$$= x^3 + 3x^2y + 3xy^2 + y^3$$
$$= x^3 + y^3 + 3xy\,(x + y)$$
$\therefore$ $$(x + y)^3 = x^3 + 3x^2y + 3xy^2 + y^3 = x^3 + y^3 + 3xy(x + y)$$

13. $$(x - y)^3 = (x - y)(x - y)^2$$
$$= (x - y)(x^2 - 2xy + y^2) \quad \text{[From product (6)]}$$
$$= x(x^2 - 2xy + y^2) - y(x^2 - 2xy + y^2)$$
$$= x^3 - 2x^2y + xy^2 - x^2y + 2xy^2 - y^3$$
$$= x^3 - 3x^2y + 3xy^2 - y^3$$
$$= x^3 - y^3 - 3xy(x - y)$$
$\therefore$ $$(x - y)^3 = x^3 - 3x^2y + 3xy^2 - y^3 = x^3 - y^3 - 3xy(x - y)$$

14. $$(x + y)(x^2 - xy + y^2) = x(x^2 - xy + y^2) + y(x^2 - xy + y^2)$$
$$= x^3 - x^2y + xy^2 + x^2y - xy^2 + y^3$$
$$= x^3 + y^3$$
$\therefore$ $$(x + y)(x^2 - xy + y^2) = x^3 + y^3$$

15. $$(x - y)(x^2 + xy + y^2) = x(x^2 + xy + y^2) - y(x^2 + xy + y^2)$$
$$= x^3 + x^2y + xy^2 - x^2y - xy^2 - y^3$$
$$= x^3 - y^3$$
$\therefore$ $$(x - y)(x^2 - xy + y^2) = x^3 - y^3$$

16. $(a + b + c)(a^2 + b^2 + c^2 - ab - bc - ca)$
$$= a(a^2 + b^2 + c^2 - ab - bc - ca) + b(a^2 + b^2 + c^2 - ab - bc - ca) + c(a^2 + b^2 + c^2 - ab - bc - ca)$$
$$= a^3 + ab^2 + ac^2 - a^2b - abc - a^2c + a^2b + b^3 + bc^2 - ab^2 - b^2c - abc + a^2c + b^2c + c^3 - abc - bc^2 - ac^2$$
$$= a^3 + b^3 + c^3 - 3abc$$
$\therefore$ $$(a + b + c)(a^2 + b^2 + c^2 - ab - bc - ca) = a^3 + b^3 + c^3 - 3abc$$

17. If $a + b + c = 0$ then from product (16)
$$a^3 + b^3 + c^3 - 3abc = 0 \quad \Rightarrow \quad a^3 + b^3 + c^3 = 3abc$$

18. $$(x + a)(x + b)(x + c) = (x + a)[x^2 + x(b + c) + bc] \quad \text{[From product (1)]}$$
$$= (x + a)(x^2 + bx + cx + bc)$$
$$= x(x^2 + bx + cx + bc) + a(x^2 + bx + cx + bc)$$
$$= x^3 + bx^2 + cx^2 + bcx + ax^2 + abx + cax + abc$$
$$= x^3 + ax^2 + bx^2 + cx^2 + abx + bcx + cax + abc$$
$$= x^3 + x^2(a + b + c) + x(ab + bc + ca) + abc$$
$\therefore$ $$(x + a)(x + b)(x + c) = x^3 + x^2(a + b + c) + x\,(ab + bc + ca) + abc$$

## Illustrative Examples

**Example 1.** Expand :

(i) $(2x + 3y)^2$ (ii) $(4x - y)^2$ (iii) $\left(\frac{1}{2}x + \frac{3}{5}y\right)^2$ (iv) $\left(xy - \frac{1}{2}z\right)^2$

(v) $(a + b - 2c)^2$ (vi) $\left(\frac{x}{3} - \frac{y}{2} + z\right)^2$

**Solution.** (i) $(2x+3y)^2 = (2x)^2 + (3y)^2 + 2(2x)(3y)$ [Using product (5)]

$= 4x^2 + 9y^2 + 12xy$ Ans.

(ii) $(4x-y)^2 = (4x)^2 + y^2 - 2(4x)(y)$ [Using product (6)]

$= 16x^2 + y^2 - 8xy$ Ans.

(iii) $\left(\frac{1}{2}x + \frac{3}{5}y\right)^2 = \left(\frac{1}{2}x\right)^2 + \left(\frac{3}{5}y\right)^2 + 2\left(\frac{1}{2}x\right)\left(\frac{3}{5}y\right)$

$= \frac{1}{4}x^2 + \frac{9}{25}y^2 + \frac{3}{5}xy$ Ans.

(iv) $\left(xy - \frac{1}{2}z\right)^2 = (xy)^2 + \left(\frac{1}{2}z\right)^2 - 2(xy)\left(\frac{1}{2}z\right)$

$= x^2y^2 + \frac{1}{4}z^2 - xyz$ Ans.

(v) $(a+b-2c)^2 = a^2 + b^2 + (-2c)^2 + 2ab + 2b(-2c) + 2a(-2c)$ [Using product (11)]

$= a^2 + b^2 + 4c^2 + 2ab - 4bc - 4ac$ Ans.

(vi) $\left(\frac{x}{3} - \frac{y}{2} + z\right)^2 = \left(\frac{x}{3}\right)^2 + \left(-\frac{y}{2}\right)^2 + z^2 + 2\left(\frac{x}{3}\right)\left(-\frac{y}{2}\right) + 2\left(-\frac{y}{2}\right)(z) + 2\left(\frac{x}{3}\right)(z)$

$= \frac{x^2}{9} + \frac{y^2}{4} + z^2 - \frac{1}{3}xy - yz + \frac{2}{3}xz$ Ans.

**Example 2.** Expand :

(i) $\left(2x + \frac{3}{x}\right)^2$ (ii) $\left(5x - \frac{1}{x}\right)^2$

**Solution.** (i) $\left(2x + \frac{3}{x}\right)^2 = (2x)^2 + \left(\frac{3}{x}\right)^2 + 2(2x)\left(\frac{3}{x}\right) = 4x^2 + \frac{9}{x^2} + 12$ Ans.

(ii) $\left(5x - \frac{1}{x}\right)^2 = (5x)^2 + \left(\frac{1}{x}\right)^2 - 2(5x)\left(\frac{1}{x}\right) = 25x^2 + \frac{1}{x^2} - 10$ Ans.

**Example 3.** Find the product :

(i) $(x+2)(x+4)$ (ii) $(x+3)(x-8)$ (iii) $(x-1)(x-5)$ (iv) $(2x+1)(2x+6)$

**Solution.** (i) $(x+2)(x+4) = x^2 + x(2+4) + (2)(4)$

$= x^2 + 6x + 8$ Ans.

(ii) $(x+3)(x-8) = x^2 + x(3-8) + 3(-8)$

$= x^2 - 5x - 24$ Ans.

(iii) $(x-1)(x-5) = x^2 - x(1+5) + (-1)(-5)$

$= x^2 - 6x + 5$ Ans.

(iv) $(2x+1)(2x+6) = (2x)^2 + 2x(1+6) + (1)(6)$

$= 4x^2 + 14x + 6$ Ans.

**Example 4.** Simplify :

(i) $(x+3y)(x-3y)$ (ii) $(2x+5y)(2x-5y)$

**Solution.** (i) $(x+3y)(x-3y) = (x)^2 - (3y)^2$

$= x^2 - 9y^2$ Ans.

(ii) $(2x+5y)(2x-5y) = (2x)^2 - (5y)^2$

$= 4x^2 - 25y^2$ Ans.

**Example 5.** Simplify :

(i) $(x+y+1)(x+y-1)$ (ii) $\left(a+\frac{1}{a}+2\right)\left(a+\frac{1}{a}-2\right)$

(iii) $(2x-y+z)(2x+y+z)$ (iv) $(2x-y)(2x+y)(4x^2+y^2)$

**Solution.** (i) $(x+y+1)(x+y-1) = (z+1)(z-1)$ (where $x+y=z$)

$\therefore$ $= z^2 - 1^2 = z^2 - 1 = (x+y)^2 - 1$

$= x^2 + y^2 + 2xy - 1$ **Ans.**

(ii) $\left(a+\frac{1}{a}+2\right)\left(a+\frac{1}{a}-2\right) = (x+2)(x-2)$ (where $a+\frac{1}{a}=x$)

$= x^2 - 2^2 = x^2 - 4 = \left(a+\frac{1}{a}\right)^2 - 4$

$= a^2 + \frac{1}{a^2} + 2 - 4 = a^2 + \frac{1}{a^2} - 2$ **Ans.**

(iii) $(2x-y+z)(2x+y+z) = (2x+z-y)(2x+z+y)$

$= (a-y)(a+y)$ (where $2x+z=a$)

$= a^2 - y^2 = (2x+z)^2 - y^2$

$= (2x)^2 + z^2 + 2(2x)(z) - y^2$

$= 4x^2 + z^2 + 4xz - y^2$

$= 4x^2 - y^2 + z^2 + 4xz$ **Ans.**

(iv) $(2x-y)(2x+y)(4x^2+y^2) = \{(2x)^2 - y^2\}(4x^2+y^2)$

$= (4x^2 - y^2)(4x^2 + y^2)$

$= (4x^2)^2 - (y^2)^2 = 16x^4 - y^4$ **Ans.**

**Example 6.** Expand :

(i) $(3x+2y+1)(3x+2y+5)$ (ii) $(x-2y+3)(x-2y+6)$

**Solution.** (i) $(3x+2y+1)(3x+2y+5) = (z+1)(z+5)$ (where $3x+2y=z$)

$= z^2 + z(1+5) + (1)(5)$

$= z^2 + 6z + 5$

$= (3x+2y)^2 + 6(3x+2y) + 5$

$= (3x)^2 + (2y)^2 + 2(3x)(2y) + 18x + 12y + 5$

$= 9x^2 + 4y^2 + 12xy + 18x + 12y + 5$ **Ans.**

(ii) $(x-2y+3)(x-2y+6) = (z+3)(z+6)$ (where $x-2y=z$)

$= z^2 + (3+6)z + (3)(6)$

$= z^2 + 9z + 18$

$= (x-2y)^2 + 9(x-2y) + 18$

$= x^2 + (2y)^2 - 2x(2y) + 9x - 18y + 18$

$= x^2 + 4y^2 - 4xy + 9x - 18y + 18$ **Ans.**

**Example 7.** Expand :

(i) $(a+4b)^3$ (ii) $(4x+3y)^3$

**Solution.** (i) $(a+4b)^3 = a^3 + 3a^2(4b) + 3a(4b)^2 + (4b)^3$

$= a^3 + 12a^2b + 48ab^2 + 64b^3$ **Ans.**

(ii) $(4x+3y)^3 = (4x)^3 + 3(4x)^2(3y) + 3(4x)(3y)^2 + (3y)^3$

$= 64x^3 + 144x^2y + 108xy^2 + 27y^3$ **Ans.**

**Example 8.** Expand :

(i) $(2x - y)^3$ (ii) $\left(a - \frac{2}{b}\right)^3$

**Solution.** (i) $(2x - y)^3 = (2x)^3 - 3(2x)^2y + 3(2x)y^2 - y^3$

$= 8x^3 - 12x^2y + 6xy^2 - y^3$ Ans.

(ii) $\left(a - \frac{2}{b}\right)^3 = a^3 - 3a^2\left(\frac{2}{b}\right) + 3a\left(\frac{2}{b}\right)^2 - \left(\frac{2}{b}\right)^3$

$= a^3 - \frac{6a^2}{b} + \frac{12a}{b^2} - \frac{8}{b^3}$ Ans.

**Example 9.** Simplify : $(2x + 3y)^3 - (2x - 3y)^3$

**Solution.** $(2x + 3y)^3 - (2x - 3y)^3 = [(2x)^3 + 3(2x)^2(3y) + 3(2x)(3y)^2 + (3y)^3]$

$- [(2x)^3 - 3(2x)^2(3y) + 3(2x)(3y)^2 - (3y)^3]$

$= (8x^3 + 36x^2y + 54xy^2 + 27y^3) - (8x^3 - 36x^2y + 54xy^2 - 27y^3)$

$= 8x^3 + 36x^2y + 54xy^2 + 27y^3 - 8x^3 + 36x^2y - 54xy^2 + 27y^3$

$= 72x^2y + 54y^3$ Ans.

**Example 10.** Expand : $(x + 2y + 3)^3$

**Solution.** $(x + 2y + 3)^3 = (z + 3)^3$ (where $x + 2y = z$)

$= z^3 + 3z^2(3) + 3z(3)^2 + 3^3$

$= z^3 + 9z^2 + 27z + 27$

$= (x + 2y)^3 + 9(x + 2y)^2 + 27(x + 2y) + 27$

$= x^3 + 3x^2(2y) + 3x(2y)^2 + (2y)^3 + 9[x^2 + 2x(2y) + (2y)^2] + 27x + 54y + 27$

$= x^3 + 6x^2y + 12xy^2 + 8y^3 + 9x^2 + 36xy + 36y^2 + 27x + 54y + 27$ Ans.

**Example 11.** Simplify :

(i) $(x + 2y)(x^2 - 2xy + 4y^2)$ (ii) $(3a + 2b)(9a^2 - 6ab + 4b^2)$

**Solution.** (i) $(x + 2y)(x^2 - 2xy + 4y^2) = (x + 2y)\{x^2 - x(2y) + (2y)^2\}$

$= x^3 + (2y)^3$

$= x^3 + 8y^3$ Ans.

(ii) $(3a + 2b)(9a^2 - 6ab + 4b^2)$

$= (3a + 2b)\{(3a)^2 - (3a)(2b) + (2b)^2\}$

$= (3a)^3 + (2b)^3$

$= 27a^3 + 8b^3$ Ans.

**Example 12.** Simplify :

(i) $(2x - y)(4x^2 + 2xy + y^2)$ (ii) $(4a - 3b)(16a^2 + 12ab + 9b^2)$

**Solution.** (i) $(2x - y)(4x^2 + 2xy + y^2) = (2x - y)\{(2x)^2 + (2x)y + y^2\}$

$= (2x)^3 - y^3$

$= 8x^3 - y^3$ Ans.

(ii) $(4a - 3b)(16a^2 + 12ab + 9b^2)$

$= (4a - 3b)\{(4a)^2 + (4a)(3b) + (3b)^2\}$

$= (4a)^3 - (3b)^3$

$= 64a^3 - 27b^3$ Ans.

**Example 13.** Simplify : $(3x+2y)(9x^2-6xy+4y^2)+(3x-2y)(9x^2+6xy+4y^2)$

**Solution.** $(3x+2y)(9x^2-6xy+4y^2)+(3x-2y)(9x^2+6xy+4y^2)$

$= (3x+2y)\{(3x)^2-(3x)(2y)+(2y)^2\}+(3x-2y)\{(3x)^2+(3x)(2y)+(2y)^2\}$

$= (3x)^3+(2y)^3+(3x)^2-(2y)^3 = 27x^3+27x^3 = 54x^3$ Ans.

**Example 14.** Find the product :

(i) $(x+1)(x+2)(x+3)$ (ii) $(x+2)(x-5)(x+6)$

**Solution.** We know that

$(x+a)(x+b)(x+c) = x^3+(a+b+c)x^2+(ab+bc+ca)x+abc$

(i) $(x+1)(x+2)(x+3) = x^3+(1+2+3)x^2+(1\times2+2\times3+3\times1)x+1\times2\times3$

$= x^3+6x^2+11x+6$ Ans.

(ii) $(x+2)(x-5)(x+6) = x^3+(2-5+6)x^2+\{(2)(-5)+(-5)(6)+(6)(2)\}x+(2)(-5)(6)$

$= x^3+3x^2-28x-60$ Ans.

**Example 15.** Find the coefficient of $x$ and constant term in $(x+2)(x-6)(x+4)$.

**Solution.** $(x+2)(x-6)(x+4) = x^3+(2-6+4)x^2+\{(2)(-6)+(-6)(4)+(4)(2)\}x+(2)(-6)(4)$

$= x^3-28x-48$

$\therefore$ Coefficient of $x = -28$ and constant term $= -48$ Ans.

**Example 16.** Using suitable identity, find the value of :

(i) $99^3$ (ii) $103^3$

**Solution.** (i) $99^3 = (100-1)^3 = 100^3-3(100)^2(1)+3(100)(1)^2-(1)^3$

$= 1000000-30000+300-1 = 970299$ Ans.

(ii) $103^3 = (100+3)^3 = 100^3+3(100)^2\cdot 3+3(100)(3)^2+3^3$

$= 1000000+90000+2700+27 = 1092727$ Ans.

**Example 17.** Find the product :

(i) $(a+2b+3c)(a^2+4b^2+9c^2-2ab-6bc-3ca)$

(ii) $(3x-y+2z)(9x^2+y^2+4z^2+3xy+2yz-6zx)$

**Solution.** (i) $(a+2b+3c)(a^2+4b^2+9c^2-2ab-6bc-3ca)$

$= (a+2b+3c)\{a^2+(2b)^2+(3c)^2-a(2b)-(2b)(3c)-(3c)a\}$

$= (a)^3+(2b)^3+(3c)^3-3(a)(2b)(3c) = a^3+8b^3+27c^3-18abc$ Ans.

(ii) $(3x-y+2z)(9x^2+y^2+4z^2+3xy+2yz-6zx)$

$= \{3x+(-y)+2z\}\{(3x)^2+(-y)^2+(2z)^2-(3x)(-y)-(-y)(2z)-(2z)(3x)\}$

$= (3x)^3+(-y)^3+(2z)^3-3(3x)(-y)(2z) = 27x^3-y^3+8z^3+18xyz$ Ans.

**Example 18.** Prove that :

$(x+y)^3+(y+z)^3+(z+x)^3-3(x+y)(y+z)(z+x) = 2(x^3+y^3+z^3-3xyz)$

**Solution.** Let $x+y=a$, $y+z=b$, $z+x=c$

$\therefore$ L.H.S. $= (x+y)^3+(y+z)^3+(z+x)^3-3(x+y)(y+z)(z+x)$

$= a^3+b^3+c^3-3abc$

$= (a+b+c)(a^2+b^2+c^2-ab-bc-ca)$

$= (x+y+y+z+z+x)[(x+y)^2+(y+z)^2+(z+x)^2-(x+y)(y+z)$
$-(y+z)(z+x)-(z+x)(x+y)]$

$= (2x+2y+2z)[x^2+y^2+2xy+y^2+z^2+2yz+z^2+x^2+2zx-xy-xz-y^2$
$-yz-yz-xy-z^2-zx-zx-yz-x^2-xy]$

$= 2(x+y+z)(x^2+y^2+z^2-xy-yz-zx)$

$= 2(x^3+y^3+z^3-3xyz) =$ R.H.S. Hence Proved.

**Example 19.** Simplify : $(a - 2b)^3 + (2b - 3c)^3 + (3c - a)^3$

**Solution.** Let $x = a - 2b$, $y = 2b - 3c$, $z = 3c - a$

$\therefore \quad x + y + z = a - 2b + 2b - 3c + 3c - a = 0$

$\Rightarrow \quad x^3 + y^3 + z^3 = 3xyz$

$\Rightarrow \quad (a - 2b)^3 + (2b - 3c)^3 + (3c - a)^3 = 3(a - 2b)(2b - 3c)(3c - a)$ **Ans.**

**Example 20.** Without actually calculating the cube, find the values of the following :

(i) $18^3 + (-10)^3 + (-8)^3$ (ii) $\left(\frac{1}{3}\right)^3 + \left(\frac{1}{4}\right)^3 - \left(\frac{7}{12}\right)^3$

**Solution.** (i) Let $x = 18$, $y = -10$, $z = -8$

$\therefore \quad x + y + z = 18 + (-10) + (-8) = 0$

$\Rightarrow \quad x^3 + y^3 + z^3 = 3xyz$

$\Rightarrow \quad (18)^3 + (-10)^3 + (-8)^3 = 3(18)(-10)(-8) = 4320$ **Ans.**

(ii) Let $x = \frac{1}{3}$, $y = \frac{1}{4}$, $z = -\frac{7}{12}$

$\therefore \quad x + y + z = \frac{1}{3} + \frac{1}{4} - \frac{7}{12} = \frac{4 + 3 - 7}{12} = 0$

$\Rightarrow \quad x^3 + y^3 + z^3 = 3xyz$

$\Rightarrow \quad \left(\frac{1}{3}\right)^3 + \left(\frac{1}{4}\right)^3 + \left(-\frac{7}{12}\right)^3 = 3\left(\frac{1}{3}\right)\left(\frac{1}{4}\right)\left(-\frac{7}{12}\right)$

$\Rightarrow \quad \left(\frac{1}{3}\right)^3 + \left(\frac{1}{4}\right)^3 - \left(\frac{7}{12}\right)^3 = -\frac{7}{48}$ **Ans.**

**Example 21.** If $3x = 2y - 4$, find the value of $27x^3 - 8y^3 + 72xy$.

**Solution.** We have, $3x = 2y - 4$

$\Rightarrow \quad 3x - 2y + 4 = 0$

$\Rightarrow \quad 3x + (-2y) + 4 = 0$

$\Rightarrow \quad (3x)^3 + (-2y)^3 + 4^3 = 3(3x)(-2y)(4)$

$\Rightarrow \quad 27x^3 - 8y^3 + 64 = -72xy$

$\Rightarrow \quad 27x^3 - 8y^3 + 72xy = -64$ **Ans.**

**Example 22.** If $x = 5$, $y = 3$, $z = 2$, find the value of $\dfrac{x^3 + y^3 + z^3 - 3xyz}{x^2 + y^2 + z^2 - xy - yz - zx}$.

**Solution.**

$$\frac{x^3 + y^3 + z^3 - 3xyz}{x^2 + y^2 + z^2 - xy - yz - zx} = \frac{(x + y + z)(x^2 + y^2 + z^2 - xy - yz - zx)}{x^2 + y^2 + z^2 - xy - yz - zx}$$

$$= x + y + z = 5 + 3 + 2 = 10$$ **Ans.**

**Example 23.** Simplify : $\dfrac{(x^2 - y^2)^3 + (y^2 - z^2)^3 + (z^2 - x^2)^3}{(x - y)^3 + (y - z)^3 + (z - x)^3}$

**Solution.** $\because \quad (x^2 - y^2) + (y^2 - z^2) + (z^2 - x^2) = 0$

$\therefore \quad (x^2 - y^2)^3 + (y^2 - z^2)^3 + (z^2 - x^2)^3 = 3(x^2 - y^2)(y^2 - z^2)(z^2 - x^2)$ ...(i)

Again, $(x - y) + (y - z) + (z - x) = 0$

$$\therefore \quad (x-y)^3+(y-z)^3+(z-x)^3 = 3(x-y)(y-z)(z-x) \quad \text{...(ii)}$$

Now, $$\frac{(x^2-y^2)^3+(y^2-z^2)^3+(z^2-x^2)^3}{(x-y)^3+(y-z)^3+(z-x)^3} = \frac{3(x^2-y^2)(y^2-z^2)(z^2-x^2)}{3(x-y)(y-z)(z-x)} \quad \text{[From (i) and (ii)]}$$

$$= \frac{(x-y)(x+y)(y-z)(y+z)(z-x)(z+x)}{(x-y)(y-z)(z-x)}$$

$$= (x+y)(y+z)(z+x)$$ **Ans.**

**Example 24.** If $a+b+c=0$, find the value of $\frac{(b+c)^2}{bc}+\frac{(c+a)^2}{ca}+\frac{(a+b)^2}{ab}$.

**Solution.** We have, $a+b+c=0$

$$\Rightarrow \quad a^3+b^3+c^3 = 3abc$$

$$\Rightarrow \quad \frac{a^3}{abc}+\frac{b^3}{abc}+\frac{c^3}{abc} = \frac{3abc}{abc}$$

$$\Rightarrow \quad \frac{a^2}{bc}+\frac{b^2}{ca}+\frac{c^2}{ab} = 3$$

$$\Rightarrow \quad \frac{(-a)^2}{bc}+\frac{(-b)^2}{ca}+\frac{(-c)^2}{ab} = 3$$

$$\Rightarrow \quad \frac{(b+c)^2}{bc}+\frac{(c+a)^2}{ca}+\frac{(a+b)^2}{ab} = 3 \qquad (\because\ b+c=-a,\ c+a=-b \text{ and } a+b=-c)$$ **Ans.**

**Example 25.** If $ab+bc+ca=0$, then find the value of $\frac{1}{a^2-bc}+\frac{1}{b^2-ca}+\frac{1}{c^2-ab}$.

**Solution.** Given, $ab+bc+ca=0$ ...(i)

$$\Rightarrow \quad ab+ca=-bc,\ ab+bc=-ca \text{ and } bc+ca=-ab$$

$$\therefore \quad \frac{1}{a^2-bc}+\frac{1}{b^2-ca}+\frac{1}{c^2-ab} = \frac{1}{a^2+ab+ca}+\frac{1}{b^2+ab+bc}+\frac{1}{c^2+bc+ca}$$

$$= \frac{1}{a(a+b+c)}+\frac{1}{b(a+b+c)}+\frac{1}{c(a+b+c)}$$

$$= \frac{bc+ca+ab}{abc(a+b+c)} = 0 \qquad \text{[From (i)]}$$ **Ans.**

**Example 26.** Using suitable identity, evaluate the following :

$$\frac{26\times26\times26+24\times24\times24}{26\times26-26\times24+24\times24}$$

**Solution.**

$$\frac{26\times26\times26+24\times24\times24}{26\times26-26\times24+24\times24} = \frac{(26)^3+(24)^3}{(26)^2-26\times24+(24)^2}$$

$$= \frac{(26+24)(26^2-26\times24+24^2)}{26^2-26\times24+24^2}$$

$$= (26+24) = 50$$ **Ans.**

# Exercise 3A

**1.** Expand the following :

(i) $(x+3y)^2$ (ii) $(3x-2y)^2$ (iii) $\left(\frac{1}{3}x+\frac{1}{2}y\right)^2$ (iv) $\left(2x-\frac{1}{3}y\right)^2$

(v) $(3x+y-5z)^2$ (vi) $\left(\frac{x}{2}-\frac{3y}{5}+z\right)^2$

**2.** Expand the following :

(i) $\left(5x+\frac{1}{x}\right)^2$ (ii) $\left(3x-\frac{1}{2x}\right)^2$

**3.** Find the product :

(i) $(x+1)(x+5)$ (ii) $(x+2)(x-6)$ (iii) $(x-4)(x-6)$ (iv) $(3x+1)(3x+5)$

**4.** Find the product :

(i) $(3a-2b)(3a+2b)$ (ii) $(5x+3y)(5x-3y)$

**5.** Find the product :

(i) $(x+2y+3)(x+2y-3)$ (ii) $\left(x-\frac{1}{x}+4\right)\left(x-\frac{1}{x}-4\right)$ (iii) $(3x+y+2)(3x-y+2)$ (iv) $(x+2)(x-2)(x^2+4)$

**6.** Expand the following :

(i) $(x+3y+2)(x+3y+5)$ (ii) $(2x-3y+1)(2x-3y-5)$

**7.** Expand the following :

(i) $(2x+3y)^3$ (ii) $(3a+b)^3$ (iii) $\left(2x+\frac{1}{x}\right)^3$ (iv) $\left(2x+\frac{1}{2x}\right)^3$

**8.** Expand the following :

(i) $(3x-5y)^3$ (ii) $(x-3y)^3$ (iii) $\left(3x-\frac{1}{x}\right)^3$ (iv) $\left(3x-\frac{1}{3x}\right)^3$

**9.** Simplify the following :

(i) $(2a+b)^2+(2a-b)^2$ (ii) $(a+5b)^2-(a-5b)^2$ (iii) $(a+b)^3+(a-b)^3$ (iv) $(2x+5y)^3-(2x-5y)^3$

**10.** Expand the following :

(i) $(x+y+1)^3$ (ii) $(x-2y+3)^3$

**11.** Find the product :

(i) $(3x+y)(9x^2-3xy+y^2)$ (ii) $(x+5y)(x^2-5xy+25y^2)$

**12.** Find the product :

(i) $(3x-2y)(9x^2+6xy+4y^2)$ (ii) $\left(a-\frac{1}{a}\right)\left(a^2+\frac{1}{a^2}+1\right)$

**13.** Simplify the following :

(i) $(a+2b)(a^2-2ab+4b^2)+(a-2b)(a^2+2ab+4b^2)$ (ii) $(3x+5y)(9x^2-15xy+25y^2)-(3x-5y)(9x^2+15xy+25y^2)$

**14.** Find the product :

(i) $(x+3)(x+5)(x+7)$ (ii) $(x-1)(x+3)(x+2)$

**15.** Find the coefficient of $x$ and constant term in the product $(x+3)(x+4)(x+5)$.

**16.** Find the coefficient of $x^2$ in the product $(x-1)(x-5)(x-6)$.

**17.** Using suitable identity, find the value of :

(i) $102^2$ (ii) $98^2$ (iii) $(10.5)^2$ (iv) $101^3$

(v) $98^3$ (vi) $(1.1)^3$

**18.** Find the product :

(i) $(3a + b + 5c)(9a^2 + b^2 + 25c^2 - 3ab - 5bc - 15ac)$

(ii) $(x - 2y + 5z)(x^2 + 4y^2 + 25z^2 + 2xy + 10yz - 5xz)$

(iii) $(3a - 4b - c)(9a^2 + 16b^2 + c^2 + 12ab - 4bc + 3ca)$

**19.** Simplify :

(i) $(3x - 4y)^3 + (4y - 5z)^3 + (5z - 3x)^3$ (ii) $(a - 4b)^3 + (4b - 3c)^3 + (3c - a)^3$

**20.** Without actually calculating the cube, find the values of the following :

(i) $(35)^3 + (-15)^3 + (-20)^3$ (ii) $\left(-\frac{8}{15}\right)^3 + \left(\frac{1}{3}\right)^3 + \left(\frac{1}{5}\right)^3$

**21.** Using suitable identity, evaluate the following :

(i) $\frac{92 \times 92 \times 92 + 8 \times 8 \times 8}{92 \times 92 - 92 \times 8 + 8 \times 8}$ (ii) $\frac{(103)^3 - (3)^3}{(103)^2 + 103 \times 3 + (3)^2}$

**22.** If $a + b + 2c = 0$, then prove that $a^3 + b^3 + 8c^3 = 6abc$.

**23.** If $x + 2y - 5 = 0$, then prove that $x^3 + 8y^3 + 30xy = 125$.

**24.** If $4x - 5y - 2 = 0$, then prove that $64x^3 - 125y^3 - 120xy = 8$.

**25.** If $4x + 2y + z = 0$, show that

$$\frac{(4x + 2y)^2}{xy} + \frac{2(4x + z)^2}{xz} + \frac{4(2y + z)^2}{zx} = 24$$

**26.** If $\frac{2a}{3b} = \frac{3b}{4c}$, show that

$$(2a - 3b + 4c)(2a + 3b + 4c) = 4a^2 + 9b^2 + 16c^2.$$

## Answers

**1.** (i) $x^2 + 6xy + 9y^2$ (ii) $9x^2 - 12xy + 4y^2$ (iii) $\frac{1}{9}x^2 + \frac{1}{3}xy + \frac{1}{4}y^2$ (iv) $4x^2 - \frac{4}{3}xy + \frac{1}{9}y^2$

(v) $9x^2 + y^2 + 25z^2 + 6xy - 10yz - 30xz$ (vi) $\frac{1}{4}x^2 + \frac{9}{25}y^2 + z^2 - \frac{3}{5}xy + xz - \frac{6}{5}yz$

**2.** (i) $25x^2 + 10 + \frac{1}{x^2}$ (ii) $9x^2 - 3 + \frac{1}{4x^2}$ **3.** (i) $x^2 + 6x + 5$ (ii) $x^2 - 4x - 12$ (iii) $x^2 - 10x + 24$ (iv) $9x^2 + 18x + 5$

**4.** (i) $9a^2 - 4b^2$ (ii) $25x^2 - 9y^2$

**5.** (i) $x^2 + 4xy + 4y^2 - 9$ (ii) $x^2 + \frac{1}{x^2} - 18$ (iii) $9x^2 - y^2 + 12x + 4$ (iv) $x^4 - 16$

**6.** (i) $x^2 + 6xy + 9y^2 + 7x + 21y + 10$ (ii) $4x^2 - 12xy + 9y^2 - 8x + 12y - 5$

**7.** (i) $8x^3 + 36x^2y + 54xy^2 + 27y^3$ (ii) $27a^3 + 27a^2b + 9ab^2 + b^3$ (iii) $8x^3 + 12x + \frac{6}{x} + \frac{1}{x^3}$ (iv) $8x^3 + 6x + \frac{3}{2x} + \frac{1}{8x^3}$

**8.** (i) $27x^3 - 135x^2y + 225xy^2 - 125y^3$ (ii) $x^3 - 9x^2y + 27xy^2 - 27y^3$ (iii) $27x^3 - 27x + \frac{9}{x} - \frac{1}{x^3}$ (iv) $27x^3 - 9x + \frac{1}{x} - \frac{1}{27x^3}$

**9.** (i) $8a^2 + 2b^2$ (ii) $20\,ab$ (iii) $2a^3 + 6ab^2$ (iv) $120x^2y + 250y^3$

**10.** (i) $x^3 + 3x^2y + 3xy^2 + y^3 + 3x^2 + 6xy + 3y^2 + 3x + 3y + 1$ (ii) $x^3 - 6x^2y + 12xy^2 - 8y^3 + 9x^2 - 36xy + 36y^2 + 27x - 54y + 27$

**11.** (i) $27x^3 + y^3$ (ii) $x^3 + 125y^3$ **12.** (i) $27x^3 - 8y^3$ (ii) $a^3 - \frac{1}{a^3}$

**13.** (i) $2a^3$ (ii) $250y^3$ **14.** (i) $x^3 + 15x^2 + 71x + 105$ (ii) $x^3 + 4x^2 + x - 6$

**15.** (i) Coefficient of $x = 47$, constant term = 60 **16.** Coefficient of $x^2 = -12$

**17.** (i) 10404 (ii) 9604 (iii) 110.25 (iv) 1030301 (v) 941192 (vi) 1.331

**18.** (i) $27a^3 + b^3 + 125c^3 - 45abc$ (ii) $x^3 - 8y^3 + 125z^3 + 30xyz$ (iii) $27a^3 - 64b^3 - c^3 - 36abc$

**19.** (i) $3(3x - 4y)(4y - 5z)(5z - 3x)$ (ii) $3(a - 4b)(4b - 3c)(3c - a)$

**20.** (i) 31500 (ii) $\frac{-8}{75}$ **21.** (i) 100 (ii) 100

## Some Applications of Special Products

### Illustrative Examples

**Example 1.** If $x + y = 8$ and $xy = 15$, find the values of :

(i) $x^2 + y^2$ (ii) $x - y$ (iii) $x^2 - y^2$ (iv) $x^3 - y^3$

**Solution.** (i) From the identity,

$$x^2 + y^2 + 2xy = (x + y)^2$$

We get $$x^2 + y^2 + 2(15) = (8)^2$$

$\Rightarrow$ $$x^2 + y^2 = 64 - 30$$
$$= 34$$ Ans.

(ii) From the identity,

$$(x - y)^2 = x^2 + y^2 - 2xy$$

We get $$(x - y)^2 = 34 - 2 \times 15 = 4$$

$\Rightarrow$ $$x - y = \pm 2$$ Ans.

(iii) $$x^2 - y^2 = (x + y)(x - y)$$
$$= 8(\pm 2) = \pm 16$$ Ans.

(iv) $$x^3 - y^3 = (x - y)(x^2 + y^2 + xy)$$
$$= (\pm 2)(34 + 15)$$
$$= \pm 98$$ Ans.

**Example 2.** If $x + \frac{1}{x} = 4$, find the values of :

(i) $x^2 + \frac{1}{x^2}$ (ii) $x - \frac{1}{x}$ (iii) $x^2 - \frac{1}{x^2}$

**Solution.** (i) Given, $$x + \frac{1}{x} = 4$$

$\Rightarrow$ $$\left(x + \frac{1}{x}\right)^2 = 4^2$$

$\Rightarrow$ $$x^2 + \frac{1}{x^2} + 2 = 16$$

$\Rightarrow$ $$x^2 + \frac{1}{x^2} = 16 - 2 = 14$$ Ans.

(ii) $$\left(x - \frac{1}{x}\right)^2 = x^2 + \frac{1}{x^2} - 2$$
$$= 14 - 2 = 12$$

$\Rightarrow$ $$x - \frac{1}{x} = \pm\sqrt{12} = \pm 2\sqrt{3}$$ Ans.

(iii) $$x^2 - \frac{1}{x^2} = \left(x - \frac{1}{x}\right)\left(x + \frac{1}{x}\right)$$
$$= (\pm 2\sqrt{3})(4)$$
$$= \pm 8\sqrt{3}$$ Ans.

**Example 3.** If $x - \frac{1}{x} = 2$, find the values of :

(i) $x^2 + \frac{1}{x^2}$ (ii) $x^3 - \frac{1}{x^3}$ (iii) $x^4 + \frac{1}{x^4}$

**Solution.** (i)

$$x - \frac{1}{x} = 2$$

$$\Rightarrow \left(x - \frac{1}{x}\right)^2 = 2^2 \Rightarrow x^2 + \frac{1}{x^2} - 2 = 4$$

$$\Rightarrow x^2 + \frac{1}{x^2} = 6$$ **Ans.**

(ii)

$$x - \frac{1}{x} = 2$$

$$\Rightarrow \left(x - \frac{1}{x}\right)^3 = 2^3 \Rightarrow x^3 - \frac{1}{x^3} - 3\left(x - \frac{1}{x}\right) = 8$$

$$\Rightarrow x^3 - \frac{1}{x^3} - 3(2) = 8 \Rightarrow x^3 - \frac{1}{x^3} = 14$$ **Ans.**

(iii) From part (i),

$$x^2 + \frac{1}{x^2} = 6$$

$$\Rightarrow \left(x^2 + \frac{1}{x^2}\right)^2 = 6^2 \Rightarrow \left(x^4 + \frac{1}{x^4}\right) + 2 = 36$$

$$\Rightarrow x^4 + \frac{1}{x^4} = 34$$ **Ans.**

**Example 4.** If $x^2 - 6x + 1 = 0$, find the values of :

(i) $x^2 + \frac{1}{x^2}$ (ii) $x^4 + \frac{1}{x^4}$ where, $x \neq 0$

**Solution.** (i) $x^2 - 6x + 1 = 0$

Divide both sides by $x$, we get

$$x - 6 + \frac{1}{x} = 0$$

$$\Rightarrow x + \frac{1}{x} = 6 \Rightarrow \left(x + \frac{1}{x}\right)^2 = 6^2$$

$$\Rightarrow x^2 + \frac{1}{x^2} + 2 = 36 \Rightarrow x^2 + \frac{1}{x^2} = 34$$ **Ans.**

(ii) From part (i),

$$x^2 + \frac{1}{x^2} = 34$$

$$\Rightarrow \left(x^2 + \frac{1}{x^2}\right)^2 = 34^2 \Rightarrow x^4 + \frac{1}{x^4} + 2 = 1156$$

$$\Rightarrow x^4 + \frac{1}{x^4} = 1154$$ **Ans.**

**Example 5.** If $x^2 + \frac{1}{x^2} = 14$, find the values of :

(i) $x + \frac{1}{x}$ (ii) $x - \frac{1}{x}$ (iii) $x^2 - \frac{1}{x^2}$

**Solution.** (i) $x^2 + \frac{1}{x^2} = 14$

$\Rightarrow x^2 + \frac{1}{x^2} + 2 = 14 + 2 \Rightarrow \left(x + \frac{1}{x}\right)^2 = 16$

$\Rightarrow x + \frac{1}{x} = \pm 4$ Ans.

(ii) $x^2 + \frac{1}{x^2} = 14$

$\Rightarrow x^2 + \frac{1}{x^2} - 2 = 14 - 2 \Rightarrow \left(x - \frac{1}{x}\right)^2 = 12$

$\Rightarrow x - \frac{1}{x} = \pm 2\sqrt{3}$ Ans.

(iii) $x^2 - \frac{1}{x^2} = \left(x - \frac{1}{x}\right)\left(x + \frac{1}{x}\right) = (\pm 2\sqrt{3})\ (\pm 4) = \pm 8\sqrt{3}$ Ans.

**Example 6.** If $3x^2 - 4x - 3 = 0$, find the values of :

(i) $x - \frac{1}{x}$ (ii) $x + \frac{1}{x}$ (iii) $x^2 + \frac{1}{x^2}$

**Solution.** (i) $3x^2 - 4x - 3 = 0$

Dividing by $3x$, we get

$x - \frac{4}{3} - \frac{1}{x} = 0 \Rightarrow x - \frac{1}{x} = \frac{4}{3}$ Ans.

(ii) $\left(x + \frac{1}{x}\right)^2 = x^2 + \frac{1}{x^2} + 2$

$= \left(x^2 + \frac{1}{x^2} - 2\right) + 4 = \left(x - \frac{1}{x}\right)^2 + 4 = \left(\frac{4}{3}\right)^2 + 4 = \frac{16}{9} + 4 = \frac{52}{9}$

$\Rightarrow x + \frac{1}{x} = \pm \frac{2\sqrt{13}}{3}$

(iii) $x - \frac{1}{x} = \frac{4}{3}$

$\left(x - \frac{1}{x}\right)^2 = \frac{16}{9}$

$\Rightarrow x^2 + \frac{1}{x^2} - 2 = \frac{16}{9} \Rightarrow x^2 + \frac{1}{x^2} = \frac{16}{9} + 2 = \frac{34}{9}$ Ans.

**Example 7.** If $x^4 + \frac{1}{x^4} = 47$, find the values of :

(i) $x^2 + \frac{1}{x^2}$ (ii) $x + \frac{1}{x}$ (iii) $x^3 + \frac{1}{x^3}$

**Solution.** (i) $$x^4 + \frac{1}{x^4} = 47$$

$$\Rightarrow \quad x^4 + \frac{1}{x^4} + 2 = 47 + 2 = 49 \quad \Rightarrow \quad \left(x^2 + \frac{1}{x^2}\right)^2 = 7^2$$

$$\Rightarrow \quad x^2 + \frac{1}{x^2} = 7 \quad \left(\because x^2 + \frac{1}{x^2} \text{ is always positive}\right)$$ **Ans.**

(ii) $$x^2 + \frac{1}{x^2} = 7$$

$$\Rightarrow \quad x^2 + \frac{1}{x^2} + 2 = 7 + 2 \quad \Rightarrow \quad \left(x + \frac{1}{x}\right)^2 = 9$$

$$\Rightarrow \quad x + \frac{1}{x} = \pm\sqrt{9} = \pm 3$$ **Ans.**

(iii) $$x^3 + \frac{1}{x^3} = x^3 + \frac{1}{x^3} + 3\left(x + \frac{1}{x}\right) - 3\left(x + \frac{1}{x}\right)$$

$$= \left(x + \frac{1}{x}\right)^3 - 3\left(x + \frac{1}{x}\right)$$

When $x + \frac{1}{x} = 3$, $x^3 + \frac{1}{x^3} = (3)^3 - 3(3) = 27 - 9 = 18$ **Ans.**

When $x + \frac{1}{x} = -3$, $x^3 + \frac{1}{x^3} = (-3)^3 - 3(-3) = -27 + 9 = -18$ **Ans.**

**Example 8.** If $x = \sqrt{2} + 1$, find the values of :

(i) $x + \frac{1}{x}$ (ii) $x^2 + \frac{1}{x^2}$ (iii) $x^3 + \frac{1}{x^3}$

**Solution.** (i) $$x = \sqrt{2} + 1$$

$$\Rightarrow \quad \frac{1}{x} = \frac{1}{\sqrt{2}+1} = \frac{1}{\sqrt{2}+1} \times \frac{\sqrt{2}-1}{\sqrt{2}-1} = \frac{\sqrt{2}-1}{(\sqrt{2})^2 - (1)^2} = \sqrt{2} - 1$$

$$x + \frac{1}{x} = \sqrt{2} + 1 + \sqrt{2} - 1 = 2\sqrt{2}$$ **Ans.**

(ii) $$x + \frac{1}{x} = 2\sqrt{2}$$

$$\Rightarrow \quad \left(x + \frac{1}{x}\right)^2 = (2\sqrt{2})^2 \quad \Rightarrow \quad x^2 + \frac{1}{x^2} + 2 = 8$$

$$\Rightarrow \quad x^2 + \frac{1}{x^2} = 6$$ **Ans.**

(iii) $$x + \frac{1}{x} = 2\sqrt{2}$$

$$\Rightarrow \quad \left(x + \frac{1}{x}\right)^3 = (2\sqrt{2})^3 \quad \Rightarrow \quad x^3 + \frac{1}{x^3} + 3\left(x + \frac{1}{x}\right) = 16\sqrt{2}$$

$$\Rightarrow \quad x^3 + \frac{1}{x^3} + 3(2\sqrt{2}) = 16\sqrt{2} \quad \Rightarrow \quad x^3 + \frac{1}{x^3} = 10\sqrt{2}$$ **Ans.**

**Example 9.** If $x + y = 5$ and $x^2 + y^2 = 17$, find :

(i) $xy$ (ii) $x^3 + y^3$

**Solution.** (i)

$$x + y = 5$$
$$\Rightarrow (x + y)^2 = 5^2$$
$$\Rightarrow x^2 + y^2 + 2xy = 25$$
$$\Rightarrow 17 + 2xy = 25$$
$$\Rightarrow 2xy = 8$$
$$\Rightarrow xy = 4$$

Ans.

(ii)

$$x + y = 5$$
$$\Rightarrow (x + y)^3 = 5^3$$
$$\Rightarrow x^3 + y^3 + 3xy\ (x + y) = 125$$
$$\Rightarrow x^3 + y^3 + 3\ (4)\ (5) = 125$$
$$\Rightarrow x^3 + y^3 = 125 - 60$$
$$= 65$$

Ans.

**Example 10.** If $a + b + c = 10$, $a^2 + b^2 + c^2 = 50$, find the value of $ab + bc + ca$.

**Solution.**

$$a + b + c = 10$$
$$\Rightarrow (a + b + c)^2 = 10^2$$
$$\Rightarrow a^2 + b^2 + c^2 + 2\ (ab + bc + ca) = 100$$
$$\Rightarrow 50 + 2\ (ab + bc + ca) = 100$$
$$\Rightarrow 2\ (ab + bc + ca) = 50$$
$$\Rightarrow ab + bc + ca = 25$$

Ans.

**Example 11.** If $a + b + c = 12$ and $ab + bc + ca = 45$, find the value of $a^2 + b^2 + c^2$.

**Solution.**

$$a + b + c = 12$$
$$\Rightarrow (a + b + c)^2 = 12^2$$
$$\Rightarrow a^2 + b^2 + c^2 + 2\ (ab + bc + ca) = 144$$
$$\Rightarrow a^2 + b^2 + c^2 + 2\ (45) = 144$$
$$\Rightarrow a^2 + b^2 + c^2 = 144 - 90 = 54$$

Ans.

**Example 12.** If $a - b + c = 8$, $a^2 + b^2 + c^2 = 22$, find the value of $ab + bc - ca$.

**Solution.**

$$a - b + c = 8$$
$$\Rightarrow (a - b + c)^2 = 8^2$$
$$\Rightarrow a^2 + b^2 + c^2 + 2\ (-\ ab - bc + ca) = 64$$
$$\Rightarrow 22 - 2\ (ab + bc - ca) = 64$$
$$\Rightarrow -2\ (ab + bc - ca) = 64 - 22 = 42$$
$$\Rightarrow ab + bc - ca = -21$$

Ans.

**Example 13.** If $a + b + c = 4$, $ab + bc + ca = 5$, and $abc = 2$, find the value of $a^3 + b^3 + c^3$.

**Solution.**

$$a + b + c = 4$$
$$\Rightarrow (a + b + c)^2 = 4^2$$
$$\Rightarrow a^2 + b^2 + c^2 + 2ab + bc + ca = 16$$
$$\Rightarrow a^2 + b^2 + c^2 + 2\ (5) = 16$$
$$\Rightarrow a^2 + b^2 + c^2 = 6$$

Ans.

Now,

$$a^3 + b^3 + c^3 = (a^3 + b^3 + c^3 - 3abc) + 3\ abc$$
$$= (a + b + c)\ \{a^2 + b^2 + c^2 - (ab + bc + ca)\} + 3\ abc$$
$$= 4(6 - 5) + 3 \times 2$$
$$= 4 + 6 = 10$$

Ans.

**Example 14.** If the sum of two numbers is 8 and the sum of their squares is 40, find the product of two numbers.

**Solution.** Let $x$ and $y$ be two numbers, then $x + y = 8$ and $x^2 + y^2 = 40$.

Now, $x + y = 8$

$\Rightarrow (x + y)^2 = 8^2$

$\Rightarrow x^2 + y^2 + 2xy = 64$

$\Rightarrow 40 + 2xy = 64$

$\Rightarrow 2xy = 24$

$\Rightarrow xy = 12.$

$\therefore$ Product of two numbers is 12. **Ans.**

**Example 15.** If the sum of two numbers is 10 and the sum of their cubes is 370, find the sum of the squares of two numbers.

**Solution.** Let $x$ and $y$ be two numbers, then $x + y = 10$ and $x^3 + y^3 = 370$

Now, $(x + y) = 10$

$\Rightarrow (x + y)^3 = 10^3$

$\Rightarrow x^3 + y^3 + 3xy\,(x + y) = 1000$

$\Rightarrow 370 + 3xy\,(10) = 1000$

$\Rightarrow 30xy = 630$

$\Rightarrow xy = 21$

$\therefore x^2 + y^2 = (x^2 + y^2 + 2xy) - 2xy$

$= (x + y)^2 - 2xy$

$= 10^2 - 2 \times 21 = 100 - 42 = 58$ **Ans.**

**Example 16.** If the number $y$ is 6 less than the number $x$ and the sum of the squares of these two numbers is 68, find the product of two numbers.

**Solution.** Given $y = x - 6$ and $x^2 + y^2 = 68$

Now, $y = x - 6$

$\Rightarrow x - y = 6$

$\Rightarrow (x - y)^2 = 6^2$

$\Rightarrow x^2 + y^2 - 2xy = 36$

$\Rightarrow 68 - 2xy = 36$

$\Rightarrow -2xy = 36 - 68 = -32$

$\Rightarrow xy = 16$

$\therefore$ Product of two numbers is 16. **Ans.**

## Exercise 3B

1. If $x + y = 10$ and $xy = 21$, find the value of $x^2 + y^2$.
2. If $x - y = 6$ and $xy = 27$, find the value of $x^2 + y^2$.
3. If $5a - b = 9$ and $ab = 2$, find the value of $25a^2 + b^2$.
4. If $3x + 2y = 13$ and $xy = 6$, find the value of $9x^2 + 4y^2$.
5. If $x + y = 7$ and $x - y = 2$, find the values of :
   (i) $x^2 + y^2$ (ii) $xy$
6. If $x^2 + y^2 = 58$ and $xy = 21$, find the values of :
   (i) $x + y$ (ii) $x - y$
7. If $x + y = 6$ and $xy = 8$, find the values of :
   (i) $x - y$ (ii) $x^2 + y^2$ (iii) $x^3 + y^3$
8. If $a - b = 2$ and $ab = 3$, find the values of :
   (i) $a + b$ (ii) $a^2 + b^2$ (iii) $a^3 + b^3$
9. If $x + \frac{1}{x} = 3$, find the value of $x^2 + \frac{1}{x^2}$.

**10.** If $x - \frac{1}{x} = 2$, find the values of :

(i) $x + \frac{1}{x}$ (ii) $x^2 + \frac{1}{x^2}$

**11.** If $x + \frac{1}{x} = 5$, find the values of :

(i) $x - \frac{1}{x}$ (ii) $x^2 + \frac{1}{x^2}$ (iii) $x^4 + \frac{1}{x^4}$

**12.** If $x + \frac{1}{x} = 4$, find the values of :

(i) $x^2 + \frac{1}{x^2}$ (ii) $x^3 + \frac{1}{x^3}$

**13.** If $x - \frac{1}{x} = 7$, find the values of :

(i) $x^2 + \frac{1}{x^2}$ (ii) $x^3 - \frac{1}{x^3}$ (iii) $x^4 + \frac{1}{x^4}$

**14.** If $x - \frac{1}{x} = 4$, find the values of :

(i) $x^2 + \frac{1}{x^2}$ (ii) $x^3 - \frac{1}{x^3}$

**15.** If $x^2 - 6x + 1 = 0$, find the values of :

(i) $x^2 + \frac{1}{x^2}$ (ii) $x^3 + \frac{1}{x^3}$ (iii) $x^4 + \frac{1}{x^4}$

**16.** If $x - \frac{2}{x} = 2$, find the value of $x^3 - \frac{8}{x^3}$.

**17.** If $x^2 + \frac{1}{x^2} = 23$, find the values of :

(i) $x + \frac{1}{x}$ (ii) $x^4 + \frac{1}{x^4}$

**18.** If $x^2 + \frac{1}{x^2} = 27$, find the values of :

(i) $x - \frac{1}{x}$ (ii) $x^4 + \frac{1}{x^4}$

**19.** If $a = \frac{1}{4-a}$, find the values of :

(i) $a^2 + \frac{1}{a^2}$ (ii) $a^3 + \frac{1}{a^3}$

**20.** If $x = 3 + 2\sqrt{2}$, find the values of :

(i) $\frac{1}{x}$ (ii) $x + \frac{1}{x}$ (iii) $x^2 + \frac{1}{x^2}$

21. If $x = 5 - 2\sqrt{6}$, find the values of :

(i) $\frac{1}{x}$  (ii) $x - \frac{1}{x}$  (iii) $x^2 + \frac{1}{x^2}$

22. If $x = 7 + 4\sqrt{3}$, find the values of :

(i) $\frac{1}{x}$  (ii) $x + \frac{1}{x}$  (iii) $x^3 + \frac{1}{x^3}$

23. If $x = 3 + 2\sqrt{2}$, find the value of $\sqrt{x} + \frac{1}{\sqrt{x}}$.

24. If $x + y + z = 6$, $x^2 + y^2 + z^2 = 14$, find the value of $xy + yz + zx$.

25. If $x + y - z = 0$, $xy - yz - zx = -8$, find the value of $x^2 + y^2 + z^2$.

26. If $a - b + c = 4$, $ab + bc - ac = 17$, find the value of $a^2 + b^2 + c^2$.

27. If $a^2 + b^2 + c^2 = 38$ and $ab + bc + ca = 13$, find the value of $a + b + c$.

28. If $x - y = 2$, and $x^2 + y^2 = 34$, find the values of :

(i) $xy$  (ii) $x^3 - y^3$

29. The sum of two numbers is 10 and the sum of their squares is 68. Find the product of the numbers.

30. The sum of two numbers is 5 and the sum of their cubes is 35. Find the product of the numbers.

31. The number $x$ is 4 more than the number $y$ and their product is 21. Find the sum of the squares of two numbers.

## Answers

**1.** 58  **2.** 90  **3.** 101  **4.** 97  **5.** (i) $\frac{53}{2}$ (ii) $\frac{45}{4}$

**6.** (i) $\pm 10$ (ii) $\pm 4$  **7.** (i) $\pm 2$ (ii) 20 (iii) 72

**8.** (i) $\pm 4$ (ii) 10 (iii) $\pm 28$  **9.** 7  **10.** (i) $\pm 2\sqrt{2}$ (ii) 6

**11.** (i) $\pm\sqrt{21}$ (ii) 23 (iii) 527  **12.** (i) 14 (ii) 52  **13.** (i) 51 (ii) 364 (iii) 2599

**14.** (i) 18 (ii) 76  **15.** (i) 34 (ii) 198 (iii) 1154  **16.** 20

**17.** (i) $\pm 5$ (ii) 527  **18.** (i) $\pm 5$ (ii) 727  **19.** (i) 14 (ii) 52

**20.** (i) $3 - 2\sqrt{2}$ (ii) 6 (iii) 34  **21.** (i) $5 + 2\sqrt{6}$ (ii) $-4\sqrt{6}$ (iii) 98

**22.** (i) $7 - 4\sqrt{3}$ (ii) 14 (iii) 2702

**23.** $2\sqrt{2}$  **24.** 11  **25.** 16  **26.** 50  **27.** $\pm 8$  **28.** (i) 15 (ii) 98

**29.** 16  **30.** 6  **31.** 58

# Exercise 3C

## Multiple Choice Questions

Choose the correct answer from the given four options in each of the following questions :

1. $96 \times 104$ is equal to :

(a) 9974  (b) 9964  (c) 9984  (d) 9994

2. If $x + y = 11$ and $xy = 30$ then $x^2 + y^2$ is equal to :

(a) 61  (b) 56  (c) 58  (d) 65

3. If $\frac{a}{b} + \frac{b}{a} = 1$ then the value of $a^3 + b^3$ is :

(a) $-1$  (b) 0  (c) 1  (d) 2

4. The value of $102^2 - 98^2$ is :

(a) 600  (b) 2400  (c) 1600  (d) 800

5. If $x-y=1$ and $xy=2$, then the value of $x^3-y^3$ is :
(a) 5 (b) 6 (c) 7 (d) 8

6. If $x+\frac{1}{x}=9$, then the value of $x^2+\frac{1}{x^2}$ is :
(a) 77 (b) 79 (c) 83 (d) 85

7. If $x-\frac{1}{x}=3$, then the value of $x^3-\frac{1}{x^3}$ is :
(a) 27 (b) 36 (c) 45 (d) 18

8. If $a+b+c=0$, then $a^3+b^3+c^3$ is equal to :
(a) 3 *abc* (b) 2 *abc* (c) *abc* (d) 0

9. The value of $88^3+12^3-100^3$ is equal to :
(a) –316800 (b) 1168 (c) 1210028 (d) 314688

10. If $a+b+c=16$ and $ab+bc+ca=40$ then $a^2+b^2+c^2$ is equal to :
(a) 136 (b) 156 (c) 176 (d) 196

### Answers

**1.** (c) **2.** (a) **3.** (b) **4.** (d) **5.** (c) **6.** (b) **7.** (b) **8.** (a) **9.** (a) **10.** (c)

## Assertion-Reason Type Questions

In the following questions, a statement of Assertion (A) and a statement of Reason (R) are given:
(a) Both Assertion (A) and Reason (R) are true and Reason (R) is the correct explanation of Assertion (A).
(b) Both Assertion (A) and Reason (R) are true and Reason (R) is not the correct explanation of Assertion (A).
(c) Assertion (A) is true but Reason (R) is false.
(d) Assertion (A) is false but Reason (R) is true.

1. **Assertion :** $98\times 102=9996$
**Reason :** $(a+b)(a-b)=a^2-b^2$
2. **Assertion :** $x+y=8$, $xy=15$ then $x^2+y^2=34$
**Reason :** $x^2+y^2-2xy=(x-y)^2$
3. **Assertion :** $(2x-y)^3=8x^3+12x^2y+6xy^2-y^3$
**Reason :** $(a-b)^3=a^3-3a^2b+3ab^2-b^3$
4. **Assertion :** $18^3+(-10)^3+(-8)^3=4320$
**Reason :** $(x+y+z)^2=x^2+y^2+z^2+2xy+2yz+2zx$

### Answers

**1.** (a) **2.** (c) **3.** (d) **4.** (b)

## Valid Statements Questions

In the following questions, two statements (i) and (ii) are given. Choose the valid statement.
(a) Only (i) (b) Only (ii) (c) Both (i) and (ii) (d) Neither (i) nor (ii)

1. (i) If $a+b+c=0$ then $a^3+b^3+c^3=0$
(ii) If $x-\frac{1}{x}=3$ then $x^3-\frac{1}{x^3}=36$
2. (i) If $x-y=2$ and $x^2+y^2=34$ then $xy=15$
(ii) $(a+b)^2=a^2+2ab+b^2$

3. (i) If $x^2 - 6x + 1 = 0$ then $x^2 + \frac{1}{x^2} = 34$

(ii) $x^3 + y^3 = (x + y)(x^2 + xy + y^2)$

4. (i) $(x + y + 1)(x - y - 1) = x^2 + (y + 1)^2$

(ii) $(x + 9y)(x - 9y) = x^2 - 9y^2$

## Answers

**1.** (b) **2.** (c) **3.** (a) **4.** (d)

## SUMMARY of the Chapter

- $(x + a)(x + b) = x^2 + x(a + b) + ab$
- $(x + a)(x - b) = x^2 + x(a - b) - ab$
- $(x - a)(x + b) = x^2 - x(a - b) - ab$
- $(x - a)(x - b) = x^2 - x(a + b) + ab$
- $(x + y)^2 = x^2 + 2xy + y^2$
- $(x - y)^2 = x^2 - 2xy + y^2$
- $(x + y)(x - y) = x^2 - y^2$
- $\left(a + \frac{1}{a}\right)^2 = a^2 + \frac{1}{a^2} + 2, a \neq 0$
- $\left(a - \frac{1}{a}\right)^2 = a^2 + \frac{1}{a^2} - 2, a \neq 0$
- $\left(a + \frac{1}{a}\right)\left(a - \frac{1}{a}\right) = a^2 - \frac{1}{a^2}, a \neq 0$
- $(x + y + z)^2 = x^2 + y^2 + z^2 + 2(xy + yz + zx)$
- $(x + y)^3 = x^3 + 3x^2y + 3xy^2 + y^3 = x^3 + y^3 + 3xy(x + y)$
- $(x - y)^3 = x^3 - 3x^2y + 3xy^2 - y^3 = x^3 - y^3 - 3xy(x - y)$
- $(x + y)(x^2 - xy + y^2) = x^3 + y^3$
- $(x - y)(x^2 + xy + y^2) = x^3 - y^3$
- $(a + b + c)(a^2 + b^2 + c^2 - ab - bc - ca) = a^3 + b^3 + c^3 - 3abc$
- If $a + b + c = 0$, then $a^3 + b^3 + c^3 = 3abc$
- $(x + a)(x + b)(x + c) = x^3 + x^2(a + b + c) + x(ab + bc + ca) + abc$

# CHAPTER TEST

1. Expand :

   (i) $(3x - 5y)^2$ (ii) $(a + 4b)^2$

2. Using identity, find the value of $(103)^2$.

3. Without calculating the cubes, evaluate the following :

$$30^3 - 18^3 - 12^3$$

4. The sum of two positive numbers is 6 and the sum of their cubes is 72. Find the product of two numbers.

5. If $x + y = 8$ and $xy = 12$, find the values of :

   (i) $x^2 + y^2$ (ii) $x^3 + y^3$

6. If $x + \frac{1}{x} = \frac{5}{2}$, find the values of :

   (i) $x - \frac{1}{x}$ (ii) $x^2 + \frac{1}{x^2}$

7. If $x^2 + \frac{1}{x^2} = 34$, find the values of :

   (i) $x + \frac{1}{x}$ (ii) $x^4 + \frac{1}{x^4}$

8. If $a + b + c = 12$ and $a^2 + b^2 + c^2 = 100$, find the value of $ab + bc + ca$.

9. Find the coefficient of $x^2$ in the product of $(x + 3)(x + 4)(x + 7)$.

10. If $\frac{a}{2b} = \frac{2b}{3c}$, show that $(a - 2b + 3c)(a + 2b + 3c) = a^2 + 4b^2 + 9c^2$.

## *Answers*

**1.** (i) $9x^2 - 30xy + 25y^2$ **6.** $a^2 + 8ab + 16b^2$ **2.** 10609

**3.** 19440 **4.** 8 **5.** (i) 40 (ii) 224

**6.** (i) $\pm\frac{3}{2}$ (ii) $\frac{17}{4}$ **7.** (i) $\pm 6$ (ii) 1154 **8.** 22 **9.** 14

Chapter

# 4 FACTORISATION

## Syllabus

- $a^2 - b^2$
- $a^3 \pm b^3$
- $ax^2 + bx + c$, by splitting the middle term.

## INTRODUCTION

We are familiar with the product of two prime numbers, *i.e.*,

$$5 \times 7 = 35$$

The product of 5 and 7 is 35.

$\Rightarrow$ 5 and 7 are the factors of 35.

Similarly, for algebraic expressions, we are also familiar with the product of two algebraic expressions, *i.e.*,

$(x + 3)(x + 5) = x^2 + (3 + 5)x + (3)(5) = x^2 + 8x + 15$

The product of $(x + 3)$ and $(x + 5)$ is $x^2 + 8x + 15$.

$\Rightarrow$ $(x + 3)$ and $(x + 5)$ are the factors of $x^2 + 8x + 15$.

$\Rightarrow$ Factors of $x^2 + 8x + 15$ are $(x + 3)$ and $(x + 5)$.

So, we can say that, when an algebraic expression can be written as the product of two or more algebraic expressions, then each of these expressions is called a factor of the given algebraic expression.

## Factorisation

The method of finding the factors of an algebraic expression is called factorisation.

or

The reverse process of multiplication is called factorisation.

*Examples*

Product :

1. $(x + 1)(x + 2) = x^2 + 3x + 2$
2. $(3x + 1)(x - 2) = 3x^2 - 5x - 2$
3. $(2y + 1)(3y - 4) = 6y^2 - 5y - 4$
4. $(a + b)(a - b) = a^2 - b^2$
5. $(x + y)(x^2 - xy + y^2) = x^3 + y^3$

Factors :

1. $x^2 + 3x + 2 = (x + 1)(x + 2)$
2. $3x^2 - 5x - 2 = (3x + 1)(x - 2)$
3. $6y^2 - 5y - 4 = (2y + 1)(3y - 4)$
4. $a^2 - b^2 = (a + b)(a - b)$
5. $x^3 + y^3 = (x + y)(x^2 - xy + y^2)$

## Factorisation by Taking Common Factor

If the different terms are given in an algebraic expression then we find the highest common factor (H.C.F.) of all these terms. We write this H.C.F. and starts a bracket. Now, we divide each term by this H.C.F. and write the quotients within the bracket alongwith their signs.

## Illustrative Examples

**Example 1.** Factorise the following :

(i) $ax + ay$

(ii) $3xy + 5xz$

(iii) $x^2 - 5x + x^3$

(iv) $a^2bc^2 + 3abc^3 - 4ab^2c$

**Solution.** (i) Given terms are $ax$ and $ay$.

H.C.F of $ax$ and $ay$ is $a$.

$\therefore$ $ax + ay = a(x + y)$ Ans.

(ii) Given terms are $3xy$ and $5xz$.

H.C.F of $3xy$ and $5xz$ is $x$.

$\therefore$ $3xy + 5xz = x(3y + 5z)$ Ans.

(iii) Given terms are $x^2$, $5x$ and $x^3$

H.C.F of $x^2$, $5x$, $x^3$ is $x$.

$\therefore$ $x^2 - 5x + x^3 = x(x - 5 + x^2)$ Ans.

(iv) Given terms are $a^2bc^2$, $3abc^3$ and $4ab^2c$

H.C.F of $a^2bc^2$, $3abc^3$ and $4ab^2c$ is $abc$.

$\therefore$ $a^2bc^2 + 3abc^3 - 4ab^2c = abc(ac + 3c^2 - 4b)$ Ans.

**Example 2.** Factorise the following:

(i) $a(x+y)+b(x+y)$

(ii) $3x(y+2z)+p(y+2z)-2q(y+2z)$

(iii) $4x(a+b)+3x^2(a+b)-x^3(a+b)$

**Solution.** (i) $a(x+y)+b(x+y)=(x+y)(a+b)$ Ans.

(ii) $3x(y+2z)+p(y+2z)-2q(y+2z)=(y+2z)(3x+p-2q)$ Ans.

(iii) $4x(a+b)+3x^2(a+b)-x^3(a+b)=x(a+b)(4+3x-x^2)$ Ans.

**Example 3.** Factorise the following : $a(x^2+1)^2+a^2(x^2+1)$

**Solution.** $a(x^2+1)^2+a^2(x^2+1)=a(x^2+1)(x^2+1+a)$ Ans.

**Example 4.** Factorise the following : $2(2a-b)^4-6c(2a-b)^3$

**Solution.** $2(2a-b)^4-6c(2a-b)^3=2(2a-b)^3(2a-b-3c)$ Ans.

**Example 5.** Factorise the following : $x(2y-3z)+2p(-2y+3z)$

**Solution.** $x(2y-3z)+2p(-2y+3z)=x(2y-3z)-2p(2y-3z)=(2y-3z)(x-2p)$ Ans.

## Exercise 4A

Factorise the following : (1 to 15)

1. $bx-by$
2. $ax-ay+az$
3. $2x^2+7x-3xz$
4. $x^3y^4-4x^4y^3$
5. $\pi r^2-2\pi r$
6. $x^2yz+xyz^2+xy^2z$
7. $42a^2bc^4-56a^3b^2c^3$
8. $a^2(x+y)+b^2(x+y)$
9. $p(x^2+1)-2q(x^2+1)$
10. $20(x-y)^2-30(x-y)^3$
11. $5(a-2b)^3+15(a-2b)^2-25(a-2b)$
12. $16(3x+y)^3-24(3x+y)$
13. $a(x^2+y^2-z^2)-b(-x^2-y^2+z^2)$
14. $p(a^2+a-b)+q(b-a-a^2)$
15. $p^2(q^2+r^2)+p(q^2+r^2)+(q^2+r^2)^2$

### Answers

1. $b(x-y)$ 2. $a(x-y+z)$ 3. $x(2x+7-3z)$ 4. $x^3y^3(y-4x)$ 5. $\pi r(r-2)$ 6. $xyz(x+z+y)$
7. $14a^2bc^3(3c-4ab)$ 8. $(x+y)(a^2+b^2)$ 9. $(x^2+1)(p-2q)$ 10. $10(x-y)^2(2-3x+3y)$
11. $5(a-2b)(a^2-4ab+4b^2+3a-6b-5)$ 12. $8(3x+y)(18x^2+12xy+2y^2-3)$ 13. $(x^2+y^2-z^2)(a+b)$
14. $(a^2+a-b)(p-q)$ 15. $(q^2+r^2)(p^2+p+q^2+r^2)$

## Factorisation by Grouping Method

If there is no common factor in all terms of a given algebraic expression and it can be taken in two or more groups then we take the common factor from each group and factorise the given algebraic expression.

## Illustrative Examples

**Example 1.** Factorise : $px+py+qx+qy$.

**Solution.** $px+py+qx+qy$

$=(px+py)+(qx+qy)$ (making two groups)

$=p(x+y)+q(x+y)$ (taking common factor from each group)

$=(x+y)(p+q)$ Ans.

**Example 2.** Factorise : $x^3 + 5x^2 + x + 5$

**Solution.**
$$x^3 + 5x^2 + x + 5 = (x^3 + 5x^2) + (x + 5)$$
$$= x^2 (x + 5) + 1(x + 5)$$
$$= (x + 5)(x^2 + 1)$$
Ans.

**Example 3.** Factorise : $x^4 + a^2 x^2 + px^2 + pa^2$

**Solution.**
$$x^4 + a^2 x^2 + px^2 + pa^2 = (x^4 + a^2 x^2) + (px^2 + pa^2)$$
$$= x^2(x^2 + a^2) + p(x^2 + a^2)$$
$$= (x^2 + a^2)(x^2 + p)$$
Ans.

**Example 4.** Factorise : $x^4 + x^3 + x^2 + x$

**Solution.**
$$x^4 + x^3 + x^2 + x = x(x^3 + x^2 + x + 1)$$
$$= x[(x^3 + x^2) + (x + 1)]$$
$$= x[x^2 (x + 1) + 1(x + 1)]$$
$$= x(x + 1)(x^2 + 1)$$
Ans.

**Example 5.** Factorise : $x(x+3y - z) - 3yz$

**Solution.**
$$x(x + 3y - z) - 3yz = x^2 + 3xy - xz - 3yz$$
$$= x(x + 3y) - z(x + 3y)$$
$$= (x + 3y)(x - z)$$
Ans.

**Example 6.** Factorise : $x^2y + x + 2xy + 2$

**Solution.**
$$x^2y + x + 2xy + 2 = x(xy + 1) + 2(xy + 1)$$
$$= (xy + 1)(x + 2)$$
Ans.

**Example 7.** Factorise : $x^2 + x(a + 2b) + 2ab$

**Solution.**
$$x^2 + x(a + 2b) + 2ab = x^2 + xa + 2bx + 2ab$$
$$= x(x + a) + 2b(x + a)$$
$$= (x + a)(x + 2b)$$
Ans.

**Example 8.** Factorise : $x^2 - ax - bx + ab$

**Solution.**
$$x^2 - ax - bx + ab = x(x - a) - b(x - a)$$
$$= (x - a)(x - b)$$
Ans.

**Example 9.** Factorise : $x^2 - \left(a + \frac{1}{a}\right)x + 1$

**Solution.**
$$x^2 - \left(a + \frac{1}{a}\right)x + 1 = x^2 - ax - \frac{x}{a} + 1$$
$$= x^2 - ax - \frac{x}{a} + \frac{a}{a} \qquad \left(\because \frac{a}{a} = 1\right)$$
$$= x(x - a) - \frac{1}{a}(x - a)$$
$$= (x - a)\left(x - \frac{1}{a}\right)$$
Ans.

**Example 10.** Factorise : $(2x - y)^2 - 6x + 3y$

**Solution.**
$$(2x - y)^2 - 6x + 3y = (2x - y)^2 - 3(2x - y)$$
$$= (2x - y)(2x - y - 3)$$
Ans.

**Example 11.** Factorise : $x^2 + y^2 + 2xy - 5x - 5y$

**Solution.**
$$x^2 + y^2 + 2xy - 5x - 5y = (x^2 + y^2 + 2xy) - 5(x + y)$$
$$= (x + y)^2 - 5(x + y)$$
$$= (x + y)(x + y - 5) \quad \text{Ans.}$$

**Example 12.** Factorise : $x^2 + \frac{1}{x^2} + 2 - 3x - \frac{3}{x}$

**Solution.**
$$x^2 + \frac{1}{x^2} + 2 - 3x - \frac{3}{x} = \left(x^2 + \frac{1}{x^2} + 2\right) - 3\left(x + \frac{1}{x}\right)$$
$$= \left(x + \frac{1}{x}\right)^2 - 3\left(x + \frac{1}{x}\right) = \left(x + \frac{1}{x}\right)\left(x + \frac{1}{x} - 3\right) \quad \text{Ans.}$$

**Example 13.** Factorise : $(ax + by)^2 + (bx - ay)^2$

**Solution.**
$$(ax + by)^2 + (bx - ay)^2 = a^2x^2 + b^2y^2 + 2abxy + b^2x^2 + a^2y^2 - 2abxy$$
$$= (a^2x^2 + a^2y^2) + (b^2x^2 + b^2y^2)$$
$$= a^2(x^2 + y^2) + b^2(x^2 + y^2)$$
$$= (x^2 + y^2)(a^2 + b^2) \quad \text{Ans.}$$

**Example 14.** Factorise : $a(x^2 + 1) - x(a^2 + 1)$

**Solution.**
$$a(x^2 + 1) - x(a^2 + 1) = ax^2 + a - xa^2 - x = ax^2 - xa^2 - x + a$$
$$= ax(x - a) - 1(x - a) = (x - a)(ax - 1) \quad \text{Ans.}$$

**Example 15.** Factorise : $(a - b)^2 - 3(a - b) - z(a - b) + 3z$

**Solution.**
$$(a - b)^2 - 3(a - b) - z(a - b) + 3z = (a - b)(a - b - 3) - z(a - b - 3)$$
$$= (a - b - 3)(a - b - z) \quad \text{Ans.}$$

## Exercise 4B

Factorise the following :

1. $ab + bc + ad + cd$
2. $x^2 + x + bx + b$
3. $ax + ay + az + bx + by + bz$
4. $ax^2 + bx^2 + ay^2 + by^2$
5. $x^3 - 3x^2 - 2x + 6$
6. $x^4 + 2x^3 + 3x^2 + 6x$
7. $1 - a - b + ab$
8. $2ax - 4ay - bx + 2by$
9. $x(x + 2y - z) - 2yz$
10. $x^2 + x(1 + p) + p$
11. $x^2 - x(3a + 2b) + 6ab$
12. $x^2 + \frac{1}{x^2} - 2 - 3x + \frac{3}{x}$
13. $x^2 + y^2 + 2xy - 2x - 2y$
14. $(ax - by)^2 - (bx - ay)^2$
15. $x^2 + y^2 - 2(xy - xz + yz)$
16. $x^2 - \left(\frac{a}{b} + \frac{b}{a}\right)x + 1$
17. $ab(x^2 + y^2) - xy(a^2 + b^2)$
18. $x^2 + \left(a + \frac{1}{a}\right)x + 1$

### Answers

1. $(a + c)(b + d)$
2. $(x + 1)(x + b)$
3. $(x + y + z)(a + b)$
4. $(a + b)(x^2 + y^2)$
5. $(x - 3)(x^2 - 2)$
6. $x(x + 2)(x^2 + 3)$
7. $(1 - a)(1 - b)$
8. $(x - 2y)(2a - b)$
9. $(x + 2y)(x - z)$
10. $(x + 1)(x + p)$
11. $(x - 3a)(x - 2b)$
12. $\left(x - \frac{1}{x}\right)\left(x - \frac{1}{x} - 3\right)$
13. $(x + y)(x + y - 2)$
14. $(x^2 - y^2)(a^2 - b^2)$
15. $(x - y)(x - y + 2z)$
16. $\left(x - \frac{a}{b}\right)\left(x - \frac{b}{a}\right)$
17. $(ax - by)(bx - ay)$
18. $\left(x + \frac{1}{a}\right)(x + a)$

## Factors of Algebraic Expression $(x^2 - y^2)$

We know that $(x + y)(x - y) = x^2 - y^2$

$\therefore$ Factors of $x^2 - y^2$ are $(x + y)$ and $(x - y)$

$\Rightarrow$ $(x^2 - y^2) = (x + y)(x - y)$

## Illustrative Examples

**Example 1.** Factorise the following :

(i) $x^2 - 4y^2$ (ii) $9x^2 - 1$ (iii) $x^4 - y^4$ (iv) $8x^3 - 18xy^2$

**Solution.** (i) $x^2 - 4y^2 = (x)^2 - (2y)^2$

$= (x + 2y)(x - 2y)$ Ans.

(ii) $9x^2 - 1 = (3x)^2 - (1)^2$

$= (3x + 1)(3x - 1)$ Ans.

(iii) $x^4 - y^4 = (x^2)^2 - (y^2)^2$

$= (x^2 + y^2)(x^2 - y^2)$

$= (x^2 + y^2)(x + y)(x - y)$ Ans.

(iv) $8x^3 - 18xy^2 = 2x(4x^2 - 9y^2)$

$= 2x[(2x)^2 - (3y)^2]$

$= 2x(2x + 3y)(2x - 3y)$ Ans.

**Example 2.** Factorise the following :

(i) $a^2 - (b + c)^2$ (ii) $x^2 - 2xy + y^2 - z^2$

**Solution.** (i) $a^2 - (b + c)^2 = \{a + (b + c)\}\{a - (b + c)\}$

$= (a + b + c)(a - b - c)$ Ans.

(ii) $x^2 - 2xy + y^2 - z^2 = (x^2 - 2xy + y^2) - z^2$

$= (x - y)^2 - z^2$

$= (x - y + z)(x - y - z)$ Ans.

**Example 3.** Factorise the following :

(i) $x(x - a) - y(y - a)$ (ii) $x^3 - px^2 - x + p$

**Solution.** (i) $x(x - a) - y(y - a) = x^2 - ax - y^2 + ay$

$= (x^2 - y^2) - ax + ay$

$= (x + y)(x - y) - a(x - y)$

$= (x - y)(x + y - a)$ Ans.

(ii) $x^3 - px^2 - x + p = x^2(x - p) - 1(x - p)$

$= (x - p)(x^2 - 1)$

$= (x - p)(x^2 - 1^2)$

$= (x - p)(x + 1)(x - 1)$ Ans.

**Example 4.** Factorise the following :

(i) $4a^2 - x^2 + 2xy - y^2$ (ii) $a^2 + b^2 + 2ab - c^2 - d^2 + 2cd$

**Solution.** (i) $4a^2 - x^2 + 2xy - y^2 = 4a^2 - (x^2 - 2xy + y^2)$

$= (2a)^2 - (x - y)^2$

$= \{2a + (x - y)\}\{2a - (x - y)\}$

$= (2a + x - y)(2a - x + y)$ Ans.

(ii) $a^2 + b^2 + 2ab - c^2 - d^2 + 2cd = (a^2 + b^2 + 2ab) - (c^2 + d^2 - 2cd)$
$= (a + b)^2 - (c - d)^2$
$= \{(a + b) + (c - d)\}\ \{(a + b) - (c - d)\}$
$= (a + b + c - d)\ (a + b - c + d)$ Ans.

**Example 5.** Factorise the following :
(i) $4x^4 + y^4$ (ii) $x^4 + 5x^2 + 9$ (iii) $x^4 - 7x^2y^2 + y^4$

**Solution.** (i) $4x^4 + y^4 = (2x^2)^2 + (y^2)^2$
$= (2x^2)^2 + (y^2)^2 + 2(2x^2)(y^2) - 2(2x^2)(y^2)$
$= (2x^2 + y^2)^2 - 4x^2y^2$
$= (2x^2 + y^2)^2 - (2xy)^2$
$= (2x^2 + y^2 + 2xy)\ (2x^2 + y^2 - 2xy)$ Ans.

(ii) $x^4 + 5x^2 + 9 = (x^2)^2 + 3^2 + 5x^2$
$= (x^2)^2 + 3^2 + 2(x^2)\ (3) - 2(x^2)\ (3) + 5x^2$
$= (x^2 + 3)^2 - x^2$
$= (x^2 + 3 + x)\ (x^2 + 3 - x)$
$= (x^2 + x + 3)\ (x^2 - x + 3)$ Ans.

(iii) $x^4 - 7x^2y^2 + y^4 = (x^2)^2 + (y^2)^2 - 7x^2y^2$
$= (x^2)^2 + (y^2)^2 + 2x^2y^2 - 2x^2y^2 - 7x^2y^2$
$= (x^2 + y^2)^2 - 9x^2y^2 = (x^2 + y^2)^2 - (3xy)^2$
$= (x^2 + y^2 + 3xy)\ (x^2 + y^2 - 3xy)$ Ans.

**Example 6.** Express $(x^2 + 2x + 5)(x^2 - 2x + 5)$ as the difference of two squares.

**Solution.** $(x^2 + 2x + 5)(x^2 - 2x + 5) = (x^2 + 5 + 2x)(x^2 + 5 - 2x)$
$= (x^2 + 5)^2 - (2x)^2$ Ans.

## Exercise 4C

Factorise the following : (1 to 27)

1. $4x^2 - y^2$
2. $x^2 - 9y^2$
3. $16x^2 - 9y^2$
4. $96x^2 - 216y^2$
5. $4x^2 - 25$
6. $120 - 30x^2$
7. $5x^3 - 80x$
8. $(a + b)^2 - 9$
9. $8 - 2(x - 1)^2$
10. $4 - (x - y)^2$
11. $36x^2 - 4(y - z)^2$
12. $(x - 4)\ (x + 4) + 7$
13. $x^2 - 4y^2 - 2x + 4y$
14. $x + 3y - x^2 + 9y^2$
15. $9x^2 - 4(x + y)^2$
16. $x^2 - 2xy + y^2 - 16$
17. $(x + y)^3 - x - y$
18. $x^2 - 25y^2 + 2x - 10y$
19. $4x^2 - a^2 + 2a - 1$
20. $9 - x^2 + 2xy - y^2$
21. $(1 - x^2)\ (1 - y^2) + 4xy$
22. $(a^2 - b^2)\ (c^2 - d^2) - 4abcd$
23. $x^4 + 4$
24. $x^4 + x^2 + 1$
25. $4x^4 + y^4 + 3x^2y^2$
26. $x^4 - 14x^2 + 1$
27. $x^2 + \dfrac{1}{x^2} - 14$
28. Express each of the following as the difference of two squares:
(i) $(x^2 + x + 1)\ (x^2 - x + 1)$ (ii) $(x^2 + 5x + 6)\ (x^2 - 5x - 6)$

## Answers

| | | |
|---|---|---|
| **1.** $(2x+y)(2x-y)$ | **2.** $(x+3y)(x-3y)$ | **3.** $(4x+3y)(4x+3y)$ |
| **4.** $24(2x+3y)(2x-3y)$ | **5.** $(2x+5)(2x-5)$ | **6.** $30(2+x)(2-x)$ |
| **7.** $5x(x+4)(x-4)$ | **8.** $(a+b+3)(a+b-3)$ | **9.** $2(x+1)(3-x)$ |
| **10.** $(2+x-y)(2-x+y)$ | **11.** $4(3x+y-z)(3x-y+z)$ | **12.** $(x+3)(x-3)$ |
| **13.** $(x-2y)(x+2y-2)$ | **14.** $(x+3y)(1-x+3y)$ | **15.** $(5x+2y)(x-2y)$ |
| **16.** $(x-y+4)(x-y-4)$ | **17.** $(x+y)(x+y+1)(x+y-1)$ | **18.** $(x-5y)(x+5y+2)$ |
| **19.** $(2x+a-1)(2x-a+1)$ | **20.** $(3+x-y)(3-x-y)$ | **21.** $(1+xy+x-y)(1+xy-x+y)$ |
| **22.** $(ac-bd+bc+ad)(ac-bd-bc-ad)$ | | **23.** $(x^2+2x+2)(x^2-2x+2)$ |
| **24.** $(x^2+x+1)(x^2-x+1)$ | **25.** $(2x^2+y^2+xy)(2x^2+y^2-xy)$ | **26.** $(x^2+4x+1)(x^2-4x+1)$ |
| **27.** $\left(x+\frac{1}{x}+4\right)\left(x+\frac{1}{x}-4\right)$ | **28.** (i) $(x^2+1)^2-(x)^2$ (ii) $(x^2)^2-(5x+6)^2$ | |

## Factorisation of Trinomials

Here, we will discuss two types of trinomials of degree 2.

1. $x^2+bx+c$ 2. $ax^2+bx+c,\ a \neq 0$

### 1. Factorisation of Trinomial of the Type $x^2+bx+c$

Consider the following algebraic expressions in trinomial form $x^2+bx+c$ :

(i) $x^2+8x+12 = x^2+(6+2)\,x+12$

(ii) $x^2-8x+12 = x^2-(6+2)\,x+12$

(iii) $x^2+4x-12 = x^2+(6-2)\,x-12$

(iv) $x^2-4x-12 = x^2-(6-2)\,x-12$

Here, constant term $(c) = 12 = 6 \times 2$

In case (i) and case (ii), constant term $= +12$.

So, we take two factors 6 and 2 of 12 whose sum is 8.

In case (iii) and case (iv), constant term $= -12$.

So, we take two factors 6 and 2 of 12 whose difference is 4.

#### Method of Factorisation

After taking two factors of the constant term as discussing in the above examples, we get 4 terms which can be divided into two groups, each has two terms. Now, it can be factorised by grouping method.

### 2. Factorisation of Trinomial of the Type $ax^2+bx+c,\ a \neq 0$

Multiply $a$ and $c$ and obtain $ac$. Now take two factors of $ac$ as discussing in the factorisation of trinomial $x^2+bx+c$.

## Illustrative Examples

**Example 1.** Factorise the following :

(i) $x^2+7x+12$ (ii) $x^2-7x+12$ (iii) $x^2+x-12$ (iv) $x^2-x-12$

**Solution.** (i)

$$\begin{aligned} x^2+7x+12 &= x^2+(4+3)x+12 \quad (4\times 3=12,\ 4+3=7)\\ &= x^2+4x+3x+12\\ &= x(x+4)+3(x+4)\\ &= (x+4)(x+3) \end{aligned}$$

Ans.

(ii)

$$\begin{aligned} x^2-7x+12 &= x^2-(4+3)x+12 \quad (4\times 3=12,\ 4+3=7)\\ &= x^2-4x-3x+12\\ &= x(x-4)-3(x-4)\\ &= (x-4)(x-3) \end{aligned}$$

Ans.

(iii) $x^2 + x - 12 = x^2 + (4 - 3)x - 12$ $(4 \times 3 = 12, 4 - 3 = 1)$

$= x^2 + 4x - 3x - 12$

$= x(x + 4) - 3(x + 4)$

$= (x + 4)(x - 3)$ Ans.

(iv) $x^2 - x - 12 = x^2 - (4 - 3)x - 12$ $(4 \times 3 = 12, 4 - 3 = 1)$

$= x^2 - 4x + 3x - 12$

$= x(x - 4) + 3(x - 4)$

$= (x - 4)(x + 3)$ Ans.

**Example 2.** Factorise the following :

(i) $x^2 + 17x + 72$ (ii) $x^2 - 35x + 150$ (iii) $x^2 + x - 380$ (iv) $x^2 - 3x - 810$

**Solution.** (i) $x^2 + 17x + 72 = x^2 + (9+8)x + 72$ $(9 \times 8 = 72, 9 + 8 = 17)$

$= x^2 + 9x + 8x + 72$

$= x(x + 9) + 8(x + 9)$

$= (x + 9)(x + 8)$ Ans.

(ii) $x^2 - 35x + 150 = x^2 - (30 + 5)x + 150$ $(30 \times 5 = 150, 30 + 5 = 35)$

$= x^2 - 30x - 5x + 150$

$= x(x - 30) - 5(x - 30)$

$= (x - 30)(x - 5)$ Ans.

(iii) $x^2 + x - 380 = x^2 + (20 - 19)x - 380$ $(20 \times 19 = 380, 20 - 19 = 1)$

$= x^2 + 20x - 19x - 380$

$= x(x + 20) - 19(x + 20)$

$= (x + 20)(x - 19)$ Ans.

(iv) $x^2 - 3x - 810 = x^2 - (30 - 27)x - 810$ $(30 \times 27 = 810, 30 - 27 = 3)$

$= x^2 - 30x + 27x - 810$

$= x(x - 30) + 27(x - 30)$

$= (x - 30)(x + 27)$ Ans.

**Example 3.** Factorise the following :

(i) $8x^2 + 14x + 5$ (ii) $8x^2 - 14x + 5$ (iii) $8x^2 + 6x - 5$ (iv) $8x^2 - 6x - 5$

**Solution.** (i) $8x^2 + 14x + 5 = 8x^2 + (10 + 4)x + 5$ $(8 \times 5 = 40, 10 \times 4 = 40, 10+4 = 14)$

$= 8x^2 + 10x + 4x + 5$

$= 2x(4x + 5) + 1(4x + 5)$

$= (4x + 5)(2x + 1)$ Ans.

(ii) $8x^2 - 14x + 5 = 8x^2 - (10 + 4)x + 5$ $(8 \times 5 = 40, 10 \times 4 = 40, 10+4 = 14)$

$= 8x^2 - 10x - 4x + 5$

$= 2x(4x - 5) - 1(4x - 5)$

$= (4x - 5)(2x - 1)$ Ans.

(iii) $8x^2 + 6x - 5 = 8x^2 + (10 - 4)x - 5$ $(8 \times 5 = 40, 10 \times 4 = 40, 10 - 4 = 6)$

$= 8x^2 + 10x - 4x - 5$

$= 2x(4x + 5) - 1(4x + 5)$

$= (4x + 5)(2x - 1)$ Ans.

(iv) $8x^2 - 6x - 5 = 8x^2 - (10 - 4)x - 5$ $(8 \times 5 = 40, 10 \times 4 = 40, 10 - 4 = 6)$

$= 8x^2 - 10x + 4x - 5$

$= 2x(4x - 5) + 1(4x - 5)$

$= (4x - 5)(2x + 1)$ Ans.

**Example 4.** Factorise the following :

(i) $6x^2 + x - 35$ (ii) $4 - x - 5x^2$ (iii) $4x^2 + 12x + 5$ (iv) $8x^2 - 27x + 9$

**Solution.** (i) $6x^2 + x - 35 = 6x^2 + (15 - 14)x - 35$ $(6 \times 35 = 210,\ 15 \times 14 = 210,\ 15 - 14 = 1)$

$= 6x^2 + 15x - 14x - 35$

$= 3x\,(2x + 5) - 7(2x + 5)$

$= (2x + 5)(3x - 7)$ **Ans.**

(ii) $4 - x - 5x^2 = 4 - (5 - 4)x - 5x^2$ $(4 \times 5 = 20,\ 5 \times 4 = 20,\ 5 - 4 = 1)$

$= 4 - 5x + 4x - 5x^2$

$= 1\,(4 - 5x) + x(4 - 5x)$

$= (4 - 5x)(1 + x)$ **Ans.**

(iii) $4x^2 + 12x + 5 = 4x^2 + (10 + 2)x + 5$ $(5 \times 4 = 20,\ 10 \times 2 = 20,\ 10 + 2 = 12)$

$= 4x^2 + 10x + 2x + 5$

$= 2x\,(2x + 5) + 1\,(2x + 5)$

$= (2x + 5)(2x + 1)$ **Ans.**

(iv) $8x^2 - 27x + 9 = 8x^2 - (24 + 3)x + 9$ $(8 \times 9 = 72,\ 24 \times 3 = 72,\ 24 + 3 = 27)$

$= 8x^2 - 24x - 3x + 9$

$= 8x\,(x - 3) - 3(x - 3)$

$= (x - 3)(8x - 3)$ **Ans.**

**Example 5.** Factorise the following :

(i) $4x^2 - 5\sqrt{2}\,x - 7$ (ii) $4\sqrt{5}x^2 - 23x + 3\sqrt{5}$

**Solution.** (i) $4x^2 - 5\sqrt{2}\,x - 7 = 4x^2 - (7\sqrt{2} - 2\sqrt{2})x - 7$ $(7 \times 4 = 28,\ 7\sqrt{2} \times 2\sqrt{2} = 28,\ 7\sqrt{2} - 2\sqrt{2} = 5\sqrt{2})$

$= 4x^2 - 7\sqrt{2}x + 2\sqrt{2}x - 7$

$= \sqrt{2}x\,(2\sqrt{2}x - 7) + 1\,(2\sqrt{2}x - 7)$

$= (2\sqrt{2}x - 7)\,(\sqrt{2}x + 1)$ **Ans.**

(ii) $4\sqrt{5}x^2 - 23x + 3\sqrt{5} = 4\sqrt{5}x^2 - (20 + 3)x + 3\sqrt{5}$ $(4\sqrt{5} \times 3\sqrt{5} = 60,\ 20 \times 3 = 60,\ 20 + 3 = 23)$

$= 4\sqrt{5}x^2 - 20x - 3x + 3\sqrt{5}$

$= 4\sqrt{5}x\,(x - \sqrt{5}) - 3\,(x - \sqrt{5})$

$= (x - \sqrt{5})(4\sqrt{5}x - 3)$ **Ans.**

**Example 6.** Factorise the following :

(i) $x^4 + 18x^2 + 80$ (ii) $x^4 - 10x^2y^2 + 9y^4$

**Solution.** (i) $x^4 + 18x^2 + 80 = x^4 + (10 + 8)x^2 + 80$ $(10 \times 8 = 80,\ 10 + 8 = 18)$

$= x^4 + 10x^2 + 8x^2 + 80$

$= x^2\,(x^2 + 10) + 8(x^2 + 10)$

$= (x^2 + 10)(x^2 + 8)$ **Ans.**

(ii) $x^4 - 10x^2y^2 + 9y^4 = x^4 - (1 + 9)x^2y^2 + 9y^4$ $(1 \times 9 = 9,\ 1 + 9 = 10)$

$= x^4 - x^2y^2 - 9x^2y^2 + 9y^4$

$= x^2\,(x^2 - y^2) - 9y^2(x^2 - y^2)$

$= (x^2 - y^2)\,(x^2 - 9y^2)$

$= (x^2 - y^2)\,\{x^2 - (3y)^2\}$

$= (x + y)(x - y)\,(x + 3y)(x - 3y)$ **Ans.**

**Example 7.** Factorise the following :
(i) $(x-3y)^2-2x+6y-24$ (ii) $6(2x+y)^2-26x-13y+5$

**Solution.** (i)
$$\begin{aligned}(x-3y)^2-2x+6y-24 &= (x-3y)^2-2(x-3y)-24\\ &= p^2-2p-24 && \text{(where } p=x-3y)\\ &= p^2-(6-4)p-24 && (6\times4=24,\ 6-4=2)\\ &= p^2-6p+4p-24\\ &= p(p-6)+4(p-6)\\ &= (p-6)(p+4)\\ &= (x-3y-6)(x-3y+4)\end{aligned}$$
Ans.

(ii)
$$\begin{aligned}6(2x+y)^2-26x-13y+5 &= 6(2x+y)^2-13(2x+y)+5\\ &= 6p^2-13p+5 && \text{(where } p=2x+y)\\ &= 6p^2-(10+3)p+5 && (6\times5=30,\ 10\times3=30,\ 10+3=13)\\ &= 6p^2-10p-3p+5\\ &= 2p(3p-5)-1(3p-5)\\ &= (3p-5)(2p-1)\\ &= \{3(2x+y)-5\}\{2(2x+y)-1\}\\ &= (6x+3y-5)(4x+2y-1)\end{aligned}$$
Ans.

**Example 8.** Factorise : $x^2+\frac{7}{2}x+3$

**Solution.**
$$\begin{aligned}x^2+\frac{7}{2}x+3 &= \frac{2x^2+7x+6}{2}\\ &= \frac{1}{2}[2x^2+7x+6]\\ &= \frac{1}{2}[2x^2+(4+3)x+6]\\ &= \frac{1}{2}[2x^2+4x+3x+6] && (2\times6=12,\ 4\times3=12,\ 4+3=7)\\ &= \frac{1}{2}[2x(x+2)+3(x+2)]\\ &= \frac{1}{2}(x+2)(2x+3)\end{aligned}$$
Ans.

**Example 9.** Factorise the following :
(i) $(x^2-2x)(x^2-2x-3)-4$ (ii) $5-(3x^2-2x)(6-3x^2+2x)$

**Solution.** (i)
$$\begin{aligned}(x^2-2x)(x^2-2x-3)-4 &= p(p-3)-4 && \text{(where } x^2-2x=p)\\ &= p^2-3p-4\\ &= p^2-(4-1)p-4\\ &= p^2-4p+p-4 && (4\times1=4,\ 4-1=3)\\ &= p(p-4)+1(p-4)\\ &= (p-4)(p+1)\\ &= (x^2-2x-4)(x^2-2x+1)\\ &= (x^2-2x-4)(x-1)^2\end{aligned}$$
Ans.

(ii) $5 - (3x^2 - 2x)(6 - 3x^2 + 2x) = 5 - (3x^2 - 2x)\{6 - (3x^2 - 2x)\}$

$= 5 - p(6 - p)$ (where $p = 3x^2 - 2x$)

$= 5 - 6p + p^2 = p^2 - 6p + 5$

$= p^2 - (5 + 1)p + 5$ $(1 \times 5 = 5, 1 + 5 = 6)$

$= p^2 - 5p - p + 5$

$= p(p - 5) - 1(p - 5)$

$= (p - 5)(p - 1)$

$= (3x^2 - 2x - 5)(3x^2 - 2x - 1)$

$= \{3x^2 - (5 - 3)x - 5\}\{3x^2 - (3 - 1)x - 1\}$

$= \{3x^2 - 5x + 3x - 5\}\{3x^2 - 3x + x - 1\}$

$= \{x(3x - 5) + 1(3x - 5)\}\{3x(x - 1) + 1(x - 1)\}$

$= (3x - 5)(x + 1)(x - 1)(3x + 1)$ Ans.

## Exercise 4D

Factorise the following :

1. $x^2 + 3x + 2$
2. $x^2 + 9x + 20$
3. $x^2 - 8x + 15$
4. $x^2 - 27x + 180$
5. $x^2 + 10x - 24$
6. $x^2 - 5x - 50$
7. $x^2 - 18x - 63$
8. $3x^2 + 13x + 14$
9. $3x^2 + 7x + 2$
10. $6y^2 + 19y + 15$
11. $15 - 4x - 4x^2$
12. $11 - 8x - 3x^2$
13. $x^3 - 5x^2 + 6x$
14. $7x^2 + 10xy - 8y^2$
15. $3\sqrt{2}x^2 - 11x + 4\sqrt{2}$
16. $2\sqrt{3}x^2 + x - 5\sqrt{3}$
17. $x^2 + \frac{11x}{6} - \frac{5}{3}$
18. $x^2 + \frac{7}{6}x - \frac{5}{6}$
19. $x(2x - y) - y^2$
20. $x(6x - 7) - 5$
21. $12(x + y)^2 - x - y - 1$
22. $(3x - 2y)^2 - 6(3x - 2y) - 135$
23. $x^4 - 5x^2 + 4$
24. $x^4 - 20x^2y^2 + 64y^4$
25. $(x^2 - x)^2 - 26(x^2 - x) + 120$
26. $(x^2 + 2x)^2 - 18(x^2 + 2x) + 45$
27. $(2x^2 - x)(2x^2 - x - 4) + 3$

### *Answers*

1. $(x + 1)(x + 2)$
2. $(x + 4)(x + 5)$
3. $(x - 3)(x - 5)$
4. $(x - 12)(x - 15)$
5. $(x + 12)(x - 2)$
6. $(x - 10)(x + 5)$
7. $(x - 21)(x + 3)$
8. $(x + 2)(3x + 7)$
9. $(x + 2)(3x + 1)$
10. $(2y + 3)(3y + 5)$
11. $(5 + 2x)(3 - 2x)$
12. $(11 + 3x)(1 - x)$
13. $x(x - 2)(x - 3)$
14. $(7x - 4y)(x + 2y)$
15. $(3x - 4\sqrt{2})(\sqrt{2}x - 1)$
16. $(x + \sqrt{3})(2\sqrt{3}x - 5)$
17. $\frac{1}{6}(2x + 5)(3x - 2)$
18. $\frac{1}{6}(3x + 5)(2x - 1)$
19. $(2x + y)(x - y)$
20. $(3x - 5)(2x + 1)$
21. $(4x + 4y + 1)(3x + 3y - 1)$
22. $(3x - 2y - 15)(3x - 2y + 9)$
23. $(x - 1)(x + 1)(x - 2)(x + 2)$
24. $(x - 2y)(x + 2y)(x - 4y)(x + 4y)$
25. $(x - 3)(x + 2)(x - 5)(x + 4)$
26. $(x + 5)(x - 3)(x + 3)(x - 1)$
27. $(2x + 1)(x - 1)(2x - 3)(x + 1)$

## Factors of $(x^3 + y^3)$

We know that $(x + y)(x^2 - xy + y^2) = x^3 + y^3$

$\Rightarrow$ $(x^3 + y^3) = (x + y)(x^2 - xy + y^2)$

## Factors of $(x^3 - y^3)$

We know that $(x - y)(x^2 + xy + y^2) = x^3 - y^3$

$\Rightarrow$ $(x^3 - y^3) = (x - y)(x^2 + xy + y^2)$

# Illustrative Examples

**Example 1.** Factorise the following :

(i) $x^3 + 8$ (ii) $8x^3 + 27$ (iii) $x^3 + 64y^3$ (iv) $125x^3 + 8y^3$

**Solution.** (i)

$$x^3 + 8 = x^3 + (2)^3$$
$$= (x + 2)\{x^2 - x(2) + 2^2\}$$
$$= (x + 2)(x^2 - 2x + 4) \quad \text{Ans.}$$

(ii)

$$8x^3 + 27 = (2x)^3 + (3)^3$$
$$= (2x + 3)\{(2x)^2 - (2x)(3) + (3)^2\}$$
$$= (2x + 3)(4x^2 - 6x + 9) \quad \text{Ans.}$$

(iii)

$$x^3 + 64y^3 = (x)^3 + (4y)^3$$
$$= (x + 4y)\{(x)^2 - (x)(4y) + (4y)^2\}$$
$$= (x + 4y)(x^2 - 4xy + 16y^2) \quad \text{Ans.}$$

(iv)

$$125x^3 + 8y^3 = (5x)^3 + (2y)^3$$
$$= (5x + 2y)\{(5x)^2 - (5x)(2y) + (2y)^2\}$$
$$= (5x + 2y)(25x^2 - 10xy + 4y^2) \quad \text{Ans.}$$

**Example 2.** Factorise the following :

(i) $x^3 - 1$ (ii) $125x^3 - 27$ (iii) $x^3 - 64y^3$ (iv) $8x^3 - 27y^3$

**Solution.** (i)

$$x^3 - 1 = x^3 - 1^3$$
$$= (x - 1)\{x^2 + (x)(1) + 1^2\}$$
$$= (x - 1)(x^2 + x + 1) \quad \text{Ans.}$$

(ii)

$$125x^3 - 27 = (5x)^3 - (3)^3$$
$$= (5x - 3)\{(5x)^2 + (5x)(3) + 3^2\}$$
$$= (5x - 3)(25x^2 + 15x + 9) \quad \text{Ans.}$$

(iii)

$$x^3 - 64y^3 = x^3 - (4y)^3$$
$$= (x - 4y)\{(x)^2 + (x)(4y) + (4y)^2\}$$
$$= (x - 4y)(x^2 + 4xy + 16y^2) \quad \text{Ans.}$$

(iv)

$$8x^3 - 27y^3 = (2x)^3 - (3y)^3$$
$$= (2x - 3y)\{(2x)^2 + (2x)(3y) + (3y)^2\}$$
$$= (2x - 3y)(4x^2 + 6xy + 9y^2) \quad \text{Ans.}$$

**Example 3.** Factorise the following :

(i) $\frac{1}{8}a^3 + 27$ (ii) $\frac{x^3}{27} - \frac{y^3}{64}$

**Solution.** (i)

$$\frac{1}{8}a^3 + 27 = \left(\frac{1}{2}a\right)^3 + (3)^3$$
$$= \left(\frac{1}{2}a + 3\right)\left\{\left(\frac{1}{2}a\right)^2 - \left(\frac{1}{2}a\right)(3) + 3^2\right\}$$
$$= \left(\frac{1}{2}a + 3\right)\left(\frac{1}{4}a^2 - \frac{3}{2}a + 9\right) \quad \text{Ans.}$$

(ii)
$$\frac{x^3}{27}-\frac{y^3}{64}=\left(\frac{x}{3}\right)^3-\left(\frac{y}{4}\right)^3$$
$$=\left(\frac{x}{3}-\frac{y}{4}\right)\left\{\left(\frac{x}{3}\right)^2+\left(\frac{x}{3}\right)\left(\frac{y}{4}\right)+\left(\frac{y}{4}\right)^2\right\}$$
$$=\left(\frac{x}{3}-\frac{y}{4}\right)\left(\frac{x^2}{9}+\frac{xy}{12}+\frac{y^2}{16}\right)$$
Ans.

**Example 4.** Factorise the following :

(i) $27x^4-xy^3$ (ii) $8x^3-\dfrac{1}{8x^3}$

**Solution.** (i)
$$27x^4-xy^3=x(27x^3-y^3)$$
$$=x\{(3x)^3-y^3\}$$
$$=x(3x-y)\{(3x)^2+(3x)y+y^2\}$$
$$=x(3x-y)(9x^2+3xy+y^2)$$
Ans.

(ii)
$$8x^3-\frac{1}{8x^3}=(2x)^3-\left(\frac{1}{2x}\right)^3$$
$$=\left(2x-\frac{1}{2x}\right)\left\{(2x)^2+(2x)\left(\frac{1}{2x}\right)+\left(\frac{1}{2x}\right)^2\right\}$$
$$=\left(2x-\frac{1}{2x}\right)\left(4x^2+1+\frac{1}{4x^2}\right)$$
Ans.

**Example 5.** Factorise the following :

(i) $64x^3-(2x-3y)^3$ (ii) $(x+y)^3-8(x-y)^3$

**Solution.** (i)
$$64x^3-(2x-3y)^3=(4x)^3-(2x-3y)^3$$
$$=\{(4x)-(2x-3y)\}\{(4x)^2+4x(2x-3y)+(2x-3y)^2\}$$
$$=(4x-2x+3y)(16x^2+8x^2-12xy+4x^2-12xy+9y^2)$$
$$=(2x+3y)(28x^2-24xy+9y^2)$$
Ans.

(ii)
$$(x+y)^3-8(x-y)^3=(x+y)^3-(2x-2y)^3$$
$$=\{(x+y)-(2x-2y)\}\{(x+y)^2+(x+y)(2x-2y)+(2x-2y)^2\}$$
$$=(x+y-2x+2y)(x^2+y^2+2xy+2x^2-2y^2+4x^2+4y^2-8xy)$$
$$=(3y-x)(7x^2+3y^2-6xy)$$
Ans.

**Example 6.** Factorise : $x^6-26x^3-27$

**Solution.**
$$x^6-26x^3-27=x^6-(27-1)x^3-27$$
$$=x^6-27x^3+x^3-27$$
$$=x^3(x^3-27)+1(x^3-27)$$
$$=(x^3-27)(x^3+1)$$
$$=(x^3-3^3)(x^3+1^3)$$
$$=(x-3)[x^2+x(3)+3^2](x+1)\{x^2-x(1)+1^2\}$$
$$=(x-3)(x^2+3x+9)(x+1)(x^2-x+1)$$
Ans.

**Example 7.** Factorise : $x^6 - y^6$

**Solution.**
$$\begin{aligned} x^6 - y^6 &= (x^3)^2 - (y^3)^2 \\ &= (x^3 + y^3)(x^3 - y^3) \\ &= (x + y)(x^2 - xy + y^2)(x - y)(x^2 + xy + y^2) \end{aligned}$$
Ans.

**Example 8.** Factorise : $x^3 - 64y^3 + x^2 - 16y^2$

**Solution.**
$$\begin{aligned} x^3 - 64y^3 + x^2 - 16y^2 &= x^3 - (4y)^3 + x^2 - (4y)^2 \\ &= (x - 4y)\{x^2 + x(4y) + (4y)^2\} + (x + 4y)(x - 4y) \\ &= (x - 4y)(x^2 + 4xy + 16y^2) + (x + 4y)(x - 4y) \\ &= (x - 4y)(x^2 + 4xy + 16y^2 + x + 4y) \end{aligned}$$
Ans.

## Exercise 4E

Factorise the following :

1. $x^3 + 64$
2. $27x^3 + 8$
3. $x^3 + 8y^3$
4. $8x^3 + 125y^3$
5. $x^3 - 8$
6. $125x^3 - 64$
7. $x^5 - 64x^2$
8. $64x^3 - \frac{27}{y^3}$
9. $\frac{x^3}{8} - y^3$
10. $27x^3 + \frac{1}{27x^3}$
11. $xy^7 - x^7y$
12. $64x^4 - 1000x$
13. $(2x + y)^3 + (x + y)^3$
14. $(2x + 3y)^3 - (x + y)^3$
15. $8x^3 - (x - y)^3$
16. $x^6 - 63x^3 - 64$
17. $x^9 + y^9$
18. $x^6 - 7x^3 - 8$
19. $x^6 - 19x^3 - 196$
20. $x^3 + 3x^2y + 3xy^2 + 9y^3$
21. $x^3 + 8y^3 + x^2 - 4y^2$
22. $4x^2 - 9y^2 - 8x^3 + 27y^3$

### Answers

1. $(x + 4)(x^2 - 4x + 16)$
2. $(3x + 2)(9x^2 - 6x + 4)$
3. $(x + 2y)(x^2 - 2xy + 4y^2)$
4. $(2x + 5y)(4x^2 - 10xy + 25y^2)$
5. $(x - 2)(x^2 + 2x + 4)$
6. $(5x - 4)(25x^2 + 20x + 16)$
7. $x^2(x - 4)(x^2 + 4x + 16)$
8. $\left(4x - \frac{3}{y}\right)\left(16x^2 + \frac{12x}{y} + \frac{9}{y^2}\right)$
9. $\left(\frac{x}{2} - y\right)\left(\frac{x^2}{4} + \frac{xy}{2} + y^2\right)$
10. $\left(3x + \frac{1}{3x}\right)\left(9x^2 + \frac{1}{9x^2} - 1\right)$
11. $xy(y - x)(y + x)(y^2 + xy + x^2)(y^2 - xy + x^2)$
12. $8x(2x - 5)(4x^2 + 10x + 25)$
13. $(3x + 2y)(3x^2 + 3xy + y^2)$
14. $(x + 2y)(7x^2 + 19xy + 13y^2)$
15. $(x + y)(7x^2 - 4xy + y^2)$
16. $(x + 1)(x - 4)(x^2 - x + 1)(x^2 + 4x + 16)$
17. $(x + y)(x^2 - xy + y^2)(x^6 - x^3y^3 + y^6)$
18. $(x - 2)(x + 1)(x^2 - x + 1)(x^2 + 2x + 4)$
19. $(x - 3)(x + 2)(x^2 - 2x + 4)(x^2 + 3x + 9)$
20. $(x + 3y)(x^2 + 3y^2)$
21. $(x + 2y)(x^2 - 2xy + 4y^2 + x - 2y)$
22. $(2x - 3y)(2x + 3y - 4x^2 - 6xy - 9y^2)$

## Exercise 4F

### Multiple Choice Questions

Choose the correct answer from the given four options in each of the following questions :

1. $x^2 - y^2$ is equal to :
(a) $(x - y)(x - y)$ (b) $(x + y)(x + y)$ (c) $(x - y)(x + y)$ (d) $(x - 2y)(2x - y)$

2. $x^3 - y^3$ is equal to :
(a) $(x - y)(x^2 + xy + y^2)$ (b) $(x + y)(x^2 + xy + y^2)$ (c) $(x - y)(x^2 - xy + y^2)$ (d) $(x + y)(x^2 - xy + y^2)$

3. $x^2 + 9x + 20$ is equal to :
(a) $(x + 4)(x + 5)$ (b) $(x + 4)(x - 5)$
(c) $(x + 2)(x + 10)$ (d) $(x + 10)(x - 2)$

4. $(17)^2 - (13)^2$ is equal to :
(a) 80 (b) 90 (c) 100 (d) 120

5. Factors of $x^4 + 4y^4$ are :
(a) $(x^2 + 2xy + 2y^2)(x^2 - 2xy + 2y^2)$ (b) $(x^2 + 2y^2)(x^2 + 2y^2)$
(c) $(x^2 - 2y^2)(x^2 - 2y^2)$ (d) none of these

6. Factors of $(3 - x - 4x^2)$ are :
(a) $(4x + 3)(1 - x)$ (b) $(3 - 4x)(1 + x)$ (c) $(4x + 3)(1 + x)$ (d) $(3 - 4x)(1 - x)$

7. Factors of $x^3 - 3x^2 - x + 3$ are :
(a) $(x - 1)(x + 1)(x - 3)$ (b) $(x - 1)(x + 1)(x + 3)$ (c) $(x - 1)(x + 2)(x - 3)$ (d) $(x - 1)(x - 2)(x - 3)$

8. One factor of $(x - y)^3 - (x^3 - y^3)$ is :
(a) $3xy$ (b) $x^2y^2$ (c) $x + y$ (d) $x^3y^3$

9. Factors of $9x^2 - 16y^2$ are :
(a) $(3x - 4y)(3x - 4y)$ (b) $(4x - 3y)(4x + 3y)$ (c) $(3x + 4y)(3x - 4y)$ (d) $(4x + 3y)(4x + 3y)$

10. Factors of $x^2 + \left(a + \frac{1}{a}\right)x + 1$ are :
(a) $(x + a)\left(x + \frac{1}{a}\right)$ (b) $(x + a)\left(x - \frac{1}{a}\right)$ (c) $(x - a)\left(x + \frac{1}{a}\right)$ (d) $(x - a)\left(x - \frac{1}{a}\right)$

### *Answers*

**1.** (c) **2.** (a) **3.** (a) **4.** (d) **5.** (a) **6.** (b) **7.** (a) **8.** (a) **9.** (c) **10.** (a)

## Valid Statements *Questions*

In the following questions, two statements (i) and (ii) are given. Choose the valid statement.
(a) Only (i) (b) Only (ii) (c) Both (i) and (ii) (d) Neither (i) nor (ii)

1. (i) $x^2 - y^2 + 2xy = (x + y)^2$
(ii) $x^2 - \left(a + \frac{1}{a}\right)x + 1 = (x - a)\left(x + \frac{1}{a}\right)$

2. (i) $8x^3 - y^3 = (2x - y)(4x^2 + 2xy + y^2)$
(ii) $16x^2 - 9y^2 = (4x - 3y)(4x + 3y)$

3. (i) $4x^4 + y^4 = (2x^2 + y^2 + 2xy)(2x^2 + y^2 - 2xy)$
(ii) $x^2 - 7x - 8 = (x + 8)(x - 1)$

4. (i) $4x^2 - 5\sqrt{2}\,x - 7 = (2\sqrt{2}x + 7)(\sqrt{2}x - 1)$
(ii) $x^2 + x + px + p = (x + 1)(x + p)$

### *Answers*

**1.** (d) **2.** (c) **3.** (a) **4.** (b)

## SUMMARY *of the Chapter*

- The reverse process of multiplication is called factorisation.
- Factorisation can be determined by the following methods:
  1. Taking out common factor.
  2. Grouping of terms.
  3. Using the following identities.

$$a^2 - b^2 = (a + b)(a - b)$$
$$a^3 + b^3 = (a + b)(a^2 - ab + b^2)$$
$$a^3 - b^3 = (a - b)(a^2 + ab + b^2)$$

# CHAPTER TEST

1. Factorise : $x^2 - 7x - 260$
2. Factorise : $x^3 + 6x^2 - x - 6$
3. Factorise : $x^4 + 4$
4. Factorise : $x^2 + \left(\frac{a}{b} + \frac{b}{a}\right)x + 1$
5. Factorise : $(x^2 - x)(x^2 - x - 14) + 24$
6. Factorise : $(x^2 + y^2 - z^2)^2 - 4x^2y^2$
7. Factorise : $24xy - 16x^2 - 9y^2 + z^2$
8. Factorise : $8x^3 + 2x + 30$
9. Factorise : $x^4 - 27x$
10. Factorise : $x^4 + 5x^2y^2 + 9y^4$

## *Answers*

1. $(x - 20)(x + 13)$
2. $(x + 6)(x + 1)(x - 1)$
3. $(x^2 + 2x + 2)(x^2 - 2x + 2)$
4. $\left(x + \frac{a}{b}\right)\left(x + \frac{b}{a}\right)$
5. $(x - 2)(x + 1)(x - 4)(x + 3)$
6. $(x + y + z)(x + y - z)(x - y - z)(x - y + z)$
7. $(z + 4x - 3y)(z - 4x + 3y)$
8. $2(2x + 3)(2x^2 - 3x + 5)$
9. $x(x - 3)(x^2 + 3x + 9)$
10. $(x^2 + 3y^2 - xy)(x^2 + 3y^2 + xy)$

Chapter

# 5 SIMULTANEOUS LINEAR EQUATIONS

## Syllabus

- Simultaneous Linear Equations in two variables. (With numerical coefficients only)
- Solving algebraically by:
  - Elimination
  - Substitution and
  - Cross Multiplication method
- Solving simple problems by framing appropriate equations.

## INTRODUCTION

We are familiar with a linear equation in one variable. Its general form is $ax + b = 0, a \neq 0$ where $a$, $b$ are real numbers. It has a unique solution $x = \frac{-b}{a}$.

Now, we shall study the linear equations in two variables, methods of solving a pair of linear equations in two variables and their some applications.

## Linear Equation in Two Variables

The equation of the form $ax + by + c = 0, a \neq 0, b \neq 0$ where $a$, $b$, $c$ are real numbers, is called a linear equation in two variables $x$ and $y$.

## Solution of a Linear Equation in Two Variables

For the linear equation in two variables $x$ and $y$,

$$ax + by + c = 0, a \neq 0, b \neq 0.$$

a pair of values of $x$ and $y$, which satisfy the given equation, is called a solution of the linear equation.

If $x = \alpha, y = \beta$ is a solution, then

$$a\alpha + b\beta + c = 0$$

*For example :* Consider the linear equation

$$3x + 2y - 13 = 0$$

This equation is satisfied by $x = 3$ and $y = 2$.

$\therefore$ $x = 3$ and $y = 2$ is a solution of the linear equation $3x + 2y - 13 = 0$.

**Remark**

A linear equation in two variables has infinitely many solutions.

**NOTE**

The graph of a linear equation in two variables represents a straight line in *XY*-plane which contains infinitely many point. Every point on this line is a solution of the linear equation.

## Simultaneous Linear Equations

Consider two equations in two variables $x$ and $y$ :

$$a_1 x + b_1 y + c_1 = 0$$
$$a_2 x + b_2 y + c_2 = 0$$

These two equations simultaneously are called a system of simultaneous linear equations in two variables.

A pair of values of $x$ and $y$ is called a solution of the system of simultaneous linear equations if it satisfies both the equations.

*For example :* Consider the pair of linear equations in two variables $x$ and $y$.

$$x + 3y = 7$$
$$2x + y = 4$$

$x = 1$, $y = 2$ satisfies both the equations, so $x = 1$, $y = 2$ is the solution of the above pair of linear equations.

**NOTE**

If a system of linear equations has only one solution, it is called consistent and independent. In this chapter we shall discuss only consistent and independent system of simultaneous linear equations in two variables.

## Methods of Solving a Pair of Linear Equations in Two Variables

We shall discuss the following three methods of solving a pair of linear equations in two variables:

- Substitution method
- Elimination method
- Cross-multiplication method

## Substitution Method

### Steps

- From any one equation, find the value of one variable in terms of other variable.
- Substitute the value of this variable in other equation and obtained an equation in one variable.
- Solve this equation of one variable and find the value of the variable.
- Substitute the value of this variable in any one of the given equations and find the value of other variable.

## Illustrative Examples

**Example 1.** Solve : $x + y = 3$
$3x + 2y = 8$

**Solution.** Given, $x + y = 3$ ...(i)
$3x + 2y = 8$ ...(ii)
From equation (i),
$x + y = 3 \Rightarrow y = 3 - x$ ...(iii)
Put this value in equation (ii)
$3x + 2(3 - x) = 8 \Rightarrow 3x + 6 - 2x = 8 \Rightarrow x = 8 - 6 = 2$
Put this value in equation (iii)
$y = 3 - 2 = 1$
$\therefore$ $x = 2, y = 1$ Ans.

**Example 2.** Solve: $x - y = 5$
$2x + 3y = 20$

**Solution.** Given, $x - y = 5$ ...(i)
$2x + 3y = 20$ ...(ii)
From equation (i),
$x - y = 5 \Rightarrow x = 5 + y$ ...(iii)
Put this value in equation (ii)
$2(5 + y) + 3y = 20 \Rightarrow 10 + 2y + 3y = 20$
$\Rightarrow 5y = 20 - 10 = 10 \Rightarrow y = 2$
Put this value in equation (iii)
$x = 5 + 2 = 7$
$\therefore$ $x = 7, y = 2$ Ans.

**Example 3.** Solve : $2x + 3y = 13$
$3x + 2y = 12$

**Solution.** Given, $2x + 3y = 13$ ...(i)
$3x + 2y = 12$ ...(ii)
From equation (i),
$2x + 3y = 13 \Rightarrow 3y = 13 - 2x \Rightarrow y = \frac{13 - 2x}{3}$ ...(iii)

Put this value in equation (ii)
$$3x + \frac{2(13 - 2x)}{3} = 12 \Rightarrow \frac{9x + 26 - 4x}{3} = 12$$
$$\Rightarrow 5x + 26 = 36 \Rightarrow 5x = 10 \Rightarrow x = 2$$

Put this value in equation *(iii)*

$$y = \frac{13 - 2 \times 2}{3} = 3$$

$\therefore$ $x = 2, y = 3$ Ans.

**Example 4.** Solve : $4x - 3y = 7$, $2x + 5y = 23$

**Solution.** Given, $4x - 3y = 7$ ...(i)

$2x + 5y = 23$ ...(ii)

From equation *(i)*

$$4x - 3y = 7 \Rightarrow 4x = 7 + 3y \Rightarrow x = \frac{7 + 3y}{4} \quad ...(iii)$$

Put this value in equation *(ii)*

$$\frac{2\,(7 + 3y)}{4} + 5y = 23 \Rightarrow \frac{14 + 6y + 20y}{4} = 23$$

$$\Rightarrow 14 + 26\,y = 92 \Rightarrow 26\,y = 78 \Rightarrow y = 3$$

Put this value in equation *(iii)*

$$x = \frac{7 + 3 \times 3}{4} = 4$$

$\therefore$ $x = 4, y = 3$ Ans.

**Example 5.** Solve : $\sqrt{2}x + \sqrt{3}y = 0$, $\sqrt{3}x - \sqrt{5}y = 0$

**Solution.** Given $\sqrt{2}x + \sqrt{3}y = 0$ ...(i)

$\sqrt{3}x - \sqrt{5}y = 0$ ...(ii)

From equation *(ii)*,

$$\sqrt{3}x - \sqrt{5}y = 0 \Rightarrow x = \frac{\sqrt{5}}{\sqrt{3}}\,y \quad ...(iii)$$

Put this value in equation *(i)*

$$\sqrt{2} \cdot \frac{\sqrt{5}}{\sqrt{3}}\,y + \sqrt{3}y = 0 \Rightarrow y\left(\sqrt{2} \cdot \frac{\sqrt{5}}{3} + \sqrt{3}\right) = 0 \Rightarrow y = 0$$

Put this value in equation *(iii)*

$$x = \frac{\sqrt{5}}{\sqrt{3}} \times 0 = 0$$

$\therefore$ $x = 0, y = 0$ Ans.

**Example 6.** Solve $3x + y = 16$ and $x + 2y = 7$. Hence, find the value of $k$ for which $kx + 3y = 13$.

**Solution.** Given $3\,x + y = 16$ ...(i)

$x + 2y = 7$ ...(ii)

From equation *(i)*

$$3x + y = 16 \Rightarrow y = 16 - 3x \quad ...(iii)$$

Put this value in equation *(ii)*

$$x + 2(16 - 3x) = 7 \Rightarrow x + 32 - 6x = 7$$

$$\Rightarrow -5x = -25 \Rightarrow x = 5$$

Put this value in equation *(iii)*

$$y = 16 - 3 \times 5 = 1$$

$\therefore$ $x = 5, y = 1$ Ans.

Put these values in the equation $kx + 3y = 13$

$\therefore$ $5k + 3 \times 1 = 13 \Rightarrow 5k = 10$

$\Rightarrow$ $k = 2$ Ans.

**Example 7.** Solve: $\frac{2x}{3}+\frac{y}{5}=3$, $\frac{x}{6}+\frac{3y}{10}=2$

**Solution.** Given: $\frac{2x}{3}+\frac{y}{5}=3$ ...(i)

$\frac{x}{6}+\frac{3y}{10}=2$ ...(ii)

From equation (i)

$\frac{2x}{3}+\frac{y}{5}=3 \Rightarrow \frac{y}{5}=3-\frac{2x}{3}=\frac{9-2x}{3} \Rightarrow y=\frac{45-10x}{3}$ ...(iii)

Put this value in equation (ii)

$\frac{x}{6}+\frac{3}{10}\left(\frac{45-10x}{3}\right)=2 \Rightarrow \frac{x}{6}+\frac{45-10x}{10}=2 \Rightarrow \frac{5x+135-30x}{30}=2$

$\Rightarrow 135-25x=60 \Rightarrow -25x=-75 \Rightarrow x=3$

Put this value in equation (iii)

$y=\frac{45-10\times 3}{3}=5$

$\therefore$ $x=3, y=5$ Ans.

**Example 8.** Solve : $0.3x+0.7y=1.3$
$0.7x+0.2y=1.6$

**Solution.** Given, $0.3x+0.7y=1.3$ ...(i)

$0.7x+0.2y=1.6$ ...(ii)

Multiply both sides by 10

$3x+7y=13$ ...(iii)

$7x+2y=16$ ...(iv)

From equation (iii)

$3x+7y=13 \Rightarrow 3x=13-7y \Rightarrow x=\frac{13-7y}{3}$ ...(v)

Put this value in equation (iv)

$\frac{7(13-7y)}{3}+2y=16 \Rightarrow \frac{91-49y+6y}{3}=16$

$\Rightarrow 91-43y=48 \Rightarrow -43y=-43 \Rightarrow y=1$

Put this value in equation (v)

$x=\frac{13-7\times 1}{3}=2$

$\therefore$ $x=2, y=1$ Ans.

## Exercise 5A

Solve the following simultaneous equations by substitution method.

1. $x+y=3,\ x-7y=-5$
2. $2x+y=4,\ 3x+2y=7$
3. $3x+4y=13,\ 5x+9y=24$
4. $3x+4y=37,\ 7x+9y=85$
5. $3x-2y=0,\ 5x+y=13$
6. $x+5y=28,\ 4x+15y=87$
7. $x+2y=5,\ 3x-y=8$
8. $7x-10y=11,\ 3x-7y=2$
9. $4(x+4)-3(y+2)=5,\ 3(x-1)+2y+1=24$
10. $\frac{2x}{3}+\frac{y}{4}=3,\ \frac{x}{3}-\frac{y}{4}=0$
11. $0.2x+0.5y=2.1,\ 0.3x+0.4y=2.8$
12. $0.4x+0.5y=2.5,\ 0.3x-0.1y=1.4$
13. Solve $x+y=5$ and $3x+y=13$. Hence find the value of $k$ if $3x+ky=16$.
14. Solve $3x-2y=1$ and $2x+5y=7$. Hence find the value of $k$ if $2x+7y=k$.

## Answers

**1.** $x = 2, y = 1$ **2.** $x = 1, y = 2$ **3.** $x = 3, y = 1$ **4.** $x = 7, y = 4$ **5.** $x = 2, y = 3$ **6.** $x = 3, y = 5$
**7.** $x = 3, y = 1$ **8.** $x = 3, y = 1$ **9.** $x = 4, y = 7$ **10.** $x = 3, y = 4$ **11.** $x = 8, y = 1$ **12.** $x = 5, y = 1$
**13.** $x = 4, y = 1, k = 4$ **14.** $x = 1, y = 1, k = 9$

## Elimination Method

### Steps

- Multiply one or both equations as required, by some number to make the coefficient of either variable equal numerically.
- If the coefficients of this variable in both equations have same sign then subtract one equation from the other. It the coefficients of this variable in both equations have opposite signs, then add two equations to eliminate this variable.
- Now we get an equation containing one variable only. Solve this equation to find the value of this variable.
- Put the value of this variable in any of the two given equations to find the value of the other variable.

## Illustrative Examples

**Example 1.** Solve : $x + y = 7$
$x - y = 1$

**Solution.** Given equations are

$$x + y = 7 \quad \ldots(i)$$
$$x - y = 1 \quad \ldots(ii)$$

Here, the coefficients of $y$ are equal and of opposite signs.
So, adding equations *(i)* and *(ii)*,

$$\begin{array}{r} x + y = 7 \\ x - y = 1 \\ \hline 2x = 8 \end{array}$$

$\Rightarrow \quad x = 4$

Put $x = 4$ in equation *(i)*,

$$x + y = 7 \quad \Rightarrow \quad 4 + y = 7$$

$\Rightarrow \quad y = 7 - 4 = 3$

$\therefore \quad x = 4, y = 3$ **Ans.**

**Example 2.** Solve : $x + 2y = 7$
$3x - y = 0$

**Solution.** Given equations are

$$x + 2y = 7 \quad \ldots(i)$$
$$3x - y = 0 \quad \ldots(ii)$$

Multiply equation *(ii)* by 2,

$$6x - 2y = 0 \quad \ldots(iii)$$

Adding equations *(i)* and *(iii)*,

$$\begin{array}{r} x + 2y = 7 \\ 6x - 2y = 0 \\ \hline 7x \quad = 7 \end{array}$$

$\Rightarrow \quad x = 1$

Put $x = 3$ in equation *(i)*,

$$x + 2y = 7 \quad \Rightarrow \quad 1 + 2y = 7$$

$\Rightarrow \quad 2y = 7 - 1 = 6 \quad \Rightarrow \quad y = 3$

$\therefore \quad x = 1, y = 3$ **Ans.**

**Example 3.** Solve: $5x - 2y = 16$
$3x + 5y = 22$

**Solution.** Given equations are

$$5x - 2y = 16 \quad \ldots(i)$$
$$3x + 5y = 22 \quad \ldots(ii)$$

Multiply equation *(i)* by 5 and equation *(ii)* by 2,

$$25x - 10y = 80$$
$$6x + 10y = 44$$

Adding, we get $31x = 124$

$\Rightarrow$ $x = 4$

Put $x = 4$ in equation *(i)*,

$$5x - 2y = 16 \Rightarrow 5 \times 4 - 2y = 16$$

$\Rightarrow$ $-2y = 16 - 20 = -4 \Rightarrow y = 2$

$\therefore$ $x = 4, y = 2$ Ans.

**Example 4.** Solve : $19x + 15y = 83$
$15x + 19y = 87$

**Solution.** Given equations are

$$19x + 15y = 83 \quad \ldots(i)$$
$$15x + 19y = 87 \quad \ldots(ii)$$

Adding equations *(i)* and *(ii)*,

$$19x + 15y = 83$$
$$15x + 19y = 87$$
$$34x + 34y = 170$$

$\Rightarrow$ $x + y = 5$ ...*(iii)*

Subtracting equation *(ii)* from *(i)*,

$$19x + 15y = 83$$
$$15x + 19y = 87$$
$$- \quad - \quad -$$
$$4x - 4y = -4$$

$\Rightarrow$ $x - y = -1$ ...*(iv)*

Adding equations *(iii)* and *(iv)*,

$$x + y = 5$$
$$x - y = -1$$
$$2x = 4$$

$\Rightarrow$ $x = 2$

Put $x = 2$ in equation *(iii)*

$$x + y = 5 \Rightarrow 2 + y = 5$$

$\Rightarrow$ $y = 5 - 2 = 3$

$\therefore$ $x = 2, y = 3$ Ans.

**Example 5.** Solve : $4x + 3y = 10$ and $x - 2y = 8$. Hence, find the value of $k$ if $kx + 5y = 2$.

**Solution.** Given equations are

$$4x + 3y = 10 \quad \ldots(i)$$
$$x - 2y = 8 \quad \ldots(ii)$$

Multiply equation *(ii)* by 4 and subtracting from equation *(i)*,

$$4x + 3y = 10$$
$$4x - 8y = 32$$
$$- \quad + \quad -$$
$$11y = -22$$

$\Rightarrow$ $y = -2$

Put $y = -2$ in equation *(i)*,

$$4x + 3y = 10 \Rightarrow 4x + 3(-2) = 10$$
$$\Rightarrow 4x = 10 + 6 = 16 \Rightarrow x = 4$$
$$\therefore x = 4, y = -2$$ Ans.

Put $x = 4$, $y = -2$ in the equation $kx + 5y = 2$,

$$kx + 5y = 2 \Rightarrow 4k + 5(-2) = 2$$
$$\Rightarrow 4k = 2 + 10 = 12$$
$$\therefore k = 3$$ Ans.

**Example 6.** Solve : $\frac{3x}{2} - \frac{y}{5} = 14$, $\frac{x}{8} + \frac{y}{10} = 0$

**Solution.** Given equations are

$$\frac{3x}{2} - \frac{y}{5} = 14 \Rightarrow \frac{30x}{2} - \frac{10y}{5} = 140$$ (Multiply both sides by 10)

$$\Rightarrow 15x - 2y = 140$$ ...*(i)*

and $$\frac{x}{8} + \frac{y}{10} = 0 \Rightarrow \frac{40x}{8} + \frac{40y}{10} = 0$$ (Multiply both sides by 40)

$$\Rightarrow 5x + 4y = 0$$ ...*(ii)*

Multiply equation *(i)* by 2 and adding in equation *(ii)*,

$$30x - 4y = 280$$
$$5x + 4y = 0$$
$$35x = 280$$
$$\Rightarrow x = 8$$

Put $x = 8$ in equation *(ii)*,

$$5x + 4y = 0 \Rightarrow 5 \times 8 + 4y = 0$$
$$\Rightarrow 4y = -40 \Rightarrow y = -10$$
$$\therefore x = 8, y = -10$$ Ans.

**Example 7.** Solve : $0.3x + 0.4y = 1.3$
$0.4x - 0.5y = 0.7$

**Solution.** Given $0.3x + 0.4y = 1.3$
$0.4x - 0.5y = 0.7$

Multiply both equations by 10,

$$3x + 4y = 13$$ ...*(i)*
$$\Rightarrow 4x - 5y = 7$$ ...*(ii)*

Multiply equation *(i)* by 5 and equation *(ii)* by 4 and adding them

$$15x + 20y = 65$$
$$16x - 20y = 28$$
$$31x = 93$$
$$\Rightarrow x = 3$$

Put $x = 3$ in equation *(i)*

$$3 \times 3 + 4y = 13 \Rightarrow 4y = 13 - 9 = 4$$
$$\Rightarrow y = 1$$
$$\therefore x = 3, y = 1$$ Ans.

**Example 8.** Solve : $\frac{2x+7}{5} + \frac{2y+7}{3} = 4$, $\frac{3x-2}{10} + \frac{y+7}{5} = 2$

**Solution.** Given $$\frac{2x+7}{5} + \frac{2y+7}{3} = 4 \Rightarrow \frac{6x + 21 + 10y + 35}{15} = 4$$

$$\Rightarrow 6x + 10y + 56 = 60 \Rightarrow 6x + 10y = 4$$
$$\Rightarrow 3x + 5y = 2$$ ...*(i)*

and $\frac{3x-2}{10}+\frac{y+7}{5}=2 \Rightarrow \frac{3x-2+2y+14}{10}=2$

$\Rightarrow 3x+2y+12=20 \Rightarrow 3x+2y=8$ ...(ii)

Subtracting equation (ii) from equation (i)

$$\begin{array}{r} 3x+5y=2 \\ 3x+2y=8 \\ - \quad - \quad - \\ \hline 3y=-6 \end{array}$$

$\Rightarrow y=-2$

Put $y=-2$ in equation (i),

$3x+5(-2)=2 \Rightarrow 3x=2+10=12$

$\Rightarrow x=4$

$\therefore x=4, y=-2$ Ans.

**Example 9.** Solve : $ax+by=a+b$, $bx-ay=b-a$

**Solution.** Given, $ax+by=a+b$ ...(i)

$bx-ay=b-a$ ...(ii)

Multiply equation (i) by $a$ and equation (ii) by $b$ and adding them

$$\begin{array}{r} a^2x+aby=a^2+ab \\ b^2x-aby=b^2-ab \\ \hline (a^2+b^2)x=a^2+b^2 \end{array}$$

$\Rightarrow x=1$

Put $x=1$ in equation (i),

$a+by=a+b \Rightarrow by=b$

$\Rightarrow y=1$

$\therefore x=1, y=1$ Ans.

**Example 10.** Can the following system of equations hold simultaneously?

$$3x+y=11$$
$$x+2y=7$$
$$5x-2y=21$$

**Solution.** Given,

$3x+y=11$ ...(i)

$x+2y=7$ ...(ii)

$5x-2y=11$ ...(iii)

Adding equations (ii) and (iii)

$$\begin{array}{r} x+2y=7 \\ 5x-2y=11 \\ \hline 6x \quad =18 \end{array}$$

$\Rightarrow x=3$

Put $x=3$ in equation (ii)

$3+2y=7 \Rightarrow 2y=4 \Rightarrow y=2$

$\therefore$ Solution of equation (ii) and equation (iii) is

$x=3, y=2$

From equation (i)

L.H.S. $=3x+y=3\times 3+2=11=$ R.H.S.

Equation (i) is satisfied from the solution of equation (ii) and equation (iii)

$\therefore$ Given system of equations hold simultaneously. Ans.

## Exercise 5B

Solve the following systems of equations by elimination method :

1. $4x + 3y = 13, x + y = 4$
2. $5x + 8y = 44, 3x + 5y = 27$
3. $2x - 3y = 24, x - y = 13$
4. $2x + 5y = 9,\ x - y = 1$
5. $5x + 4y = -13, x - 2y = 3$
6. $11x - 16y = 35, 4x - 9y = 0$
7. $\frac{x}{2} + \frac{y}{3} = 3, 3x + y = 12$
8. $6x - \frac{8}{y} = 14,\ 2x - \frac{14}{y} = -1$
9. $3x = 4 - 5y, 2x - y = 7$
10. $x = y + 4, 4x - 9y = 11$
11. $2(x + 1) + 3(y - 2) = 19, 3(x + 2) + 2(y - 1) = 26$
12. $3(x - 2) + 5(y + 1) = 20,\ 4(x - 1) + 3(y + 3) = 22$
13. $\frac{x+1}{3} + \frac{y-3}{4} = 3,\ \frac{x-2}{3} + \frac{y+1}{2} = 5$
14. $18x + 23y = -5, 23x + 18y = 5$
15. $0.7x + 0.3y = 1.1, 0.2x + 0.5y = -0.1$
16. $\frac{x}{a} + \frac{y}{b} = a + b,\ \frac{x}{a^2} + \frac{y}{b^2} = 2, a \neq 0, b \neq 0$
17. $\frac{x}{a} = \frac{y}{b}; ax + by = a^2 + b^2, a \neq 0, b \neq 0$
18. $(a - b)\,x + (a + b)\,y = a^2 - 2ab - b^2, (a + b)\,(x + y) = a^2 + b^2$
19. $2bx + ay = 2ab, bx - ay = 4ab$
20. $x + y = a - b, ax - by = a^2 + b^2$
21. Can the following system of equations hold simultaneously?

$$5x + 2y = 26$$
$$2x + 3y = 17$$
$$3x + 5y = 27$$

22. If the system of following equations hold simultaneously, find the value of $k$.

$$4x + 3y = 11$$
$$x - y = 1$$
$$3x + ky = 10$$

### Answers

1. $x = 1, y = 3$ 2. $x = 4,\ y = 3$ 3. $x = 15, y = 2$ 4. $x = 2, y = 1$ 5. $x = -1, y = -2$ 6. $x = 9, y = 4$ 7. $x = 2, y = 6$ 8. $x = 3,\ y = 2$ 9. $x = 3, y = -1$ 10. $x = 5, y = 1$ 11. $x = 4,\ y = 5$ 12. $x = 2, y = 3$ 13. $x = 5,\ y = 7$ 14. $x = 1, y = -1$ 15. $x = 2, y = -1$ 16. $x = a^2, y = b^2$ 17. $x = a, y = b$ 18. $x = a + b, y = \frac{-2ab}{a^2 + b^2}$ 19. $x = 2a, y = -2b$ 20. $x = a, y = -b$ 21. Yes 22. $k = 4$

### Cross-Multiplication Method

Consider the following system of simultaneous linear equations in two variables :

$$a_1x + b_1y + c_1 = 0 \quad \ldots(i)$$
$$a_2x + b_2y + c_2 = 0 \quad \ldots(ii)$$

where $\frac{a_1}{a_2} \neq \frac{b_1}{b_2}$, *i.e.*, $a_1b_2 - a_2b_1 \neq 0$

Multiply equation *(i)* by $b_2$ and equation *(ii)* by $b_1$ and subtracting,

$$a_1b_2x + b_1b_2y + c_1b_2 = 0$$
$$\underset{-}{a_2b_1x} + \underset{-}{b_1b_2y} + \underset{-}{c_2b_1} = 0$$
$$\overline{(a_1b_2 - a_2b_1)x + c_1b_2 - c_2b_1 = 0}$$

$$\Rightarrow \quad x = \frac{b_1c_2 - b_2c_1}{a_1b_2 - a_2b_1}$$

Multiply equation *(i)* by $a_2$ and equation *(ii)* by $a_1$ and subtracting,

$$\begin{array}{r} a_1a_2x + a_2b_1y + a_2c_1 = 0 \\ a_1a_2x + a_1b_2y + a_1c_2 = 0 \\ - \qquad - \qquad - \quad \\ \hline (a_2b_1 - a_1b_2)y + a_2c_1 - a_1c_2 = 0 \end{array}$$

$\Rightarrow$ $$y = \frac{c_2a_1 - a_2c_1}{a_2b_1 - a_1b_2}, = \frac{a_2c_1 - c_2a_1}{a_1b_2 - a_2b_1}$$

$\therefore$ $$x = \frac{b_1c_2 - b_2c_1}{a_1b_2 - a_2b_1},\ y = \frac{a_2c_1 - c_2a_1}{a_1b_2 - a_2b_1}$$

$\Rightarrow$ $$\frac{x}{b_1c_2 - b_2c_1} = \frac{1}{a_1b_2 - a_2b_1},\ \frac{y}{a_2c_1 - c_2a_1} = \frac{1}{a_1b_2 - a_2b_1}$$

$\Rightarrow$ $$\frac{x}{b_1c_2 - b_2c_1} = \frac{y}{a_2c_1 - c_2a_1} = \frac{1}{a_1b_2 - a_2b_1}$$

$\Rightarrow$ $$\frac{x}{\begin{matrix} b_1 & \nearrow\!\!\!\!\searrow & c_1 \\ b_2 & & c_2 \end{matrix}} = \frac{y}{\begin{matrix} c_1 & \nearrow\!\!\!\!\searrow & a_1 \\ c_2 & & a_2 \end{matrix}} = \frac{1}{\begin{matrix} a_1 & \nearrow\!\!\!\!\searrow & b_1 \\ a_2 & & b_2 \end{matrix}}$$

The arrows between the two numbers show that they are to be multiplied. The arrows in downward direction(↘) show the term with a plus sign and the arrows in upward direction (↗) show the term with a negative sign.

## Illustrative Examples

**Example 1.** Solve by cross-multiplication method:

$$3x + 2y = 19$$
$$5x + y = 20$$

**Solution.** Given equations are

$$3x + 2y - 19 = 0$$
$$5x + y - 20 = 0$$

Using cross multiplication method,

$\Rightarrow$ $$\frac{x}{\begin{matrix} 2 & \nearrow\!\!\!\!\searrow & -19 \\ 1 & & -20 \end{matrix}} = \frac{y}{\begin{matrix} -19 & \nearrow\!\!\!\!\searrow & 3 \\ -20 & & 5 \end{matrix}} = \frac{1}{\begin{matrix} 3 & \nearrow\!\!\!\!\searrow & 2 \\ 5 & & 1 \end{matrix}}$$ $\Rightarrow$ $$\frac{x}{-40 + 19} = \frac{y}{-95 + 60} = \frac{1}{3 - 10}$$

$\Rightarrow$ $$\frac{x}{-21} = \frac{y}{-35} = \frac{1}{-7}$$ $\Rightarrow$ $$x = \frac{-21}{-7} \text{ and } y = \frac{-35}{-7}$$

$\Rightarrow$ $$x = 3 \text{ and } y = 5$$

Ans.

**Example 2.** Solve by cross-multiplication method:

$5x - 2y = 11,\qquad 3x + y = 11$

**Solution.** Given,

$$5x - 2y - 11 = 0$$
$$3x + y - 11 = 0$$

Using cross-multiplication method,

$$\frac{x}{\begin{matrix} -2 & \nearrow\!\!\!\!\searrow & -11 \\ 1 & & -11 \end{matrix}} = \frac{y}{\begin{matrix} -11 & \nearrow\!\!\!\!\searrow & 5 \\ -11 & & 3 \end{matrix}} = \frac{1}{\begin{matrix} 5 & \nearrow\!\!\!\!\searrow & -2 \\ 3 & & 1 \end{matrix}}$$ $\Rightarrow$ $$\frac{x}{22 + 11} = \frac{y}{-33 + 55} = \frac{1}{5 + 6}$$

$$\Rightarrow \quad \frac{x}{33} = \frac{y}{22} = \frac{1}{11} \qquad \Rightarrow \quad x = \frac{33}{11} \text{ and } y = \frac{22}{11}$$

$$\Rightarrow \quad x = 3 \text{ and } y = 2$$ **Ans.**

**Example 3.** Solve by cross-multiplication method:
$4x + 3y = 5, \quad 3x + 4y = 2$

**Solution.** Given,

$$4x + 3y - 5 = 0$$
$$3x + 4y - 2 = 0$$

Using cross-multiplication method,

$$\Rightarrow \quad \frac{x}{\begin{matrix} 3 & \times & -5 \\ 4 & & -2 \end{matrix}} = \frac{y}{\begin{matrix} -5 & \times & 4 \\ -2 & & 3 \end{matrix}} = \frac{1}{\begin{matrix} 4 & \times & 3 \\ 3 & & 4 \end{matrix}} \qquad \Rightarrow \quad \frac{x}{-6+20} = \frac{y}{-15+8} = \frac{1}{16-9}$$

$$\Rightarrow \quad \frac{x}{14} = \frac{y}{-7} = \frac{1}{7} \qquad \Rightarrow \quad x = \frac{14}{7} \text{ and } y = \frac{-7}{7}$$

$$\Rightarrow \quad x = 2 \text{ and } y = -1$$ **Ans.**

**Example 4.** Solve by cross-multiplication method.
$4x - 3y = -5$
$-x + 2y = 5$

**Solution.** Given,

$$4x - 3y + 5 = 0$$
$$-x + 2y - 5 = 0$$

Using cross-multiplication method,

$$\frac{x}{\begin{matrix} -3 & \times & 5 \\ 2 & & -5 \end{matrix}} = \frac{y}{\begin{matrix} 5 & \times & 4 \\ -5 & & -1 \end{matrix}} = \frac{1}{\begin{matrix} 4 & \times & -3 \\ -1 & & 2 \end{matrix}} \qquad \Rightarrow \quad \frac{x}{15-10} = \frac{y}{-5+20} = \frac{1}{8-3}$$

$$\Rightarrow \quad \frac{x}{5} = \frac{y}{15} = \frac{1}{5} \qquad \Rightarrow \quad x = \frac{5}{5} \text{ and } y = \frac{15}{5}$$

$$\Rightarrow \quad x = 1 \text{ and } y = 3$$ **Ans.**

**Example 5.** Solve by cross-multiplication method:
$2ax + by = 2ab, \quad ax - by = 4ab$

**Solution.** Given,

$$2ax + by - 2ab = 0$$
$$ax - by - 4ab = 0$$

Using cross-multiplication method,

$$\frac{x}{\begin{matrix} b & \times & -2ab \\ -b & & -4ab \end{matrix}} = \frac{y}{\begin{matrix} -2ab & \times & 2a \\ -4ab & & a \end{matrix}} = \frac{1}{\begin{matrix} 2a & \times & b \\ a & & -b \end{matrix}} \qquad \Rightarrow \quad \frac{x}{-4ab^2 - 2ab^2} = \frac{y}{-2a^2b + 8a^2b} = \frac{1}{-2ab - ab}$$

$$\Rightarrow \quad \frac{x}{-6ab^2} = \frac{y}{6a^2b} = \frac{1}{-3ab} \qquad \Rightarrow \quad x = \frac{-6ab^2}{-3ab} \text{ and } y = \frac{6a^2b}{-3ab}$$

$$\Rightarrow \quad x = 2b \text{ and } y = -2a$$ **Ans.**

## Exercise 5C

**Using cross-multiplication method, solve the following system of simultaneous linear equations:**

1. $3x + 2y = 7,\ 2x + 3y = 8$
2. $3x + 4y = 25,\ 4x + 5y = 32$
3. $4x + 3y = 5,\ 2x + 5y = -1$
4. $2x - y = 9,\ 5x + y = 26$
5. $3x - 7y = 2,\ 4x - 3y = 9$
6. $x - 3y - 5 = 0,\ 3x + 2y - 8 = 0$
7. $x - 2y + 1 = 0,\ x + y + 4 = 0$
8. $9x - 4y = 200,\ 7x - 3y = 200$
9. $ax + by = a - b,\ bx - ay = a + b$
10. $5x + 7y = 31,\ 7x + 5y = 29$

### Answers

1. $x = 1, y = 2$
2. $x = 3, y = 4$
3. $x = 2, y = -1$
4. $x = 5, y = 1$
5. $x = 3, y = 1$
6. $x = \frac{34}{11}, y = \frac{-7}{11}$
7. $x = -3, y = -1$
8. $x = 200, y = 400$
9. $x = 1, y = -1$
10. $x = 2, y = 3$

## Equations Reducible to Linear Equations in Two Variables

There are such equations which are not linear but can be converted into linear equations in two variables by some substitutions. In this section, we shall discuss such types of equations.

## Illustrative Examples

**Example 1.** Solve : $\frac{16}{x} + \frac{3}{y} = \frac{121}{5},\ \frac{15}{x} + \frac{2}{y} = 17,\ x \neq 0,\ y \neq 0$

**Solution.** Given,

$$\frac{16}{x} + \frac{3}{y} = \frac{121}{5} \qquad \text{...(i)}$$

$$\frac{15}{x} + \frac{2}{y} = 17 \qquad \text{...(ii)}$$

Put $\frac{1}{x} = u$ and $\frac{1}{y} = v$

Given equations become

$$16u + 3v = \frac{121}{5} \quad \Rightarrow \quad 80u + 15v = 121 \qquad \text{...(iii)}$$

and $\quad 15u + 2v = 17 \qquad \text{...(iv)}$

Multiply equation *(iii)* by 2 and equation *(iv)* by 15 and subtracting

$$\begin{array}{r} 160u + 30v = 242 \\ \underset{-}{225u} + \underset{-}{30v} = \underset{-}{255} \\ \hline -65u \quad = -13 \end{array}$$

$$\Rightarrow \quad u = \frac{-13}{-65} = \frac{1}{5} \quad \Rightarrow \quad \frac{1}{x} = \frac{1}{5} = x = 5$$

Put $u = \frac{1}{5}$ in equation *(iv)*,

$$15 \times \frac{1}{5} + 2v = 17 \quad \Rightarrow \quad 2v = 17 - 3 = 14$$

$\Rightarrow \quad v = 7 \quad \Rightarrow \quad \frac{1}{y} = 7 \quad \Rightarrow \quad y = \frac{1}{7}$

$\therefore \quad x = 5, \ y = \frac{1}{7}$ **Ans.**

**Example 2.** Solve: $\frac{1}{x} + \frac{5}{y} = 6$

$\frac{1}{y} - \frac{5}{x} = -4, \ x \neq 0, y \neq 0$

**Solution.** Given,

$$\frac{1}{x} + \frac{5}{y} = 6 \quad \ldots(i)$$

$$\frac{1}{y} - \frac{5}{x} = -4 \quad \ldots(ii)$$

Put $\frac{1}{x} = u, \frac{1}{y} = v$

Given equations become

$$u + 5v = 6 \quad \ldots(iii)$$

$$v - 5u = -4$$

$$-5u + v = -4 \quad \ldots(iv)$$

Multiply equation *(iii)* by 5 and adding in equation *(iv)*

$$\begin{aligned} 5u + 25v &= 30 \\ -5u + v &= -4 \\ \hline 26v &= 26 \end{aligned}$$

$\Rightarrow \quad v = 1 \quad \Rightarrow \quad \frac{1}{y} = 1 \quad \Rightarrow \quad y = 1$

Put $v = 1$ in equation *(iii)*,

$u + 5 \times 1 = 6 \quad \Rightarrow \quad v = 1 \quad \Rightarrow \quad \frac{1}{x} = 1$

$\Rightarrow \quad x = 1$

$\therefore \quad x = 1, y = 1$ **Ans.**

**Example 3.** Solve: $4x + 3y = 5xy$

$8x + 7y = 11xy$

$x \neq 0, y \neq 0$

**Solution.** Given,

$4x + 3y = 5xy$

$\Rightarrow \quad \frac{4x}{xy} + \frac{3y}{xy} = 5$ (Dividing each term by $xy$)

$\Rightarrow \quad \frac{4}{y} + \frac{3}{x} = 5$

$\Rightarrow \quad \frac{3}{x} + \frac{4}{y} = 5 \quad \ldots(i)$

and $\quad 8x + 7y = 11xy$

$\Rightarrow \quad \frac{8x}{xy} + \frac{7y}{xy} = 11$ (Dividing each term by $xy$)

$$\Rightarrow \qquad \frac{8}{y} + \frac{7}{x} = 11$$

$$\Rightarrow \qquad \frac{7}{x} + \frac{8}{y} = 11 \qquad \text{...(ii)}$$

Put $\frac{1}{x} = u$ and $\frac{1}{y} = v$ in equations *(i)* and *(ii)*

$$3u + 4v = 5 \qquad \text{...(iii)}$$
$$7u + 8v = 11 \qquad \text{...(iv)}$$

Multiply equation *(iii)* by 2

$$6u + 8v = 10 \qquad \text{...(v)}$$

Subtracting equation *(v)* from equation *(iv)*

$$\begin{array}{r} 7u + 8v = 11 \\ 6u + 8v = 10 \\ - \quad - \quad - \\ \hline u \qquad = 1 \end{array}$$

$$\Rightarrow \qquad \frac{1}{x} = 1 \qquad \Rightarrow \qquad x = 1$$

Put $u = 1$ in equation *(iii)*,

$$3 \times 1 + 4v = 5 \qquad \Rightarrow \qquad 4v = 5 - 3 = 2$$

$$\Rightarrow \qquad v = \frac{2}{4} \qquad \Rightarrow \qquad \frac{1}{y} = \frac{1}{2} \qquad \Rightarrow \qquad y = 2$$

$\therefore \qquad x = 1, y = 2$ **Ans.**

**Example 4.** Solve : $\frac{6}{x+1} + \frac{3}{y+2} = 5, \qquad \frac{3}{x+1} + \frac{1}{y+2} = 2$

**Solution.** Let $\frac{1}{x+1} = u$ and $\frac{1}{y+2} = v$

Given,

$$\frac{6}{x+1} + \frac{1}{y+2} = 5$$

$$\Rightarrow \qquad 6u + 3v = 5 \qquad \text{...(i)}$$

and $\qquad \frac{3}{x+1} + \frac{1}{y+2} = 2 \qquad \Rightarrow \qquad 3u + v = 2 \qquad \text{...(ii)}$

Multiply equation *(ii)* by 2

$$\Rightarrow \qquad 6u + 2v = 4 \qquad \text{...(iii)}$$

Subtracting equation *(iii)* from equation *(i)*

$$\begin{array}{r} 6u + 3v = 5 \\ 6u + 2v = 4 \\ - \quad - \quad - \\ \hline v \; = 1 \end{array}$$

$$\Rightarrow \qquad \frac{1}{y+2} = 1 \qquad \Rightarrow \qquad y + 2 = 1 \qquad \Rightarrow \qquad y = -1$$

Put $v = 1$ in equation *(i)*,

$$6u + 3 \times 1 = 5 \qquad \Rightarrow \qquad 6u = 2 \qquad \Rightarrow \qquad u = \frac{2}{6}$$

$$\Rightarrow \qquad \frac{1}{x+1} = \frac{1}{3} \qquad \Rightarrow \qquad x + 1 = 3 \qquad \Rightarrow \qquad x = 2$$

$\therefore \qquad x = 2, y = -1$ **Ans.**

**Example 5.** Solve : $\frac{3}{\sqrt{x}} + \frac{4}{\sqrt{y}} = 3$, $\frac{6}{\sqrt{x}} - \frac{2}{\sqrt{y}} = 1$

**Solution.** Let $\frac{1}{\sqrt{x}} = u$ and $\frac{1}{\sqrt{y}} = v$

Given,

$$\frac{3}{\sqrt{x}} + \frac{4}{\sqrt{y}} = 3$$

$\Rightarrow$ $3u + 4v = 3$ ...(i)

and $\frac{6}{\sqrt{x}} - \frac{2}{\sqrt{y}} = 1$ $\Rightarrow$ $6u - 2v = 1$ ...(ii)

Multiply equation (ii) by 2

$12u - 4v = 2$ ...(iii)

Adding equation (i) and equation (iii)

$$\begin{array}{r} 3u + 4v = 3 \\ 12u - 4v = 2 \\ \hline 15u \quad = 5 \end{array}$$

$\Rightarrow$ $u = \frac{5}{15}$ $\Rightarrow$ $u = \frac{1}{3}$ $\Rightarrow$ $\frac{1}{\sqrt{x}} = \frac{1}{3}$

$\Rightarrow$ $\sqrt{x} = 3$ $\Rightarrow$ $x = 9$

Put $u = \frac{1}{3}$ in equation (i),

$3 \times \frac{1}{3} + 4v = 3$ $\Rightarrow$ $4v = 3 - 1 = 2$ $\Rightarrow$ $v = \frac{2}{4}$

$\Rightarrow$ $\frac{1}{\sqrt{y}} = \frac{1}{2}$ $\Rightarrow$ $\sqrt{y} = 2$ $\Rightarrow$ $y = 4$

$\therefore$ $x = 9, y = 4$ **Ans.**

**Example 6.** Solve: $\frac{10}{x+y} + \frac{3}{x-y} = 5$, $\frac{5}{x+y} - \frac{2}{x-y} = -1$

**Solution.** Let $\frac{1}{x+y} = u$ and $\frac{1}{x-y} = v$

$\because$ Given, $\frac{10}{x+y} + \frac{3}{x-y} = 5$

$\Rightarrow$ $10u + 3v = 5$ ...(i)

and $\frac{5}{x+y} - \frac{2}{x-y} = -1$ $\Rightarrow$ $5u - 2v = -1$ ...(ii)

Multiply equation (ii) by 2 and subtracting from equation (i)

$$\begin{array}{r} 10u + 3v = 5 \\ 10u - 4v = -2 \\ - \quad + \quad + \\ \hline 7v = 7 \end{array}$$

$\Rightarrow$ $v = 1$ $\Rightarrow$ $\frac{1}{x-y} = 1$ $\Rightarrow$ $x - y = 1$ ...(iii)

Put $v = 1$ in equation (i),

$10u + 3 \times 1 = 5$ $\Rightarrow$ $10u = 2$ $\Rightarrow$ $u = \frac{1}{5}$

$\Rightarrow \quad \dfrac{1}{x+y} = \dfrac{1}{5} \quad \Rightarrow \quad x + y = 5 \quad \ldots(iv)$

Adding equation *(iii)* and equation *(iv)*

$$\begin{aligned} x - y &= 1 \\ x + y &= 5 \\ \hline 2x &= 6 \end{aligned}$$

$\Rightarrow \quad x = 3$

Put $x = 3$ in equation *(iv)*

$3 + y = 5 \quad \Rightarrow \quad y = 2$

$\therefore \quad x = 3, y = 2$ **Ans.**

**Example 7.** Solve $\dfrac{30}{3x+y} - \dfrac{16}{3x-y} = 1, \quad \dfrac{10}{3x+y} + \dfrac{32}{3x-y} = 5$

**Solution.** Let $\dfrac{1}{3x+y} = u$ and $\dfrac{1}{3x-y} = v$

$\because$ Given, $\dfrac{30}{3x+y} - \dfrac{16}{3x-y} = 1$

$\Rightarrow \quad 30u - 16v = 1 \quad \ldots(i)$

and $\dfrac{10}{3x+y} + \dfrac{32}{3x-y} = 5 \quad \Rightarrow \quad 10u + 32v = 5 \quad \ldots(ii)$

Multiply equation *(i)* by 2 and adding in equation *(ii)*,

$$\begin{aligned} 60u - 32v &= 2 \\ 10u + 32v &= 5 \\ \hline 70u \quad &= 7 \end{aligned}$$

$\Rightarrow \quad u = \dfrac{1}{10}$

$\Rightarrow \quad \dfrac{1}{3x+y} = \dfrac{1}{10} \quad \Rightarrow \quad 3x + y = 10 \quad \ldots(iii)$

Put $u = \dfrac{1}{10}$ in equation *(ii)*,

$10 \times \dfrac{1}{10} + 32v = 5 \quad \Rightarrow \quad 32v = 4 \quad \Rightarrow \quad v = \dfrac{1}{8}$

$\Rightarrow \quad \dfrac{1}{3x-y} = \dfrac{1}{8} \quad \Rightarrow \quad 3x - y = 8 \quad \ldots(iv)$

Adding equations *(iii)* and *(iv)*,

$$\begin{aligned} 3x + y &= 10 \\ 3x - y &= 8 \\ \hline 6x &= 18 \end{aligned}$$

$\Rightarrow \quad x = 3$

Put $x = 3$ in equation *(iii)*,

$3 \times 3 + y = 10 \quad \Rightarrow \quad y = 1$

$\therefore \quad x = 3, y = 1$ **Ans.**

# Exercise 5D

**Solve the following pairs of linear equations:**

1. $\frac{9}{x}+\frac{2}{y}=4,\ \frac{12}{x}+\frac{6}{y}=7,\ x\neq 0, y\neq 0$
2. $\frac{8}{x}+\frac{1}{y}=3,\ \frac{16}{x}-\frac{3}{y}=1,\ x\neq 0, y\neq 0$
3. $\frac{2}{x}+\frac{2}{y}=1,\ \frac{6}{x}-\frac{9}{y}=-2,\ x\neq 0, y\neq 0$
4. $\frac{1}{2x}-\frac{3}{4y}=1,\ \frac{4}{x}-\frac{1}{y}=3,\ x\neq 0, y\neq 0$
5. $3x+5y=2xy,\ 21x-15y=4xy,\ x\neq 0,\ y\neq 0$
6. $7x+4y=6xy,\ x+3y=-4xy,\ x\neq 0,\ y\neq 0$
7. $7x-4y=\frac{3}{2}xy,\ x+y=\frac{7}{2}xy,\ x\neq 0,\ y\neq 0$
8. $\frac{9}{\sqrt{x}}+\frac{2}{\sqrt{y}}=4,\ \frac{3}{\sqrt{x}}+\frac{4}{\sqrt{y}}=3,\ x\neq 0,\ y\neq 0$
9. $\frac{10}{x+1}-\frac{2}{y-1}=\frac{3}{2},\quad \frac{5}{x+1}+\frac{8}{y-1}=3$
10. $\frac{4}{x+2}-\frac{6}{y-1}=-1,\quad \frac{2}{x+2}+\frac{3}{y-1}=1$
11. $\frac{10}{x+y}-\frac{1}{x-y}=1,\quad \frac{5}{x+y}+\frac{3}{x-y}=4$
12. $\frac{6}{2x+y}+\frac{5}{2x-y}=3,\quad \frac{9}{2x+y}-\frac{10}{2x-y}=1$

## Answers

**1.** $x=3, y=2$ **2.** $x=4, y=1$ **3.** $x=6, y=3$ **4.** $x=2, y=-1$ **5.** $x=5, y=3$ **6.** $x=-\frac{1}{2}, y=\frac{1}{2}$ **7.** $x=\frac{11}{23}, y=\frac{22}{31}$ **8.** $x=9, y=4$ **9.** $x=4, y=5$ **10.** $x=6, y=5$ **11.** $x=3, y=2$ **12.** $x=2, y=-1$

## Word Problems

**Example 1.** The sum of two numbers is 28 and their difference is 4. Find the numbers.

**Solution.** Let two numbers be $x$ and $y$.

$\therefore$ $x+y=28$ ...(i)

$x-y=4$ ...(ii)

Adding equations (i) and (ii), we get

$2x=32 \Rightarrow x=16$

Put $x=16$ in equation (i),

$16+y=28 \Rightarrow y=12$

$\therefore$ Two numbers are 16 and 12. Ans.

**Example 2.** The sum of two numbers is 65. If the larger number exceeds four times the smaller one by 5. Find the numbers.

**Solution.** Let the two numbers be $x$ and $y$, and $x>y$.

$\therefore$ $x+y=65$ ...(i)

$x-4y=5$ ...(ii)

Subtracting equation (ii) from (i),

$5y=60 \Rightarrow y=12$

Putting, $y=12$ in equation (i),

$x+12=65 \Rightarrow x=53$

Hence, two numbers are 53 and 12. Ans.

**Example 3.** The sum of two numbers is 9. The sum of their reciprocals is $\frac{1}{2}$. Find the numbers.

**Solution.** Let the two numbers be $x$ and $y$.

$\therefore$ $x+y=9$ ...(i)

and $\frac{1}{x}+\frac{1}{y}=\frac{1}{2}$ ...(ii)

$\Rightarrow$ $\frac{y+x}{xy}=\frac{1}{2}$

$\Rightarrow$ $xy = 2(x+y)$ $\Rightarrow$ $xy = 2 \times 9$ [From (i)]

$\Rightarrow$ $xy = 18$

we know that

$$(x-y)^2 = (x+y)^2 - 4xy$$

$\Rightarrow$ $(x-y)^2 = (9)^2 - 4(18) = 81 - 72 = 9$

$\therefore$ $x - y = \pm 3$

If $x - y = 3$ ...(iii)

Now, from equations *(iii)* and *(i)*,

$$x - y = 3$$
$$x + y = 9$$

On adding, $2x = 12$

$\therefore$ $x = 6$

$\therefore$ $y = 9 - 6$

$= 3$ [From (i)]

If $x - y = -3$ ...(iv)

Now, from equations *(iv)* and *(i)*,

$$x - y = -3$$
$$x + y = 9$$

On adding, $2x = 6$

$\therefore$ $x = 3$

$\therefore$ $y = 9 - 3$

$= 6$ [From (i)]

$\therefore$ Two numbers are 3 and 6. **Ans.**

**Example 4.** If the numerator of a fraction is increased by 2, it becomes $\frac{1}{2}$. If its denominator is increased by 3, it becomes $\frac{1}{3}$. Find the fraction.

**Solution.** Let the fraction be $\frac{x}{y}$.

First condition gives

$$\frac{x+2}{y}=\frac{1}{2}$$

$\Rightarrow$ $2x + 4 = y$

$\Rightarrow$ $2x - y = -4$ ...(i)

second condition gives

$$\frac{x}{y+3}=\frac{1}{3}$$

$\Rightarrow$ $3x = y + 3$

$\Rightarrow$ $3x - y = 3$ ...(ii)

Subtracting equation *(i)* from equation *(ii)*,

$$3x - y = 3$$
$$2x - y = -4$$
$$- \quad + \quad +$$

$$x = 7$$

Put $x = 7$ in equation *(i)*,

$$2(7) - y = -4$$

$\Rightarrow$ $y = 14 + 4$

$\Rightarrow$ $y = 18$

$\therefore$ Fraction $= \dfrac{7}{18}$ **Ans.**

**Example 5.** If we add 1 to the numerator and subtract 1 from the denominator, a fraction reduces to 1. It becomes $\frac{2}{3}$ if we subtract 1 from numerator. What is the fraction?

**Solution.** Let fraction $= \dfrac{x}{y}$

According to the problem

$$\frac{x+1}{y-1} = 1 \Rightarrow x + 1 = y - 1 \Rightarrow x - y = -2 \quad ...(i)$$

and $$\frac{x-1}{y} = \frac{2}{3} \Rightarrow 3x - 3 = 2y \Rightarrow 3x - 2y = 3 \quad ...(ii)$$

Multiply equation *(i)* by 2 and subtracting from equation *(ii)*

$$\begin{array}{r} 3x - 2y = 3 \\ 2x - 2y = -4 \\ - \quad + \quad + \\ \hline x \quad = 7 \end{array}$$

Put $x = 7$ in equation *(i)*,

$$7 - y = -2 \Rightarrow y = 9$$

$\therefore$ Fraction $\dfrac{x}{y} = \dfrac{7}{9}$ **Ans.**

**Example 6.** Sum of the digits of a two-digit number is 9. The number obtained by reversing the order of the digits of the given number exceed the given number by 45. Find the given number.

**Solution.** Let digit at unit's digit be $x$ and ten's digit be $y$.

$\therefore$ Number $= 10y + x$

On reversing the digits, the new number $= 10x + y$

$\therefore$ $x + y = 9$ ...*(i)*

and $10x + y = 45 + (10y + x)$

$\Rightarrow$ $9x - 9y = 45$

$\Rightarrow$ $x - y = 5$ ...*(ii)*

Adding equations *(i)* and *(ii)*,

$$2x = 14 \Rightarrow x = 7$$

Put $x = 7$ in equation *(i)*,

$$7 + y = 9 \Rightarrow y = 9 - 7 = 2$$

$\therefore$ Number $= 10y + x = 10 \times 2 + 7 = 27$ **Ans.**

**Example 7.** The sum of the digits of a two-digit number is 9. Also, eight times this number is thrice the number obtained by reversing the order of the digits. Find the number.

**Solution.** Let two digit number $= 10x + y$

$\therefore$ $x + y = 9$ ...*(i)*

and $8(10x + y) = 3 \times$ Number formed by reversing the digits.

$= 3(10y + x)$

$\Rightarrow$ $80x + 8y = 30y + 3x$

$$\Rightarrow \quad 77x - 22y = 0$$

$$\Rightarrow \quad 7x - 2y = 0 \quad \ldots(ii)$$

Multiply equation *(i)* by 2 and adding in equation *(ii)*

$$2x + 2y = 18$$
$$7x - 2y = 0$$
$$9x = 18 \quad \Rightarrow \quad x = 2$$

Put $x = 2$ in equation *(i)*

$$2 + y = 9$$

$$\Rightarrow \quad y = 9 - 2 = 7$$

$\therefore$ Number $= 10 \times 2 + 7 = 27$ **Ans.**

**Example 8.** A two digit number is equal to 4 times the sum of its digits. If the digits are reversed, the number is increased by 36. Find the number.

**Solution.** Let two digit number be $10x + y$.

First condition gives

$$10x + y = 4(x + y)$$

$$\Rightarrow \quad 6x - 3y = 0$$

$$\Rightarrow \quad 2x - y = 0 \quad \ldots(i)$$

Second condition gives

$$10x + y + 36 = 10y + x$$

$$\Rightarrow \quad 9x - 9y = -36$$

$$\Rightarrow \quad x - y = -4 \quad \ldots(ii)$$

Subtracting equation *(ii)* from equation *(i)*,

$$2x - y = 0$$
$$x - y = -4$$
$$- \quad + \quad\quad +$$
$$x = 4$$

Put $x = 4$ in equation *(i)*

$$2(4) - y = 0 \quad \Rightarrow \quad y = 8$$

$\therefore$ Numbers $= 10\,(4) + 8 = 48$ **Ans.**

**Example 9.** The cost of 3 notebooks and 2 pens is ₹ 140. The cost of 2 notebooks and 3 pens is ₹ 110. Find the cost of 1 notebook and the cost of 1 pen.

**Solution.** Let cost of 1 notebook = ₹ $x$

and cost of 1 pen = ₹ $y$

First condition gives

$$3x + 2y = 140 \quad \ldots(i)$$

second condition gives

$$2x + 3y = 110 \quad \ldots(ii)$$

Multiply equation *(i)* by 2 and equation *(ii)* by 3 and subtracting them.

$$6x + 4y = 280$$
$$6x + 9y = 330$$
$$- \quad\quad - \quad\quad -$$
$$-5y = -50$$

$$\Rightarrow \quad y = 10$$

Put $y = 10$ in equation *(i)*,

$$3x + 2 \times 10 = 140 \quad \Rightarrow \quad 3x = 140 - 20 = 120 \quad \Rightarrow \quad x = 40$$

$\therefore$ Cost of 1 notebook = ₹ 40 **Ans.**

and cost of 1 pen = ₹ 10 **Ans.**

**Example 10.** A person has ₹ 5 and ₹ 10 coins. He has 50 coins in all and their total cost is ₹ 400. How many coins of each type he have?

**Solution.** Let number of ₹ 5 coins = $x$
and number of ₹ 10 coins = $y$
First condition gives

$$x + y = 50 \quad \text{...(i)}$$

Second condition gives

$$5x + 10y = 400 \Rightarrow x + 2y = 80 \quad \text{...(ii)}$$

Subtracting equation *(i)* from equation *(ii)*,

$$\begin{array}{r} x + 2y = 80 \\ x + y = 50 \\ - \quad - \quad - \\ \hline y = 30 \end{array}$$

Put $y = 30$ in equation *(i)*,

$$30 + y = 50 \Rightarrow y = 20$$

∴ Number of ₹ 5 coins = 30 Ans.
and number of ₹ 10 coins = 20 Ans.

**Example 11.** Two numbers are in the ratio 3 : 4. If thrice the larger added to the smaller, the sum is 75. Find the numbers.

**Solution.** Let two numbers be $x$ and $y$,

$$\therefore \quad \frac{x}{y} = \frac{3}{4}$$

$$\Rightarrow \quad x = \frac{3y}{4} \quad \text{...(i)}$$

and $$x + 3y = 75$$

$$\Rightarrow \quad \left(\frac{3y}{4}\right) + 3y = 75 \quad \text{[From equation (i)]}$$

$$\Rightarrow \quad \frac{3y + 12y}{4} = 75$$

$$\Rightarrow \quad 15y = 300$$

$$\Rightarrow \quad y = 20$$

Put $y = 20$ in equation *(i)*,

$$x = \frac{3 \times 20}{4} = 15$$

∴ Two numbers are 15 and 20. Ans.

**Example 12.** The ratio of the monthly incomes of $A$ and $B$ is 9 : 7 and the ratio of their monthly expenditures is 4 : 3. If each saves ₹ 200 per month, find their monthly income.

**Solution.** Let the monthly income of $A$ = ₹ $9x$
∴ The monthly income of $B$ = ₹ $7x$
Let the monthly expenditure of $A$ = ₹ $4y$
∴ The monthly expenditure of $B$ = ₹ $3y$
According to the given condition

$$9x - 4y = 200 \quad \text{...(i)}$$

$$7x - 3y = 200 \quad \text{...(ii)}$$

Multiply equation *(i)* by 3 and equation *(ii)* by 4

$$\begin{array}{r} 27x - 12y = 600 \\ 28x - 12y = 800 \\ - \quad + \quad - \\ \hline -x = -200 \end{array} \quad \text{(On subtracting)}$$

$$\therefore \quad x = 200$$

⇒ Monthly income of $A = 9 \times 200$ = ₹ 1800 Ans.
and Monthly income of $B = 7 \times 200$ = ₹ 1400 Ans.

**Example 13.** Four years ago, the father's age was 5 times the age of his son. After four years, the father's age will be 3 times the age of his son. Find their present ages.

**Solution.** Let, present age of father = $x$ years
and present age of son = $y$ years.
Four years ago,
Father's age = $(x - 4)$ years
Son's age = $(y - 4)$ years
$\therefore$ First condition gives

$$x - 4 = 5(y - 4)$$

$$\Rightarrow \quad x = 5y - 16 \qquad \ldots(i)$$

After four years
Father's age = $(x + 4)$ years
Son's age = $(y + 4)$ years
$\therefore$ second condition gives

$$x + 4 = 3(y + 4)$$

$$\Rightarrow \quad 5y - 16 + 4 = 3y + 12 \qquad \text{[From equation } (i)\text{]}$$

$$\Rightarrow \quad 5y - 3y = 12 + 12$$

$$\Rightarrow \quad 2y = 24$$

$$\Rightarrow \quad y = 12$$

Put $y = 12$ in equation $(i)$

$$x = 5 \times 12 - 16 = 44$$

$\therefore$ Present age of father = 44 years **Ans.**
and present age of son = 12 years **Ans.**

**Example 14.** Twenty years hence father's age will be two times the age of his son. Five years ago, father was seven times as old as his son. Find their present ages.

**Solution.** Let present age of son be $x$ years and the present age of father be $y$ years.
Twenty years hence, the age of son = $x + 20$
and the age of father = $y + 20$
First condition gives

$$2(x + 20) = y + 20 \quad \Rightarrow \quad 2x - y = -20 \qquad \ldots(i)$$

Five years ago, age of son = $(x - 5)$ years
and age of father = $(y - 5)$ years
Second condition gives,

$$7(x - 5) = y - 5 \quad \Rightarrow \quad 7x - y = 30 \qquad \ldots(ii)$$

Subtracting equation $(i)$ from $(ii)$,

$$5x = 50 \quad \Rightarrow \quad x = 10$$

Put $x = 10$ in equation $(i)$

$$3 \times 10 - y = -10 \quad \Rightarrow \quad 30 - y = -10$$

$$\Rightarrow \quad -y = -40 \quad \Rightarrow \quad y = 40$$

Hence, present age of son is 10 years and present age of father is 40 years. **Ans.**

**Example 15.** 10 years ago, Shyam was four times as old as Qadir. Five years ago, Shyam was thrice as old as Qadir. Find their present ages.

**Solution.** Let present age of Shyam = $x$ years
and present age of Qadir = $y$ years
10 years ago,
Shyam's age = $(x - 10)$ years
Qadir's age = $(y - 10)$ years
First condition gives

$$x - 10 = 4(y - 10) \quad \Rightarrow \quad x = 4y - 30 \qquad \ldots(i)$$

5 years ago,
Shyam's age = $(x - 5)$ years
Qadir's age = $(y - 5)$ years
Second condition gives,

$$x - 5 = 3(y - 5)$$

$\Rightarrow$ $4y - 30 - 5 = 3y - 15$ [From equation *(i)*]

$$y = 20$$

Put $y = 20$ in equation *(i)*

$$x = 4 \times 20 - 30 = 50$$

$\therefore$ Present age of Shyam = 50 years **Ans.**
and present age of Qadir = 20 years **Ans.**

**Example 16.** A lending library has a fixed charge for the first three days and an additional charge for each day thereafter. Ravi paid ₹ 38 for a book kept for seven days, while Sushant paid ₹ 30 for the book he kept for five days. Find the fixed charge and the charge for each extra day.

**Solution.** Let the fixed charges for first 3 days = ₹ $x$
and the charge per day after it = ₹ $y$
First condition gives,
charges for 7 days = ₹ 38

$\Rightarrow$ $x + (7 - 3)y = 38$ $\Rightarrow$ $x + 4y = 38$ ...*(i)*

and charges for 5 days = ₹ 30

$\Rightarrow$ $x + (5 - 3)y = 30$ $\Rightarrow$ $x + 2y = 30$ ...*(ii)*

Subtracting equation *(ii)* from equation *(i)*

$$\begin{array}{r} x + 4y = 38 \\ x + 2y = 30 \\ - \quad - \quad - \\ \hline 2y = 8 \end{array} \Rightarrow y = 4$$

Put $y = 4$ in equation *(ii)*

$$x + 2 \times 4 = 30 \Rightarrow x = 22$$

$\therefore$ Fixed charges = ₹ 22
and charges per day after first three days = ₹ 4 **Ans.**

**Example 17.** A part of monthly hostel charges is fixed and the remaining depends on the number of days one has taken food in mess. A student Gopal takes food for 25 days and pays ₹ 1250 as hostel charges. Another student Sushant takes food for 22 days and pays ₹ 1160 as hostel charges. Find the fixed charges and the cost of food per day.

**Solution.** Let fixed charges = ₹ $x$
and the cost of food per day = ₹ $y$
$\therefore$ First condition gives

$x + 25y = 1250$ $\Rightarrow$ $x = 1250 - 25y$ ...*(i)*

and second condition gives

$$x + 22y = 1160$$

$\Rightarrow$ $1250 - 25y + 22y = 1160$ [From equation *(i)*]

$\Rightarrow$ $-3y = -90$ $\Rightarrow$ $y = 30$

Put $y = 30$ in equation *(i)*,

$$x = 1250 - 25 \times 30 = 500$$

$\therefore$ Fixed charges = ₹ 500 **Ans.**
and cost of food per day = ₹ 30 **Ans.**

**Example 18.** A shopkeeper sold a chair and a table for ₹ 1590 and makes a profit of 10% on chair and 15% on table. By selling them for ₹ 1560, he gets a profit of 15% on the chair and 10% on the table. Find the cost price of a chair and the cost price of a table.

**Solution.** Let cost price of a chair = ₹ $x$
and cost price of a table = ₹ $y$

$\therefore$ First condition gives

$x + 10\%$ of $x$ + $y + 15\%$ of $y = 1590$

$$\Rightarrow \quad x + \frac{10x}{100} + y + \frac{15y}{100} = 1590 \quad \Rightarrow \quad 110x + 115y = 159000$$

$$\Rightarrow \quad 22x + 23y = 31800 \quad \text{...(i)}$$

Second condition gives

$$x + 15\% \text{ of } x + y + 10\% \text{ of } y = 1560$$

$$\Rightarrow \quad x + \frac{15x}{100} + y + \frac{10y}{100} = 1560$$

$$\Rightarrow \quad 115x + 110y = 156000 \quad \Rightarrow \quad 23x + 22y = 31200 \quad \text{...(ii)}$$

Adding equation *(i)* and equation *(ii)*

$$45x + 45y = 63000 \quad \Rightarrow \quad x + y = 1400 \quad \text{...(iii)}$$

Subtracting equation *(ii)* from equation *(i)*,

$$-x + y = 600$$

$$\Rightarrow \quad -x + 1400 - x = 600 \quad \text{[From equation (i)]}$$

$$\Rightarrow \quad 2x = 800 \quad \Rightarrow \quad x = 400$$

Put $x = 400$ in equation *(iii)*

$$400 + y = 1400 \quad \Rightarrow \quad y = 1000$$

$\therefore$ cost of a chair = ₹ 400 **Ans.**
and cost of a table = ₹ 1000 **Ans.**

**Example 19.** 2 men and 7 boys can finish a work in 4 days, while 4 men and 4 boys can finish the same work in 3 days. How long would it take one man or one boy to do it?

**Solution.** Let 1 man can do a piece of work in $x$ days while a boy can do a piece of work in $y$ days.

$\therefore$ One man's one day work $= \frac{1}{x}$

and one boy's one day work $= \frac{1}{y}$

According to given conditions,

$$\frac{2}{x} + \frac{7}{y} = \frac{1}{4} \quad \text{...(i)}$$

and

$$\frac{4}{x} + \frac{4}{y} = \frac{1}{3} \quad \text{...(ii)}$$

Multiplying equation *(i)* by 2 and *(ii)* by 1, we get

$$\frac{4}{x} + \frac{14}{y} = \frac{1}{2} \quad \text{...(iii)}$$

$$\frac{4}{x} + \frac{4}{y} = \frac{1}{3} \quad \text{...(iv)}$$

Subtracting equation *(iv)* from *(iii)*, we get

$$\frac{14}{y} - \frac{4}{y} = \frac{1}{2} - \frac{1}{3} \quad \Rightarrow \quad \frac{10}{y} = \frac{1}{6} \quad \Rightarrow \quad y = 60$$

Substituting $y = 60$ in equation *(i)*, we get

$$\frac{2}{x} + \frac{7}{60} = \frac{1}{4} \quad \Rightarrow \quad \frac{2}{x} = \frac{1}{4} - \frac{7}{60}$$

$$\Rightarrow \quad \frac{2}{x} = \frac{8}{60} \quad \Rightarrow \quad 8x = 120 \quad \text{or} \quad x = 15$$

Hence, one man would do the work in 15 days and one boy in 60 days. **Ans.**

**Example 20.** 4 men and 3 women can do a piece of work in 14 days. 5 men and 15 women can do the same piece of work in 10 days. In how many days, one man can finish the same work?

**Solution.** Let one man can do the work in '$x$' days.

One woman can do the work in '$y$' days.

$\therefore$ One day work of one man $= \frac{1}{x}$

and one day work of one woman $= \frac{1}{y}$

$\therefore$ First condition gives,

$$\frac{4}{x} + \frac{3}{y} = \frac{1}{14} \qquad \ldots(i)$$

Second condition gives,

$$\frac{5}{x} + \frac{15}{y} = \frac{1}{4} \qquad \ldots(ii)$$

Multiply equation *(i)* by 5 and subtracting from equation *(ii)*

$$\frac{5}{x} + \frac{15}{y} = \frac{1}{4}$$

$$\frac{20}{x} + \frac{15}{y} = \frac{5}{14}$$

$$- \quad - \quad -$$

$$\frac{-15}{x} = \frac{1}{4} - \frac{5}{14}$$

$$\frac{-15}{x} = \frac{7-10}{28} = \frac{-3}{28} \qquad \text{(On subtracting)}$$

$\Rightarrow$ $x = 140$

$\therefore$ One man can finish the work in 140 days. **Ans.**

**Example 21.** Two places $A$ and $B$ are 220 km apart on a highway. A car starts from $A$ and another starts from $B$ at the same time. If they go in the same direction, they meet after 22 hours. If they go in opposite direction, they meet in 2 hours. Find the speeds of two cars.

**Solution.** Let the speed of two cars be $x$ km/hr and $y$ km/hr.

When cars move in same direction, they meet at point $C$ (say).

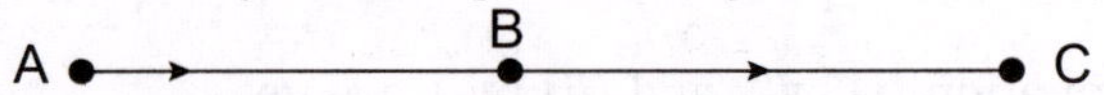


$\therefore$ Distance covered by car starting from $A$ in 22 hours = $22x$

and distance covered by car starting from $B$ in 22 hours = $22y$

$\therefore$ $22x - 22y = 220 \quad \Rightarrow \quad x - y = 10 \qquad \ldots(i)$

When cars move in opposite direction, they meet at point $D$ (say)

$\therefore$ Distance covered by car starting from $A$ in 2 hours = $2x$

and distance covered by car starting from $B$ in 2 hours = $2y$

$\therefore$ $2x + 2y = 220 \quad \Rightarrow \quad x + y = 110 \qquad \ldots(ii)$

Adding equations *(i)* and *(ii)*,

$$x - y = 10$$

$$x + y = 110$$

$$2x = 120$$

$\Rightarrow$ $x = 60$

Put $x = 60$ in equation *(ii)*,

$$60 + y = 110 \quad \Rightarrow \quad y = 50$$

$\therefore$ Speeds of two cars = 60 km/hr and 50 km/hr **Ans.**

**Example 22.** A teacher divides some money among some students equally. If there were 2 students less, each student will get ₹ 10 more. If there were 3 students more, each student will get ₹ 10 less. Find the number of students and the money received by each student.

**Solution.** Let number of students $= x$

and money received by each student = ₹ $y$.

$\therefore$ Total money = ₹ $x \cdot y$

If number of students $= (x - 2)$

then money received by each student = ₹ $(y + 10)$

$\therefore$ Total money = ₹ $(x - 2)(y + 10)$

So, $(x - 2)(y + 10) = xy$

$\Rightarrow \quad xy + 10x - 2y - 20 = xy$

$\Rightarrow \quad 5x - y = 10$

$\Rightarrow \quad y = 5x - 10$ ...*(i)*

If number of students $= x + 3$

then money received by each student = ₹ $(y - 10)$

$\therefore$ Total money = ₹ $(x + 3)(y - 10)$

So, $(x + 3)(y - 10) = xy$

$\Rightarrow \quad xy - 10x + 3y - 30 = xy$

$\Rightarrow \quad -10x + 3y = 30$

$\Rightarrow \quad -10x + 3(5x - 10) = 30$ [From equation *(i)*]

$\Rightarrow \quad -10x + 15x - 30 = 30$

$\Rightarrow \quad 5x = 60$

$\Rightarrow \quad x = 12$

Put $x = 12$ in equation *(i)*

$y = 5 \times 12 - 10 = 60$

$\therefore$ Number of students = 12 **Ans.**

and money received by each student = ₹ 50 **Ans.**

**Example 23.** The sum of the digits of a two digit number is 9. The result of dividing this number by the number with digits reversed is $\frac{8}{3}$. Find the number.

**Solution.** Let two digit number $= 10x + y$

$\therefore \quad x + y = 9 \quad \Rightarrow \quad y = 9 - x$ ...*(i)*

and $\quad \dfrac{10x + y}{10y + x} = \dfrac{8}{3} \quad \Rightarrow \quad 30x + 3y = 80y + 8x$

$\Rightarrow \quad 22x - 77y = 0 \quad \Rightarrow \quad 2x - 7y = 0$

$\Rightarrow \quad 2x - 7(9 - x) = 0$ [From equation *(i)*]

$\Rightarrow \quad 2x - 63 + 7x = 0 \quad \Rightarrow \quad x = 7$

Put $x = 7$ in equation *(i)*,

$$y = 9 - 7 = 2$$

$\therefore$ Number $= 10x + y = 10 \times 7 + 2 = 72$ **Ans.**

**Example 24.** A boat goes 30 km upstream and 66 km downstream in 12 hours. In 13 hours it can go 40 km upstream and 55 km downstream. Determine the speed of the stream and that of the boat in still water.

**Solution.** Let the speed of the boat in still water is $x$ km/hr and the speed of the stream is $y$ km/hr.

$\therefore$ Speed of boat upstream $= (x - y)$ km/hr

and speed of boat downstream $= (x + y)$ km/hr

We know that, $\text{speed} = \dfrac{\text{distance}}{\text{time}}$

According to given condition,

$$\text{Time taken in going 30 km upstream} = \frac{30}{x - y} \text{ hr}$$

$$\text{Time taken in 66 km downstream} = \frac{66}{x + y} \text{ hr}$$

$$\therefore \quad \frac{30}{x - y} + \frac{66}{x + y} = 12 \quad \ldots(i)$$

Similarly in second condition,

$$\frac{40}{x - y} + \frac{55}{x + y} = 13 \quad \ldots(ii)$$

Let $\dfrac{1}{x - y} = a$ and $\dfrac{1}{x + y} = b$, we get

$$30a + 66b = 12 \quad \ldots(iii)$$

and $$40a + 55b = 13 \quad \ldots(iv)$$

Multiplying equation *(iii)* by 4 and *(iv)* by 3, we get

$$120a + 264b = 48 \quad \ldots(v)$$

$$120a + 165b = 39 \quad \ldots(vi)$$

Subtracting equation *(vi)* from *(v)*, we get

$$99b = 9 \quad \Rightarrow \quad b = \frac{1}{11}$$

Putting $b = \dfrac{1}{11}$ in equation *(iii)*, we get

$$30a + 66 \times \frac{1}{11} = 12 \quad \Rightarrow \quad 30a = 6$$

$$\Rightarrow \quad a = \frac{1}{5} \quad \Rightarrow \quad \frac{1}{x - y} = \frac{1}{5} \quad \Rightarrow \quad x - y = 5 \quad \ldots(vii)$$

and $$b = \frac{1}{11} \quad \Rightarrow \quad \frac{1}{x + y} = \frac{1}{11} \quad \Rightarrow \quad x + y = 11 \quad \ldots(viii)$$

From equations *(vii)* and *(viii)*, we get

$$x = 8, y = 3$$

$\therefore$ Speed of boat in still water = 8 km/h **Ans.**

and speed of stream = 3 km/h **Ans.**

**Example 25.** Aaru travels 300 km to her home partly by train and partly by bus. She takes 4 hours if she travels 60 km by train and the remaining by bus. If she travels 100 km by train and the remaining by bus, she takes 10 minutes longer. Find the speed of the train and the speed of the bus.

**Solution.** Let speed of bus = $y$ km/h

Speed of train = $x$ km/h

In first case,

distance covered by train = 60 km

distance covered by bus = (300 – 60) km = 240 km

$$\therefore \quad \frac{60}{x} + \frac{240}{y} = 4 \quad \ldots(i)$$

In second case,
distance covered by train = 100 km
distance covered by bus = (300–100) km = 200 km

$$\therefore \quad \frac{100}{x} + \frac{200}{y} = 4\text{hr} + \frac{10}{60}\text{hr} = \frac{25}{6} \quad \ldots(ii)$$

Multiply equation *(i)* by 10 and equation *(ii)* by 6 and subtracting

$$\frac{600}{x} + \frac{2400}{y} = 40$$

$$\frac{600}{x} + \frac{1200}{y} = 25$$

$$- \quad - \quad -$$

$$\frac{1200}{y} = 15$$

$$\Rightarrow \quad y = 80$$

Put $y = 80$ in equation *(i)*

$$\frac{60}{x} + \frac{240}{80} = 4$$

$$\Rightarrow \quad \frac{60}{x} = 1 \quad \Rightarrow \quad x = 60$$

∴ Speed of train = 60 km/h **Ans.**
and speed of bus = 80 km/h **Ans.**

## Exercise 5E

1. The sum of two numbers is 40 and their difference is 16. Find the numbers.
2. The sum of two numbers is 28. Thrice the smaller is 20 more than the larger. Find two numbers.
3. The sum of two numbers is 35. If twice the smaller added to larger, the result is 50. Find the numbers.
4. Two numbers are in the ratio 8 : 9. If 12 is added to both the numbers, their ratio becomes 12 : 13. Find the numbers.
5. If one is added to both numerator and denominator of a fraction, it becomes $\frac{1}{2}$. If 2 is added to the denominator of the fraction, it becomes $\frac{1}{3}$. Find the fraction.
6. The sum of numerator and denominator of a fraction is 18. If 3 is added to both numerator and denominator of the fraction it becomes $\frac{1}{2}$. Find the fraction.
7. The unit digit of a two digit number is 1 more than twice its tens digit. If the digits are reversed, the new number is 45 more than the original number. Find the number.
8. The tens digits of a two digit number is one more than thrice the unit digit. The sum of its digits is 9. Find the number.
9. The sum of digits of a two digit number is 8. If 18 is added to the number, its digits interchange. Find the number.
10. The ratio of the annual income of *A* and *B* is 5 : 4 and the ratio of their expenditures is 11 : 8. If each saves ₹ 4000. Find their annual incomes.
11. The ratio of the annual income of *A* and *B* is 6 : 5 and the ratio of their expenditures is 5 : 4. If each saves ₹ 10000, find their annual incomes.
12. *A* is 12 years older than *B*. 4 years ago, *A* was twice as old as *B*. Find the present ages of *A* and *B*.
13. 6 years hence, Ravi will be twice as old as his son. 18 years ago, Ravi was six times of his son's age. Find their present ages.
14. The present age of Sharman is twice the sum of the ages of his two sons. Six years ago, his age was 5 times the sum of the ages of two sons. Find the present age of Sharman.

**15.** The cost of 3 notebooks and 5 pens is ₹ 265. The cost of 2 notebooks and 9 pens is ₹ 205. Find the cost of one notebook and cost of one pen.

**16.** The railway fare from Delhi to Meerut for 3 adults and 2 children is ₹ 250 and for 2 adults and 3 children is ₹ 225. Find the fare for one adult and for one child.

**17.** A person divides some money among some students equally. If there were 5 more students, each student will get ₹ 4 less. If there were 5 students less, each student will get ₹ 6 more. Find the total money.

**18.** *A* and *B* have some money with them. *B* said to *A* if you give me ₹ 50, my money will be equal to your money. *A* said to *B* if you give me ₹ 100, my money will be equal to four times of your money. How much money did *A* and *B* have initially?

**19.** Shama has some ₹ 2 and some ₹ 5 coins. The total number of coins are 50 and their total cost is ₹ 190. Find the number of ₹ 2 coins and of ₹ 5 coins.

**20.** Two places *A* and *B* are 120 km apart on a highway. *A* car starts from *A* and another starts from *B* at the same time. If they go in the same direction they meet in 3 hours. If they go in opposite direction, they meet in one hour. Find the speeds of car *A* and car *B*.

**21.** A shopkeeper purchases a table and a chair for ₹ 1400. If he sold them for ₹ 1630, he makes a profit of 20% on the table and 10% on the chair. Find the cost of one table and that of one chair.

**22.** 2 men and 5 boys together can do a piece of work in 4 days while 1 man and 2 boys together can do the same work in 9 days. Find the time taken by : (a) one man alone, (b) one boy alone to complete the work.

**23.** The result of dividing two digit number by the number with digits reversed is $1\frac{3}{4}$ and the sum of the digits of number is 9. Find the number.

**24.** The fare of a taxi is fixed and the remaining depends on the distance covered per km. Rahim goes 30 km by a taxi and paid ₹ 400 while Kamal goes 40 km by a taxi and paid ₹ 500. Find the fixed fare and the fare per km.

**25.** Half the perimeter of a rectangular garden whose breadth is 4 m less than its length of 36 m. Find the length and breadth of the garden.

**26.** The area of a rectangle gets reduced by 9 sq. units if its length is reduced by 5 units and breadth is increased by 3 units. If we increase the length by 3 units and breadth by 2 units, then the area is increased by 67 sq. units. Find the length and breadth of the rectangle.

**27.** The students of a class are made to stand in rows (complete). If one student is extra in a row, there would be 2 rows less and if one student is less in a row, there would be 3 rows more. Find the number of students in the class.

**28.** Ritu can row downstream 20 km in 2 hours and upstream 4 km in 2 hours. Find her speed of rowing in still water and the speed of the current.

**29.** A boat goes 44 km downstream in 4 hours and takes 4 hours 48 minutes longer in the same return journey. Find the speed of boat in still water and the speed of current.

**30.** Kavita travels 28 km to her home partly by rickshaw and partly by bus. She takes half an hour if she travels 4 km by rickshaw and the remaining distance by bus. If she travels 8 km by rickshaw and the remaining distance by bus, she takes 9 minutes longer. Find the speed to rickshaw and the speed of the bus.

**31.** In a $\Delta ABC$, $\angle C = 3\angle B = 2(\angle A + \angle B)$. Find all angles of $\Delta ABC$.

**32.** Ravi invests some money at 12% simple interest and some other money at 10% simple interest and receives ₹ 2600 as yearly interest. If he had interchanged the amounts, he would have received ₹ 80 more as yearly interest. How much did he invest at different rates?

## *Answers*

**1.** 28, 12 **2.** 12, 16 **3.** 15, 20 **4.** 24, 27 **5.** $\frac{3}{7}$ **6.** $\frac{5}{13}$ **7.** 49
**8.** 27 **9.** 35 **10.** ₹ 15000, ₹ 12000 **11.** ₹ 60000, ₹ 50000
**12.** 28 years, 16 years **13.** 54 years, 24 years **14.** 36 years **15.** ₹ 80, ₹ 5
**16.** ₹ 60, ₹ 35 **17.** ₹ 600 **18.** ₹ 300, ₹ 200 **19.** 20, 30 **20.** 80 km/h, 40 km/h **21.** ₹ 900, ₹ 500
**22.** (a) 18 days, (b) 36 days **23.** 63 **24.** ₹ 100, ₹ 10 per km **25.** 20 m, 16 m **26.** 17 units, 9 units
**27.** 60 **28.** 6 km/h, 4 km/h **29.** 8 km/h, 3 km/h **30.** 20 km/h, 80 km/h
**31.** $\angle A = 20°$, $\angle B = 40°$, $\angle C = 120°$ **32.** ₹ 10000 at 12% and ₹14000 at 10%

# Exercise 5F

## Multiple Choice Questions

Choose the correct answer from the given four options in each of the following questions :

1. If $x + 2y = 7$ and $3x + y = 6$, then $(x, y)$ is equal to :
(a) (1, 2) (b) (1, 3) (c) (2, 1) (d) (3, 1)

2. If $2x + 3y = -5$ and $3x + 2y = 0$, then $x$ is equal to :
(a) $-3$ (b) 3 (c) $-2$ (d) 2

3. If $34x + 43y = -9$, $43x + 34y = 9$, then $x + y$ is equal to :
(a) 0 (b) 18 (c) 9 (d) 2

4. If $x + y = 5$ and $x - y = 3$ then $3x + 2y$ is equal to :
(a) 14 (b) 10 (c) 5 (d) $-5$

5. If $x = 2 - y$ and $2y = x - 11$ then the value of $y$ is :
(a) $-5$ (b) 5 (c) $-3$ (d) 3

6. If $\frac{2}{x} + \frac{3}{y} = 13$ and $\frac{5}{x} - \frac{4}{y} = -2$ then $(x, y)$ is equal to :
(a) $\left(\frac{1}{2}, \frac{1}{3}\right)$ (b) $\left(\frac{1}{3}, \frac{1}{2}\right)$ (c) $\left(\frac{1}{2}, -\frac{1}{3}\right)$ (d) $\left(\frac{1}{3}, -\frac{1}{2}\right)$

7. If $\frac{20}{x+y} + \frac{3}{x-y} = 7$ and $\frac{8}{x-y} - \frac{15}{x+y} = 5$ then $(x, y)$ is :
(a) $(-3, 5)$ (b) $(5, -3)$ (c) (2, 3) (d) (3, 2)

8. $x = a$, $y = b$ is the solution of the pair of equations $3x + y = 10$ and $x - y = 2$, then $(a, b)$ is equal to :
(a) (3, 1) (b) (1, 3) (c) (2, 5) (d) (5, 2)

9. If $2x - \frac{3}{y} = 9$ and $3x + \frac{7}{y} = 2$ then the value of $x$ is :
(a) $-3$ (b) 3 (c) 2 (d) $-2$

10. $(a - b)x + (a + b)y = a^2 - 2ab - b^2$, $(a + b)(x + y) = a^2 + b^2$ gives the following solution :
(a) $x = a + b, y = \frac{-2ab}{a+b}$ (b) $x = \frac{-2ab}{a+b}, y = a + b$ (c) $x = a + b, y = \frac{2ab}{a+b}$ (d) $x = \frac{2ab}{a+b}, y = a + b$

### Answers

| | | | | | | | | | |
|---|---|---|---|---|---|---|---|---|---|
| **1.** (b) | **2.** (d) | **3.** (a) | **4.** (a) | **5.** (c) | **6.** (a) | **7.** (d) | **8.** (a) | **9.** (b) | **10.** (a) |

## Valid Statements Questions

In the following questions, two statements (i) and (ii) are given. Choose the valid statement.

(a) Only (i) (b) Only (ii) (c) Both (i) and (ii) (d) Neither (i) nor (ii)

1. (i) The sum of two numbers is 40 and their difference is 8. The numbers will be 24 and 16.
(ii) If $x + 3y = 10$ and $x + y = 4$ then $x = 2$,

2. (i) If $77x + 63y = 123$ and $63x + 77y = 17$ then $x + y = 5$.
(ii) $3x + 2y = 7$ and $2x + 3y = 8$ gives $x = 2, y = 1$.

3. (i) The solution of $3x + 4y = 25$ and $4x + 5y = 32$ is $x = 2, y = 1$.
(ii) $x = 1, y = 1$ is a solution of $ax + by = a + b$.

4. (i) $x = 3, y = 1$ is a solution of $9x - 7y = 20$.
(ii) $x = 4, y = -1$ is a solution of $x - y = 5$.

### Answers

| | | | |
|---|---|---|---|
| **1.** (a) | **2.** (d) | **3.** (b) | **4.** (c) |

## SUMMARY *of the Chapter*

- An equation of the form $ax + by + c = 0$, $a \neq 0$ $b \neq 0$, where $a$, $b$, $c$ are real numbers is said to be a linear equation in two variables.
- For the linear equation $ax + by + c = 0$ in two variables $x$ and $y$, $x = \alpha$, $y = \beta$ is called its solution if $a\alpha + b\beta + c = 0$
- A linear equation $ax + by + c = 0$, $a \neq 0$, $b \neq 0$ in two variables $x$ and $y$ has infinitely many solutions.
- A pair of linear equations in two variables can be solve by the following methods:
  1. Substitution method 2. Elimination method 3. Cross-multiplication method
- The word problems can be solved in the following two steps:
  1. Converting them into linear expressions and then into linear equations.
  2. Solving them from any one of the above given three methods.

# CHAPTER TEST

1. Solve the following pair of linear equations by eliminition method

$$2x + 5y = 30, 3x + y = 19$$

2. Solve the following pair of linear equations by substitution method

$$3x + 4y = 1, x + 5y = -7$$

3. Solve the following pair of linear equations by cross-multiplication method

$$4x + y = 9, 3x - 7y = -1$$

4. Solve : $\frac{2}{\sqrt{x}} + \frac{3}{\sqrt{y}} = 2$

$\frac{4}{\sqrt{x}} - \frac{9}{\sqrt{y}} = -1$

5. Solve : $\frac{1}{(x+2y)} + \frac{10}{3(3x-2y)} = -3$

$\frac{75}{x+2y} - \frac{36}{3x-2y} = 61$

6. Solve : $65x + 56y = 18$

$56x + 65y = -18$

7. Solve : $2ax - 2by + a + 4b = 0$

$2bx + 2ay + b - 4a = 0$

8. A fraction becomes $\frac{4}{5}$ if 1 is added to both numerator and denominator. If 3 is added to both numerator and denominator, it becomes $\frac{5}{6}$. Find the fraction.
9. A boat goes 30 km upstream and 44 km downstream in 10 hours. In 13 hours it goes 40 km upstream and 55 km downstream. Find the speed of stream and the speed of boat in still water.
10. The sum of the digits of a two digit number is 10. If 36 is added to the number, the digits reversed. Find the number.

## Answers

**1.** $x = 5,\ y = 4$ **2.** $x = 3,\ y = -2$ **3.** $x = 2,\ y = 1$ **4.** $x = 4,\ y = 9$ **5.** $x = \frac{1}{2}, y = \frac{5}{4}$ **6.** $x = 2, y = -2$

**7.** $x = -\frac{1}{2}, y = 2$ **8.** $\frac{7}{9}$ **9.** 3 km/h, 8 km/h **10.** 37

Chapter

# 6 INDICES/EXPONENTS

## Syllabus

- Handling positive, fractional, negative and "zero" indices.
- Simplification of expressions involving various exponents.
- $a^m \times a^n = a^{m+n}$, $a^m \div a^n - a^{m-n}$, $(a^m)^n = a^{mn}$, etc. Use of laws of exponents.

## INTRODUCTION

A product which contains the same number many times, that number of times the same number occur, is called the power of that number, *e.g.*

$$3 \times 3 \times 3 \times 3 = 3^4$$

which is the fourth power of the same number 3. And $a \cdot a \cdot a \dots \cdot a$ ($n$ factors), where $a \neq 0$, is the $n^{th}$ power of '$a$'. It can be written as follows:

$$a \cdot a \cdot a \dots \cdot a \ (n \text{ factors}) = a^n.$$

Here, '$a$' is called the base and '$n$' is called the index or exponent.

### Exponent or Index

An exponent or index is a number which shows how many times a non-zero number, (called base) is multiplied.

### Laws of Indices

1. Product Rule : $a^m \times a^n = a^{m+n}$
2. Quotient Rule : $a^m \div a^n = a^{m-n}$
3. Power Rule : $(a^m)^n = a^{m \times n}$
4. $(a \times b)^m = a^m \times b^m$
5. $\left(\dfrac{a}{b}\right)^m = \dfrac{a^m}{b^m}$
6. $a^{-m} = \dfrac{1}{a^m}$
7. $a^0 = 1$

Proof : From product rule

$$a^m \times a^n = a^{m+n}$$

Put $m = 0$, $a^0 \times a^n = a^{0+n}$

$\Rightarrow \quad a^0 \times a^n = a^n \quad \Rightarrow \quad a^0 = 1$

8. $a^m = b^m,\ m \neq 0 \quad \Rightarrow \quad a = b$
9. $a^m = a^n,\ a \neq 1 \quad \Rightarrow \quad m = n$
10. If $x$ and $y$ are two different positive prime numbers, then

$$x^a y^b = x^c . y^d \quad \Rightarrow \quad a = c \ \text{ and } \ b = d$$

## Illustrative Examples

**Example 1.** Simplify the following:

(i) $a^3 \times a^4$ (ii) $\dfrac{a^5 \times a^9}{a^4}$

**Solution.** (i) $a^3 \times a^4 = a^{3+4}$ (By product rule)

$= a^7$ Ans.

(ii) $\dfrac{a^5 \times a^9}{a^4} = \dfrac{a^{5+9}}{a^4}$ (By product rule)

$= \dfrac{a^{14}}{a^4} = a^{14-4}$ (By quotient rule)

$= a^{10}$ Ans.

**Example 2.** Simplify the following:

(i) $\dfrac{2\,(ab)^3\ (3a^3\ b^2)^4}{(a^2\ b)^3}$ (ii) $\dfrac{(x^3y^2)^2\ (2xy)^4}{(xy^2)^3}$

**Solution.** (i) $\dfrac{2(ab)^3(3a^3b^2)^4}{(a^2b)^3} = \dfrac{2\ a^3b^3 . 3^4\ (a^3)^4 (b^2)^4}{(a^2)^3\ b^3}$

$= \dfrac{2\ a^3b^3 . 81\ a^{12}b^8}{a^6\ b^3}$

$= 162\ a^{3+12-6}\ .\ b^{3+8-3}$

$= 162\ a^9b^8$ Ans.

(ii) $\dfrac{(x^3y^2)^2(2xy)^4}{(xy^2)^3} = \dfrac{(x^3)^2(y^2)^2.\ 2^4x^4y^4}{x^3(y^2)^3} = \dfrac{16x^6y^4.\ x^4y^4}{x^3y^6} = 16x^{6+4-3}.y^{4+4-6} = 16x^7y^2$ Ans.

**Example 3.** Simplify the following :

$$\frac{2^{2n}\times 8^{n+1}}{2^{n-1}\times 4^{2n}}$$

**Solution.** $\dfrac{2^{2n}\times 8^{n+1}}{2^{n-1}\times 4^{2n}} = \dfrac{2^{2n}\times (2^3)^{n+1}}{2^{n-1}\times (2^2)^{2n}} = \dfrac{2^{2n}\times 2^{3n+3}}{2^{n-1}\times 2^{4n}} = \dfrac{2^{2n+3n+3}}{2^{n-1+4n}} = \dfrac{2^{5n+3}}{2^{5n-1}} = 2^{(5n+3)-(5n-1)}$

$= 2^4 = 16$ Ans.

**Example 4.** If $a = b^{2x}$, $b = c^{2y}$ and $c = a^{2z}$, prove that $8xyz = 1$.

**Solution.** $a = b^{2x} \Rightarrow a = (c^{2y})^{2x}$ $(\because b = c^{2y})$

$\Rightarrow a = c^{4xy} \Rightarrow a = (a^{2z})^{4xy}$ $(\because c = a^{2z})$

$\Rightarrow a = a^{8xyz} \Rightarrow 8xyz = 1$ Hence Proved.

**Example 5.** Simplify : $\dfrac{1}{1+x^{p-q}} + \dfrac{1}{1+x^{q-p}}$

**Solution.** $\dfrac{1}{1+x^{p-q}} + \dfrac{1}{1+x^{q-p}} = \dfrac{1}{1+\dfrac{x^p}{x^q}} + \dfrac{1}{1+\dfrac{x^q}{x^p}} = \dfrac{1}{\dfrac{x^q+x^p}{x^q}} + \dfrac{1}{\dfrac{x^p+x^q}{x^p}}$

$= \dfrac{x^q}{x^q+x^p} + \dfrac{x^p}{x^q+x^p} = \dfrac{x^q+x^p}{x^q+x^p} = 1$ Ans.

**Example 6.** If $a^x = b^y = c^z$ and $b^2 = ac$, then show that

$$y = \frac{2xz}{x+z}$$

**Solution.** Let $a^x = b^y = c^z = k$

$\therefore\ a^x = k \Rightarrow (a^x)^{\frac{1}{x}} = k^{\frac{1}{x}} \Rightarrow a = k^{\frac{1}{x}}$

Similarly, $b = k^{\frac{1}{y}}$ and $c = k^{\frac{1}{z}}$

Now, $b^2 = ac \Rightarrow \left(k^{\frac{1}{y}}\right)^2 = k^{\frac{1}{x}}.\ k^{\frac{1}{z}} \Rightarrow k^{\frac{2}{y}} = k^{\frac{1}{x}+\frac{1}{z}}$

$\Rightarrow \dfrac{2}{y} = \dfrac{1}{x} + \dfrac{1}{z} \Rightarrow \dfrac{2}{y} = \dfrac{z+x}{xz} \Rightarrow y = \dfrac{2xz}{x+z}$ Hence Proved.

**Example 7.** If $2^x \cdot 3^y = 288$, find the values of $x$ and $y$.

**Solution.** $2^x \cdot 3^y = 2{\cdot}2{\cdot}2{\cdot}2{\cdot}2{\cdot}3{\cdot}3 = 2^5{\cdot}3^2$

On comparing,

$x = 5,\ y = 2$ Ans.

**Example 8.** If $2^a.3^b.5^c = 36000$, find the values of $a$, $b$ and $c$.

**Solution.** $2^a.3^b.5^c = 36000 = 2{\cdot}2{\cdot}2{\cdot}2{\cdot}2{\cdot}3{\cdot}3{\cdot}5{\cdot}5{\cdot}5 = 2^5.3^2.5^3$

On comparing

$a = 5,\ b = 2,\ c = 3$ Ans.

**Example 9.** Simplify : $\left[1-\{1-(1-n)^{-1}\}^{-1}\right]^{-1}$

**Solution.** $$\left[1-\{1-(1-n)^{-1}\}^{-1}\right]^{-1}=\left[1-\left(1-\frac{1}{1-n}\right)^{-1}\right]^{-1}=\left[1-\left(\frac{1-n-1}{1-n}\right)^{-1}\right]^{-1}$$
$$=\left[1-\left(\frac{-n}{1-n}\right)^{-1}\right]^{-1}=\left[1-\frac{n-1}{n}\right]^{-1}$$
$$=\left[\frac{n-n+1}{n}\right]^{-1}=\left[\frac{1}{n}\right]^{-1}=n$$ **Ans.**

**Example 10.** If $2^x = 3^y = 108^z$, find the relation between $x$, $y$ and $z$.

**Solution.** Let $2^x = 3^y = 108^z = k$

$\therefore \quad 2^x = k \Rightarrow 2 = k^{\frac{1}{x}}$ ...(1)

$3^y = k \Rightarrow 3 = k^{\frac{1}{y}}$ ...(2)

and $108^z = k \Rightarrow 108 = k^{\frac{1}{z}}$

$\Rightarrow \quad 2^2.3^3 = k^{\frac{1}{z}} \Rightarrow \left(k^{\frac{1}{x}}\right)^2\left(k^{\frac{1}{y}}\right)^3 = k^{\frac{1}{z}}$ [From (1) and (2)]

$\Rightarrow \quad k^{\frac{2}{x}}\, k^{\frac{3}{y}} = k^{\frac{1}{z}} \Rightarrow k^{\frac{2}{x}+\frac{3}{y}} = k^{\frac{1}{z}} \Rightarrow \frac{2}{x}+\frac{3}{y}=\frac{1}{z}$

which is the required relation. **Ans.**

**Example 11.** If $m \neq n$ and $(m+n)^{-1}(m^{-1}+n^{-1}) = m^x n^y$, then show that $x + y = -2$.

**Solution.** Given, $(m+n)^{-1}(m^{-1}+n^{-1}) = m^x \cdot n^y \Rightarrow \frac{1}{m+n}\left(\frac{1}{m}+\frac{1}{n}\right) = m^x n^y$

$\Rightarrow \quad \frac{1}{m+n}\left(\frac{n+m}{mn}\right) = m^x n^y \Rightarrow \frac{1}{mn} = m^x n^y \Rightarrow m^{-1} n^{-1} = m^x n^y$

On comparing, we get

$x = -1$ and $y = -1$

$\therefore \quad x + y = (-1) + (-1) = -2$ **Hence Proved.**

**Example 12.** Prove that

$$\left(\frac{a^x}{a^{-y}}\right)^{x-y}\left(\frac{a^y}{a^{-z}}\right)^{y-z}\left(\frac{a^z}{a^{-x}}\right)^{z-x} = 1$$

**Solution.** $$\text{L.H.S.} = \left(\frac{a^x}{a^{-y}}\right)^{x-y}\left(\frac{a^y}{a^{-z}}\right)^{y-z}\left(\frac{a^z}{a^{-x}}\right)^{z-x}$$
$$= (a^{x+y})^{x-y}(a^{y+z})^{y-z}(a^{z+x})^{z-x}$$
$$= a^{(x+y)(x-y)}a^{(y+z)(y-z)}\, a^{(z+x)(z-x)}$$
$$= a^{x^2-y^2}\, a^{y^2-z^2} a^{z^2-x^2} = a^{x^2-y^2+y^2-z^2+z^2-x^2}$$
$$= a^0 = 1 = \text{R.H.S.}$$ **Hence Proved.**

# Exercise 6A

1. Simplify the following :

(i) $a^7 \times a^5$ (ii) $\frac{a^9}{a^4}$ (iii) $\frac{a^7 \times a^4}{a^3}$ (iv) $\frac{x^4 \times x^5}{x^3 \times x^{-1}}$

2. Simplify the following :

(i) $\frac{3x^4y^2\,(2xy)^5}{(2x^3y^3)^2}$ (ii) $\frac{(x^{2a+3})^5}{(x^{a+1})^3}$ (iii) $\frac{(xy^3)^2(3x^2y)^4}{(xy)^3}$ (iv) $\frac{x^3y^4z^2}{x^2y^{-1}z^3}$

3. Simplify the following :

(i) $\frac{6^{2n+6} - 6^3 \cdot 36^{n+1}}{(6^{n+2})^2}$ (ii) $\frac{2^{n+2} \times 4^{n+1}}{2^{n+1} \times 4^{n-2}}$ (iii) $\frac{5^{n+5} - 6 \times 5^{n+3}}{9 \times 5^{n+1} - 20 \times 5^n}$ (iv) $\frac{3^{n+4} \times 3^{(n-2)(n+2)}}{3^{n(n+1)} \times 9^{n+1}}$

4. Write $\frac{x^{-1} - y^{-1}}{x^{-2} - y^{-2}}$ in the simplest form.

5. Simplify : $\frac{(a^{x+y})^{x-y}\,(a^{y-z})^{y+z}}{(a^{x+z})^{x-z}}$

6. Find the values of $x$ and $y$ from the following:

(i) $2^x.3^y=144$ (ii) $3^x.5^y = 675$

7. Find the values of $x$, $y$ and $z$ from the following : $2^x.3^y.5^z = 24000$

8. If $a = b^x$, $b = c^y$ and $c = a^z$ prove that $xyz = 1$.

9. Prove that $\left(\frac{a^x}{a^y}\right)^{x+y} \cdot \left(\frac{a^y}{a^z}\right)^{y+z} \left(\frac{a^z}{a^x}\right)^{z+x} = 1$.

10. Prove that $\left(\frac{x^a}{x^b}\right)^{a^2+ab+b^2} \left(\frac{x^b}{x^c}\right)^{b^2+bc+c^2} \left(\frac{x^c}{x^a}\right)^{c^2+ca+a^2} = 1$.

11. Prove that $\frac{1}{1+x^{b-a}+x^{c-a}} + \frac{1}{1+x^{a-b}+x^{c-b}} + \frac{1}{1+x^{b-c}+x^{a-c}} = 1$.

12. Prove that $\frac{x+y+z}{(xy)^{-1}+(yz)^{-1}+(zx)^{-1}} = xyz$.

13. If $x = a^{m+n}$, $y = a^{n+l}$, $z = a^{l+m}$, prove that $x^m \cdot y^n \cdot z^l \cdot = x^n \cdot y^l \cdot z^m$

14. If $x = p^{m+n} \cdot q^l$, $y = p^{n+l} . q^m$, $z = p^{l+m} \cdot q^n$ prove that $x^{m-l} \cdot y^{n-l} \cdot z^{l-m} = 1$.

15. If $a = x \cdot y^{p-1}$, $b = x \cdot y^{q-1}$, $c = x \cdot y^{r-1}$, prove that $a^{q-r} \cdot b^{r-p} \cdot c^{p-q} = 1$.

16. If $2^x = 3^y = 72^z$, find the relation between $x$, $y$ and $z$.

17. If $3^x = 5^y = 225^z$, find the relation between $x$, $y$ and $z$.

## Answers

**1.** (i) $a^{12}$ (ii) $a^5$ (iii) $a^8$ (iv) $x^7$

**2.** (i) $24x^3y$ (ii) $x^{7a+12}$ (iii) $81x^7y^7$ (iv) $\frac{xy^5}{z}$

**3.** (i) 30 (ii) 128 (iii) 95 (iv) $3^{-2n-2}$

**4.** $\frac{xy}{x+y}$

**5.** 1

**6.** (i) $x = 4, y = 2$ (ii) $x = 3, y = 2$

**7.** $x = 6, y = 1, z = 3$

**16.** $z = \frac{xy}{2x+3y}$

**17.** $2z = \frac{xy}{x+y}$

## Fractional Indices

For fractional numbers, the laws of indices are as follows:

1. $\sqrt[n]{a} = a^{\frac{1}{n}}$ 2. $a^{\frac{m}{n}} = \sqrt[n]{a^m}$

where $a > 0$ is a real number, $m$, $n$ are integers which have no common factor other than 1.

## Illustrative Examples

**Example 1.** Simplify the following :

(i) $(32)^{\frac{1}{5}}$ (ii) $(27)^{-\frac{1}{3}}$ (iii) $(125)^{\frac{4}{3}}$ (iv) $(36)^{-\frac{1}{2}}$

**Solution.** (i) $(32)^{\frac{1}{5}} = (2^5)^{\frac{1}{5}} = 2^{5\times\frac{1}{5}} = 2^1 = 2$ Ans.

(ii) $(27)^{-\frac{1}{3}} = (3^3)^{-\frac{1}{3}} = 3^{3\times\frac{-1}{3}} = 3^{-1} = \frac{1}{3}$ Ans.

(iii) $(125)^{\frac{4}{3}} = (5^3)^{\frac{4}{3}} = 5^{3\times\frac{4}{3}} = 5^4 = 625$ Ans.

(iv) $(36)^{-\frac{1}{2}} = (6^2)^{-\frac{1}{2}} = 6^{2\times\frac{-1}{2}} = 6^{-1} = \frac{1}{6}$ Ans.

**Example 2.** Evaluate the following:

(i) $\left(\frac{25}{36}\right)^{-\frac{1}{2}}$ (ii) $\left(\frac{32}{243}\right)^{-\frac{3}{5}}$

**Solution.** (i) $\left(\frac{25}{36}\right)^{\frac{-1}{2}} = \left(\frac{5^2}{6^2}\right)^{\frac{-1}{2}} = \frac{5^{2\times-\frac{1}{2}}}{6^{2\times-\frac{1}{2}}} = \frac{5^{-1}}{6^{-1}} = \frac{6}{5}$ Ans.

(ii) $\left(\frac{32}{243}\right)^{\frac{-3}{5}} = \left(\frac{2^5}{3^5}\right)^{\frac{-3}{5}} = \frac{2^{5\times-\frac{3}{5}}}{3^{5\times-\frac{3}{5}}} = \frac{2^{-3}}{3^{-3}} = \frac{3^3}{2^3} = \frac{27}{8}$ Ans.

**Example 3.** Evaluate: $\left(\frac{25}{16}\right)^{-\frac{1}{2}} + \left(\frac{256}{81}\right)^{-\frac{1}{4}}$

**Solution.** $\left(\frac{25}{16}\right)^{-\frac{1}{2}} + \left(\frac{256}{81}\right)^{-\frac{1}{4}} = \left(\frac{5^2}{4^2}\right)^{-\frac{1}{2}} + \left(\frac{4^4}{3^4}\right)^{-\frac{1}{4}} = \frac{5^{2\times-\frac{1}{2}}}{4^{2\times-\frac{1}{2}}} + \frac{4^{4\times-\frac{1}{4}}}{3^{4\times-\frac{1}{4}}}$

$= \frac{5^{-1}}{4^{-1}} + \frac{4^{-1}}{3^{-1}} = \frac{4}{5} + \frac{3}{4} = \frac{16+15}{20} = \frac{31}{20}$ Ans.

**Example 4.** Evaluate: $\left(9^{-\frac{4}{3}} \div 27^{-\frac{2}{3}}\right) \times 3^{\frac{3}{2}}$

**Solution.** $\left(9^{-\frac{4}{3}} \div 27^{-\frac{2}{3}}\right) \times 3^{\frac{3}{2}} = \frac{9^{-\frac{4}{3}}}{27^{-\frac{2}{3}}} \times 3^{\frac{3}{2}} = \frac{(3^2)^{-\frac{4}{3}}}{(3^3)^{-\frac{2}{3}}} \times 3^{\frac{3}{2}} = \frac{3^{-\frac{8}{3}} \times 3^{\frac{3}{2}}}{3^{-2}} = 3^{-\frac{8}{3}+\frac{3}{2}+2} = 3^{\frac{-16+9+12}{6}} = 3^{\frac{5}{6}}$ Ans.

**Example 5.** If $x = 2, y = -3$, find the value of $x^x + y^y + y^x$.

**Solution.** $$x^x + y^y + y^x = 2^2 + (-3)^{-3} + (-3)^2 = 4 + \frac{1}{(-3)^3} + 9 = 13 - \frac{1}{27} = \frac{351-1}{27} = \frac{350}{27}$$ Ans.

**Example 6.** Evaluate : $\frac{\sqrt{2^6} \times \sqrt[4]{81}}{\sqrt[3]{64}} - \left(\frac{1}{4}\right)^{-2}$

**Solution.** $$\frac{\sqrt{2^6} \times \sqrt[4]{81}}{\sqrt[3]{64}} - \left(\frac{1}{4}\right)^{-2} = \frac{2^{6\times\frac{1}{2}} \times (81)^{\frac{1}{4}}}{(64)^{\frac{1}{3}}} - \frac{1}{4^{-2}} = \frac{2^3 \times (3^4)^{\frac{1}{4}}}{(2^6)^{\frac{1}{3}}} - 4^2 = \frac{2^3 \times 3^{4\times\frac{1}{4}}}{2^{6\times\frac{1}{3}}} - 16$$

$$= \frac{2^3 \times 3^1}{2^2} - 16 = 2^1 \times 3^1 - 16 = 6 - 16 = -10$$ Ans.

## Exercise 6B

1. Evaluate the following :

(i) $(243)^{\frac{1}{5}}$ (ii) $(64)^{-\frac{3}{2}}$ (iii) $(-32)^{\frac{2}{5}}$ (iv) $(216)^{\frac{4}{3}}$

2. Evaluate the following :

(i) $\left(\frac{25}{9}\right)^{\frac{3}{2}} + \left(\frac{27}{64}\right)^{-\frac{1}{3}}$ (ii) $\left(\frac{81}{256}\right)^{\frac{1}{4}} \times \left(\frac{32}{243}\right)^{\frac{-2}{5}}$ (iii) $5^{-1} \times 3^0 + 25^{\frac{1}{2}}$ (iv) $3^{-2} \times 2^0 - (27)^{-\frac{1}{3}}$

3. Evaluate the following: $(27)^{\frac{4}{3}} - 5^0 \times \left(\frac{1}{9}\right)^{-\frac{3}{2}} + (81)^{\frac{1}{2}}$

4. Evaluate the following : $\frac{\sqrt{3^4} \times \sqrt[3]{27}}{\sqrt[4]{81}} + \left(\frac{1}{2}\right)^{-2}$

5. Evaluate the following : $\frac{\sqrt[4]{2^8} \times \sqrt[5]{243} \times 5^0}{\sqrt[3]{216}}$

6. If $x = 2, y = 3$, find $x^x + y^{-y}$.

7. If $x = -2, y = -3$, find $x^x + y^y$

8. If $x = 4, y = 3$, find $x^y + y^x$

9. If $x = -1, y = 2, z = -3$, find $x^y + y^x + z^x$.

10. If $x = 2, y = 3, z = 4$, find $x^z + y^{-x} + z^y$.

### Answers

**1.** (i) 3 (ii) $\frac{1}{512}$ (iii) 4 (iv) 1296 **2.** (i) $\frac{161}{27}$ (ii) $\frac{27}{16}$ (iii) $\frac{26}{5}$ (iv) $\frac{-2}{9}$ **3.** 63

**4.** 13 **5.** 2 **6.** $\frac{109}{27}$ **7.** $\frac{23}{108}$ **8.** 145 **9.** $\frac{7}{6}$ **10.** $\frac{721}{9}$

## Exponential Equation

An equation which contains a variable in exponent form, is called an exponential equation. For example : $2^{x+1} = 32$.

### Working Method to Solve an Exponential Equation

We shall use the following axiom to solve an exponential equation– "If two equal quantities being raised to certain powers produce equal result, the indices of the powers must be equal." If $a^x = a^y$, then $x = y$, where $a \neq 0$.

In an exponential equation, we convert both terms of the equation to the same base and then equate the indices on the both sides.

# Illustrative Examples

**Example 1.** Solve: $3^{2x} = 81$

**Solution.** $3^{2x} = 81 \Rightarrow 3^{2x} = 3^4$

$\Rightarrow 2x = 4 \Rightarrow x = 2$ Ans.

**Example 2.** Solve : $2^{2x-5} = \sqrt[3]{2}$

**Solution.** $2^{2x-5} = \sqrt[3]{2} \Rightarrow 2^{2x-5} = 2^{\frac{1}{3}} \Rightarrow 2x - 5 = \frac{1}{3}$

$\Rightarrow 2x = \frac{16}{3} \Rightarrow x = \frac{8}{3}$ Ans.

**Example 3.** Solve :

$3^{2x+2} - 10 \cdot 3^x + 1 = 0$

**Solution.** $3^{2x+2} - 10 \cdot 3^x + 1 = 0 \Rightarrow 3^2 . 3^{2x} - 10 \cdot 3^x + 1 = 0$

$\Rightarrow 9 \cdot (3^x)^2 - 10 \cdot 3^x + 1 = 0$

Put $3^x = y$

$\therefore 9y^2 - 10y + 1 = 0 \Rightarrow 9y^2 - 9y - y + 1 = 0$

$\Rightarrow 9y(y-1) - 1(y-1) = 0 \Rightarrow (y-1)(9y-1) = 0$

$\Rightarrow y - 1 = 0$ or $9y - 1 = 0$

$\Rightarrow y = 1$ or $y = \frac{1}{9}$

$\Rightarrow 3^x = 1$ or $3^x = \frac{1}{3^2}$

$\Rightarrow 3^x = 3^0$ or $3^x = 3^{-2}$

$\Rightarrow x = 0$ or $x = -2$ Ans.

**Example 4.** If $a^x \cdot b^y = \sqrt[3]{a^5 \cdot b^{-2}}$, where $a \neq b$ and $a$ and $b$ are positive prime numbers, then find the values of $x$ and $y$.

**Solution.** $a^x . b^y = \sqrt[3]{a^5 \, b^{-2}} = (a^5 b^{-2})^{\frac{1}{3}} = a^{\frac{5}{3}} . b^{\frac{-2}{3}}$

On comparing,

$x = \frac{5}{3}$ and $y = -\frac{2}{3}$ Ans.

**Example 5.** If $3^{4x} = (\sqrt[3]{81})^{\frac{4}{y}} = \sqrt[3]{3}$, find the values of $x$ and $y$.

**Solution.** $3^{4x} = \sqrt[3]{3} \Rightarrow 3^{4x} = 3^{\frac{1}{3}}$

$\Rightarrow 4x = \frac{1}{3} \Rightarrow x = \frac{1}{12}$

and $(\sqrt[3]{81})^{\frac{4}{y}} = \sqrt[3]{3} \Rightarrow (81)^{\frac{1}{3} \times \frac{4}{y}} = 3^{\frac{1}{3}}$

$\Rightarrow (3^4)^{\frac{4}{3y}} = 3^{\frac{1}{3}} \Rightarrow 3^{\frac{16}{3y}} = 3^{\frac{1}{3}}$

$\Rightarrow \quad \frac{16}{3y} = \frac{1}{3} \quad \Rightarrow \quad y = 16$

$\therefore \quad x = \frac{1}{12}, y = 16$ Ans.

**Example 6.** If $9^{x+2} = 720 + 9^x$, find the value of $(3x)^{2x}$.

**Solution.** $9^{x+2} = 720 + 9^x \Rightarrow 9^x.9^2 - 9^x = 720 \Rightarrow 9^x(9^2-1) = 720$

$\Rightarrow 9^x(81-1) = 720 \Rightarrow 9^x = 9 \Rightarrow 9^x = 9^1 \Rightarrow x = 1$

Now, $(3x)^{2x} = (3 \times 1)^{2\times 1} = 3^2 = 9$ Ans.

## Exercise 6C

1. Solve the following equations:
   (i) $2^{3x-2} = 1$ (ii) $3^{5x-1} = \sqrt[4]{3}$ (iii) $5^{3x-1} = \sqrt[3]{5}$ (iv) $2^{4x+1} = \sqrt[4]{256}$
2. Solve the following equations:
   (i) $2^{3x+1} = 16 \times 2^{2x}$ (ii) $2^{4x-3} = 4 \times 2^{2x-1}$
3. Solve the following equations:
   (i) $2^{2x} - 5.2^x + 4 = 0$ (ii) $3^{2x+3} - 28.3^x + 1 = 0$ (iii) $4^{x^2} : 4^x = 16 : 1$ (iv) $3^{2x+1} = 3^{2x-1} + 216$
4. If $a^x \cdot b^{3y} = \sqrt[4]{a^3 \cdot b^{-6}}$, find the values of $x$ and $y$, where $a$ and $b$ are different positive prime numbers.
5. Solve: $\sqrt{\left(\frac{4}{3}\right)^{1-3x}} = 2\frac{10}{27}$
6. Solve: $\left(\frac{2}{5}\right)^{4x-3} = 15\frac{5}{8}$
7. If $2^{3x} = (\sqrt[3]{32})^{\frac{4}{y}} = (\sqrt{8})^5$, then find the values of $x$ and $y$.
8. If $5^{2x-1} = 5^{2x-2} + 100$, find the value of $(2x)^{3x}$.
9. If $3^{3x+1} = 3^{3x-1} + 72$, find the value of $(3x+1)^{2x}$.
10. Solve for $x$ and $y$ : $8^{3-\frac{x}{2}} - 2^{2y} = 0$ and $(\sqrt{32})^x \div 2^y = 4$

### *Answers*

**1.** (i) $\frac{2}{3}$ (ii) $\frac{1}{4}$ (iii) $\frac{4}{9}$ (iv) $\frac{1}{4}$ **2.** (i) 3 (ii) 2 **3.** (i) 0, 2 (ii) 0, –3 (iii) –1, 2 (iv) 2

**4.** $x = \frac{3}{4}, y = -\frac{1}{2}$ **5.** $\frac{-5}{3}$ **6.** 0 **7.** $x = \frac{5}{2}, y = \frac{8}{9}$ **8.** 4096 **9.** 16 **10.** $x = 2, y = 3$

## Exercise 6D

### Multiple Choice *Questions*

Choose the correct answer from the given four options in each of the following questions :

1. $x^0$ is equal to :
   (a) 0 (b) 1 (c) $x$ (d) none of these
2. $a^5 \times a^{-5}$ is equal to :
   (a) 0 (b) 1 (c) $a^{-10}$ (d) $a$

**3.** $\dfrac{x^4 \times x^3}{x^9}$ is equal to :

(a) $x^2$ (b) $x$ (c) $\dfrac{1}{x}$ (d) $\dfrac{1}{x^2}$

**4.** If $x = 3$, $y = 2$, then the value of $x^x + y^y$ is :

(a) 42 (b) 35 (c) 31 (d) 17

**5.** $(81)^{0.18} \times (81)^{0.07}$ is equal to :

(a) 9 (b) 3 (c) 27 (d) 81

**6.** If $2^{2x+2} - 5 \cdot 2^x + 1 = 0$, then the value of $x$ is :

(a) 0 (b) 1 (c) –1 (d) 2

**7.** If $2^x \cdot 3^y = 288$, then the value of $y$ is :

(a) 1 (b) 2 (c) –2 (d) –1

**8.** If $a = b^x$, $b = c^y$, $c = a^z$, then the value of 8 $xyz$ is :

(a) 1 (b) 2 (c) 4 (d) 8

**9.** $\left(\dfrac{a^x}{a^{-y}}\right)^{x-y} \left(\dfrac{a^y}{a^{-z}}\right)^{y-z} \left(\dfrac{a^z}{a^{-x}}\right)^{z-x}$ is equal to :

(a) 0 (b) 1 (c) $a$ (d) $a^{xyz}$

**10.** $\dfrac{3^{n+1} \times 9^{n-1}}{3^n \times 9^{n+1}}$ is equal to :

(a) 27 (b) 9 (c) $\dfrac{1}{9}$ (d) $\dfrac{1}{27}$

## Answers

| 1. | (b) | 2. | (b) | 3. | (d) | 4. | (c) | 5. | (b) | 6. | (a) | 7. | (b) | 8. | (d) | 9. | (b) | 10. | (d) |
|---|---|---|---|---|---|---|---|---|---|---|---|---|---|---|---|---|---|---|---|

## Valid Statements *Questions*

In the following questions, two statements (i) and (ii) are given. Choose the valid statement.

(a) Only (i) (b) Only (ii) (c) Both (i) and (ii) (d) Neither (i) nor (ii)

**1.** (i) If $x = 2$, $y = 1$ then $x^x + y^y = 5$.

(ii) If $a = b^x$, $b = c^y$, $c = a^z$ then $xyz = 1$.

**2.** (i) If $m \neq n$ and $(m + n)^{-1}(m^{-1} + n^{-1}) = m^x n^y$ then $x + y = 2$.

(ii) If $2^x = 3^y = 108^z$ then $\dfrac{2}{y} + \dfrac{3}{z} = \dfrac{1}{x}$

**3.** (i) $\left(\dfrac{a^x}{a^y}\right)^{x+y} \cdot \left(\dfrac{a^y}{a^z}\right)^{y+z} \left(\dfrac{a^z}{a^x}\right)^{z+x} = 1$

(ii) $a^m \times a^n = a^{m-n}$

**4.** (i) $(64)^{-3/2} = 512$

(ii) $5^{-1} \times 3^0 = \dfrac{1}{5}$

## Answers

| 1. | (c) | 2. | (d) | 3. | (a) | 4. | (b) |
|---|---|---|---|---|---|---|---|

## SUMMARY *of the Chapter*

- $a^m \times a^n = a^{m+n}$
- $a^m \div a^n = a^{m-n}$
- $(a^m)^n = a^{mn}$
- $(a \times b)^m = a^m \times b^m$
- $\left(\frac{a}{b}\right)^m = \frac{a^m}{b^m}$
- $a^{-m} = \frac{1}{a^m}$
- $a^0 = 1$
- $\sqrt[n]{a} = a^{1/n}$
- $a^n = b^n, n \neq 0 \Rightarrow a = b$
- $a^m = a^n \Rightarrow m = n$, when $a \neq 1$.

# CHAPTER TEST

1. Simplify : $\dfrac{2^{2n}\times 8^{n+1}}{2^{n-1}\times 4^{2n}}$

2. If $2^x\cdot 3^y = 288$, find the values of $x$ and $y$.

3. Simplify : $5^{-1}\times 3^0 + 36^{\frac{1}{2}}$

4. If $x = 2$, $y = 3$, find the value of $x^{-y}+y^{-x}$.

5. Solve : $2^{3x+1} = 16\times 4^x$

6. If $a^x = b^y = c^z$ and $b^2 = ac$, prove that
$$y = \frac{2xz}{x+z}.$$

7. Prove that:
$$\frac{1}{1+x^{b-a}+x^{c-a}}+\frac{1}{1+x^{a-b}+x^{c-b}}+\frac{1}{1+x^{b-c}+x^{a-c}} = 1$$

8. If $a = b^{2x}$, $b = c^{2y}$, $c = a^{2z}$, prove that $8\,xyz = 1$.

9. Evaluate : $\dfrac{\sqrt{3^6}\times\sqrt[3]{27}}{\sqrt[4]{81}}+\left(\dfrac{1}{2}\right)^{-2}$

10. If $3^{3x+1} = 3^{3x-1}+72$, find the value of $(x+2)^{5x}$.

## *Answers*

**1.** 16 **2.** $x = 5, y = 2$ **3.** $\dfrac{31}{5}$ **4.** $\dfrac{17}{72}$ **5.** $x = 3$ **9.** 31 **10.** 243

Chapter

# 7 LOGARITHMS

## Syllabus

**(a) Logarithmic form and exponential form :** interchanging.
**(b) Lows of Logarithms and their uses.**

- Expansion of expression with the help of laws of logarithms

  *e.g.* $y = \frac{a^4 \times b^2}{c^3}$

  $\log y = 4 \log a + 2 \log b - 3 \log c$ etc.

## INTRODUCTION

We use logarithms to make easier the complicated calculations. It is commonly used in mathematics, physics, chemistry, etc.

## Logarithm

Let $a$, $b$ and $n$ are three real numbers and $a \neq 1$. If $a^n = b$, then '$n$' is called the logarithm of '$b$' at the base '$a$'. It can be written as

$$\log_a b = n$$

So, $a^n = b \Rightarrow \log_a b = n$

$\log_a b = n$ is the logarithmic form.

While $a^n = b$ is the exponential form.

*e.g.,*

$$2^4 = 16 \quad \Leftrightarrow \quad \log_2 16 = 4$$
$$5^3 = 125 \quad \Leftrightarrow \quad \log_5 125 = 3$$
$$4^{-2} = \frac{1}{16} \quad \Rightarrow \quad \log_4 \frac{1}{16} = -2$$

**Remark**

Here $a \neq 1$ and it is a positive real number. So, $a^n$ is always greater than zero, *i.e.*, positive for every rational number $n$.

$\Rightarrow$ $a^n = b$ is always a positive real number.

$\Rightarrow$ Logarithms are defined only for positive real numbers.

**NOTES**

(1) We know that
$a^0 = 1 \quad \Rightarrow \quad \log_a 1 = 0$

(2) We know that
$a^1 = a \quad \Rightarrow \quad \log_a a = 1$
where $a$ is any positive real number except 1.

(3) $\log_a x = \log_a y \Rightarrow x = y$

## Common Logarithm

Consider $\log_a x = b$

If $a = 10$, then $\log_{10} x$ is called the common logarithm, *i.e.*, logarithms with base 10 are called common logarithms. $\log_{10} x$ can also be written as $\log x$.

## Illustrative Examples

**Example 1.** Express the following in the logarithmic form:

(i) $3^5 = 243$ (ii) $4^2 = 16$
(iii) $3^3 = 27$ (iv) $8^2 = 64$

**Solution.**
(i) $3^5 = 243 \Rightarrow \log_3 243 = 5$ Ans.
(ii) $4^2 = 16 \Rightarrow \log_4 16 = 2$ Ans.
(iii) $3^3 = 27 \Rightarrow \log_3 27 = 3$ Ans.
(iv) $8^2 = 64 \Rightarrow \log_8 64 = 2$ Ans.

**Example 2.** Express the following in the logarithmic form:

(i) $10^{-3} = 0.001$ (ii) $2^{-4} = \frac{1}{16}$
(iii) $5^{-2} = \frac{1}{25}$ (iv) $4^{-3} = \frac{1}{64}$

**Solution.**
(i) $10^{-3} = 0.001 \Rightarrow \log_{10} 0.001 = -3$ Ans.
(ii) $2^{-4} = \frac{1}{16} \Rightarrow \log_2 \frac{1}{16} = -4$ Ans.
(iii) $5^{-2} = \frac{1}{25} \Rightarrow \log_5 \frac{1}{25} = -2$ Ans.
(iv) $4^{-3} = \frac{1}{64} \Rightarrow \log_4 \frac{1}{64} = -3$ Ans.

**Example 3.** Convert the following in exponential form:

(i) $\log_4 16 = 2$ (ii) $\log_5 625 = 4$ (iii) $\log_{10} 1000 = 3$ (iv) $\log_3 81 = 4$

**Solution.** (i) $\log_4 16 = 2 \Rightarrow 4^2 = 16$ **Ans.**

(ii) $\log_5 625 = 4 \Rightarrow 5^4 = 625$ **Ans.**

(iii) $\log_{10} 1000 = 3 \Rightarrow 10^3 = 1000$ **Ans.**

(iv) $\log_3 81 = 4 \Rightarrow 3^4 = 81$ **Ans.**

**Example 4.** Convert the following in exponential form:

(i) $\log_{10} 0.01 = -2$ (ii) $\log_4 \frac{1}{128} = -\frac{7}{2}$

**Solution.** (i) $\log_{10} 0.01 = -2 \Rightarrow 10^{-2} = 0.01$ **Ans.**

(ii) $\log_4 \frac{1}{128} = -\frac{7}{2} \Rightarrow 4^{-7/2} = \frac{1}{128}$ **Ans.**

**Example 5.** Evaluate each of the following by converting into exponential form :

(i) $\log_2 16$ (ii) $\log_8 2$ (iii) $\log_{\sqrt{3}} 81$ (iv) $\log_5 0.008$

**Solution.** (i) Let $\log_2 16 = x$

$\Rightarrow 2^x = 16 \Rightarrow 2^x = 2^4 \Rightarrow x = 4$

$\therefore \log_2 16 = 4$ **Ans.**

(ii) Let $\log_8 2 = x$

$\Rightarrow 8^x = 2 \Rightarrow (2^3)^x = 2 \Rightarrow 2^{3x} = 2^1 \Rightarrow 3x = 1$

$\Rightarrow x = \frac{1}{3}$

$\therefore \log_8 2 = \frac{1}{3}$ **Ans.**

(iii) Let $\log_{\sqrt{3}} 81 = x$

$\Rightarrow (\sqrt{3})^x = 81 \Rightarrow (3^{1/2})^x = 81 \Rightarrow 3^{x/2} = 3^4 \Rightarrow \frac{x}{2} = 4$

$\Rightarrow x = 8]$

$\therefore \log_{\sqrt{3}} 81 = 8$ **Ans.**

(iv) Let $\log_5 0.008 = x$

$\Rightarrow 5^x = 0.008 \Rightarrow 5^x = \frac{8}{1000} = \frac{1}{125} \Rightarrow 5^x = \frac{1}{5^3} \Rightarrow 5^x = 5^{-3} \Rightarrow x = -3$

$\therefore \log_5 0.008 = -3$ **Ans.**

**Example 6.** Solve for $x$:

(i) $\log_3 x = 2$ (ii) $\log_{27} x = \frac{2}{3}$ (iii) $\log_{10} x = -2$ (iv) $\log_{\sqrt{2}} x = 8$

**Solution.** (i) $\log_3 x = 2$

$\Rightarrow x = 3^2 \Rightarrow x = 9$ **Ans.**

(ii) $\log_{27} x = \frac{2}{3} \Rightarrow x = 27^{\frac{2}{3}} = (3^3)^{\frac{2}{3}} = 3^{3\times\frac{2}{3}} = 3^2 \Rightarrow x = 9$ **Ans.**

(iii) $\log_{10} x = -2 \Rightarrow x = 10^{-2} \Rightarrow x = 0.01$ **Ans.**

(iv) $\log_{\sqrt{2}} x = 8$

$x = (\sqrt{2})^8 = 2^{\frac{1}{2}\times 8} = 2^4 \Rightarrow x = 16$ **Ans.**

**Example 7.** Solve for $x$:

(i) $\log_x 7 = 1$ (ii) $\log_x 16 = -2$ (iii) $\log_x 25 = 4$

(iv) $\log(2x - 4) = 2$ (v) $\log_2(x^2 - 4) = 5$ (vi) $\log x = -3$

**Solution.** (i) $\log_x 7 = 1$

$\Rightarrow x^1 = 7 \Rightarrow x = 7$ **Ans.**

(ii) $\log_x 16 = -2$

$\Rightarrow x^{-2} = 16 \Rightarrow (x^{-1})^2 = 4^2 \Rightarrow x^{-1} = 4 \Rightarrow x = \frac{1}{4}$ **Ans.**

(iii) $\log_x 25 = 4$

$\Rightarrow x^4 = 25 \Rightarrow x^4 = 5^2 = (\sqrt{5})^4 \Rightarrow x = \sqrt{5}$ **Ans.**

(iv) $\log(2x - 4) = 2$

$\Rightarrow \log_{10}(2x - 4) = 2 \Rightarrow 2x - 4 = 10^2 \Rightarrow 2x = 104 \Rightarrow x = 52$ **Ans.**

(v) $\log_2(x^2 - 4) = 5$

$\Rightarrow x^2 - 4 = 2^5 = 32 \Rightarrow x^2 = 36 \Rightarrow x = \pm 6$ **Ans.**

(vi) $\log x = -3$

$\Rightarrow \log_{10} x = -3 \Rightarrow x = 10^{-3} \Rightarrow x = 0.001$ **Ans.**

**Example 8.** Evaluate the following:

(i) $\log_{3\sqrt{2}} 18$ (ii) $\log_{2\sqrt{3}} 144$

**Solution.** (i) Let $\log_{3\sqrt{2}} 18 = x$

$\Rightarrow (3\sqrt{2})^x = 18 \Rightarrow (3\sqrt{2})^x = (3\sqrt{2})^2 \Rightarrow x = 2 \Rightarrow \log_{3\sqrt{2}} 18 = 2$ **Ans.**

(ii) Let $\log_{2\sqrt{3}} 144 = x$

$\Rightarrow (2\sqrt{3})^x = 144 \Rightarrow (2\sqrt{3})^x = (2\sqrt{3})^4 \Rightarrow x = 4 \Rightarrow \log_{2\sqrt{3}} 144 = 4$ **Ans.**

**Example 9.** If $\log_{10} x = a$, $\log_{10} y = b$ and $\log_{10} z = c$,

(i) express $10^{3a-1}$ in terms of $x$. (ii) express $10^{2b-2}$ in terms of $y$.

(iii) express $10^{5c+2}$ in terms of $z$.

**Solution.** (i) $\log_{10} x = a$

$\Rightarrow 10^a = x$

$$\therefore \quad 10^{3a-1} = \frac{10^{3a}}{10} = \frac{1}{10}(10^a)^3 = \frac{1}{10}x^3$$ **Ans.**

(ii) $\log_{10} y = b$

$\Rightarrow 10^b = y$

$$\therefore \quad 10^{2b-2} = \frac{10^{2b}}{10^2} = \frac{1}{100}(10^b)^2 = \frac{1}{100}y^2$$ **Ans.**

(iii) $\log_{10} z = c$

$\Rightarrow 10^c = z$

$$\therefore \quad 10^{5c+2} = 10^2 \cdot 10^{5c} = 100 \cdot (10^c)^5 = 100 \cdot z^5$$ **Ans.**

**Example 10.** If $\log_2 x = a$, $\log_3 y = a$, find $48^{2a-1}$ in terms of $x$ and $y$.

**Solution.** $\log_2 x = a \Rightarrow 2^a = x$

$\log_3 y = a \Rightarrow 3^a = y$

$$\therefore \quad 48^{2a-1} = \frac{48^{2a}}{48} = \frac{1}{48}(2^4 \cdot 3)^{2a} = \frac{1}{48}2^{8a} \cdot 3^{2a} = \frac{1}{48}(2^a)^8 (3^a)^2 = \frac{1}{48}x^8 y^2$$ **Ans.**

# Exercise 7A

**1.** Express the following in logarithmic form:

(i) $8^3 = 512$ (ii) $5^3 = 125$ (iii) $3^2 = 9$

(iv) $10^{-2} = 0.01$ (v) $3^{-3} = \frac{1}{27}$ (vi) $2^{-5} = \frac{1}{32}$

**2.** Express the following in exponential form :

(i) $\log_5 125 = 3$ (ii) $\log_6 36 = 2$ (iii) $\log_4 256 = 4$

(iv) $\log_2 0.125 = -3$ (v) $\log_4 \frac{1}{32} = -\frac{5}{2}$ (vi) $\log_{10} 0.0001 = -4$

**3.** Evaluate the following :

(i) $\log_{6\sqrt{2}} 72$ (ii) $\log_{\sqrt{3}} 27$

**4.** Evaluate the following by converting into exponential form:

(i) $\log_5 625$ (ii) $\log_2 8$ (iii) $\log_{0.5} 64$ (iv) $\log_5 0.04$

(v) $\log_{\sqrt{3}} 9$ (vi) $\log_3 \frac{1}{3}$ (vii) $\log_9 243$ (viii) $\log_{32} 2$

**5.** Solve for $x$ :

(i) $\log_2 x = 3$ (ii) $\log_{125} x = \frac{1}{3}$ (iii) $\log_{\sqrt{2}} x = 4$ (iv) $\log_3 x = -2$

**6.** Solve for $x$ :

(i) $\log_x 81 = 4$ (ii) $\log_x 32 = -5$ (iii) $\log_x 8 = 1$ (iv) $\log_x \frac{1}{2} = -1$

(v) $\log_x 16 = \frac{1}{2}$ (vi) $\log_3 (x^2 - 19) = 4$ (vii) $\log (2x + 4) = 1$ (viii) $\log x = -1$

**7.** If $\log_{10} x = y$, express $10^{3y-1}$ in terms of $x$.

**8.** If $\log_{10} x = a$, $\log_{10} y = b$,

(i) express $10^{a-1}$ in terms of $x$.

(ii) express $10^{3b-2}$ in terms of $y$.

(iii) If $\log_{10} c = 2a - b$, find $c$ in terms of $x$ and $y$.

**9.** If $\log_2 x = a$, $\log_3 y = a$, find $24^{2a+1}$ in terms of $x$ and $y$.

**10.** If $\log_2 y = x$, $\log_3 z = x$, express $12^x$ in terms of $y$ and $z$.

**11.** If $\log_2 x = a$, $\log_5 y = a$, find $20^{2a-1}$ in terms of $x$ and $y$.

**12.** If $\log x = a$, $\log y = b$, express $x^3 y^2$ in terms of $a$ and $b$.

## Answers

**1.** (i) $\log_8 512 = 3$ (ii) $\log_5 125 = 3$ (iii) $\log_3 9 = 2$ (iv) $\log_{10} 0.01 = -2$ (v) $\log_3 \frac{1}{27} = -3$ (vi) $\log_2 \frac{1}{32} = -5$

**2.** (i) $5^3 = 125$ (ii) $6^2 = 36$ (iii) $4^4 = 256$ (iv) $2^{-3} = 0.125$ (v) $4^{-5/2} = \frac{1}{32}$ (vi) $10^{-4} = 0.0001$

**3.** (i) 2 (ii) 6

**4.** (i) 5 (ii) 3 (iii) –6 (iv) –2 (v) 4 (vi) –1 (vii) $\frac{5}{2}$ (viii) $\frac{1}{5}$

**5.** (i) 8 (ii) 5 (iii) 4 (iv) $\frac{1}{9}$

**6.** (i) 3 (ii) 0.5 (iii) 8 (iv) 2 (v) 256 (vi) $\pm 10$ (vii) 3 (viii) 0.1

**7.** $\frac{x^3}{10}$ **8.** (i) $\frac{x}{10}$ (ii) $\frac{y^3}{100}$ (iii) $c = \frac{x^2}{y}$ **9.** $24\, x^6 y^2$ **10.** $y^2 z$ **11.** $\frac{x^4 y^2}{20}$ **12.** $10^{3a+2b}$

## Laws of Logarithms

1. $\log_a (mn) = \log_a m + \log_a n$. Its general form is $\log_a (mnp\ldots) = \log_a m + \log_a n + \log_a p + \ldots$
2. $\log_a \left(\frac{m}{n}\right) = \log_a m - \log_a n$
3. $\log_a (m^n) = n \log_a m$

**Remember**

1. $\log_a (a^x) = x \log_a a = x$  2. $a^{\log_a x} = x$

## Base Changing Formula

$$\log_a m = \frac{\log_b m}{\log_b a}, m > 0, a, b > 0, a \neq 1, b \neq 1$$

**Remember**

1. $\log_b m = \log_a m \times \log_b a$  2. $\log_b a \times \log_a b = 1$  3. $\log_b a = \frac{1}{\log_a b}$

# Illustrative Examples

**Example 1.** Evaluate the following:

(i) $\frac{\log 36}{\log \sqrt{6}}$  (ii) $\log_5 250 - \log_5 2$

**Solution.** (i) $\frac{\log 36}{\log \sqrt{6}} = \frac{\log(6^2)}{\log (6^{1/2})} = \frac{2 \log 6}{\frac{1}{2} \log 6} = 4$ Ans.

(ii) $\log_5 250 - \log_5 2 = \log_5 \left(\frac{250}{2}\right) = \log_5 (125) = \log_5 (5^3) = 3 \log_5 5 = 3 \times 1 = 3$ Ans.

**Example 2.** Evaluate the following : $\log_{27} 81 - \log_9 243$

**Solution.** $\log_{27} 81 - \log_9 243 = \frac{\log 81}{\log 27} - \frac{\log 243}{\log 9} = \frac{\log(3^4)}{\log(3^3)} - \frac{\log(3^5)}{\log(3^2)} = \frac{4 \log 3}{3 \log 3} - \frac{5 \log 3}{2 \log 3}$

$= \frac{4}{3} - \frac{5}{2} = \frac{8-15}{6} = -\frac{7}{6}$ Ans.

**Example 3.** Express the following in terms of log 2 and log 3:

(i) log 36  (ii) log 45  (iii) log 7.5  (iv) 14.4

**Solution.** (i) $\log 36 = \log(2^2 \times 3^2) = \log 2^2 + \log 3^2 = 2\log 2 + 2 \log 3$ Ans.

(ii) $\log 45 = \log (3^2 \times 5) = \log 3^2 + \log 5 = 2 \log 3 + \log\left(\frac{10}{2}\right)$

$= 2 \log 3 + \log 10 - \log 2 = 1 + 2 \log 3 - \log 2$ Ans.

(iii) $\log 7.5 = \log\left(\frac{75}{10}\right) = \log\left(\frac{15}{2}\right) = \log\left(\frac{30}{4}\right) = \log\left(\frac{3 \times 10}{2^2}\right)$

$= \log 3 + \log 10 - \log 2^2 = 1 + \log 3 - 2 \log 2$ Ans.

(iv) $\log 14.4 = \log\left(\frac{144}{10}\right) = \log\left(\frac{2^4 \times 3^2}{10}\right) = \log 2^4 + \log 3^2 - \log 10 = 4 \log 2 + 2 \log 3 - 1$ **Ans.**

**Example 4.** Evaluate the following :

(i) $3 \log 5 + \log 8 + \log 3 - \frac{1}{2} \log 9$

(ii) $\log 100 + 2 \log(0.01) + \log 5 + \frac{1}{3} \log 8$

**Solution.** (i)

$$3 \log 5 + \log 8 + \log 3 - \frac{1}{2} \log 9 = \log 5^3 + \log 8 + \log 3 - \log\left(9^{\frac{1}{2}}\right)$$

$$= \log 125 + \log 8 + \log 3 - \log 3 = \log(125 \times 8)$$

$$= \log 1000 = \log(10^3) = 3 \log 10 = 3 \times 1 = 3$$ **Ans.**

(ii)

$$\log 100 + 2 \log(0.01) + \log 5 + \frac{1}{3} \log 8 = \log 100 + \log(0.01)^2 + \log 5 + \frac{1}{3} \log(2^3)$$

$$= \log(100 \times 0.01 \times 0.01 \times 5) + \frac{1}{3} \times 3 \log 2$$

$$= \log(0.05) + \log 2 = \log(0.05 \times 2)$$

$$= \log(0.1) = \log(10^{-1}) = -1 \log 10 = -1 \times 1 = -1$$ **Ans.**

**Example 5.** Prove that : $\log 288 = 5 \log 2 + 2 \log 3$.

**Solution.**

$$\text{L.H.S.} = \log 288 = \log(32 \times 9) = \log(2^5 \times 3^2)$$

$$= \log(2^5) + \log(3^2) = 5 \log 2 + 2 \log 3 = \text{R.H.S.}$$ **Ans.**

**Example 6.** Evaluate without using log table: $4 \log 2 + \log 75 - \log 60 + \log 50$

**Solution.**

$$4 \log 2 + \log 75 - \log 60 + \log 50 = \log(2^4) + \log 75 - \log 60 + \log 50$$

$$= \log\left(\frac{2^4 \times 75 \times 50}{60}\right) = \log 1000 = \log(10^3)$$

$$= 3 \log 10 = 3 \times 1 = 3 \qquad (\because \log 10 = \log_{10} 10)$$ **Ans.**

**Example 7.** Prove that: $\log 8 \div \log 4 = \frac{3}{2}$

**Solution.**

$$\text{L.H.S.} = \log 8 \div \log 4 = \frac{\log 8}{\log 4} = \frac{\log(2^3)}{\log(2^2)} = \frac{3 \log 2}{2 \log 2} = \frac{3}{2} = \text{R.H.S.}$$ **Hence Proved.**

**Example 8.** Prove that: $7 \log \frac{16}{15} + 5 \log \frac{25}{24} + 3 \log \frac{81}{80} = \log 2$ .

**Solution.**

$$\text{L.H.S.} = 7 \log \frac{16}{15} + 5 \log \frac{25}{24} + 3 \log \frac{81}{80}$$

$$= 7(\log 16 - \log 15) + 5(\log 25 - \log 24) + 3(\log 81 - \log 80)$$

$$= 7\left[\log(2^4) - \log(3 \times 5)\right] + 5\left[\log(5^2) - \log(2^3 \times 3)\right] + 3\left[\log(3^4) - \log(2^4 \times 5)\right]$$

$$= 7(4 \log 2 - \log 3 - \log 5) + 5(2 \log 5 - 3 \log 2 - \log 3) + 3(4 \log 3 - 4 \log 2 - \log 5)$$

$$= 28 \log 2 - 7 \log 3 - 7 \log 5 + 10 \log 5 - 15 \log 2 - 5 \log 3 + 12 \log 3 - 12 \log 2 - 3 \log 5$$

$$= \log 2 = \text{R.H.S.}$$ **Hence Proved.**

**Example 9.** Prove that : $5^{\log 16} = 4^{\log 25}$.

**Solution.** Let $5^{\log 16} = x$

$\Rightarrow \quad \log (5^{\log 16}) = \log x$

$\Rightarrow \quad \log x = \log 16 \log 5$

$= \log (4^2) \log 5 = 2 \log 4 \log 5 = 2 \log 5 \log 4$

$= \log (5^2) \log 4 = \log 25 \log 4 = \log (4^{\log 25})$

$\Rightarrow \quad x = 4^{\log 25} \quad \Rightarrow \quad 5^{\log 16} = 4^{\log 25}$

Hence Proved.

**Example 10.** Express the following as a single logarithm:
$3 \log 2 + 2 \log 3 - 1$

**Solution.** $3 \log 2 + 2 \log 3 - 1 = \log (2^3) + \log (3^2) - \log 10 = \log \dfrac{2^3 \times 3^2}{10} = \log 7.2$ Ans.

**Example 11.** If $3 \log x + 1 = \log 5 + 7 \log 2$, then find the value of $x$.

**Solution.** $3 \log x + 1 = \log 5 + 7 \log 2$

$\Rightarrow \quad 3 \log x = \log 5 + \log 2^7 - 1 = \log 5 + \log 2^7 - \log 10$

$= \log \dfrac{5 \times 2^7}{10} = \log (2^6) = 6 \log 2$

$\Rightarrow \quad \log x = 2 \log 2 = \log 2^2 \quad \Rightarrow \quad x = 4$ Ans.

**Example 12.** If $\log x = \log 7 - \log 2 + \log 32 - 2 \log 3 - \log \dfrac{7}{45}$, find the value of $x$.

**Solution.** $\log x = \log 7 - \log 2 + \log 32 - 2 \log 3 - \log \dfrac{7}{45}$

$= \log 7 - \log 2 + \log(2^5) - 2 \log 3 - \log 7 + \log 45$

$= -\log 2 + 5 \log 2 - 2 \log 3 + \log(3^2 \times 5)$

$= 4 \log 2 - 2 \log 3 + \log 3^2 + \log 5$

$= \log 2^4 - 2 \log 3 + 2 \log 3 + \log 5$

$= \log (2^4 \times 5) = \log 80 \quad \Rightarrow \quad x = 80$ Ans.

**Example 13.** If $\log_{10} (x + 5) + \log_{10} (x - 5) = 2 + \log_{10} 2 + \log_{10} 3$ find the value of $x$.

**Solution.** $\log_{10} (x + 5) + \log_{10} (x - 5) = 2 + \log_{10} 2 + \log_{10} 3$

$\Rightarrow \quad \log_{10}\{(x + 5)(x - 5)\} = 2 \log_{10} 10 + \log_{10} 2 + \log_{10} 3$

$\Rightarrow \quad \log_{10} (x^2 - 25) = \log_{10} (10^2 \times 2 \times 3) \quad \Rightarrow \quad x^2 - 25 = 600$

$\Rightarrow \quad x^2 = 625 \quad \Rightarrow \quad x = 25 \quad (\because \; x \neq -25)$ Ans.

**Example 14.** If $2 \log_{10} x + \dfrac{3}{2} \log_{10} y = 1$, find the relation between $x$ and $y$.

**Solution.** $2 \log_{10} x + \dfrac{3}{2} \log_{10} y = 1$

$\Rightarrow \quad 4 \log_{10} x + 3 \log_{10} y = 2$

$\Rightarrow \quad \log_{10} (x^4) + \log_{10} (y^3) = 2 \log_{10} 10$

$\Rightarrow \quad \log_{10} (x^4 y^3) = \log_{10}(10^2) \quad \Rightarrow \quad x^4 y^3 = 100$

which is the required relation. Ans.

**Example 15.** Express the following in terms of log 2 and log 3 :
(i) log 288 (ii) log 2160

**Solution.** (i) $\log 288 = \log (2^5 \times 3^2) = \log (2^5) + \log (3^2) = 5 \log 2 + 2 \log 3$ Ans.
(ii) $\log 2160 = \log (2^3 \times 3^3 \times 10) = \log (2^3) + \log (3^3) + \log 10 = 3 \log 2 + 3 \log 3 + 1$ Ans.

**Example 16.** If $\log 2 = x$ and $\log 3 = y$, express log 1536 in terms of $x$ and $y$.

**Solution.** $\log 1536 = \log (512 \times 3) = \log 512 + \log 3 = \log (2^9) + \log 3 = 9 \log 2 + \log 3 = 9x + y$ Ans.

**Example 17.** Solve for $x$ :
(i) $\log_2 (\log_5 x) = 2$ (ii) $\log_x 75 = 2 - \log_x 3$

**Solution.** (i) $\log_2 (\log_5 x) = 2 \Rightarrow \log_5 x = 2^2 = 4 \Rightarrow x = 5^4 = 625$ Ans.
(ii) $\log_x 75 = 2 - \log_x 3 \Rightarrow \log_x 75 + \log_x 3 = 2 \Rightarrow \log_x (75 \times 3) = 2$
$\Rightarrow x^2 = 225 \Rightarrow x = 15$ Ans.

**Example 18.** Solve for $x$ : $\log_{10} x + \log_{10} (3x - 7) = 1$.

**Solution.** $\log_{10} x + \log_{10} (3x - 7) = 1$
$\Rightarrow \log_{10} \{x (3x - 7)\} = \log_{10} 10 \Rightarrow 3x^2 - 7x = 10$
$\Rightarrow 3x^2 - 7x - 10 = 0 \Rightarrow (3x - 10)(x + 1) = 0$
$\Rightarrow 3x - 10 = 0$ or $x + 1 = 0 \Rightarrow x = \dfrac{10}{3}$ or $x = -1$

but $x$ cannot be negative.

$\therefore \quad x = \dfrac{10}{3}$ Ans.

**Example 19.** Solve for $x$ : $3^{\log x} - 2^{\log x} = 2^{\log x+1} - 3^{\log x-1}$

**Solution.** $3^{\log x} - 2^{\log x} = 2^{\log x+1} - 3^{\log x-1}$
$\Rightarrow 3^{\log x} + 3^{\log x-1} = 2^{\log x+1} + 2^{\log x} \Rightarrow 3^{\log x}(1 + 3^{-1}) = 2^{\log x} + (2^1 + 1)$
$\Rightarrow 3^{\log x}\left(1 + \dfrac{1}{3}\right) = 2^{\log x}(2 + 1) \Rightarrow 3^{\log x}.\left(\dfrac{4}{3}\right) = 2^{\log x}.3$
$\Rightarrow \dfrac{3^{\log x}}{2^{\log x}} = \dfrac{9}{4} \Rightarrow \left(\dfrac{3}{2}\right)^{\log x} = \left(\dfrac{3}{2}\right)^2$
$\Rightarrow \log x = 2 \Rightarrow x = 10^2 = 100$ Ans.

**Example 20.** Solve for $x$ : $\log_5 \left(5^{\frac{1}{x}} + 125\right) = \log_5 6 + 1 + \dfrac{1}{2x}$.

**Solution.** $\log_5 \left(5^{\frac{1}{x}} + 125\right) = \log_5 6 + 1 + \dfrac{1}{2x} = \log_5 6 + \log_5 5 + \dfrac{1}{2x}$
$\Rightarrow \log_5 (5^{\frac{1}{x}} + 125) - \log_5 6 - \log_5 5 = \dfrac{1}{2x} \Rightarrow \log_5 \left(\dfrac{5^{1/x} + 125}{6 \times 5}\right) = \dfrac{1}{2x}$
$\Rightarrow \dfrac{5^{\frac{1}{x}} + 125}{30} = 5^{\frac{1}{2x}} \Rightarrow 5^{\frac{1}{x}} + 125 = 30.5^{\frac{1}{2x}}$
$\Rightarrow (5^{1/2x})^2 - 30 \cdot 5^{1/2x} + 125 = 0 \Rightarrow y^2 - 30y + 125 = 0,$ where $5^{\frac{1}{2x}} = y$
$\Rightarrow y^2 - 25y - 5y + 125 = 0 \Rightarrow y(y - 25) - 5(y - 25) = 0$
$\Rightarrow (y - 25)(y - 5) = 0 \Rightarrow y - 25 = 0$ or $y - 5 = 0$
$\Rightarrow y = 25$ or $y = 5 \Rightarrow 5^{\frac{1}{2x}} = 5^2$ or $5^{\frac{1}{2x}} = 5^1$

$\Rightarrow \quad \frac{1}{2x} = 2 \quad$ or $\quad \frac{1}{2x} = 1 \quad \Rightarrow \quad x = \frac{1}{4} \quad$ or $\quad x = \frac{1}{2}$ Ans.

**Example 21.** If $\log_{10}(xy) = 1$ and $\log_{\sqrt{3}}\left(\frac{6x}{5y}\right) = 2$, then find the values of $x$ and $y$.

**Solution.**

$$\log_{\sqrt{3}}\left(\frac{6x}{5y}\right) = 2$$

$$\Rightarrow \frac{6x}{5y} = (\sqrt{3})^2 \quad \Rightarrow \quad x = \frac{5y}{2} \qquad \ldots(i)$$

and $\log_{10}(xy) = 1 \quad \Rightarrow \quad xy = 10^1 = 10$

$$\Rightarrow \frac{5y}{2} \cdot y = 10 \text{ [from (i)]} \quad \Rightarrow \quad y^2 = 4 \quad \Rightarrow \quad y = \pm 2$$

If $y = 2$, then from $(i)$, $x = \frac{5 \times 2}{2} = 5$

If $y = -2$, then from $(ii)$, $x = \frac{5 \times (-2)}{2} = -5$

$\therefore \quad x = 5, y = 2 \quad$ or $\quad x = -5, y = -2$ Ans.

**Example 22.** If $x = \log\frac{1}{2}$, $y = \log\frac{2}{5}$ and $z = \log 5$, find the value of $x + y + z$.

**Solution.** $x + y + z = \log\frac{1}{2} + \log\frac{2}{5} + \log 5 = \log\left(\frac{1}{2} \times \frac{2}{5} \times 5\right) = \log 1 = 0$ Ans.

**Example 23.** If $2a = \log x$, $b^2 = \log y$ and $4a - 5b^2 = \log z$, then find the relation between $x$, $y$ and $z$.

**Solution.**

$$4a - 5b^2 = 2\log z$$

$$\Rightarrow 2\log x - 5\log y = 2\log z \quad \Rightarrow \quad \log x^2 - \log y^5 = \log z^2$$

$$\Rightarrow \log\frac{x^2}{y^5} = \log z^2 \quad \Rightarrow \quad \frac{x^2}{y^5} = z^2 \quad \Rightarrow \quad x^2 = y^5 z^2$$ Ans.

**Example 24.** If $\log\frac{a+b}{3} = \frac{\log a + \log b}{2}$, then prove that : $a^2 + b^2 = 7ab$.

**Solution.**

$$\log\frac{a+b}{3} = \frac{\log a + \log b}{2}$$

$$\Rightarrow 2\log\frac{a+b}{3} = \log a + \log b \quad \Rightarrow \quad \log\left(\frac{a+b}{3}\right)^2 = \log(a \cdot b)$$

$$\Rightarrow \frac{(a+b)^2}{9} = ab \quad \Rightarrow \quad (a+b)^2 = 9ab$$

$$\Rightarrow a^2 + b^2 + 2ab = 9ab \quad \Rightarrow \quad a^2 + b^2 = 7ab$$

Hence Proved.

**Example 25.** If $a = 1 + \log_x yz$, $b = 1 + \log_y zx$, $c = 1 + \log_z xy$, then solve that : $ab + bc + ca = abc$.

**Solution.**

$$a = 1 + \log_x yz = \log_x x + \log_x yz = \log_x (xyz)$$

$$\Rightarrow \frac{1}{a} = \frac{1}{\log_x(xyz)} = \log_{xyz} x$$

Similarly, $\frac{1}{b} = \log_{xyz} y$ and $\frac{1}{c} = \log_{xyz} z$

Now, $\frac{1}{a} + \frac{1}{b} + \frac{1}{c} = \log_{xyz} x + \log_{xyz} y + \log_{xyz} z$

$$\Rightarrow \quad \frac{bc + ca + ab}{abc} = \log_{xyz}(xyz) = 1 \quad \Rightarrow \quad ab + bc + ca = abc$$ Ans.

**Example 26.** If $\frac{\log x}{y - z} = \frac{\log y}{z - x} = \frac{\log z}{x - y}$, then show that : $x^x \cdot y^y \cdot z^z = 1$.

**Solution.** Let $\frac{\log x}{y - z} = \frac{\log y}{z - x} = \frac{\log z}{x - y} = k$

$\Rightarrow \quad \log x = k(y - z), \log y = k(z - x), \log z = k(x - y)$

Now, $\quad x \log x + y \log y + z \log z = kx(y - z) + ky(z - x) + kz(x - y)$

$\Rightarrow \quad \log(x^x) + \log(y^y) + \log(z^z) = k(xy - xz + yz - xy + zx - yz)$

$\Rightarrow \quad \log(x^x \cdot y^y \cdot z^z) = 0 \quad \Rightarrow \quad x^x \cdot y^y \cdot z^z = 10^0$

$\Rightarrow \quad x^x \cdot y^y \cdot z^z = 1$ Hence Proved.

## Exercise 7B

1. Evaluate the following:
   (i) $\frac{1}{2}\log 625 + \log 8 - \frac{1}{4}\log 16$
   (ii) $\log 100 + 2\log 0.01 - \frac{1}{2}\log 5^{-4} + \frac{2}{3}\log 8$
   (iii) $\log 5 + 3\log 2 - 2\log 6 + 2\log 3$
   (iv) $2\log 2 + 4\log 3 + \log 5 - \log 7.5 - \log 2.16$
2. Evaluate the following :
   (i) $\log_{16} 32 - \log_9 27$
   (ii) $\log_{625} 125 + \log_{64} 16$
3. Express the following in terms of log 2 and log 3:
   (i) log 24 (ii) log 72 (iii) log 13.5 (iv) log 180
4. Prove the following :
   (i) $2\log\frac{15}{4} + \log\frac{81}{5} - 3\log\frac{9}{4} + \log 100 = 3 + \log 2$
   (ii) $\log\frac{125}{147} = 3 - 3\log 2 - 2\log 7 - \log 3$
   (iii) $\log\frac{35}{33} - \log\frac{135}{99} + \log\frac{24}{7} = 3\log 2 - \log 3$
   (iv) $2\log_{10} 20 + \log 5 - \log 2 = 3$
5. Express each of the following as a single logarithm:
   (i) $2\log 5 + 3\log 2 - 1$
   (ii) $2\log 3 + \log 7 + 3\log 5 - 2$
6. If $\log 2 = x$ and $\log 3 = y$, express each of the following in terms of $x$ and $y$.
   (i) log 36 (ii) log 250 (iii) log 14.4
7. Prove that : $4^{\log 9} = 3^{\log 16}$.
8. If $\log x = a + b$ and $\log y = a - b$, express $\log(x^2 y)$ in terms of $a$ and $b$.
9. If $\log x = 3a + 2b$ and $\log y = 2a - b$, express $\log(x^3 y^2)$ in terms of $a$ and $b$.
10. If $x = \log\frac{2}{3}, y = \log\frac{3}{7}, z = \log\frac{7}{2}$, find the value of :
    (i) $x + y + z$
    (ii) $2^{x+y+z}$
11. If $x = \log\frac{3}{7}, y = \log\frac{10}{7}, z = \log\frac{10}{3}$, find the value of:
    (i) $x - y + z$
    (ii) $5^{x-y+z}$
12. Find the value of $x$ in the following cases:
    (i) $\log_{10} x = \log_{10} 2 + 2$.
    (ii) $\log x = -2 + 3\log 2 - 5\log 3 + 2\log 72 + \log 3$
    (iii) $\log(x + 2) + \log(x - 2) = \log 2 + \log 3 + 1$
    (iv) $\log(x + 4) + \log(x - 4) = 4\log 2 + \log 3$
    (v) $\log(3x + 2) + \log(3x - 2) = 1 + \log 2 + \log 7$
    (vi) $\log_2 x + \log_8 x + \log_{32} x = \frac{23}{15}$
    (vii) $\log_3 x + \log_9 x + \log_{81} x = \frac{7}{4}$

13. Prove that: $(1+\log_a b).\log_{ab} x = \log_a x$.

14. Prove that: $(\log x)^2 - (\log y)^2 = \log\left(\frac{x}{y}\right)\cdot\log(xy)$.

15. If $\log\frac{x+y}{2} = \frac{\log x + \log y}{2}$, prove that $x = y$.

16. If $2\log\frac{x-y}{2} = \log x + \log y$, prove that $x^2 + y^2 - 6xy = 0$.

17. If $\log(x+y) = \log x + \log y$, prove that: $y = \frac{x}{x-1}$.

18. If $\log(x+y) = \log x - \log y$, prove that $x = \frac{y^2}{1-y}$.

19. If $x^2 + y^2 = 34xy$, prove that $\log\left(\frac{x+y}{6}\right) = \frac{1}{2}(\log x + \log y)$.

20. Show that: $\log_b a \cdot \log_c d = \log_c a \cdot \log_b d$.

21. If $\frac{1}{\log_a x} + \frac{1}{\log_c x} = \frac{2}{\log_b x}$, then prove that $b^2 = ac$.

22. Show that : $\frac{1}{\log_{36} 12} + \frac{1}{\log_6 12} + \frac{1}{\log_8 12} = 3$

23. If $x = \log_a(bc)$, $y = \log_b(ca)$, $z = \log_c(ab)$, prove that $\frac{1}{1+x} + \frac{1}{1+y} + \frac{1}{1+z} = 1$

## Answers

**1.** (i) 2 (ii) 0 (iii) 1 (iv) 2 **2.** (i) $-\frac{1}{4}$ (ii) $\frac{13}{6}$

**3.** (i) $3\log 2 + \log 3$ (ii) $3\log 2 + 2\log 3$ (iii) $3\log 3 - \log 2$ (iv) $1 + \log 2 + 2\log 3$

**5.** (i) $\log 20$ (ii) $\log\frac{315}{4}$ **6.** (i) $2x + 2y$ (ii) $3 - 2x$ (iii) $4x + 2y - 1$

**8.** $3a + b$ **9.** $13a + 4b$

**10.** (i) 0 (ii) 1 **11.** (i) 0 (ii) 1

**12.** (i) 200 (ii) 5.12 (iii) 8 (iv) 8 (v) 4 (vi) 2 (vii) 3

# Exercise 7C

## Multiple Choice Questions

Choose the correct answer from the given four options in each of the following questions :

1. If $\log(2x+5) = 2$, then $x$ is equal to :
   (a) 40 (b) 42.5 (c) 47.5 (d) 48

2. $\log_{\sqrt{2}}\sqrt{8}$ is equal to :
   (a) 3 (b) 4 (c) 16 (d) 5

3. The value of $4^{\log 3} - 3^{\log 4}$ is :
   (a) 0 (b) 1 (c) 3 (d) 12

4. If $x = \log 2$, $y = \log 3$, then $\log 12$ is equal to :
   (a) $2x + 3y$ (b) $2x + y$ (c) $3x + 2y$ (d) $x + 2y$

5. If $\log_x 9 - \log_x 3 - \log_x 27 = 2$, then $x$ is equal to :
   (a) 9 (b) 3 (c) $\frac{1}{9}$ (d) $\frac{1}{3}$

6. If $\log_2 x = a$ and $\log_5 y = a$, then $100^{3a-1}$ is equal to :

(a) $\frac{x^6y^6}{100}$ (b) $\frac{x^3y^3}{100}$ (c) $\frac{x^2y^2}{100}$ (d) $\frac{xy}{100}$

7. $\log_4 32 - \log_8 32$ is equal to :

(a) $\frac{1}{3}$ (b) $\frac{1}{2}$ (c) $\frac{7}{6}$ (d) $\frac{5}{6}$

8. $3 - 5\log_{10} 2$ is equal to :

(a) $\log\frac{225}{4}$ (b) $\log\frac{125}{4}$ (c) $\log\frac{75}{4}$ (d) $\log\frac{25}{4}$

9. If $\log(x+y) = \log x + \log y$, then $y$ is equal to :

(a) $\frac{x}{x-1}$ (b) $\frac{x+1}{x}$ (c) $\frac{x-1}{x}$ (d) $\frac{x}{x+1}$

10. If $\log\left(\frac{x+y}{5}\right) = \frac{\log x + \log y}{2}$, then correct relation is :

(a) $x^2 + y^2 + 23xy = 0$ (b) $x^2 + y^2 - 23xy = 0$ (c) $x^2 + y^2 + 27xy = 0$ (d) $x^2 + y^2 + 27xy = 0$

### Answers

| | | | | | | | | | |
|---|---|---|---|---|---|---|---|---|---|
| 1. (c) | 2. (a) | 3. (a) | 4. (b) | 5. (d) | 6. (a) | 7. (d) | 8. (b) | 9. (a) | **10. (b)** |

## Valid Statements *Questions*

In the following questions, two statements (i) and (ii) are given. Choose the valid statement.

**(a)** Only (i) (b) Only (ii) (c) Both (i) and (ii) (d) Neither (i) nor (ii)

1. (i) $\log(m \cdot n) = \log m + \log n$

(ii) $3 - 5\log_{10} 2 = \log_{10} 125 - \log_{10} 4$

2. (i) $\log 288 = 5\log 2 + 2\log 3$

(ii) $3\log 2 + 2\log 3 - 1 = \log 72$

3. (i) $\log m - \log n = \log(m^n)$

(ii) If $\log_{10}(x+5) + \log_{10}(x-5) = \log 600$, then $x = 5$.

4. (i) $5^{\log 4} = 4^{\log 5}$

(ii) If $x = \log\frac{1}{2}, y = \log\frac{2}{3}, z = \log 3$, then $x + y + z = 0$

### Answers

| | | | |
|---|---|---|---|
| 1. (c) | 2. (a) | 3. (d) | 4. (c) |

## SUMMARY *of the Chapter*

1. If $a$, $b$ and $m$ are three real numbers and $a \neq 1$ such that $a^m = b$, then $m$ is called **the** logarithm of $b$ at the base $a$ and is written as

$$\log_a b = m$$

Here, $a^m = b$ is called the exponential form.

2. Laws of logarithm

   (i) $\log_a (m \cdot n) = \log_a m + \log_a n,\ a \neq 1$

   (ii) $\log_a \left(\frac{m}{n}\right) = \log_a m - \log_a n,\ a \neq 1$

   (iii) $\log_a (m^n) = n \log_a m,\ a \neq 1$

   (iv) $\log_a 1 = 0,\ a \neq 1$

   (v) $\log_a a = 1,\ a \neq 1$

   (vi) $\log_a m = \frac{\log_b m}{\log_b a}$

   (vii) $\log_b a \times \log_a b = 1$

# CHAPTER TEST

1. Express $2^5 = 32$ in logarithmic form.
2. Find $x$ if $\log_3 x = 4$.
3. Solve for $x$ :
   $2 \log_{10} x + 1 = \log_{10} 360.$
4. If $\log \dfrac{x+y}{4} = \dfrac{\log x + \log y}{2}$, prove that $x^2 + y^2 = 14\, xy$.
5. Prove that: $2^{\log 3} = 3^{\log 2}$
6. Express log 288 in terms of log 2 and log 3.
7. If $\dfrac{\log x}{y-z} = \dfrac{\log y}{z-x} = \dfrac{\log z}{x-y}$, then prove that $x^x . y^y . z^z = 1$.
8. If $\log_{10} x = p$ and $\log_{10} y = q$ :
   (i) Write $10^{p-1}$ in terms of $x$
   (ii) Write $10^{2q-1}$ in terms of $y$
   (iii) If $\log_{10} z = 2p - q$, find $z$ in terms of $x$ and $y$.
9. Solve for $x$ :
   $\log_{10} x - \log_{10}(2x-3) = 1.$
10. Show that:
   $$\frac{1}{\log_3 180} + \frac{1}{\log_{10} 180} + \frac{1}{\log_6 180} = 1$$

## *Answers*

1. $\log_2 32 = 5$  2. 81  3. 6  6. 5 log 2 + 2 log 3

8. (i) $\dfrac{x}{10}$ (ii) $\dfrac{y^2}{10}$ (iii) $\dfrac{x^2}{y}$  9. $\dfrac{30}{19}$

UNIT IV : GEOMETRY

# Chapter 8

# TRIANGLES

## Syllabus

**(a) Congruency :** Four cases : SSS, SAS, AAS, and RHS. Illustration through cutouts. Simple applications.

**(b) Problems based on :**

- Angles opposite equal sides are equal and converse.
- If two sides of a triangle are unequal, then the greater angle is opposite the greater side and converse.
- Sum of any two sides of a triangle is greater than the third side.
- Of all straight lines that can be drawn to a given line from a point outside it, the perpendicular is the shortest.

## INTRODUCTION

We know that a plane figure bounded by three line segments is called a triangle. It consists of three vertices, three line segments and three angles. In the figure given alongside, a triangle *ABC* is shown.

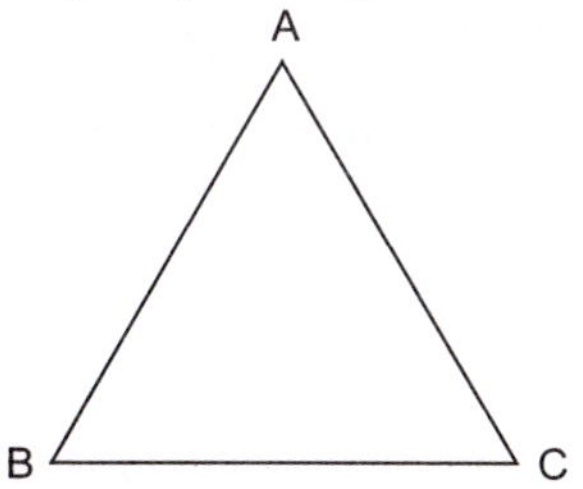


Vertices : *A, B* and *C*.

Line Segments : *AB, BC,* and *CA*.

Angles : $\angle A = \angle BAC$, $\angle B = \angle ABC$, $C = \angle ACB$.

**NOTE**

The three sides and three angles of a triangle are called six elements of a triangle. A vertex of a triangle is the point of intersection of two sides, *e.g.*, *B* is the point of intersection of line segments (sides) *AB* and *BC*.

The side opposite to vertex *A* is *BC*.

## Types of Triangles

Triangles can be divided on the basis of its sides and on the basis of its angles.

### 1. Types of Triangles on the Basis of its Sides

#### (i) Scalene Triangle

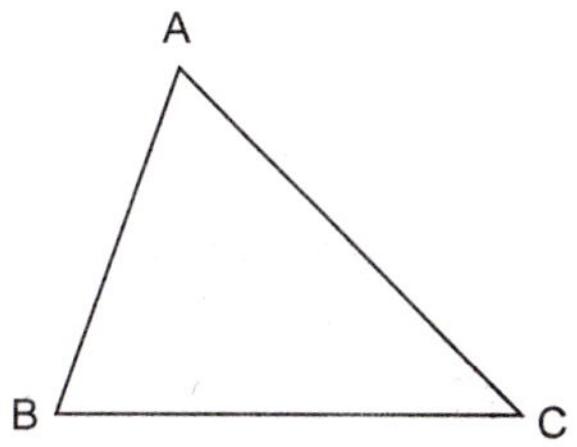


If all three sides of a triangle are different, it is called a scalene triangle. In the adjoining figure,

$$AB \neq BC \neq CA$$

$\therefore$ $\Delta ABC$ is a scalene triangle.

#### (ii) Isosceles Triangle

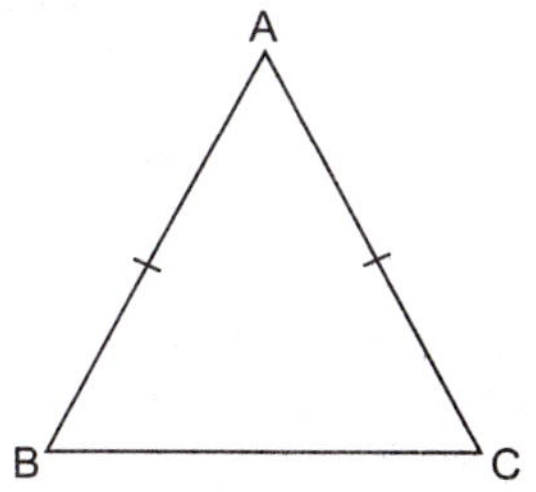


If any two sides of a triangle are equal, it is called an isosceles triangle. In the adjoining figure,

$$AB = AC$$

$\therefore$ $\Delta ABC$ is an isosceles triangle.

#### (iii) Equilateral Triangle

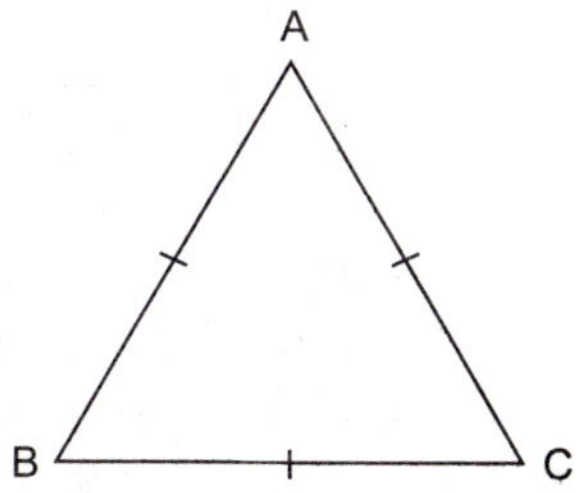


If all three sides of a triangle are equal, it is called an equilateral triangle. In the adjoining figure,

$$AB = BC = CA$$

$\therefore$ $\Delta ABC$ is an equilateral triangle.

**NOTE**

All the equilateral triangles are also called isosceles triangles.

### 2. Types of Triangles on the Basis of its Angles

#### (i) Acute-angled Triangle

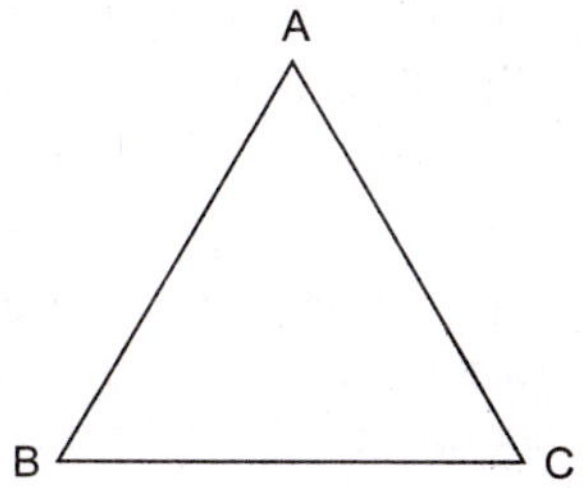


If all the three angles of a triangle are acute angles (*i.e.*, less than 90°), it is called an acute-angled triangle. In the adjoining figure each angle is less than 90°, so $\Delta ABC$ is an acute-angled triangle.

**NOTE**

An equilateral triangle is an acute-angled triangle.

### (ii) Right-angled Triangle

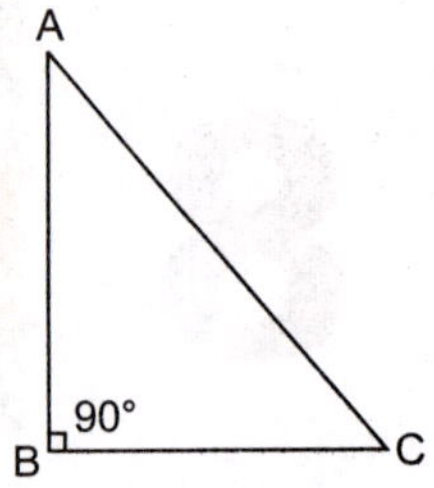


If an angle of a triangle is right angle (*i.e.*, 90°), it is called a right-angled triangle. In the adjoining figure,

$$\angle B = 90°$$

$\therefore$ $\Delta ABC$ is a right-angled triangle.

**Remember**

The side opposite to the right angle in a right-angled triangle is called hypotenuse.

### (iii) Obtuse-angled Triangle

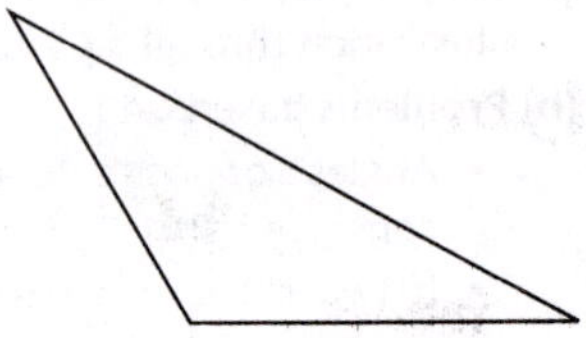

If an angle of a triangle is obtuse (*i.e.*, more than 90°) it is called an obtuse-angled triangle. In the adjoining figure,

$$\angle ABC > 90°$$

$\therefore$ $\Delta ABC$ is an obtuse-angled triangle.

**NOTE**

Two angles in a triangle can never be right angles or obtuse angles.

## Terms Related to a Triangle

### (i) Orthocentre

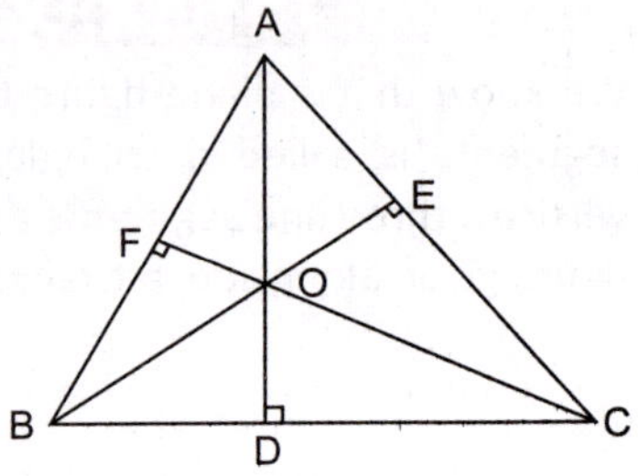


We know that the perpendicular drawn from a vertex to opposite side in a triangle is called the altitude of the triangle. A triangle has three altitudes. In the adjoining figure; $AD$, $BE$, and $CF$ perpendiculars to $BC$, $AC$ and $AB$, respectively.

$\therefore$ $$AD \perp BC,\ BE \perp AC \text{ and } CF \perp AB$$

$AD$, $BE$, and $CF$ are three altitudes. These three altitudes always pass through a point $O$, which is called the orthocentre of $\Delta ABC$.

### (ii) Centroid

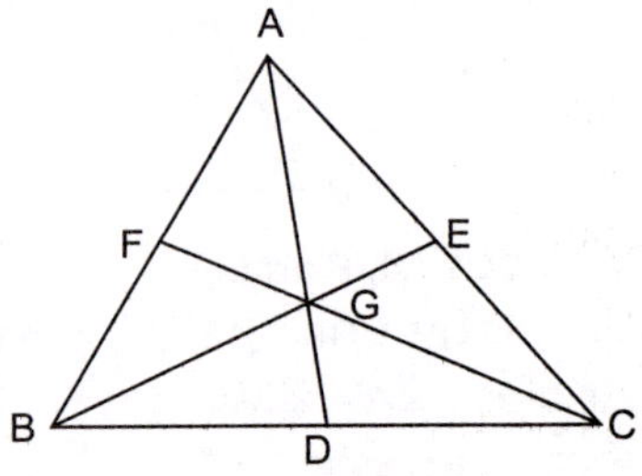


The line segment joining a vertex of a triangle to the mid-point of the opposite side is called a median of the triangle. In the adjoining figure; $D$, $E$ and $F$ are the mid-points of the sides $BC$, $CA$, and $AB$ respectively.

$\therefore$ $AD$, $BE$, and $CF$, are three medians of $\Delta ABC$.

These three medians always pass through a point $G$ which is called the centroid of $\Delta ABC$. For point $G$, $AG : GD = BG : GE = CG : GF = 2 : 1$

### (iii) Incentre and Incircle

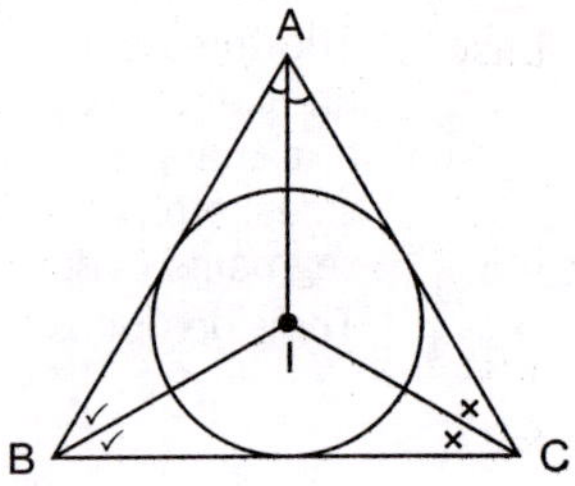


A line bisecting an interior angle of a triangle is called the internal bisector of the angle of the triangle. In the adjoining figure,

$$\angle BAI = \angle CAI,\ \angle CBI = \angle ABI,\ \angle ACI = \angle BCI$$

A triangle has three internal bisectors of its angles. The three angle bisectors of a triangle always pass through a point which is called the incentre of the triangle. Here, $I$ is the incentre of the triangle.

**Remember**

A circle can be drawn with centre *I* which touches all three sides of the triangle. This circle is called the incircle of the triangle.

### (iv) Circumcentre and Circumcircle

A line bisecting a side and perpendicular to it is called the right bisector of the side of the triangle. In the adjoining figure,

$$BD = CD,\ CE = AE, \text{ and } AF = FB$$

and $$\angle ODB = 90°, \angle OEC = 90°, \angle OFA = 90°$$

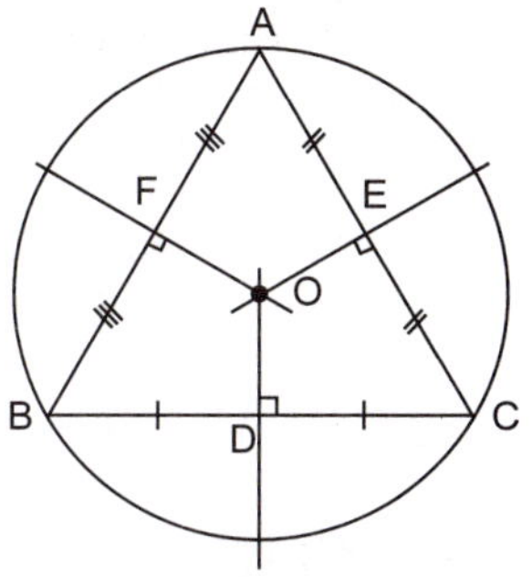


∴ $OD$, $OE$, and $OF$ are the right bisectors of the sides $BC$, $CA$, and $AB$, respectively. All three right bisectors of a triangle always pass through a point, which is called the circumcentre of the triangle.

Here '$O$' is the circumcentre of $\Delta ABC$.

**Remember**

A circle can be drawn with centre *O* and radius *OA* which passes through the vertices *A, B*, and *C*, of $\Delta ABC$. This circle is called the circumcircle of triangle.

## Angle Sum Property of a Triangle

The sum of three angles of a triangle is 180°.

In the adjoining figure, a $\Delta ABC$ is given in which $\angle A + \angle B + \angle C = 180°$.

Given $\Delta ABC$.

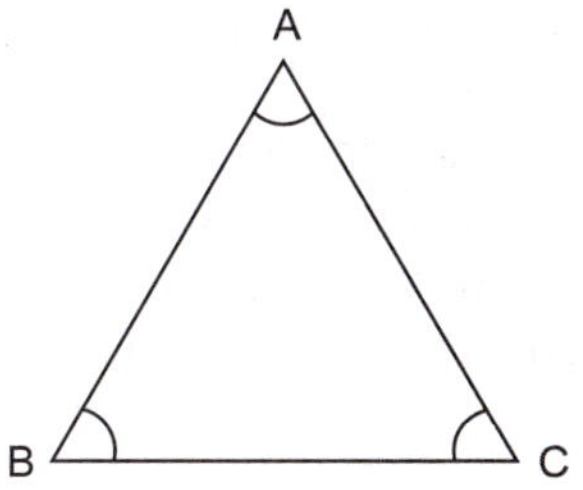


To prove : $\angle ABC + \angle BCA + \angle CAB = 180°$

Construction : Produce $BC$ to $D$ and draw $CE \parallel BA$.

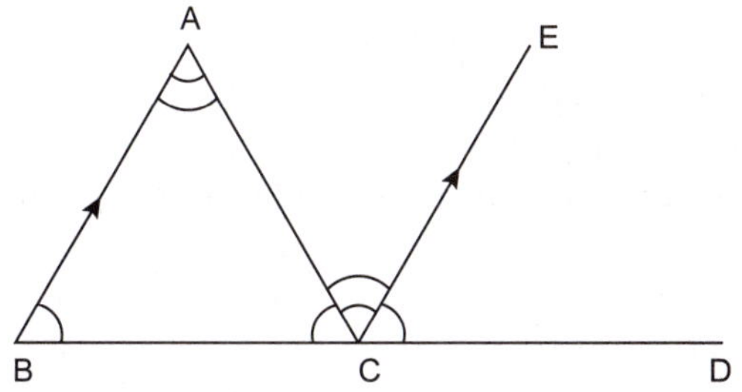


| Proof : Statements | | Reasons |
|---|---|---|
| $\angle BAC = \angle ACE$ | ...(i) | Alternate angles |
| $\angle ABC = \angle ECD$ | ...(ii) | Corresponding angles |
| $\angle BAC + \angle ABC = \angle ACE + \angle ECD$ | | Adding eq. *(i)* and *(ii)* |
| $\Rightarrow \angle BAC + \angle ABC + \angle ACB = \angle ACE + \angle ECD + \angle ACB$ | | Adding $\angle ACB$ on both sides |
| $= \angle BCD = 180°$ | | Straight angle |

Hence Proved.

## Exterior Angle Property of a Triangle

An exterior angle of a triangle is equal to the sum of its interior opposite angles.

In the adjoining figure, $\angle ACD = \angle A + \angle B$, where $\angle A$ and $\angle B$ are interior opposite angles for exterior angle $ACD$.

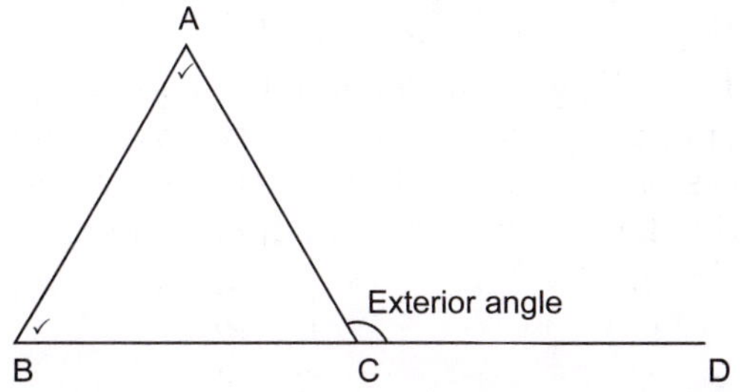

## Congruence of Triangles

Two geometrical figures are said to be congruent figures if they have exactly the same shape and the same size.

Two triangles are said to be congruent if they have exactly the same shape and the same figure.

or

Two triangles are said to be congruent if one triangle can be superposed on the other to cover it exactly.

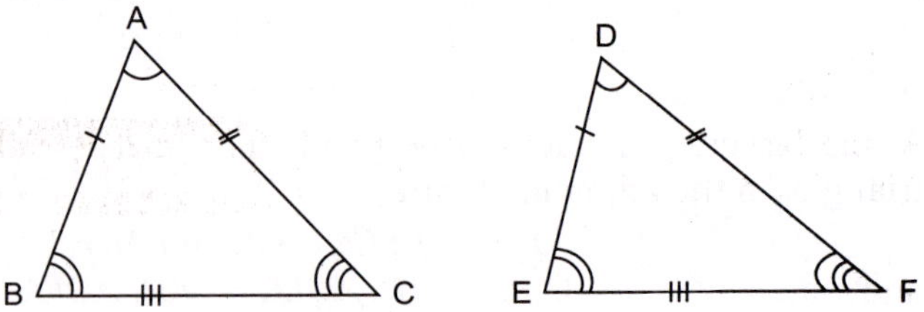


Consider, $\Delta ABC$ and $DEF$.

Here, (a) $AB = DE$, $AC = DF$ and $BC = EF$

(b) $\angle A = \angle D$, $\angle B = \angle E$, and $\angle C = \angle F$,

$\therefore$ $\Delta ABC$ and $\Delta DEF$ are congruent which can be written as

$$\Delta ABC \cong \Delta DEF$$

**NOTE**

The corresponding parts of congruent triangles are also congruent. It is abbreviated as CPCT.

### Criteria for Congruence of Triangles

To prove that two triangles are congruent, it is not necessary to prove that all six elements of one triangle are equal to the corresponding six elements of another triangle.

Let us perform an activity.

Draw two triangles $\Delta ABC$ and $\Delta PQR$ such that $AB = PQ = 5$ cm, $BC = QR = 6.5$ cm, and $CA = RP = 5$ cm. If we place $\Delta ABC$ on $\Delta PQR$ such that $A$ is on $P$ and $B$ is on $Q$ then we observe that $C$ lies on $R$. It shows that $\Delta ABC$ completely and exactly covers $\Delta PQR$, so $\Delta ABC \cong PQR$.

Thus, we obtained the following rule.

#### SSS Congruence Rule

Two triangles are congruent if the three sides of one triangle are equal to the three sides of another triangle. It is called side–side–side (SSS) congruence rule for triangles. In the adjoining figures,

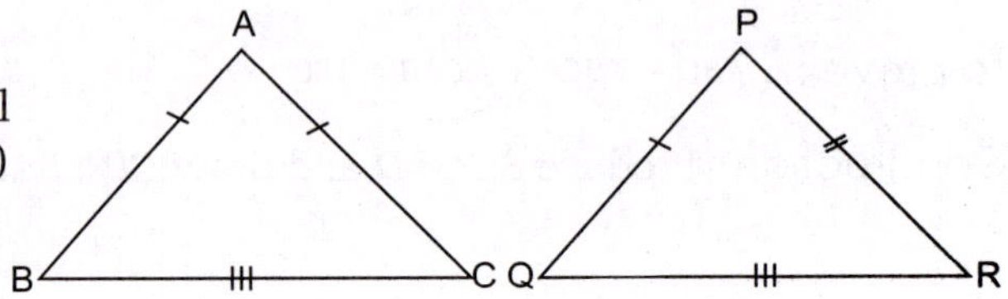


$AB = PQ$

$BC = QR$

and $AC = PR$

$\therefore$ $\Delta ABC \cong \Delta PQR$ (SSS criteria)

Let us perform another activity.

Consider two triangles $\Delta ABC$ and $\Delta PQR$ in which $AB = 5$ cm, $BC$, 6 cm, $\angle B = 60°$, $PQ = 5$ cm, $QR = 6$ cm and $\angle Q = 60°$. If we place side $AB$ on side $PQ$, point $B$ on point $Q$ and side $BC$ on side $QR$, we observe that $\Delta ABC$ completely and exactly covers $\angle PQR$. So,

$$\Delta ABC \cong \Delta PQR$$

Thus, we obtained the following rule.

#### SAS Congruence Rule

Two triangles are congruent if two sides and the included angle of one triangle are equal to two sides and the included angle to the other triangle. It is called side-angle-side (SAS) congruence rule for triangles. In the adjoining figures,

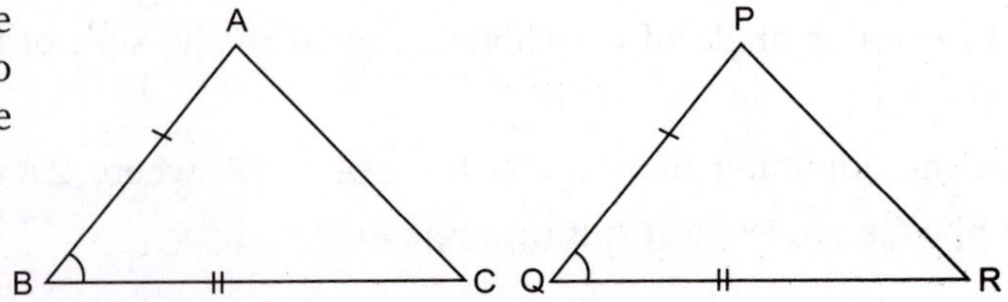


$AB = PQ$

$\angle B = \angle Q$

$BC = QR$

$\therefore$ $ABC \cong \Delta PQR$ (SAS criteria)

**Remember**

For SAS congruence rule, the equality of included angles is necessary.

## Illustrative Examples

**Example 1.** If $\Delta PQR \cong \Delta EDF$, then is it true to say that $PR = EF$? Give reason.

**Solution.** True,

$\because \quad \Delta PQR \cong \Delta EDF$

$\therefore \quad PR = EF$ (CPCT) Ans.

**Example 2.** In the adjoining figure, $AP = AQ$ and $AB$ bisects $\angle PAQ$. Show that $\Delta ABP \cong \Delta ABD$. What can you say about $BP$ and $BQ$?

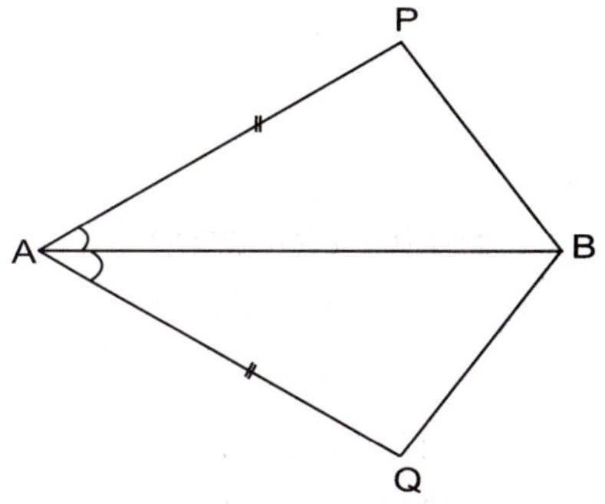


**Solution.**

| | Statements | Reasons |
|---|---|---|
| 1. | $AB = AQ$ | Given |
| 2. | $\angle BAP = \angle BAQ$ | $AB$ bisects $\angle PAQ$ |
| 3. | $AB = AB$ | Common |
| 4. | $\Delta ABP \cong \Delta ABQ$ | SAS criteria |
| 5. | $BP = BQ$ | CPCT Hence Proved. |

**Example 3.** In the adjoining figure, $AD = BC$ and $BD = AC$. Prove that $\angle ADB = \angle BCA$ and $\angle DAB = \angle CBA$.

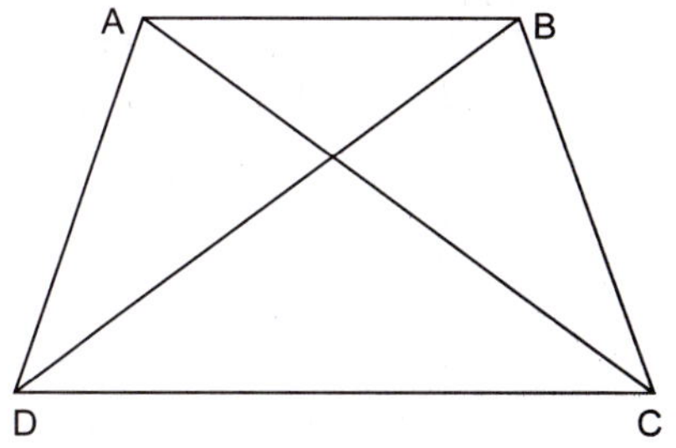


**Solution.**

| | Statements | Reasons |
|---|---|---|
| 1. | $AD = BC$ | Given |
| 2. | $BA = AB$ | Common |
| 3. | $BD = AC$ | Given |
| 4. | $\Delta ABD \cong \Delta BAC$ | SSS criteria |
| 5. | $\angle ADB = \angle BCA$ | CPCT |
| 6. | $\angle DAB \cong \angle CBA$ | CPCT Hence Proved. |

**Example 4.** In the adjoining figure, $M$ and $N$ are the mid-points of $AB$ and $AC$ respectively in $\Delta ABC$ and $AB = AC$. Show that $BN = CM$.

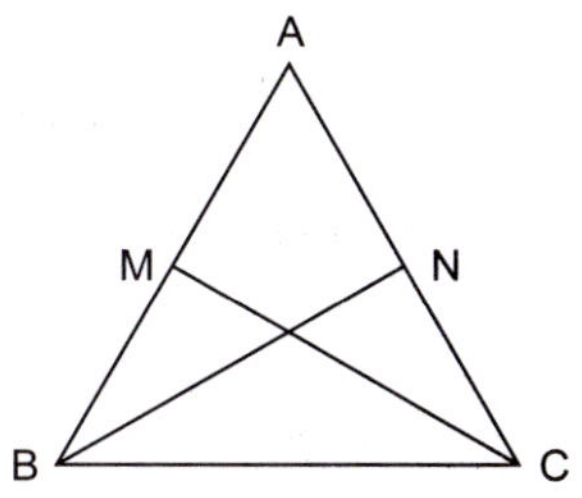


**Solution.**

| | Statements | Reasons |
|---|---|---|
| 1. | $AB = AC$ | Given |
| 2. | $\angle ACB = \angle ABC$ | Angles opposite to equal sides in $\Delta ABC$ |
| 3. | $AB = 2\ BM$ | $M$ is the mid-point of $AB$ |
| 4. | $AC = 2\ CN$ | $N$ is the mid-point of $AC$ |
| 5. | $2\ BM = 2\ CN$ | From (1), (3) and (4) |
| 6. | $BM = CN$ | Dividing by 2 in (5) |
| 7. | In $\Delta MBC$ and $\Delta NCB$ | $M$ is mid-point of $AC$ |
| | $BM = CN$ | From (6) |
| | $\angle MBC = \angle NCB$ | From (2) |
| | $BC = CB$ | Common |
| 8. | $\therefore \Delta MBC \cong \Delta NCB$ | SAS criteria |
| 9. | $CM = BN$ | CPCT |

Hence Proved.

**Example 5.** In the adjoining figure, $AB = AC$, $P$ and $Q$ are points on $BA$ and $CA$ produced respectively such that $AP = AQ$. Prove that :

(i) $\Delta APC \cong \Delta AQB$

(ii) $CP = BQ$

(iii) $\angle ACP = \angle ABQ$

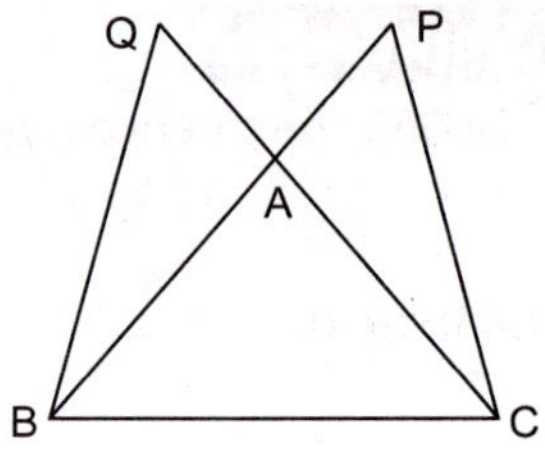


**Solution.**

| | Statements | Reasons |
|---|---|---|
| 1. | $AC = AB$ | Given |
| 2. | $\angle PAC = \angle QAB$ | Vertically opposite angles |
| 3. | $AP = AQ$ | Given |
| 4. | $\Delta APC \cong \Delta AQB$ | SAS criteria |
| 5. | $CP = BQ$ | CPCT |
| 6. | $\angle ACB = \angle ABQ$ | CPCT |

Hence Proved.

**Example 6.** In the adjoining figure, $AB = AD$, $AC = AE$ and $\angle BAD = \angle EAC$. Show that : $BC = DE$.

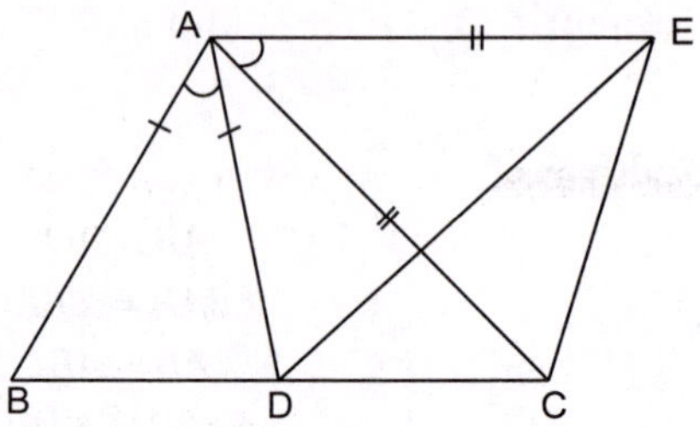


**Solution.** Given, $\angle BAD = \angle EAC$

Adding $\angle CAD$ on both sides, we get

$$\angle BAD + \angle CAD = \angle EAC + \angle CAD$$

$\Rightarrow$ $\angle BAC = \angle EAD$ ...(i)

In $\Delta BAC$ and $\Delta DAE$,

$BA = DA$ (Given)

$\angle BAC = \angle DAE$ [From (i)]

$AC = AE$ (Given)

$\therefore$ $\Delta BAC \cong \Delta DAE$ (SAS criteria)

$\Rightarrow$ $BC = DE$ (CPCT)

Hence Proved.

**Example 7.** In the adjoining figure, two sides $AB$, $BC$, and median $AM$ of one triangle $ABC$ are respectively equal to two sides $PQ$, $QR$ and median $PN$ of triangle $PQR$. Show that :

(i) $\Delta ABM \cong \Delta PQN$

(ii) $\Delta ABC \cong \Delta PQR$.

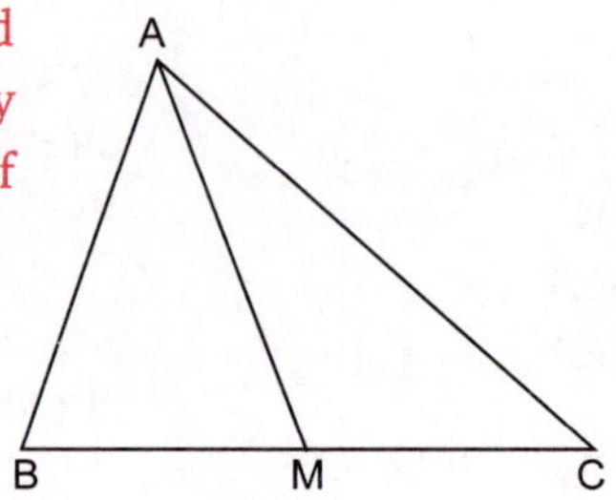


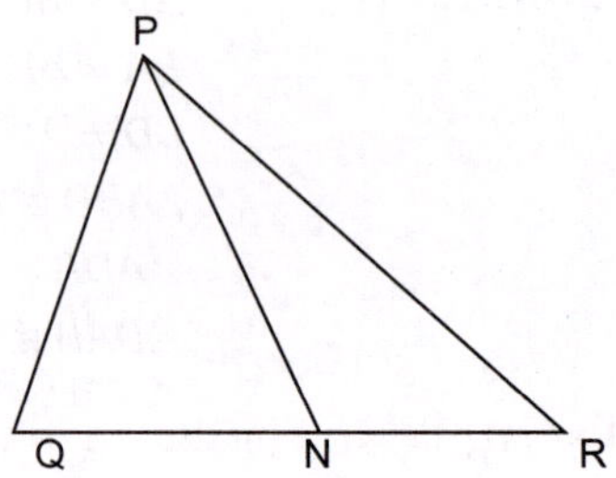


**Solution.** (i) $BC = QR$ (Given)

$\Rightarrow$ $\frac{1}{2}BC = \frac{1}{2}QR$ $\Rightarrow$ $BM = QN$ ...(i)

In $\Delta ABM$ and $\Delta PQN$

$AB = PQ$ (Given)

$BM = QN$ [From (i)]

$AM = PN$ (Given)

$\therefore$ $\Delta ABM \cong \Delta PQN$ (SSS criteria)

(ii) From part (i)

$\Delta ABM \cong \Delta PQN$

$\Rightarrow$ $\angle B = \angle Q$ (CPCT) ...(ii)

In $\Delta ABC$ and $\Delta PQR$

$AB = PQ$ (Given)

$\angle B = \angle Q$ [From (ii)]

$BC = QR$ (Given)

$\therefore$ $\Delta ABC \cong \Delta PQR$ (SAS criteria)

Hence Proved.

**Example 8.** In the adjoining figure, $AB = CD$, $CE = BF$ and $\angle ACE = \angle DBF$. Prove that :

(i) $\Delta ACE \cong \Delta DBF$

(ii) $AE = DF$.

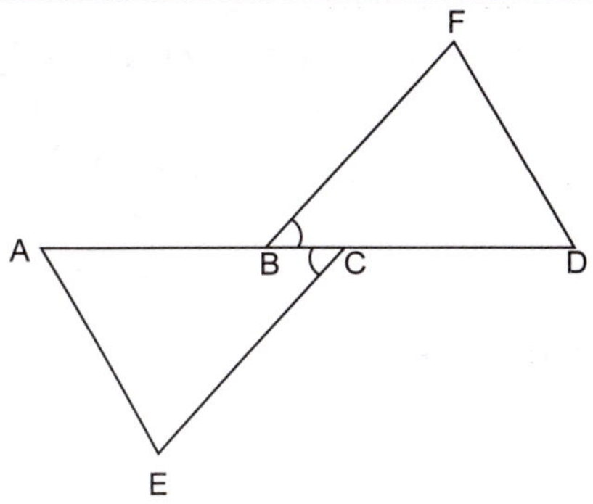


**Solution.** (i)

$AB = CD$ (Given)

$AB + BC = CD + BC$ (Adding $BC$ on both sides)

$\Rightarrow AC = DB$

In $\Delta ACE$ and $\Delta DBF$

$AC = DB$ (Proved above)

$\angle ACE = \angle DBF$ (Given)

$CE = BF$ (Given)

$\therefore \Delta ACE \cong \Delta DBF$ (SAS criteria)

(ii) $\because \Delta ACE \cong \Delta DBF$

$\therefore AE = DF$ (CPCT)

Hence Proved.

**Example 9.** From the adjoining figure, find the values of $x$ and $y$.

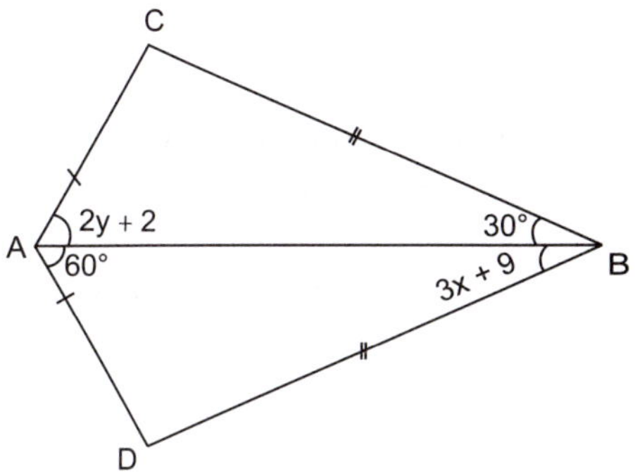


**Solution.** In $\Delta ABD$ and $\Delta ABC$,

$AD = AC$ (Given)

$AB = AB$ (Common)

$BD = BC$ (Given)

$\therefore \Delta ABD \cong \Delta ABC$ (SAS criteria)

$\Rightarrow \angle ABD = \angle ABC$ and $\angle BAD = \angle BAC$ (CPCT)

$\Rightarrow 3x + 9 = 30°$ and $60° = 2y + 2$

$\Rightarrow x = 7°$ and $y = 29°$ Ans.

**Example 10.** In the adjoining figure, $AB = DC$ and $AB \parallel DC$. Prove that : $AD = BC$.

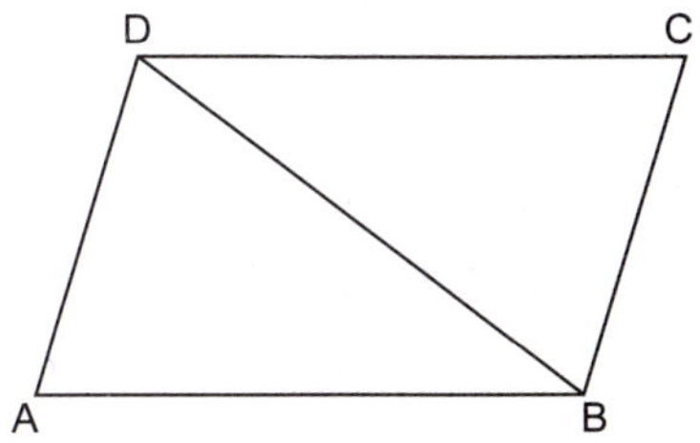


**Solution.**

| | Statements | Reasons |
|---|---|---|
| 1. | $AB = CD$ | Given |
| 2. | $\angle ABD = \angle CDB$ | Alternate angles as $AB \parallel CD$ and $BD$ is a transversal |
| 3. | $BD = DB$ | Common |
| 4. | $\Delta ABD \cong \Delta CDB$ | SAS criteria |
| 5. | $AD = CB$ | CPCT |

Hence Proved.

**Example 11.** Two line segments $AB$ and $CD$ bisect each other at $O$. Prove that :

(i) $AC = DB$

(ii) $\angle CAB = \angle ABD$

(iii) $AC \parallel DB$

(iv) $AD = CB$.

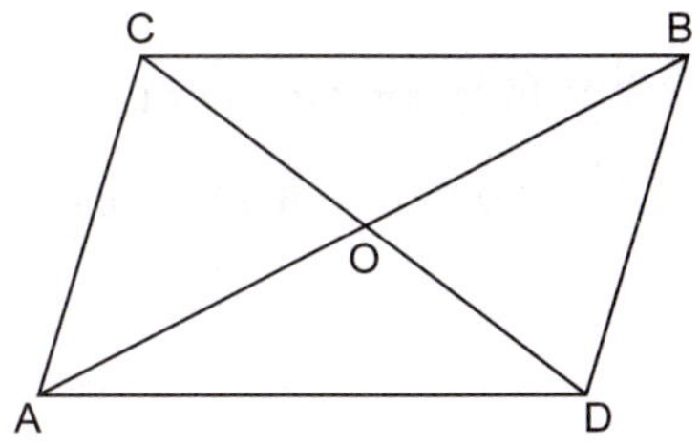


**Solution.** (i) In $\Delta OAC$ and $\Delta OBD$

$OA = OB$ ($\because$ $CD$ bisects $AB$)

$\angle AOC = \angle BOD$ (Vertically opposite angles)

$OC = OD$ ($\because$ $AB$ bisects $CD$)

$\therefore \Delta OAC \cong \Delta OBD$ (SAS criteria)

$\Rightarrow AC = BD$ (CPCT)

(ii) $\because \Delta OAC \cong \Delta OBD$

$\therefore \angle CAO = \angle DBO$ (CPCT)

$\Rightarrow \angle CAB = \angle DBA \quad \Rightarrow \quad \angle CAB = \angle ABD$

(iii) $\because \angle CAB = \angle ABD$ and $AB$ is a transversal

$\therefore \quad AC \parallel DB$

(iv) In $\square ABCD$

$AC = DB$ and $AC \parallel DB$

$\therefore ABCD$ is a parallelogram. $\Rightarrow$ $AD = CB$ **Hence Proved.**

## Exercise 8A

1. If $\Delta ABC \cong \Delta PQR$, is it true to say that $AB = PR$ ? Why?
2. In the adjoining figure, $AB = AC$, $AP = AQ$. Prove that :
   (i) $\Delta APC \cong \Delta AQB$ (ii) $CP = BQ$ (iii) $\angle APC = \angle AQB$

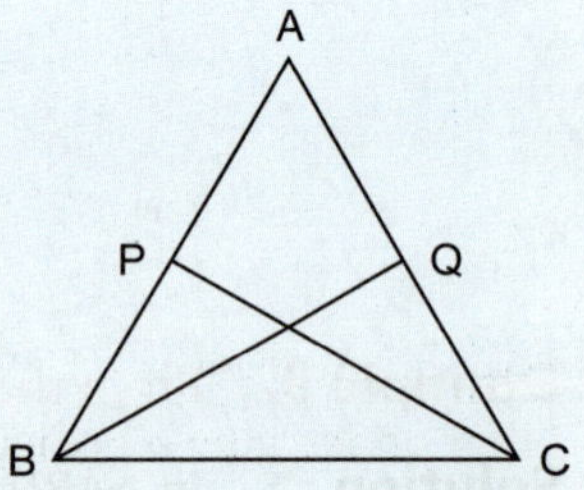


3. $AB$ is a line segment and line $l$ is its perpendicular bisector. If $P$ is a point on line $l$, show that $P$ is equidistant from $A$ and $B$.

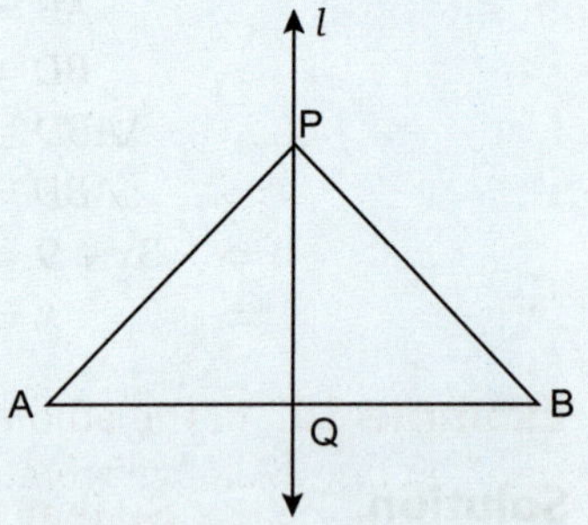


4. In the adjoining figure, $OA = OB$, and $OC = OD$. Show that :
   (i) $\Delta OAD \cong \Delta OBC$ (ii) $AD \parallel CB$.

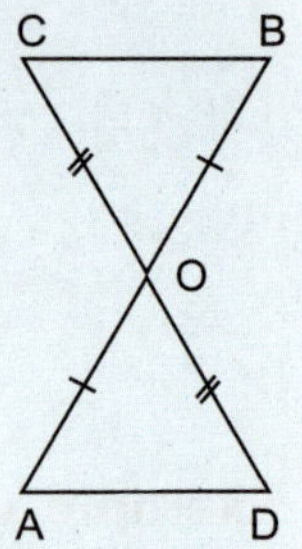


5. In quadrilateral $ABCD$, $AB = BC$ and $AD = CD$. Show that $BD$ bisects $\angle ABC$ and $\angle ADC$ both.
6. From the adjoining figure, find the values of $x$ and $y$.

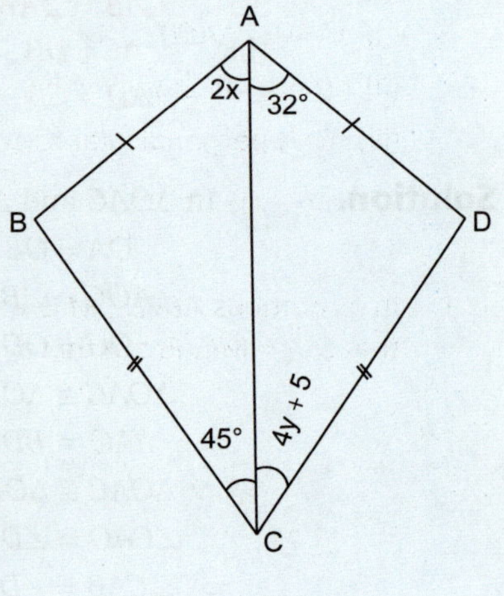

**7.** In the adjoining figure, $AB = PQ$, $BR = CQ$, $\angle ABC = \angle PQR = 90°$. Prove that $AC = PR$.

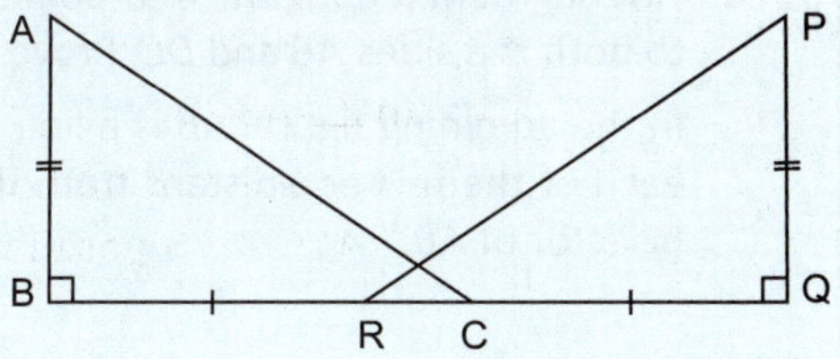


**8.** In the adjoining figure, $AB = AC$ and $AP$ is the bisector of $\angle A$. Prove that :

(i) $P$ is the mid-point of $BC$

(ii) $AP$ is perpendicular to $BC$

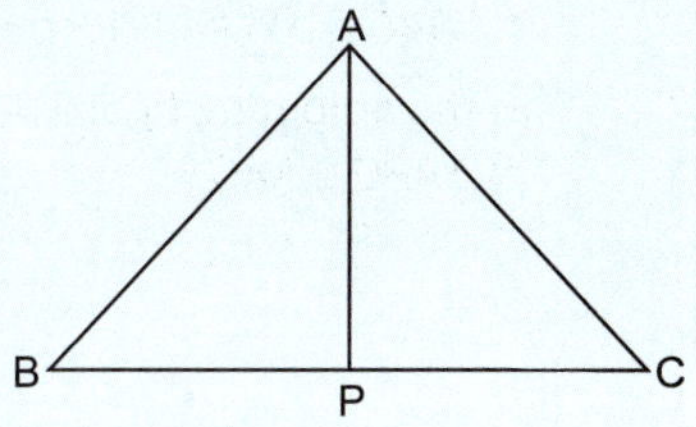


**9.** In the adjoining figure, $ABCD$ is a quadrilateral in which $AD = BC$ and $\angle DAB = \angle CBA$. Prove that:

(i) $\Delta ABD \cong \Delta BAC$ (ii) $BD = AC$ (iii) $\angle ABD = \angle BAC$

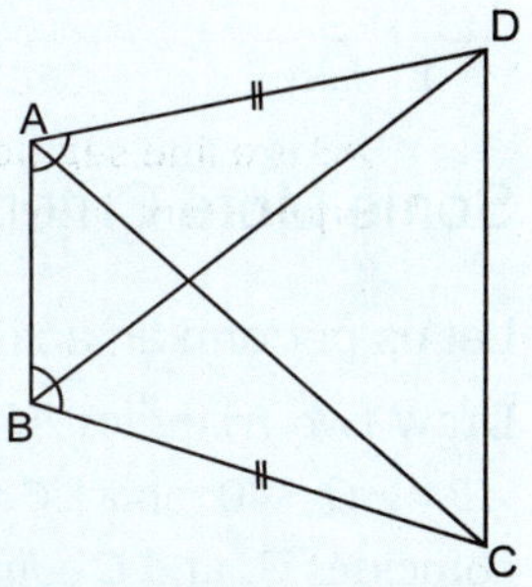


**10.** In the adjoining figure, $OA = OB$, $OC = OD$ and $\angle AOB = \angle COD$. Prove that: $AC = BD$.

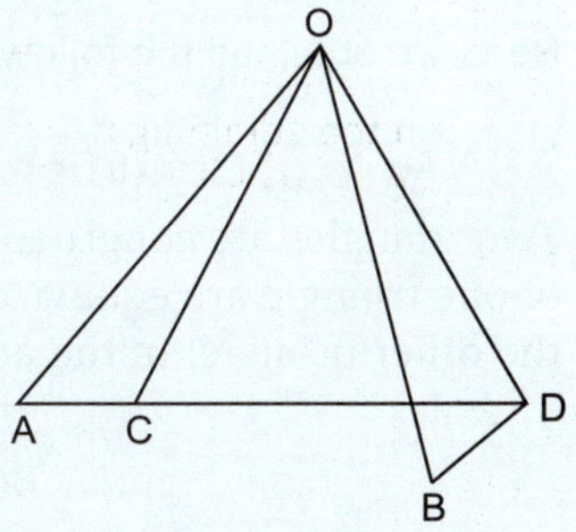


**11.** In the adjoining figure, $AB = AC$ and $D$ is the mid-point of $BC$. Use SSS criteria of congruency and prove that :

(i) $\Delta ABD \cong \Delta ACD$

(ii) $AD$ bisects $\angle A$.

(iii) $AD$ is perpendicular to $BC$.

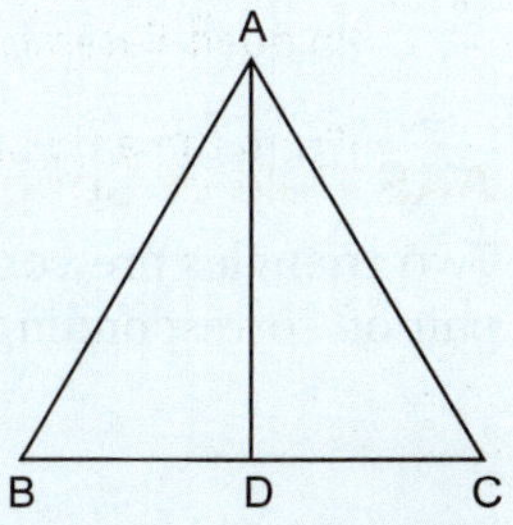


**12.** In a rhombus $ABCD$ , $M$ is any point in its interior as shown in the adjoining figure, such that $MA = MC$. Prove that $B$, $M$, $D$ are collinear.

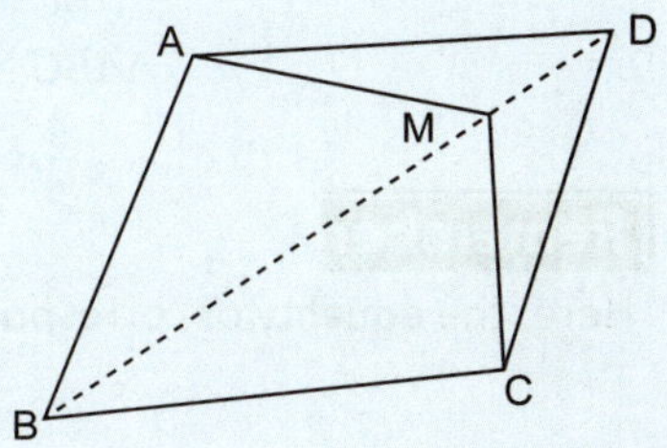

**13.** Line segment joining the mid-points $M$ and $N$ of parallel sides $AB$ and $DC$ respectively of a trapezium $ABCD$ is perpendicular to both the sides $AB$ and $DC$. Prove that : $AD = BC$.

**14.** In the adjoining figure, $AB$ is a line segment, $P$ and $Q$ are points on opposite sides of $AB$ such that each of them is equidistant from the points $A$ and $B$. Show that the line $PQ$ is the perpendicular bisector of $AB$.

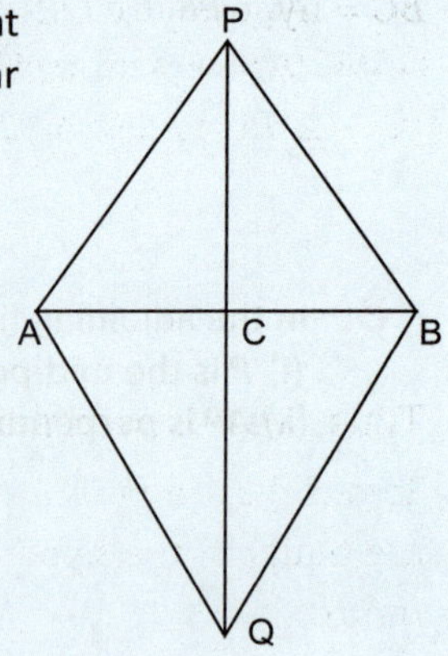


## *Answers*

**1.** false **6.** $x = 16°, y = 10°$

## Some More Criteria for Congruence of Triangles

Let us perform an activity.

Draw two triangles $ABC$ and $PQR$ such that $BC = QR = 5$ cm, $\angle B = \angle Q = 40°$ and $\angle C = \angle R = 45°$. Place side $BC$ on $QR$ so that $B$ coincides $Q$, and $C$ coincides $R$ then we observe that $A$ lies on $P$. Thus $\Delta ABC$ covers $\Delta PQR$ completely and exactly :

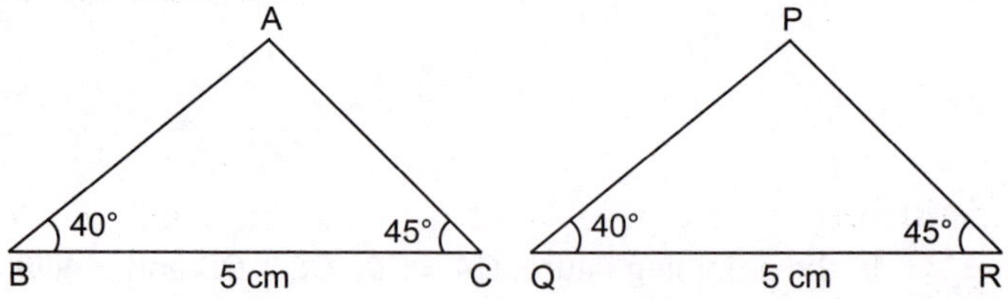


$\therefore$ $\Delta ABC \cong \Delta PQR$

Here, we obtained the following rule :

### ASA Rule of Congruency

Two triangles are congruent if two angles and the included side of one triangle are equal to two angles and the included side of the other triangle. In the adjoining figures,

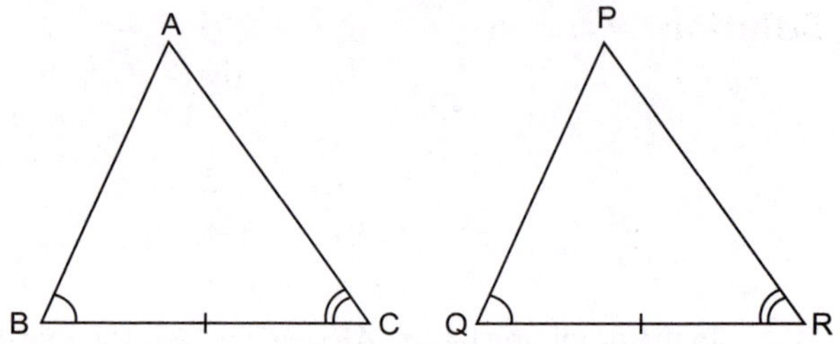


$\angle B = \angle Q$

$BC = QR$

$\angle C = \angle R$

$\therefore$ $\Delta ABC \cong \Delta PQR$ (ASA criteria)

### AAS Rule of Congruency

Two triangles are congruent if any two pairs of angles and a pair of corresponding sides are equal. In the adjoining figures,

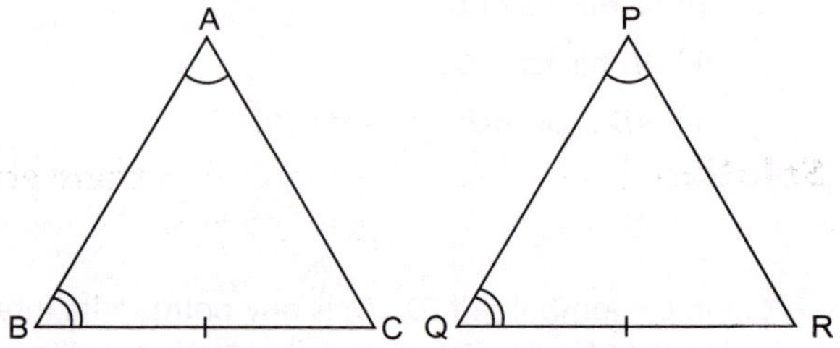


$\angle A = \angle P$

$\angle B = \angle Q$

$BC = QR$

$\therefore$ $\Delta ABC \cong \Delta PQR$ (AAS criteria)

**Remember**

Here, the equality of corresponding sides is necessary.

Let us perform an activity.

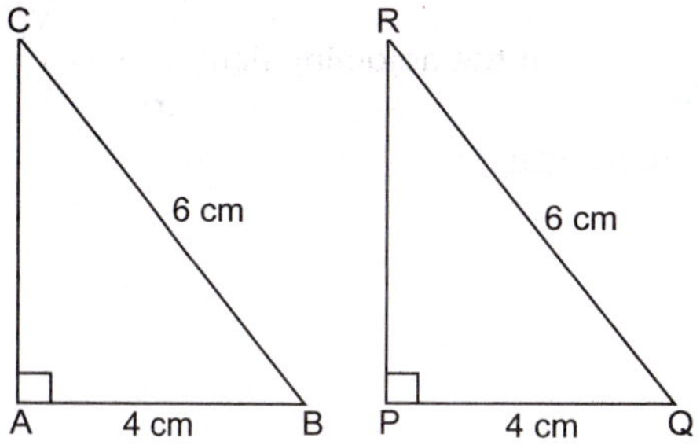


Draw two right-angled triangles $ABC$ and $PQR$ such that hypotenuse $BC$ = hypotenuse $QR$ = 6 cm, side $AB$ = side $PQ$ = 4 cm and $\angle A = \angle P = 90°$. Place $\Delta ABC$ over $\Delta PQR$, so that $A$ is on $P$ and $B$ is on $Q$. We observe that $C$ lies on $R$.

$\therefore$ $\Delta ABC$ covers $\Delta PQR$ completely and exactly. So,

$$\Delta ABC \cong PQR \qquad \text{(RHS criteria)}$$

Thus, we obtained the following criteria

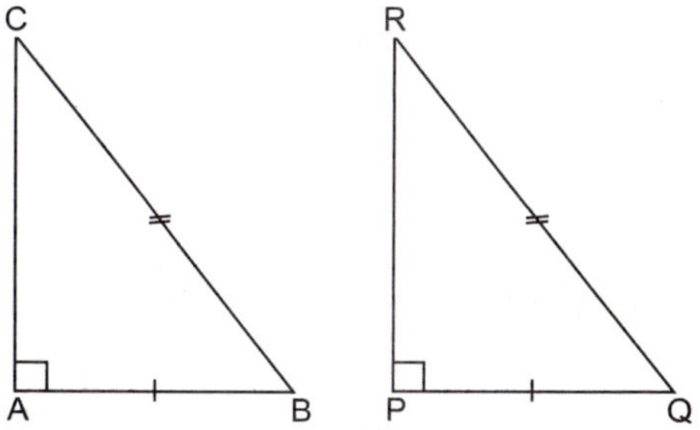


Two right triangles are congruent if the hypotenuse and one side of one triangle are equal to the hypotenuse and one side of the other triangle. In the adjoining figures,

$$\angle A = \angle P = 90°$$
$$BC = QR$$
$$AB = PQ$$
$\therefore$ $$\Delta ABC \cong \Delta PQR \qquad \text{(RHS criteria)}$$

## Illustrative Examples

**Example 1.** "If two angles and one side of a triangle are equal to two angles and one side of another triangle, then the triangles must be congruent." Is the statement true ? Why?

**Solution.** No, sides must be the corresponding sides.

**Example 2.** In the adjoining figure, $AB = AC$ and $\angle ABE = \angle ACD$. Prove that :
(i) $\Delta ABE \cong \Delta ACD$ (ii) $BE = CD$.

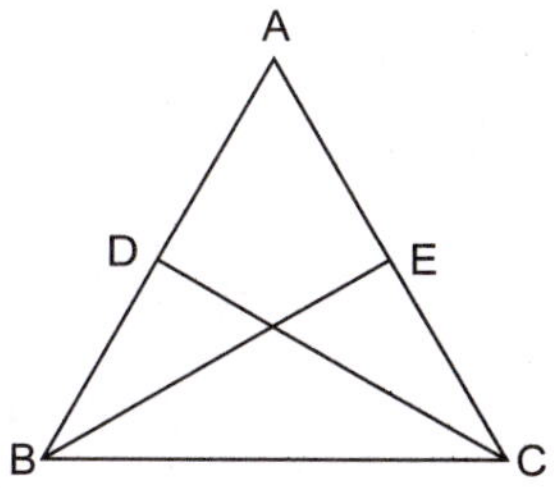


**Solution.** (i) In $\Delta ABE$ and $\Delta ACD$

$\angle ABE = \angle ACD$ (Given)
$AB = AC$ (Given)
$\angle BAE = \angle CAD$ (Common)
$\therefore$ $\Delta ABE \cong \Delta ACD$ (ASA criteria)

(ii) $\because$ $\Delta ABE$ and $\Delta ACD$ [From part (i)]
$\therefore$ $BE = CD$ (CPCT)

Hence Proved.

**Example 3.** In the adjoining figure, line segment $AB$ is parallel to another line segment $CD$, $P$ is mid-point of $AC$. Show that :
(i) $\Delta APB \cong \Delta DPC$
(ii) $P$ *is also a mid-point of* $BD$.

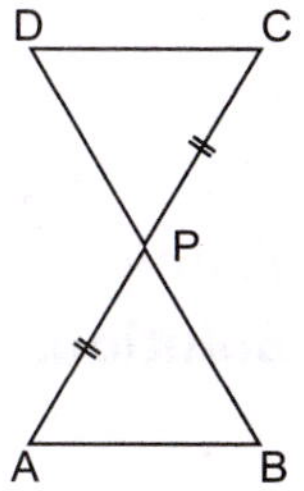


**Solution.** (i) $AB \parallel CD$ and $BC$ is a transversal

$\therefore$ $\angle ABP = \angle DCP$ (Alternate angles)

In $\Delta APB$ and $\Delta DPC$

$PA = PC$ ($P$ is the mid-point of $AC$.)
$\angle ABP = \angle DCP$ (Proved above)
$\angle APB = \angle DPC$ (Vertically opposite angles)
$\therefore$ $\Delta APB \cong \Delta DPC$ (AAS criteria)

(ii) $PB = PC$ (CPCT)

$\Rightarrow$ $P$ is the mid-point of $BD$.

Hence Proved.

**Example 4.** In the adjoining figure, $AD$ is median of $\Delta ABC$, $BM$ and $CN$ are perpendiculars drawn from $B$ and $C$ respectively on $AD$ and $AD$ produced. Prove that $BM = CN$.

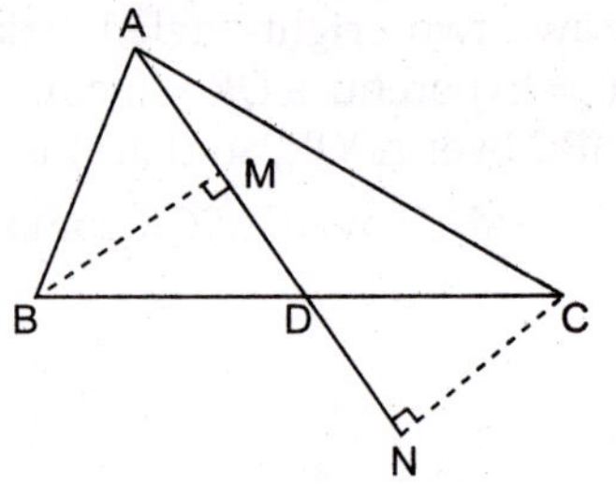


**Solution.**

| | Statements | Reasons |
|---|---|---|
| 1. | $\angle BMD = \angle CND$ | Each 90° |
| 2. | $\angle BDM = \angle CDN$ | Vertically opposite angles |
| 3. | $BD = CD$ | $D$ is the mid-point of $BC$. |
| 4. | $\Delta BMD \cong \Delta CND$ | AAS criteria |
| 5. | $BM = CN$ | CPCT |

Hence Proved.

**Example 5.** In the adjoining figure, the line $l$ is the bisector of angle $A$ and $B$ at any point on line $l$. If $BM \perp AP$ and $BN \perp AQ$. Show that :

(i) $\Delta AMB \cong \Delta ANB$.

(ii) $B$ *is equidistant from the arms of* $\angle A$.

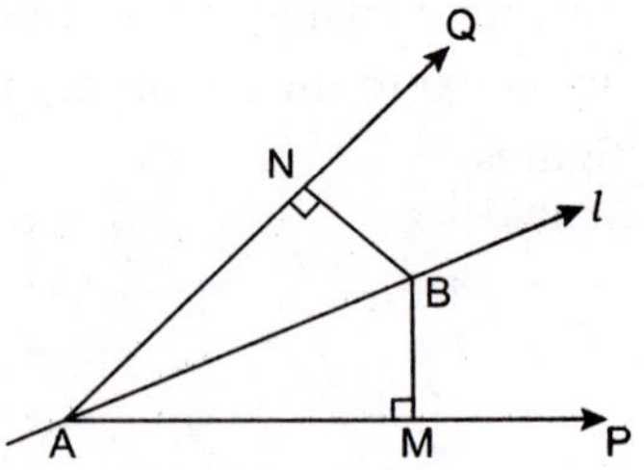


**Solution.** (i) In $\Delta AMB$ and $\Delta ANB$,

$\angle AMB = \angle ANB$ (Each 90°)

$\angle BAM = \angle BAN$ ($l$ is bisector of $\angle A$)

$AB = AB$ (Common)

$\therefore \Delta AMB \cong \Delta ANB$ (AAS criteria)

(ii) $\because \Delta AMB \cong \Delta ANB$ [From part (i)]

$BM = BN$ (CPCT)

*i.e.*, $B$ is equidistant from the arms of $\angle A$.

Hence Proved.

**Example 6.** In the adjoining figure, two lines $AB$ and $CD$ intersect each other at point $O$ such that $BC \parallel DA$ and $BC = DA$. Prove that $O$ is the mid-point of both the line segments $AB$ and $CD$.

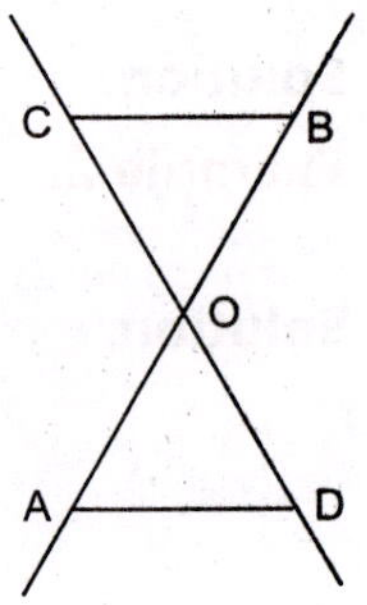


**Solution.** $BC \parallel DA$ and $AB$ is a transversal.

$\therefore \angle CBO = \angle AOD$ (Alternate angles)

$BC \parallel DA$ and $CD$ is a transversal.

$\therefore \angle OCB = \angle ODA$ (Alternate angles)

Now, in $\Delta OBC$ and $\Delta OAD$,

$\angle CBO = \angle DAO$ (Proved above)

$\angle OCB = \angle ODA$ (Proved above)

$BC = AD$ (Given)

$\therefore \Delta OBC \cong \Delta OAD$ (AAS criteria)

$\Rightarrow OB = OA$ and $OC = OD$ (CPCT)

Hence, $O$ is the mid-point of both the line segments $AB$ and $CD$.

Hence Proved.

**Example 7.** From the adjoining figure, find the value of $x$ and $y$.

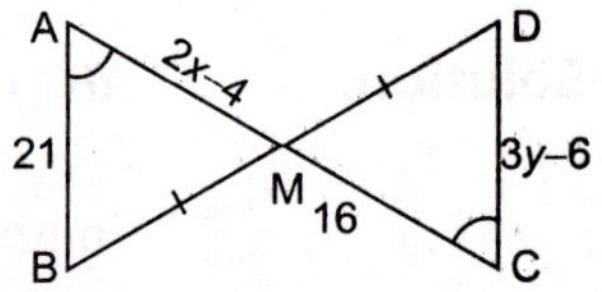


**Solution.** In $\Delta ABM$ and $\Delta CDM$,

$\angle BAM = \angle DCM$ (Given)

$\angle AMB = \angle CMD$ (Vertically opposite angles)

$BM = DM$ (Given)

$\therefore \Delta ABM \cong \Delta CDM$ (AAS criteria)

$\Rightarrow AB = CD$ and $AM = CM$ (CPCT)

$\Rightarrow 21 = 3y - 6$ and $2x - 4 = 16$

$3y = 27$ $\quad$ $2x = 20$

$\Rightarrow y = 9$ and $x = 10$

Ans.

**Example 8.** In the adjoining figure, $BQ$ and $DP$ are prependiculars to the line segment $AC$. If $BQ = DP$ then prove that $AC$ bisects $BD$.

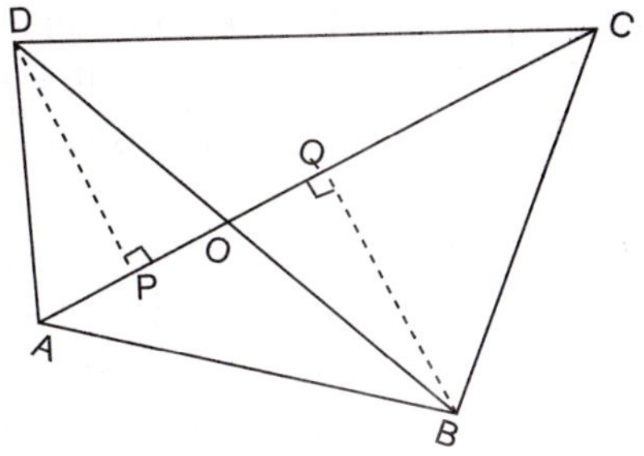


**Solution.**

| Statements | Reasons |
|---|---|
| 1. $\angle POD = \angle QOB$ | Vertically opposite angles |
| 2. $\angle OPD = \angle OQB$ | Each 90° |
| 3. $DP = BQ$ | Given |
| 4. $\Delta OPD \cong \Delta OQB$ | AAS criteria |
| 5. $OD = OB$ | CPCT |

Hence, $O$ is the mid-point of $BD$.

$\Rightarrow$ $AC$ bisects $BD$

Hence Proved.

**Example 9.** In the adjoining figure, $\angle B = \angle E$, $\angle BAD = \angle EAC$ and $BD = EC$. Prove that $\Delta ABC \cong \Delta AED$.

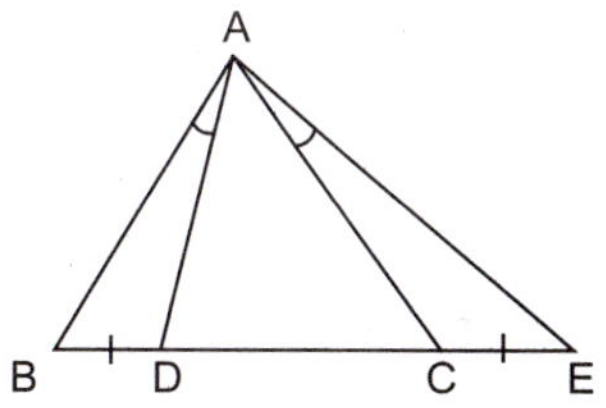


**Solution.** In $\Delta ABD$ and $\Delta AEC$,

$\angle BAD = \angle EAC$ (Given)

$\angle ABD = \angle AEC$ (Given)

$BD = EC$ (Given)

$\therefore$ $\Delta ABD \cong \Delta AEC$ (AAS Criteria)

$\Rightarrow$ $AB = AE$ (CPCT) ...(i)

Given, $BD = EC$

$\Rightarrow$ $BD + CD = EC + CD$ (Adding $CD$ on both sides)

$\Rightarrow$ $BC = ED$ ...(ii)

In $\Delta ABC$ and $\Delta AED$,

$BC = ED$ [From eq. *(ii)*]

$\angle ABC = \angle AED$ (Given)

$AB = AE$ [From *(i)*]

$\therefore$ $\Delta ABC \cong \Delta AED$ (SAS criteria)

Hence Proved.

**Example 10.** In the adjoining figure, $AD \perp BC$, $AD \perp EF$ and $\angle EAB = \angle FAC$. Prove that $\Delta ABD \cong \Delta ACD$.

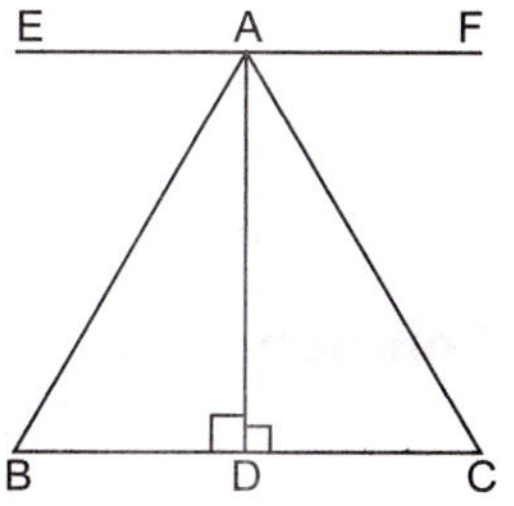


**Solution.** $AD \perp EF$

$\Rightarrow$ $\angle DAE = \angle DAF$ ...(i)

$\angle EAB = \angle FAC$ ...(ii) (Given)

Subtracting eqns. *(ii)* from *(i)*, we get

$$\angle DAE - \angle EAB = \angle DAF - \angle FAC$$

$\Rightarrow$ $\angle BAD = \angle CAD$ ...(iii)

In $\Delta ABD$ and $\Delta ACD$,

$\angle BAD = \angle CAD$ [From eqn. *(iii)*]

$AD = DC$ (Common)

$\angle ADB = \angle ACD$ (Each 90°)

$\therefore$ $\Delta ABD \cong \Delta ADC$ (ASA criteria)

Hence Proved.

**Example 11.** In the adjoining figure, $AB = AD$, $\angle BAM = \angle NAD$ and $\angle MAC = \angle CAN$. Prove that $AM = AN$.

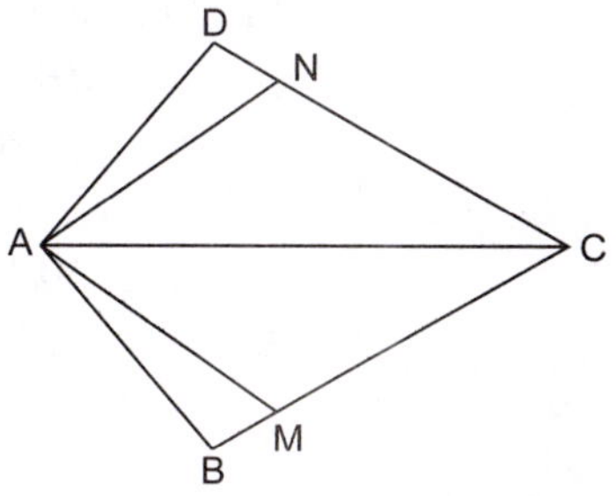


**Solution.** Given,

$\angle BAM = \angle NAD$ ...(i)

and $\angle MAC = \angle CAN$ ...(ii)

adding eqn. *(i)* and *(ii)* we get

$$\angle BAM + \angle MAC = \angle NAD + \angle CAN$$

$\Rightarrow$ $\angle BAC = \angle CAD$

In $\Delta ABC$ and $\Delta ADC$,

$AB = AD$ (Given)

$\angle BAC = \angle DAC$ (Proved above)

$AC = AC$ (Common)

$\therefore \quad \Delta ABC \cong \Delta ADC$ (SAS criteria)

$\Rightarrow \quad \angle ABC = \angle ADC$ (CPCT)

$\Rightarrow \quad \angle ABM = \angle ADN$

In $\Delta ABM$ and $\Delta ADN$,

$\angle ABM = \angle ADN$ (Proved above)

$AB = AD$ (Given)

$\angle BAM = \angle DAN$ (Given)

$\therefore \quad \Delta ABM \cong \Delta ADN$ (ASA criteria)

$\Rightarrow \quad AM = AN$ (CPCT)

Hence Proved.

**Example 12.** In the adjoining figure, $AB$ is a line segment and $P$ is its mid-point. $D$ and $E$ are points on the same side of $AB$ such that, $\angle BAD = \angle ABE$ and $\angle EPA = \angle DPB$. Prove that:

(i) $\Delta DAP \cong \Delta EBP$

(ii) $AD = BE$.

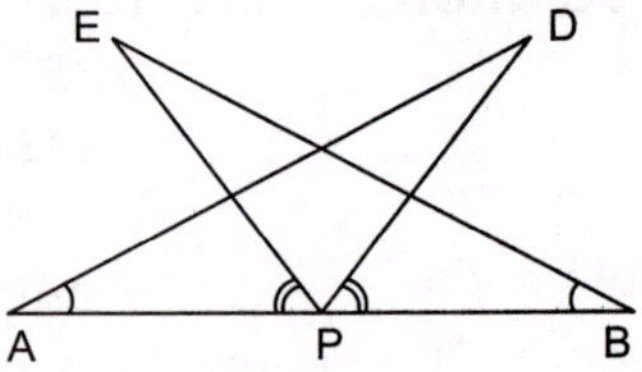


**Solution.** (i) Given that,

$$\angle EPA = \angle DPB \quad \ldots(i)$$

Adding $\angle EPD$ on both sides, we get

$$\angle EPA + \angle EPD = \angle DPB + \angle EPD$$

$$\Rightarrow \quad \angle EPB = \angle DPA$$

In $\Delta DAP$ and $\Delta EBP$,

$\angle DPA = \angle EPB$ (Proved above)

$PA = PB$ ($P$ is the mid-point of $AB$.)

$\angle PAD = \angle PBE$ (Given)

$\therefore \quad \Delta DAP \cong \Delta EBP$ (ASA criteria)

(ii) $AD = BE$ (CPCT)

Hence Proved.

**Example 13.** In the adjoining figure, $PQ = RQ$ and $\angle PAR = \angle PBR$. Prove that $BP = AR$.

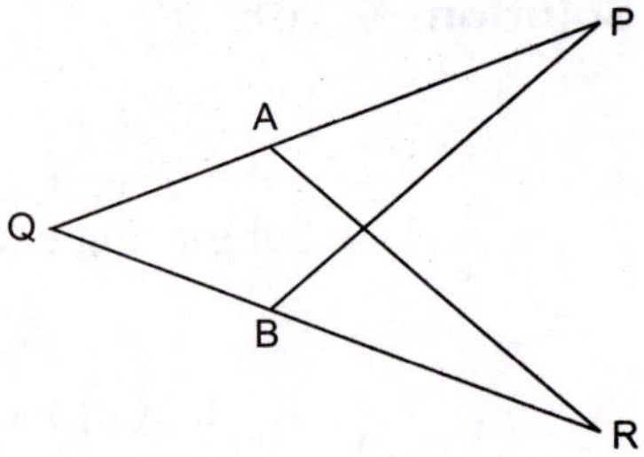


**Solution.** In $\Delta AQR$,

$\angle PAR$ is the exterior angle.

$\therefore \quad \angle PAR = \angle Q + \angle ARQ$

In $\Delta BPQ$,

$\angle PBR$ is the exterior angle.

$\therefore \quad \angle PBR = \angle Q + \angle BPQ$

but $\quad \angle PAR = \angle PBR$ (Given)

$\therefore \quad \angle Q + \angle ARQ = \angle Q + \angle BPQ$

$\Rightarrow \quad \angle ARQ = \angle BPQ$

In $\Delta BPQ$ and $\Delta ARQ$,

$\angle BPQ = \angle ARQ$ (Proved above)

$PQ = RQ$ (Given)

$\angle Q = \angle Q$ (Common)

$\therefore \quad \Delta BPQ \cong \Delta ARQ$ (ASA criteria)

$\Rightarrow \quad BP = AR$ (CPCT)

Hence Proved.

**Example 14.** In the adjoining figure, $\angle BCD = \angle ADC$ and $\angle BCA = \angle ADB$. Show that :

(i) $\Delta ACD \cong \Delta BDC$

(ii) $AD = BC$

(iii) $\angle A = \angle B$.

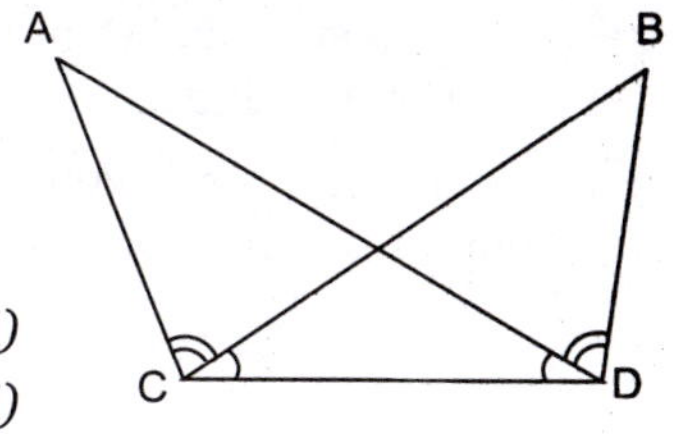


**Solution.** Given, $\angle BCD = \angle ADC$ ...(i)

and $\angle ACB = \angle ADB$ ...(ii)

Adding eqns. (i) and (ii), we get

$\angle BCD + \angle ACB = \angle ADC + \angle ADB$

$\Rightarrow \angle ACD = \angle BDC$

(i) In $\Delta ACD$ and $\Delta BDC$,

$\angle ACD = \angle BDC$ (Proved above)

$CD = DC$ (Common)

$\angle ADC = \angle BCD$ (Given)

$\therefore \Delta ACD \cong \Delta BCD$ (ASA criteria)

(ii) $AD = BC$ (CPCT)

(iii) $\angle A = \angle B$ (CPCT)

Hence Proved.

**Example 15.** In $\Delta ABC$, the internal bisectors of $\angle B$ and $\angle C$ meet at $O$. Prove that $OA$ is also the internal bisector of $\angle A$.

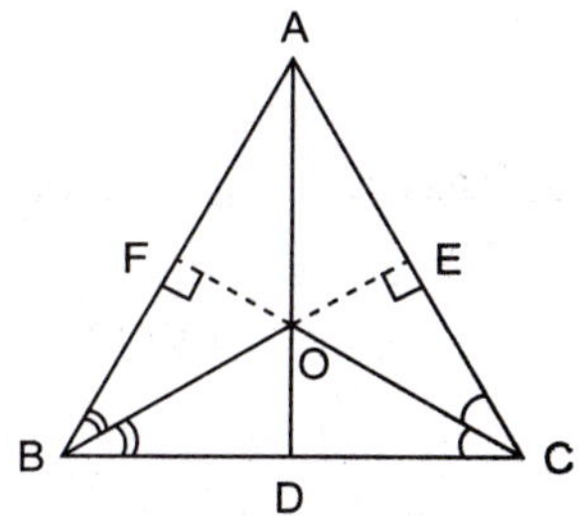


**Solution.** Draw $OD \perp BC$, $OE \perp CA$ and $OF \perp AB$.

| Statements | Reasons |
|---|---|
| 1. $\angle ODC = \angle OEC$ | Each 90° |
| 2. $\angle OCD = \angle OCE$ | $OC$ bisects $\angle C$. |
| 3. $OC = OC$ | Common |
| 4. $\Delta ODC \cong \Delta OEC$ | AAS criteria |
| 5. $OD = OE$ | CPCT |
| 6. $OD = OF$ | By proving $\Delta OBD \cong \Delta OBF$ |
| 7. $OE = OF$ | From (5) and (6) |
| 8. $\angle OEA = \angle OFA$ | Each 90° |
| 9. $OA = OA$ | Common |
| 10. $\Delta OAE \cong \Delta OAF$ | RHS criteria |
| 11. $\angle OAE = \angle OAF$ | CPCT |

$\Rightarrow OA$ bisects $\angle A$

Hence Proved.

## Exercise 8B

1. In $\Delta ABC$ and $\Delta PQR$, $\angle A = \angle R$ and $\angle B = \angle P$. Which side of $\Delta ABC$ should be equal to $\Delta PQR$, so that the two triangles are congruent. Give reason.

2. In $\Delta ABC$ and $\Delta PQR$, $AB = PQ$ and $AC = PR$. Which angle of $\Delta ABC$ should be equal to $\Delta PQR$, so that the two triangles are congruent. Give reason.

3. In the adjoining figure, $BE = CD$ and $\angle BEA = \angle CDA$. Prove that $AE = AD$.

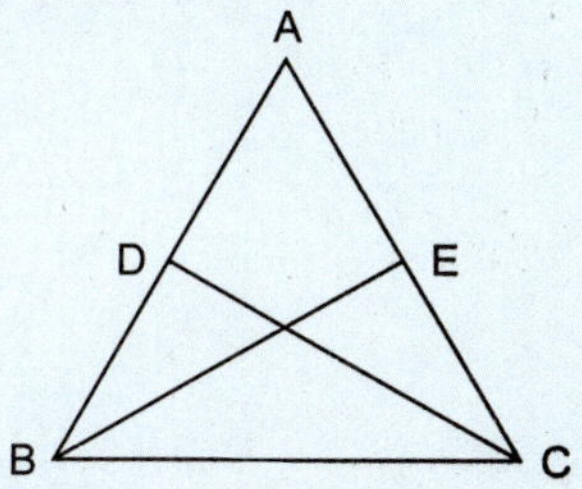

**4.** $P$ is a point equidistant from two lines $m$ and $n$ intersecting at a point $M$. Show that the line $MP$ bisects the angle between the lines $m$ and $n$.

**5.** In the adjoining figure, $l$ and $m$ are two parallel lines intersected by another pair of parallel lines $p$ and $q$. Show that :

$$\Delta ABC \cong \Delta CDA.$$

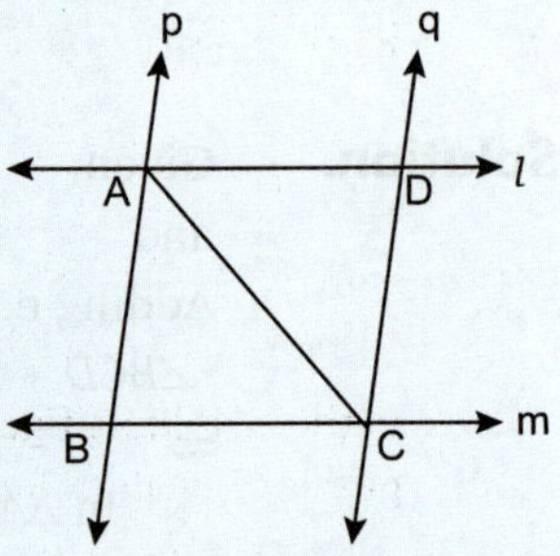


**6.** In the adjoining figure, $AD$ and $BC$ are equal perpendiculars to the line segment $AB$. Show that : $CD$ bisects $AB$.

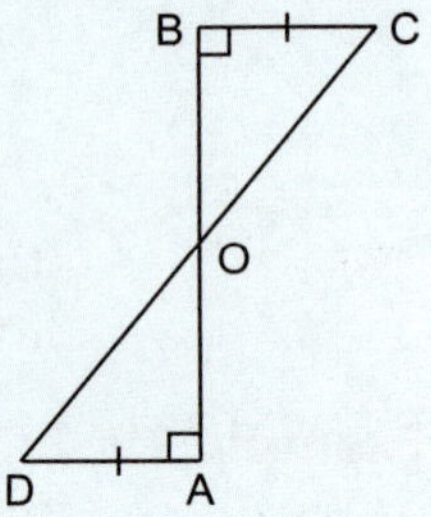


**7.** In quadrilateral $ABCD$, the diagonal $AC$ bisects $\angle A$ and $\angle C$ both. Prove that $AB = AD$ and $CB = CD$.

**8.** In a rectangle $ABCD$, $X$ and $Y$ are points on the sides $AD$ and $BC$ respectively such that $AY = BX$. Prove that: $BY = AX$ and $\angle BAY = \angle ABX$.

**9.** $ABC$ is an isosceles triangle with $AB = AC$. If $AP \perp BC$, then show that : $\angle B = \angle C$.

**10.** In the adjoining figure, $\angle ABC = \angle ACB$. $M$ and $N$ are points on the sides $AC$ and $AB$ respectively such that $BN = CM$. Prove that :

(i) $\Delta NBC \cong \Delta MCB$

(ii) $\Delta PNB \cong \Delta PMC$

(iii) $PB = PC$.

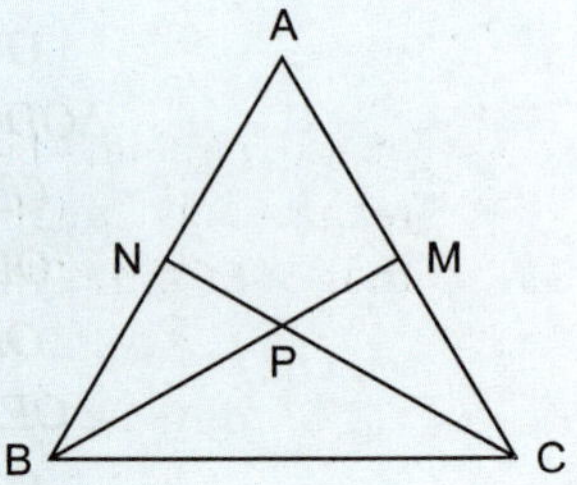


**11.** In the adjoining figure, $BA \perp AC$, $PQ \perp PR$, such that $BA = PQ$ and $BR = CQ$. Show that : $\Delta ABC \cong \Delta PQR$.

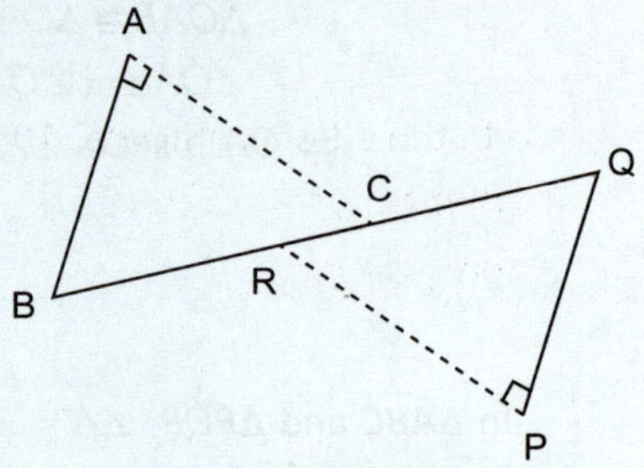


**12.** From the adjoining figure, find the value of $x$ and $y$.

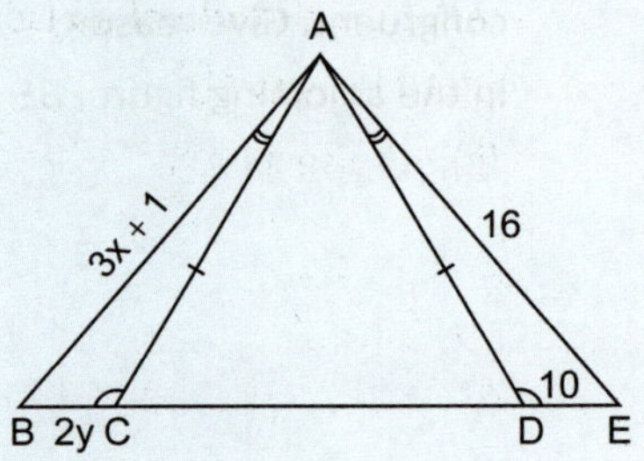

**13.** In the adjoining figure, $AB \parallel DC$ and $\angle C = \angle D$. Prove that:

(i) $AD = BC$

(ii) $AC = BD$.

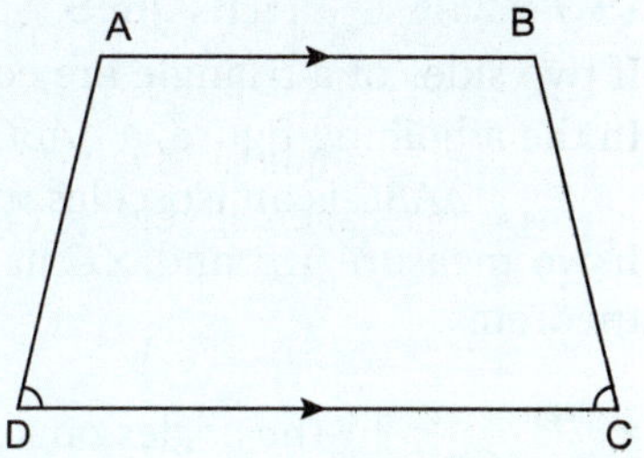


**14.** In the adjoining figure, $ABCD$ is a squre and $R$ is the mid-point of $AB$. $PQ$ is any line segment passing through $R$ which meets $AD$ at $P$ and $CB$ produced at $Q$. Prove that $R$ is the mid-point of $PQ$.

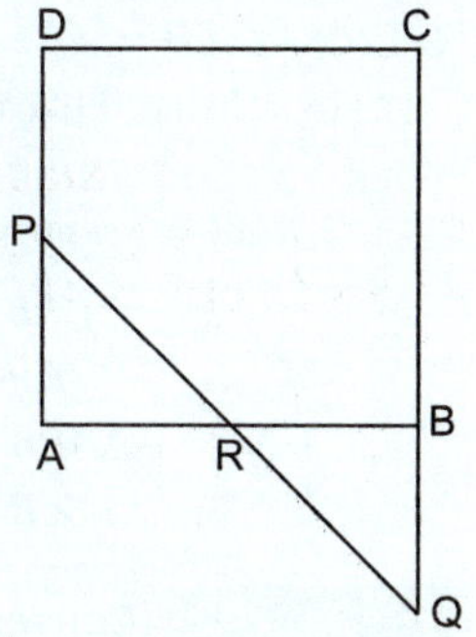


**15.** In the adjoining figure, $AB = CD$ and $\angle ABC = \angle BCD$. Prove that :

(i) $AC = BD$

(ii) $BP = CP$.

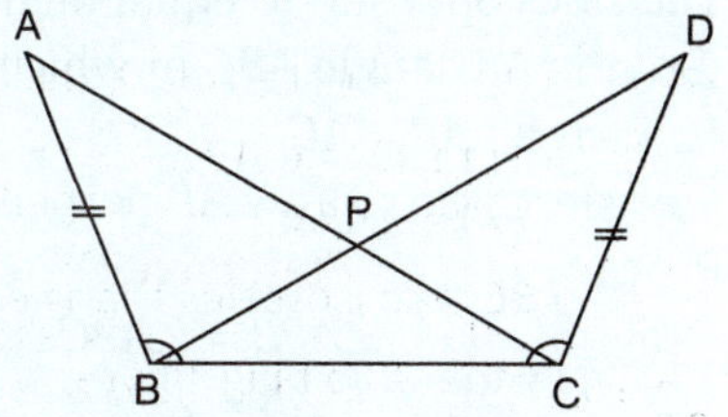


**16.** In the adjoining figure, two sides $AB$, $AC$ and altitude $AM$ of $\Delta ABC$ are respectively equal to two sides $PQ$, $PR$ and altitude $PN$ of $\Delta PQR$. Prove that $\Delta ABC \cong \Delta PQR$.

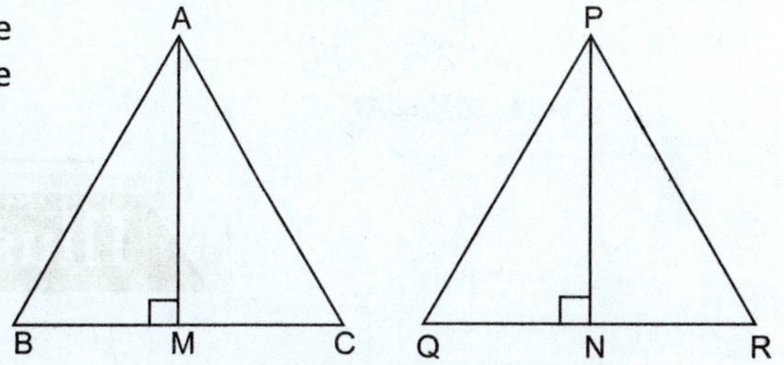


**17.** In the adjoining figure, $AB \parallel FD$, $AC \parallel GE$ and $BD = EC$. Prove that:

(i) $BG = DF$

(ii) $EG = CF$.

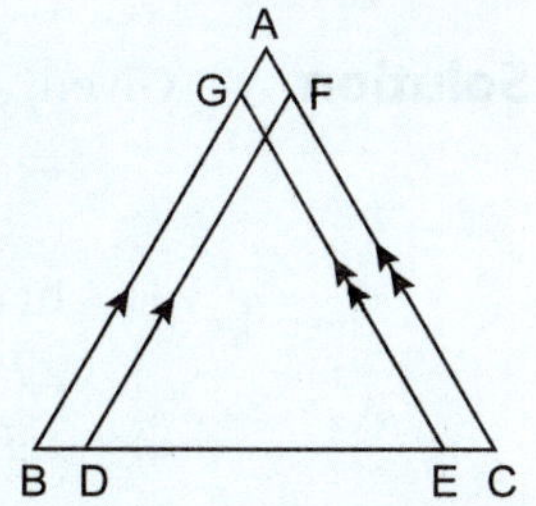


**18.** $AD$ is an altitude of an isosceles triangle $ABC$ in which $AB = AC$. Show that :

(i) $AD$ bisects $BC$

(ii) $AD$ bisects $\angle A$.

## Answers

**1.** $AB = RP$ **2.** $\angle A = \angle P$ **12.** $x = 5, y = 5$

## Isosceles Triangles

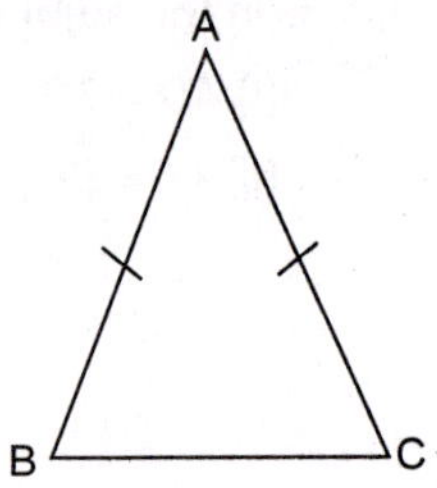


If two sides of a triangle are equal, it is called an isosceles triangle.

In the adjoining figure, a $\Delta ABC$ is given in which $AB = AC$.

$\therefore$ $\Delta ABC$ is an isosceles triangle.

If we measure $\angle B$ and $\angle C$ in this triangle, we find that $\angle B = \angle C$. So, we obtained the following theorems:

**Theorem 1** The angles opposite to equal sides in an isosceles triangle are equal.

Given: An isosceles triangle $ABC$ in which $AB = AC$.

To Prove: $\angle B = \angle C$.

Construction : Draw $AP$ perpendicular to $BC$.

Proof :

| | Statements | Reasons |
|---|---|---|
| 1. | $\angle APB = \angle APC$ | Each 90° |
| 2. | $AB = AC$ | Given |
| 3. | $AP = AP$ | Common |
| 4. | $\Delta APB \cong \Delta APC$ | RHS criteria |
| 5. | $\angle B = \angle C$ | CPCT |

Hence Proved.

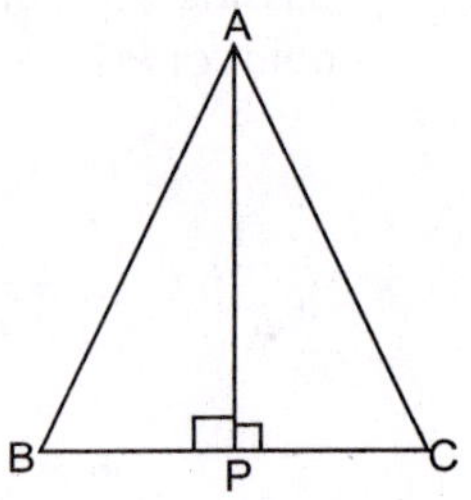


**Theorem 2.** (Converses of theorem-1)

The sides opposite to equal angles in an isosceles triangle are equal.

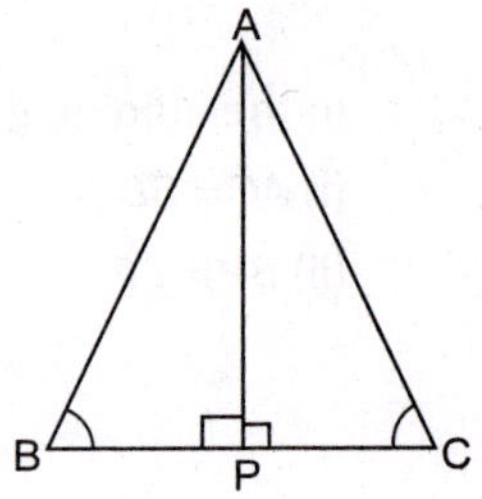


Given : A triangle $ABC$ in which $\angle B = \angle C$.

To Prove : $AB = AC$

Construction : Draw $AP$ perpendicular to $BC$

Proof :

| | Statements | Reasons |
|---|---|---|
| 1. | $\angle APB = \angle APC$ | Each 90° |
| 2. | $\angle B = \angle C$ | Given |
| 3. | $AP = AP$ | Common |
| 4. | $\Delta APB \cong \Delta APC$ | AAS criteria |
| 5. | $AB = AC$ | CPCT |

Hence Proved.

# Illustrative Examples

**Example 1.** In an isosceles triangle $PQR$, $PQ = QR$ and $\angle Q = 90°$. Find $\angle P$ and $\angle R$.

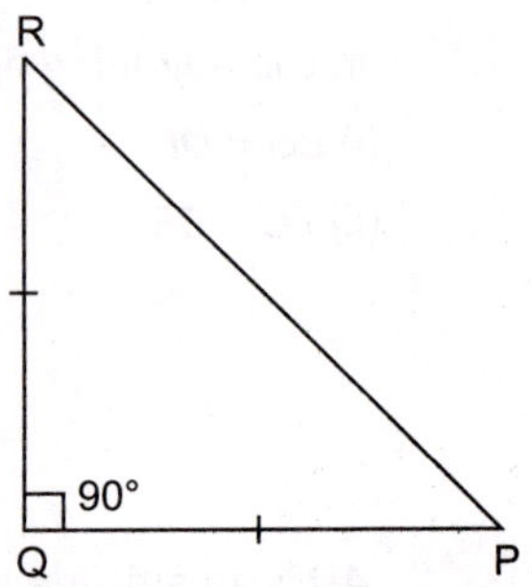


**Solution.** Given, $PQ = QR$

$\Rightarrow$ $\angle R = \angle P$ (Angles opposite to equal sides in a triangle are equal.)

In $\Delta PQR$,

$\angle P + \angle Q + \angle R = 180°$ (Angle sum property in a triangle)

$\Rightarrow$ $\angle P + 90° + \angle P = 180°$ ($\because$ $\angle R = \angle P$)

$\Rightarrow$ $2\angle P = 90°$ $\Rightarrow$ $\angle P = 45°$

$\therefore$ $\angle P = 45°$ and $\angle R = 45°$ Ans.

**Example 2.** In the adjoining figure, $AB = AC$ and $\angle BAC = 50°$. Find $\angle ACD$.

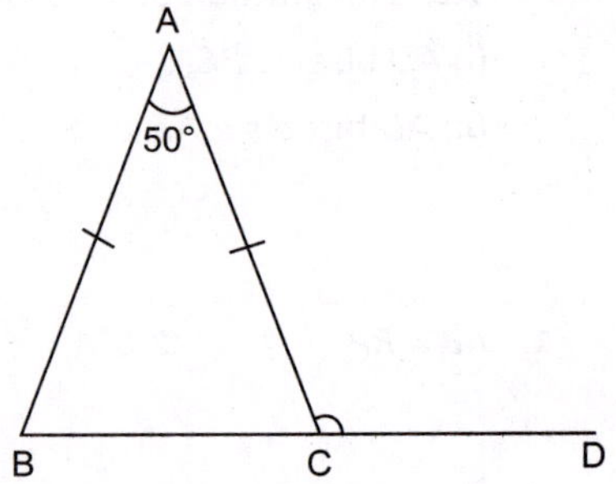


**Solution.** In $\Delta ABC$

$AC = AB$ (Given)

$\Rightarrow$ $\angle ABC = \angle ACB$ (Angles opposite to equal sides in a triangle are equal.)

and, $\angle ABC + \angle ACB + \angle BAC = 180°$

$\Rightarrow$ $\angle ACB + \angle ACB + 50° = 180°$

$\Rightarrow$ $2\angle ACB = 130°$ $\Rightarrow$ $\angle ACB = 65°$

Now, $\angle ACB + \angle ACD = 180°$ (Straight angle)

$\Rightarrow$ $65° + \angle ACD = 180°$ $\Rightarrow$ $\angle ACD = 115°$ Ans.

**Example 3.** In the adjoining figure, $AB = AD$ and $BC = CD$. Find $\angle ADC$.

**Solution.** Join $BD$.

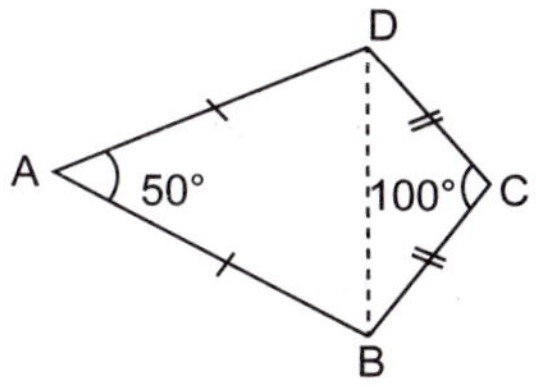


In $\Delta ABD$,

$AB = AD$ (Given)

$\Rightarrow$ $\angle ADB = \angle ABD$ ...(i) (Angles opposite to equal sides in a triangle are equal.)

In $\Delta BCD$,

$BC = CD$ (Given)

$\Rightarrow$ $\angle BDC = \angle CBD$ ... (ii) (Angles opposite to equal sides in a triangle are equal.)

Adding eqns. (i) and (ii), we get

$$\angle ADB + \angle BDC = \angle ABD + \angle CBD$$

$$\angle ADC = \angle ABC \quad \text{...(iii)}$$

In ▱$ABCD$,

$$\angle A + \angle B + \angle C + \angle D = 360°$$

$\Rightarrow$ $50° + \angle D + 100° + \angle D = 360°$

$\Rightarrow$ $2\angle D = 210°$ $\Rightarrow$ $\angle D = 105°$ Ans.

**Example 4.** In the adjoining figure, $PR = RS$, $PQ = QR$ and $\angle PQR = 56°$. Find the value of $x$.

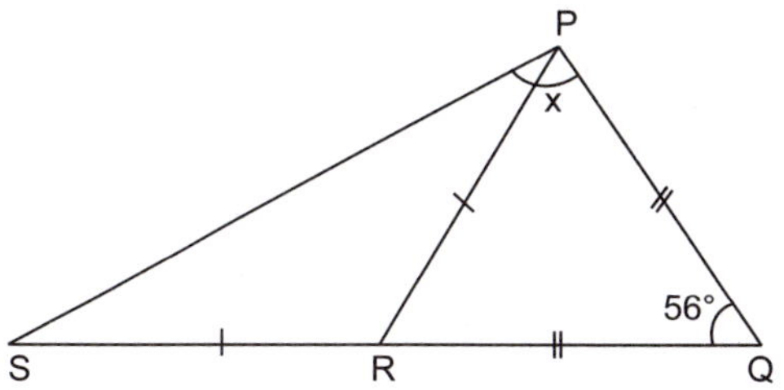


**Solution.** In $\Delta PQR$,

$PQ = QR$ (Given)

$\Rightarrow$ $\angle PRQ = \angle RPQ$

and $\angle RPQ + \angle PRQ + \angle PQR = 180°$

$\Rightarrow$ $\angle PRQ + \angle PRQ + 56° = 180°$

$\Rightarrow$ $2\angle PRQ = 124°$ $\Rightarrow$ $\angle PRQ = 62°$

$\angle PRS + \angle PRQ = 180°$ (Straight angles)

$\Rightarrow$ $\angle PRS + 62° = 180°$ $\Rightarrow$ $\angle PRS = 118°$

In $\Delta PRS$,

$PR = SR$

$\Rightarrow$ $\angle PSR = \angle SPR$ (Angles opposite to equal sides in a triangle are equal.)

and $\angle PSR + \angle SPR + \angle PRS = 180°$ (Angle sum property in a triangle)

$\Rightarrow$ $\angle PSR + \angle PSR + 118° = 180°$ $\Rightarrow$ $2\angle PSR = 62°$

$\Rightarrow$ $\angle PSR = 31°$ $\Rightarrow$ $\angle PSQ = 31°$

In $\Delta PQS$,

$\angle SPQ + \angle PSQ + \angle PQS = 180°$ (Angle sum property in a triangle)

$\Rightarrow$ $31° + x + 56° = 180°$ $\Rightarrow$ $x = 93°$ Ans.

**Example 5.** In the adjoining figure, $AB = BC = CA = CD$. Find $\angle ACD$ and $\angle ADC$.

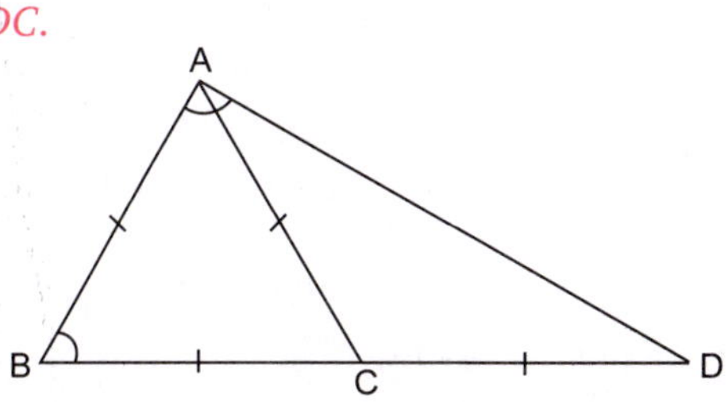


**Solution.** In $\Delta ABC$,

$$AB = BC = CA$$

$\Rightarrow$ $\Delta ABC$ is an equilateral triangle.

$\Rightarrow$ $\angle BAC = \angle ABC = \angle ACB = 60°$

$\angle BCD = 180°$

$\Rightarrow$ $\angle BCA + \angle ACD = 180°$ $\Rightarrow$ $60° + \angle ACD = 180°$

$\Rightarrow$ $\angle ACD = 120°$ Ans.

In $\Delta ACD$,

$AC = CD$ (Given)

$\Rightarrow \angle ADC = \angle CAD$ ...(i) (Angles opposite to equal sides are equal.)

Now, $\angle ACD + \angle ADC + \angle CAD = 180°$

$\Rightarrow 120° + \angle ADC + \angle ADC = 180°$ [From (i)]

$\Rightarrow 2\angle ADC = 180° - 120° = 60° \Rightarrow \angle ADC = 30°$

Ans.

**Example 6.** In $\Delta ABC$, the bisector $AD$ of $\angle A$ is perpendicular to the side $BC$. Show that $AB = AC$ and $\Delta ABC$ is isosceles.

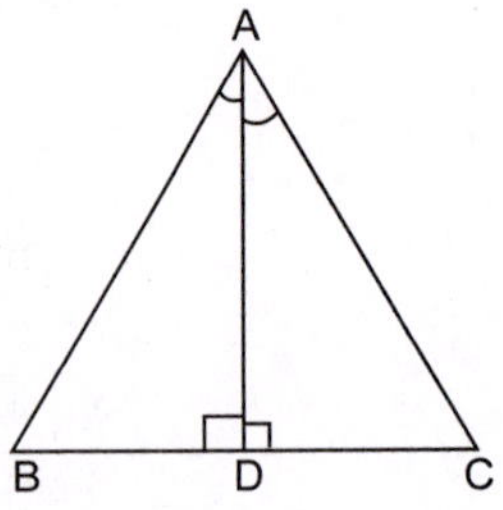


**Solution.** In $\Delta ABD$ and $\Delta ACD$,

$\Rightarrow \angle BAD = \angle CAD$ ($AD$ is the bisector of $\angle A$)

$AD = AD$ (Common)

$\angle ADB = \angle ADC$ (Each 90°)

$\therefore \Delta ABD \cong \Delta ACD$ (ASA criteria)

$\Rightarrow AB = AC \Rightarrow \Delta ABC$ is isosceles.

Hence Proved.

**Example 7.** In $\Delta ABC$, $BP$ and $CQ$ are perpendiculars on sides $AC$ and $AB$, respectively, such that $BP = CQ$. Prove that:

(i) $\Delta ABP \cong \Delta ACQ$

(ii) $\Delta ABC$ *is isosceles*

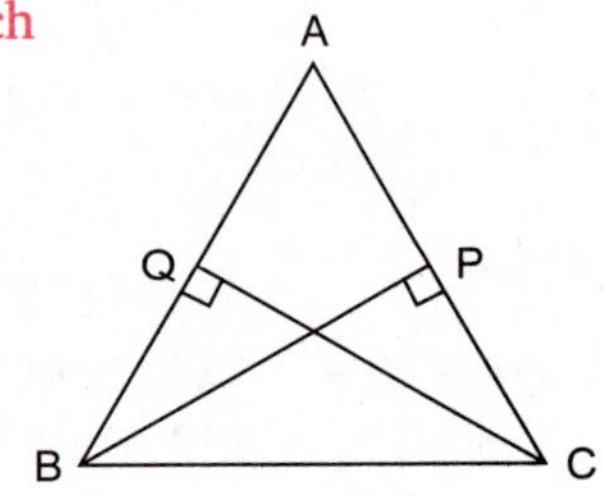


**Solution.** (i) In $\Delta ABP$ and $\Delta ACQ$,

$\angle APB = \angle AQC$ (Each 90°)

$\angle BAP = \angle CAQ$ (Common)

$BP = CQ$ (Given)

$\therefore \Delta ABP \cong \Delta CAQ$ (ASA criteria)

(ii) $\because \Delta ABP \cong \Delta ACQ$

$\therefore AB = AC \Rightarrow \Delta ABC$ is isosceles.

Hence Proved.

**Example 8.** In the adjoining figure, $ABCD$ is a square and $M$ is the mid-point of $AD$. Prove that $\angle MBC = \angle MCB$.

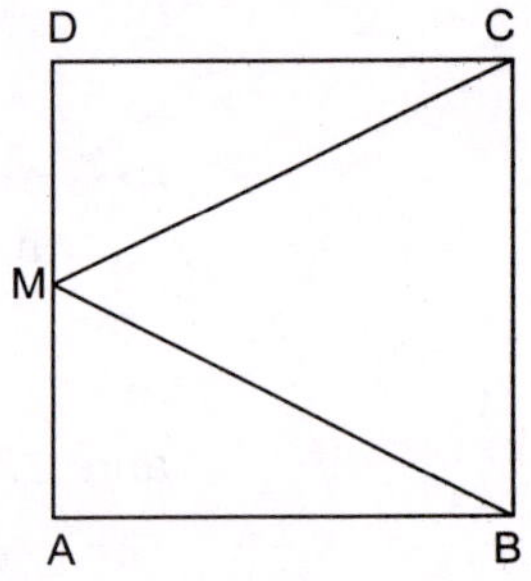


**Solution.**

| | Statements | Reasons |
|---|---|---|
| 1. | $AB = DC$ | Side of a square |
| 2. | $\angle MAB = \angle MDC$ | Each 90° |
| 3. | $AM = DM$ | $M$ is the mid-point of $AD$ |
| 4. | $\Delta ABM \cong \Delta DCM$ | SAS criteria |
| 5. | $BM = CM$ | CPCT |
| 6. | $\angle MCB = \angle MBC$ | Opposite angle of equal sides in $\Delta MBC$ |

Hence Proved.

**Example 9.** In the adjoining figure, $AB \parallel CD$, $\angle SRB = 80°$ and $PR = QR$. Find $\angle PRQ$.

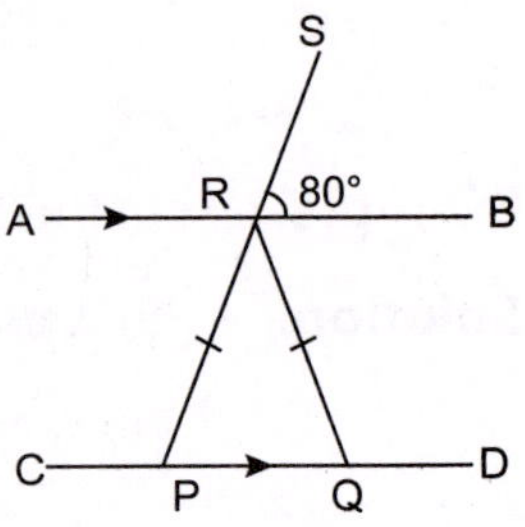


**Solution.** $AB \parallel CD$ and $SRP$ is a transversal.

$\therefore \angle RPQ = \angle SRB = 80°$ (Corresponding angles)

In $\Delta PQR$,

$QR = PR$ (Given)

$\Rightarrow \angle QPR = \angle PRQ$ (Angles opposite to equal sides in a triangle are equal.)

$\Rightarrow \angle QPR = 80°$

Now, $\angle PQR + \angle QPR + \angle PRQ = 180°$

$\Rightarrow 80° + 80° + \angle PRQ = 180°$

$\Rightarrow \angle PRQ = 20°$

Ans.

**Example 10.** *ABC is an isosceles triangle in which AB = AC and BM and CN are altitudes. Show that : BM = CN.*

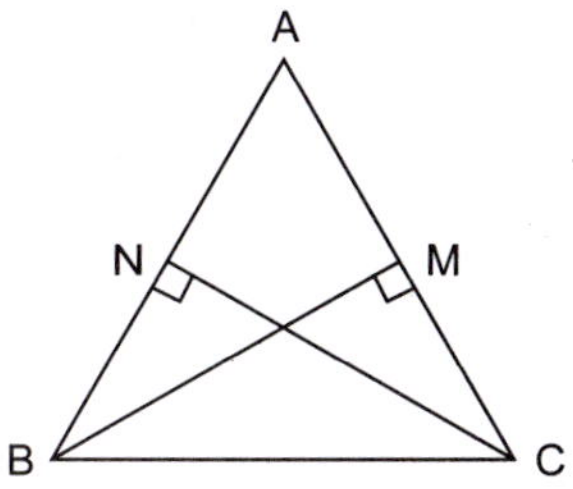


**Solution.** In $\Delta ABC$,

$AB = AC$ (Given)

$\Rightarrow \angle ACB = \angle ABC$ ...(i) (Angles opposite to equal sides in a triangle are equal.)

In $\Delta BMC$ and $\Delta CNB$,

$\angle BCM = \angle CBN$ [From (i)]

$\angle BMC = \angle CNB$ (Each 90°)

$BC = CB$ (Common)

$\therefore \Delta BMC \cong \Delta CNB$ (AAS criteria)

$\Rightarrow BM = CN$ (CPCT)

Hence Proved.

**Example 11.** *In the adjoining figure, AB = AC, CH = CB, HK || BC. If ∠CAD = 132°. Find ∠CHK.*

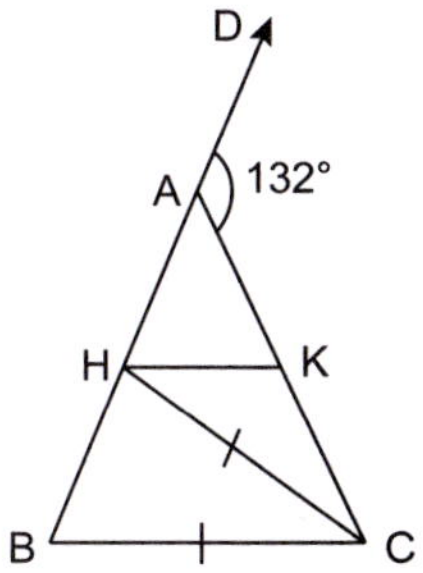


**Solution.** In $\Delta ABC$,

$AB = AC$ (Given)

$\Rightarrow \angle ACB = \angle ABC$ (Angles opposite to equal sides in a triangle are equal.)

$\angle CAD = \angle ACB + \angle ABC$ (Exterior angle property)

$\Rightarrow 132° = \angle ACB + \angle ACB$

$\Rightarrow 2\angle ACB = 132° \Rightarrow \angle ACB = 66°$

$\angle ABC = 66°$

$\angle HBC = 66°$

In $\Delta HBC$,

$CH = CB$ (Given)

$\Rightarrow \angle CBH = \angle CHB \Rightarrow \angle CHB = 66°$

From angle sum property,

$$\angle HBC + \angle CHB + \angle BCH = 180°$$

$\Rightarrow 66° + 66° + \angle BCH = 180° \Rightarrow \angle BCH = 48°$

Now, $HK \parallel BC$ and $CH$ is a transversal.

$\therefore \angle CHK = \angle BCH$ (Alternate angles)

$\Rightarrow \angle CHK = 48°$

Ans.

**Example 12.** *In the adjoining figure, ABC is an isosceles triangle in which AB = AC. If P and Q are points on BC such that BQ = PC, then show that AP = AQ.*

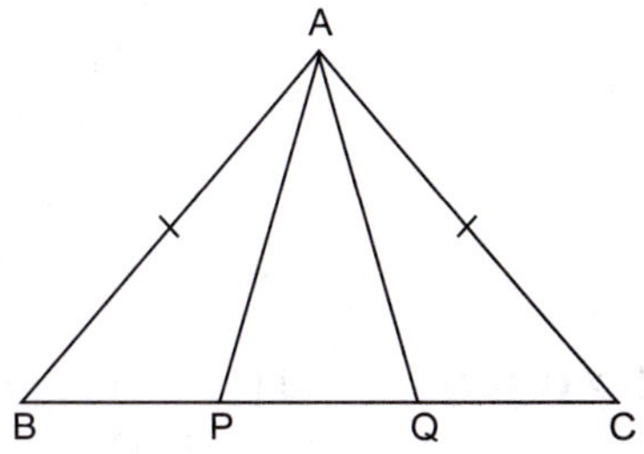


**Solution.** In $\Delta ABC$,

$AC = AB$ (Given)

$\Rightarrow \angle ABC = \angle ACB$ (Angles opposite to equal sides in a triangle are equal.)

$\Rightarrow \angle ABP = \angle ACQ$

and $BQ = PC$

$\Rightarrow BP + PQ = PQ + CQ \Rightarrow BP = PQ$

Now, in $\Delta ABP$ and $\Delta ACQ$,

$AB = AC$ (Given)

$\angle ABP = \angle ACQ$ (Proved above)

$BP = CQ$ (Proved above)

$\therefore \Delta ABP \cong \Delta ACQ$ (SAS criteria)

$\Rightarrow AP = AQ$ (CPCT)

Hence Proved.

**Example 13.** In the adjoining figure, $AP$, $BQ$ and $CR$ are the altitudes of $\Delta ABC$. If $AP = BQ = CR$, prove that $\Delta ABC$ is an equilateral triangle.

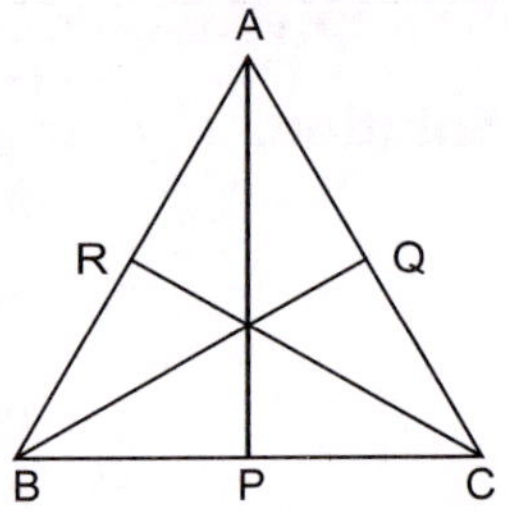


**Solution.** In $\Delta ABQ$ and $\Delta ACR$,

$\angle BAQ = \angle CAR$ (Common)

$\angle AQB = \angle ARC$ (Each 90°)

$BQ = CR$ (Given)

$\therefore \Delta ABQ \cong \Delta ACR$ (AAS criteria)

$\Rightarrow AB = AC$ ...(i)

Similarly, we can prove that

$BC = AC$ ...(ii)

From eqns. *(i)* and *(ii)*, we get

$AB = BC = CA$

$\Rightarrow \Delta ABC$ is an equilateral triangle.

Hence Proved.

**Example 14.** In the adjoining figure, $OA = OD$ and $\angle CAP = \angle BDQ$. Prove that $\Delta OBC$ is an isosceles triangle.

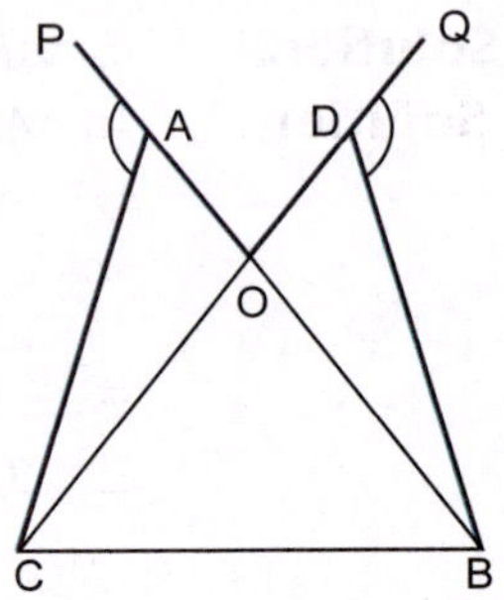


**Solution.** $\angle CAP + \angle OAC = 180°$ (Linear pair)

and $\angle BDQ + \angle ODB = 180°$ (Linear pair)

$\therefore \angle CAP + \angle OAC = \angle BDQ + \angle ODB$

but $\angle CAP = \angle BDQ$

$\therefore \angle OAC = \angle ODB$

In $\Delta OAC$ and $\angle ODB$,

$\angle OAC = \angle ODB$ (Proved above)

$OA = OD$ (Given)

$\angle AOC = \angle DOB$ (Vertically opposite angles)

$\therefore \Delta OAC \cong \Delta ODB$ (ASA criteria)

$\Rightarrow OC = OB$ (CPCT)

$\Rightarrow \Delta OBC$ is an isosceles triangle.

Hence Proved.

**Example 15.** In the adjoining figure, $P$ and $Q$ are points on side $BC$ of $\Delta ABC$ such that $BP = CQ$ and $AP = AQ$. Show that $\Delta ABP \cong \Delta ACQ$.

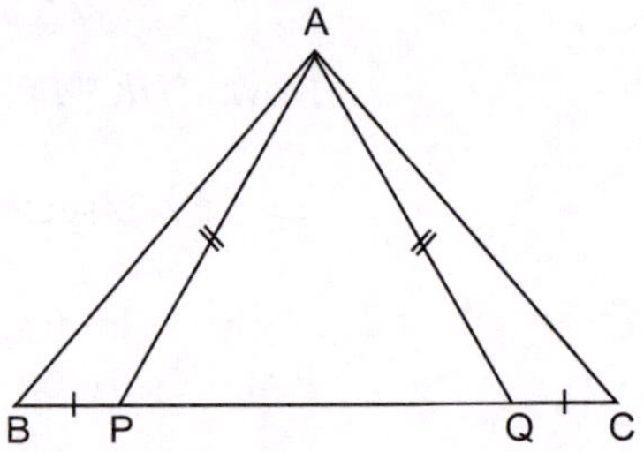


**Solution.** In $\Delta APQ$,

$AP = AQ$ (Given)

$\Rightarrow \angle AQP = \angle APQ$ (Angles opposite to equal sides in a triangle are equal.)

$\Rightarrow 180° - \angle AQP = 180° - \angle APQ$ (Given)

$\Rightarrow \angle AQC = \angle APB$

In $\Delta ABP$ and $\Delta ACQ$,

$BP = CQ$ (Given)

$\angle APB = \angle AQC$ (Proved above)

$AP = AQ$ (Given)

$\therefore \Delta ABP \cong \Delta ACQ$

Hence proved.

**Example 16.** In the adjoining figure, $\angle EAB = \angle EBA$ and $AC = BD$. Prove that $AD = BC$.

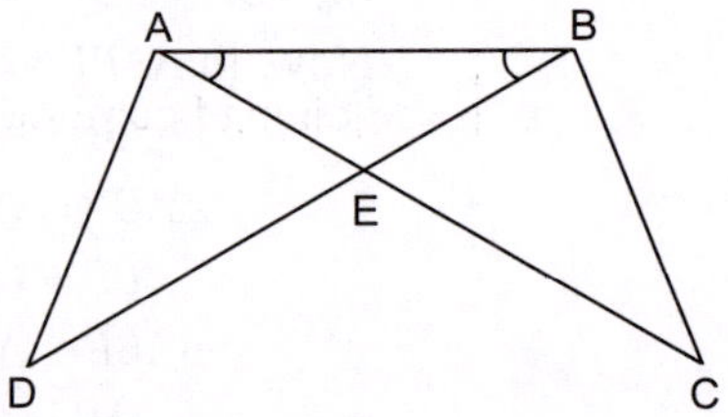


**Solution.** In $\Delta AEB$,

$\angle EAB = \angle EBA$

$\Rightarrow EB = EA$ ...*(i)*

Given that,

$\Rightarrow BD = AC$ ...*(ii)*

Subtracting equation *(i)* from *(ii)*, we get

$BD - EB = AC - EA$

$DE = CE$

In $\Delta AED$ and $\Delta BEC$,

| | |
|---|---|
| $AE = BE$ | (Given) |
| $\angle AED = \angle BEC$ | (Vertically opposite angles) |
| $DE = CE$ | (Proved above) |
| $\therefore \Delta AED \cong \Delta BEC$ | (SAS criteria) |
| $AD = BC$ | (CPCT) |

Hence Proved.

**Example 17.** In an isosceles triangle $ABC$, in which $AB = AC$, the bisectors of $\angle B$ and $\angle C$ intersect each other at $O$. Show that :

(i) $OB = OC$

(ii) $OA$ bisects $\angle A$.

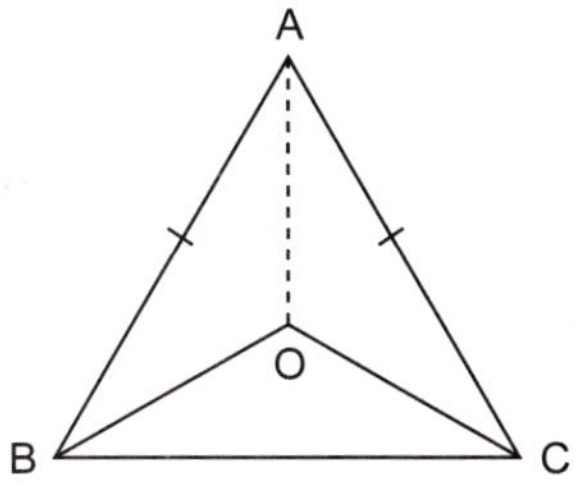


**Solution.** In $\Delta ABC$,

(i) $AB = AC$

$\Rightarrow \angle ACB = \angle ABC$ (Angles opposite to equal sides in a triangle are equal.)

$\Rightarrow \frac{1}{2}\angle ACB = \frac{1}{2}\angle ABC$

$\Rightarrow \angle OCB = \angle OBC$ ($\because$ $OC$ and $OB$ are bisectors of $\angle C$ and $\angle B$, respectively.)

$\Rightarrow OB = OC$ (Sides opposite to equal angles in a triangle are equal.)

(ii) $\frac{1}{2}\angle ABC = \frac{1}{2}\angle ACB$

$\Rightarrow \angle ABO = \angle ACO$ ($OB$ and $OC$ are the bisectors of $\angle B$ and $\angle C$, respectively.)

In $\Delta OAB$ and $\Delta OAC$

| | |
|---|---|
| $OB = OC$ | (Proved above) |
| $\angle ABO = \angle ACO$ | (Proved above) |
| $AB = AC$ | (Given) |
| $\therefore \Delta OAB \cong \Delta OAC$ | (SAS criteria) |
| $\Rightarrow \angle OAB = \angle OAC$ | (CPCT) |

$\Rightarrow$ $OA$ bisects $\angle A$.

Hence Proved.

## Exercise 8C

1. In $\Delta ABC$, $AB = AC$, and $\angle BAC = 30°$. Find the value of $x$.

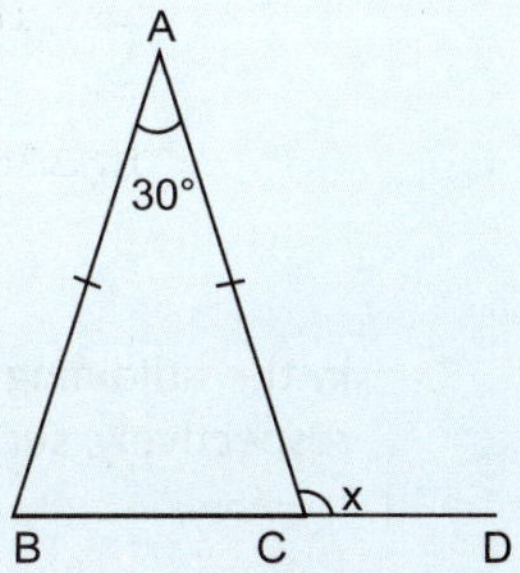


2. In the adjoining figure, $AC = CD = BD$ and $\angle CBD = 40°$. Find $\angle ACD$.

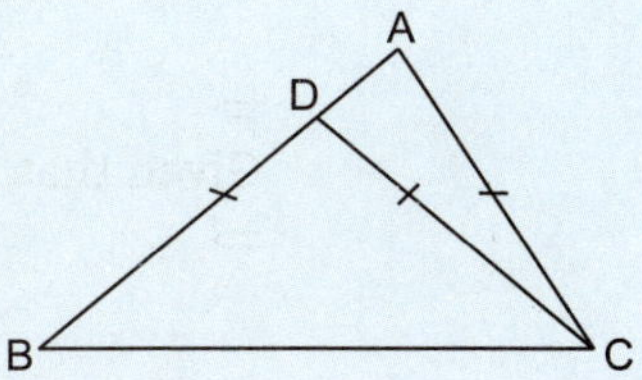

3. In the adjoining figure, $AC = BC = CD$ and $\angle ADC = 40°$. Find $\angle BAC$.

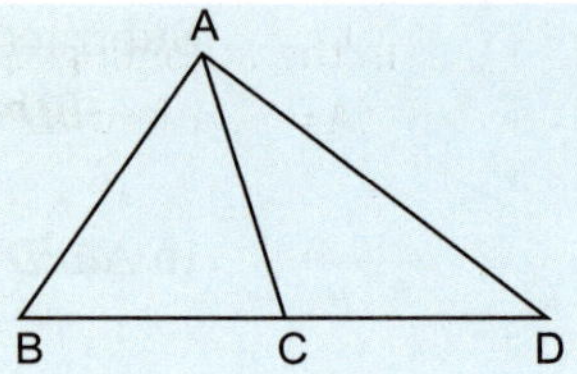


4. In the adjoining figure, $AC = BC$ and $CD = AD$. If $\angle ADC = 60°$. Find $\angle BAC$.

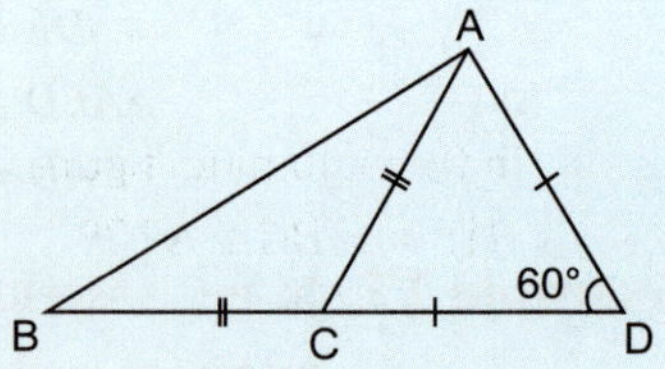


5. Show that angles of an equilateral triangle are 60° each.

6. In the adjoining figure, $BC = CD$. Find $\angle ACB$.

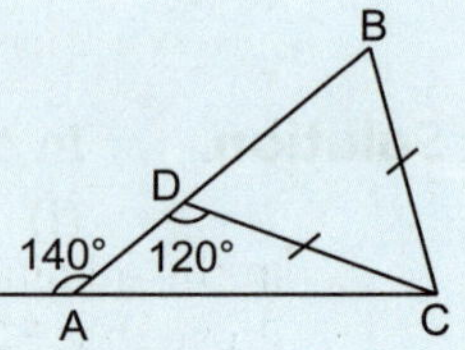


7. In the adjoining figure, $ABC$ and $DBC$ are two isosceles triangles on the same base $BC$. Prove that $\angle ABD = \angle ACD$.

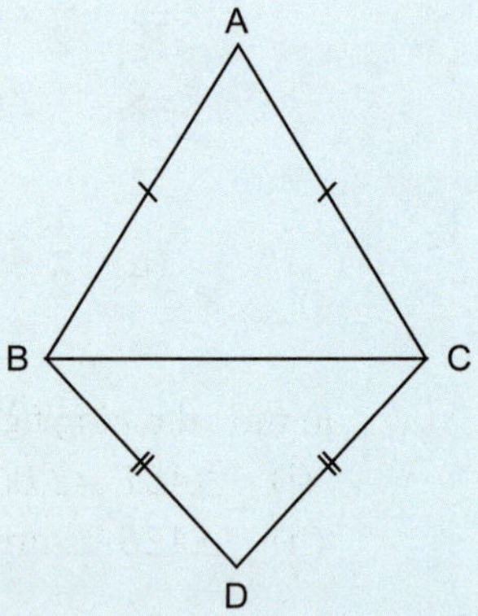


8. In the adjoining figure, $ABC$ is an isosceles triangle in which $AB = AC$. Its side $BA$ is produced to $D$ such that $AD = AB$. Show that $\angle BCD = 90°$.

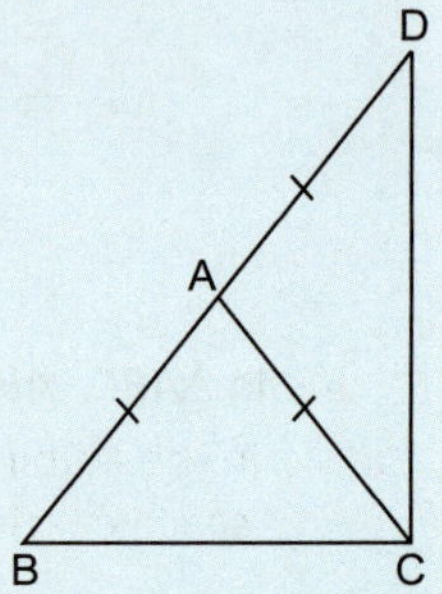


9. In the adjoining figure, $D$ is the mid-point of $BC$. $DE$ and $DF$ are perpendiculars to $AB$ and $AC$ respectively, such that $DE = DF$. Prove that $\Delta ABC$ is an isosceles triangle.

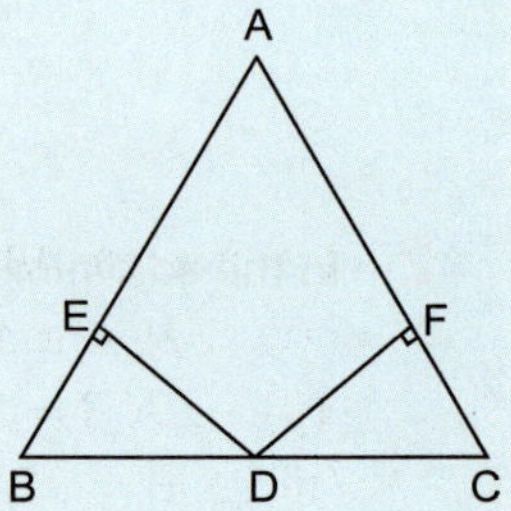

**10.** In the adjoining figure, $ABC$ is an isosceles triangle in which $AB = AC$ and $PQ$ is parallel to $BC$. If $\angle A = 40°$, find $\angle PQC$.

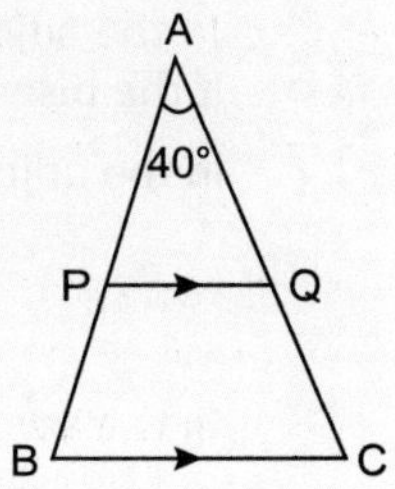


**11.** In the adjoining figure, $AB = AC$ and $BE$, $CF$ are the bisectors of $\angle B$, $\angle C$ respectively. Prove that:

(i) $\Delta EBC \cong \Delta FCB$

(ii) $BE = CF$

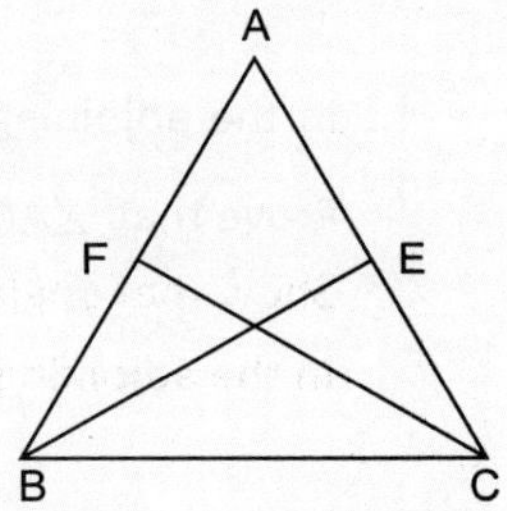


**12.** In the adjoining figure, $ABC$ is a right-angled triangle, right-angled at $A$ such that $AB = AC$. Bisector of $\angle A$ meets $BC$ at $D$. Prove that $BC = 2AD$.

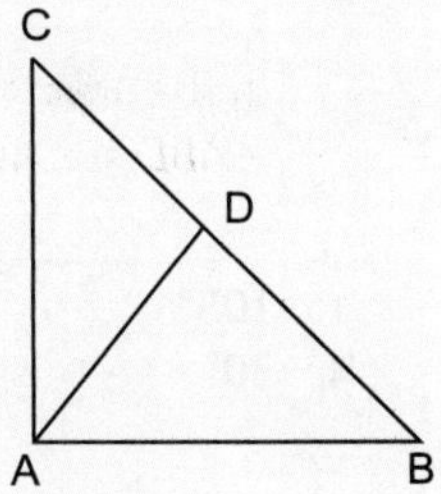


**13.** In the adjoining figure, $\Delta CDE$ is an equilateral triangle and $ABCD$ is a square. Show that:

(i) $\Delta ADE \cong \Delta BCE$

(ii) $\Delta AEB$ is an isosceles triangle.

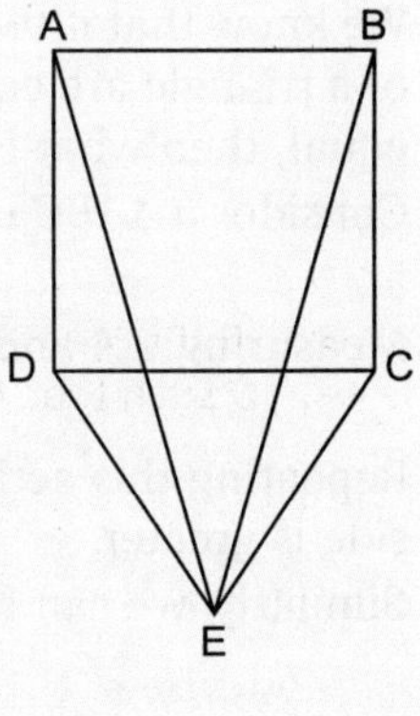


**14.** In the adjoining figure, $ABCD$ is a square and $ABE$ is an equilateral triangle. Prove that $\Delta ECD$ is an isosceles triangle.

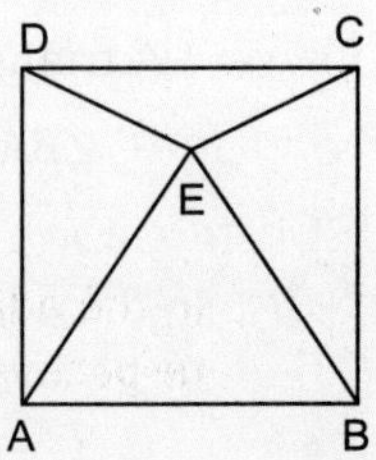


**15.** In a triangle $ABC$, $AB = AC$, $D$ and $E$ are points on the sides $AB$ and $AC$, respectively such that $BD = CE$. Show that:

(i) $\Delta DBC \cong \Delta ECB$

(ii) $\Delta DCB = \Delta EBC$

(iii) $OB = OC$, where $O$ is the point of intersection of $BE$ and $CD$.

**16.** If the bisector of an angle of a triangle also bisects the opposite side, prove that the triangle is isosceles.

**17.** In the adjoining figure, $AB = BC$ and $AC = CD$. Prove that $\angle BAD : \angle ADB = 3 : 1$.

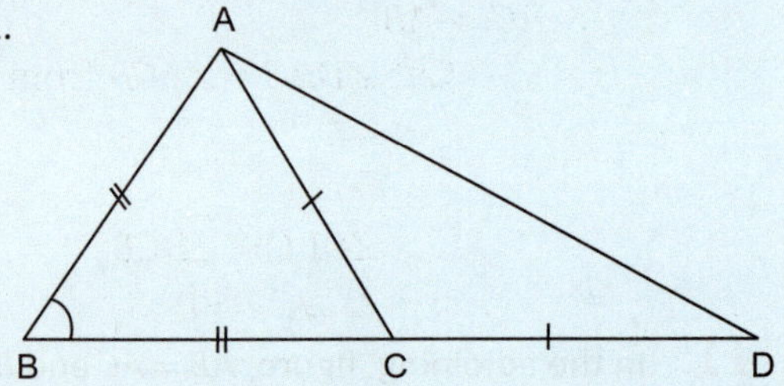


**18.** In the adjoining figure, $ABCD$ is a square and $ADE$ is an equilateral triangle.

Prove that $\angle ACE = \frac{1}{2}\angle DAE$.

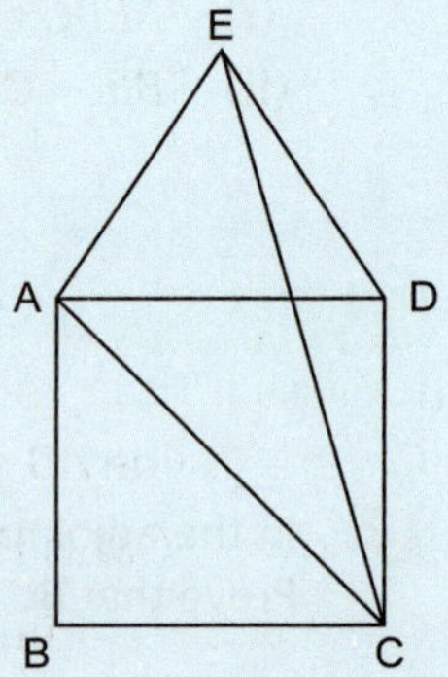


## *Answers*

| | | |
|---|---|---|
| **1.** 105° | **2.** 20° | **3.** 50° |
| **4.** 30° | **6.** 80° | **10.** 110°. |

## Inequalities in a Triangle

We know that if two sides of a triangle are equal then angles opposite to them are also equal and conversely if two angles of a triangle are equal then sides opposite to them are also equal. Here, a question arise, if two sides of a triangle are not equal, then what is the relation between the angles opposite to these sides?

Consider a $\Delta ABC$ in which

$$BC > AB$$

Measuring $\angle A$ and $\angle C$, we find that

$$\angle A > \angle C$$

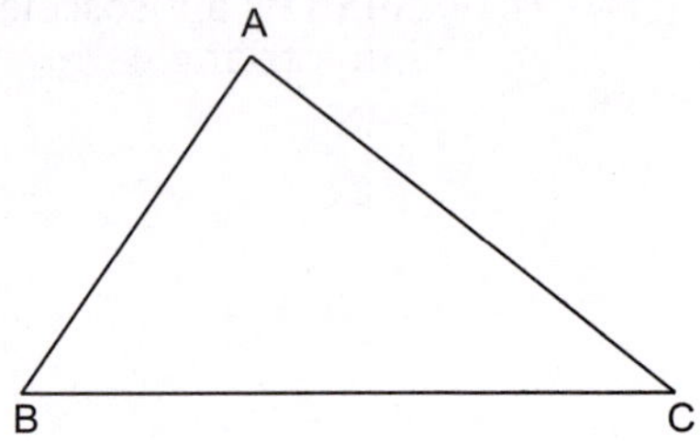


Repeating this activity with more triangles, we find that the angle opposite to larger side is greater.

Similarly, we can find that the side opposite to larger angle is larger.

**Theorem 1** If two sides of a triangle are unequal, then the longer side has greater angle opposite to it.

Given : A triangle $ABC$ in which $BC > AB$.

To Prove : $\angle BAC > \angle ACB$.

Construction : Cut $BD = AB$ from $BC$ and join $AD$.

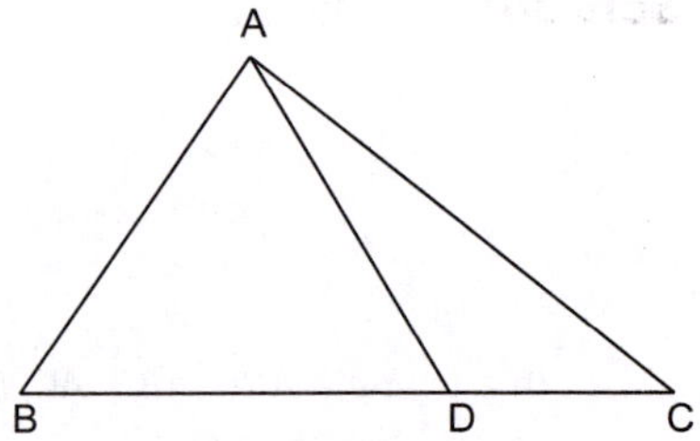


Proof :

| | Statements | Reasons |
|---|---|---|
| 1. | $AB = BD$ | By construction |
| 2. | $\angle ADB = \angle BAD$ | Angles opposite to equal sides in triangle are equal. |
| 3. | $\angle ADB > \angle DCA$ | $\angle ADB$ is the exterior angle. |
| 4. | $\angle ADB > \angle BCA$ | $\angle DCA = \angle BCA$ |
| 5. | $\angle BAD > \angle BCA$ | From (2) and (4) |
| 6. | $\angle BAC > \angle BCA$ | $\angle BAD = \angle BAC$ |

Hence Proved.

**Theorem 2** If two angles of a triangle are unequal, the greater angle has the greater side opposite to it.

Given : A $\Delta ABC$ in which $\angle ABC > \angle ACB$

To Prove : $AC > AB$.

Construction : Cut $\angle DBC = \angle ACB$ from $\angle ABC$ and point $D$ lines on $AC$.

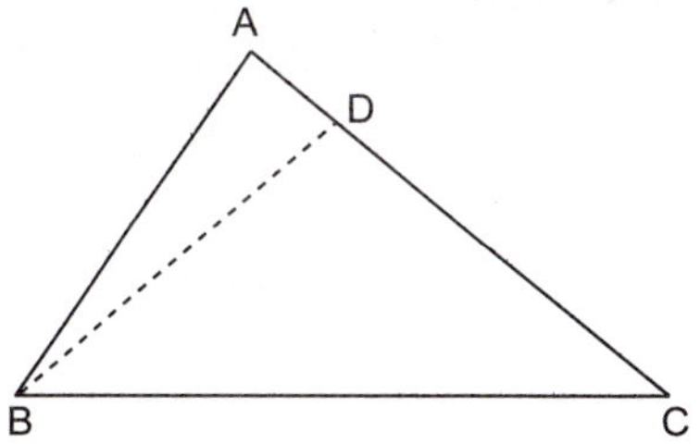


Proof :

| | Statements | Reasons |
|---|---|---|
| 1. | $\angle DBC = \angle DCB$ | By construction |
| 2. | $DC = BD$ | Sides opposite to equal angles in a triangle are equal. |
| 3. | $BD + AD > AB$ | Sum of any two sides of a triangle is greater than the third side. |
| 4. | $DC + AD > AB$ | From (2) and (3) |
| 5. | $AC > AB$ | $DC + AD = AC$ |

Hence Proved.

**Theorem 3** Of all the line segments that can be drawn to a given straight line from a given point outside it, the perpendicular is the shortest.

Given : A line $AB$ and $OM$ is perpendicular from point $O$ to $AB$.

To Prove : $OM$ is the shortest of all the lines that can be drawn from $O$ to $AB$

Construction : Take a point $N$ on $AB$ other than $M$ and join $ON$.

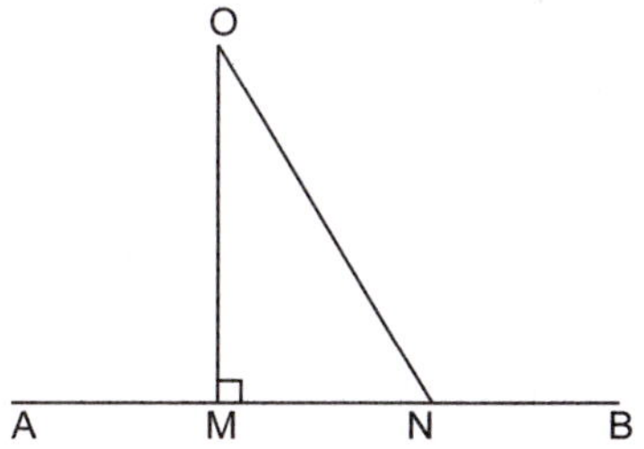


Proof :

In $\Delta OMN$,

$\angle OMN > \angle ONM$ $\quad (\because \angle OMN = 90°)$

$\Rightarrow$ $ON > OM$ (Side opposite to greater angle in a triangle is greater.)

Similarly, we can show that $OM$ is smaller than any other line segment that can be drawn from $O$ to $AB$.

$\therefore$ OM is the shortest line segment drawn from $O$ to $AB$. Hence Proved.

Corollary 1. In a triangle, the sum of any two sides is always greater than the third side.

In $\Delta ABC$,

$$AB + BC > AC, \quad BC + AC > AB, \quad AB + AC > BC$$

Corollary 2. In a triangle, the difference of any two sides of a triangle is always smaller than the third side.

In $\Delta ABC$,

$$AB - BC < AC, AB - AC < BC, BC - AC < AB$$

# Illustrative Examples

**Example 1.** In $\Delta ABC$, $\angle A = 100°$, $\angle C = 30°$, find (i) the longest side, (ii) the smallest side of $\Delta ABC$.

**Solution.** In $\Delta ABC$,

$$\angle A + \angle B + \angle C = 180°$$

$$\Rightarrow \quad 100° + \angle B + 30° = 180° \quad \Rightarrow \quad \angle B = 50°$$

(i) In $\Delta ABC$,

The largest angle $= \angle A = 100°$

$\therefore$ The opposite side $BC$ of $\angle A$ will be the longest.

$\therefore$ The longest side $= BC$ Ans.

(ii) In $\Delta ABC$, The smallest angle $= \angle C = 30°$

$\therefore$ The opposite side $AB$ of $\angle C$ will be the smallest.

$\therefore$ The smallest side $= AB$.

**Example 2.** In $\Delta ABC$, $D$ is any point on side $BC$. Prove that : $AB + BC + CA > 2AD$.

**Solution.** In $\Delta ABC$, $D$ is any point on side $BC$. We know that the sum of any two sides of triangle is greater than the third side.

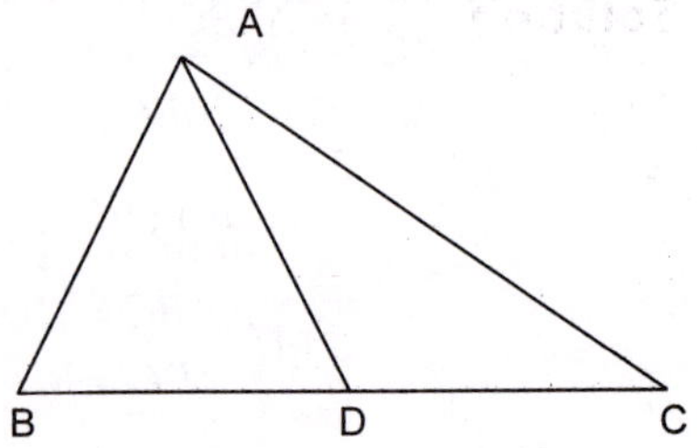


$\therefore$ In $\Delta ABD$,

$$AB + BD > AD \quad \ldots(i)$$

In $\Delta ACD$,

$$AC + CD > AD \quad \ldots(ii)$$

Adding *(i)* and *(ii)*, we get

$$AB + BD + AC + CD > AD + AD$$

$$\Rightarrow \quad AB + (BD + CD) + CA > 2AD$$

$$\Rightarrow \quad AB + BC + CA > 2AD$$

Hence Proved.

**Example 3.** In a quadrilateral $ABCD$, $AB$ is the smallest and $CD$ is the largest side. Prove that :

(i) $\angle B > \angle D$ (ii) $\angle A > \angle C$

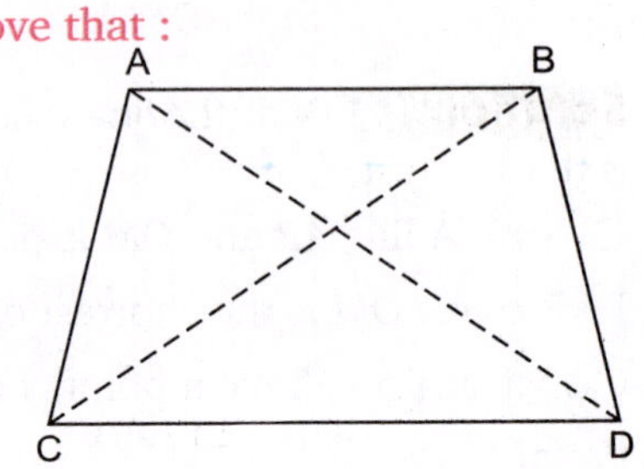


**Solution.** (i) Join $BD$

In $\Delta ABD$,

$$AD > AB \quad (\because AB \text{ is the smallest.})$$

$$\Rightarrow \quad \angle ABD > \angle ADB \quad \ldots(i)$$

In $\Delta BCD$,

$$CD > BC \quad (\because CD \text{ is largest})$$

$$\Rightarrow \quad \angle CBD > \angle BDC \quad \ldots(ii)$$

Adding *(i)* and *(ii)*, we get

$$\angle ABD + \angle CBD > \angle ADB + \angle BDC$$

$$\Rightarrow \quad \angle ABC > \angle ADC \quad \Rightarrow \quad \angle B > \angle D$$

(ii) Join $AC$.

In $\Delta ABC$,

$$BC > AB \quad (\because AB \text{ is the smallest.})$$

$$\Rightarrow \quad \angle BAC > \angle ACB \quad \ldots(iii)$$

In $\Delta ACD$,

$$CD > AC \quad (\because CD \text{ is largest})$$

$$\Rightarrow \quad \angle CAD > \angle ACD \quad \ldots(iv)$$

Adding *(iii)* and *(iv)*, we get

$$\angle BAC + \angle CAD > \angle ACB + \angle ACD$$

$$\Rightarrow \quad \angle BAD > \angle BCD \quad \Rightarrow \quad \angle A > \angle C$$

Hence Proved.

**Example 4.** In the adjoining figure, find :

(i) The longest side of $\Delta ABC$

(ii) The smallest side of $\Delta ABC$.

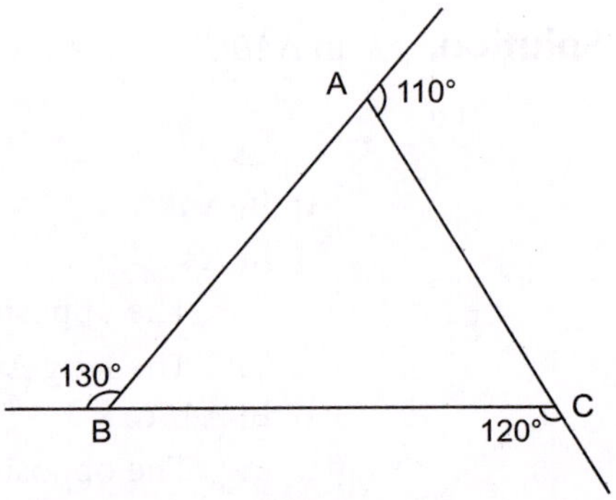


**Solution.**

$$\angle A = 180° - 110° = 70°$$

$$\angle B = 180° - 130° = 50°$$

$$\angle C = 180° - 120° = 60°$$

(i) The greatest angle $= \angle A$

$\Rightarrow$ The longest side $= BC$ **Ans.**

(ii) The smallest angle $= \angle B$

$\Rightarrow$ The smallest side $= AC$ **Ans.**

**Example 5.** In $\Delta ABC$, $BC = CA$ and $\angle A = 40°$. Find the longest side of $\Delta ABC$.

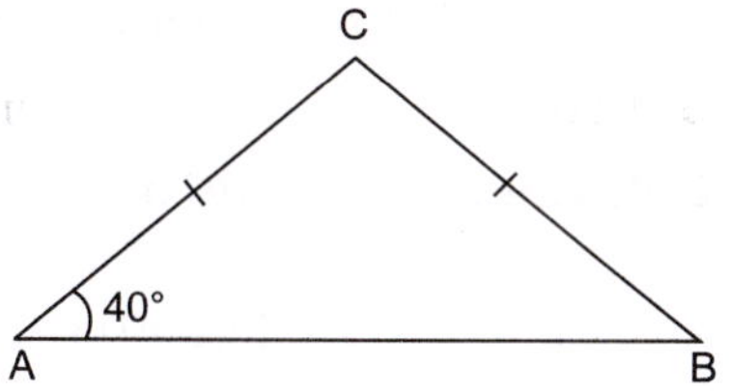


**Solution.** In $\Delta ABC$,

$$AC = BC$$

$$\Rightarrow \quad \angle B = \angle A$$

(Angles opposite to equal sides in a triangle are equal.)

$$\Rightarrow \quad \angle B = 40°$$

and
$$\angle A + \angle B + \angle C = 180°$$

$$\Rightarrow \quad 40° + 40° + \angle C = 180° \quad \Rightarrow \quad \angle C = 100°$$

$\therefore$ The largest angle of $\Delta ABC$ is $\angle C$.

$\Rightarrow$ The longest side of $\Delta ABC$ is $AB$. **Ans.**

**Example 6.** In the adjoining figure, $AD$ bisects $\angle BAC$. Write $AB$, $BD$ and $CD$ in the descending order of their lengths.

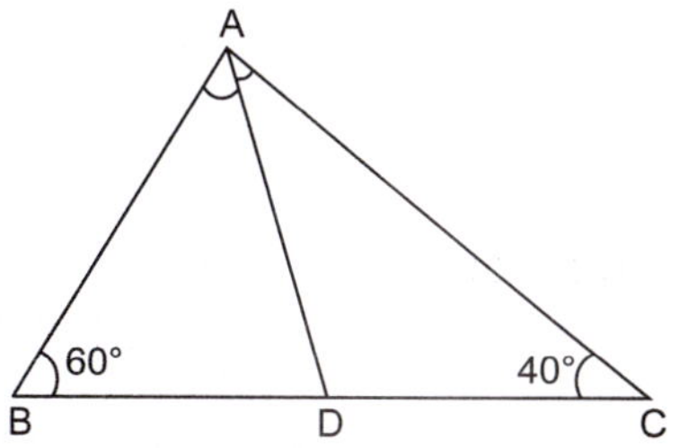


**Solution.** In $\Delta ABC$,

$$\angle BAC = 180° - (\angle ABC + \angle ACB)$$
$$= 180° - (60° + 40°) = 80°$$

$$\therefore \quad \angle BAD = \angle CAD = \frac{1}{2}\angle BAC = \frac{1}{2} \times 80° = 40°$$

In $\Delta ABD$,

$$\angle ADB, = 180° - (\angle ABD + \angle BAD)$$
$$= 180° - (60° + 40°) = 80°$$

$$\therefore \quad \angle ADB > \angle ABD > \angle BAD$$

$$\Rightarrow \quad AB > AD > BD \quad \text{...(i)}$$

In $\Delta ACD$,

$$\angle CAD = \angle ACD = 40° \quad \Rightarrow \quad CD = AD$$

Put $AD = CD$ in *(i)*.

$$AB > CD > BD$$ **Ans.**

**Example 7.** If $D$ be any point on the base $BC$ of an isosceles $\Delta ABC$ in which $AB = AC$, then prove that:
(i) $AB > AD$ (ii) $AC > AD$

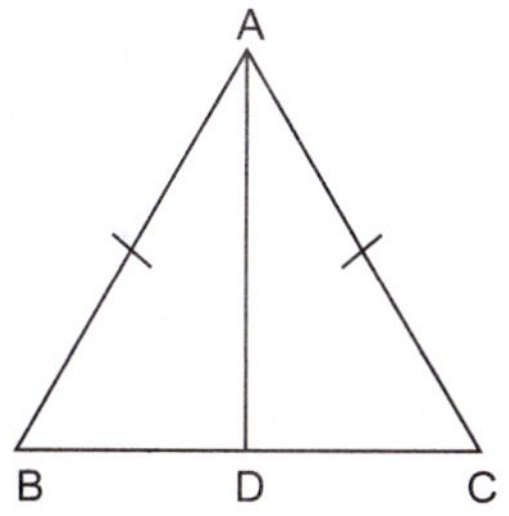


**Solution.** In $\Delta ABC$,

$$AB = AC$$

$$\Rightarrow \quad \angle ACB = \angle ABC \quad \text{...(i)}$$

(i) In $\Delta ACD$,

$\angle ADB = \angle ACD + \angle CAD$ [$\because$ $\angle ADB$ is the exterior angle.]

$\Rightarrow$ $\angle ADB > \angle ACD$

$\Rightarrow$ $\angle ADB > \angle ACB$ [$\because$ $\angle ACD = \angle ACB$]

$\Rightarrow$ $\angle ADB > \angle ABC$ [From equation *(i)*]

$\Rightarrow$ $\angle ADB > \angle ABD$ [$\because$ $\angle ABC = \angle ABD$]

$\Rightarrow$ $AB > AD$ **Hence Proved.**

(ii) In $\Delta ABD$,

$\angle ADC = \angle ABD + \angle BAD$ [$\because$ $\angle ADC$ is the exterior angle.]

$\Rightarrow$ $\angle ADC > \angle ABD$

$\Rightarrow$ $\angle ADC > \angle ABC$ [$\because$ $\angle ABD = \angle ABC$]

$\Rightarrow$ $\angle ADC > \angle ACB$ [From equation *(i)*]

$\Rightarrow$ $\angle ADC > \angle ACD$ [$\because$ $\angle ACB = \angle ACD$]

$\Rightarrow$ $AC > AD$ **Hence Proved.**

**Example 8.** Prove that the sum of any two sides of a triangle is greater than twice the median with respect to the third side.

**Solution.** Let $ABC$ be any triangle and $AD$ be the median from $A$ to $BC$. We have to prove that

$$AB + AC > 2AD$$

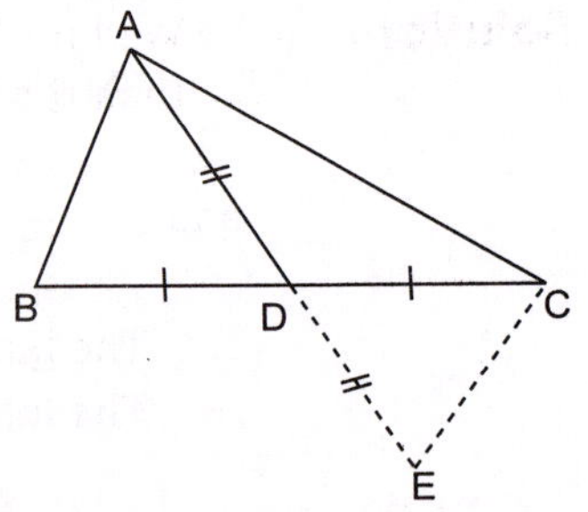


Produce $AD$ to $E$ such that

$$AD = DE$$

Join $CE$.

In $\Delta ABD$ and $\Delta ECD$,

$BD = CD$ ($D$ is mid-point of $BC$.)

$\angle ADB = \angle EDC$ (Vertically opposite angles)

$AD = DE$ (By construction)

$\therefore$ $\Delta ABD \cong \Delta ECD$ (SAS criteria)

$\Rightarrow$ $AB = EC$ (CPCT)

In $\Delta AEC$.

$EC + AC > AE$ (sum of two sides of a triangle is greater than the third side.)

$\Rightarrow$ $AB + AC > AE$ ($AB = EC$)

$\Rightarrow$ $AB + AC > AD + DE$

$\Rightarrow$ $AB + AC > AD + AD$ ($DE = AD$)

$\Rightarrow$ $AB + AC > 2AD$

Hence Proved.

**Example 9.** Prove that the sum of lengths of altitudes of a triangle is less than the perimeter of the triangle.

**Solution.** Let $ABC$ be a triangle and $AD \perp BC$, $BE \perp CA$, and $CF \perp AB$. We know that of all the line segments that can be drawn to a given line from a point not lying on it, the perpendicular line segment is the shortest.

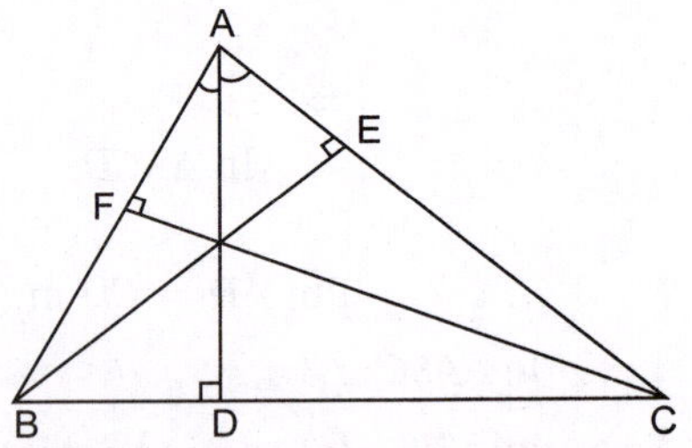


$AD \perp BC \Rightarrow AD < AB$ ...(i)

$BE \perp CA \Rightarrow BE < BC$ ...(ii)

$CF \perp AB \Rightarrow CF < CA$ ...(iii)

On adding (i), (ii) and (iii), we get,

$$AD + BE + CF < AB + BC + CA$$

Hence, the sum of lengths of altitudes of a triangle is less than the perimeter of the triangle.

Hence Proved.

**Example 10.** $\Delta ABC$ is an isosceles triangle in which $AB = AC$. If $D$ is any point on $BC$ produced, then prove that $AD > AB$

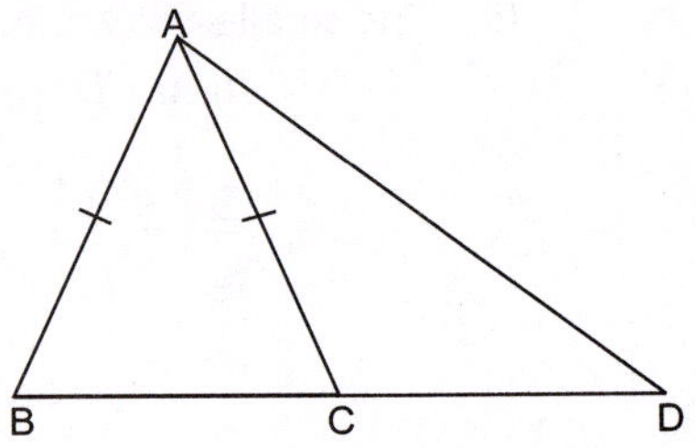


**Solution.** In $\Delta ABC$,

$$AB = AC$$

$\Rightarrow$ $\angle ACB = \angle ABC$ ...(i)

In $\Delta ACD$,

$\angle ACB = \angle ADC + \angle CAD$ ($\because$ $\angle ACB$ is the exterior angle.)

$\Rightarrow$ $\angle ACB > \angle ADC$

$\Rightarrow$ $\angle ABC > \angle ADC$ [From equation (i)]

$\Rightarrow$ $\angle ABD > \angle ADB$

$\Rightarrow$ $AD > AB$

Hence Proved.

**Example 11.** In the adjoining figure, the diagonals $AC$ and $BD$ of a quadrilateral $ABCD$ intersect at point '$O$'. Prove that:

(i) $AB + BC + CD + DA < 2\,(AC + BD)$

(ii) $AB + BC + CD + DA > AC + BD$

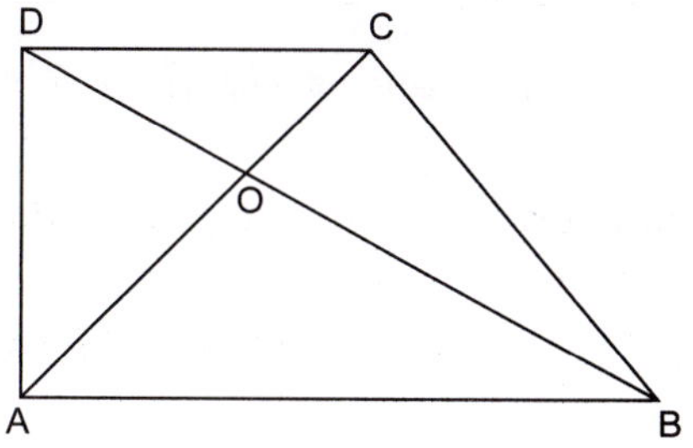


**Solution.** (i) We know that the sum of any two sides of a triangle is greater than the third side.

$\therefore$ In $\Delta OAB$, $OA + OB > AB$ ...(i)

In $\Delta OBC$, $OB + OC > BC$ ...(ii)

In $\Delta OCD$, $OC + OD > CD$ ...(iii)

In $\Delta DAO$, $OD + OA > DA$ ...(iv)

Adding (i), (ii), (iii) and (iv), we get

$OA + OB + OB + OC + OC + OD + OD + OA > AB + BC + CD + DA$

$\Rightarrow \quad 2(OA + OC) + 2(OB + OD) > AB + BC + CD + DA$

$\Rightarrow \quad 2\,AC + 2\,BD > AB + BC + CD + DA$

$\Rightarrow \quad 2(AC + BD) > AB + BC + CD + DA$

$\Rightarrow \quad AB + BC + CD + DA < 2(AC + BD)$

(ii) In $\Delta ABC$, $AB + BC > AC$ ...(v)

In $\Delta BCD$, $BC + CD > BD$ ...(vi)

In $\Delta CDA$, $CD + DA > AC$ ...(vii)

In $\Delta DAB$, $DA + AB > BD$ ...(viii)

Adding (v), (vi), (vii) and (viii)

$AB + BC + BC + CD + CD + DA + DA + AB > AC + BD + AC + BD$

$\Rightarrow \quad 2(AB + BC + CD + DA) > 2(AC + BD)$

$\Rightarrow \quad AB + BC + CD + DA > AC + BD$

Hence Proved.

## Exercise 8D

1. In $\Delta ABC$, $\angle A = 30°$, $\angle B = 90°$. Find the longest side of $\Delta ABC$.
2. In $\Delta ABC$, $\angle A = 68°$, $AB = AC$. Find the longest side of $\Delta ABC$.
3. Show that in a right-angled triangle, the hypotenuse is the longest side.
4. In $\Delta ABC$, $AB = 4$ cm, $BC = 5$ cm and $CA = 6$ cm. Find the longest angle of $\Delta ABC$.
5. From the adjoining figure, find:
   (i) The longest side of $\Delta ABC$
   (ii) The smallest side of $\Delta ABC$.

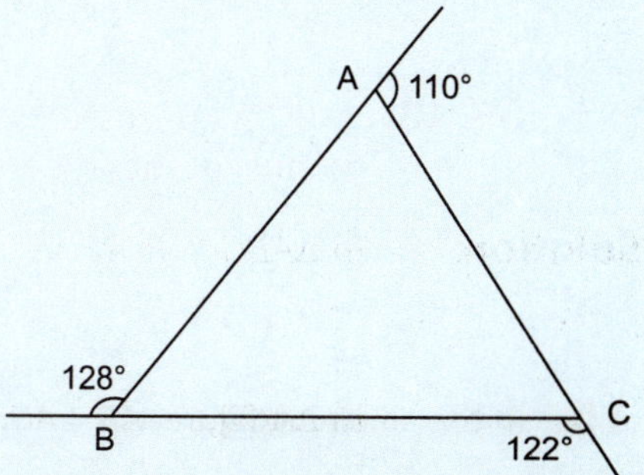


6. From the adjoining figure, find:
   (i) The longest side of $\Delta ABC$
   (ii) The nature of $\angle BAC$.

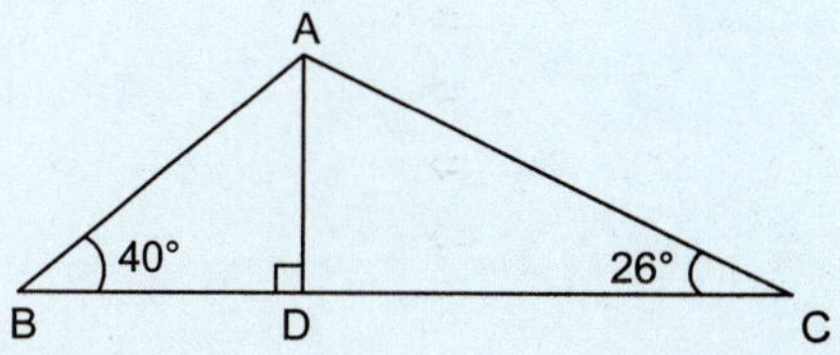

**7.** In the adjoining figure $\angle DBC > \angle BCE$. prove that $AB > AC$.

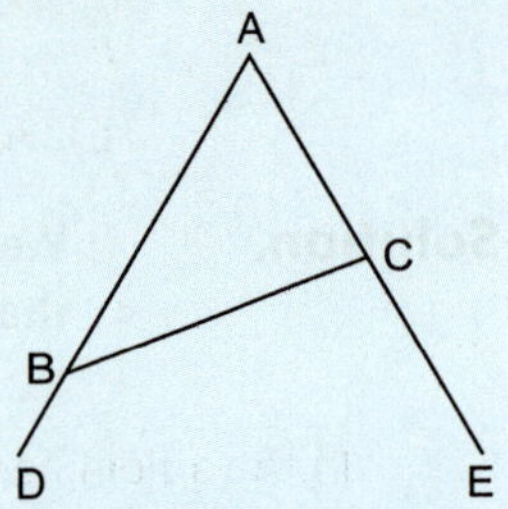


**8.** In a quadrilateral $ABCD$. Prove that:

(a) $BC + CD + DA > AB$ (b) $AB + BC + CD + DA > 2AC$ (c) $AB + BC + CD + DA > 2BD$

**9.** In $\Delta ABC$, if $AB < AC < BC$, then:

(a) What is the relation between $\angle A$ and $\angle C$ ?

(b) What is the relation between the values of $(AB + AC)$ and $BC$ ?

(c) What is the relation between the values of $(BC - AB)$ and $AC$ ?

(d) Which is the largest angle of $\Delta ABC$.

**10.** Let '$O$' be any point in the interior of $\Delta ACB$. Prove that:

(a) $AB + AC > OB + OC$ (b) $AB + BC + CA > (OA + OB + OC)$ (c) $AB + BC + CA < 2(OA + OB + OC)$.

**11.** In the adjoining figure, $AD = DE$. Prove that $AB + BC > CE$.

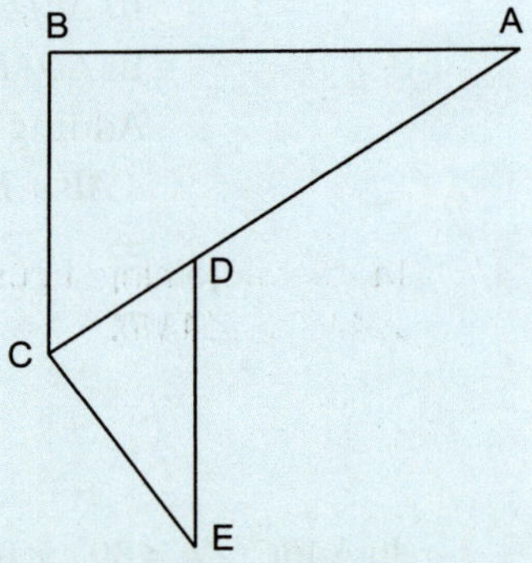


**12.** Prove that the sum of three medians of a triangle is less than the perimeter of the triangle.

**13.** If $P$ is any interior point of $\Delta ABC$, prove that $\angle BPC > \angle BAC$.

**14.** In the adjacent figure, $BE = DE$. Prove that $AC + BC > CD$.

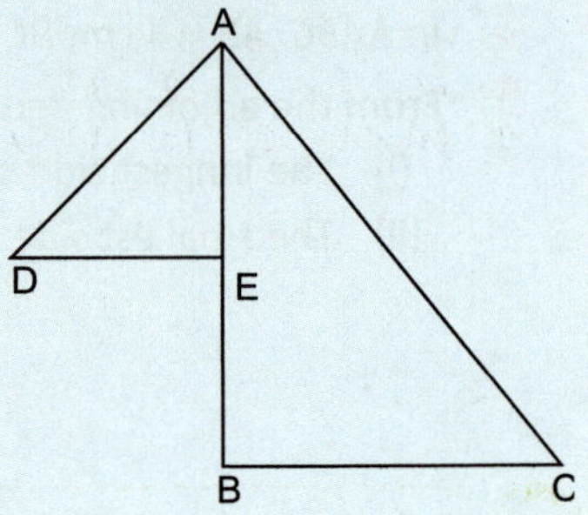


**15.** In the adjoining figure, $AB = AD$. Prove that $BC > CD$.

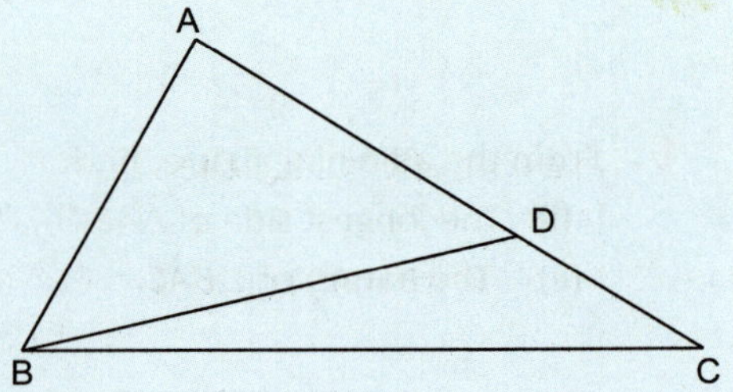

**16.** In the adjoining figure, $x > y > z$. Write the sides of $\Delta ABC$ in ascending order.

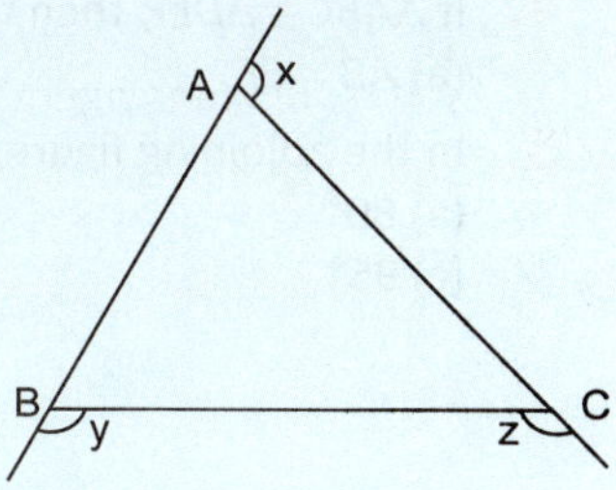


**17.** In the adjoining figure $AB > AC$. If $OB$ and $OC$ are the bisectors of $\angle ABC$ and $\angle ACB$, respectively, then prove that $OB > OC$.

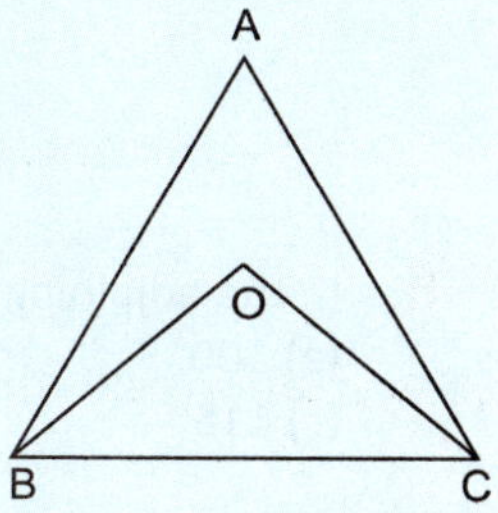


**18.** In the adjoining figure $OB$ and $OC$ are the bisectors of $\angle DBC$ and $\angle ECB$, respectively. If $AC > AB$ prove that $OB > OC$.

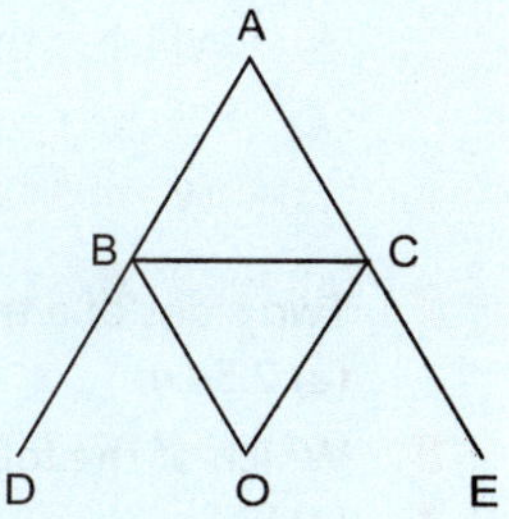


**19.** In the adjoining figure, $AC > AB$ and $AM$ is the bisector of $\angle BAC$. Prove that $\angle AMC > \angle AMB$.

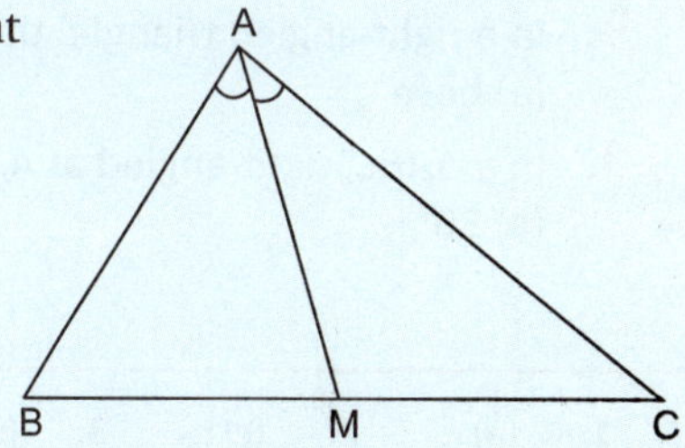


## Answers

**1.** $AC$ **2.** $BC$ **4.** $\angle B$ **5.** (a) $BC$ (b) $AC$ **6.** (i) $BC$ (ii) Obtuse-angled triangle
**9.** (a) $\angle A > \angle C$ (b) $AB + AC > BC$ (c) $BC - AB < AC$ (d) $\angle A$ **16.** $BC < AC < AB$

# Exercise 8E

## Multiple Choice Questions

Choose the correct answer from the given four options in each of the following questions :

**1.** In $\Delta PQR$, $\angle R < \angle Q$, then :
(a) $PR > PQ$ (b) $PR < PQ$ (c) $QR > PQ$ (d) $QR < AB$

**2.** In $\Delta ABC$, $AB = AC$ and $\angle A = 100°$, then $\angle C$ is equal to :
(a) 30° (b) 35° (c) 40° (d) 80°

**3.** In $\Delta ABC$, the correct relation is :
(a) $AB - BC > CA$ (b) $BC - CA > AB$ (c) $AB + BC < AC$ (d) $AB < BC + AC$

**4.** If $\Delta ABC \cong \Delta DEF$, then the correct statement is :

(a) $AB = EF$ (b) $BC = EF$ (c) $\angle B = \angle F$ (d) $\angle A = \angle E$

**5.** In the adjoining figure, $AD = CD = BD$. $\angle ABC$ is equal to :

(a) 80° (b) 90°
(c) 95° (d) 100°

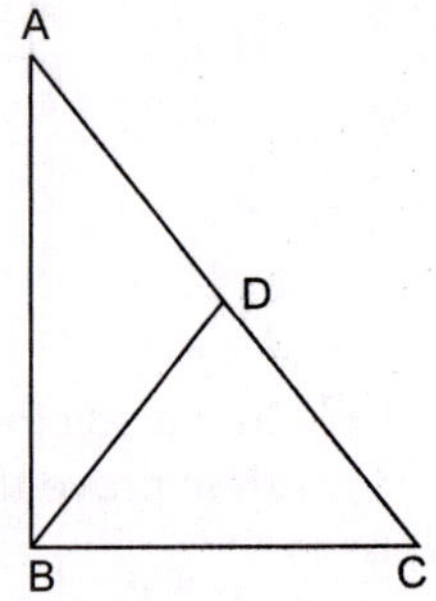


**6.** In the adjoining figure, the value of $x$ is :

(a) 100° (b) 105°
(c) 115° (d) 130°

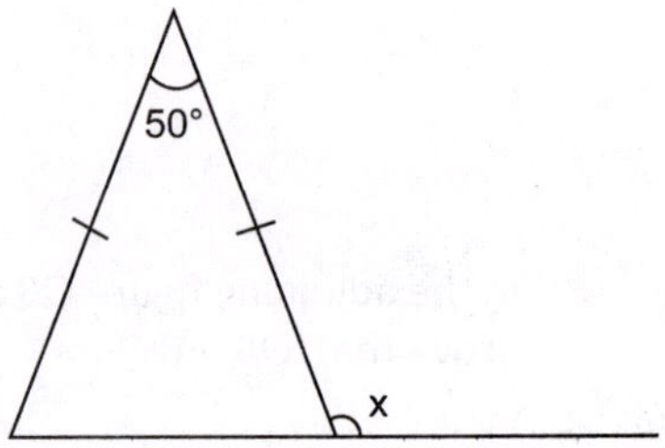


**7.** Two sides of a triangle are 3 cm and 6 cm, the length of third side of triangle cannot be :

(a) 2.5 cm (b) 3.5 cm (c) 4 cm (d) 8 cm

**8.** Which of the following is not the criterion for the congruency of two triangles?

(a) SAS (b) SSS (c) RHS (d) ASS

**9.** In a right-angled triangle, the longest side is :

(a) base (b) altitude (c) hypotenuse (d) can't say

**10.** In a $\Delta ABC$, right-angled at $A$, it is given that $AB = AC$, $\angle C$ is equal to :

(a) 30° (b) 45° (c) 60° (d) 90°

## Answers

**1.** (a) **2.** (c) **3.** (d) **4.** (b) **5.** (b) **6.** (c) **7.** (a) **8.** (d) **9.** (c) **10.** (b).

## SUMMARY *of the Chapter*

- A closed figure bounded by three line segments is called a triangle.
- A triangle has three vertices, three sides and three angles.
- The sum of three interior angles of a triangle is 180°. It is called angle sum property in a triangle.
- An exterior angle of a triangle is equal to the sum of its two interior opposite angles.
- Two triangles are said to be congruent if and only if they have exactly the same shape and same size.
- Criteria for congruency of two triangles :
  - (i) SSS : Three sides of a triangle are equal to three sides of the other triangle.
  - (ii) SAS : Two sides and the included angle of a triangle are equal to the two sides and the included angle of the other triangle.
  - (iii) ASA : Two angles and the included side of a triangle are equal to the two angles and the included side of the other triangle.
  - (iv) AAS : Two angles and one non-included side of a triangle are equal to two angles and the corresponding side of the other triangle.
  - (v) RHS : The hypotenuse and one side of a right-angled triangle are equal to the hypotenuse and one side of other right-angled triangle.
- The angles opposite to equal sides in a triangle are equal.
- The sides opposite to equal angles in a triangle are equal.
- If two sides of a triangle are unequal, then the longer side has greater angle opposite to it.
- If two angles of a triangle are unequal, then the greater angle has longer side opposite to it.
- The sum of two sides of a triangle is greater than the third side.
- The difference between any two sides of a triangle is less than the third side.
- Of all the line segments that can be drawn to a given line from a point not lying on it, the perpendicular line segment is the shortest.

# CHAPTER TEST

1. In $\Delta ABC$, $\angle A = 65°$, $\angle B = 60°$. Write the sides of $\Delta ABC$ in descending order.
2. In the adjoining figure, $\angle BCD = \angle ADC$ and $\angle ADB = \angle BCA$ Show that:

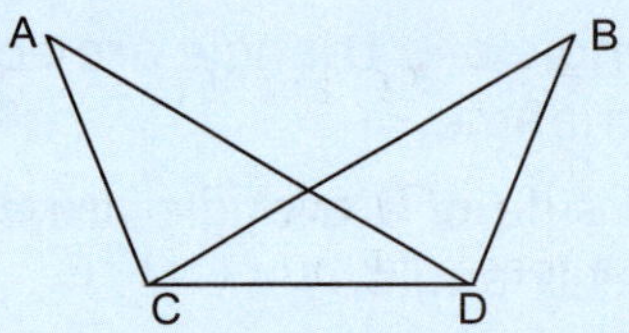


   (i) $\Delta ACD \cong \Delta BDC$
   (ii) $BC = AD$
   (iii) $\angle A = \angle B$
3. In the adjoining figure, $AC = AE$ and $\angle x = \angle y$. Prove that : $BE = CD$.

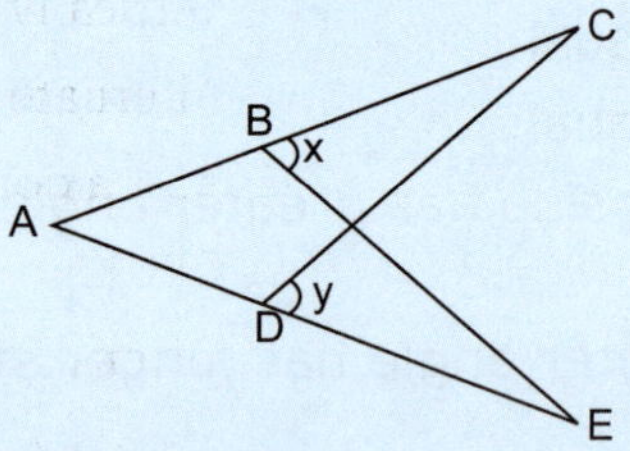


4. In the adjoining figure, $AB = PQ$, $BR = CQ$, $AB \perp BC$ and $PQ \perp RQ$. Prove that $AC = PR$.

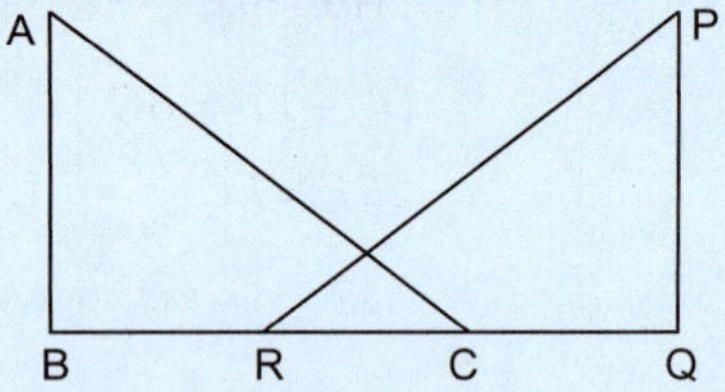


5. In the adjoining figure, $AB = DC$ and $AB \parallel DC$. Prove that $AD = BC$.

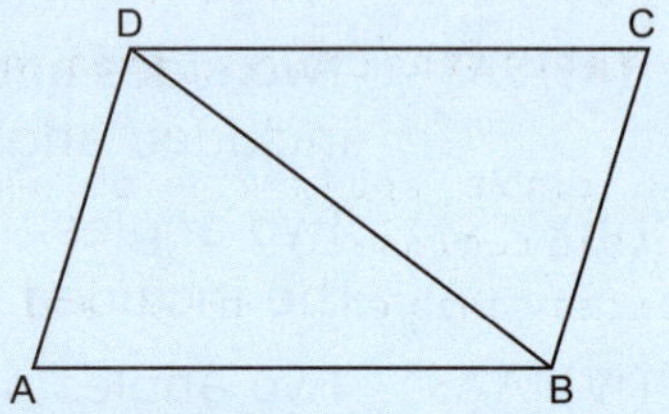


6. $ABCD$ is a rectangle. $X$ and $Y$ are points on sides $AD$ and $BC$ respectively, such that $AY = BX$. Prove that $BY = AX$ and $\angle BAY = \angle ABX$.
7. In $\Delta ABC$, the bisector $AD$ of $\angle A$ is perpendicular to the side $BC$. Show that $AB = AC$.
8. Prove that of all the line segments that can be drawn to a given line from a point not lying on it, the perpendicular line segment is the shortest.
9. Prove that the sum of the lengths of altitudes of a triangle is less than the perimeter of the triangle.
10. In the adjoining figure, $ABC$ and $MBC$ are two isosceles triangles on the base $BC$ and vertices $A$ and $M$ are on the same side of $BC$. If $AM$ is extended to meet $BC$ at $N$, prove that :

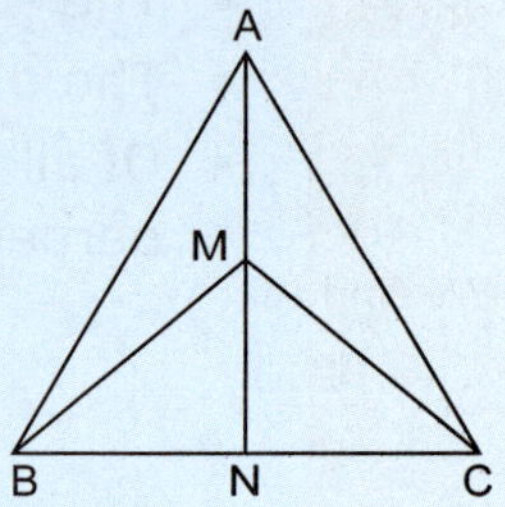


   (i) $\Delta ABM \cong \Delta ACM$
   (ii) $\Delta ABN \cong \Delta ACN$
   (iii) $AN$ bisects $\angle A$ as well as $\angle M$.
   (iv) $AN$ is the perpendicular bisector of $BC$.

## Answer

1. $BC > AC > AB$.

Chapter

# 9 MID-POINT THEOREM

## Syllabus

- Mid-point theorem and its converse, equal intercept theorem :
  (i) Proof and simple applications of mid-point theorem and its converse.
  (ii) Equal intercept theorem : proof and simple application.

## INTRODUCTION

We are familiar with different properties of a triangle. In this chapter, we shall discuss the mid-point theorem and its converse, in a triangle. For this, let us perform the following activity:

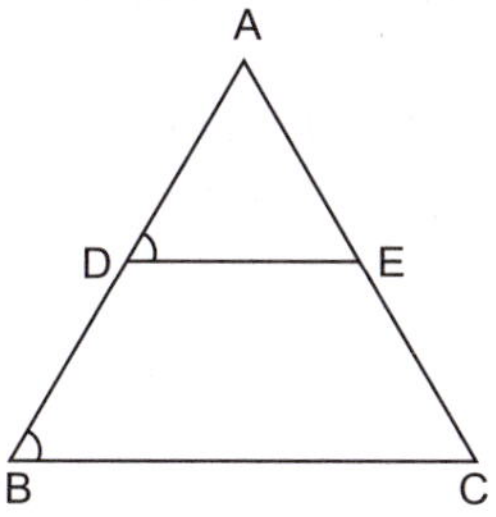


Draw a $\Delta ABC$. Mark $D$ and $E$ as the mid-points of the sides $AB$ and $AC$, respectively. Measure

(i) $DE$ and $BC$

(ii) $\angle ADE$ and $\angle ABC$.

We find that,

$$DE = \frac{1}{2}BC \text{ and } \angle ADE = \angle ABC$$

For two lines $DE$ and $BC$, the line $AB$ is a transversal. So $\angle ADE$ and $\angle ABC$ are corresponding angles, which are equal.

So, $DE \parallel BC$

Repeat this activity with several triangles, each time we get the same result. This result is called the mid-point theorem.

## Mid-point Theorem

The line segment joining the mid-points of two sides of a triangle is parallel to the third side and is equal to half of it.

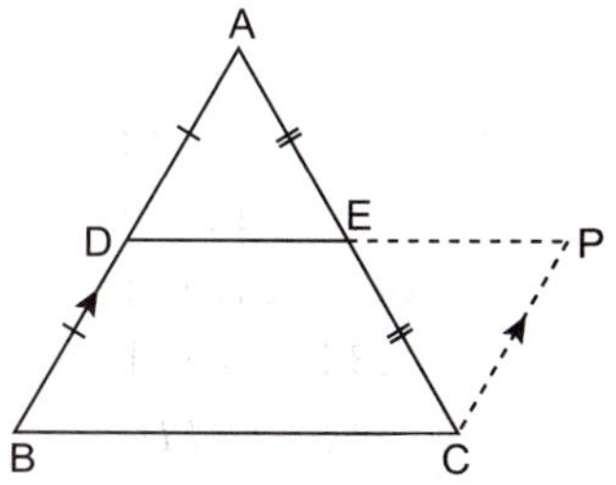


**Given :** A triangle $ABC$ in which $D$ and $E$ are the mid-points of the sides $AB$ and $AC$, respectively.

**To Prove:** $DE \parallel BC$ and $DE = \frac{1}{2}BC$

**Construction :** Draw $CP$ parallel to $BA$ which meets $DE$ produced at $P$.

**Proof :**

| | Statement | Reason |
|---|---|---|
| | In $\Delta ADE$ and $\Delta CPE$, | |
| | $AE = CE$ | Given |
| | $\angle AED = \angle CEP$ | Vertically opposite angles |
| | $\angle EAD = \angle ECP$ | Alternate angles |
| $\therefore$ | $\Delta ADE \cong \Delta CPE$ | ASA axiom |
| $\Rightarrow$ | $AD = CP$ and $DE = PE$ ...(i) | CPCT |
| But | $AD = BD$ | Given |
| $\therefore$ | $CP = BD$ | |

Now, $CP = BD$ and $CP \parallel BD$

$\therefore$ $BCPD$ is a parallelogram.

$\Rightarrow$ $DP \parallel BC$ and $DP = BC$

$\Rightarrow$ $DE \parallel BC$ and $DE + EP = BC$

$\Rightarrow$ $DE \parallel BC$ and $2DE = BC$ [From eqn. (i)]

$\Rightarrow$ $DE \parallel BC$ and $DE = \frac{1}{2}BC$ **Hence Proved.**

### Converse of Mid-point Theorem

The straight line drawn through the mid-point of one side of a triangle, parallel to another side, bisects the third side.

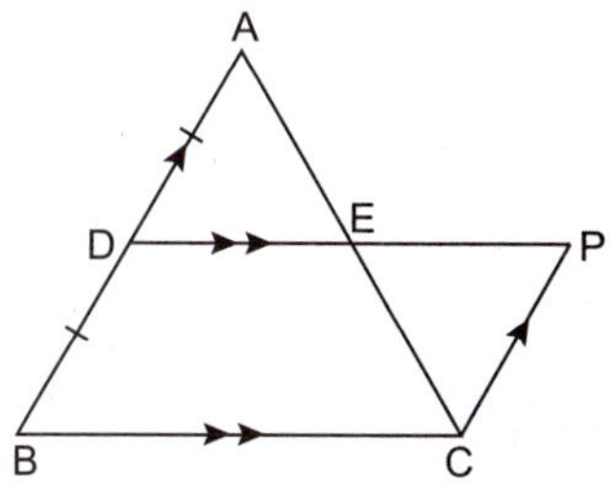


**Given :** A triangle $ABC$ in which $D$ is the mid-point of $AB$ and $DE \parallel BC$.

**To Prove :** $E$ bisects $AC$, *i.e.*, $AE = EC$.

**Construction :** Draw $CP \parallel BA$ which meets $DE$ produced at $P$.

**Proof :** Statement | Reason

| Statement | Reason |
|---|---|
| $BCPD$ is a parallelogram. | $BC \parallel DP$ and $BD \parallel CP$ |
| $CP = BD$ | Opposite sides of parallelogram |
| $\Rightarrow$ $CP = DA$ | $BD = DA$ (Given) |
| In $\Delta ADE$ and $\Delta CPE$, | |
| $AD = CP$ | Proved above |
| $\angle DAE = \angle PCE$ | Alternate angles |
| $\angle ADE = \angle CPE$ | Alternate angles |
| $\therefore$ $\Delta ADE \cong \Delta CPE$ | ASA axiom |
| $\Rightarrow$ $AE = CE$ | CPCT |

*i.e.,* $E$ is the mid-point of $AC$.

**Hence Proved.**

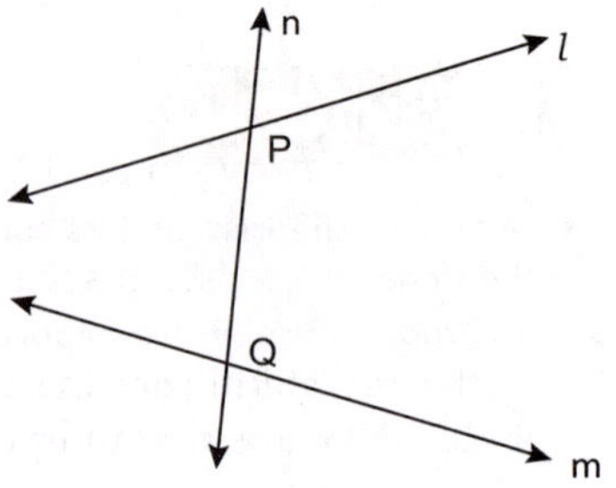


## Intercepts

If a line $n$ intersects two lines $l$ and $m$, drawn in a plane at two points $P$ and $Q$, respectively, then the line segment $PQ$ is called the intercept made on line $n$ by the lines $l$ and $m$.

## Equal Intercept Theorem

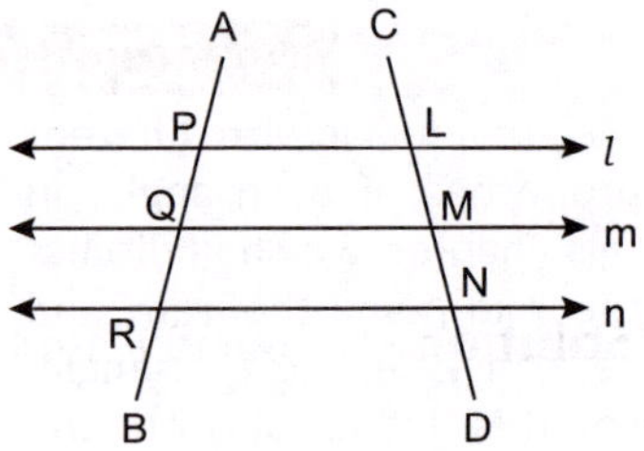


If a transversal makes equal intercepts on three or more parallel lines, then any other line cutting these three or more parallel lines, will also make equal intercepts.

**Given :** Three lines $l \parallel m \parallel n$ and a transversal $AB$ makes equal intercepts on these lines, *i.e.,* $PQ = QR$. $CD$ is another transversal whose intercepts between these lines are $LM$ and $MN$.

**To Prove :** $LM = MN$

**Construction :** Draw $PS \parallel CD \parallel QT$

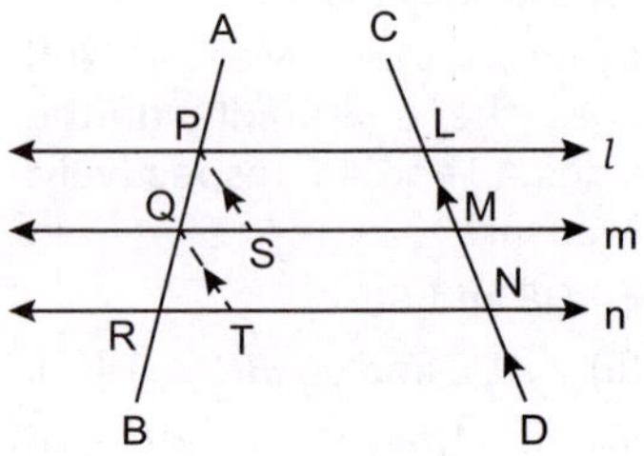


**Proof :**

| Statement | | Reason |
|---|---|---|
| In $\Delta PQS$ and $\Delta QRT$, | | |
| $PQ = QR$ | | Given |
| $\angle PQS = \angle QRT$ | | Corresponding angles |
| $\angle QPS = \angle RQT$ | | Corresponding angles |
| $\therefore$ $\Delta PQS \cong \Delta QRT$ | | ASA axiom |
| $\Rightarrow$ $PS = QT$ | ...(*i*) | CPCT |
| Now, $PSML$ is a parallelogram | | $PS \parallel LM$ and $LP \parallel MS$ |
| $\therefore$ $PS = LM$ | ...(*ii*) | Opposite sides of parallelogram |
| Again, $QTNM$ is a parallelogram | | $QT \parallel MN$ and $QM \parallel TN$ |
| $\therefore$ $QT = MN$ | ...(*iii*) | Opposite sides of parallelogram |
| $\therefore$ $LM = MN$ | | From eqns. (*i*), (*ii*) and (*iii*) |

**Hence Proved.**

# Illustrative Examples

**Example 1.** In the adjoining figure, $AD = 4$ cm, $AE = 4.2$ cm and $DE = 6$ cm. If $D$ and $E$ are the mid-points of $AB$ and $AC$, respectively. Find the perimeter of $\Delta ABC$.

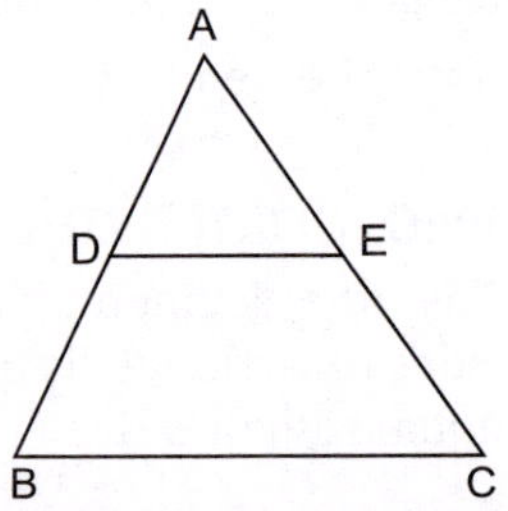


**Solution.**

$AB = 2AD = 2 \times 4 = 8$ cm

$AC = 2AE = 2 \times 4.2 = 8.4$ cm

$\because$ $D$ and $E$ are the mid-points of $AB$ and $AC$, respectively.

$\therefore$ $BC = 2DE = 2 \times 6 = 12$ cm

Now, perimeter of $\Delta ABC = AB + BC + CA = 8 + 8.4 + 12 = 28.4$ cm **Ans.**

**Example 2.** In the adjoining figure, $ABCD$ is a parallelogram. $X$ and $Y$ are the mid-points of $AD$ and $BC$, respectively. Prove that $AE = EF = FC$.

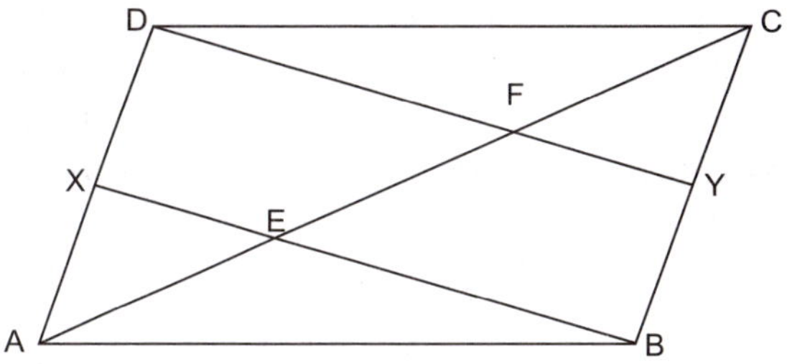


**Solution.** Here $DX = \frac{1}{2} AD$

and $BY = \frac{1}{2} BC$

$\therefore$ $DX = BY$ $(\because AD = BC)$

$\because$ $AD \parallel BC$

$\therefore$ $DX \parallel BY$

Now, $DX = BY$ and $DX \parallel BY$

$\therefore$ $\square DXBY$ is a parallelogram.

$\Rightarrow$ $BX \parallel DY$

Now, in $\Delta ADF$, $X$ is the mid-point of $AD$ (Given)

and $XE \parallel DE$ $(\because BX \parallel DY)$

$\therefore$ $XE$ bisects $AF$

$\Rightarrow$ $AE = EF$ ...(i)

Similarly, in $\Delta CEB$

$Y$ is the mid-point of $CB$. (Given)

and $FY \parallel BE$ $(\because BX \parallel DY)$

$\therefore$ $YF$ bisects $CE$.

$\Rightarrow$ $CF = EF$ ...(ii)

From equations (i) and (ii)

$AE = EF = CF$

Hence Proved.

**Example 3.** $D$, $E$ and $F$ are the mid-points of the sides $BC$, $CA$ and $AB$ respectively of an equilateral triangle $ABC$. Show that $\Delta DEF$ is also an equilateral triangle.

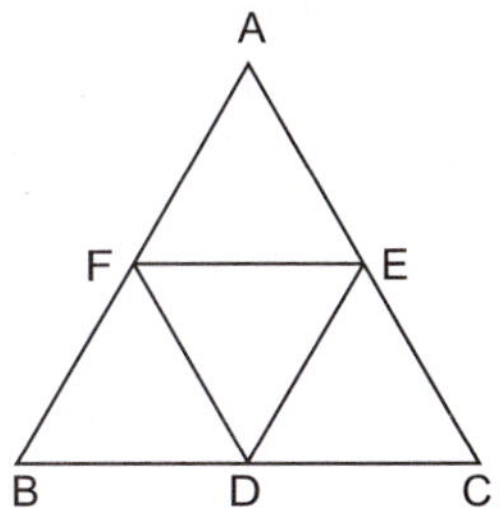


**Solution.** $E$ and $F$ are the mid-points of $AC$ and $AB$, respectively.

$\therefore$ $EF = \frac{1}{2} BC$ ...(i)

Similarly, $DF = \frac{1}{2} AC$ ...(ii)

and $DE = \frac{1}{2} AB$ ...(iii)

$\because$ $\Delta ABC$ is an equilateral triangle.

$\therefore$ $AB = BC = CA$

From (i), (ii) and (iii),

$\Rightarrow \frac{1}{2} AB = \frac{1}{2} BC = \frac{1}{2} CA \Rightarrow DE = EF = FD \Rightarrow \Delta DEF$ is also an equilateral triangle.

Hence Proved.

**Example 4.** In the adjoining figure, $X$ and $Y$ are mid-points of sides $AB$ and $AC$, respectively, of $\Delta ABC$. If $BC = 6$ cm, $AB = 7$ cm and $AC = 8$ cm, then find the perimeter of trapezium $XBCY$.

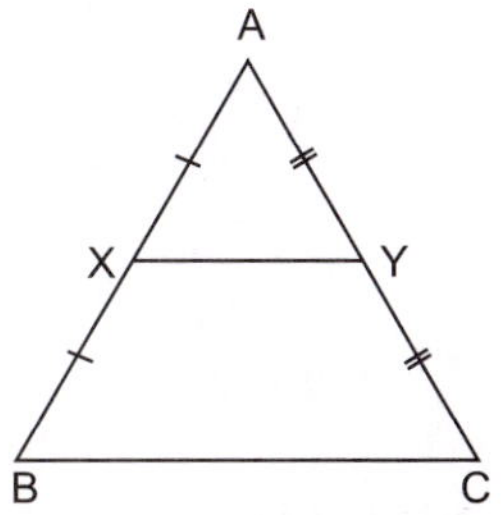


**Solution.** $X$ is the mid-point of $AB$ and $Y$ is the mid-point of $AC$, so

$$XY \parallel BC \text{ and } XY = \frac{1}{2} BC = \frac{1}{2} \times 6 \text{ cm} = 3 \text{ cm}$$

$$XB = \frac{1}{2} AB = \frac{1}{2} \times 7 \text{ cm} = 3.5 \text{ cm}$$

$$YC = \frac{1}{2} AC = \frac{1}{2} \times 8 \text{ cm} = 4 \text{ cm}$$

$\therefore$ Perimeter of trapezium $XBCY = XB + BC + CY + XY = (3.5 + 6 + 4 + 3)$ cm $= 16.5$ cm Ans.

**Example 5.** In $\Delta ABC$, $D$ is the mid-point of $BC$ and $E$ is the mid-point of $AD$. A line through $B$ and $E$ meets $AC$ at point $F$. Prove that $AF = \frac{1}{3} AC$.

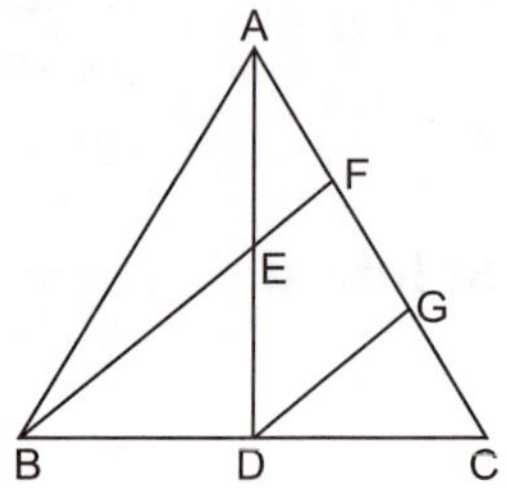


**Solution.** Draw $DG \parallel BEF$.

In $\Delta ADG$, $E$ is the mid-point of $AD$ (Given)

and $EF \parallel DG$ (By construction)

$\therefore$ $F$ is the mid-point of $AG$

*i.e.,* $AF = FG$ ...(i)

Again, in $\Delta CFB$, $D$ is the mid-point of $CB$ (Given)

and $DG \parallel BF$ (By construction)

$\therefore$ $G$ is the mid-point of $CF$

*i.e.,* $FG = CG$ ...(ii)

From equations *(i)* and *(ii)*

$$AF = FG = CG$$

$$\Rightarrow \quad AF = \frac{1}{3} AC$$

Hence Proved.

**Example 6.** Prove that the figure obtained by joining the mid-points of the adjacent sides of a quadrilateral is a parallelogram.

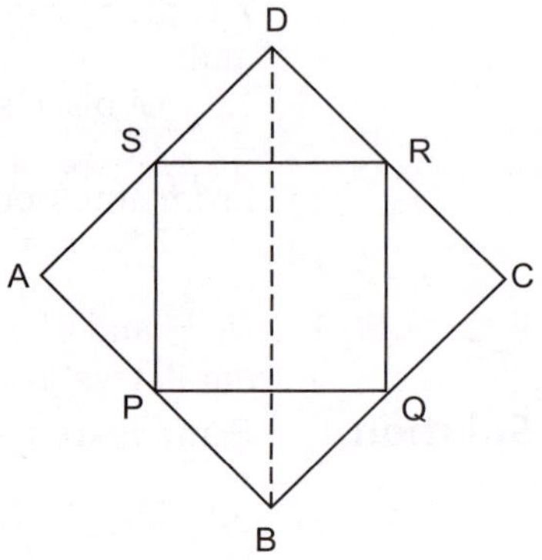


**Solution.** Given : A quadrilateral $ABCD$ in which $P$, $Q$, $R$ and $S$ are the mid-points of $AB$, $BC$, $CD$ and $DA$, respectively.

To Prove : $\square PQRS$ is a parallelogram.

Construction : Join $BD$.

Proof : In $\Delta ABD$, $P$ is the mid-point of $AB$ and $S$ is the mid-point of $AD$.

$$\therefore \quad PS = \frac{1}{2} BD \text{ and } PS \parallel BD \quad \text{...(i)}$$

Again, in $\Delta CBD$, $Q$ is the mid-point of $CB$ and $R$ is the mid-point of $CD$.

$$\therefore \quad QR = \frac{1}{2} BD \text{ and } QR \parallel BD \quad \text{...(ii)}$$

From equations *(i)* and *(ii)*

$$PS = \frac{1}{2} BD = QR \text{ and } PS \parallel BD \parallel QR$$

$\Rightarrow$ $PS = QR$ and $PS \parallel QR$ $\Rightarrow$ $\square PQRS$ is a parallelogram.

Hence Proved.

**Example 7.** Show that the quadrilateral formed by joining the mid-points of the adjacent sides of a rectangle is a rhombus.

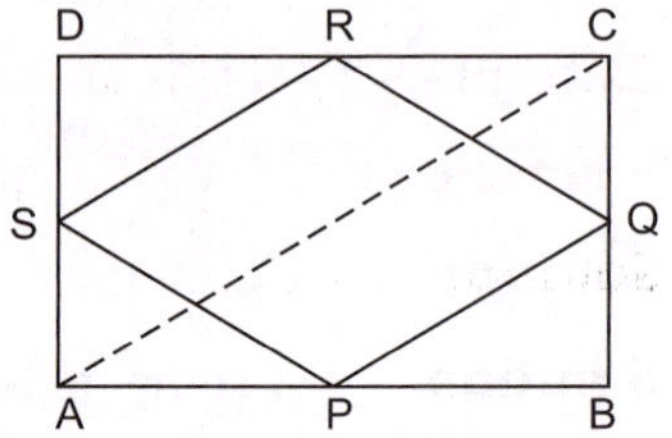


**Solution.** Given : A rectangle $ABCD$, in which $P$, $Q$, $R$ and $S$ are the mid-points of $AB$, $BC$, $CD$ and $DA$, respectively.

To Prove : $\square PQRS$ is a rhombus.

Construction : Join $AC$.

Proof : In $\Delta DAC$, $S$ is the mid-point of $DA$ and $R$ is the mid-point of $DC$.

$$\therefore \quad SR = \frac{1}{2} AC \text{ and } SR \parallel AC \quad \text{...(i)}$$

In $\Delta BAC$, $P$ is the mid-point of $BA$ and $Q$ is the mid-point of $BC$.

$$\therefore \quad PQ = \frac{1}{2} AC \text{ and } PQ \parallel AC \quad \text{...(ii)}$$

From equations *(i)* and *(ii)*

$$PQ = \frac{1}{2}AC = SR \text{ and } SR \parallel AC \parallel PQ$$

$\Rightarrow$ $PQ = SR$ and $PQ \parallel SR$ $\Rightarrow$ $\square PQRS$ is a parallelogram.

Now, in $\Delta APS$ and $\Delta BPQ$,

$AP = BP$ (Given)

$AS = BQ$ $\left(AS = \frac{1}{2}AD = \frac{1}{2}BC = BQ\right)$

and $\angle PAS = \angle PBQ$ (Each 90°)

$\therefore$ $\Delta APS \cong \Delta BPQ$ (SAS axiom)

$\Rightarrow$ $PS = PQ$ (CPCT)

Now, $\square PQRS$ is a parallelogram and its two adjacent sides $PS$ and $PQ$ are equal.

$\therefore$ $\square PQRS$ is a rhombus.

Hence Proved.

**Example 8.** **$ABCD$ is a rhombus and $P, Q, R, S$ are the mid-points of the sides $AB, BC, CD, DA$, respectively. Show that the quadrilateral $PQRS$ is a rectangle.**

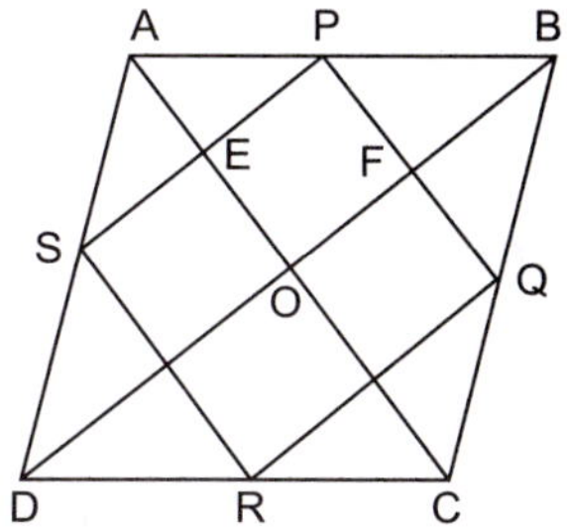


**Solution.** Here, $ABCD$ is a rhombus. $P, Q, R, S$ are the mid-points of the sides $AB$, $BC$, $CD$, $DA$, respectively.

We have to show that $PQRS$ is a rectangle.

In $\Delta ABC$,

$P$ and $Q$ are the mid-points of the sides $AB$ and $BC$, respectively.

$\therefore$ $PQ \parallel AC$ and $PQ = \frac{1}{2}AC$

Similarly, $SR \parallel AC$ and $SR = \frac{1}{2}AC$

$\therefore$ $PQ \parallel SR$ and $PQ = SR$

$\Rightarrow$ $\square PQRS$ is a parallelogram.

In $\Delta ABD$,

$P$ and $S$ are the mid-points of $AB$ and $AD$, respectively.

So, $PS \parallel BD$

$\Rightarrow$ $EP \parallel OF$ and $PF \parallel EO$

$\therefore$ $\square OEPF$ is a parallelogram.

But $\angle EOF = 90°$ (diagonals of a rhombus bisect each other at right angles)

And the opposite angles in parallelogram are equal.

$\therefore$ $\angle EPF = \angle EOF = 90°$

Now, $PQRS$ is a parallelogram in which one angle, *i.e.*, $\angle P = 90°$.

Hence, $PQRS$ is a rectangle.

Hence Proved.

**Example 9.** **$ABC$ is an isosceles triangle in which $AB = AC$ and $D, E, F$ are the mid-points of the sides $BC, CA, AB$, respectively. Show that $AD$ and $EF$ bisect each other at right angles.**

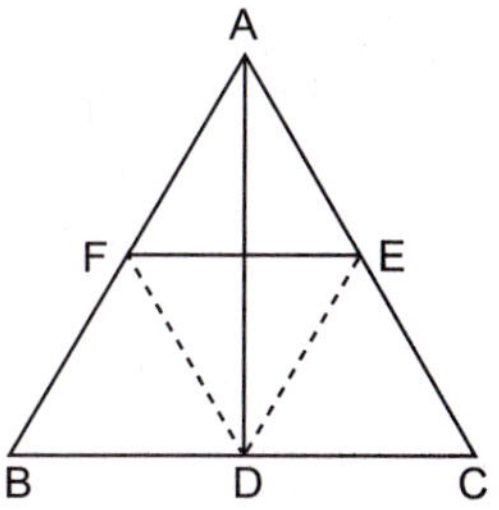


**Solution.** Here, $ABC$ is an isosceles triangle in which

$AB = AC$

Join $DE$ and $DF$.

In $\Delta ABC$,

$D$ and $E$ are the mid-points of $CB$ and $CA$ respectively, so

$$ED \parallel AB \text{ and } ED = \frac{1}{2}AB \quad \ldots(i)$$

Again, $D$ and $F$ are the mid-points of $BC$ and $BA$ respectively, so

$$DF \parallel CA \text{ and } DF = \frac{1}{2}CA \quad \ldots(ii)$$

From *(i)* and *(ii)*, we get

$$ED \parallel AB \text{ and } DF \parallel CA$$

$\Rightarrow$ $$ED \parallel AF \text{ and } DF \parallel AE$$

Therefore, *DEAF* is a parallelogram.

Given that $AB = AC$

$\Rightarrow$ $\frac{1}{2} AB = \frac{1}{2} AC$ $\Rightarrow$ $ED = FD$ [From *(i)* and *(ii)*]

Now, *DEAF* is a parallelogram and $ED = FD$

$\Rightarrow$ *DEAF* is a rhombus.

We know that the diagonals of a rhombus bisect each other at right angles.

$\Rightarrow$ diagonals *AD* and *FE* bisect each other at right angles. Hence Proved.

**Example 10.** *ABC* is a triangle, right angled at *C*. A line through the mid-point *O* of hypotenuse *AB* and parallel to *BC* intersects *AC* to *D*. Prove that

(i) *D* is mid-point of *AC*.

(ii) $OD \perp AC$

(iii) $CO = OA = \frac{1}{2} AB$

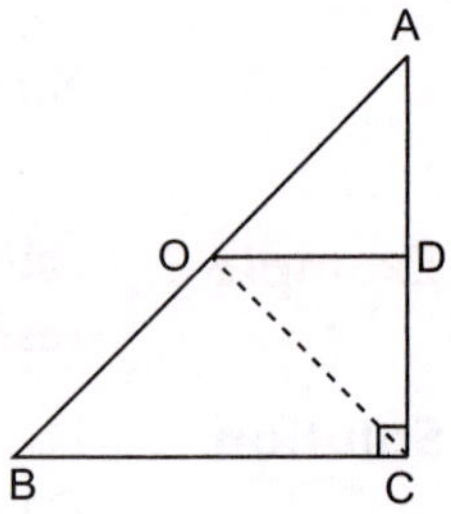


**Solution.** (i) In $\Delta ABC$,

*O* is the mid-point of *AB* and $OD \parallel BC$, therefore, by the converse of mid-point theorem,

*D* is the mid-point of *AC*.

(ii) $OD \parallel BC$ and *AC* is a transversal,

$\therefore$ $\angle BCD + \angle CDO = 180°$ (Sum of co-interior angles)

$\Rightarrow$ $90° + \angle CDO = 180°$ ($\angle BCA = 90°$)

$\Rightarrow$ $\angle CDO = 90°$ $\Rightarrow$ $OD \perp AC$

(iii) In $\Delta AOD$ and $\Delta COD$,

$AD = DC$ [From part *(i)*]

$\angle ADO = \angle CDO$ (Each 90°)

$OD = OD$ (Common)

$\therefore$ $\Delta AOD \cong \Delta COD$ (SAS criteria)

$\Rightarrow$ $AO = CO$ (CPCT)

Since *O* is the mid-point of *AB*

$\therefore$ $AO = \frac{1}{2} AB$

Hence, $CO = AO = \frac{1}{2} AB$ Hence Proved.

**Example 11.** In the adjoining figure *D, E, F* are the mid-points of the sides *AB, BC, CA* respectively of a $\Delta ABC$. Show that $\Delta ABC$ is divided into four congruent triangles by joining the points *D, E* and *F*.

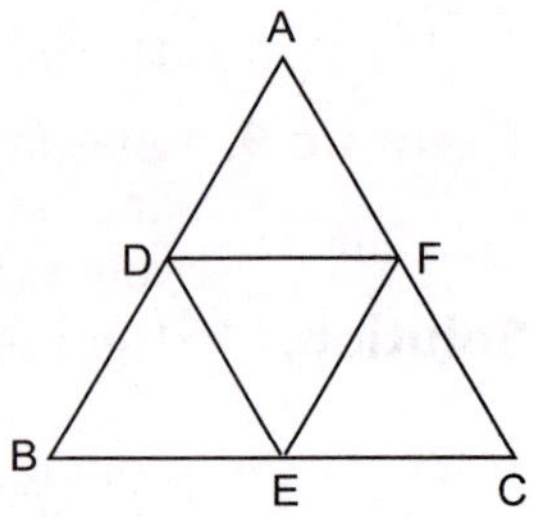


**Solution.** In $\Delta ABC$, *D* and *E* are the mid-points of *BA* and *BC* respectively, so by the mid-point theorem, $DE \parallel AC$.

Similarly, $FE \parallel BA$ and $DF \parallel BC$

$\Rightarrow$ *ADEF, BEFD* and *CFDE* are all parallelograms.

We know that the diagonal of a parallelogram divides it into two congruent triangles.

$\therefore$ $\Delta ADF \cong \Delta DEF$

$\Delta BDE \cong \Delta DEF$

$\Delta CEF \cong \Delta DEF$

Hence, $\Delta ADF \cong \Delta BDE \cong \Delta CEF \cong \Delta DEF$

$\Rightarrow$ All four triangles are congruent. Hence Proved.

**Example 12.** $E$ and $F$ are the mid-points of non-parallel sides $AD$ and $BC$ respectively of a trapezium $ABCD$. Prove that $EF \parallel AB$ and $EF = \frac{1}{2}(AB + CD)$.

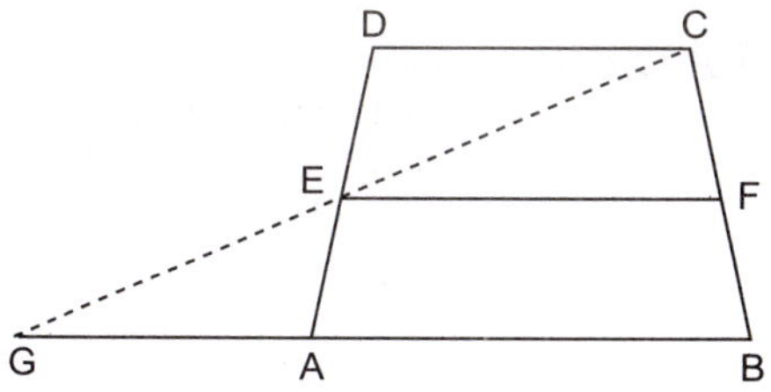


**Solution.** $ABCD$ is a trapezium in which $AB \parallel DC$ and $E$, $F$ are the mid-point of $AD$, $BC$ respectively.

Join $CE$ and produces it to meet $BA$ produced at $G$.

In $\Delta EDC$ and $\Delta EAG$,

$ED = EA$ ($E$ is mid-point of $AD$)

$\angle CED = \angle GEA$ (Vertically opposite angles)

$\angle ECD = \angle EGA$ (Alternate angles, $DC \parallel AB \Rightarrow DC \parallel GB$ and $CG$ is a transversal)

$\therefore$ $\Delta EDC \cong \Delta EAG$ (AAS criteria)

$\Rightarrow$ $CD = GA$ and $EC = EG$ (CPCT)

In $\Delta CGB$,

$E$ and $F$ are mid-points of $CG$ and $BC$, respectively. ($\because EC = EG$)

$\therefore$ By mid-point theorem,

$$EF \parallel AB \text{ and } EF = \frac{1}{2} GB$$

$$\Rightarrow \quad EF \parallel AB \text{ and } EF = \frac{1}{2}(GA + AB)$$

$$\Rightarrow \quad EF \parallel AB \text{ and } EF = \frac{1}{2}(CD + AB)$$

Hence Proved.

**Example 13.** $P$, $Q$, $R$ are the mid-points of the sides $BC$, $CA$, $AB$, respectively, of a $\Delta ABC$. $PR$ and $BQ$ meet at $X$, $CR$ and $PQ$ meet at $Y$, prove that $XY = \frac{1}{4} BC$.

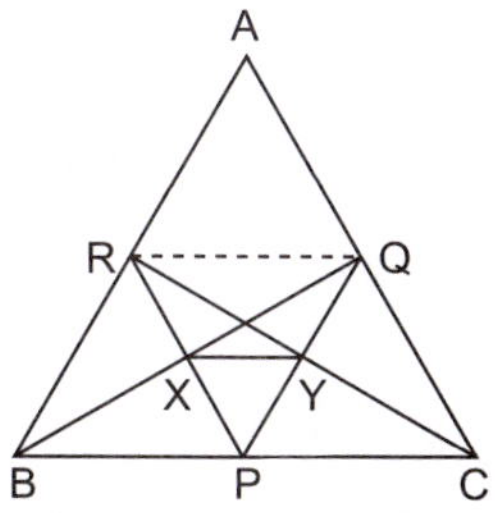


**Solution.** $ABC$ is a triangle. $P$, $Q$, $R$ are the mid-points of $BC$, $CA$, $AB$ respectively. $PR$ and $BQ$ meet at $X$, $CR$ and $PQ$ meet at $Y$. Join $RQ$ and $XY$.

$R$ and $Q$ are mid-points of sides $AB$ and $AC$, respectively, therefore, by mid-point theorem,

$$RQ \parallel BC \text{ and } RQ = \frac{1}{2} BC$$

$\Rightarrow$ $RQ \parallel BC$ and $RQ = BP$ ($P$ is mid-point of $BC$)

$\Rightarrow$ $BPQR$ is a parallelogram.

We know that the diagonals of a parallelogram bisect each other.

$\therefore$ $X$ is the mid-point of $PR$.

Again, $$RQ \parallel BC \text{ and } RQ = \frac{1}{2} BC$$

$\Rightarrow$ $RQ \parallel PC$ and $RQ = PC$

$\Rightarrow$ $PCQR$ is a parallelogram.

$\Rightarrow$ $Y$ is mid-point of $PQ$.

In $\Delta PQR$,

$X$ and $Y$ are the mid-points of $PR$ and $PQ$ respectively, therefore by mid-point theorem,

$$XY \parallel RQ \text{ and } XY = \frac{1}{2} RQ$$

$$\therefore \quad XY = \frac{1}{2} RQ = \frac{1}{2}\left(\frac{1}{2} BC\right) = \frac{1}{4} BC$$

Hence Proved.

**Example 14.** In the adjoining figure, two points $A$ and $B$ lie on the same side of a line '$l$' and $AD \perp l$, $BE \perp l$. If $C$ is the mid-point of $AB$, prove that $CD = CE$.

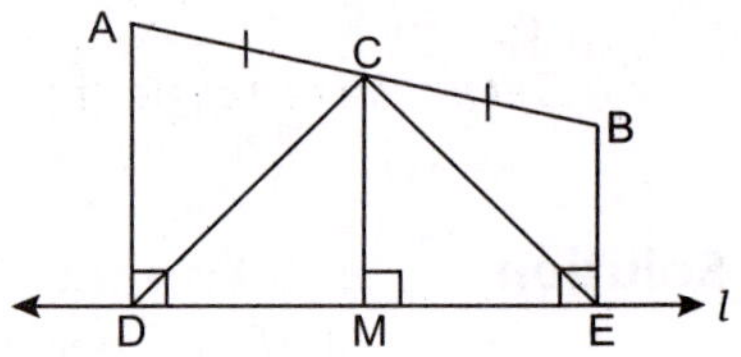


**Solution.** Draw $CM \perp l$.

$\therefore$ $AD \parallel CM \parallel BE$

$\because$ $AD \parallel CM \parallel BE$ and a transversal $AB$ makes equal intercepts

*i.e.,* $AC = BC$

$\therefore$ The other transversal $DE$ will also make the equal intercepts,

*i.e.,* $DM = EM$

Now, in $\Delta CDM$ and $\Delta CEM$

$DM = EM$ (Proved above)

$\angle DMC = \angle EMC$ (Each 90°)

and $CM = CM$ (Common)

$\therefore$ $\Delta CDM \cong \Delta CEM$ (SAS axiom)

$\Rightarrow$ $CD = CE$ (CPCT)

Hence Proved.

**Example 15.** In the adjoining figure, $ABCD$ is a parallelogram. $E$ and $F$ are the mid-points of $AB$ and $DC$ respectively. A line $PR$ meets $AD$, $EF$ and $BC$ at $P$, $Q$ and $R$ respectively. Prove that $PQ = QR$.

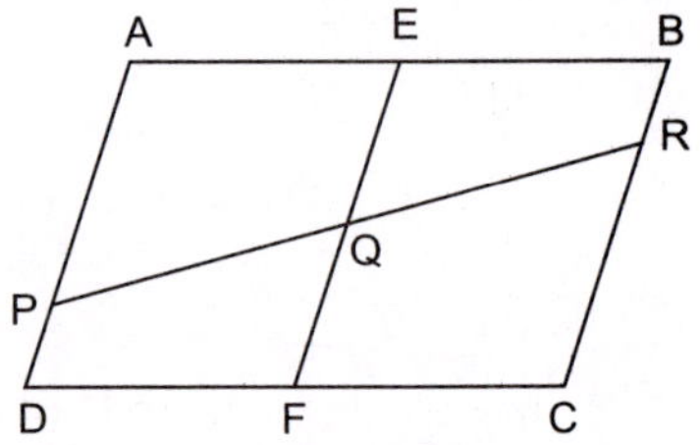


**Solution.**

$AE = \frac{1}{2} AB$ ($\because$ $E$ is the mid-point of $AB$)

$DF = \frac{1}{2} DC$ ($\because$ $F$ is the mid-point of $DC$)

$\therefore$ $AE = DF$ ($\because$ $AB = DC$)

Also $AE \parallel DF$

$\therefore$ ◻$AEFD$ is a parallelogram.

$\Rightarrow$ $AD \parallel EF$

Now, $AD \parallel EF \parallel BC$ and a transversal $AB$ makes equal intercepts, *i.e.*, $AE = EB$.

$\therefore$ Another transversal $PR$ will also make equal intercepts, *i.e.*, $PQ = QR$. Hence Proved.

## Exercise 9A

1. In the adjoining figure, $ABC$ is a triangle in which $\angle B = 90°$. $M$ and $N$ are the mid-points of sides $AB$ and $AC$, respectively. If $AB = 5$ cm, $BC = 12$ cm, find
   (i) Perimeter of ◻$MNCB$
   (ii) Area of ◻$MNCB$

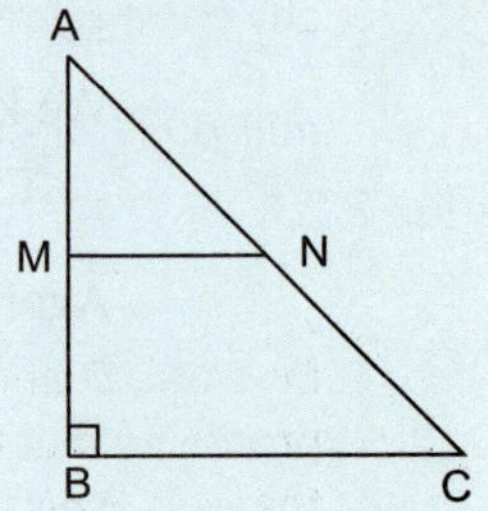


2. $\Delta ABC$ is an isosceles triangle in which $AB = AC$. If $P$, $Q$ and $R$ are the mid-points of the sides $AB$, $BC$ and $CA$, respectively, prove that $\Delta PQR$ is also an isosceles triangle.
3. In the adjoining figure; $P$, $Q$ and $R$ are the mid-points of the sides $BC$, $CA$ and $AB$, respectively, of $\Delta ABC$. Prove that ◻$RQPB$ is a parallelogram.

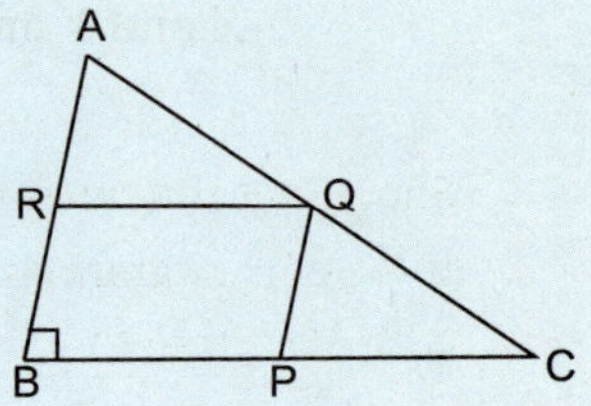

4. □$PQRS$ is a rectangle. If $A$, $B$ and $C$ are the mid-points of sides $PQ$, $PS$ and $QR$, respectively. Prove that $AB + AC = \frac{1}{2}(PR + SQ)$.

5. In the adjoining figure, $ABCD$ is a trapezium in which $AB \parallel DC$ and $M$ is the mid-point of $AD$. If $MN \parallel DC$ meets $BC$ at $N$, prove that $N$ is the mid-point of $BC$.

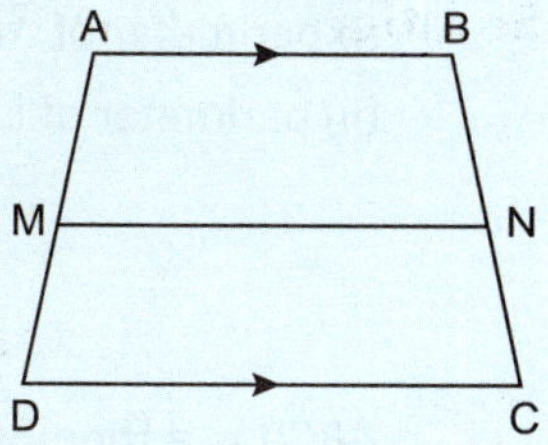


6. Show that the straight lines joining the mid-points of the opposite sides of a quadrilateral bisect each other.

7. In $\Delta ABC$, $M$ and $N$ are the mid-points of $AB$ and $AC$ respectively and $R$ be any point on $BC$. Use intercept theorem, prove that $MN$ bisects $AR$.

8. In the adjoining figure, □$ABCD$ is a parallelogram. $P$ is the mid-point of $CD$ and $DQ \parallel PB$ meets $CB$ produced at $R$. Prove that:

(i) $AD = \frac{1}{2}CR$

(ii) $DR = 2\,PB$

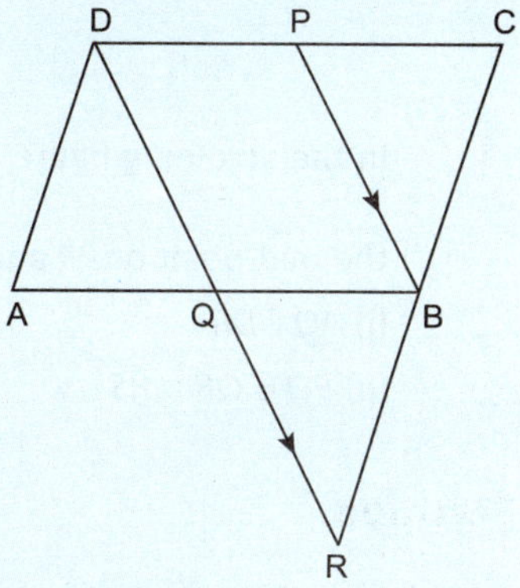


9. In a trapezium $ABCD$, $AB \parallel CD$. $M$ and $N$ are two points on $AD$ dividing it into three equal parts. Line segments $MP$ and $NQ$ are parallel to $AB$ which meet $BC$ at $P$ and $Q$, respectively. Prove that $BP = PQ = CQ$, *i.e.*, $P$ and $Q$ divide $BC$ into three equal parts.

10. In the adjoining figure, $ABCD$ is a trapezium in which $AB \parallel DC$. If $M$ and $N$ are the mid-points of $BD$ and $AC$, respectively, prove that $MN = \frac{1}{2}(CD - AB)$.

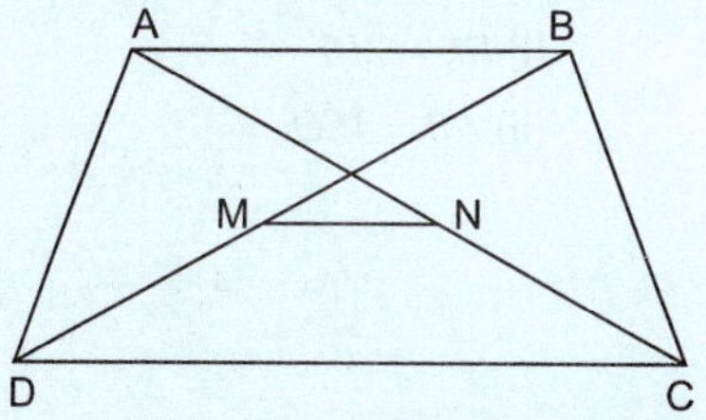


11. In the adjoining figure, $ABCD$ is a parallelogram in which $P$ is the mid-point of $DC$. If $Q$ is any point on $AC$ such that $CQ = \frac{1}{4}CA$ and $PQ$ produced meet $BC$ at $R$, prove that $R$ is the mid-point of $BC$.

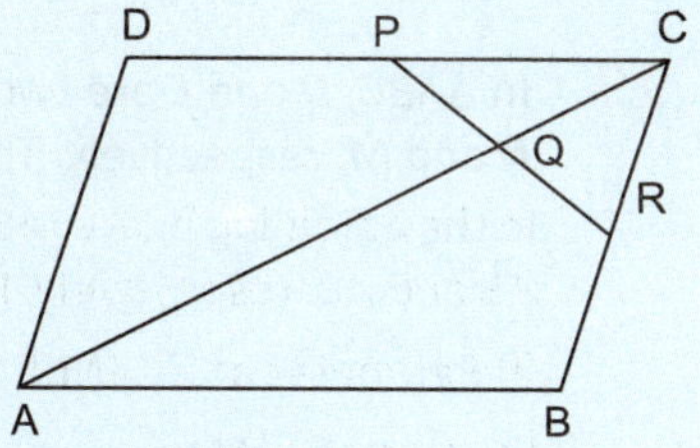


12. In $\Delta ABC$, $D$ and $E$ are the mid-points of $AC$ and $AB$, respectively. $BD$ and $CE$ produced meet a line through $A$ parallel to $BC$ at $M$ and $N$, respectively. Prove that $AM = AN$.

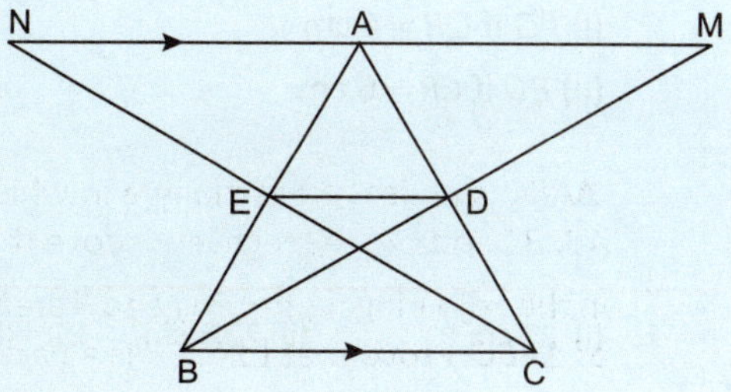


13. Show that the quadrilateral formed by joining the mid-points of the adjacent sides of a square, is a square.

14. In a parallelogram $ABCD$, the diagonals $AC$ and $BD$ intersect at point $O$. If $P$ is the mid-point of $BC$, prove that

(i) $PO \parallel AB$ (ii) $PO = \frac{1}{2}AB$

**15.** In the adjoining figure; $D$, $E$ and $F$ are the mid-points of $BC$, $CA$ and $AB$, respectively. If $AB = 6$ cm, $BC = 8$ cm and $AC = 5.6$ cm, find :

(i) perimeter of $\Delta DEF$

(ii) perimeter of $\square ABDE$

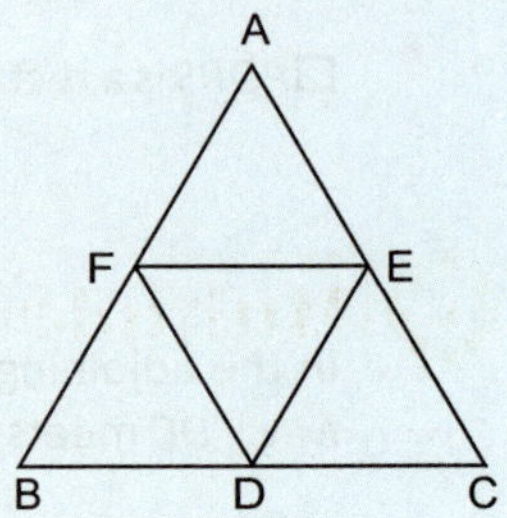


**16.** $ABCD$ is a rhombus. $EABF$ is a straight line such that $EA = AB = BF$. Prove that $ED$ and $FC$ when produced, meet at right angles.

**17.** In the adjoining figure; $AP = \frac{1}{2} AB$ and $D$ is the mid-point of $AB$, $Q$ is the mid-point of $PR$ and $DR \parallel BS$. Prove that:

(i) $AQ \parallel DR$

(ii) $PQ = QR = RS$

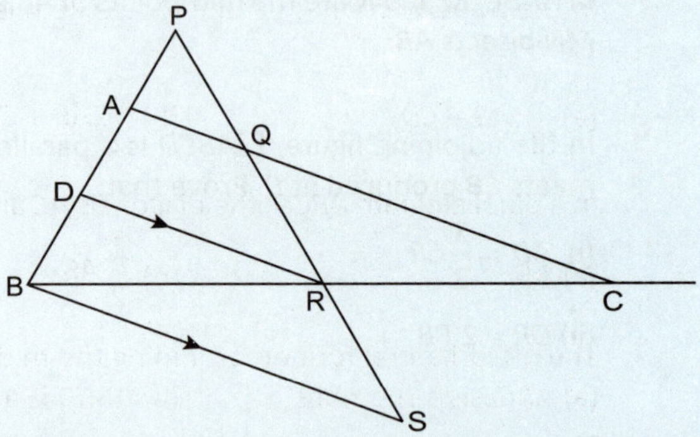


**18.** In the adjoining figure; $CE = \frac{1}{2} AC$ and $D$ is the mid-point of $BC$. Prove that:

(i) $DE = 2DF$

(ii) $AB = 4CQ$

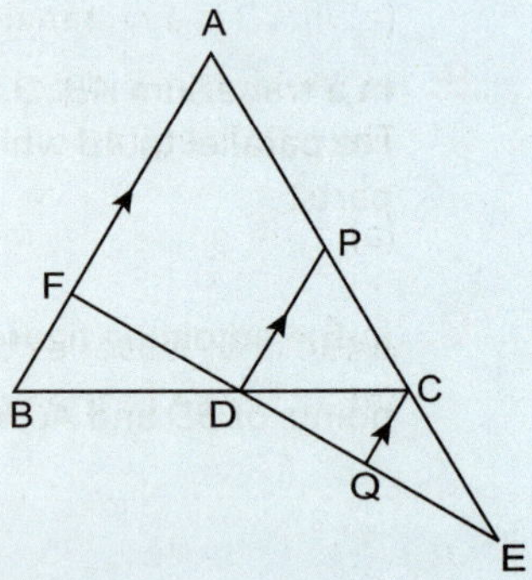


**19.** In $\Delta ABC$; $D$ and $E$ are two points on $AB$ such that $AD = DE = EB$. Through $D$ and $E$, lines are drawn parallel to $AC$ meet $BC$ at $N$ and $M$, respectively. Through $N$ and $M$, lines are drawn parallel to $AB$ meet $AC$ at $Q$ and $P$. Prove that $AP = PQ = CQ$.

**20.** In the following figure, $l \parallel m \parallel n$ and $AB = BC$, find:

(i) $PQ$ if $QR = 4$ cm

(ii) $BO$ if $CR = 6$ cm

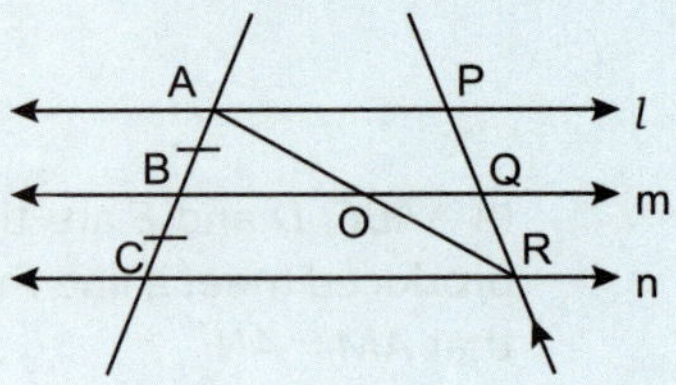


## Answers

**1.** (i) 27 cm (ii) 22.5 cm$^2$ **15.** (i) 9.8 cm (ii) 15.8 cm **20.** (i) 4 cm (ii) 3 cm

# Exercise 9B

## Multiple Choice Questions

Choose the correct answer from the given four options in each of the following questions :

1. In the trapezium *ABCD*, *P* and *Q* are the mid-points of non-parallel sides *AD* and *BC*, respectively. Then *PQ* is equal to :

   (a) $\frac{1}{2}(AB - CD)$ (b) $\frac{1}{2}(AB + CD)$ (c) $\frac{1}{3}(AB - CD)$ (d) $\frac{1}{3}(AB + CD)$

2. In the trapezium *ABCD*, *P* and *Q* are the mid-points of *AC* and *BD* respectively and $AB \parallel CD$ with $AB > CD$. Then *PQ* is equal to :

   (a) $\frac{1}{2}(AB - CD)$ (b) $\frac{1}{2}(AB + CD)$ (c) $\frac{1}{3}(AB - CD)$ (d) $\frac{1}{3}(AB + CD)$

3. In a parallelogram *ABCD*, the diagonals *AC* and *BD* intersect at point *M*. If *P* is the mid-point of side *AD*, then *PM* is equal to :

   (a) *AB* (b) $\frac{1}{2}AB$ (c) $\frac{1}{3}AB$ (d) $\frac{1}{4}AB$

4. The quadrilateral formed by joining the mid-points of the sides of a quadrilateral *ABCD*, taken in order, is a rhombus, if :

   (a) *ABCD* is a rhombus (b) *ABCD* is a parallelogram (c) $AC = BD$ (d) $AC \perp BD$

5. The quadrilateral formed by joining the mid-point of a quadrilateral *ABCD*, taken in order is a rectangle, if :

   (a) *ABCD* is a rectangle (b) *ABCD* is a parallelogram (c) $AC \perp BD$ (d) $AC = BD$

6. In $\Delta ABC$, the mid-points of the sides *BC*, *CA* and *AB* are *P*, *Q* and *R* respectively. *PR* and *BQ* meet at *X*. *CR* and *PQ* meet at *Y*. Then *XY* is equal to :

   (a) $\frac{1}{2}BC$ (b) $\frac{1}{3}BC$ (c) $\frac{1}{4}BC$ (d) $\frac{1}{5}BC$

7. $\Delta ABC$ is an isosceles triangle. *P*, *Q* and *R* are the mid-points of the sides *BC*, *CA* and *AB*, respectively. Then $\Delta PQR$ is :

   (a) an isosceles triangle (b) a scalene triangle (c) an equilateral triangle (d) can't say

### Answers

**1.** (b) **2.** (a) **3.** (b) **4.** (c) **5.** (c) **6.** (c) **7.** (a)

## SUMMARY *of the Chapter*

- **Mid-point Theorem.** A line segment joining the mid-points of two sides of a triangle is parallel to the third side and is equal to half of it.
- **Converse of Mid-point Theorem.** The straight line drawn through the mid-point of one side of a triangle, parallel to another side, bisects the third side.
- **Equal Intercept Theorem.** If a transversal makes equal intercepts on three or more parallel lines then any other line cutting these three or more parallel lines, will also make equal intercepts.

# CHAPTER TEST

**1.** In $\Delta ABC$, $D$ is the mid-point of $BC$ and $E$ is the mid-point of $AD$. A line through $B$ and $E$ meets $AC$ at $F$. Prove that $AF = \frac{1}{3}AC$.

**2.** $\Delta ABC$ is an obtuse-angled triangle in which $\angle B$ is obtuse angle. $D$ and $E$ are the mid-points of sides $AB$ and $BC$, respectively. $F$ is a point on side $AC$ such that $EF \parallel AB$. Show that $BEFD$ is a parallelogram.

**3.** Use intercept theorem to prove that the straight line drawn through the mid-point of one side of a triangle and parallel to another side, bisects the third side.

**4.** Show that the quadrilateral formed by joining the mid-points of the adjacent sides of a square is a square.

**5.** In $\square ABCD$; $AD = BC$. $P$, $Q$, $R$ and $S$ are the mid-points of $AB$, $BD$, $CD$ and $AC$ respectively, prove that $PQRS$ is a rhombus.

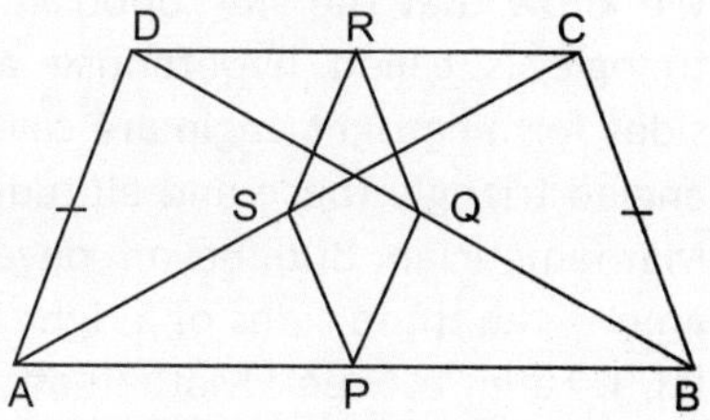


**6.** In the adjoining figure, $AB = AD$ and $BC = CD$. $P$, $Q$ and $R$ are the mid-points of the sides $AB$, $BC$ and $CD$, respectively. If $PS \parallel QR$, prove that

(i) $\angle PQR = 90°$

(ii) $S$ is the mid-point of $AD$

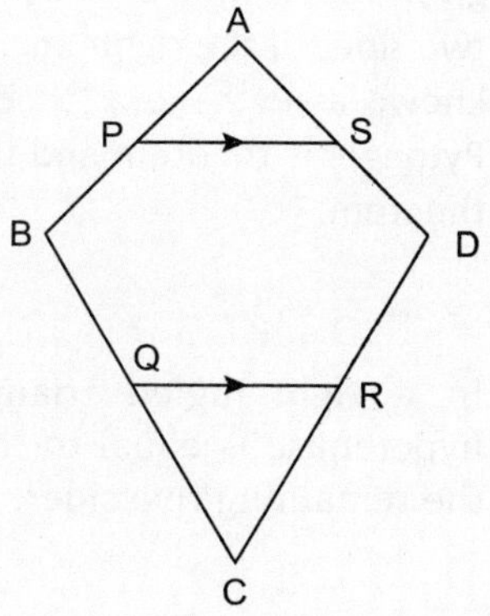


**7.** $\square PQRS$ is a rectangle. If $A$, $B$ and $C$ are the mid-points of $PQ$, $PS$ and $QR$, respectively, prove that $AB + AC = \frac{1}{2}(PR + SQ)$.

Chapter

# 10 PYTHAGORAS THEOREM

**Syllabus**

- Area based proof and simple applications of Pythagoras Theorem and its converse.

## INTRODUCTION

We have studied about the various type of triangles. In this chapter, we shall discuss a right- angled triangle. We know that the side opposite to right angle in a triangle is called hypotenuse and the other two sides forming right angle are called the legs of right-angled triangle (base and altitude). The great Indian Mathematician Buddhayan developed the relation among the three sides of a right-angled triangle (600 B.C.). Later, a Greek Mathematician Pythagoras had given the relation between hypotenuse and the other two sides of the right- angled triangle. This relation is known as Pythagoras theorem. Now, we shall study Pythagoras theorem and the converse of Pythagoras theorem.

## Pythagoras Theorem

In a right-angled triangle, the square on the hypotenuse is equal to the sum of the squares on the remaining two sides.

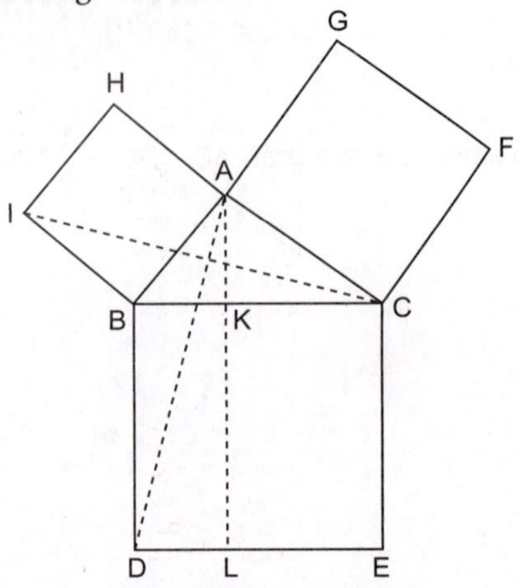


Given : A right-angled triangle $ABC$ in which $\angle BAC = 90°$

To Prove : $BC^2 = AB^2 + AC^2$

Construction : Draw $AKL \,||\, BD$ from $A$ intersecting $BC$ at and $DE$ at $L$. Join $IC$ and $AD$.

Proof :

| Statement | Reason |
|---|---|
| $\angle BAC + \angle BAH = 180°$ | Each 90° |
| $\Rightarrow$ $HAC$ is a straight line | |
| $\angle IBA = \angle CBD$ | Each 90° |
| $\Rightarrow$ $\angle IBA + \angle ABC = \angle CBD + \angle ABC$ | Adding $\angle ABC$ on both sides |
| $\Rightarrow$ $\angle IBC = \angle ABD$ | |
| In $\Delta IBC$ and $\Delta ABD$ | |
| $IB = AB$ | Sides of a square |
| $BC = BD$ | Sides of a square |
| $\angle IBC = \angle ABD$ | Proved above |
| $\therefore$ $\Delta IBC \cong \Delta ABD$ | (SAS criteria) |
| $\Rightarrow$ Area of $\Delta IBC$ = Area of $\Delta ABD$. | |
| Area of $\Delta IBC = \frac{1}{2} \times$ Area of $\square IBAH$ | $\Delta IBC$ and $\square IBAH$ are on same base $IB$ and between the parallel lines $IB$ and $HAC$. |
| Area of $\Delta ABD = \frac{1}{2} \times$ Area of $\square BDLK$ | $\Delta ABD$ and $\square BDLK$ are on the same base $BD$ and between the parallel lines $BD$ and $AKL$ |
| $\therefore$ Area of $\square IBAH$ = Area of $\square BDLK$ ...(i) | |
| Similarly, we can prove that : | |
| Area of $\square ACFG$ = Area of $\square ECKL$ ...(ii) | |
| Area of $\square IBAH$ + Area of $\square ACFG$ = Area of $\square BDLK$ + Area of $\square ECKL$ | Adding (i) and (ii) |
| $\Rightarrow$ Area of $\square IBAH$ + Area of $\square ACFG$ = Area of $\square BDEC$ | |
| $\Rightarrow$ $AB^2 + AC^2 = BC^2$ | |

Hence Proved.

## Converse of Pythagoras Theorem

If the square on the largest side of a triangle is equal to the sum of the squares on the remaining two sides, then the triangle is a right angled triangle and the angle opposite to largest side is a right angle.

**Given :** In $\Delta ABC$,

$$BC^2 = AB^2 + AC^2$$

**To Prove :**

$$\angle BAC = 90^\circ$$

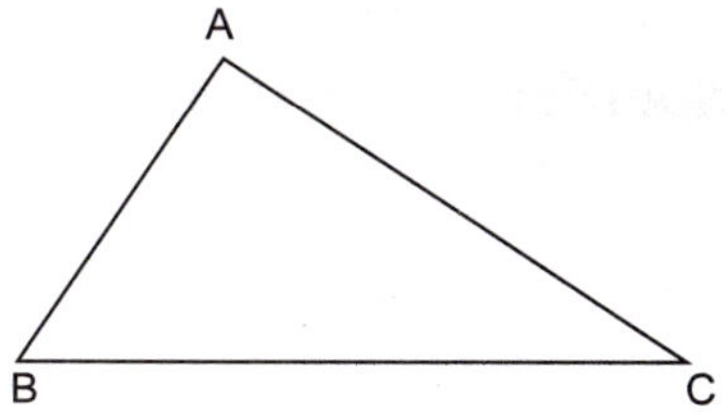


**Construction :** Construct $\Delta PQR$ in which

$PQ = AB$, $PR = AC$ and $\angle QPR = 90^\circ$

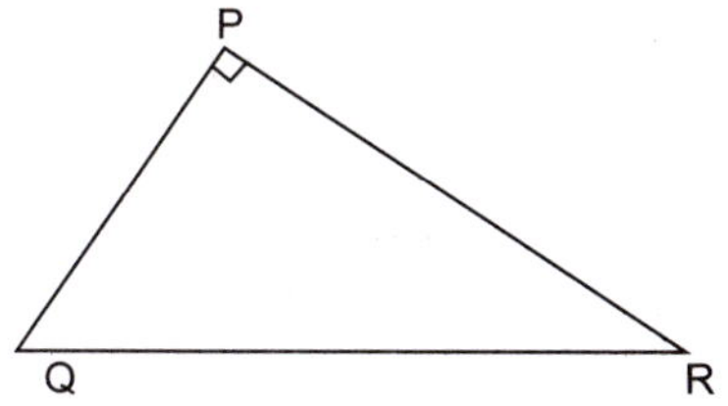


**Proof :**

| Statement | Reason |
|---|---|
| In $\Delta PQR$, | |
| $\angle P = 90^\circ$ | By construiction |
| $QR^2 = PQ^2 + PR^2$ | By Pythagoras theorem |
| $QR^2 = AB^2 + AC^2$ | By construction |
| $QR^2 = BC^2$ | Given $BC^2 = AB^2 + AC^2$ |
| $QR = BC$ | |
| In $\Delta ABC$ and $\Delta PQR$, | |
| $AB = PQ$ | By construction |
| $AC = PR$ | By construction |
| $BC = QR$ | Proved above |
| $\therefore$ $\Delta ABC \cong \Delta PQR$ | SSS Criteria |
| $\angle BAC = \angle QPR$ | CPCT |
| $\angle BAC = 90^\circ$ | $\angle QPR = 90^\circ$ |

Hence Proved.

**NOTE**

In $\Delta ABC$
- If $AB^2 > AC^2 + BC^2$ then $\angle ACB > 90^\circ$
- If $AB^2 < AC^2 + BC^2$ then $\angle ACB < 90^\circ$

## Illustrative Examples

**Example 1.** Find whether the given sides of the triangle form a right-angled triangle or not :
(i) 6 cm, 10 cm, 8 cm (ii) 5 cm, 6 cm, 7 cm.

**Solution.** (i) Here, largest side = 10 cm

$\therefore$ $10^2 = 100$

and $6^2 + 8^2 = 36 + 64 = 100$

$\therefore$ $10^2 = 6^2 + 8^2$

$\Rightarrow$ Given sides 6 cm, 10 cm, and 8 cm, form a right-angled triangle. Ans.

(ii) Here, largest side = 7 cm

$\therefore$ $7^2 = 49$

and $5^2 + 6^2 = 25 + 36 = 61$

$\therefore$ $7^2 \neq 5^2 + 6^2$

$\Rightarrow$ Given sides 5 cm, 6 cm, and 7 cm, do not form a right-angled triangle. Ans.

**Example 2.** In the adjoining figure, $\angle PQS = 90°$, $PR = 13$ m, $QR = 5$ m and $RS = 11$ m. Find $PS$.

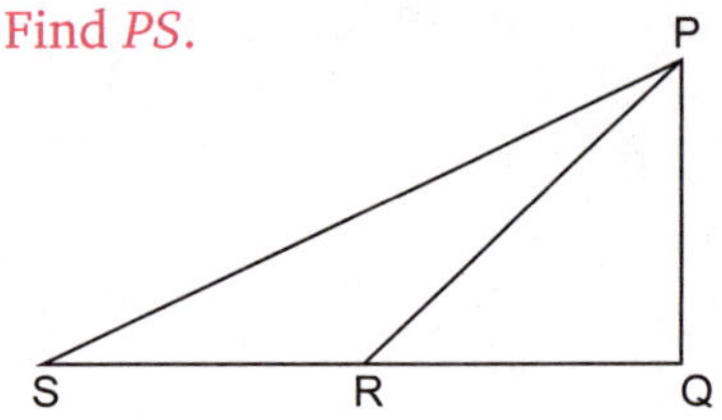


**Solution.** In $\Delta PQR$,

$$\angle PQR = 90°$$

$\therefore$ $$PQ^2 + QR^2 = PR^2$$

$\Rightarrow$ $$PQ^2 = PR^2 - QR^2 = 13^2 - 5^2 = 144$$

$\Rightarrow$ $$PQ = 12 \text{ m}$$

$$QS = QR + SR = 5\text{m} + 11\text{m} = 16\text{m}$$

In $\Delta PQS$,

$$\angle PQS = 90°$$

$\therefore$ $$PS^2 = PQ^2 + QS^2 = 12^2 + 16^2 = 400$$

$\Rightarrow$ $$PS = \mathbf{20\ m}$$ **Ans.**

**Example 3.** A ladder 40 m long rests against a wall, reaches upto a height of 32 m on the wall, find the distance of the foot of ladder from the foot of the wall.

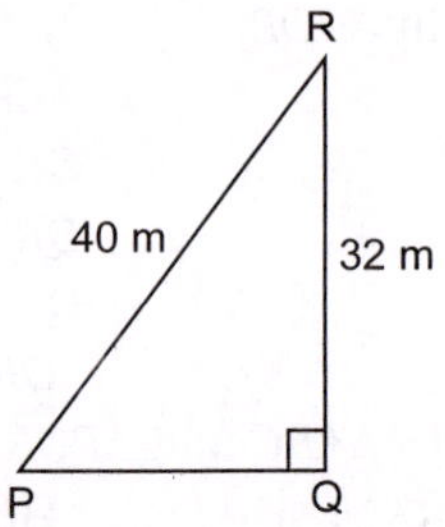


**Solution.** In the adjoining figure, $PR$ be a ladder 40 m long, reaches at point $R$ on the wall such that $QR = 32$ m.

In $\Delta PQR$,

$$\angle PQR = 90°$$

$\therefore$ $$PQ^2 + QR^2 = PR^2$$

$\Rightarrow$ $$PQ^2 = PR^2 - QR^2 = 40^2 - 32^2 = 1600 - 1024 = 576$$

$\Rightarrow$ $$PQ = \mathbf{24\ m}$$

$\therefore$ Distance of foot of ladder from the wall = **24 m** **Ans.**

**Example 4.** A 10 m long ladder is placed leaning towards a vertical wall so that it reaches upto a point 9.6 m high. If the foot of the ladder is moved 3.2 m away from the wall, find the distance by which the top of the ladder would slide downward on the wall?

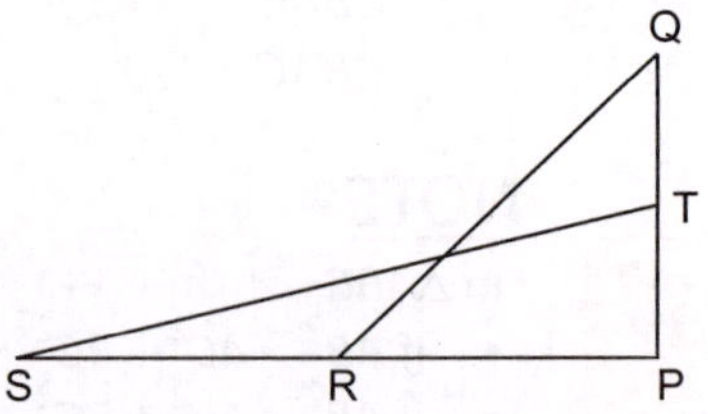


**Solution.** Let $QR$ be the ladder leaning on the wall $PQ$.

In $\Delta PQR$

given, $QR = 10$ m, $PQ = 9.6$ m

$\therefore$ $$RP^2 = QR^2 - PQ^2 = 10^2 - 9.6^2$$
$$= 100 - 92.16 = 7.84$$

$\Rightarrow$ $$RP = 2.8 \text{ m.}$$

The foot of ladder $R$ moves 3.2 m away from the wall and its new position is $S$.

$\therefore$ $$PS = PR + SR = 2.8 + 3.2 = 6 \text{ m}$$

Now, the new position of ladder be $ST$

$$ST = 10 \text{ m}$$

In $\Delta STP$,

$$PT^2 = ST^2 - PS^2 = 10^2 - 6^2 = 100 - 36 = 64$$

$\Rightarrow$ $$PT = 8\text{m}$$

$\therefore$ $$QT = PQ - PT = 9.6 - 8 = 1.6 \text{ m}$$

$\Rightarrow$ top of the ladder slides by **1.6 m** on the wall **Ans.**

**Example 5.** An aeroplane leaves an airport and flies due east at a speed of 300 km/hour. At the same time, another aeroplane leaves the same airport and flies due North at a speed of 400 km/hour. How far apart will be the two planes after 3 hours?

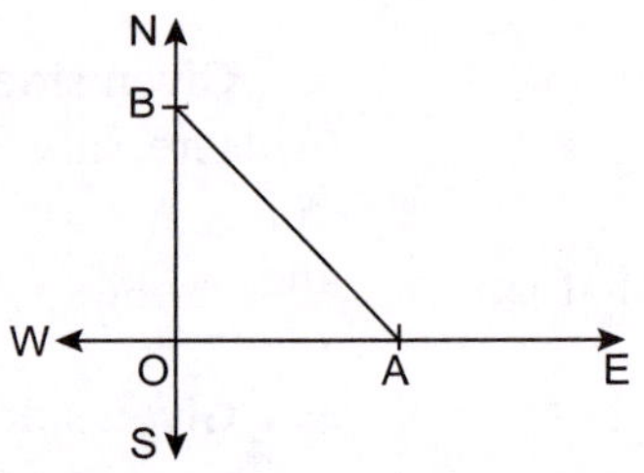


**Solution.** Let $O$, be the leaving point.

For first aeroplane,

$$OA = \text{distance covered in 3 hours}$$
$$= 300 \times 3 \text{ km} = 900 \text{ km}$$

For second aeroplane,

$$OB = \text{distance covered in 3 hours}$$
$$= 400 \times 3 \text{ km} = 1200 \text{ km}$$

In $\Delta OAB$,

$$\angle AOB = 90°$$

$\therefore$ From Pythagoras theorem, we get

$$AB^2 = OA^2 + OB^2 = 900^2 + 1200^2$$
$$= 810000 + 1440000 = 2250000$$

$\Rightarrow$ $AB = 1500$ km.

$\therefore$ distance between two aeroplanes after 3 hours = **1500 km.** Ans.

**Example 6.** Two poles of height 10 m and 15 m stand vertically on a plane ground. If the distance between their feet is 12 m, find the distance between their tops.

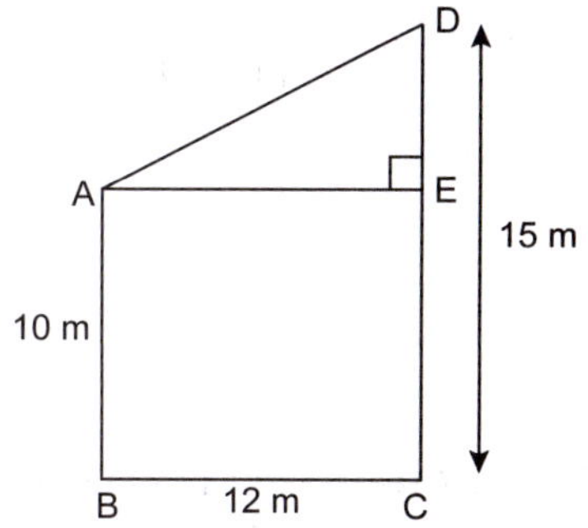


**Solution.** Let $AB$ and $CD$ be two poles of heights 10 m and 15 m respectively and the distance between their feet is $BC = 12$ m.

Draw $AE \perp DE$

$\therefore$ $EC = AB = 10$ m

and $DE = DC - CE = (15 - 10)\text{m} = 5$ m

$AE = BC = 12$ m

In $\Delta ADE$,

$\angle AED = 90°$

$\therefore$ $AD^2 = AE^2 + DE^2 = 12^2 + 5^2 = 169$

$\Rightarrow$ $AD = 13$ m

$\therefore$ distance between the tops of two poles = **13 m** Ans.

**Example 7.** The side of an equilateral triangle $ABC$ is $a$. Find each of its altitude.

**Solution.** Draw, $AM \perp BC$.

In $\Delta ABM$ and $\Delta ACM$

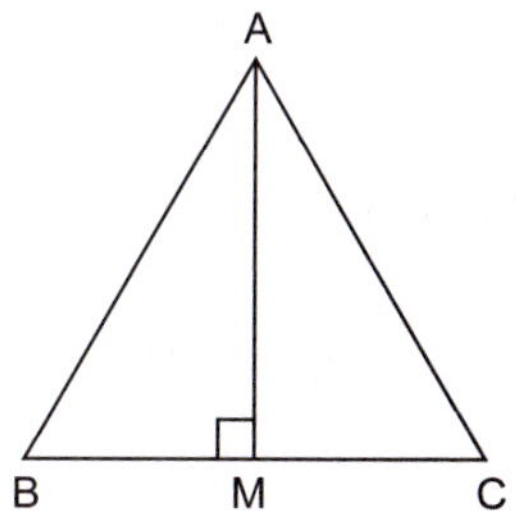


$\angle AMB = \angle AMC$ (Each 90°)

$AB = AC$ (Sides of equilateral triangle)

$AM = AM$ (Common)

$\therefore$ $\Delta ABM \cong \Delta ACM$ (R.H.S Criteria)

$\Rightarrow$ $BM = CM$ (C.P.C.T)

$\Rightarrow$ $BM + BM = CM + BM$

$\Rightarrow$ $2\,BM = BC$

$\Rightarrow$ $BM = \dfrac{a}{2}$

In $\Delta ABM$,

$\angle AMB = 90°$

$\therefore$ $AM^2 + BM^2 = AB^2$

$\Rightarrow$ $AM^2 = AB^2 - BM^2 = a^2 - \left(\dfrac{a}{2}\right)^2 = \dfrac{3}{4}a^2$

$\Rightarrow$ $AM = \dfrac{a\sqrt{3}}{2}$

Since, triangle is equilateral

$\therefore$ length of each altitude $= \dfrac{\boldsymbol{a\sqrt{3}}}{\mathbf{2}}$ Ans.

**Example 8.** In $\Delta ABC$, $\angle ABC = 90°$ and $BD = DC$, prove that:

(i) $AC^2 = AD^2 + 3\,CD^2$ (ii) $BC^2 = 4\,(AD^2 - AB^2)$

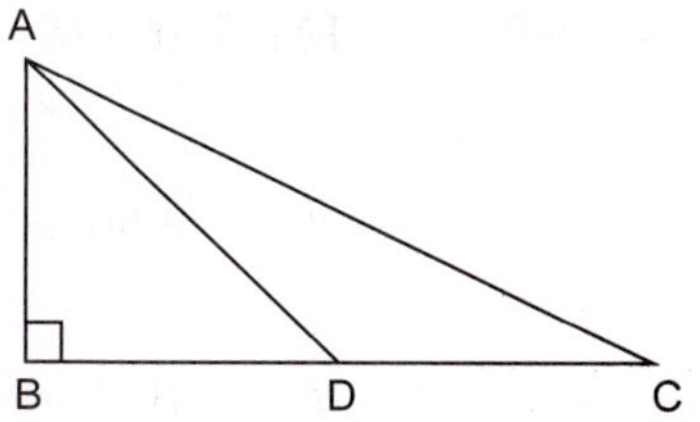


**Solution.** (i) In $\Delta ABC$,

$AC^2 = AB^2 + BC^2$

$\Rightarrow$ $AC^2 = AB^2 + (2CD)^2$ ($\because BC = 2CD$)

$\Rightarrow$ $AC^2 = AB^2 + 4CD^2$ ...(i)

In $\Delta ABD$,

$$AD^2 = AB^2 + BD^2$$

$\Rightarrow$ $$AD^2 = AB^2 + CD^2 \quad \ldots(ii) \quad (\because BD = CD)$$

Subtracting equation *(ii)* from *(i)*,we get

$$\begin{array}{r} AC^2 = AB^2 + 4CD^2 \\ AD^2 = AB^2 + CD^2 \\ - \quad - \quad - \\ \hline AC^2 - AD^2 = 3CD^2 \end{array}$$

$\Rightarrow$ $$AC^2 = AD^2 + 3CD^2$$

(ii) $$AD^2 = AB^2 + CD^2 \quad \text{[From equation (ii)]}$$

$\Rightarrow$ $$AD^2 - AB^2 = \left(\frac{1}{2}BC\right)^2 \quad (\because BD = CD = \frac{1}{2}BC)$$

$\Rightarrow$ $$AD^2 - AB^2 = \frac{1}{4}BC^2$$

$\Rightarrow$ $$4(AD^2 = AB^2) = BC^2$$

Hence Proved.

**Example 9.** In $\Delta ABC$, $AD$ is perpendicular to $BC$. Prove that : $AB^2 + CD^2 = AC^2 + BD^2$.

**Solution.** In $\Delta ABD$,

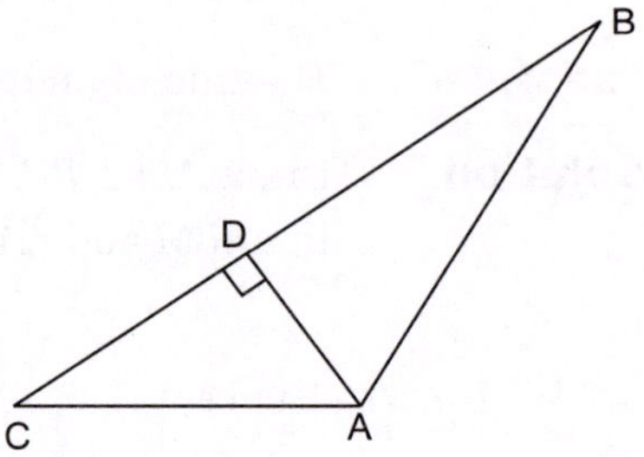


$$\angle ADB = 90°$$

From Pythagoras theorem

$$AB^2 = AD^2 + BD^2 \quad \ldots(i)$$

In $\Delta ACD$,

$$\angle ADC = 90°$$

From Pythagoras theorem

$$AC^2 = AD^2 + CD^2 \quad \ldots(ii)$$

Subtracting equation *(ii)* from *(i)*, we get

$$AB^2 - AC^2 = BD^2 - CD^2$$

$\Rightarrow$ $$AB^2 + CD^2 = AC^2 + BD^2$$

Hence Proved.

**Example 10.** In the adjoining figure, $\angle ACB$ is an obtuse angle. Prove that : $AB^2 = AC^2 + BC^2 + 2BC \cdot CD$

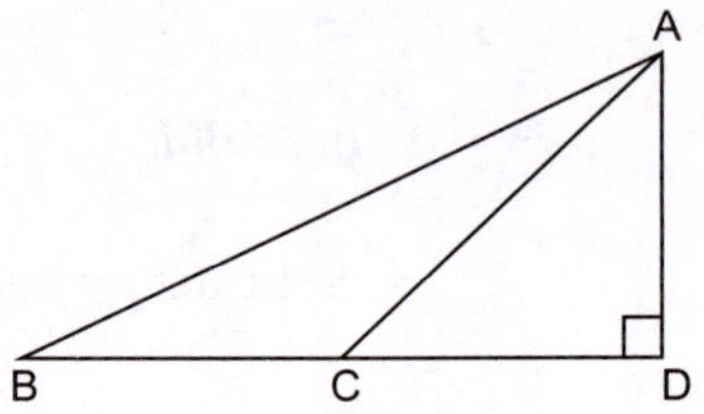


**Solution.** In $\Delta ABD$,

$$\begin{aligned} AB^2 &= BD^2 + AD^2 \\ &= (BC + CD)^2 + AD^2 \quad (\because BD = BC + CD) \\ &= BC^2 + 2BC \cdot CD + CD^2 + AD^2 \\ &= BC^2 + 2BC \cdot CD + (CD^2 + AD^2) \\ &= BC^2 + 2BC \cdot CD + AC^2 \quad (\text{In } \Delta ACD,\ AC^2 = AD^2 + CD^2) \end{aligned}$$

Hence Proved.

**Example 11.** In an isosceles triangle $ABC$, $\angle BAC = 90°$ and $AB = AC$. If $D$ is a point on side $AB$ produced, prove that :

$$BD^2 = CD^2 - 2AC \cdot AD.$$

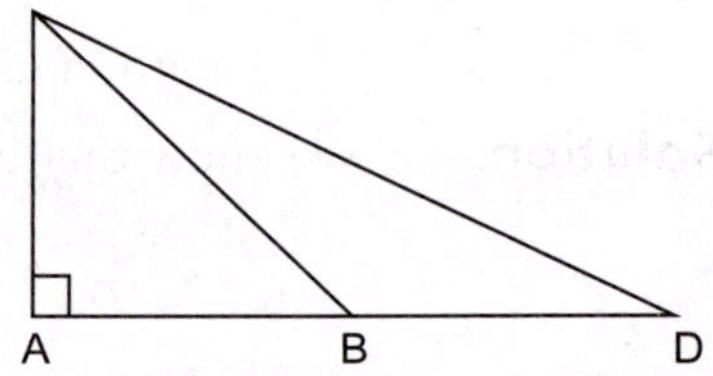


**Solution.** In $\Delta ACD$,

$$\angle CAD = 90°$$

$\therefore$ $$CD^2 = AC^2 + AD^2$$

$$= AC^2 + (AB + BD)^2 \quad (\because AD = AB + BD)$$

$$CD^2 = AC^2 + AB^2 + BD^2 + 2AB.BD$$

$\Rightarrow$ $$CD^2 = AB^2 + AB^2 + 2AB \cdot BD + BD^2 \quad (\because AC = AB)$$

$$\Rightarrow \quad CD^2 = 2AB^2 + 2AB\cdot(AD - AB) + BD^2$$
$$= 2AB^2 + 2AB\cdot AD - 2AB^2 + BD^2$$
$$= 2AB\cdot AD + BD^2$$
$$= 2AC\cdot AD + BD^2 \qquad (\because AB = AC)$$
$$\Rightarrow \quad BD^2 = CD^2 - 2AC\cdot AD$$

Hence Proved.

**Example 12.** In $\Delta ABC$, $AB = AC$ and $D$ is a point on $BC$. Prove that : $AB^2 - AD^2 = BD \times DC$.

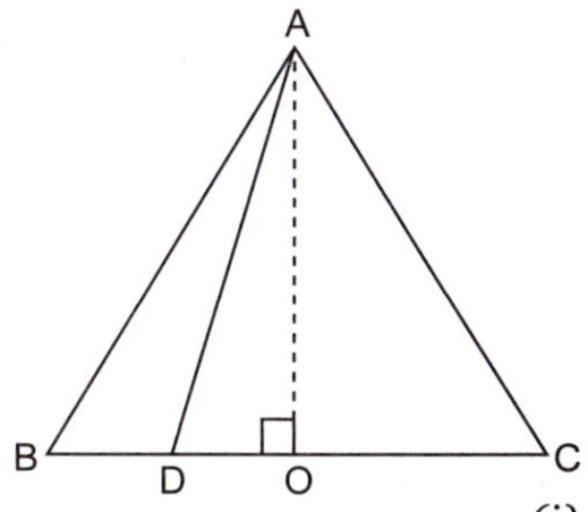


**Solution.** Draw, $AO \perp BC$.

In $\Delta ABO$ and $\Delta ACO$,

$$\angle AOB = \angle AOC \qquad \text{(Each 90°)}$$
$$AB = AC \qquad \text{(Given)}$$
$$AO = AO \qquad \text{(Common)}$$
$$\therefore \quad \Delta ABO \cong \Delta ACO \qquad \text{(R.H.S criteria)}$$
$$\Rightarrow \quad BO = CO \qquad \text{(C.P.C.T)} \qquad ...(i)$$

In $\Delta ABO$,

$$\angle AOB = 90°$$
$$\therefore \quad AB^2 = AO^2 + BO^2 \qquad ...(i)$$

In $\Delta ADO$,

$$\angle AOD = 90°$$
$$\therefore \quad AD^2 = AO^2 + DO^2 \qquad ...(ii)$$

Subtracting equation *(ii)* from *(i)*

$$AB^2 - AD^2 = BO^2 - DO^2$$
$$= (BO + DO)(BO - DO)$$
$$= (CO + DO) \times BD \qquad [\because BO = CO \text{ from } (i)]$$
$$= CD \times BD$$

Hence, $AB^2 - AD^2 = \text{CD} \times BD$

Hence Proved.

**Example 13.** In the adjoining figure, $AB = BC$ and $AD \perp CB$ produced. Prove that : $AC^2 = 2\,BC \times CD$.

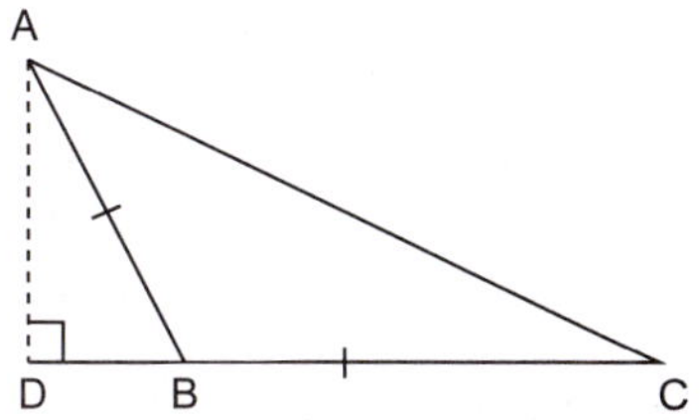


**Solution.** In $\Delta ADC$,

$$\angle ADC = 90°$$
$$\therefore \quad AC^2 = AD^2 + CD^2 \qquad ...(i)$$

In $\Delta ADB$,

$$\angle ADB = 90°$$
$$\therefore \quad AB^2 = AD^2 + BD^2 \qquad ...(ii)$$

Subtracting equation *(ii)* from *(i)*

$$AC^2 - AB^2 = CD^2 - BD^2$$
$$\Rightarrow \quad AC^2 - BC^2 = CD^2 - BD^2 \qquad (\because AB = BC \text{ given})$$
$$\Rightarrow \quad AC^2 = BC^2 + (BC + BD)^2 - BD^2$$
$$= BC^2 + BC^2 + 2BC\cdot BD + BD^2 - BD^2$$
$$= 2\,BC^2 + 2BC\cdot BD = 2\,BC\,(BC + BD) = 2\,BC \times CD$$

Hence Proved.

**Example 14.** In a rectangle $ABCD$, prove that : $AC^2 + BD^2 = AB^2 + BC^2 + CD^2 + DA^2$.

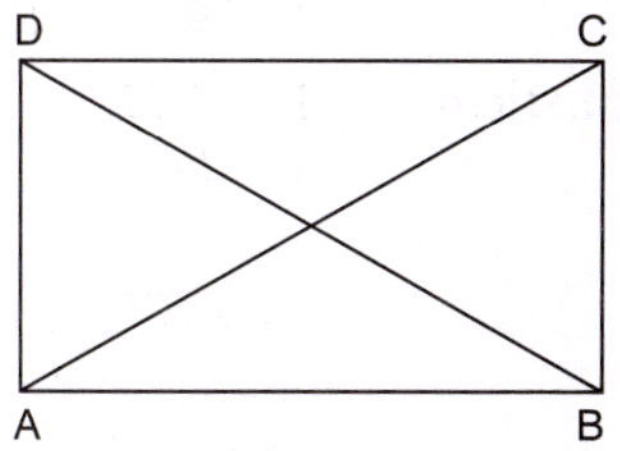


**Solution.** We know that each angle of a rectangle is a right angle.

$\therefore$ In $\Delta ABC$,

$$AC^2 = AB^2 + BC^2 \qquad ...(i)$$

In $\Delta BCD$,

$$BD^2 = BC^2 + CD^2 \qquad ...(ii)$$

In $\Delta CDA$,

$$AC^2 = CD^2 + DA^2 \quad \text{...(iii)}$$

In $\Delta DAB$,

$$BD^2 = DA^2 + AB^2 \quad \text{...(iv)}$$

Adding equations *(i)*, *(ii)*, *(iii)* and *(iv)*

$$2AC^2 + 2BD^2 = (AB^2 + BC^2) + (BC^2 + CD^2) + (CD^2 + DA^2) + (DA^2 + AB^2)$$
$$= 2AB^2 + 2BC^2 + 2CD^2 + 2DA^2$$

$\Rightarrow$ $$AC^2 + BD^2 = AB^2 + BC^2 + CD^2 + DA^2$$ **Hence Proved.**

**Example 15.** In $\Delta ABC$, $\angle ACB = 90°$ and $CD \perp AB$. If $AB = c$, $BC = a$, $AC = b$ and $CD = p$ then prove that:

(i) $pc = ab$ (ii) $\frac{1}{p^2} = \frac{1}{a^2} + \frac{1}{b^2}$

**Solution.** (i) In $\Delta ABC$, $\angle ABC = 90°$

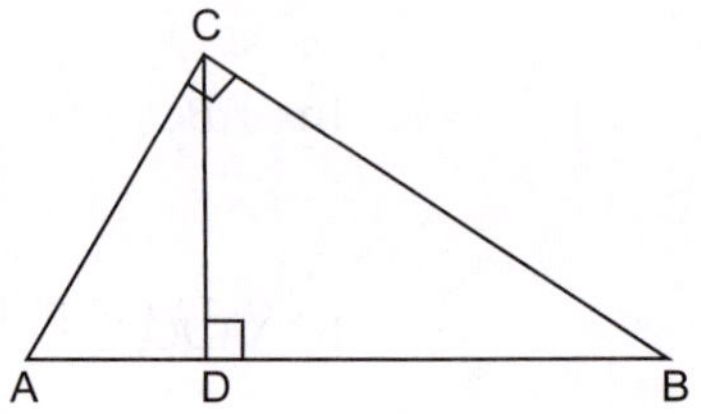


$\therefore$ $$AB^2 = AC^2 + BC^2$$

$\Rightarrow$ $$c^2 = b^2 + a^2 \quad \text{...(i)}$$

and $$\text{Area of } \Delta ABC = \frac{1}{2} AB \times CD = \frac{1}{2} \times AC \times BC$$

$\Rightarrow$ $$AB \times CD = AC \times BC$$

$\Rightarrow$ $$c \times p = b \times a \Rightarrow pc = ab \quad \text{...(ii)}$$

(ii) From equation *(ii)*

$$pc = ab \Rightarrow c = \frac{ab}{p}$$

Put this value in equation *(i)*

$$\frac{a^2b^2}{p^2} = b^2 + a^2$$

$\Rightarrow$ $$\frac{1}{p^2} = \frac{b^2 + a^2}{a^2b^2} = \frac{b^2}{a^2b^2} + \frac{a^2}{a^2b^2} = \frac{1}{a^2} + \frac{1}{b^2}$$

**Hence Proved.**

**Example 16.** In the adjoining figure, $OP \perp BC$, $OQ \perp AC$ and $OR \perp AB$. Prove that:

$$AR^2 + BP^2 + CQ^2 = AQ^2 + BR^2 + CP^2$$

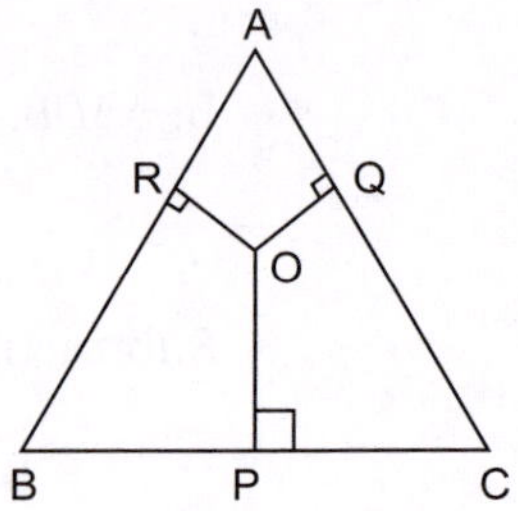


**Solution.** Join $OA$, $OB$ and $OC$.

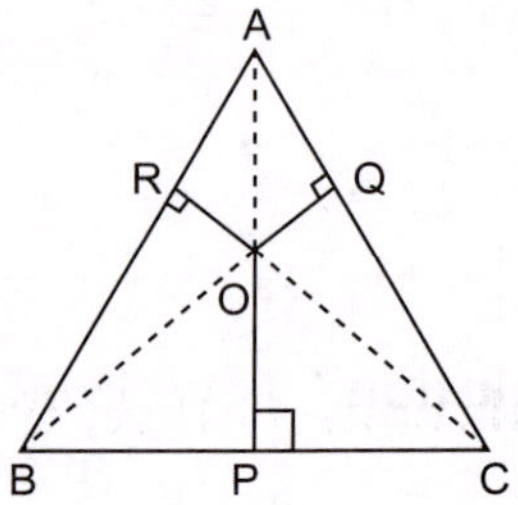


In $\Delta AOR$,

$$AO^2 = AR^2 + OR^2 \Rightarrow AR^2 = AO^2 - OR^2 \quad \text{...(i)}$$

In $\Delta AOQ$,

$$AO^2 = AQ^2 + OQ^2 \Rightarrow AQ^2 = AO^2 - OQ^2 \quad \text{...(ii)}$$

In $\Delta BOR$,

$$BO^2 = BR^2 + OR^2 \Rightarrow BR^2 = BO^2 - OR^2 \quad \text{...(iii)}$$

In $\Delta BOP$,

$$OB^2 = OP^2 + BP^2 \Rightarrow BP^2 = OB^2 - OP^2 \quad \text{...(iv)}$$

In $\Delta POC$,

$$OC^2 = OP^2 + PC^2 \Rightarrow PC^2 = OC^2 - OP^2 \quad \text{...(v)}$$

In $\Delta OCQ$,

$$OC^2 = OQ^2 + CQ^2 \Rightarrow CQ^2 = OC^2 - OQ^2 \quad \text{...(vi)}$$

Adding equations *(i)*, *(iv)* and *(vi)*

$$AR^2 + BP^2 + CQ^2 = AO^2 - OR^2 + OB^2 - OP^2 + OC^2 - OQ^2$$
$$= (AO^2 - OQ^2) + (OB^2 - OR^2) + (OC^2 - OP^2)$$
$$= AQ^2 + BR^2 + CP^2 \quad \text{[From eqns. (ii), (iii) and (v)]}$$

Hence Proved.

**Example 17.** In $\Delta ABC$, $AD \perp BC$. If $AD^2 = BD \cdot DC$, prove that : $\angle BAC = 90°$.

**Solution.** In $\Delta ABC$, $\angle D = 90°$

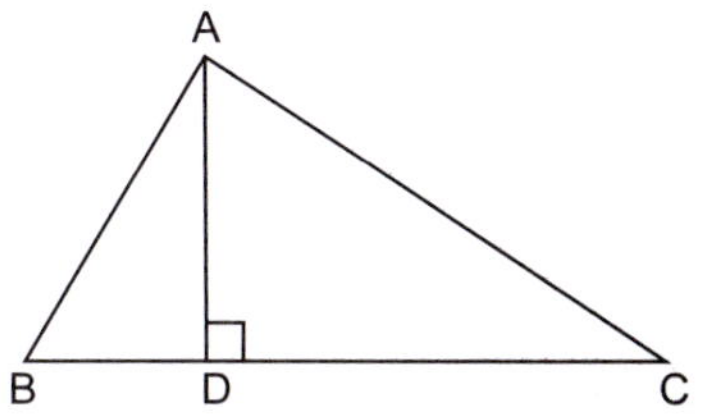


$$\therefore \quad AB^2 = AD^2 + BD^2$$
$$= BD \cdot CD + BD^2 \quad \text{(Given)}$$
$$= BD\ (CD + BD)$$
$$= BD \cdot BC \quad \ldots(i)$$

In $\Delta ACD$, $\angle D = 90°$

$$\therefore \quad AC^2 = AD^2 + CD^2$$
$$= BD \cdot CD + CD^2 \quad \text{(Given)}$$
$$= CD\ (BD + CD)$$
$$= CD \cdot BC \quad \ldots(ii)$$

Adding equations *(i)* and *(ii)*

$$AB^2 + AC^2 = BD \cdot BC + CD \cdot BC = (BD + CD) \cdot BC$$
$$= BC \cdot BC = BC^2$$
$$\Rightarrow \quad \angle BAC = 90°$$

Hence Proved.

**Example 18.** In the adjoining figure, $AD \perp BC$. If $D$ divides $BC$ in the ratio 1 : 3, prove that : $2AC^2 = 2AB^2 + BC^2$.

**Solution.** Here, $\frac{BD}{DC} = \frac{1}{3}$

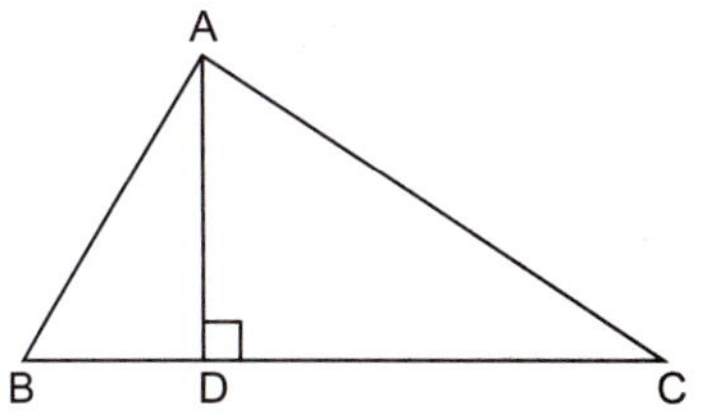


$$\Rightarrow \quad DC = 3 \cdot BD$$
$$\therefore \quad BC = BD + CD = BD + 3 \cdot BD = 4 \cdot BD$$
$$\Rightarrow \quad BD = \frac{1}{4} BC$$

In $\Delta ADC$,

$$\angle ADC = 90°$$
$$\therefore \quad AC^2 = AD^2 + DC^2 = AD^2 + (3BD)^2 = AD^2 + 9BD^2 \quad \ldots(i)$$

In $\Delta ABD$,

$$\angle ADB = 90°$$
$$\therefore \quad AB^2 = BD^2 + AD^2$$
$$\Rightarrow \quad AD^2 = AB^2 - BD^2 \quad \ldots(ii)$$

From equations *(i)* and *(ii)*, we get

$$AC^2 = (AB^2 - BD^2) + 9\ BD^2 = AB^2 + 8\ BD^2$$
$$= AB^2 + 8\left(\frac{1}{4} BC\right)^2 = AB^2 + \frac{1}{2} BC^2$$
$$\Rightarrow \quad 2 \cdot AC^2 = 2 \cdot AB^2 + BC^2$$

Hence Proved.

**Example 19.** In a quadrilateral $ABCD$, $\angle A + \angle D = 90°$. Prove that : $AC^2 + BD^2 = AD^2 + BC^2$.

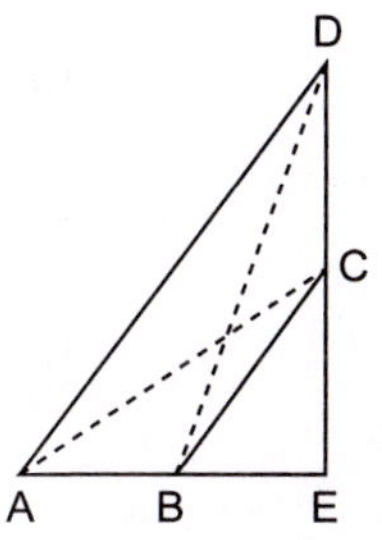


**Solution.** Here, in quadrilateral $ABCD$,

$$\angle A + \angle D = 90°$$

Produce $AB$ and $DC$ to meet at point $E$.

In $\Delta AED$,

$$\angle E = 90°$$
$$AD^2 = AE^2 + ED^2 \quad \ldots(i)$$

In $\Delta BEC$,

$$BC^2 = BE^2 + CE^2 \quad \ldots(ii)$$

In $\Delta ACE$,

$$AC^2 = AE^2 + CE^2 \quad \ldots(iii)$$

In $\Delta BDE$,

$$BD^2 = BE^2 + ED^2 \quad \ldots(iv)$$

Adding equations *(i)*, and *(ii)*, we get

$$AD^2 + BC^2 = AE^2 + ED^2 + BE^2 + CE^2$$
$$= AE^2 + CE^2 + BE^2 + ED^2$$
$$= AC^2 + BD^2$$

$\therefore$ $$AD^2 + BC^2 = AC^2 + BD^2$$ **Hence Proved.**

**Example 20.** From a point $O$ in the interior of a $\Delta ABC$, perpendiculars $OD$, $OE$ and $OF$ are drawn to the sides $BC$, $CA$ and $AB$ respectively. Prove that : $AF^2 + BD^2 + CE^2 = OA^2 + OB^2 + OC^2 - OD^2 - OE^2 - OF^2$.

**Solution.** $\Delta OAF$, $\Delta OBD$, $\Delta OCE$ are right-angled triangles.

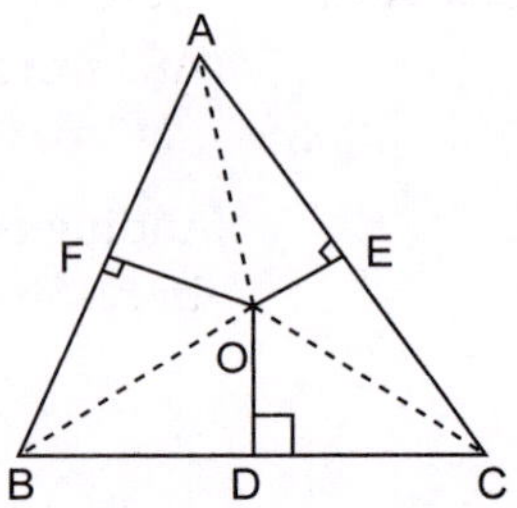


In $\Delta OAF$,

$$OA^2 = AF^2 + OF^2 \quad \ldots(i)$$

In $\Delta OBD$,

$$OB^2 = BD^2 + OD^2 \quad \ldots(ii)$$

In $\Delta OCE$,

$$OC^2 = CE^2 + OE^2 \quad \ldots(iii)$$

Adding equations *(i)*, *(ii)* and *(iii)* we get

$$OA^2 + OB^2 + OC^2 = AF^2 + BD^2 + CE^2 + OF^2 + OD^2 + OE^2$$

$\Rightarrow$ $$OA^2 + OB^2 + OC^2 - OD^2 - OE^2 - OF^2 = AF^2 + BD^2 + CE^2$$ **Hence Proved.**

**Example 21.** Prove that the sum of the square of the diagonals of a parallelogram is equal to the sum of square of its sides.

**Solution.** Let $ABCD$ be a parallelogram. Its diagonals are $AC$ and $BD$.

We have to prove that :

$$AB^2 + BC^2 + CD^2 + DA^2 = AC^2 + BD^2$$

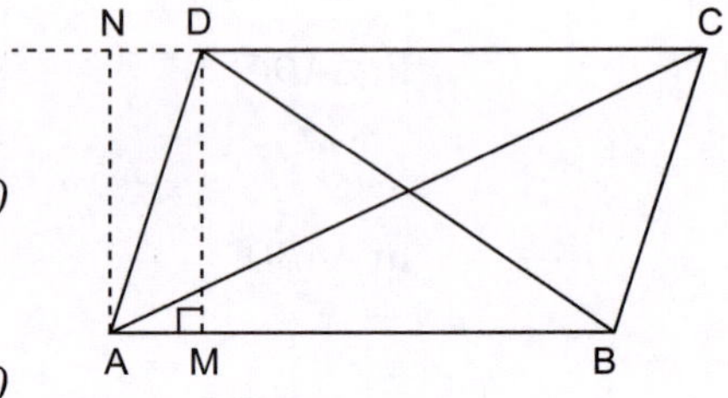


Draw $DM \perp AB$ and $AN \perp CD$ produced.

So $AMDN$ is a rectangle.

$\Rightarrow$ $$AM = DN \quad \ldots(i)$$

In $\Delta AND$,

$$\angle AND = 90°$$

$\therefore$ $$AD^2 = AN^2 + ND^2 \quad \ldots(ii)$$

In $\Delta ANC$,

$$\angle ANC = 90°$$

$\therefore$ $$AC^2 = AN^2 + NC^2 = AN^2 + (ND + CD)^2$$
$$= AN^2 + ND^2 + CD^2 + 2ND \cdot CD$$

$\Rightarrow$ $$AC^2 = AD^2 + CD^2 + 2ND \times CD \quad \ldots(iii) \text{ [using } (ii)]$$

In $\Delta AMD$,

$$\angle AMD = 90°$$

$\therefore$ $$AD^2 = AM^2 + MD^2 \quad \ldots(iv)$$

In $\Delta DMB$,

$$\Delta DMB = 90°$$

$\therefore$ $$BD^2 = MD^2 + MB^2$$
$$= MD^2 + (AB - AM)^2$$
$$= MD^2 + AM^2 + AB^2 - 2AM \times AB$$
$$= AD^2 + AB^2 - 2AM \times AB \quad \text{[From } (iv)]$$
$$= AD^2 + AB^2 - 2ND \times CD \quad \ldots(v) \quad (\because \; AM = ND \text{ and } AB = CD)$$

Adding *(iii)* and *(v)*, we get

$$AC^2 + BD^2 = AD^2 + CD^2 + AD^2 + AB^2$$
$$= BC^2 + CD^2 + AD^2 + AB^2 \quad (\because \ AD = BC)$$
$$= AB^2 + BC^2 + CD^2 + DA^2$$

Hence Proved.

**Example 22.** In the adjoining figure, $AD$ is the median of $\Delta ABC$ and $AM \perp BC$. Prove that :

(i) $AC^2 = AD^2 + BC \times DM + \frac{1}{4} BC^2$

(ii) $AB^2 = AD^2 - BC \times DM + \frac{1}{4} BC^2$

(iii) $AB^2 + AC^2 = 2AD^2 + \frac{1}{2} BC^2$

(iv) $AB^2 + AC^2 = 2(AD^2 + BD^2)$

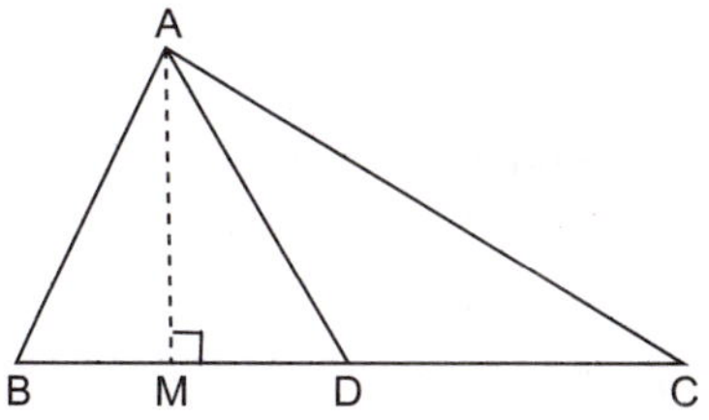


**Solution.** Here, $AC > AB$

$AD$ is the median $\Rightarrow BD = CD$

$\Rightarrow BD = CD = \frac{1}{2} BC$

In $\Delta AMD$,

$\angle AMD = 90°$

$\therefore AD^2 = AM^2 + MD^2 \Rightarrow AM^2 = AD^2 - MD^2$ ...*(i)*

(i) In $\Delta AMC$,

$\angle AMC = 90°$

$$\therefore AC^2 = AM^2 + MC^2$$
$$= (AD^2 - MD^2) + (MD + DC)^2 \quad \text{[From } (i)\text{]}$$
$$= AD^2 - MD^2 + \left(MD + \frac{1}{2} BC\right)^2$$
$$= AD^2 - MD^2 + MD^2 + MD \times BC + \frac{1}{4} BC^2$$
$$\Rightarrow AC^2 = AD^2 + MD \times BC + \frac{1}{4} BC^2 \quad ...(ii)$$

(ii) In $\Delta ABM$,

$\angle AMB = 90°$

$$\therefore AB^2 = AM^2 + BM^2$$
$$= (AD^2 - MD^2) + (BD - MD)^2 \quad \text{[From } (i)\text{]}$$
$$= (AD^2 - MD^2) + \left(\frac{1}{2} BC - MD\right)^2$$
$$= AD^2 - MD^2 + \frac{1}{4} BC^2 + MD^2 - BC \times MD$$
$$\Rightarrow AB^2 = AD^2 - MD \times BC + \frac{1}{4} BC^2 \quad ...(iii)$$

(iii) Adding equations *(ii)* and *(iii)*, we get

$$AC^2 + AB^2 = 2AD^2 + 2 \cdot \frac{1}{4} BC^2$$
$$\Rightarrow AC^2 + AB^2 = 2AD^2 + \frac{1}{2} BC^2 \quad ...(iv)$$

(iv) From equation *(iv)*

$$AB^2 + AC^2 = 2AD^2 + \frac{1}{2}BC^2 = 2AD^2 + \frac{1}{2}(2BD)^2$$

$$\Rightarrow \quad AB^2 + AC^2 = 2(AD^2 + BD^2)$$

Hence Proved.

## Exercise 10A

1. Find whether the given sides of the triangle form a right-angled triangle or not :
   (i) 3 cm, 4 cm and 5 cm. (ii) 5 cm, 13 cm and 12 cm. (iii) 8 cm, 9 cm and 12 cm.
2. A rectangular garden is 30 m broad and 40 m long. Find the length of its diagonal.
3. A ladder 13 m long rests against a vertical wall. Its top reaches to a window on the wall at 12 m high. Find the distance of the foot of the ladder from the wall.
4. Two poles of height 12 m and 24 m stand vertically on a plane ground. If the distance between their tops is 13 m. Find the distance between their feet.
5. An aeroplane leaves an airport and flies due North at a speed of 200 km\hr. At the same time another aeroplane leaves the same airport and flies due West at a speed of 150 Km\hr. How far apart will be the two aeroplanes after 4 hours.
6. A ladder 25 m long reaches a window which is 15 m above the ground on one side of the street. When it turned to the other side keeping its foot at the same point, it touches a wall at a height of 20 m from the ground. Find the width of the street.
7. The side of a rhombus is 10 cm. Its one diagonal is 12 cm. Find the length of other diagonal.
8. Find the altitude of an equilateral triangle of side '$2a$' cm.
9. Find the altitude of an equilateral triangle of side $6\sqrt{3}$ cm.
10. In $\Delta ABC$, $\angle B = 90°$. If $AC = (x + 4)$ cm, $BC = (x + 2)$ cm, and $AB = (3x + 1)$ cm, find the sides of triangle.
11. In the adjoining figure, $\angle PQR = 90°$, $PR = 10$ cm, $QR = 6$ cm and $SR = 9$ cm. Find $PS$.

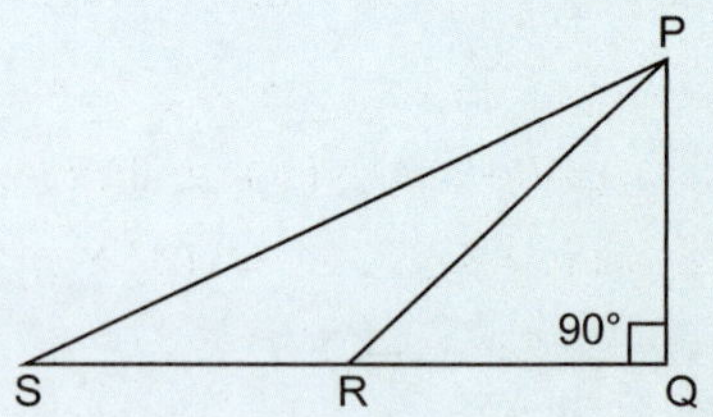


12. In the adjoining figure, $\angle RQS = 90°$, $\angle QPS = 90°$, $RS = 25$ cm, $QR = 20$ cm, $PQ = 9$ cm. Find $PS$.

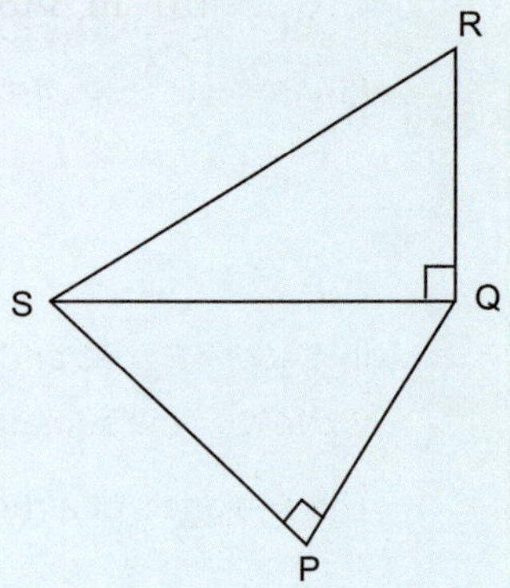


13. In the adjoining figure, $DC \| AB$. $BC = 8$ cm, $AD = 17$ cm, $CD = 24$ cm. Find
    (i) $AB$ (ii) area of trapezium $ABCD$

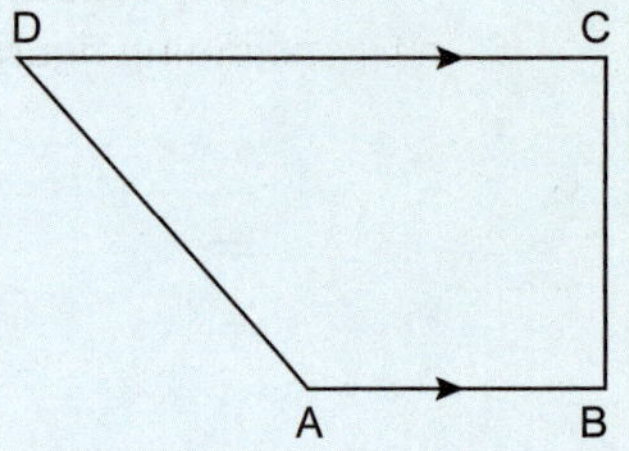

**14.** $\Delta ABC$ is an isosceles triangle in which $AB = AC = 17$ cm and $BC = 16$ cm. Find the length of perpendicular drawn from $A$ to $BC$.

**15.** In the adjoining figure, $SR \parallel PQ$ and $\angle PQR = 90°$. If $PQ = 7$ cm, $PR = 25$ cm and $SR = 17$ cm, find the length of $PS$.

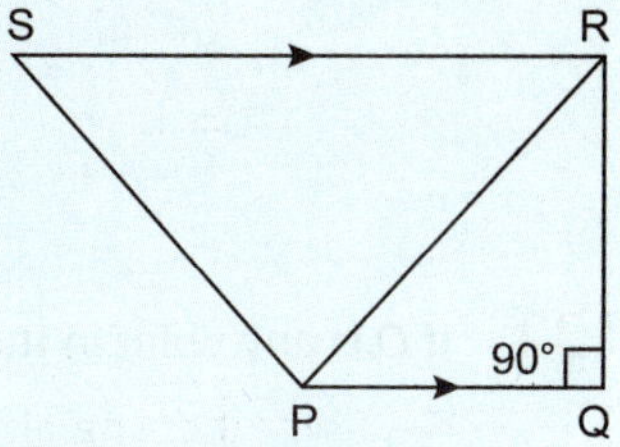


**16.** The sides of a right-angled triangle are $2x$, $x + 5$ and $3x + 1$. If the hypotenuse is $3x + 1$, find the sides of triangle.

**17.** In $\Delta ABC$, $\angle ABC = 90°$ and $D$ is any point on $BC$. Prove that : $AD^2 + BC^2 = AC^2 + BD^2$.

**18.** In $\Delta PQR$, $\angle QPR = 90°$ and $PM \perp QR$. Prove that : $PM^2 = QM.RM$.

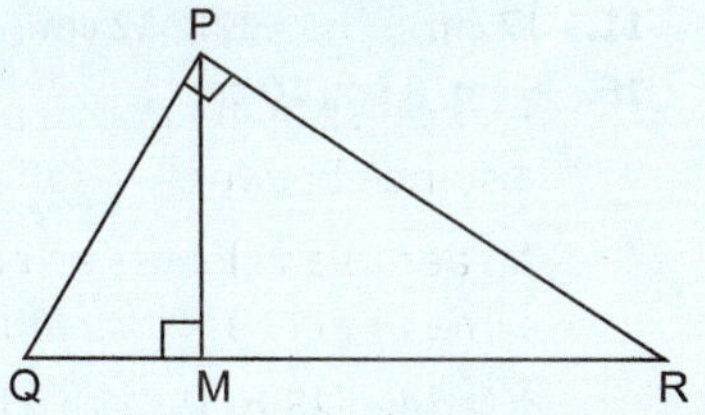


**19.** In a quadrilateral $ABCD$, $\angle B = 90°$ and $AD^2 = AB^2 + BC^2 + CD^2$. Prove that : $\angle ACD = 90°$.

**20.** $\Delta ABC$ is a isosceles triangle in which $AB = AC$ and $\angle A = 90°$. Prove that : $BC^2 = 2AC^2$.

**21.** In $\Delta ABC$, $\angle A = 90°$ and $BC^2 = 2AC^2$, prove that : $\Delta ABC$ is isosceles.

**22.** In $\Delta ABC$, $\angle ABC$ is an acute angle. Prove that : $AC^2 = AB^2 + BC^2 - 2\ BC.\ BD$.

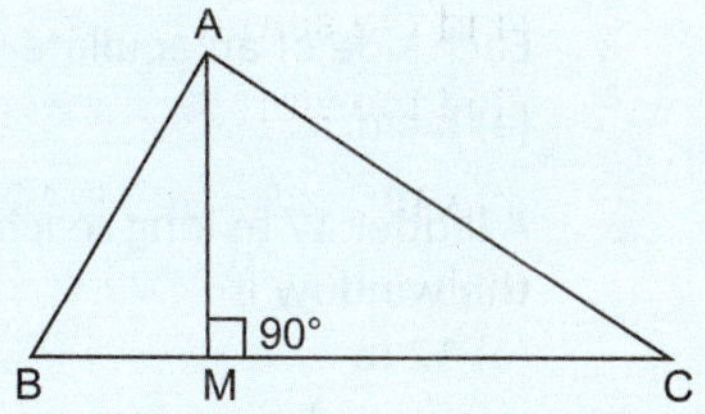


**23.** $\Delta ABC$ is an equilateral triangle. Side $BC$ is trisected at $D$. Prove that : $9\ AD^2 = 7\ AB^2$.

**24.** In $\Delta ABC$, $\angle ABC = 90°$ . $X$ and $Y$ are mid-points of the sides $AB$ and $BC$ respectively. Prove that :

(i) $CX^2 + AY^2 = 5XY^2$ (ii) $4\ (CX^2 + AY^2) = 5\ AC^2$

**25.** In the adjoining figure, $AB > AC$, $BE = EC$ and $\angle ADC = 90°$. Prove that :

(i) $AB^2 - AC^2 = 2BC.ED$

(ii) $AB^2 + AC^2 = 2\ (AE^2 + BE^2)$

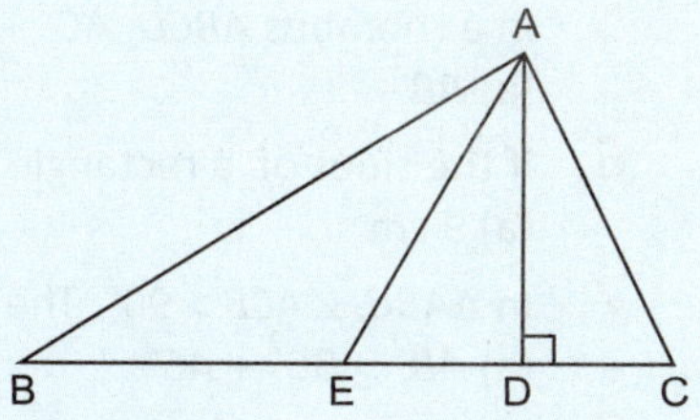


**26.** In $\Delta ABC$, $AB = AC$ and $D$ is any point on side $BC$ produced. Prove that : $AD^2 = AB^2 + BD \cdot CD$

**27.** Prove that the sum of the squares on the sides of a rhombus is equal to the sum of square on its diagonals.

**28.** The diagonals of a rhombus $ABCD$ intersect each other at $O$. Prove that : $OA^2 + OC^2 = 2AB^2 - \frac{1}{2}BD^2$.

**29.** In $\square ABCD$, $\angle B = 90°$ and $\angle D = 90°$. Prove that : $2AC^2 = AB^2 + BC^2 + CD^2 + DA^2$.

**30.** In the adjoining figure, $PQ = QR$ and $\angle PSQ = 90°$. Prove that : $PR^2 = 2\ PQ.\ RS$.

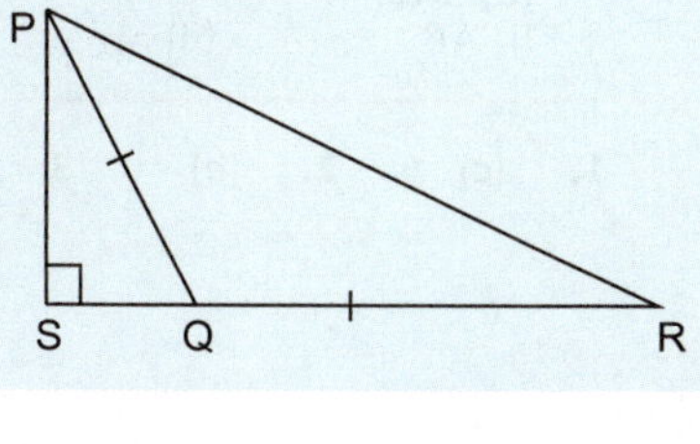

**31.** In the adjoining figure, $\angle PQR = 90°$ and $XY \parallel QR$. If $PX : QX = 1 : 2$, $PQ = 6$cm, $PY = 4$ cm, find $PR$ and $QR$.

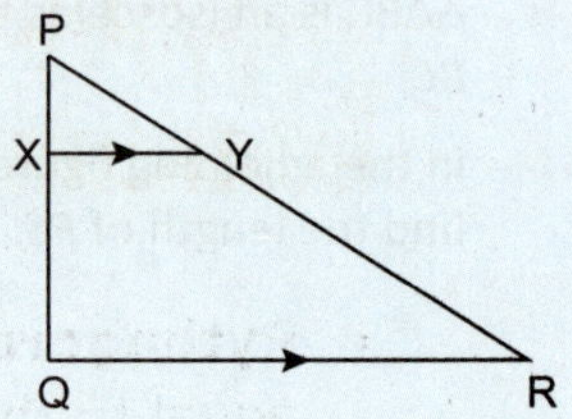


**32.** If $O$ is any point in the interior of a rectangle, $ABCD$, prove that : $OA^2 + OC^2 = OB^2 + OD^2$.

### Answers

**1.** (i) yes (ii) yes (iii) No **2.** 50 m **3.** 5 m **4.** 5 m
**5.** 1000 Km **6.** 35 m, **7.** 16 cm **8.** $a\sqrt{3}$ unit **9.** 9 cm **10.** 5 cm, 4 cm, 3 cm
**11.** 17 cm **12.** 12 cm **13.** (i) 9 cm (ii) 132 $cm^2$ **14.** 15 cm **15.** 26 cm
**16.** 6 cm, 8 cm, 10 cm **31.** 12 cm, $6\sqrt{3}$ cm

## Exercise 10B

### Multiple Choice Questions

Choose the correct answer from the given four options in each of the following questions :

**1.** Each side of an equilateral triangle is 10 cm. The length of the each its altitude is :
(a) 5 cm (b) $5\sqrt{2}$ cm (c) $5\sqrt{3}$ cm (d) $3\sqrt{5}$ cm

**2.** A ladder 17 m long reaches a window above the ground. If the distance of the foot of ladder from wall is 8 m, the height of the window is :
(a) 12 m (b) 15 m (c) 12 cm (d) 14 m

**3.** The lengths of the diagonals of a rhombus are 16 cm and 12 cm. The length of the side of rhombus is :
(a) 8 cm (b) 9 cm (c) 11 cm (d) 10 cm

**4.** In $\Delta ABC$, $BC = CA$ and $\angle ACB = 90°$. Then correct relation is :
(a) $AB^2 = 2AC^2$ (b) $2AB^2 = AC^2$ (c) $BC^2 = 2AC^2$ (d) $2BC^2 = AC^2$

**5.** In a rhombus $ABCD$, $AC^2 + BD^2$ is equal to :
(a) $AB^2$ (b) $2BC^2$ (c) $3\ CD^2$ (d) $4\ DA^2$

**6.** If the sides of a rectangle are 6 cm and 8 cm then the length of its diagonal is :
(a) 9 cm (b) 10 cm (c) 12 cm (d) 14 cm

**7.** In $\Delta ABC$, $\angle ACB > 90°$. The correct relation is :
(a) $AB^2 > BC^2 + AC^2$ (b) $BC^2 > AC^2 + AB^2$ (c) $AC^2 > AB^2 + BC^2$ (d) $AB^2 = BC^2 + AC^2$

**8.** In $\Delta ABC$, $\angle ACB < 90°$. The correct relation is :
(a) $AB^2 = BC^2 + AC^2$ (b) $BC^2 < AC^2 + AB^2$ (c) $AB^2 < BC^2 + AC^2$ (d) $AB^2 > BC^2 + AC^2$

**9.** In $\Delta ABC$, $AB = AC$ and $BD \perp AC$ then $BD^2 - CD^2$ is equal to :
(a) $2\ CD \cdot AD$ (b) $2CD \cdot AC$ (c) $2AC \cdot BC$ (d) $2BC \cdot AC$

**10.** In $\Delta ABC$, $\angle ACB = 90°$ $P$ and $Q$ are the points on $CA$ and $CB$ respectively which divides these sides in the ratio 2 : 1. Then $9(AQ^2 + BP^2)$ is equal to :
(a) $5AB^2$ (b) $8\ AB^2$ (c) $10\ AB^2$ (d) $13\ AB^2$

### Answers

**1.** (c) **2.** (b) **3.** (d) **4.** (a) **5.** (d) **6.** (b) **7.** (a) **8.** (c) **9.** (a) **10.** (d)

## SUMMARY *of the Chapter*

- **Pythagoras Theorem :** In a right-angled triangle, the square on the hypotenuse is equal to the sum of the squares on the remaining two sides containing right angle.
- **Converse of Pythagoras Theorem :** If, in any triangle, the square on the largest side of the triangle is equal to the sum of the squares on the remaining two sides, then the triangle is right-angled triangle.
- In $\Delta ABC$, if

  (i) $AB^2 = AC^2 + BC^2$, then $\angle ACB = 90°$ (right angle)

  (ii) $AB^2 > AC^2 + BC^2$, then $\angle ACB > 90°$ (obtuse angle)

  (iii) $AB^2 < AC^2 + BC^2$, then $\angle ACB < 90°$ (acute angle)

# CHAPTER TEST

1. In $\Delta ABC$, $AC = BC$ and $AB^2 = 2BC^2$. Prove that $\Delta ABC$ is a right-angled triangle.

2. In the given figure, $PQ \| SR$, $PQ = 18$ cm, $QR = 6$cm and $PS = 10$ cm. Find the area of □$PQRS$.

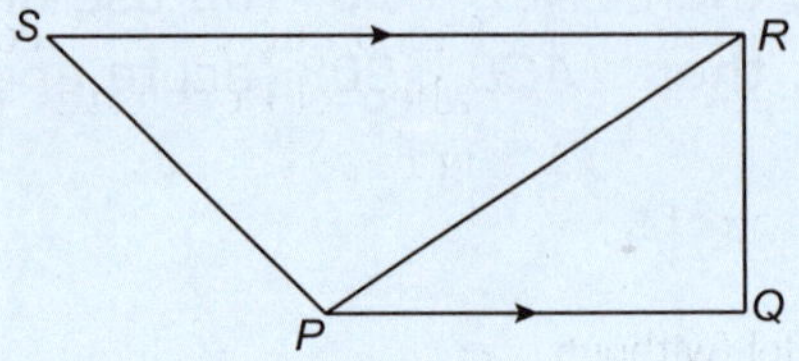


3. In the given figure, $\angle ABC = 90°$. Prove that : $AE^2 + CD^2 = AC^2 + DE^2$

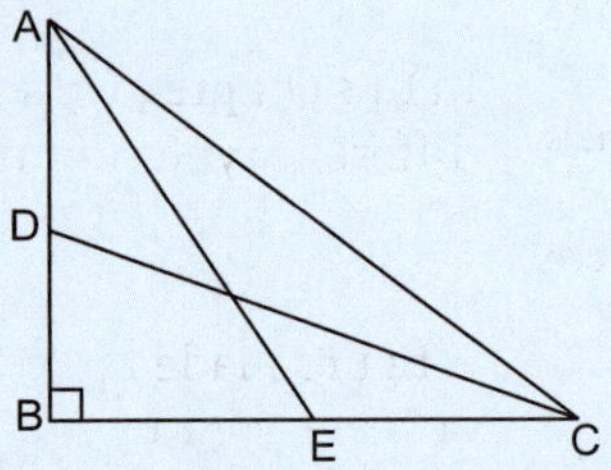


4. In an equilateral triangle $ABC$, the side $BC$ is trisected at $D$. Prove that : $9AD^2 = 7AB^2$.

5. Prove that the sum of the squares on the sides of a rhombus is equal to the sum of squares on its diagonals.

6. In $\Delta ABC$, $AB = BC = CA = 2a$. Find the length of perpendicular drawn from $A$ to $BC$.

7. In the given figure, $\angle ACB$ is an obtuse angle. Prove that : $AB^2 = AC^2 + BC^2 + 2BC \cdot CD$

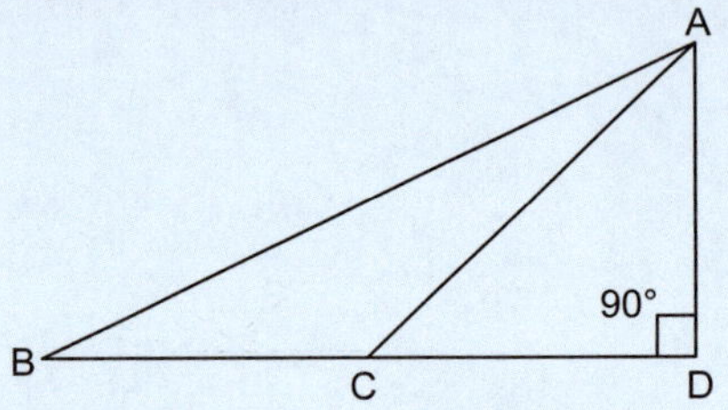


8. The side of a rhombus is 13 cm. If its one diagonal is 24 cm, find the length of other diagonal.

## *Answers*

**2.** 84 $cm^2$ **6.** $a\sqrt{3}$ cm **8.** 10 cm

# Chapter 11 RECTILINEAR FIGURES

## Syllabus

Proof and use of theorems on parallelogram.

- Both pairs of opposite sides equal (without proof).
- Both pairs of opposite angles equal.
- One pair of opposite sides equal and parallel (without proof).
- Diagonals bisect each other and bisect the parallelogram.
- Rhombus as a special parallelogram whose diagonals meet at right angles.
- In a rectangle, diagonals are equal; in a square they are equal and meet at right angles.

## INTRODUCTION

When a figure is drawn on a sheet of paper by using a pencil from one point to other point without lifting the pencil, it is called a plane figure (curve).

*For example :*

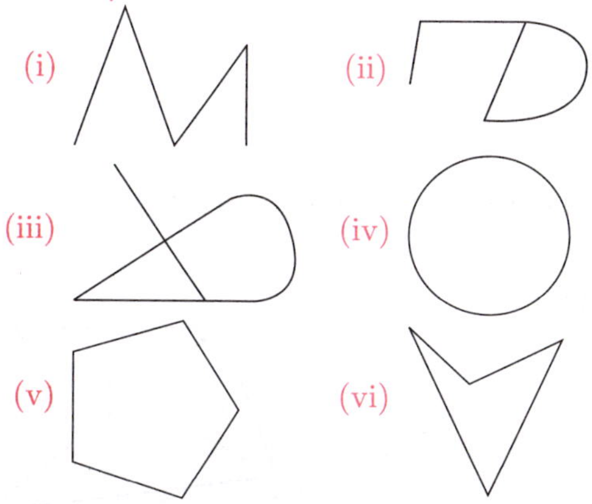


### Types of Plane Figures

There are two types of plane figures.

### (i) Open Figures (Open Curves)

The plane figures containing starting and end points different, are called open figures (curves). Figures (i), (ii) and (iii) are open figures.

### (ii) Close Figures (Close Curves)

The plane figures containing starting and end points same, are called close figures (curves). Figure (iv), (v) and (vi) are close figures.

### Simple Curve

If a curve does not cross itself at any point, it is called a simple curve.

In this chapter, we shall discuss about rectilinear figures, polygons, different types of quadrilaterals and their properties.

### Rectilinear Figures

A figure made up of line segments only, is called a rectilinear figure or plane figure.

*For example :*

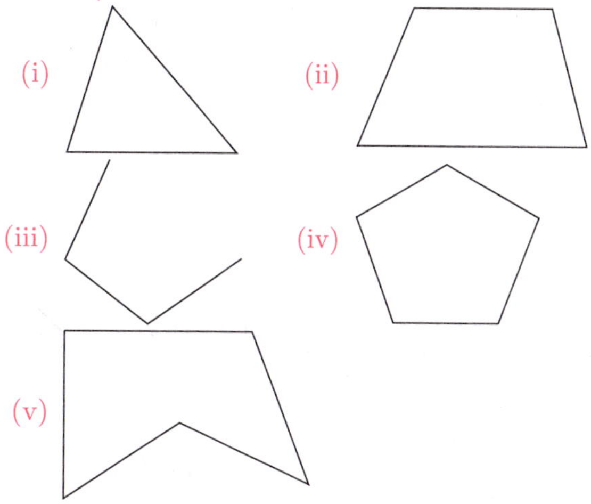


### Polygons

A closed figure made up of line segments only, is called a polygon. In the above examples (i), (ii), (iv) and (v) are polygons.

**Remark**

Every polygon is a rectilinear figure, but every rectilinear figure is not a polygon.

Remember the following in a polygon :

(i) The line segments are called the sides of the polygon.

(ii) The intersection of two consecutive sides of a polygon are called the vertices of the polygon.

(iii) The angle between two consecutive sides of a polygon is called the interior angle or simply angle of the polygon.

On the basis of the number of sides in a polygon, we can name them as follows :

| | | | | | | | |
|---|---|---|---|---|---|---|---|
| No. of sides : | 3 | 4 | 5 | 6 | 7 | 8 | 10 |
| Name of polygon : | Triangle | Quadrilateral | Pentagon | Hexagon | Heptagon | Octagon | Decagon |

## Diagonal

It is a line segment joining any two non-consecutive vertices of a polygon.

## Convex Polygon

If all interior angles of a polygon are less than 180°, it is called a convex polygon.

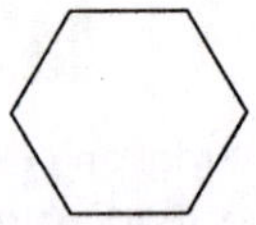
Convex Polygon

## Concave Polygon

If one or more than one of the interior angle of a polygon is more than 180°, it is called a concave polygon.

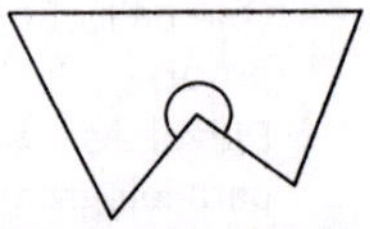
Concave Polygon

**NOTE**

In this chapter, we shall discuss only convex polygons.

## Exterior Angle

When a side of a polygon is produced, then the angle makes by this line to the next side of the polygon is called the exterior angle of the polygon.

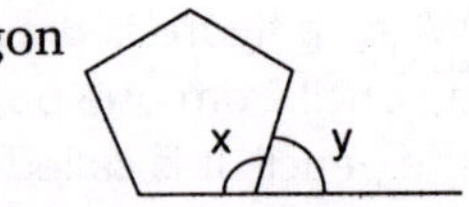


In the given figure, $x$ is the interior angle and $y$ is the adjacent exterior angle.

Here,

$$\text{interior angle} + \text{adjacent exterior angle} = 180°$$

## Regular Polygon

If all sides of a polygon are equal and all its interior angles are also equal, then it is called a regular polygon.

- All regular polygons are always convex.

## Quadrilateral

A closed plane figure bounded by four line segments is called a quadrilateral.

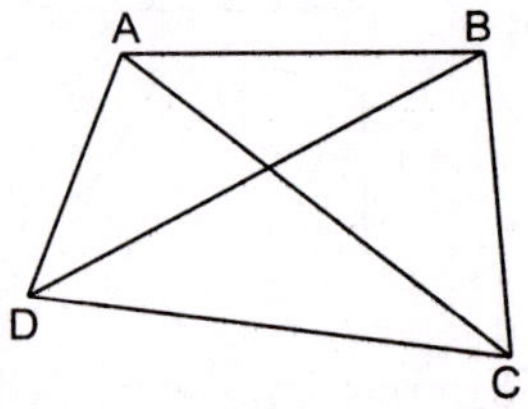


In the adjoining figure, a quadrilateral $ABCD$ is shown.

## Vertices

It has four vertices $A$, $B$, $C$ and $D$.

## Sides

It has four line segments $AB$, $BC$, $CD$ and $DA$, called its sides.

### Diagonals

The line segments joining opposite vertices of a quadrilateral are called its diagonals. Here, $AC$ and $BD$ are the diagonals.

### Angles

It has four angles : $\angle A$, $\angle B$, $\angle C$ and $\angle D$, called interior angles of the quadrilateral.

**NOTE**

Sum of interior angles of a quadrilateral = 360°.

Pair of Opposite Angles : $\angle A$, $\angle C$ and $\angle B$, $\angle D$ are the pair of opposite angles.

Pair of Adjacent Angles : $\angle A$, $\angle B$; $\angle B$, $\angle C$; $\angle C$, $\angle D$ and $\angle D$, $\angle A$ are four pairs of adjacent angles.

## Different Types of Quadrilaterals

### 1. Trapezium

If one pair of opposite sides is parallel in a quadrilateral, it is called a trapezium.

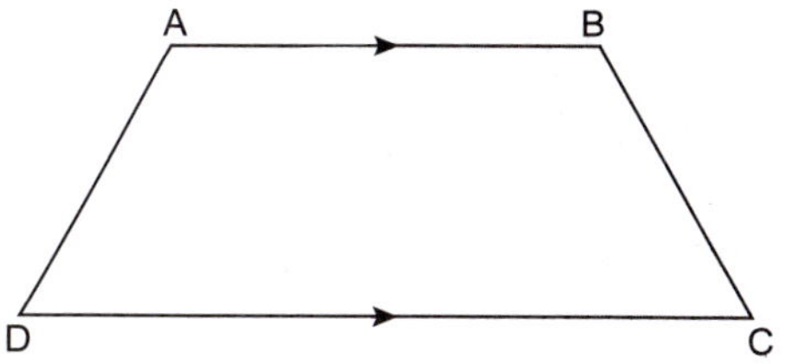


In the adjoining figure, $\square ABCD$ is shown in which $AB \parallel DC$.

$\therefore$ $\square ABCD$ is a trapezium.

In a trapezium $ABCD$ with $AB \parallel DC$, if $AD = BC$, then it is called an isosceles trapezium in which

$$\angle A = \angle B \text{ and } \angle C = \angle D.$$

### 2. Parallelogram

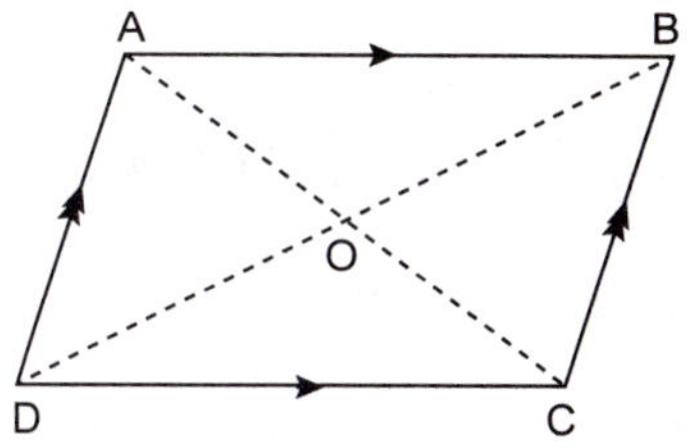


If both pairs of opposite sides are parallel in a quadrilateral, it is called a parallelogram.

In the adjoining figure, $\square ABCD$ is shown in which $AB \parallel DC$ and $DA \parallel CB$.

$\therefore$ $\square ABCD$ is a parallelogram.

In a parallelogram $ABCD$

(i) Opposite sides are parallel, *i.e.*, $AB \parallel DC$ and $DA \parallel CB$.

(ii) Opposite sides are equal, *i.e.*, $AB = DC$ and $DA = CB$.

(iii) Opposite angles are equal, *i.e.*, $\angle A = \angle C$ and $\angle B = \angle D$.

(iv) Sum of adjacent angles is 180°, *i.e.*, consecutive angles are supplementary. So

$$\angle A + \angle B = 180°; \quad \angle B + \angle C = 180°; \quad \angle C + \angle D = 180°; \quad \angle D + \angle A = 180°$$

(v) Diagonals bisect each other, *i.e.*,

$$OA = OC = \frac{1}{2} AC \text{ and } OB = OD = \frac{1}{2} BD$$

(vi) Each diagonal divides the parallelogram into two congruent triangles, *i.e.*,

$$\Delta ABC \cong \Delta CDA \text{ and } \Delta BCD \cong \Delta DAB$$

(vii) Diagonals divide the parallelogram into four triangles of equal area, *i.e.*,

$$\text{Area } (\Delta AOB) = \text{Area } (\Delta BOC) = \text{Area } (\Delta COD) = \text{Area } (\Delta DOA)$$

$$= \frac{1}{4} \text{ Area (parallelogram } ABCD)$$

## 3. Rectangle

If each angle of a parallelogram is 90°, it is called a rectangle.

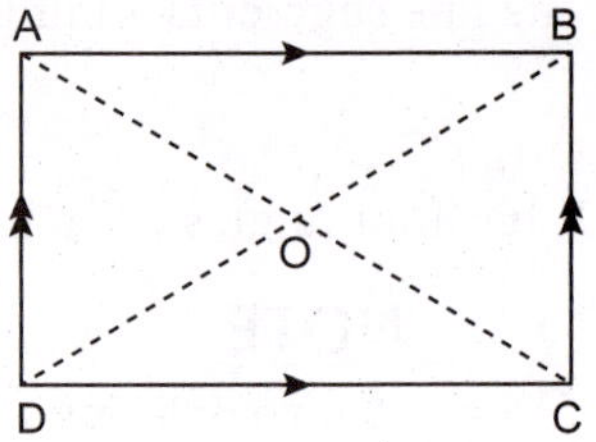


In the adjoining figure, □$ABCD$ is shown in which $AB \parallel DC$, $AD \parallel BC$ and $\angle A = \angle B = \angle C = \angle D = 90°$.

$\therefore$ $ABCD$ is a rectangle.

In the rectangle $ABCD$,

(i) $AC = BD$

(ii) diagonals bisect each other, *i.e.*,

$$OA = OB = OC = OD = \frac{1}{2}AC = \frac{1}{2}BD$$

## 4. Rhombus

If all four sides of a quadrilateral are equal, it is called a rhombus.

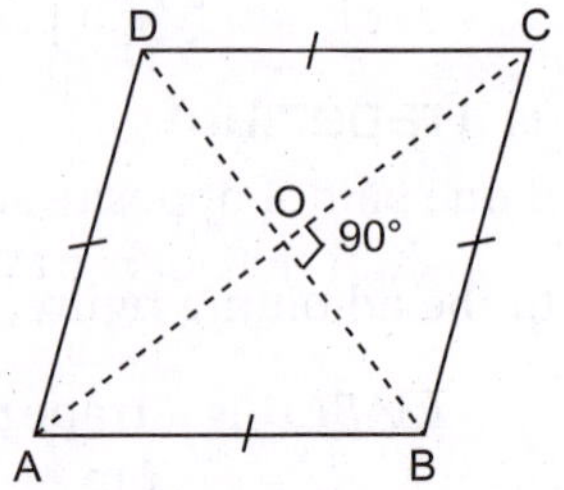


In the adjoining figure, □$ABCD$ is shown in which $AB = BC = CD = DA$.

$\therefore$ □$ABCD$ is a rhombus.

In the rhombus $ABCD$,

diagonals $AC$ and $BD$ bisect each other at right angles.

$$OA = OC = \frac{1}{2}AC \text{ and } OB = OD = \frac{1}{2}BD$$

$$\angle AOB = \angle BOC = \angle COD = \angle DOA = 90°$$

## 5. Square

If each angle of a rhombus is 90°, it is called a square.

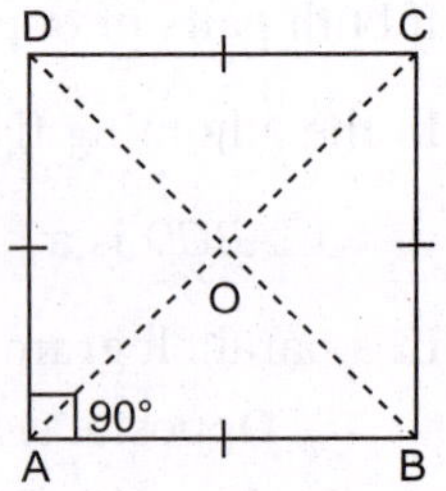


In the adjoining figure, □$ABCD$ is shown in which $AB = BC = CD = DA$

and $\angle A = \angle B = \angle C = \angle D = 90°$.

$\therefore$ □$ABCD$ is a square.

In the square $ABCD$,

(i) diagonals $AC = BD$

(ii) diagonals bisect each other at 90°.

$$OA = OB = OC = OD = \frac{1}{2}AC = \frac{1}{2}BD$$

and $$\angle AOB = \angle BOC = \angle COD = \angle DOA = 90°$$

## 6. Kite

A quadrilateral in which two pairs of adjacent sides are equal, is called a kite.

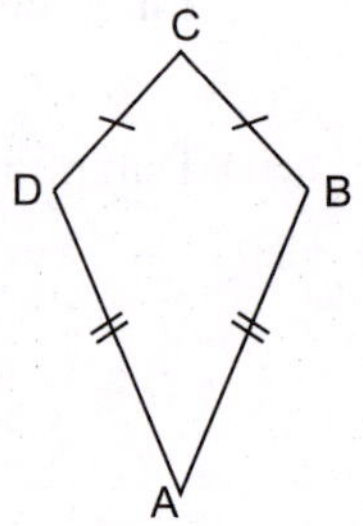


In the adjoining figure, □$ABCD$ is shown in which $AD = AB$ and $BC = CD$

$\therefore$ □$ABCD$ is a kite.

## Properties of Parallelograms

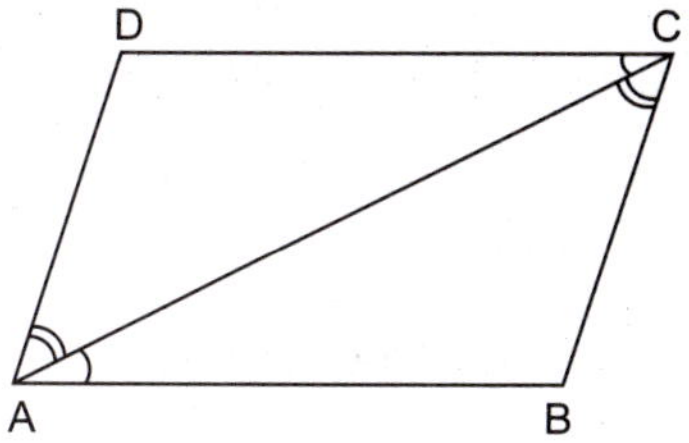


**Theorem 1** A diagonal of a parallelogram divides it into two congruent triangles.

Given : A parallelogram $ABCD$ and the diagonal $AC$ divides it into two triangles namely,

$$\Delta ABC \text{ and } \Delta CDA.$$

To Prove : $\Delta ABC \cong \Delta CDA$.

Proof :

| Statement | Reason |
|---|---|
| $\angle BCA = \angle DAC$ | Alternate angles, $AB \parallel CD$ and $AC$ is transversal |
| $AC = CA$ | Common |
| $\angle BAC = \angle DCA$ | Alternate angles, $AD \parallel BC$ and $AC$ is transversal |
| $\Delta ABC \cong \Delta CDA$ | ASA axiom of congruency |

$\therefore$ A diagonal of a parallelogram divides it into two congruent triangles. Hence Proved.

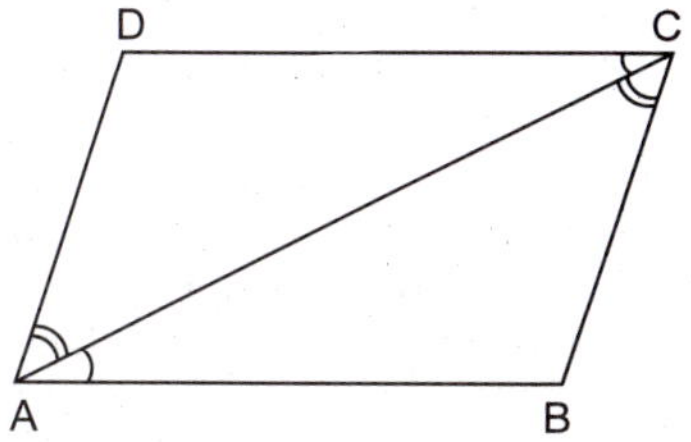


**Theorem 2** In a parallelogram, opposite sides are equal.

Given : A parallelogram $ABCD$.

To Prove : $AB = DC$ and $BC = AD$.

Construction : Join $AC$.

Proof :

| Statement | Reason |
|---|---|
| $\angle BCA = \angle DAC$ | Alternate angles, $AB \parallel CD$ and $AC$ is transversal |
| $AC = CA$ | Common |
| $\angle BAC = \angle DCA$ | Alternate angles, $AD \parallel BC$ and $AC$ is transversal |
| $\Delta ABC \cong \Delta CDA$ | ASA axiom of congruency |
| $AB = CD$ and $BC = DA$ | CPCT |

$\therefore$ Opposite sides of a parallelogram are equal. Hence Proved.

**Theorem 3 (Converse of theorem 2)** If each pair of opposite sides of a quadrilateral is equal, then it is a parallelogram.

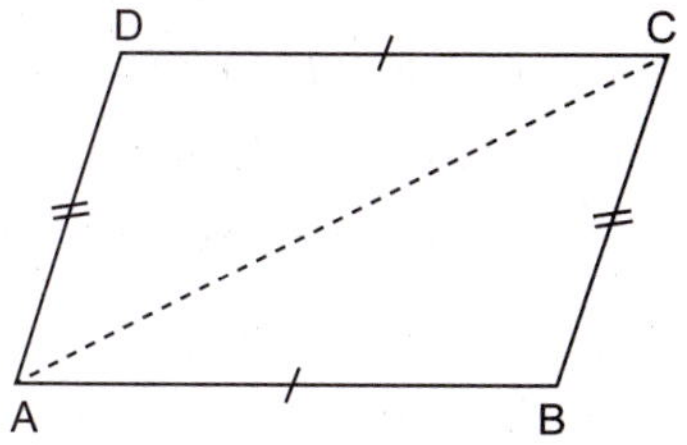


Given : A quadrilateral $ABCD$ in which $AB = DC$ and $AD = BC$.

To Prove : $ABCD$ is a parallelogram.

Construction : Join $AC$.

Proof :

| Statement | Reason |
|---|---|
| $AB = CD$ | Given |
| $BC = DA$ | Given |
| $AC = CA$ | Common |
| $\Delta ABC \cong \Delta CDA$ | SSS axiom of congruency |
| $\angle BAC = \angle DCA$ | CPCT |
| $\Rightarrow AB \parallel DC$ | Alternate angles are equal |
| $\angle ACB = \angle CAD$ | CPCT |
| $\Rightarrow BC \parallel AD$ | Alternate angles are equal |

$\therefore BC \parallel AD$ and $BA = CD \Rightarrow ABCD$ is a parallelogram. Hence Proved.

**Theorem 4** In a parallelogram, the opposite angles are equal.

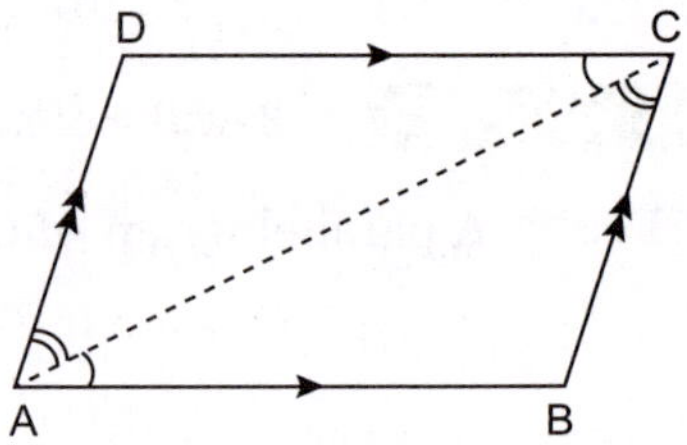


Given : A parallelogram $ABCD$ in which $AB \parallel DC$ and $AD \parallel BC$.

To Prove : $\angle A = \angle C$ and $\angle B = \angle D$.

Construction : Join $AC$.

Proof :

| Statement | | Reason |
|---|---|---|
| In $\Delta ABC$ and $\Delta CDA$, | | |
| $\angle BAC = \angle DCA$ | ...(i) | Alternate angles |
| $\angle BCA = \angle DAC$ | ...(ii) | Alternate angles |
| $AC = CA$ | | Common |
| $\therefore \quad \Delta ABC \cong \Delta CDA$ | | ASA axiom of congruency |
| $\Rightarrow \quad \angle ABC = \angle CDA$ | | CPCT |
| $\Rightarrow \quad \angle B = \angle D$ | | |

Again, from equations (i) and (ii)

$$\angle BCA + \angle DCA = \angle DAC + \angle BAC$$

$\Rightarrow \quad \angle BCD = \angle BAD \quad \Rightarrow \quad \angle C = \angle A$

$\therefore \quad \angle A = \angle C \quad$ and $\quad \angle B = \angle D$

$\Rightarrow$ Opposite angles of a parallelogram are equal.

Hence Proved.

**Theorem 5 (Converse of theorem 4)** If each pair of opposite angles of a quadrilateral is equal, then it is a parallelogram.

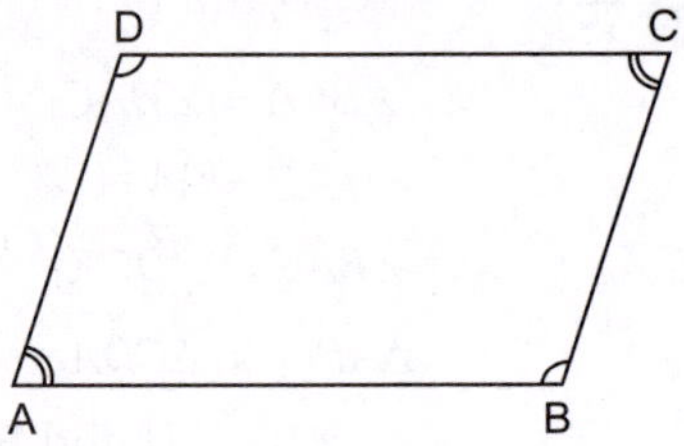


Given : A quadrilateral $ABCD$ in which

$$\angle A = \angle C \quad \text{and} \quad \angle B = \angle D$$

To Prove : $ABCD$ is a parallelogram.

Proof :

| Statement | Reason |
|---|---|
| 1. $\angle A = \angle C$ | Given |
| 2. $\angle B = \angle D$ | Given |
| 3. $\angle A + \angle B = \angle C + \angle D$ | Adding (1) and (2) |
| 4. $\angle A + \angle B + \angle C + \angle D = 360°$ | Sum of angles of a quadrilateral |
| 5. $\angle A + \angle B = \angle C + \angle D = 180°$ | From (3) and (4) |
| 6. $\angle A + \angle B = 180°$ | Sum of interior angles, formed by lines $BC$, $AD$ and transversal $AB$ |
| $\Rightarrow \quad BC \parallel AD$ | |
| Similarly, $\quad AB \parallel DC$ | |
| $\because \quad AB \parallel DC$ and $BC \parallel AD$ | |
| $\therefore \quad ABCD$ is a parallelogram. | |

Hence Proved.

**Theorem 6** If a pair of opposite sides of a quadrilateral is equal and parallel, then it is a parallelogram.

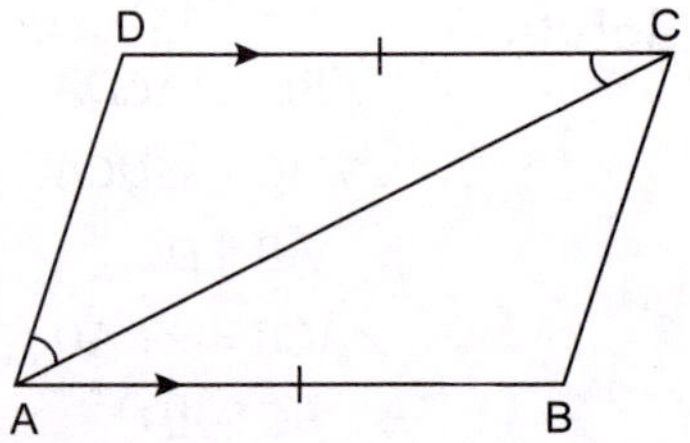


Given : A quadrilateral $ABCD$ in which $AB \parallel DC$ and $AB = DC$.

To Prove : $ABCD$ is a parallelogram.

Construction : Join $AC$.

Proof :

| Statement | Reason |
|---|---|
| $AB = CD$ | Given |
| $\angle BAC = \angle DCA$ | Alternate angles, $AB \parallel DC$ and $AC$ is a transversal |

| | | |
|---|---|---|
| | $AC = CA$ | Common |
| | $\Delta ABC \cong \Delta CDA$ | SAS axiom of congruency |
| | $\angle ACB = \angle CAD$ | CPCT |
| $\Rightarrow$ | $AD \parallel BC$ | |
| Now, | $AD \parallel BC$ and $AB \parallel DC$ | |
| $\therefore$ | $ABCD$ is a parallelogram. | |

Hence Proved.

**Theorem 7** The diagonals of a parallelogram bisect each other.

Given : A parallelogram $ABCD$ whose diagonals $AC$ and $BD$ intersect at '$O$'.

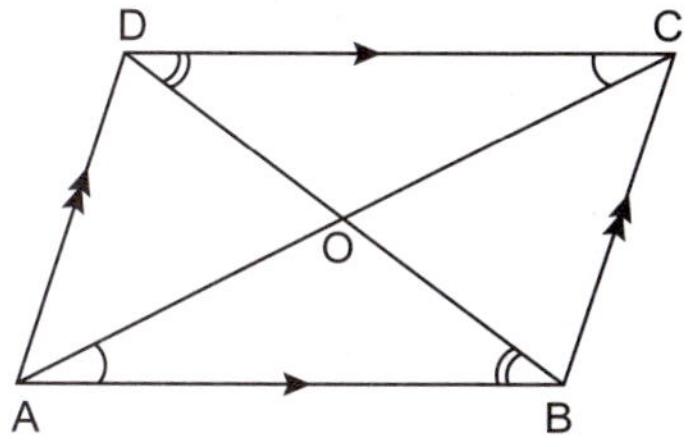


To Prove : $OA = OC$ and $OB = OD$.

Proof :

| | Statement | Reason |
|---|---|---|
| | In $\Delta OAB$ and $\Delta OCD$, | |
| | $\angle OAB = \angle OCD$ | Alternate angles |
| | $\angle OBA = \angle ODC$ | Alternate angles |
| | $AB = CD$ | Opposite sides of parallelogram |
| $\therefore$ | $\Delta OAB \cong \Delta OCD$ | ASA axiom of congruency |
| $\Rightarrow$ | $OA = OC$ | |
| and | $OB = OD$ | CPCT |

Hence Proved.

**Theorem 8** If the diagonals of a quadrilateral bisect each other, then it is a parallelogram.

Given : A quadrilateral $ABCD$ whose diagonals $AC$ and $BD$ intersect at $O$ such that $OA = OC$ and $OB = OD$.

To Prove : $ABCD$ is a parallelogram.

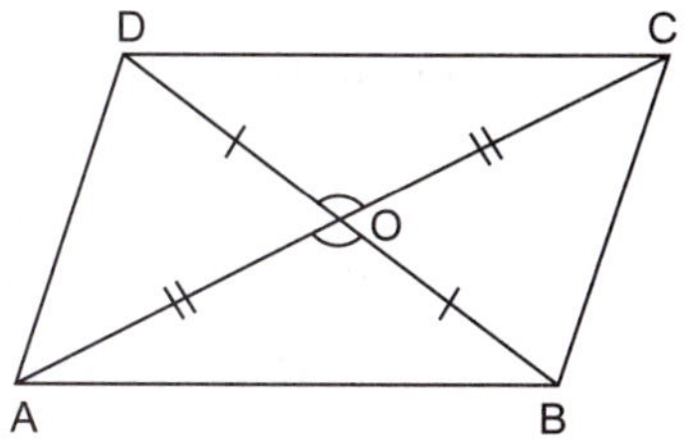


Proof :

| | Statement | Reason |
|---|---|---|
| 1. | $OA = OC$ | Given |
| 2. | $\angle AOB = \angle COD$ | Vertically opposite angles |
| 3. | $OB = OD$ | Given |
| 4. | $\Delta AOB \cong \Delta COD$ | SAS criteria |
| 5. | $\angle OAB = \angle OCD$ | CPCT |
| | $\Rightarrow \angle CAB = \angle ACD$ | Alternate angles, formed by lines |
| | $\Rightarrow AB \parallel DC$ | $AB$, $DC$ and transversal $AC$ |
| 6. | $AB = CD$ | CPCT |
| 7. | $ABCD$ is a parallelogram | $AB = CD$ and $AB \parallel DC$ |

Hence Proved.

## Illustrative Examples

**Example 1.** In a rectangle $ABCD$, diagonals $AC$ and $BD$ intersect at '$O$'. If $\angle OAB = 25°$, find :

(a) $\angle ACB$ (b) $\angle ABO$

(c) $\angle COD$ (d) $\angle BOC$

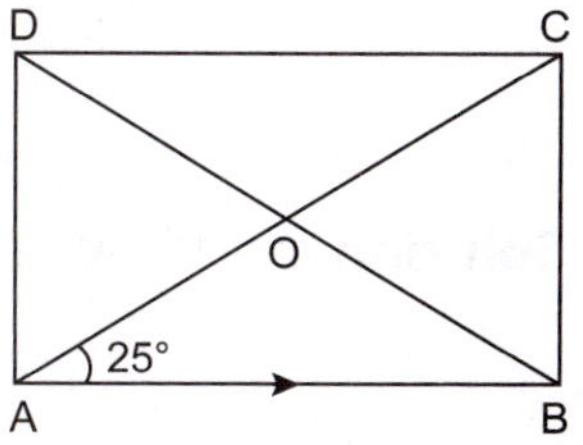


**Solution.** (a) In $\Delta ABC$,

$$\angle ABC = 90°$$

$$\therefore \quad \angle ACB = 180° - \angle ABC - \angle CAB$$
$$= 180° - 90° - 25°$$
$$= 65°$$

Ans.

(b) In $\Delta ABO$,

$$OA = OB$$

$$\therefore \quad \angle ABO = \angle OAB = 25°$$

Ans.

(c) $\angle COD = \angle AOB$ (Vertically opposite angles)

$= 180° - \angle OAB - \angle OBA$

$= 180° - 25° - 25°$

$= 130°$ Ans.

(d) $\angle BOC + \angle COD = 180°$ (Straight angle)

$\Rightarrow$ $\angle BOC = 180° - \angle COD$

$= 180° - 130°$

$= 50°$ Ans.

**Example 2.** The angles of a quadrilateral are $3x$, $8x$, $10x$ and $15x$. Find the smallest and the largest angles of the quadrilateral.

**Solution.** We know that the sum of angles of a quadrilateral is 360°.

$\therefore$ $3x + 8x + 10x + 15x = 360°$

$\Rightarrow$ $36x = 360°$

$\Rightarrow$ $x = 10°$

So, smallest angle $= 3x = 3 \times 10° = 30°$ Ans.

and largest angle $= 15x = 15 \times 10° = 150°$ Ans.

**Example 3.** One angle of a quadrilateral is 120° and the remaining three angles are in the ratio 2 : 3 : 7. Find the angles of the quadrilateral.

**Solution.** Let remaining three angles be $2x$, $3x$ and $7x$.

We know that sum of angles of a quadrilateral is 360°.

$\therefore$ $2x + 3x + 7x + 120° = 360°$

$\Rightarrow$ $12x = 240°$ $\Rightarrow$ $x = 20°$

So, $2x = 2 \times 20° = 40°$

$3x = 3 \times 20° = 60°$

$7x = 7 \times 20° = 140°$

Hence, angles of quadrilateral are 40°, 60°, 140° and 120°. Ans.

**Example 4.** The angles of a quadrilateral are in the ratio 2 : 3 : 6 : 7. Show that it is a trapezium.

**Solution.** Let angles be $\angle A = 2x$, $\angle B = 3x$, $\angle C = 6x$ and $\angle D = 7x$ in quadrilateral $ABCD$.

We know that the sum of angles of a quadrilateral is 360°.

$\therefore$ $\angle A + \angle B + \angle C + \angle D = 360°$

$\Rightarrow$ $2x + 3x + 6x + 7x = 360°$

$\Rightarrow$ $18x = 360°$

$\Rightarrow$ $x = 20°$

Now, $\angle A + \angle D = 2x + 7x = 9x = 9 \times 20° = 180°$

$\angle B + \angle C = 3x + 6x = 9x = 9 \times 20° = 180°$

$\because$ $\angle A + \angle D = \angle B + \angle C$

$\therefore$ $ABCD$ is a trapezium. Hence Proved.

**Example 5.** Three angles of a quadrilateral are equal. Is it a parallelogram? Give reason.

**Solution.** Let $ABCD$ be a quadrilateral in which

$\angle A = \angle B = \angle C = 80°$

$\therefore$ $\angle A + \angle B = 80° + 80°$

$= 160° \neq 180°$

So, $ABCD$ need not be a parallelogram. Ans.

**Example 6.** Two adjacent angles of a parallelogram are $(3x + 10°)$ and $(7x - 30°)$. Find all angles of the parallelogram.

**Solution.** Let in parallelogram $ABCD$,

$$\angle A = 3x + 10° \quad \text{and} \quad \angle B = 7x - 30°$$

We know that the sum of adjacent angles in a parallelogram is 180°.

$\therefore$ $\angle A + \angle B = 180°$

$\Rightarrow$ $3x + 10° + 7x - 30° = 180°$

$\Rightarrow$ $10x = 200°$

$\Rightarrow$ $x = 20°$

$\therefore$ $\angle A = \angle C = 3x + 10° = 3 \times 20° + 10° = 70°$

and $\angle B = \angle D = 7x - 30° = 7 \times 20° - 30° = 110°$

Hence, angles of parallelogram are 70°, 110°, 70°, 110°. **Ans.**

**Example 7.** The opposite angles of a parallelogram are $2x + 12°$ and $3x - 22°$. Find all angles of the parallelogram.

**Solution.** Let in parallelogram $ABCD$,

$$\angle A = 2x + 12° \quad \text{and} \quad \angle C = 3x - 22°$$

We know that opposite angles in a parallelogram are equal.

$\therefore$ $\angle A = \angle C$

$\Rightarrow$ $2x + 12° = 3x - 22°$

$\Rightarrow$ $x = 34°$

$\therefore$ $\angle A = 2x + 12° = 2 \times 34° + 12° = 80°$

$\angle C = 3x - 22° = 3 \times 34° - 22° = 80°$

We know that the sum of adjacent angles in a parallelogram is 180°.

$\therefore$ $\angle A + \angle B = 180°$

$\Rightarrow$ $\angle B = 180° - \angle A = 180° - 80° = 100°$

and $\angle B = \angle D$ (Opposite angles in a parallelogram)

$\Rightarrow$ $\angle B = 100°$

Hence, angles of parallelogram = 80°, 100°, 80°, 100° **Ans.**

**Example 8.** If each pair of opposite sides of a quadrilateral are equal, prove that it is a parallelogram.

**Solution.** Given : A quadrilateral $ABCD$ in which $AB = DC$ and $AD = BC$.

To Prove : $ABCD$ is a parallelogram.

Construction : Join $AC$.

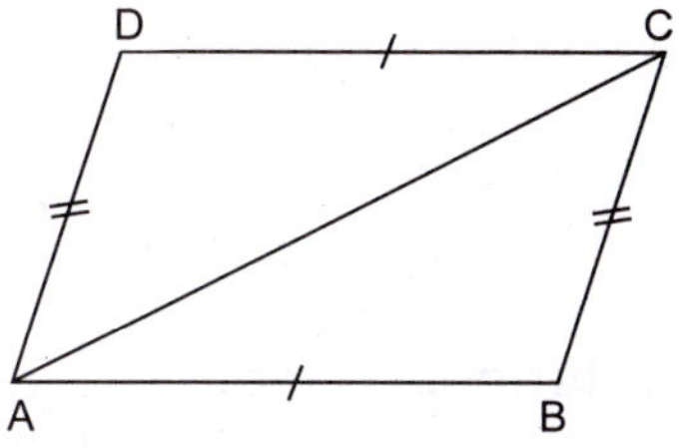


Proof :

| | Statement | Reason |
|---|---|---|
| | In $\Delta ABC$ and $\Delta CDA$, | |
| | $AB = CD$ | Given |
| | $BC = DA$ | Given |
| | $AC = CA$ | Given |
| $\therefore$ | $\Delta ABC \cong \Delta CDA$ | SSS axiom |
| $\Rightarrow$ | $\angle BAC = \angle DCA$ | CPCT |
| $\Rightarrow$ | $AB \parallel DC$ | Alternate angles are equal |
| and | $\angle BCA = \angle DAC$ | CPCT |
| $\Rightarrow$ | $BC \parallel AD$ | Alternate angles are equal |

Hence, $ABCD$ is a parallelogram. **Hence Proved.**

**Example 9.** In the adjoining figure, $ABCD$ is a parallelogram. Find the values of $x$ and $y$.

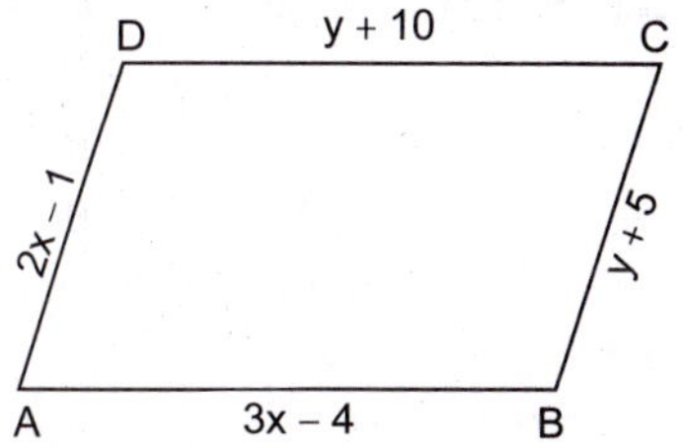


**Solution.** We know that the opposite sides of a parallelogram are equal.

$\therefore$ $AB = CD$

$\Rightarrow$ $3x - 4 = y + 10$

$\Rightarrow$ $y = 3x - 14$ ...(i)

and $AD = BC$

$\Rightarrow \quad 2x - 1 = y + 5$

$\Rightarrow \quad 2x - 1 = 3x - 14 + 5$ [From $(i)$]

$\Rightarrow \quad x = 8$

Put $x = 8$ in equation $(i)$, we get,

$y = 3 \times 8 - 14 = 10$

$\therefore \quad x = 8, y = 10$ Ans.

**Example 10.** In the adjoining figure, $ABCD$ is a square and $CDE$ is an equilateral triangle. Find :
(a) $\angle AED$ (b) $\angle EAB$ (c) reflex $\angle AEC$

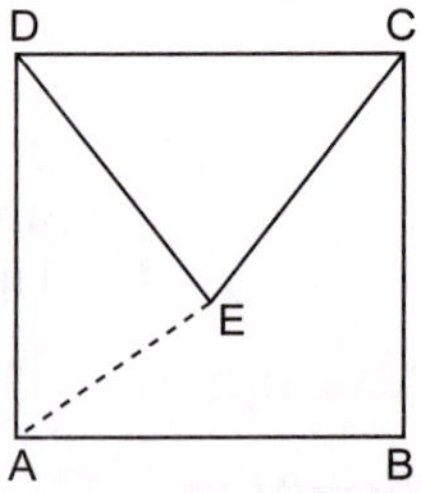


**Solution.** (a) We know that each angle of a square is 90° and each angle of an equilateral triangle is 60°.

$\therefore \quad \angle ADE = \angle ADC - \angle EDC$
$= 90° - 60° = 30°$

$AD = CD$ (Sides of a square)

and $ED = CD$ (Sides of an equilateral triangle)

$\therefore \quad AD = ED$

$\Rightarrow \quad \angle AED = \angle EAD$ (Angles opposite to equal sides in $\Delta AED$ are equal)

Now, $\angle AED + \angle EAD + \angle ADE = 180°$ (Angle sum property of $\Delta AED$)

$\Rightarrow \quad \angle AED + \angle AED + 30° = 180°$

$\Rightarrow \quad 2\angle AED = 180° - 30° = 150°$

$\Rightarrow \quad \angle AED = 75°$ Ans.

(b) $\angle EAB = \angle DAB - \angle EAD$
$= 90° - 75° = 15°$ Ans.

(c) Reflex $\angle AEC = 360° - \angle AEC$
$= 360° - (\angle AED + \angle DEC)$
$= 360° - (75° + 60°)$
$= 225°$ Ans.

**Example 11.** In the adjoining parallelogram $ABCD$, the bisectors $AM$ and $BM$ of $\angle A$ and $\angle B$ respectively meet at point $M$ on side $DC$. Prove that $AB = 2\ BC$.

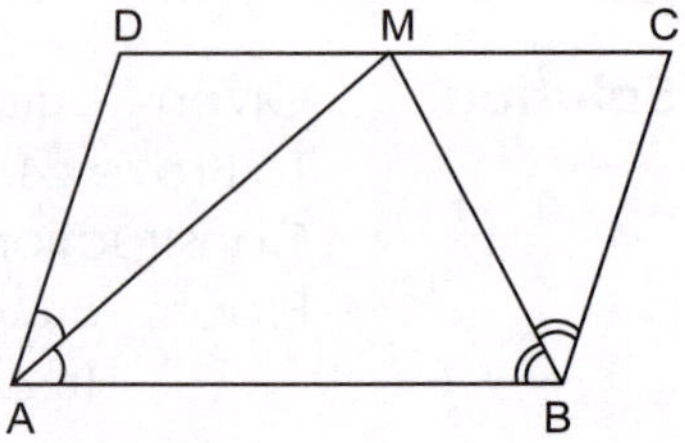


**Solution.** Proof :

| Statement | | Reason |
|---|---|---|
| 1. | $\angle MAB = \angle AMD$ | Alternate angles, $AB \parallel DM$ and $AM$ is a transversal |
| 2. | $\angle MAB = \angle DAM$ | $AM$ is the bisector of $\angle A$ |
| 3. | $\angle AMD = \angle DAM$ | From (1) and (2) |
| 4. | $AD = DM$ | Opposite sides of equal angles in $\Delta ADM$ are equal |
| 5. | $BC = DM$ | $BC = AD$ |
| 6. | $\angle MBA = \angle BMC$ | Alternate angles, $AB \parallel MC$ and $BM$ is a transversal |
| 7. | $\angle MBA = \angle CBM$ | $BM$ is the bisector of $\angle B$ |
| 8. | $\angle BMC = \angle CBM$ | From (6) and (7) |
| 9. | $BC = CM$ | Opposite sides of equal angles in $\Delta CBM$ are equal |
| 10. | $BC + BC = DM + CM$ | Adding (5) and (9) |
| 11. | $2BC = CD$ | $CD = DM + CM$ |
| 12. | $2BC = AB$ | $AB = CD$, opposite sides of parallelogram |

Hence Proved.

**Example 12.** In the adjoining parallelogram $ABCD$, $AP = PB$ and $DP$ is the bisector of $\angle ADC$. Prove that :

(a) $BC = BP$

(b) $CP$ is the bisector of $\angle BCD$

(c) $\angle DPC = 90°$

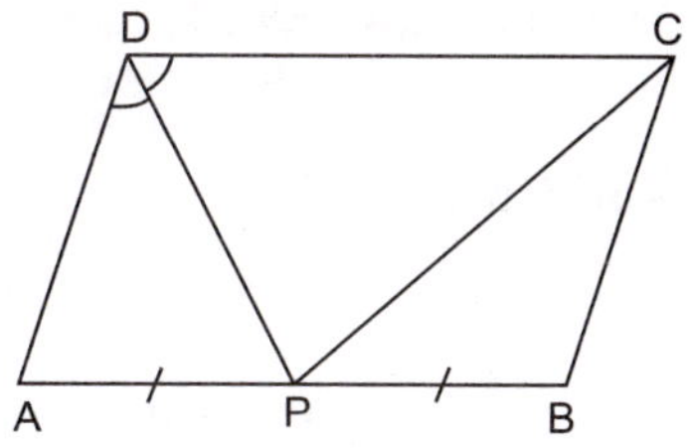


**Solution.** (a) $DC \parallel AP$ and $DP$ is a transversal.

$\therefore \quad \angle CDP = \angle DPA$ (Alternate angles)

But $\quad \angle CDP = \angle ADP$ ($DP$ bisects $\angle ADC$)

$\therefore \quad \angle DPA = \angle ADP \Rightarrow AD = AP$

But $\quad AD = BC$ (Opposite sides of parallelogram)

and $\quad AP = BP$ (Given)

$\therefore \quad BC = BP$

(b) In $\Delta BCP$,

$BC = BP$ [Proved in part (a)]

$\Rightarrow \quad \angle BPC = \angle BCP$

Now, $DC \parallel AB$ and $CP$ is a transversal.

$\therefore \quad \angle DCP = \angle BPC$ (Alternate angles)

$\therefore \quad \angle DCP = \angle BCP$

$\Rightarrow$ $CP$ bisects $\angle BCD$.

(c) Now, $\quad \angle DPC = \frac{1}{2}\angle C$ ($\because$ $CP$ bisects $\angle DCB$)

and $\quad \angle CDP = \frac{1}{2}\angle D$ ($\because$ $DP$ bisects $\angle CDA$)

$\therefore \quad \angle DPC + \angle CDP = \frac{1}{2}(\angle C + \angle D)$

$= \frac{1}{2} \times 180°$ ($\because$ $\angle C + \angle D = 180°$)

$= 90°$

$\Rightarrow \quad 180° - \angle DPC = 90°$

$\Rightarrow \quad \angle DPC = 90°$

Hence Proved.

**Example 13.** In the adjoining figure, $ABCD$ is a parallelogram and $M$ is the mid-point of $AC$. If $X$ and $Y$ are two points on $AB$ and $DC$ respectively such that $AX = CY$, then prove that :

(a) $\Delta AXM \cong \Delta CYM$

(b) $XMY$ is a straight line.

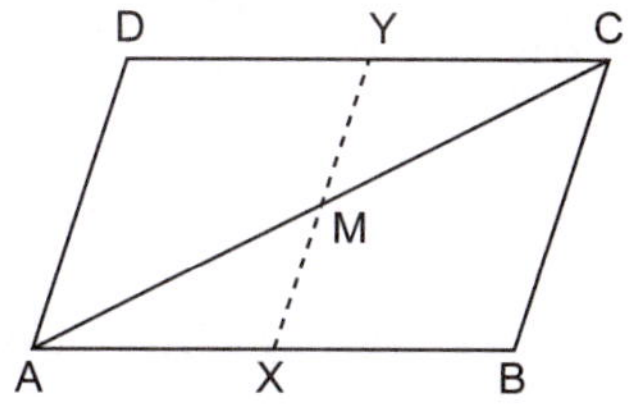


**Solution.** (a) In $\Delta AXM$ and $\Delta CYM$,

$AX = CY$ (Given)

$AM = CM$ ($M$ is the mid-point of $AC$)

$\angle XAM = \angle MCY$ (Alternate angles)

$\therefore \quad \Delta AXM \cong \Delta CYM$ (SAS criteria)

(b) Now, $\quad \Delta AXM \cong \Delta CYM$ [From part (a)]

$\Rightarrow \quad \angle AMX = \angle CMY$ ...(i) (CPCT)

Now, $\quad \angle XMC = \angle XAM + \angle AMX$ ...(ii) (Ext. angle of $\Delta AMX$)

$\Rightarrow \quad \angle CMY + \angle XMC = \angle XAM + \angle AXM + \angle AMX$

$\Rightarrow \quad \angle CMY + \angle XMC = 180°$

$\Rightarrow$ $XMY$ is a straight line.

Hence Proved.

**Example 14.** *ABCD is a parallelogram. AB is produced to E such that BE = AB. Prove that ED bisects BC.*

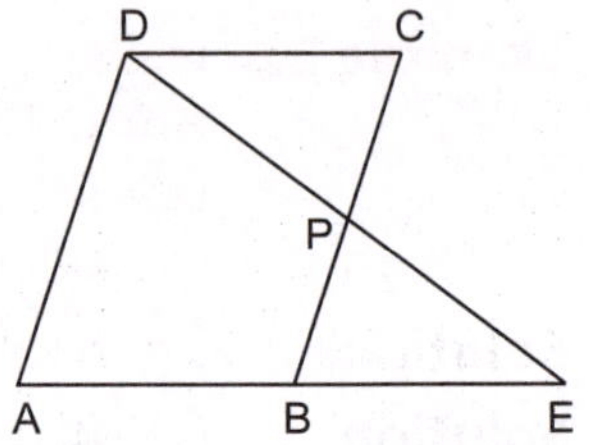


**Solution.** $AB = DC$ (Opposite sides of a parallelogram)

$BE = AB$ (Given)

$\therefore$ $BE = DC$

In $\Delta PBE$ and $\Delta PCD$,

$\angle BPE = \angle CPD$ (Vertically opposite angles)

$\angle PEB = \angle PDC$ (Alternate angles, $AD \parallel BC$ and $DE$ is a transversal)

$BE = CD$ (Proved above)

$\therefore$ $\Delta PBE \cong \Delta PCD$ (AAS axiom of congruency)

$PB = PC$ (CPCT)

$\Rightarrow$ $ED$ bisects $BC$.

Hence Proved.

**Example 15.** *ABCD is a parallelogram. AM and BN are perpendiculars on DC and DC produced respectively. Prove that AM = BN.*

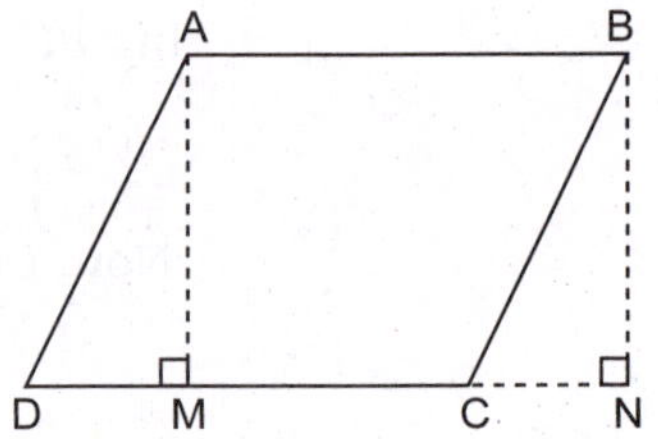


**Solution.** In $\Delta ADM$ and $\Delta BCN$,

$\angle AMD = \angle BNC$ (Each 90°)

$\angle ADM = \angle BCN$ (Corresponding angle, $AD \parallel BC$ and $DC$ is transversal)

$AD = BC$ (Opposite sides of a parallelogram)

$\therefore$ $\Delta ADM \cong \Delta BCN$ (AAS axiom of congruency)

$\Rightarrow$ $AM = BN$ (CPCT)

Hence Proved.

**Example 16.** *In a quadrilateral ABCD, AP and BP are the bisectors of ∠A and ∠B respectively. Prove that* $\angle APB = \frac{1}{2}(\angle C + \angle D)$.

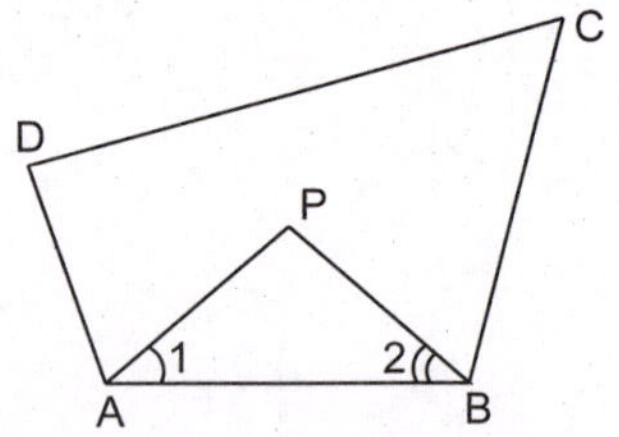


**Solution.** $AP$ and $BP$ are the bisectors of $\angle A$ and $\angle B$ respectively.

$$\angle 1 = \frac{1}{2}\angle A \text{ and } \angle 2 = \frac{1}{2}\angle B \quad \ldots(i)$$

In $\Delta APB$,

$\angle APB + \angle 1 + \angle 2 = 180°$ (Angle sum property of triangle)

$\Rightarrow$ $\angle APB = 180° - (\angle 1 + \angle 2)$

$= 180° - \frac{1}{2}(\angle A + \angle B)$ [using (i)]

$= 180° - \frac{1}{2}\{360° - (\angle C + \angle D)\} = 180° - 180° + \frac{1}{2}(\angle C + \angle D)$

$= \frac{1}{2}(\angle C + \angle D)$

Hence Proved.

**Example 17.** *In a ΔABC, median BM is produced to a point D such that DM = BM. Prove that ABCD is a parallelogram.*

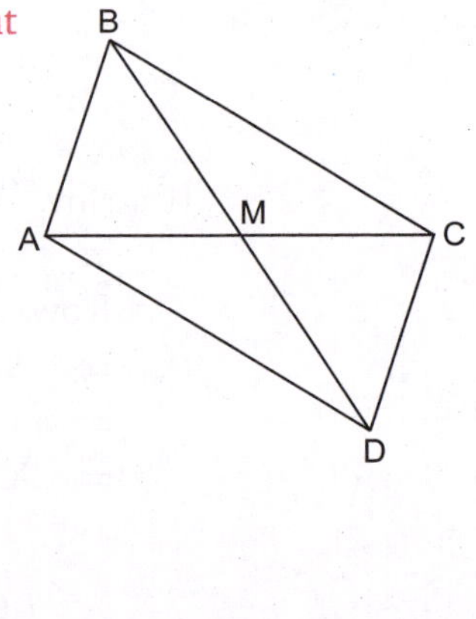


**Solution.** $BM$ is the median.

$\Rightarrow$ $M$ is the mid-point of $AC$

and $BM = DM$

$\Rightarrow$ $M$ is the mid-point of $BD$

$\therefore$ In quadrilateral $ABCD$, the diagonals $AC$ and $BD$ bisect each other.

$\Rightarrow$ $ABCD$ is a parallelogram.

**Example 18.** In the adjoining figure, $ABCD$ is an isosceles trapezium and its diagonals meet at $P$. Prove that

(a) $\angle A = \angle B$ and $\angle C = \angle D$ (b) $AC = BD$

(c) $PA = PB$ and $PC = PD$

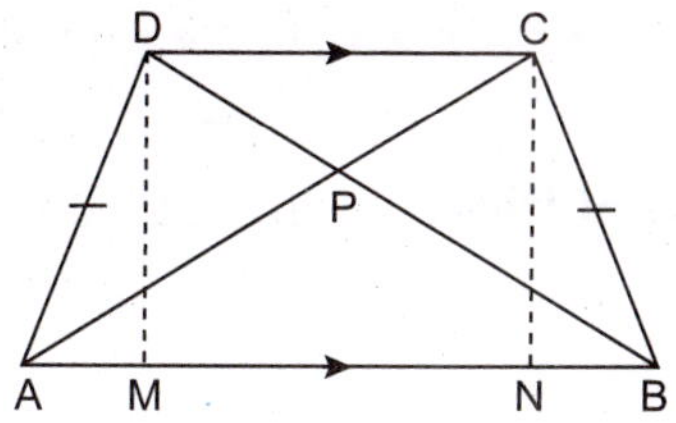


**Solution.** (a) Draw $DM \perp AB$ and $CN \perp AB$.

In $\Delta AMD$ and $\Delta BNC$,

$\angle AMD = \angle BNC$ (Each 90°)

$AD = BC$ (Given)

$DM = CN$ (Distance between parallel lines are equal)

$\therefore$ $\Delta AMD \cong \Delta BNC$ (RHS axiom of congruency)

$\therefore$ $\angle A = \angle B$ (CPCT)

Now, $\angle A + \angle D = 180°$ and $\angle B + \angle C = 180°$ ($\because AB \,||\, CD$, sum of co-interior angles is 180°)

$\Rightarrow$ $\angle A + \angle D = \angle B + \angle C$

$\Rightarrow$ $\angle D = \angle C$ ($\because \angle A = \angle B$)

Hence, $\angle A = \angle B$ and $\angle C = \angle D$

(b) In $\Delta ABD$ and $\Delta BAC$,

$AD = BC$ (Given)

$\angle A = \angle B$ (Proved above)

$AB = BA$ (Common)

$\therefore$ $\Delta ABD \cong \Delta BAC$ (SAS axiom of congruency)

$\Rightarrow$ $BD = AC$ (CPCT)

(c) In $\Delta PAD$ and $\Delta PBC$,

$\angle APD = \angle BPC$ (Vertically opposite angles)

$AD = BC$ (Given)

$\angle ADP = \angle BCP$ (Proved above)

$\therefore$ $\Delta PAD \cong \Delta BPC$ (ASA axiom of congruency)

$\Rightarrow$ $PA = PB$ and $PD = PC$ (CPCT)

Hence Proved.

**Example 19.** In the adjoining figure, $ABCD$ is a kite in which $AB = AD$ and $BC = CD$. Prove that

(a) $AC$ is the bisector of $\angle A$ and $\angle C$. (b) $AC$ is perpendicular bisector of $BD$.

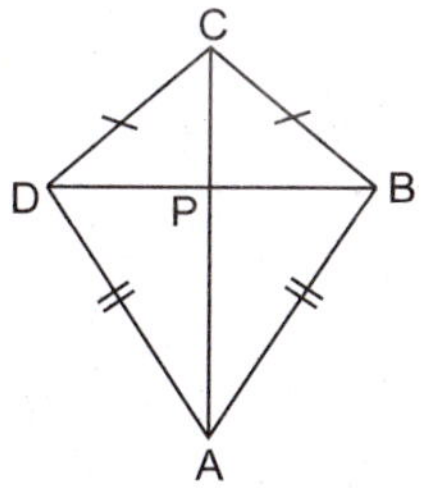


**Solution.** (a) In $\Delta ABC$ and $\Delta ADC$,

$AB = AD$ (Given)

$BC = DC$ (Given)

$AC = AC$ (Common)

$\therefore$ $\Delta ABC \cong \Delta ADC$ (SSS axiom of congruency)

$\Rightarrow$ $\angle BAC = \angle DAC$ and $\angle BCA = \angle DCA$ (CPCT)

Hence, $AC$ is the bisector of $\angle A$ and $\angle C$.

(b) In $\Delta PBC$ and $\Delta PDC$,

$BC = DC$ (Given)

$\angle BCP = \angle DCP$ (Proved above)

$PC = PC$ (Common)

$\therefore$ $\Delta PBC \cong \Delta PDC$ (SAS axiom of congruency)

$\Rightarrow$ $PB = PD$ and $\angle BPC = \angle DPC$ (CPCT)

But $\angle BPC + \angle DPC = 180°$ (Straight angle)

$\therefore$ $\angle BPC = \angle DPC = 90°$

Hence, $AC$ is perpendicular bisector of $BD$.

Hence Proved.

**Example 20.** In the adjoining figure, $ABCD$ is a parallelogram. $X$ and $Y$ are two points on diagonal $BD$ such that $DX = BY$. Prove that $AXCY$ is a parallelogram.

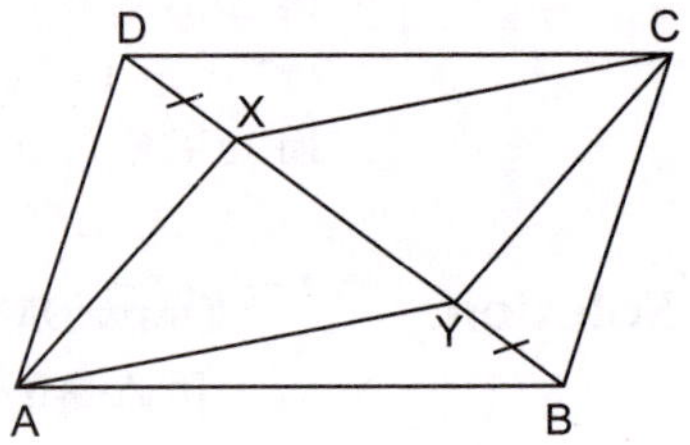


**Solution.** In $\Delta CDX$ and $\Delta ABY$,

$CD = AB$ (Opposite sides of parallelogram)

$\angle CDX = \angle ABY$ (Alternate angles)

$DX = BY$ (Given)

$\therefore$ $\Delta CDX \cong \Delta ABY$ (SAS axiom of congruency)

$\Rightarrow$ $CX = AY$ (CPCT)

Again, in $\Delta ADX$ and $\Delta CBY$,

$AD = CB$ (Opposite sides of parallelogram)

$\angle ADX = \angle CBY$ (Alternate angles)

$DX = BY$ (Given)

$\therefore$ $\Delta ADX \cong \Delta CBY$ (SAS axiom of congruency)

$\Rightarrow$ $AX = CY$ (CPCT)

Now, in $\square AXCY$, $AX = CY$ and $CX = AY$

$\therefore$ $\square AXCY$ is a parallelogram.

Hence Proved.

**Example 21.** In the adjoining figure, $ABCD$ and $PBCQ$ are parallelograms. Prove that :

(a) $APQD$ is a parallelogram.

(b) $AP = DQ$

(c) $\Delta ABP \cong \Delta DCQ$

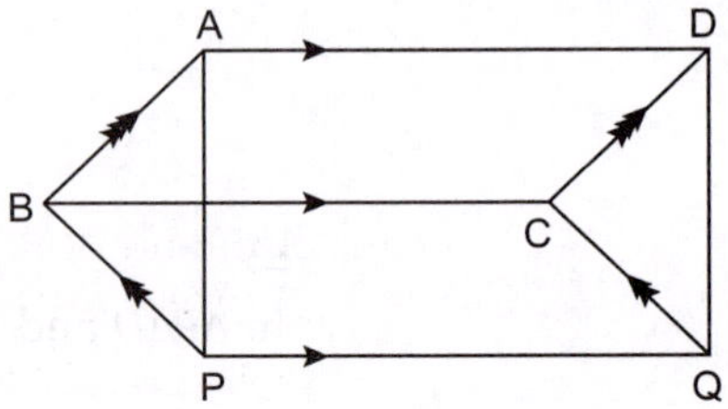


**Solution.** (a) $ABCD$ is a parallelogram.

$\therefore$ $AD \parallel BC$ and $AD = BC$ ...(i)

$PBCQ$ is a parallelogram.

$\therefore$ $PQ \parallel BC$ and $PQ = BC$ ...(ii)

From equations (i) and (ii),

$AD \parallel PQ$ and $AD = PQ$

$\Rightarrow$ $APQD$ is a parallelogram.

(b) We know that the opposite sides of a parallelogram are equal.

$\therefore$ In the parallelogram $APQD$,

$AP = DQ$

(c) In $\Delta ABP$ and $\Delta DCQ$,

$AB = DC$ (Opposite sides of a parallelogram)

$BP = CQ$ (Opposite sides of a parallelogram)

and $AP = DQ$ [Proved in (b) part]

$\therefore$ $\Delta ABP \cong \Delta DCQ$ (SSS axiom of congruency)

Hence Proved.

**Example 22.** In the adjoining figure, bisectors of $\angle A$ and $\angle C$ of quadrilateral $ABCD$ meet $DC$ produced and $BA$ produced at $N$ and $M$ respectively. Prove that $\angle M + \angle N = \frac{1}{2}(\angle A + \angle C)$.

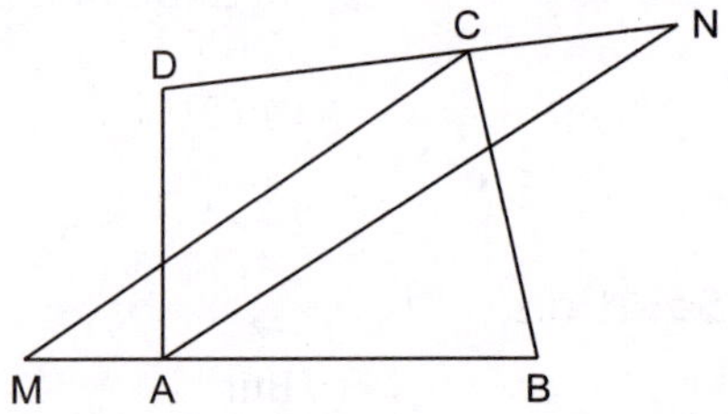


**Solution.** $AN$ is the bisector of $\angle A$.

$\therefore$ $\angle DAN = \frac{1}{2}\angle A$ ...(i)

$CM$ is the bisector of $\angle C$.

$\therefore$ $\angle BCM = \frac{1}{2}\angle C$ ...(ii)

In $\Delta ADN$,

$$\angle DAN + \angle D + \angle N = 180° \quad \ldots(iii)$$

In $\Delta BCM$,

$$\angle BCM + \angle B + \angle M = 180° \quad \ldots(iv)$$

Adding equations *(iii)* and *(iv)* we get,

$$\angle DAN + \angle D + \angle N + \angle BCM + \angle B + \angle M = 360°$$

$$\Rightarrow \quad \frac{1}{2}\angle A + \angle D + \angle N + \frac{1}{2}\angle C + \angle B + \angle M = 360° \quad \text{[From } (i) \text{ and } (ii)]$$

$$\Rightarrow \quad (\angle A + \angle B + \angle C + \angle D) + \angle M + \angle N - \frac{1}{2}\angle A - \frac{1}{2}\angle C = 360°$$

$$\Rightarrow \quad 360° + \angle M + \angle N - \frac{1}{2}\angle A - \frac{1}{2}\angle C = 360° \quad \text{(Sum of angles of a quadrilateral is 360°)}$$

$$\Rightarrow \quad \angle M + \angle N = \frac{1}{2}(\angle A + \angle C)$$

Hence Proved.

**Example 23.** Prove that the diagonals of a rectangle are equal.

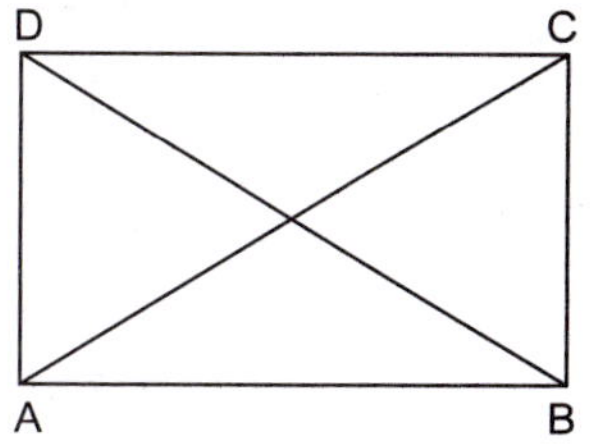


**Solution.** Given : A rectangle *ABCD* whose diagonals are *AC* and *BD*.

To Prove : $AC = BD$.

Proof :

| Statement | Reason |
|---|---|
| In $\Delta ABC$ and $\Delta BAD$, | |
| $AB = BA$ | Common |
| $\angle ABC = \angle BAD$ | Each 90° |
| $BC = AD$ | Opposite sides of a rectangle |
| $\therefore \quad \Delta ABC \cong \Delta BAD$ | SAS axiom of congruency |
| $\Rightarrow \quad AC = BD$ | CPCT |

Hence Proved.

**Example 24.** If the diagonals of a parallelogram are equal, then prove that it is a rectangle.

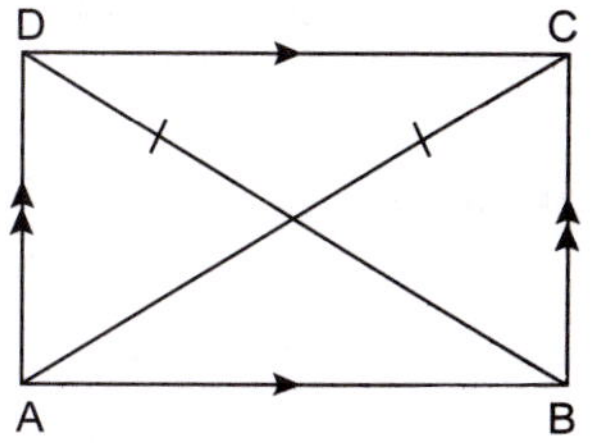


**Solution.** Given : A parallelogram *ABCD* in which $AC = BD$.

To Prove : *ABCD* is a rectangle.

Proof :

| Statement | Reason |
|---|---|
| In $\Delta ABC$ and $\Delta BAD$, | |
| $AC = BD$ | Given |
| $AB = BA$ | Common |
| $BC = AD$ | Opposite sides of a parallelogram |
| $\therefore \quad \Delta ABC \cong \Delta BAD$ | SSS axiom of congruency |
| $\Rightarrow \quad \angle ABC = \angle BAD$ | CPCT |
| But $\angle ABC + \angle BAD = 180°$ | Sum of co-interior angles is 180° |
| $\therefore \quad \angle ABC = \angle BAD = 90°$ | |
| $\Rightarrow \quad ABCD$ is a rectangle. | |

Hence Proved.

**Example 25.** Prove that the diagonals of a rhombus bisect each other at right angles.

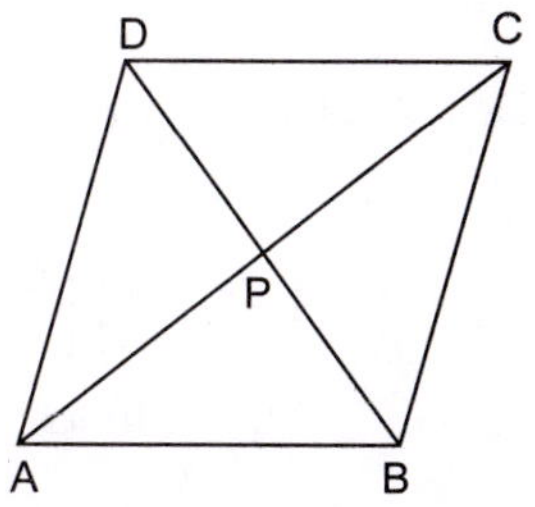


**Solution.** Given : A rhombus *ABCD* whose diagonals *AC* and *BD* intersect at '*P*'.

To Prove : $PA = PC$, $PB = PD$ and $\angle APB = \angle CPB = 90°$.

Proof :

| Statement | Reason |
|---|---|
| In $\Delta PAB$ and $\Delta PCD$, | |
| $AB = CD$ | Sides of a rhombus |

| Statement | Reason |
|---|---|
| $\angle PAB = \angle PCD$ | Alternate angles |
| $\angle PBA = \angle PDC$ | Alternate angles |
| $\therefore \quad \Delta PAB \cong \Delta PCD$ | ASA axiom of congruency |
| $\Rightarrow \quad PA = PC$ and $PB = PD$ | CPCT |
| Again, in $\Delta PAB$ and $\Delta PCB$, | |
| $PA = PC$ | Proved above |
| $PB = PB$ | Common |
| $AB = CB$ | Sides of a rhombus |
| $\therefore \quad \Delta PAB \cong \Delta PCB$ | SSS axiom of congruency |
| $\Rightarrow \quad \angle APB = \angle CPB$ | CPCT |
| But $\angle APB + \angle CPB = 180°$ | |
| $\Rightarrow \quad \angle APB = \angle CPB = 90°$ | |

Hence Proved.

**Example 26.** If the diagonals of a parallelogram cut at right angles, then prove that it is a rhombus.

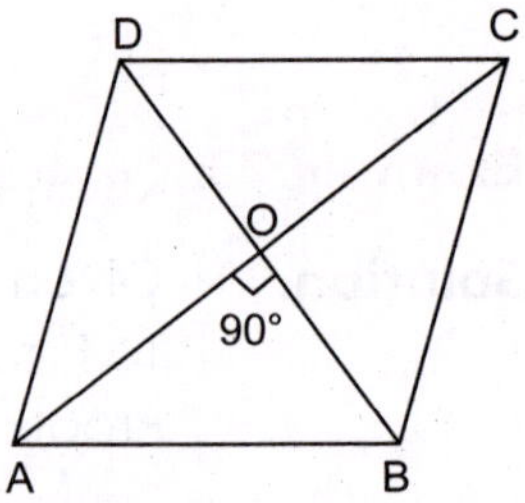


**Solution.** Given : A parallelogram $ABCD$ whose diagonals $AC$ and $BD$ intersect each other at right angle.

To Prove : $ABCD$ is a rhombus.

Proof :

| Statement | Reason |
|---|---|
| In $\Delta OAB$ and $\Delta OCB$, | |
| $OA = OC$ | Diagonals of a parallelogram bisect each other |
| $\angle AOB = \angle COB$ | Each 90° |
| $OB = OB$ | Common |
| $\therefore \quad \Delta OAB \cong \Delta OCB$ | SAS axiom of congruency |
| $\Rightarrow \quad AB = BC$ | CPCT |
| $\therefore \quad ABCD$ is a rhombus. | |

Hence Proved.

**Example 27.** Prove that the diagonals of a square are equal and perpendicular to each other.

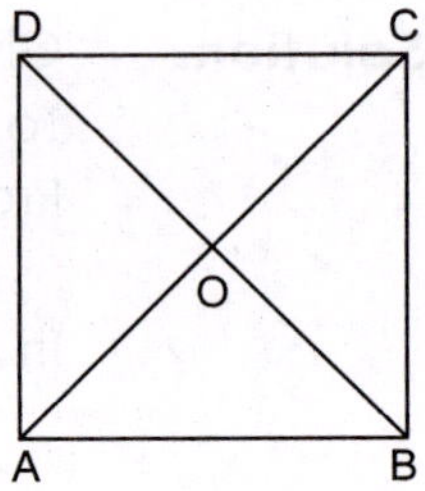


**Solution.** Given : A square $ABCD$ whose diagonals $AC$ and $BD$ intersect at '$O$'.

To Prove : $AC = BD$ and $AC \perp BD$.

Proof :

| Statement | Reason |
|---|---|
| In $\Delta ABC$ and $\Delta BAD$, | |
| $AB = BA$ | Common |
| $\angle ABC = \angle BAD$ | Each 90° |
| $BC = AD$ | Sides of square |
| $\therefore \quad \Delta ABC \cong \Delta BAD$ | SAS axiom of congruency |
| $\Rightarrow \quad AC = BD$ | CPCT |
| In $\Delta AOB$ and $\Delta COB$, | |
| $AO = CO$ | Diagonals of a parallelogram bisect each other |
| $AB = CB$ | Sides of square |
| $OB = OB$ | Common |
| $\therefore \quad \Delta AOB \cong \Delta COB$ | SSS axiom of congruency |
| $\Rightarrow \quad \angle AOB = \angle COB$ | CPCT |
| But $\angle AOB + \angle COB = 180°$ | |
| $\therefore \quad \angle AOB = \angle COB = 90°$ | |
| Hence, $\quad AC = BD$ and $AC \perp BD$. | |

Hence Proved.

**Example 28.** If the diagonals of a parallelogram are equal and intersect at right-angles, then prove that the parallelogram is a square.

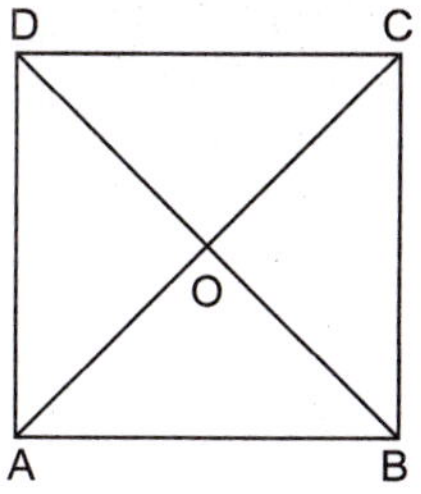


**Solution.** Given : A parallelogram $ABCD$ in which $AC = BD$ and $AC \perp BD$.

To Prove : $ABCD$ is a square.

Proof :

| | Statement | Reason |
|---|---|---|
| In $\Delta ABO$ and $\Delta ADO$, | | |
| | $BO = DO$ | Diagonals of a parallelogram bisect each other |
| | $\angle AOB = \angle AOD$ | Each 90° (Given) |
| | $AO = AO$ | Common |
| $\therefore$ | $\Delta ABO \cong \Delta ADO$ | SAS-Axiom of congruency |
| $\Rightarrow$ | $AB = AD$ | |
| But | $AB = DC$ and $AD = BC$ | Opposite sides of parallelogram |
| $\therefore$ | $AB = BC = CD = DA$ | |
| Now, in $\Delta ABC$ and $\Delta BAD$, | | |
| | $AB = BA$ | Common |
| | $AC = BD$ | Given |
| | $BC = AD$ | Opposite sides of a parallelogram |
| $\therefore$ | $\Delta ABC \cong \Delta BAD$ | |
| $\Rightarrow$ | $\angle ABC = \angle BAD$ | CPCT |
| But | $\angle ABC + \angle BAD = 180°$ | Sum of co-interior angles |
| $\therefore$ | $\angle ABC = \angle BAD = 90°$ | |

Hence, $ABCD$ is a square. Hence Proved.

## Exercise 11A

1. Find the values of $x$ and $y$ from the following parallelograms :

(i)
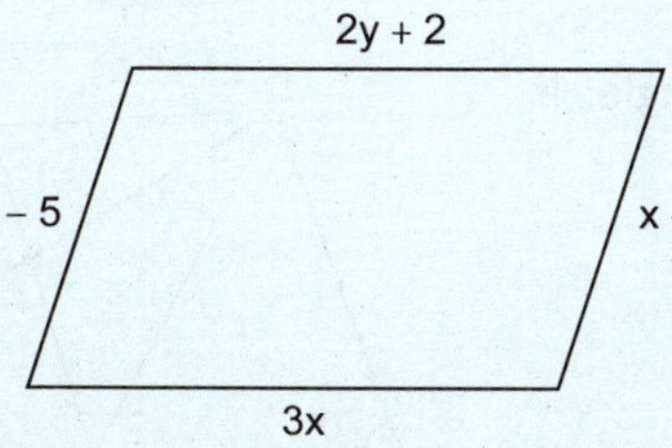


(ii)
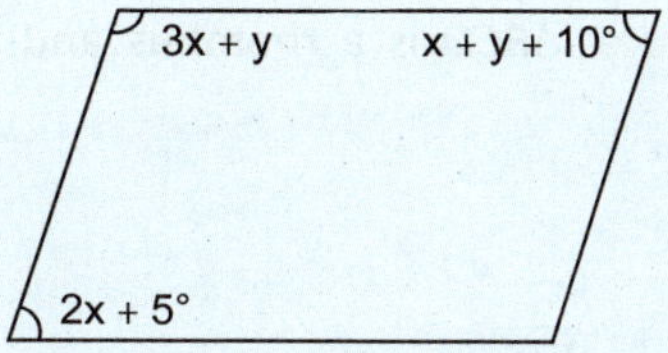


2. The angles of a quadrilateral are in the ratio 2 : 3 : 3 : 4. Find the angles.
3. Three angles of a quadrilateral are in the ratio 7 : 8 : 11 and the fourth angle is of 100°. Find the angles.
4. Two adjacent angles of a parallelogram are $2x + 10°$ and $4x - 40°$. Find the angles of the parallelogram.
5. Two opposite angles of the parallelogram are $3x - 5°$ and $x + 45°$. Find the angles of the parallelogram.
6. The angles of a quadrilateral are in the ratio 3 : 4 : 5 : 6. Show that it is a trapezium.
7. In the adjoining figure, $\square ABCD$ is a square and $\Delta ABP$ is an equilateral triangle. Find :
   (i) $\angle AOB$
   (ii) $\angle CPB$
   (iii) $\angle PCD$

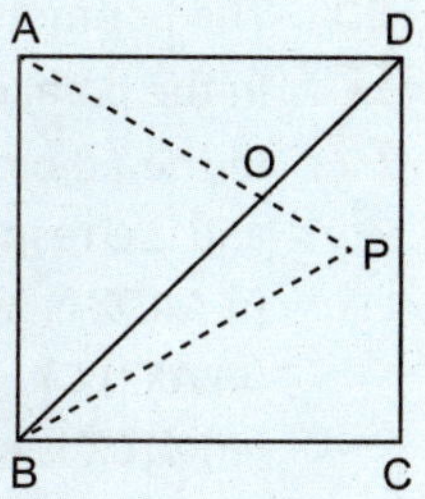

**8.** In the adjacent parallelogram *ABCD*, $AP \perp CD$ and $AQ \perp BC$. If $x : y = 5 : 4$, then find the angles of the parallelogram.

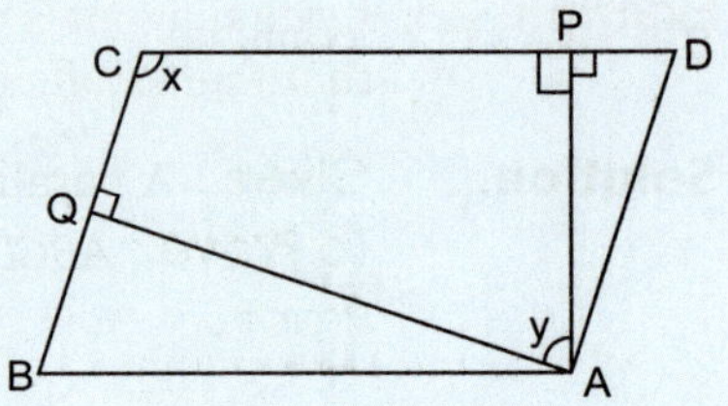


**9.** In the adjoining figure, *ABCD* is an isosceles trapezium in which $AB \parallel DC$ and $AD = BC$. If $\angle ACD = 30°$ and $\angle ADB = 25°$, then find :

(i) $\angle AOD$

(ii) $\angle CBD$

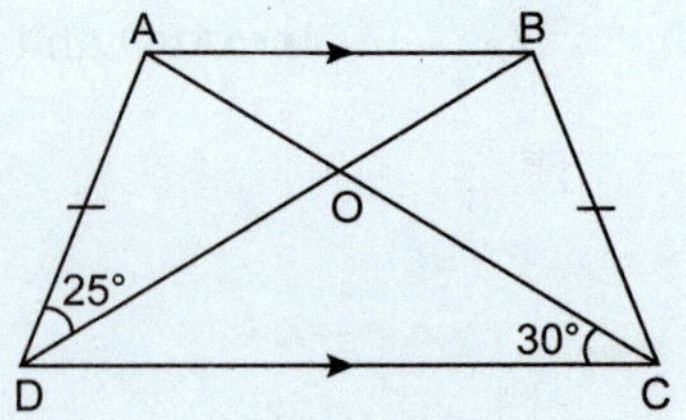


**10.** In the adjoining figure, $OC = OD$. Find :

(i) $\angle CBD$

(ii) $\angle CAD$

(iii) $\angle BCA$

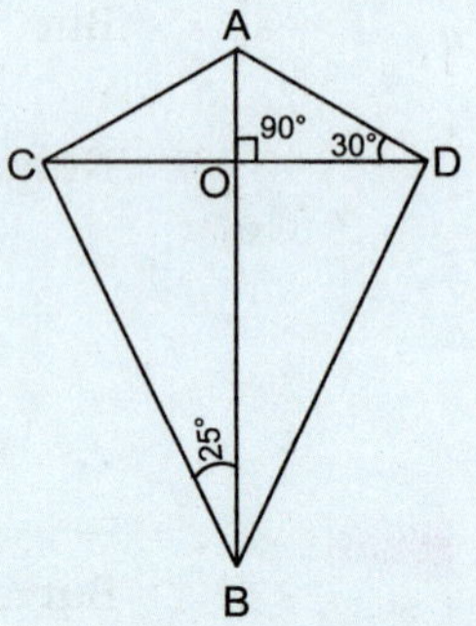


**11.** In the adjoining figure, a rectangle *ABCD* is shown. If $\angle CAB = 20°$, then find the values of *x* and *y*.

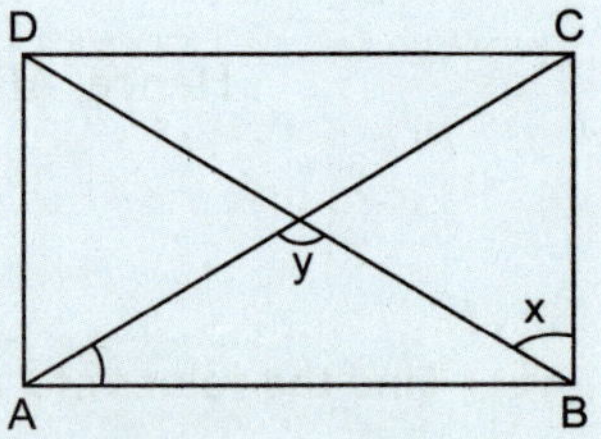


**12.** In the adjoining figure, *ABCD* is a rhombus and *ABE* is an equilateral triangle. If $\angle BCD = 70°$, find :

(i) $\angle ADE$

(ii) $\angle BDE$

(iii) $\angle BED$

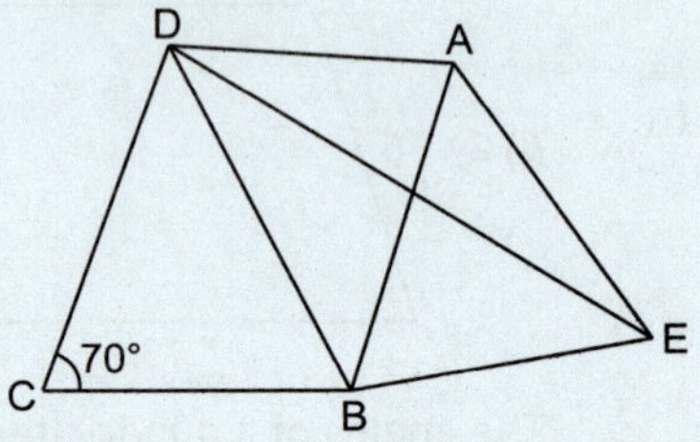


**13.** The diagonals of a rectangle *ABCD* intersect at *P* and *PAL* is an equilateral triangle such that *B* and *L* are on the same side of *AC*. If $\angle ACD = 30°$, find :

(i) $\angle ALB$ (ii) $\angle ABL$

**14.** The diagonals of a quadrilateral *ABCD* bisect each other. If $\angle A = 50°$, then find $\angle B$.

**15.** The perimeter of a parallelogram *ABCD* is 48 cm. If $BC = 3x - 2$, $DA = x + 2y + 2$ and $AB = 3y + 2$, find the values of *x* and *y*.

**16.** In the parallelogram *ABCD*, *E* and *F* are the mid-points of *AB* and *DC* respectively. Prove that *AEFD* is a parallelogram.

**17.** In the adjoining figure, *ABCD* is a parallelogram. *AX* and *CY* are the bisectors of $\angle A$ and $\angle C$ respectively. Prove that :

(i) $\Delta ADX \cong \Delta CBY$

(ii) $AX \parallel CY$

(iii) *AYCX* is a parallelogram.

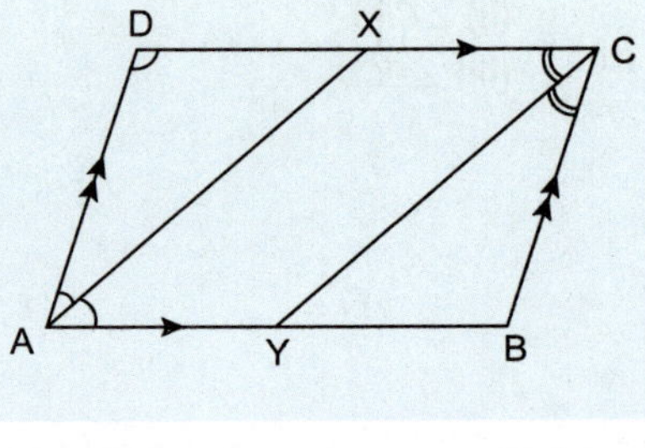

**18.** If a diagonal of a parallelogram bisects one of the angles of the parallelogram and it also bisects the opposite angle then prove that the two diagonals are perpendicular to each other.

**19.** In a square *ABCD*; *A* is joined to a point *X* on *BC* and *D* is joined to a point *Y* on *AB*. If $AX = DY$, prove that *AX* is perpendicular to *DY*.

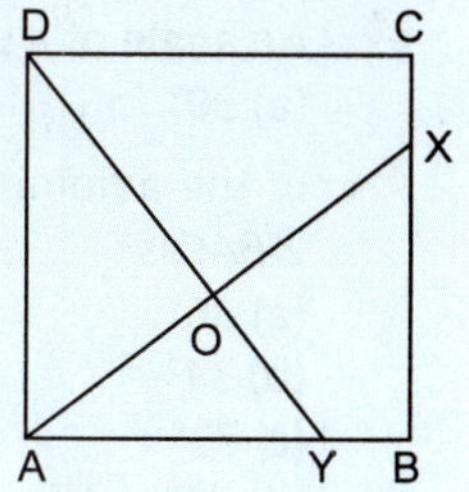


**20.** In a rhombus *ABCD*, the altitude from *D* to side *AB* bisects *AB*. Find the angles of the rhombus.

**21.** If *P* and *Q* are points of trisection of the diagonal *BD* of a parallelogram *ABCD*, prove that : $CQ \parallel AP$.

**22.** Prove that a diagonal of a rhombus bisects the angles at the vertices.

**23.** In $\Delta ABC$, median *AD* is produced to *E* such that $AD = DE$, prove that *ABEC* is a parallelogram.

**24.** In a quadrilateral *ABCD*, $AB = AD$ and $BC = CD$. Prove that :
(i) *AC* bisects $\angle BAD$ (ii) *AC* is the perpendicular bisector of *BD*.

**25.** In a parallelogram *ABCD*; *BX* is the bisector of $\angle ABC$ and *DY* is the bisector of $\angle ADC$. Prove that *BXDY* is a parallelogram.

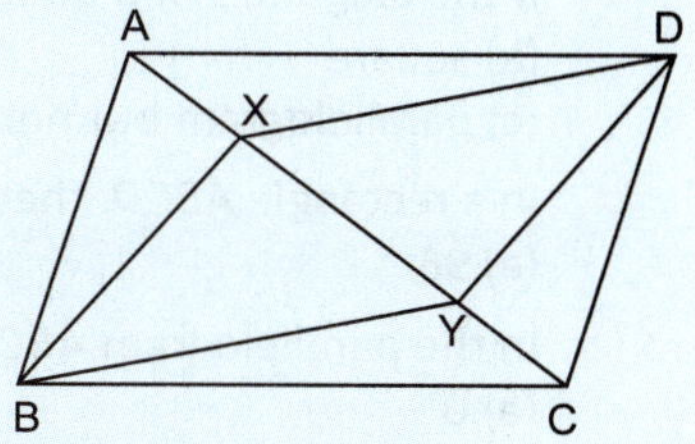


**26.** In a trapezium *ABCD*, the diagonals *AC* and *BD* intersect at point '*O*', $AB \parallel DC$ and $AD = BC$. Prove that :
(i) $\angle BAD = \angle ABC$ (ii) $\angle ADC = \angle BCD$
(iii) $AC = BD$ (iv) $OA = OB$ and $OC = OD$

**27.** Prove that the bisectors of the interior angles of a parallelogram form a rectangle.

**28.** Prove that the bisectors of the interior angles of a rectangle form a square.

**29.** The side *AB* of a parallelogram *ABCD* is produced to *X* and the bisector of $\angle CBX$ meets *DA* produced and *DC* produced at *Y* and *Z* respectively, prove that : $DY = DZ = AB + BC$.

**30.** *ABCD* is a rhombus. *RABS* is a straight line such that $RA = AB = BS$. Prove that *RD* and *SC* when produced meet at right angles.

## *Answers*

**1.** (i) $x = 4, y = 5$ (ii) $x = 30°, y = 25°$
**2.** 60°, 90°, 90°, 120°
**3.** 80°, 110°, 70°, 100°
**4.** 80°, 100°, 80°, 100°
**5.** 70°, 110°, 70°, 110°
**7.** (i) 75° (ii) 75° (iii) 15°
**8.** 100°, 80°, 100°, 80°
**9.** (i) 60° (ii) 95°
**10.** (i) 50° (ii) 120° (iii) 95°
**11.** $x = 70°, y = 140°$
**12.** (i) 25° (ii) 30° (iii) 35°
**13.** (i) 120° (ii) 30°
**14.** 130°
**15.** $x = 5, y = 3$
**20.** $\angle A = \angle C = 60°, \angle B = \angle D = 120°$

# Exercise 11B

## Multiple Choice *Questions*

Choose the correct answer from the given four options in each of the following questions :

**1.** The angles of a quadrilateral are in the ratio 3 : 3 : 5 : 7. The largest angle is :
(a) 120° (b) 140° (c) 150° (d) 160°

**2.** Three angles of a quadrilateral are equal and fourth angle is 120°. Each of three equal angles is :
(a) 80° (b) 90° (c) 100° (d) 110°

3. The two adjacent angles of a parallelogram are in the ratio 3 : 7. The largest angle of the parallelogram is :
(a) 126° (b) 140° (c) 120° (d) 98°

4. An angle of a parallelogram is half of its adjacent angle. The smallest angle of a quadrilateral is :
(a) 30° (b) 80° (c) 45° (d) 60°

5. In the adjoining figure, *ABCD* is a parallelogram. If $\angle CAD = 36°$ and $\angle ABC = 110°$, then $\angle BAC$ is :
(a) 36°
(b) 34°
(c) 72°
(d) 74°

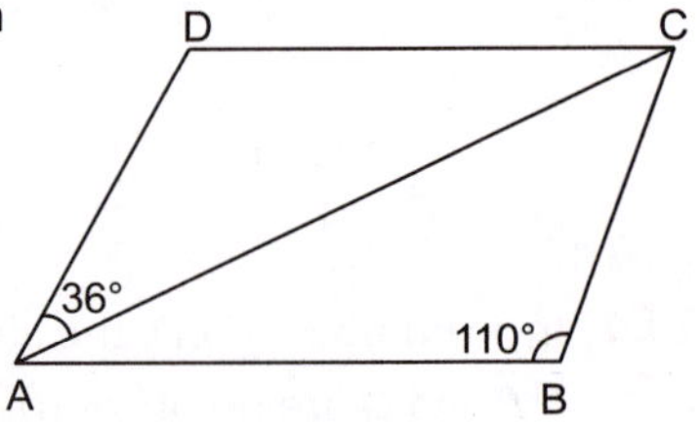


6. A quadrilateral *ABCD* is a trapezium with $AB \parallel DC$ if :
(a) $AB = BC$ (b) $\angle A + \angle D = 180°$ (c) $\angle A + \angle B = 180°$ (d) $\angle C + \angle D = 180°$

7. The sum of all four angles of a quadrilateral is :
(a) 360° (b) 270° (c) 180° (d) 720°

8. If the diagonals of a quadrilateral bisect each other at right angle then it is a :
(a) square (b) rectangle but not a square
(c) parallelogram but not a square (d) kite but not a square

9. In a rectangle *ABCD*, the diagonals *AC* and *BD* intersect at *O*. If $\angle OAB = 27°$, $\angle COD$ is equal to :
(a) 96° (b) 116° (c) 126° (d) 54°

10. In the parallelogram *ABCD*, $\angle A - \angle B - \angle C + \angle D$ is equal to :
(a) 0° (b) 90° (c) 180° (d) 360°

11. The angle between two altitudes of a parallelogram through the vertex of an obtuse angle of the parallelogram is 55°. The largest angle of the parallelogram is :
(a) 110° (b) 125° (c) 115° (d) 130°

12. In a quadrilateral *ABCD*, *AO* and *BO* are the bisectors of $\angle A$ and $\angle B$ respectively, then $(\angle C + \angle D)$ is equal to :
(a) $\angle AOB$ (b) $2\angle AOB$ (c) $3\angle AOB$ (d) $4\angle AOB$

## Answers

**1.** (b) **2.** (a) **3.** (a) **4.** (d) **5.** (b) **6.** (b) **7.** (a) **8.** (a) **9.** (c) **10.** (a)
**11.** (b) **12.** (b)

## SUMMARY of the Chapter

- Polygons : A closed figure, made up of line segments only, is called a polygon.
- Regular Polygon : If all sides of a polygon are equal and all its interior angles are also equal, then it is called a regular polygon.
- Quadrilateral : A closed figure, bounded by four line segments is called a quadrilateral.
- Different Types of Quadrilaterals—

  1. Trapezium : If one pair of opposite sides is parallel in a quadrilateral, it is called a trapezium.
  2. Parallelogram : If both pairs of opposite sides are parallel in a quadrilateral, it is called a parallelogram.
  3. Rectangle : If each angle of a parallelogram is 90°, it is called a rectangle.
  4. Rhombus : If all four sides of a quadrilateral are equal, it is called a rhombus.
  5. Square : If each angle of a rhombus is 90°, it is called a square.
  6. Kite : A quadrilateral in which two pairs of adjacent sides are equal, is called a kite.

### Theorem

1. A diagonal of a parallelogram divides it into two congruent triangles.
2. In a parallelogram, opposite sides are equal.
3. If each pair of opposite sides of a quadrilateral is equal, then it is a parallelogram.
4. In a parallelogram, opposite angles are equal.
5. If each pair of opposite angles of a quadrilateral is equal, then it is a parallelogram.
6. If a pair of opposite sides of a quadrilateral is equal and parallel, then it is a parallelogram.
7. The diagonals of a parallelogram bisect each other.
8. If the diagonals of a quadrilateral bisect each other, then it is a parallelogram.

# CHAPTER TEST

1. The angles of a quadrilateral are $7x$, $8x$, $10x$ and $11x$. Find the angles of the quadrilateral.
2. In the adjoining figure, a parallelogram $ABCD$ is shown. If $DM \perp AB$, $DN \perp BC$ and $\angle MDN = 50°$. Find the largest angle of the parallelogram.

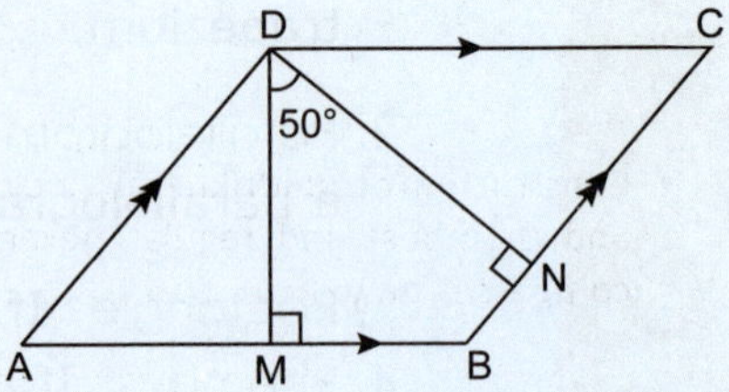


3. In the adjoining figure, a square $ABCD$ and an equilateral triangle $CDE$ are shown. Find value of $x$.

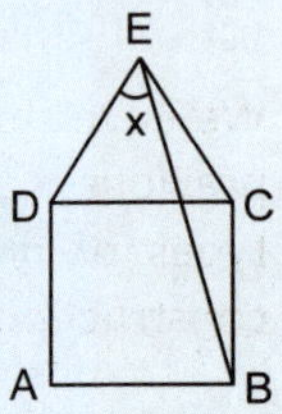


4. Prove that the bisectors of any two adjacent angles of a parallelogram meet at right angles.
5. Show that the bisectors of the angles of a parallelograms from a rectangle.
6. $ABCD$ is a parallelogram, bisectors of $\angle A$ and $\angle B$ meet at $E$ which lies on $DC$. Prove that : $AB = 2\,AD$.
7. In the adjoining figure, $\Delta ABC$ is isosceles such that $AB = AC$. $AD$ bisects exterior angle $MAC$ and $CD \parallel BA$. Show that :

   (a) $\angle DAC = \angle BCA$

   (b) $ABCD$ is a parallelogram.

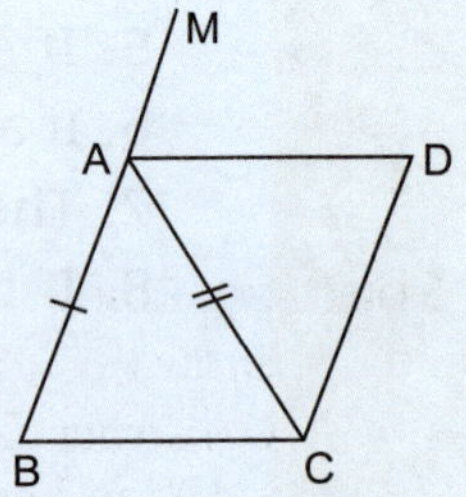


8. $ABCD$ is a parallelogram. $P$ and $Q$ are the points on diagonal $AC$ such that $AP = CQ$. Show that $BPDQ$ is a parallelogram.

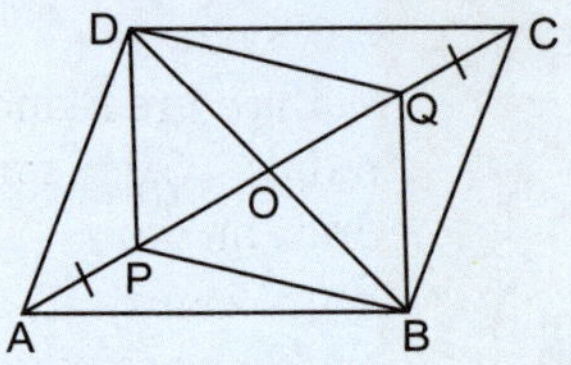


9. Prove that the diagonals of a square are equal and bisect each other at right angles.
10. $ABCD$ is a parallelogram. $AB$ is produced to $E$ such that $BE = AB$. Prove that $ED$ bisects $BC$.

## *Answers*

**1.** 70°, 80°, 100°, 110° **2.** 130° **3.** 45°

Chapter

# 12 CONSTRUCTIONS OF POLYGONS

## Syllabus

- Construction of quadrilaterals (including parallelograms and rhombus) and regular hexagon using ruler and compasses only.

## INTRODUCTION

We have studied the construction of triangles in the previous classes. Now, we shall construct different types of quadrilaterals in different cases and the construction of regular hexagon.

## Construction of Quadrilaterals

### Construction of a Quadrilateral Whose Four Sides and One Angle are Given

**Construction 1.** Construct a Quadrilateral $ABCD$ in which $AB = 6$ cm, $BC = 6.3$ cm, $CD = 6.6$ cm, $DA = 6.5$ cm and $\angle A = 60°$.

**Solution.** Steps :

(a) Draw $AB = 6$ cm.

(b) Construct $\angle DAB = 60°$ and cut $AD = 6.5$ cm.

(c) With centre $B$ and radius 6.3 cm, draw an arc.

(d) With centre $D$ and radius 6.6 cm draw another arc which cuts the first arc at $C$.

(e) Join $BC$ and $CD$.

$\therefore$ $\square ABCD$ is the required quadrilateral.

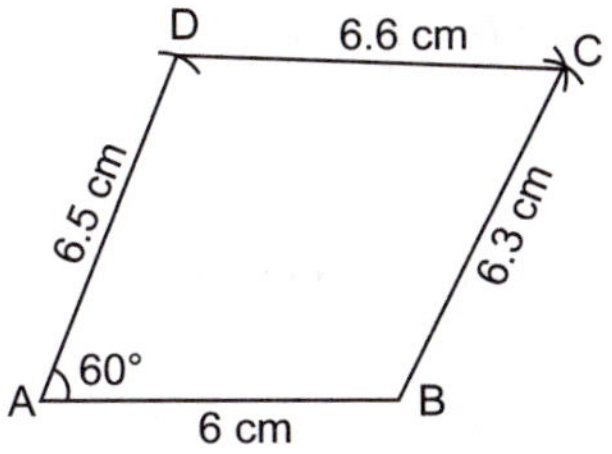


### Construction of a Quadrilateral Whose Three Sides and Two Angles are Given

**Construction 2.** Construct a quadrilateral $ABCD$ in which $AB = 6$ cm, $\angle A = 105°$, $\angle B = 75°$, $BC = 4.5$ cm and $AD = 4$ cm.

**Solution.** Steps :

(a) Draw $AB = 6$ cm.

(b) Construct $\angle DAB = 105°$ and cut $AD = 4.0$ cm.

(c) Construct $\angle ABC = 75°$ and cut $BC = 4.5$ cm.

(d) Join $CD$.

$\therefore$ $\square ABCD$ is the required quadrilateral.

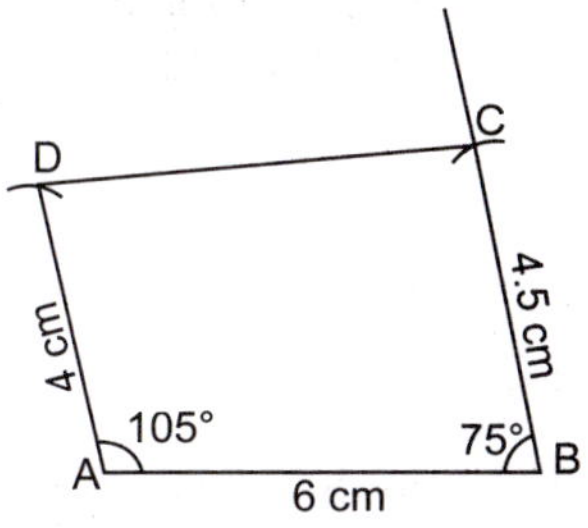


### Construction of a Quadrilateral Whose Four Sides and One Diagonal are Given

**Construction 3.** Construct a quadrilateral $ABCD$ in which $AB = 2.8$ cm, $BC = 3.8$ cm, $CD = 3.6$ cm, $DA = 4$ cm and $AC = 4.2$ cm.

**Solution.** Steps :

(a) Draw $AB = 2.8$ cm.

(b) With centre $A$ and radius 4.2 cm, draw an arc.

(c) With centre $B$ and radius 3.8 cm, draw another arc which cuts the arc in (b) part at $C$.

(d) Join $AC$ and $BC$.

(e) Draw an arc with centre $A$ and radius 4 cm.

(f) Draw another arc with centre $C$ and radius 3.6 cm, intersecting the arc in (e) at $D$.

(g) Join $CD$ and $AD$.

$\therefore$ $\square ABCD$ is the required quadrilateral.

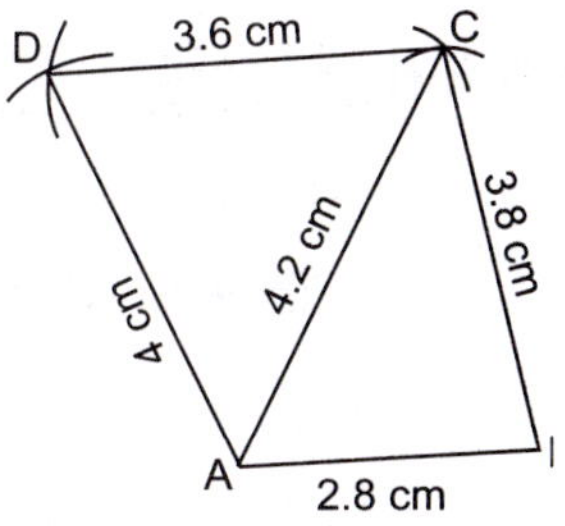


### Construction of a Quadrilateral Whose Three Sides and Two Diagonals are Given

**Construction 4.** Construct a quadrilateral $ABCD$ in which $AB = 5$ cm, $BC = 4.5$ cm, $AD = 4.8$ cm, $AC = 6.1$ cm and $BD = 4.8$ cm.

**Solution.** Steps :

(a) Draw $AB = 5$ cm.

(b) With centre $A$ and radius 6.1 cm, draw an arc. With centre $B$ and radius 4.5 cm, draw another arc which cuts the first arc at $C$.

(c) Join $AC$ and $BC$.

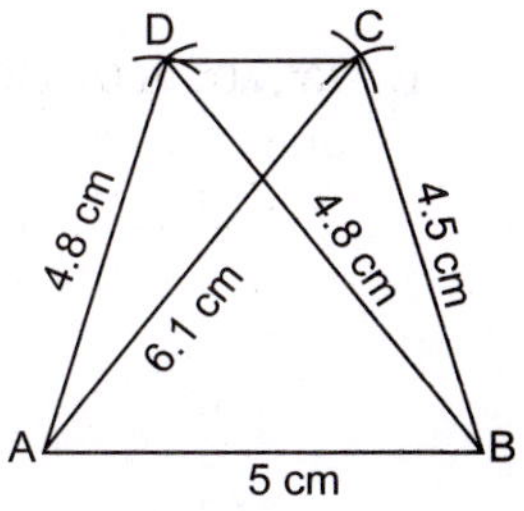

(d) With centre $A$ and radius 4.8 cm, draw an arc. With centre $B$ and radius 4.8 cm, draw another arc which cuts the first arc at $D$.

(e) Join $AD$, $BD$ and $CD$.

$\therefore$ $\square ABCD$ is the required quadrilateral.

## Construction of Parallelograms

**Construction 5.** Construct a parallelogram $ABCD$ in which $AB \parallel DC$, $BC \parallel AD$, $AB = 6$ cm, $AD = 4$ cm and $\angle DAB = 70°$.

**Solution.** Steps :

(a) Draw $AB = 6$ cm and construct $\angle DAB = 70°$.

(b) Cut $AD = 4$ cm.

(c) With centre $B$ and radius 4 cm, draw an arc.

(d) With centre $D$ and radius 6 cm, draw another arc which cuts the first arc at $C$.

(e) Join $BC$ and $CD$.

$\therefore$ $\square ABCD$ is the required parallelogram.

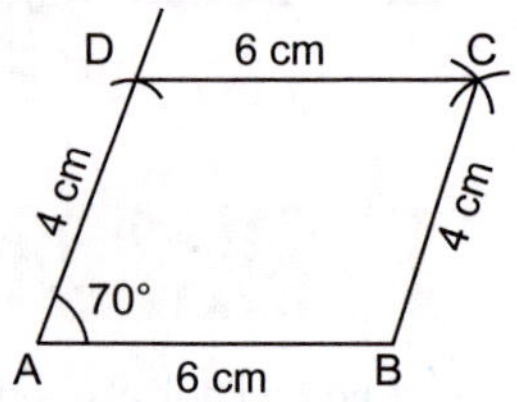


**Construction 6.** Construct a parallelogram $ABCD$ in which $AB = 6$ cm, $BC = 4.5$ cm and $AC = 7$ cm.

**Solution.** Steps :

(a) Draw $AB = 6$ cm.

(b) With centre $A$ and radius 7 cm, draw an arc. With centre $B$ and radius 4.5 cm draw another arc which cuts the first arc at $C$.

(c) Join $AC$ and $BC$.

(d) With centre $C$ and radius 6 cm draw an arc. With centre $A$ and radius 4.5 cm draw another arc which cuts the first arc at $D$.

(e) Join $AD$ and $CD$.

$\therefore$ $\square ABCD$ is the required parallelogram.

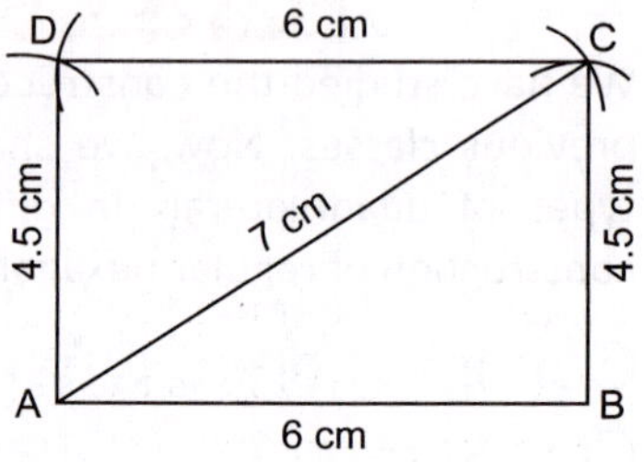


**Construction 7.** Construct a parallelogram $ABCD$ in which $AB = 5$ cm, $AC = 7.2$ cm and $BD = 6.4$ cm.

**Solution.** Steps :

(a) Draw $AB = 5$ cm.

(b) With centre $A$ and radius $\frac{7.2}{2} = 3.6$ cm draw an arc. With centre $B$ and radius $\frac{6.4}{2} = 3.2$ cm, draw another arc which cuts the first arc at $O$.

(c) Join and produce $AO$ and cut $OC = OA$.

(d) Join and produce $BO$ and cut $OD = OB$.

(e) Join $AD$, $BC$ and $CD$.

$\therefore$ $\square ABCD$ is the required parallelogram.

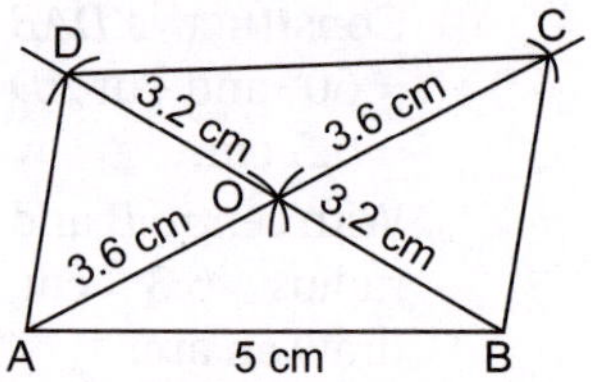


**Construction 8.** Construct a parallelogram $ABCD$ in which $AC = 5.4$ cm, $BD = 6$ cm and angle between the diagonals is 60°.

**Solution.** Steps :

(a) Draw $AC = 5.4$ cm and bisect it at point $O$.

(b) Draw $\angle COD = 60°$ and cut $OD = OB = \frac{6}{2} = 3$ cm.

(c) Join $AB$, $BC$, $CD$ and $AD$.

$\therefore$ $\square ABCD$ is the required parallelogram.

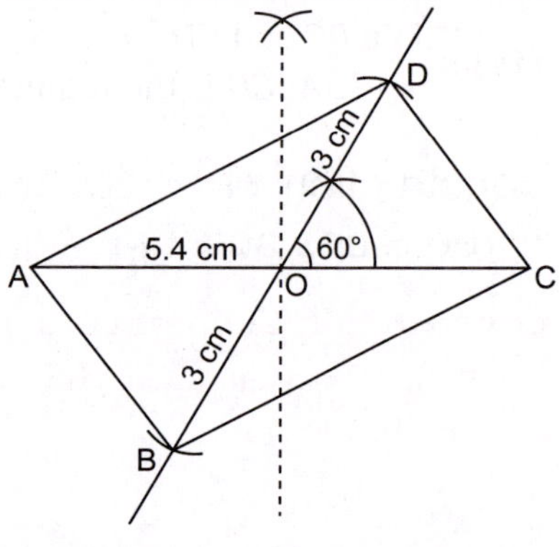

**Construction 9.** Construct a parallelogram *ABCD* in which *AB* = 6 cm, *BC* = 4 cm and the perpendicular *DM* drawn from *D* to *AB* is 3.5 cm.

**Solution.** Steps :

(a) Draw *AB* = 6 cm.

(b) Construct ∠*PAB* = 90° and cut *AQ* = 3.5 cm from *AP*.

(c) Draw *BX* || *AB*.

(d) With centre *A* and radius 4 cm, draw an arc which intersects *QX* at point *D*.

(e) Join *AD*.

(f) With centre *D* and radius 6 cm, draw an arc which intersects *DX* at *C*.

(g) Join *BC*.

∴ □*ABCD* is the required parallelogram.

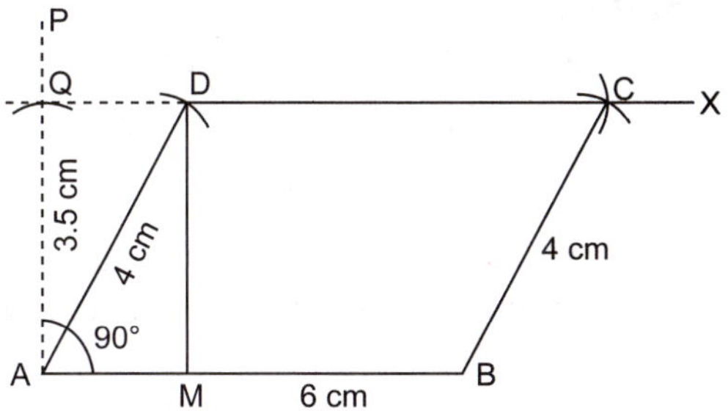


## Construction of Rectangles

**Construction 10.** Construct a rectangle *ABCD* whose sides *AB* = 6 cm, and *AD* = 4 cm.

**Solution.** Steps :

(a) Draw *AB* = 6 cm.

(b) Draw ∠*DAB* = 90° and cut *AD* = 4 cm.

(c) With centre *B* and radius 4 cm, draw an arc. With centre *D* and radius 6 cm draw another arc which intersects the first arc at *C*.

(d) Join *BC* and *DC*.

∴ □*ABCD* is the required rectangle.

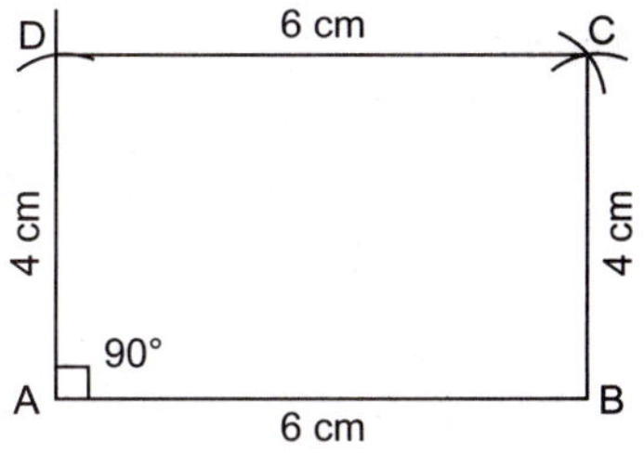


**Construction 11.** Construct a rectangle *ABCD* whose side *AB* = 5 cm and diagonal *BD* = 6 cm.

**Solution.** Steps :

(a) Draw *AB* = 5 cm.

(b) Draw ∠*DAB* = 90° and cut *BD* = 6 cm.

(c) With centre *B* and radius equal to *AD* draw an arc. With centre *D* and radius 5 cm draw another arc which intersects the first arc at *C*.

(d) Join *BC* and *DC*.

∴ □*ABCD* is the required rectangle.

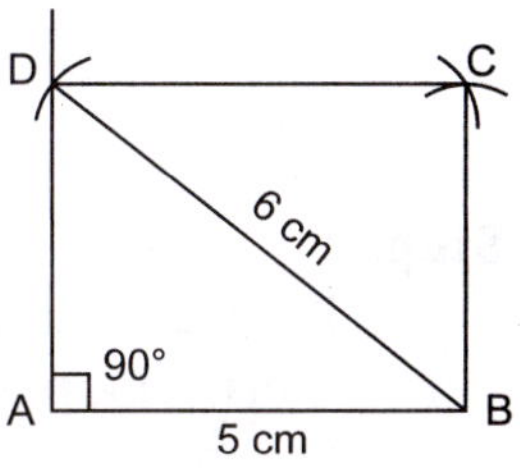


## Construction of Rhombus

**Construction 12.** Construct a rhombus *ABCD* whose diagonals *AC* = 7 cm and *BD* = 5.4 cm.

**Solution.** We know that the diagonals of a rhombus bisect each other at right angles.

**Steps** :

(a) Draw *AC* = 7 cm.

(b) Bisect *AC* at *O*.

(c) With centre *O* and radius $\frac{5.4}{2} = 2.7$ cm draw two arcs on each sides of *AC* which intersect the bisector of *AC* at *B* and *D*.

(d) Join *AB*, *BC*, *CD* and *DA*.

∴ □*ABCD* is the required rhombus.

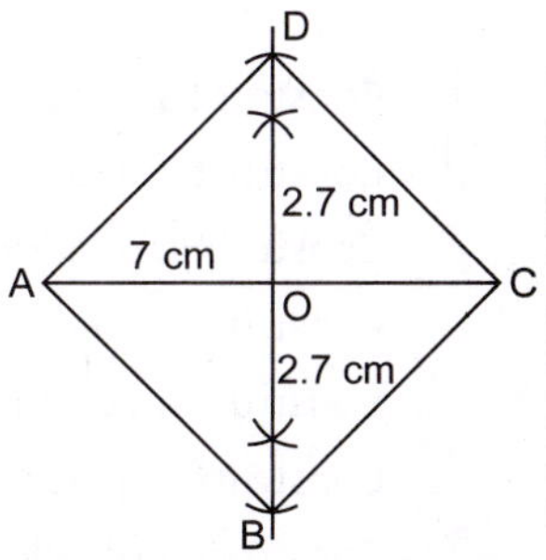

## Construction of a Trapezium

**Construction 13.** Construct a trapezium *ABCD* in which *AB* || *DC*, *AB* = 6.4 cm, *BC* = 3.2 cm, *CD* = 3 cm and *DA* = 4 cm.

**Solution.** Steps :

(a) Draw *AB* = 6.4 cm and cut *AE* = *DC* = 3 cm.

(b) With centre *B* and radius 3.2 cm, draw an arc. With centre *E* and radius *AD* = 4 cm, draw another arc which intersects the first arc at *C*.

(c) Join *BC* and *CE*.

(d) With centre *C* and radius 3 cm, draw an arc. With centre *A* and radius 4 cm, draw another arc which intersects the first arc at *D*.

(e) Join *CD* and *AD*.

∴ □*ABCD* is the required trapezium.

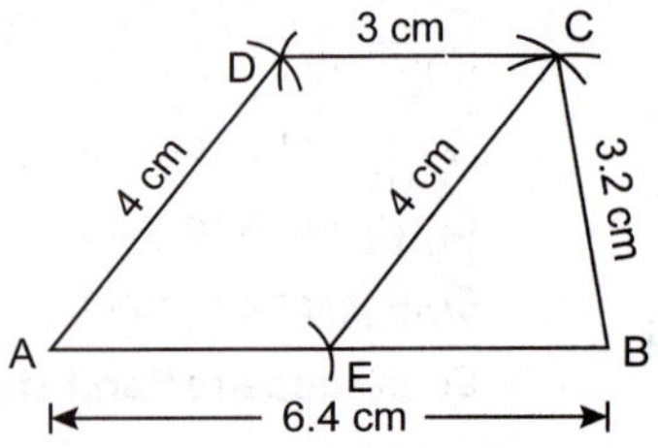


## Construction of a Regular Hexagon

**Construction 14.** Construct a regular hexagon of side 3.4 cm.

**Solution.** First Method :

**Steps :**

(a) Draw a circle of radius 3.4 cm.

(b) Take a point *A* on the circumference of this circle and draw an arc with centre *A* and radius 3.2 cm which cuts the circle at *B*.

(c) With centre *B* and radius 3.4 cm, draw an arc which cuts the circle at *C*.

(d) With centre *C* and radius 3.4 cm, draw an arc which cuts the circle at *D*.

(e) Similarly, we can find the points *E* and *F* on the circumference of the circle.

(f) Join *AB*, *BC*, *CD*, *DE*, *EF* and *FA*.

∴ *ABCDEF* is the required regular hexagon.

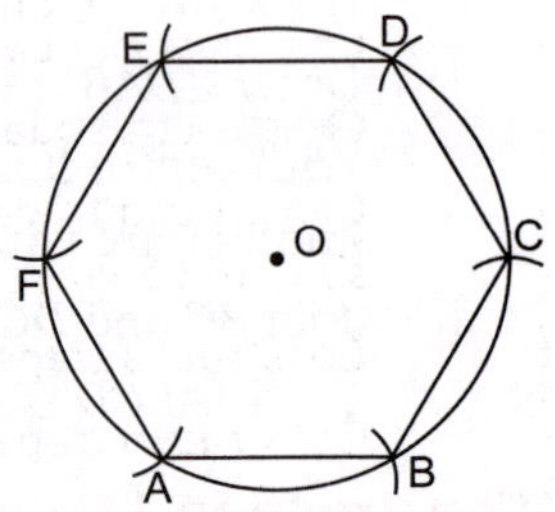


**Second Method :** The angle subtended by each side of a regular hexagon at the centre of its circumcircle is $\frac{360°}{6} = 60°$.

**Steps :**

(a) Draw a circle with centre *O* and radius 3.4 cm.

(b) Consider a point *A* on the circumference of the circle and join *OA*.

(c) Construct ∠*AOB* = 60°.

(d) With *B* as centre and radius *AB*, draw an arc which cuts the circle at *C*.

(e) With centre *C* and radius *AB*, draw an arc which cuts the circle at *D*.

(f) Similarly, we can find the points *E* and *F* on the circumference of the circle.

(g) Join *AB*, *BC*, *CD*, *DE*, *EF* and *FA*.

∴ *ABCDEF* is the required regular hexagon.

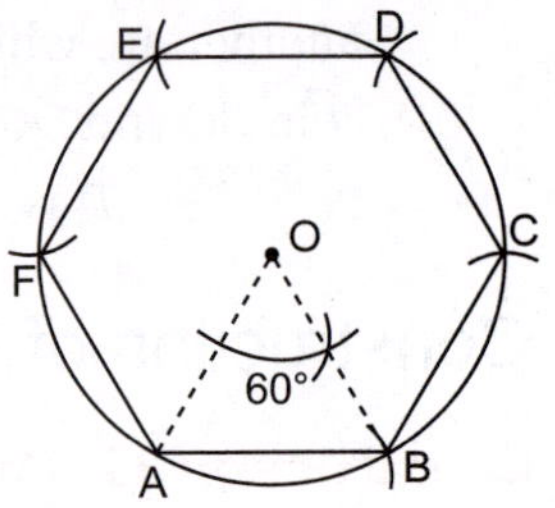


## Exercise 12A

1. Construct a quadrilateral *ABCD* in which *AB* = 6 cm, *BC* = 4.2 cm, *CD* = 4.8 cm, *DA* = 4.2 cm and *AC* = 6.6 cm.
2. Construct a quadrilateral *ABCD* in which *AB* = 5.2 cm, *BC* = 6 cm, ∠*B* = 70°, *CD* = 4.8 cm and *DA* = 4.0 cm.
3. Construct a quadrilateral *ABCD* in which *AB* = 6 cm, ∠*A* = 60°, ∠*B* = 75°, *AD* = 4 cm and *BC* = 4.8 cm.
4. Construct a quadrilateral *ABCD* in which *AB* = 4 cm, *AD* = 4.4 cm, *BD* = 5.4 cm, *BC* = 4.5 cm and *AC* = 5.2 cm.
5. Construct a quadrilateral *ABCD* in which *BC* = 6 cm, *AC* = 7 cm, *AD* = 4.2 cm, ∠*A* = 120° and *CD* = 4 cm.
6. Construct a quadrilateral *ABCD* in which *AB* = 4 cm, *BC* = 4.3 cm, *CD* = 4.2 cm, and ∠*B* = ∠*C* = 90°.
7. Construct a parallelogram *ABCD* in which *AB* = 5.5 cm, *BC* = 4.2 cm and *AC* = 7 cm.

8. Construct a parallelogram $ABCD$ in which $AB = 4.5$ cm, $AD = 5$ cm and $\angle A = 75°$.
9. Construct a parallelogram $ABCD$ in which $AB = 5.6$ cm, $AC = 6$ cm and $BD = 6.2$ cm.
10. Construct a parallelogram $ABCD$ in which $AC = 7$ cm, $BD = 8$ cm and the angle between these diagonals is 60°.
11. Construct a parallelogram $ABCD$ in which $AB = 5$ cm, $BC = 4.8$ cm and height corresponding to $AB$ is 3.5 cm.
12. Construct a parallelogram $ABCD$ in which $AB = 5$ cm, $AC = 6.4$ cm and height corresponding to $AB$ is 4 cm.
13. Construct a rectangle $ABCD$ in which $AB = 6$ cm and $BC = 4.8$ cm.
14. Construct a rectangle $ABCD$ in which $AB = 5.2$ cm, and $BD = 6.5$ cm.
15. Construct a rectangle $ABCD$ in which $AC = 5$ cm and acute angle between its diagonals is 45°.
16. Construct a rectangle $ABCD$ in which $AB = 4.8$ cm and area is 12 $cm^2$.
17. Construct a rhombus $ABCD$ in which $\angle A = 75°$ and $AB = 4$ cm.
18. Construct a rhombus $ABCD$ in which $AB = 4$ cm and $AC = 6.2$ cm.
19. Construct a rhombus $ABCD$ in which $AC = 6.4$ cm and $BD = 8$ cm.
20. Construct a rhombus $ABCD$ in which $AB = 5.2$ cm and height is 4.5 cm.
21. Construct a rhombus $ABCD$ in which $AC = 6.4$ cm and height is 4 cm.
22. Construct a square of side 4.5 cm.
23. Construct a square $ABCD$ whose one diagonal $BD = 5.6$ cm.
24. Construct a square whose perimeter is 20 cm.
25. Construct a square whose area is 23.04 $cm^2$.
26. Construct a trapezium $ABCD$ in which $AB \parallel DC$, $AB = 4.4$ cm, $\angle ABC = 90°$, $\angle DAB = 120°$ and the distance between parallel sides is 3.5 cm.
27. Construct a trapezium $ABCD$ in which $AB = 3.5$ cm, $BC = 6$ cm, $CD = 3.2$ cm, $AD = 4.5$ cm and $AD \parallel BC$.
28. Construct a trapezium $ABCD$ in which $AB = 4$ cm, $BC = 6$ cm, $CD = 3.5$ cm, $AD = 4.6$ cm and $AD \parallel BC$.
29. Construct a regular hexagon of side :
    (a) 5 cm    (b) 4.5 cm
30. Using ruler and compass only, construct a parallelogram $ABCD$ in which $AB = 4$ cm, $\angle A = 60°$ and $BC = 5$ cm.
31. Using ruler and compass only, construct a rhombus $ABCD$ in which $AB = 4$ cm and $\angle BCD = 120°$.

# CHAPTER TEST

1. Construct a square *ABCD* in which $AB = 5.0$ cm.
2. Construct a quadrilateral *PQRS* in which $PQ = 4.5$ cm, $QR = 5.6$ cm, $RS = 5.5$ cm, $PS = 6.1$ cm and $PR = 6$ cm.
3. Construct a parallelogram *ABCD* in which $AB = 6$ cm, $BC = 5$ cm and $\angle DAB = 60°$.
4. Construct a parallelogram *ABCD* in which $CD = 5$ cm, $AC = 6$ cm and $BD = 6.4$ cm.
5. Construct a ractangle *ABCD* in which $AB = 5$ cm and $BC = 4$ cm.
6. Construct a regular hexagon of side 3.0 cm.
7. Construct a rhombus *ABCD* in which $AB = 5$ cm and $AC = 8$ cm.
8. Construct a trapezium *ABCD* in which $AB \parallel CD$, $AB = 4$ cm, $\angle ABC = 80°$, $\angle DAB = 110°$ and the distance between parallel sides is 3 cm.
9. Construct a rhombus *ABCD* in which $AC = 6$ cm and $BD = 8$ cm.

Chapter

# 13 THEOREMS ON AREA

## Syllabus

Proof and use of area theorems on parallelograms :

- Parallelograms on the same base and between the same parallels are equal in area.
- The area of a triangle is half that of a parallelogram on the same base and between the same parallels.
- Triangles between the same base and between the same parallels are equal in area (without proof).
- Triangles with equal areas on the same bases have equal corresponding altitudes.

## INTRODUCTION

We are familiar with the term 'area'. It is a planar region bounded by a simple closed curve. The magnitude of area is some number along with some square units, *e.g.,* 125 $m^2$, 41 $cm^2$, 3 hectare, etc. We have already studied some results of evaluating the area of closed figures like, circle, triangle, rectangle, square, rhombus, parallelogram, etc. In this chapter, we shall study some theorems on area under some conditions.

## Axioms of Area

(i) Congruence Area Axiom : If two figures are congruent, then area bounded by these figures are equal. In the following figures :

$$\Delta ABC \cong \Delta DEF$$

$\Rightarrow$ $\quad$ Area$(\Delta ABC)$ = Area$(\Delta DEF)$

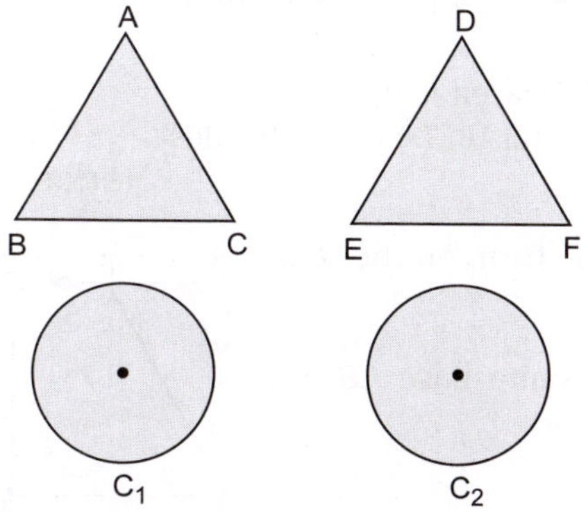


and $\quad$ Circle $C_1 \cong$ Circle $C_2$

$\Rightarrow$ $\quad$ Area (circle $C_1$) = Area (circle $C_2$)

(ii) Addition Area Axiom : In the adjoining figure, the planar region $R$ is formed by two non-overlapping planar regions $R_1$ and $R_2$, then,

$$\text{Area } (R) = \text{Area } (R_1) + \text{Area } (R_2)$$

This result is called addition area axiom.

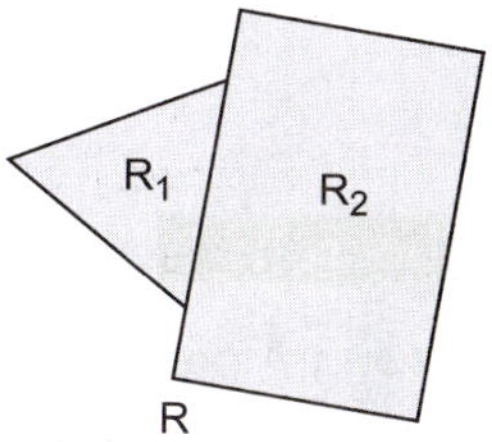


(iii) Equal Figures : Two figures are said to be equal figures if they have equal area. All two congruent figures have equal area so all congruent figures are equal figures but two equal figures need not be congruent.

*For example :*

$$\text{Area of triangle} = \frac{1}{2} \times 3 \text{ cm} \times 4 \text{ cm}$$
$$= 6 \text{ cm}^2$$

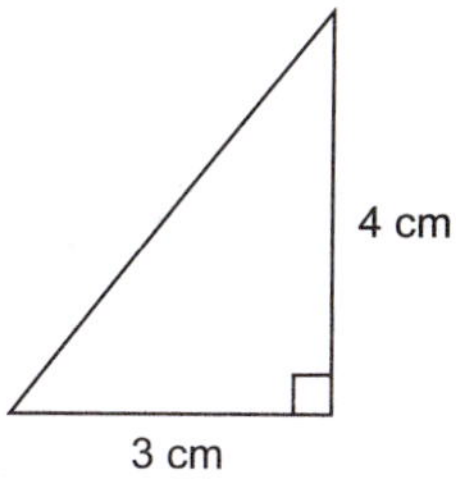


$$\text{Area of rectangle} = 3 \text{ cm} \times 2 \text{ cm}$$
$$= 6 \text{ cm}^2$$

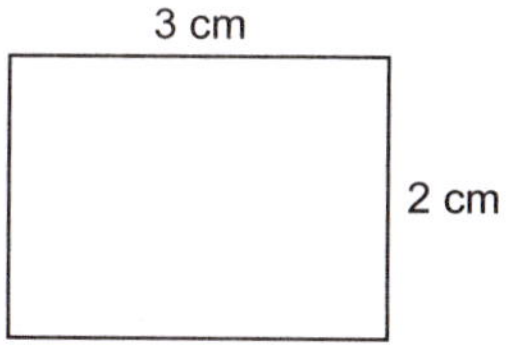


$\because$ Area of triangle = Area of rectangle

$\therefore$ Two figures are equal but they are not congruent.

## Area of Triangle

A closed figure bounded by three line segments is called a triangle.

In the adjoining figure, $ABC$ is a triangle. The part of a plane, bounded by a triangle is called the interior of that triangle.

The union of a triangle and its interior is called the triangular region and its area is called the area of the triangle.

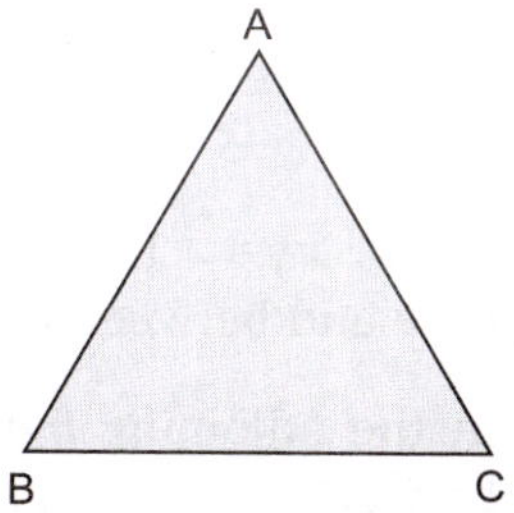

## Area of Rectangle

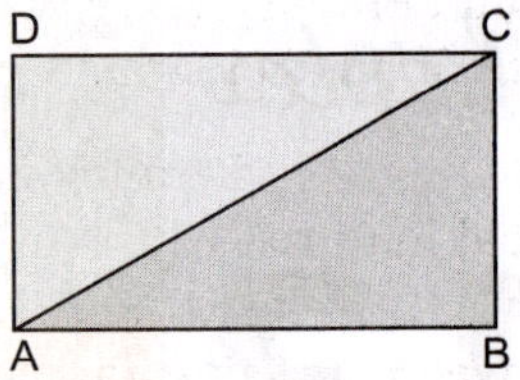


The part of a plane, bounded by a rectangle is called the interior of that rectangle. In the adjoining figure, *ABCD* is a rectangle.

The union of a rectangle and its interior is called the rectangular region and its area is called the area of the rectangle.

The area of rectangle is equal to the sum of the areas of two triangles.

$\therefore$ Area of rectangle $ABCD$ = Area of $\Delta ABC$ + Area of $\Delta ACD$.

## Area of Polygon

The union of a polygon and its interior is called the polygon region. It can be expressed as the union of a finite number of triangular region.

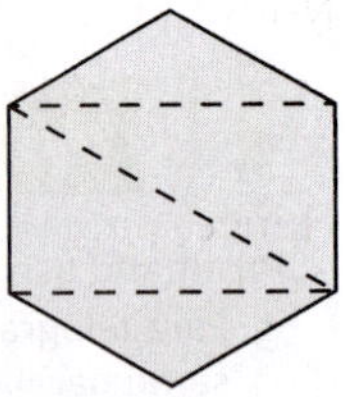

**Theorem 1** A diagonal of a parallelogram divides it into two triangles of equal areas.

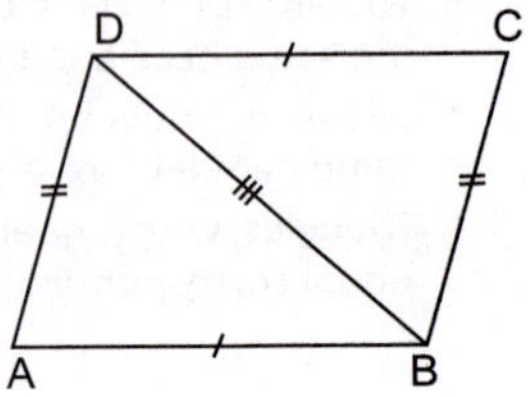


**Given :** A parallelogram *ABCD* with one diagonal *BD*.

**To Prove :** ar($\Delta ABD$) = ar($\Delta CDB$).

**Proof :**

| Statement | Reason |
|---|---|
| In $\Delta ABD$ and $\Delta CDB$ | |
| $AB = CD$ | Opposite sides of a parallelogram |
| $BD = DB$ | Common |
| $AD = CB$ | Opposite sides of a parallelogram |
| $\therefore$ $\Delta ABD \cong CDB$ | SSS axiom |
| $\Rightarrow$ Area of $\Delta ABD$ = Area of $\Delta CDB$ | Congruent area axiom |

Hence Proved.

**Theorem 2** Parallelograms on the same base and between the same parallel lines are equal in areas.

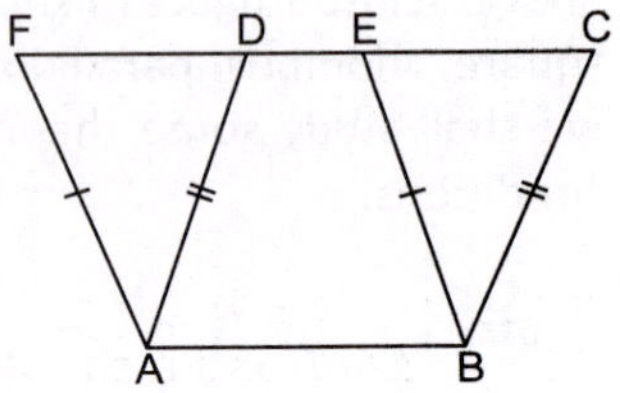


**Given :** Two parallelograms *ABCD* and *ABEF* on same base *AB* and between the same parallel lines *AB* and *FC*.

**To Prove :** Area of parallelograms *ABCD* = Area of parallelogram *ABEF*.

**Proof :**

| Statement | Reason |
|---|---|
| In $\Delta ADF$ and $\Delta BCE$ | |
| $AD = BC$ | Opposite sides of a parallelogram |
| $\angle DAF = \angle CBE$ | $BC \parallel AD$ and $BE \parallel AF$ |
| $AF = BE$ | Opposite sides of a parallelogram |
| $\therefore$ $\Delta ADF \cong \Delta BCE$ | SAS axiom |
| $\Rightarrow$ ar($\Delta ADF$) = ar($\Delta BCE$) | Congruent area axiom |
| $\Rightarrow$ ar($\Delta ADF$) + ar($\square ABED$) = ar($\Delta BCE$) + ar($\square ABED$) | Adding ar($\square ABED$) on both sides |
| $\Rightarrow$ ar(parallelogram *ABEF*) = ar(parallelogram *ABCD*) | |

Hence Proved.

**Corollary 1 :** The area of a parallelogram is equal to the area of the rectangle form on the same base and between the same parallel lines.

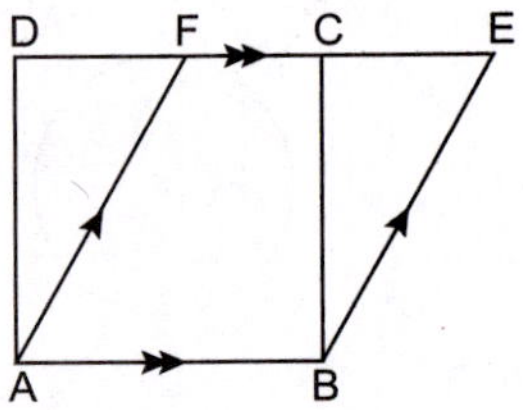


In the adjoining figure, rectangle *ABCD* and parallelogram *ABEF* are on same base *AB* and between the same parallel lines *AB* and *DE*.

$\therefore$ ar(rectangle *ABCD*) = ar(parallelogram *ABEF*)

**Corollary 2 :** Area of rectangle = Base × Height.

From Corollary 1,

Area of parallelogram $ABEF$ = Area of rectangle $ABCD = AB \times BC$ = Base × Height

**Corollary 3 :** Parallelograms on equal bases and between the same parallels are equal in area.

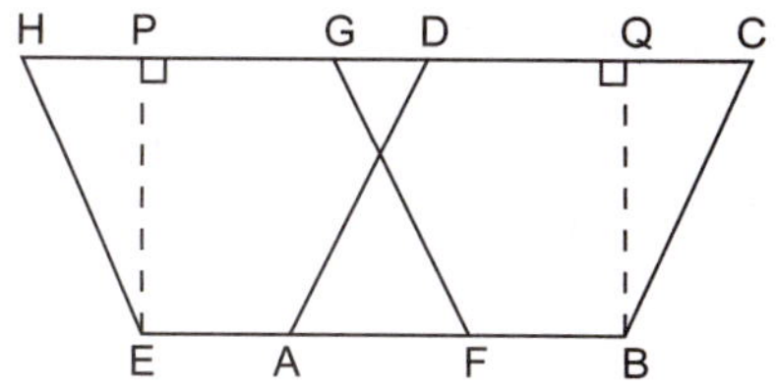


**Proof :** Let $ABCD$ and $EFGH$ be two parallelograms on equal bases $AB = EF$ and between the same parallel lines $EB$ and $HC$.

Draw $EP \perp HC$ and $BQ \perp HC$

$\because$ $EB \parallel HC$

$\therefore$ $EP = BQ$

Now, Area of || gm $ABCD = AB \times BQ$

$= EF \times EP$ ($\because$ $AB = EF$ and $BQ = EP$)

= Area of || gm $EFGH$

Hence, parallelograms on equal bases and between the same parallel lines are equal in area. **Hence Proved.**

**Theorem 3** Parallelograms on same base and having equal areas lie between the same parallel lines.

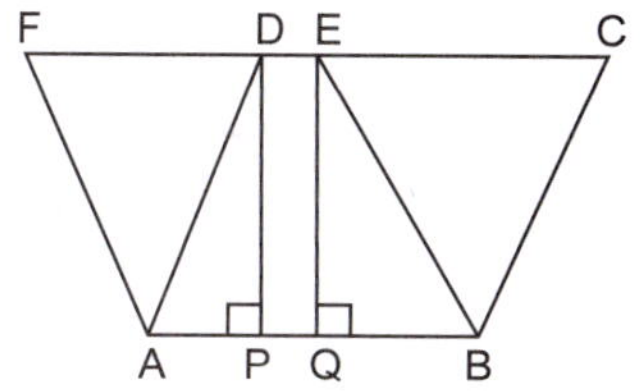


**Given :** Parallelograms $ABCD$ and $ABEF$ are on same base $AB$ such that

Area of || gm $ABCD$ = Area of || gm $ABEF$.

**To Prove :** $AB \parallel FC$.

**Construction :** Draw $DP \perp AB$ and $EQ \perp AB$

**Proof :**

| Statement | Reason |
|---|---|
| Area of \|\| gm $ABCD = AB \times DP$ | Area of \|\| gm = base × height |
| Area of \|\| gm $ABEF = AB \times EQ$ | Area of \|\| gm = base × height |
| $AB \times DP = AB \times EQ$ | Area of \|\| gm $ABCD$ = Area of \|\| gm $ABEF$ (Given) |
| $DP = EQ$ | divided by $AB$ |
| $DP \parallel EQ$ | $DP$ and $EQ$, both are perpendicular to $AB$ |
| $DPQE$ is a \|\| gm | $DP = EQ$ and $DP \parallel EQ$ |
| $DE \parallel PQ \Rightarrow FC \parallel AB$ | $DPQE$ is a \|\| gm |

**Hence Proved.**

**Corollary 1 :** Parallelograms on equal bases and having equal areas have equal corresponding altitudes.

**Corollary 2 :** Parallelograms on equal bases and having equal areas lie between the same parallel lines.

**Theorem 4** The area of a triangle is half that of a parallelogram on the same base and between the same parallel lines.

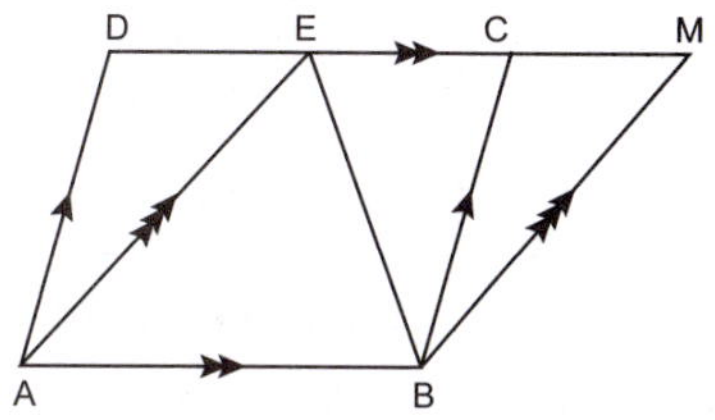


**Given :** $\Delta ABE$ and a parallelogram $ABCD$ on same base $AB$ and between the same parallel lines $AB$ and $DC$.

**To Prove :** Area of $\Delta ABE = \frac{1}{2}$ × Area of $\square ABCD$.

**Construction :** Draw $BM \parallel AE$ from $B$ which meets $DC$ produced at $M$.

**Proof :**

| Statement | Reason |
|---|---|
| $ABME$ is a parallelogram | By construction |
| Area of $\Delta ABE = \frac{1}{2}$ × Area of $\square ABME$ ...(i) | $BE$ is the diagonal of parallelogram $ABME$ |
| Area of parallelogram $ABME$ = Area of parallelogram $ABCD$ ...(ii) | Parallelogram on same base and between the same parallel lines |
| $\therefore$ Area of $\Delta ABE = \frac{1}{2}$ × Area of parallelogram $ABCD$ | From equations (i) and (ii) |

**Hence Proved.**

Corollary 1 : Area of triangle = $\frac{1}{2}$ × Base × Height.

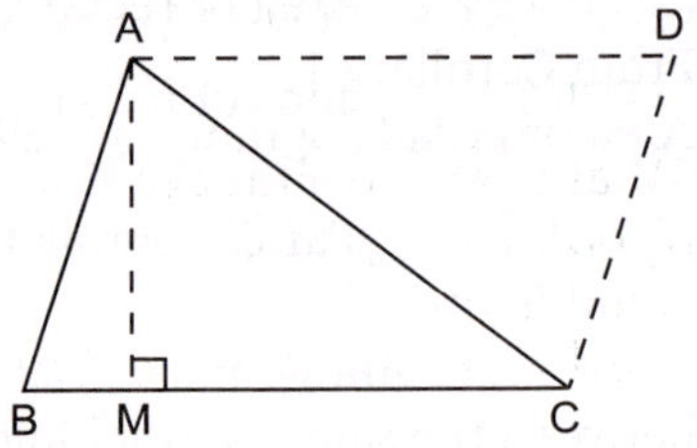


Proof : Let *ABC* be a triangle with base *BC* and $AM \perp BC$.
Draw $AD \parallel BC$ and $CD \parallel BA$ intersecting each other at point *D*.

$\therefore$ *ABCD* is a || gm.

Now, $\Delta ABC$ and || gm *ABCD* are on same base *BC* and between the same parallel lines *BC* and *AD*.

$$\therefore \quad \text{Area of } \Delta ABC = \frac{1}{2} \times \text{Area of || gm } ABCD = \frac{1}{2} \times BC \times AM = \frac{1}{2} \times \text{Base} \times \text{Height}$$

Corollary 2 : Area of a trapezium = $\frac{1}{2}$ × Sum of parallel sides × Height.

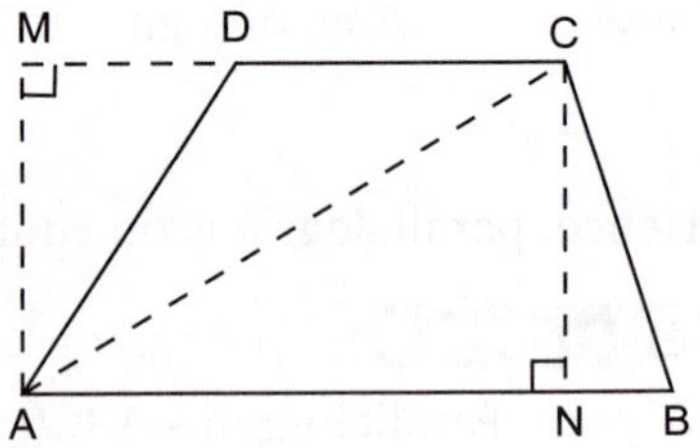


Proof : In the adjoining figure, *ABCD* be a trapezium in which $AB \parallel DC$.

Join *AC*.

Draw $CN \perp AB$ and $AM \perp CD$ produced.

$\because$ $AB \parallel CD$

$\therefore$ $CN = AM$

Now,

$$\text{Area of trapezium } ABCD = \text{Area of } \Delta ABC + \text{Area of } \Delta ACD$$

$$= \frac{1}{2} \times AB \times CN + \frac{1}{2} \times CD \times AM$$

$$= \frac{1}{2} \times AB \times CN + \frac{1}{2} \times CD \times CN \qquad (\because AM = CN)$$

$$= \frac{1}{2} \times (AB + CD) \times CN$$

$$= \frac{1}{2} \times \text{Sum of parallel sides} \times \text{Height}$$

**Theorem 5** Triangles on the same base (or equal bases) and between the same parallel lines are equal in area.

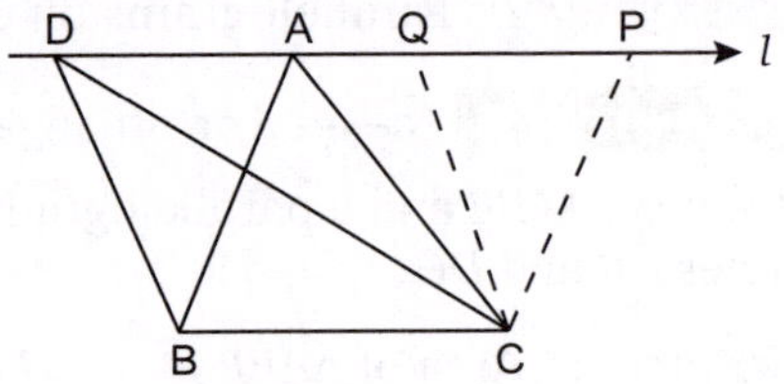


Given : $\Delta ABC$ and $\Delta DBC$ are on same base *BC* and between the same parallel lines *BC* and *l*.

To Prove : Area of $\Delta ABC$ = Area of $\Delta DBC$.

Construction : Draw $CE \parallel BA$ meet *l* at *P* and draw $CQ \parallel BD$ meet *l* at *Q*.

Proof :

| Statement | Reason |
|---|---|
| 1. *ABCP* is a parallelogram | $AB \parallel PC$ and $AP \parallel BC$ |
| 2. *BCQD* is a parallelogram | $BC \parallel DQ$ and $BD \parallel CQ$ |
| 3. Area of || gm *ABCP* = Area of || gm *BCQD* | Both parallelograms on the same base *BC* and between the same parallel lines *BC* and *l*. |
| 4. Area of $\Delta ABC = \frac{1}{2}$ × Area of || gm *ABCP* | Area of a Δ is half that of a || gm on the same base and between the same parallel lines |
| 5. Area of $\Delta DBC = \frac{1}{2}$ × Area of || gm *DBCQ* | Area of a Δ is half that of a || gm on the same base and between the same parallel lines |
| 6. Area of $\Delta ABC$ = Area of $\Delta DBC$ | From (3), (4) and (5) |

Hence Proved.

**Theorem 6** Triangles with equal areas on the same bases have equal corresponding altitudes.

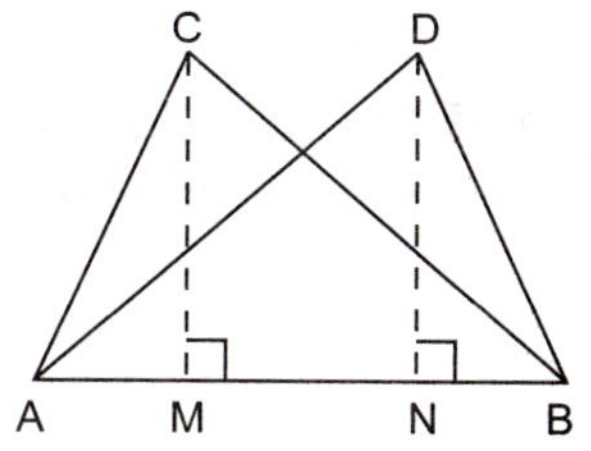


**Given :** $\Delta ABC$ and $\Delta ABD$ on the same base $AB$ and area of $\Delta ABC$ = area of $\Delta ABD$.
$CM$ and $DN$ are altitudes from $C$ and $D$ respectively to $AB$.

**To Prove :** $CM = DN$.

**Proof :**

| Statement | Reason |
|---|---|
| Area of $\Delta ABC = \frac{1}{2} \times AB \times CM$ | Area of $\Delta = \frac{1}{2} \times$ Base $\times$ Height |
| Area of $\Delta ABD = \frac{1}{2} \times AB \times DN$ | |
| $\therefore \frac{1}{2} \times AB \times CM = \frac{1}{2} \times AB \times DN$ | Area of $\Delta ABC$ = Area of $\Delta ABD$ |
| $\Rightarrow CM = DN$ | |

Hence Proved.

## Illustrative Examples

**Example 1.** In the adjoining figure, ar(|| gm $ABCD$) = 30 cm$^2$. Find :
(i) ar(|| gm $ABEF$) (ii) ar($\Delta AEB$)

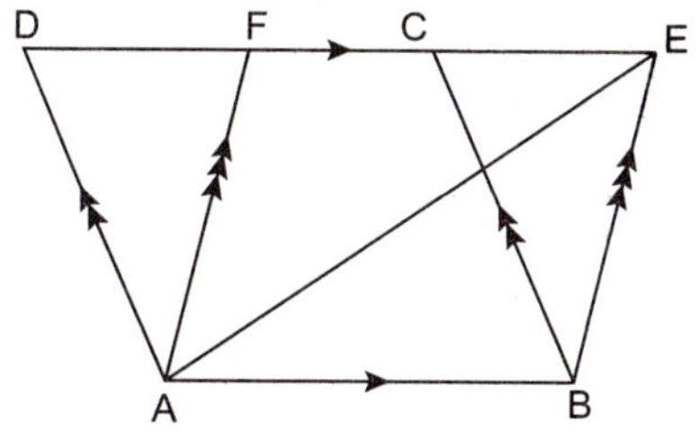


**Solution.** (i) Here, parallelograms $ABCD$ and $ABEF$ are on same base $AB$ and between the same parallel lines $AB$ and $DE$.

$\therefore$ ar(|| gm $ABEF$) = ar(|| gm $ABCD$) = 30 cm$^2$ Ans.

(ii) $\Delta ABE$ and || gm $ABEF$ are on same base $AB$ and between the same parallel lines $AB$ and $FE$.

$\therefore$ ar($\Delta ABE$) $= \frac{1}{2} \cdot$ ar(|| gm $ABEF$) $= \frac{1}{2} \times 30$ cm$^2$ = 15 cm$^2$ Ans.

**Example 2.** The area of a parallelogram is 240 cm$^2$. The ratio of its base and corresponding altitude is 5 : 3. Find the base and corresponding altitude.

**Solution.** Let base = $5x$.

$\therefore$ Corresponding altitude = $3x$

Now, Area of || gm = Base × Corresponding altitude

$\Rightarrow 240 = (5x)(3x)$

$\Rightarrow x^2 = 16 \Rightarrow x = 4$

$\therefore$ Base = $5x = 5 \times 4$ cm = 20 cm Ans.

and Corresponding altitude = $3x = 3 \times 4$ cm = 12 cm Ans.

**Example 3.** In the adjoining figure, $ABCD$ is a rectangle in which $AB = 5$ cm, $BC = 4$ cm.
If $AP \parallel BQ$, find :
(i) ar(|| gm $ABQP$) (ii) ar($\Delta ABP$)

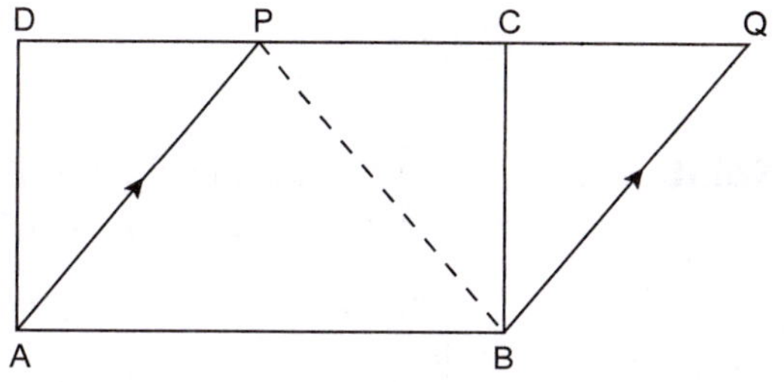


**Solution.** (i) $ABQP$ is a parallelogram because $AB \parallel PQ$ and $AP \parallel BQ$.
Parallelogram $ABQP$ and rectangle $ABCD$ are on same base $AB$ and between the same parallel lines $AB$ and $DQ$.

$\therefore$ ar(|| gm $ABQP$) = area of rectangle $ABCD$

$= AB \times BC = 5$ cm × 4 cm = 20 cm$^2$ Ans.

(ii) $\Delta ABP$ and || gm $ABQP$ are on same base $AB$ and between the same parallel lines $AB$ and $PQ$.

$\therefore$ ar($\Delta ABP$) $= \frac{1}{2}$ ar(|| gm $ABQP$) $= \frac{1}{2} \times 20$ cm$^2$ = 10 cm$^2$. Ans.

**Example 4.** In quadrilateral $ABCD$, $BD = 6$ cm, $AB = DC = 4$ cm, $\angle BDC = \angle ABD = 90°$. Show that $ABCD$ is a parallelogram.

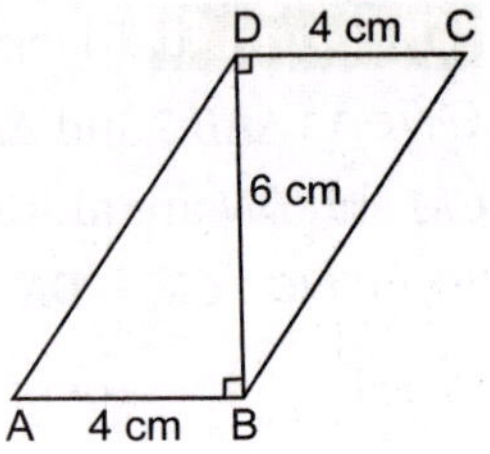


**Solution.** $\angle ABD = \angle CDB$ (each 90°)
and $BD$ is a transversal.

$\therefore$ $AB \parallel DC$ and $AB = DC$

$\therefore$ $ABCD$ is a parallelogram.

**Example 5.** In the adjoining figure, $BD = 2\ CD$.
If area of $\Delta ABC = 48\ \text{cm}^2$, find the area of $\Delta ADC$.

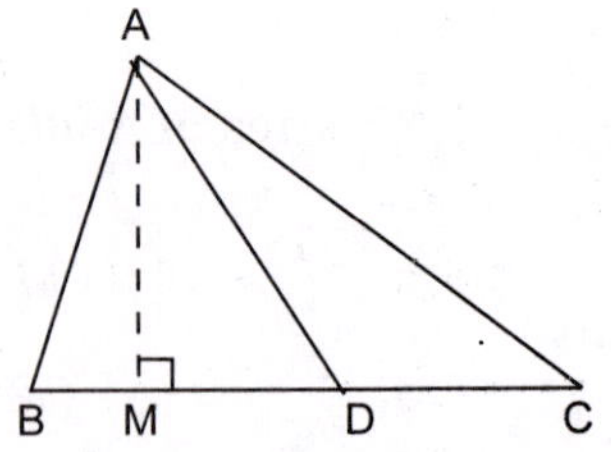


**Solution.** Draw $AM \perp BC$.

$$\text{Area of } \Delta ABC = \frac{1}{2} \times BC \times AM$$

$$\Rightarrow \quad \frac{1}{2} \times BC \times AM = 48 \quad \text{...(i)}$$

Given that, $BD = 2CD$

$\Rightarrow$ $BD + CD = 2CD + CD$ $\Rightarrow$ $BC = 3\ CD$

From *(i)*,

$$\frac{1}{2} \times 3\ CD \times AM = 48 \quad \Rightarrow \quad \frac{1}{2} \times CD \times AM = 16$$

$\Rightarrow$ Area of $\Delta ACD = 16\ \text{cm}^2$ **Ans.**

**Example 6.** In the adjoining figure, $ABCD$ and $ABPQ$ are two parallelograms.
If ar(|| gm $ABCD$) = 50 cm², find :
(i) ar(|| gm $ABPQ$)
(ii) ar($\Delta ABR$)
(iii) ar($\Delta BDC$)

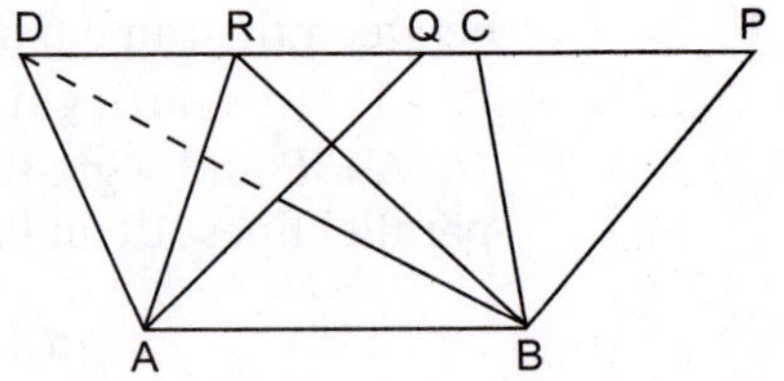


**Solution.** (i) Parallelograms $ABCD$ and $ABPQ$ are on same base $AB$ and between the same parallel lines $AB$ and $DP$

$\therefore$ ar(|| gm $ABPQ$) = ar(|| gm $ABCD$) = 50 cm² **Ans.**

(ii) $\Delta ABR$ and parallelogram $ABCD$ are on same base $AB$ and between the same parallel lines $AB$ and $DC$.

$$\therefore \quad \text{ar}(\Delta ABR) = \frac{1}{2}\ \text{ar(|| gm } ABCD) = \frac{1}{2} \times 50\ \text{cm}^2 = 25\ \text{cm}^2$$ **Ans.**

(iii) $\Delta BDC$ and parallelogram $ABCD$ are on same base $CD$ and between the same parallel lines $CD$ and $AB$.

$$\therefore \quad \text{ar}(\Delta BDC) = \frac{1}{2}\ \text{ar(|| gm } ABCD) = \frac{1}{2} \times 50\ \text{cm}^2 = 25\ \text{cm}^2$$ **Ans.**

**Example 7.** In the adjoining figure, $ABCD$ is a parallelogram in which $M$ and $N$ are the mid-points of $DC$ and $AB$ respectively. If ar(|| gm $ABCD$) = 56 cm², find :
(i) ar($\Delta BCE$) (ii) ar(|| gm $BNMC$)

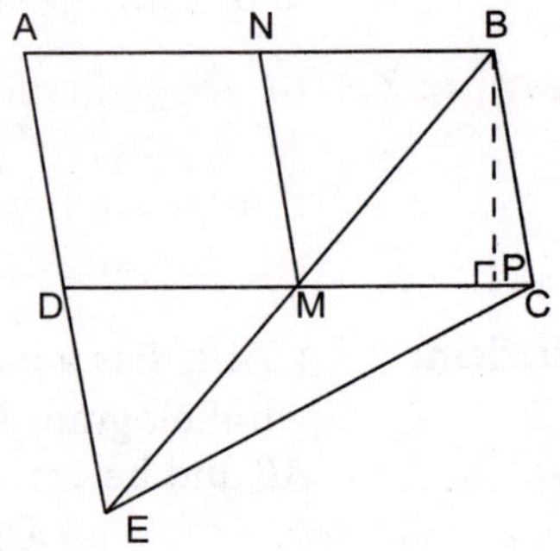


**Solution.** (i) $\Delta BCE$ and parallelogram $ABCD$ are on same base $BC$ and between the same parallel lines $CB$ and $EA$.

$$\therefore \quad \text{ar}(\Delta BCE) = \frac{1}{2} \cdot \text{ar(|| gm } ABCD) = \frac{1}{2} \times 56\ \text{cm}^2 = 28\ \text{cm}^2$$ **Ans.**

(ii) ar(|| gm $BNMC$) = Base × Corresponding height

$= CM \times BP$ (where $BP \perp MC$)

$$= \frac{1}{2} \times DC \times BP = \frac{1}{2} \times \text{ar(|| gm } ABCD)$$

$$= \frac{1}{2} \times 56\ \text{cm}^2 = 28\ \text{cm}^2$$ **Ans.**

**Example 8.** Prove that the median $AM$ of the $\Delta ABC$ divides it into two triangles of equal areas.

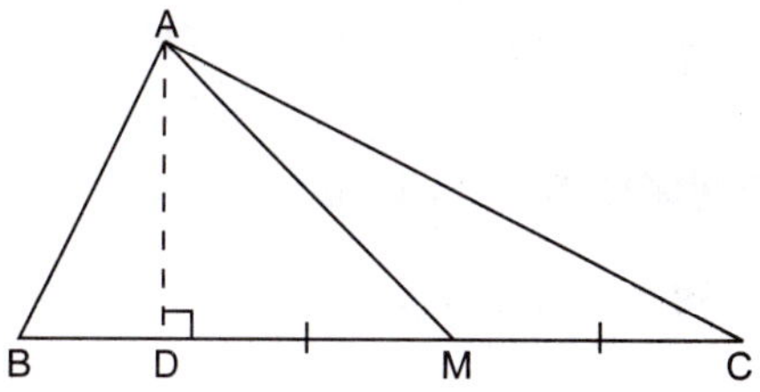


**Solution.** Draw $AD \perp BC$.

$$\text{Area of } \Delta ABM = \frac{1}{2} \times \text{Base} \times \text{Height}$$

$$= \frac{1}{2} \times BM \times AD$$

$$= \frac{1}{2} \times CM \times AD \qquad (\because \; BM = CM)$$

$$= \text{Area of } \Delta ACM$$

$\therefore$ Median $AM$ of $\Delta ABC$ divides it into two triangles of equal areas. **Hence Proved.**

**Example 9.** In the adjoining figure, $ABCD$ is a parallelogram whose area is 60 $cm^2$. The diagonals $AC$ and $BD$ intersect each other at $O$. If $M$ is mid-point of $AO$, find the area of $\Delta BOM$.

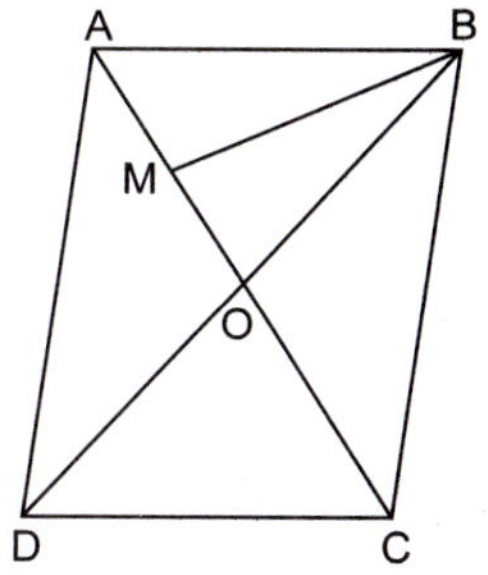


**Solution.** In $\Delta AOB$,

$M$ is mid-point of $AO$.

$$\therefore \quad \text{Area of } \Delta BOM = \frac{1}{2} \times \text{Area of } \Delta AOB \qquad ...(i)$$

We know that the diagonals of a parallelogram bisect each other.

$\therefore$ $O$ is the mid-point of $AC$.

In $\Delta ABC$,

$$\text{Area of } \Delta AOB = \frac{1}{2} \times \text{Area of } \Delta ABC \qquad ...(ii)$$

We know that the diagonal of a || gm divides it into two triangles of equal area.

$$\therefore \quad \text{Area of } \Delta ABC = \frac{1}{2} \times \text{Area of || gm } ABCD = \frac{1}{2} \times 60 = 30 \text{ cm}^2$$

From $(ii)$,

$$\text{Area of } \Delta AOB = \frac{1}{2} \times 30 = 15 \text{ cm}^2$$

From $(i)$,

$$\text{Area of } \Delta BOM = \frac{1}{2} \times 15 = 7.5 \text{ cm}^2$$

**Ans.**

**Example 10.** $PQRS$ is a parallelogram. $M$ and $N$ are any two points lying on $QR$ and $RS$ respectively. Show that, area of $\Delta PSM$ = area of $\Delta PQN$.

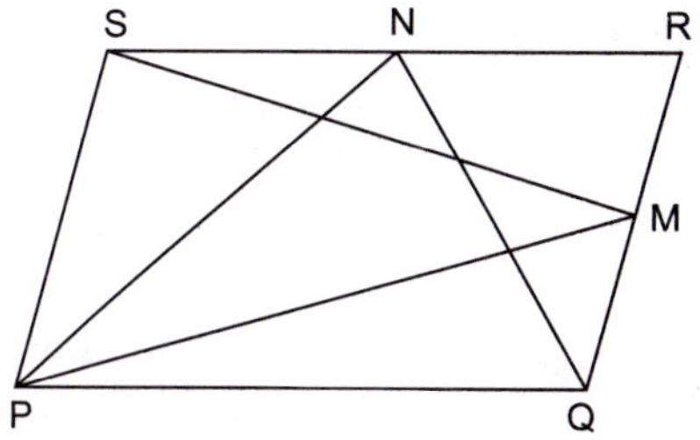


**Solution.** $\Delta PSM$ and || gm $PQRS$ are on same base $PS$ and between the same parallel lines $PS$ and $QR$.

$$\therefore \quad \text{Area of } \Delta PSM = \frac{1}{2} \times \text{Area of || gm } PQRS \qquad ...(i)$$

$\Delta PQN$ and || gm $PQRS$ are on same base $PQ$ and between the same parallel lines $PQ$ and $RS$.

$$\therefore \quad \text{Area of } \Delta PQN = \frac{1}{2} \times \text{Area of || gm } PQRS \qquad ...(ii)$$

From eqs. $(i)$ and $(ii)$, we get

$$\text{Area of } \Delta PSM = \text{Area of } \Delta PQN$$

**Hence Proved.**

**Example 11.** In the adjoining figure, $BD = 3\ CD$. If ar($\Delta ABC$) = 120 cm$^2$, find ar($\Delta ADC$).

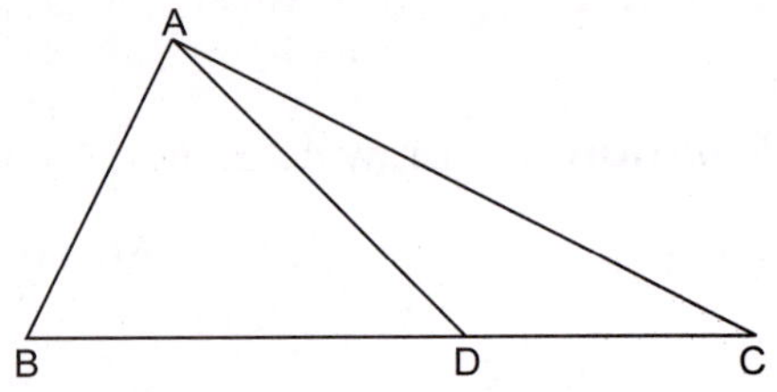


**Solution.** Given,

$$BD = 3\ CD$$
$$\Rightarrow \quad BD + CD = 3\ CD + CD$$
$$\Rightarrow \quad BC = 4\ CD$$
$$\Rightarrow \quad CD = \frac{1}{4}\ BC \quad \text{...(i)}$$

Draw $AM \perp BC$.

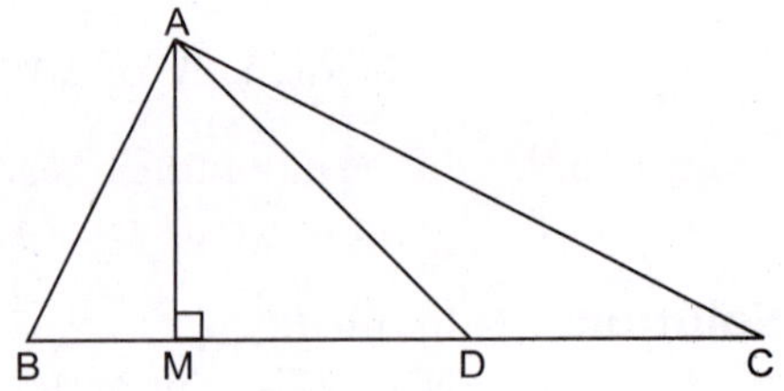


$$\text{ar}(\Delta ADC) = \frac{1}{2} \times DC \times AM$$
$$= \frac{1}{2} \times \frac{1}{4} BC \times AM \quad \text{[From (i)]}$$
$$= \frac{1}{4} \times \left(\frac{1}{2} \times BC \times AM\right)$$
$$= \frac{1}{4} \times \text{ar}(\Delta ABC) = \frac{1}{4} \times 120 \text{ cm}^2 = 30 \text{ cm}^2$$

**Ans.**

**Example 12.** $ABCD$ is a parallelogram. $M$ is any point on $BC$. $AM$ and $DC$ are produced to meet at $N$. Prove that area of $\Delta ADN$ = area of $\square ABNC$.

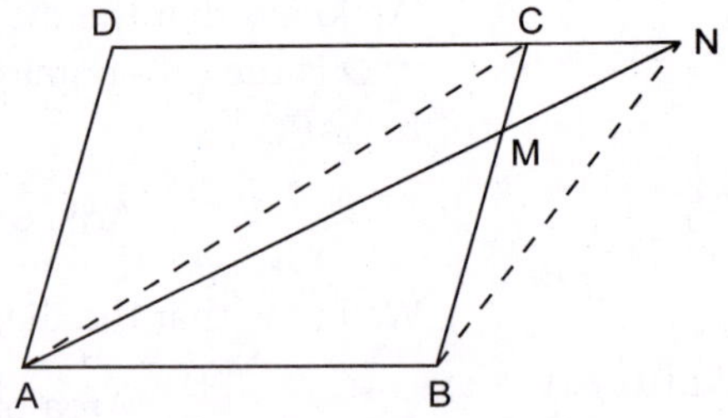


**Solution.** Join $AC$ and $BN$.

$\Delta ACN$ and $\Delta BCN$ are on same base $CN$ and between the same parallel lines $CN$ and $AB$.

$\therefore$ Area of $\Delta ACN$ = Area of $\Delta BCN$ ...(i)

We know that the diagonal $AC$ of the || gm $ABCD$ divides it into two triangles of equal area.

$\therefore$ Area of $\Delta DAC$ = Area of $\Delta ABC$ ...(ii)

Adding (i) and (ii), we get

Area of $\Delta ACN$ + Area of $\Delta DAC$ = Area of $\Delta BCN$ + Area of $\Delta ABC$

$\Rightarrow$ Area of $\Delta ADF$ = Area of $\square ABNC$

**Hence Proved.**

**Example 13.** The diagonals $AC$ and $BD$ of a quadrilateral $ABCD$ intersect at point '$O$'. If $BO = OD$, then prove that the area of $\Delta ABC$ and $\Delta ADC$ are equal.

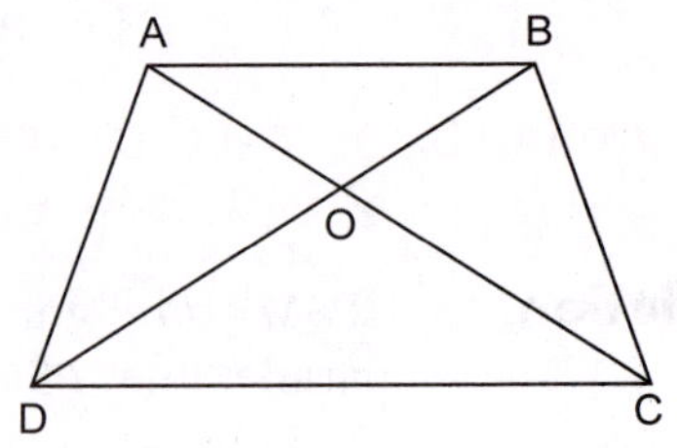


**Solution.** Given that, $BO = DO$

In $\Delta ABD$, $AO$ is the median.

$\therefore$ Area of $\Delta ABO$ = Area of $\Delta ADO$ ...(i)

In $\Delta BCD$, $CO$ is the median,

$\therefore$ Area of $\Delta BCO$ = Area of $\Delta DCO$ ...(ii)

Adding equations (i) and (ii), we get

Area of $\Delta ABO$ + Area of $\Delta BCO$ = Area of $\Delta ADO$ + Area of $\Delta DCO$

$\Rightarrow$ Area of $\Delta ABC$ = Area of $\Delta ACD$

**Hence Proved.**

**Example 14.** $ABCD$ is a trapezium in which $AB \parallel DC$ and the diagonals $AC$ and $BD$ intersect each other at $O$. Prove that area of $\Delta DAO$ = area of $\Delta BCO$.

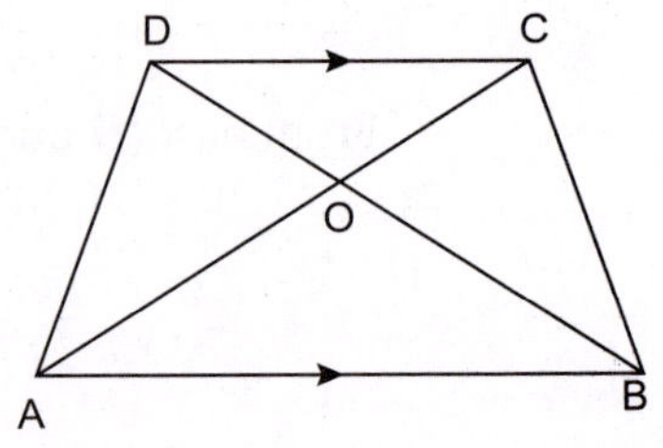


**Solution.** Proof :

| Statement | Reason |
|---|---|
| 1. $AB \parallel DC$ | Given |
| 2. Area of $\Delta ABD$ = Area of $\Delta ABC$ | Triangles are on the same base and between the same parallel lines $AB$ and $DC$. |

3. Area of $\Delta DAO$ + Area of $\Delta AOB$
   = Area of $\Delta AOB$ + Area of $\Delta BCO$ — Addition area axiom
4. Area of $\Delta DAO$ = Area of $\Delta BCO$ — Subtracting area of $\Delta AOB$ from both sides

Hence Proved.

**Example 15.** The diagonals $AC$ and $BD$ of a quadrilateral $ABCD$ intersect each other at $O$ such that area of $\Delta OAD$ = area of $\Delta OBC$. Prove that $ABCD$ is a trapezium.

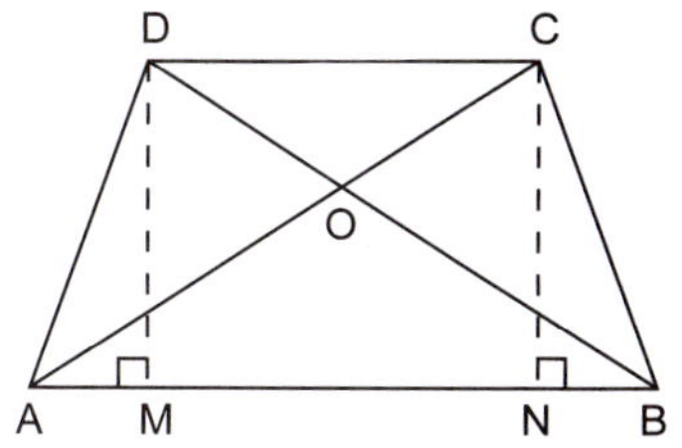


**Solution.** Draw $DM \perp AB$ and $CN \perp AB$.

$\Rightarrow$ $DM \parallel CN$

Given that,

$$\text{Area of } \Delta OAD = \text{Area of } \Delta OBC$$

$\Rightarrow$ Area of $\Delta OAD$ + Area of $\Delta OAB$ = Area of $\Delta OBC$ + Area of $\Delta OAB$

$\Rightarrow$ Area of $\Delta ABD$ = Area of $\Delta ABC$

$\Rightarrow$ $\frac{1}{2} \times AB \times DM = \frac{1}{2} \times AB \times CN$

$\Rightarrow$ $DM = CN$

Now, $DM \parallel CN$ and $DM = CN$

So, $DMNC$ is a parallelogram.

$\therefore$ $DC \parallel MN$

$\Rightarrow$ $DC \parallel AB$

$\Rightarrow$ $ABCD$ is a trapezium.

Hence Proved.

**Example 16.** In the adjoining figure, $ABCD$ is a quadrilateral. A line $DM$ drawn parallel to diagonal $AC$ from point $D$, meets $BC$ produced at $M$. Prove that area of $\Delta ABM$ = area of $\square ABCD$.

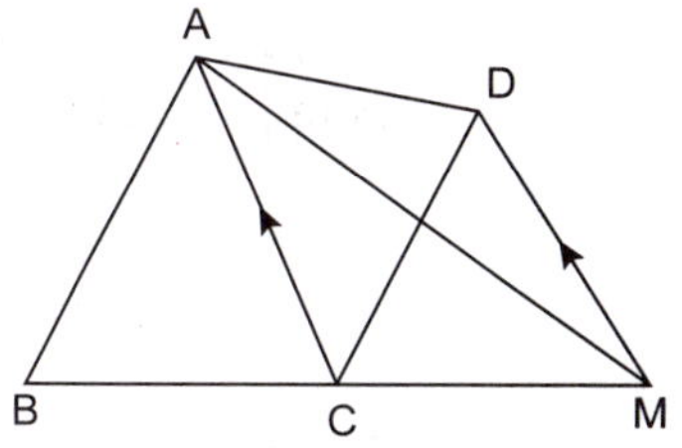


**Solution.** Here, $AC \parallel DM$.

$\Delta ACP$ and $\Delta ACD$ are on same base $AC$ and between the same parallel lines $AC$ and $DM$.

$\therefore$ Area of $\Delta ACM$ = Area of $\Delta ACD$

Adding area of $\Delta ABC$ on both sides,

Area of $\Delta ACM$ + Area of $\Delta ABC$ = Area of $\Delta ACD$ + Area of $\Delta ABC$

$\Rightarrow$ Area of $\Delta ABM$ = Area of $\square ABCD$.

Hence Proved.

**Example 17.** $P$ is an interior point of the parallelogram $ABCD$. Prove that area of $\Delta APB$ + area of $\Delta CPD$ = area of $\Delta APD$ + area of $\Delta BPC$.

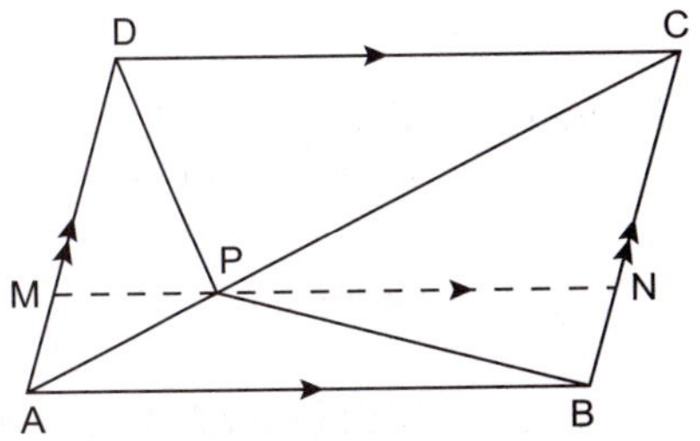


**Solution.** Draw $MN \parallel AB \parallel DC$.

$\Delta DCP$ and parallelogram $DCNM$ are on same base $DC$ and between the same parallel lines $DC$ and $MN$.

$\therefore$ Area of $\Delta DCP = \frac{1}{2} \times$ Area of parallelogram $DCNM$ ...(i)

Similarly, $\Delta ABP$ and parallelogram $ABNM$ are on same base $AB$ and between the same parallel lines $AB$ and $MN$.

$\therefore$ Area of $\Delta ABP = \frac{1}{2} \times$ Area of parallelogram $ABNM$ ...(ii)

Adding equations (i) and (ii),

Area of $\Delta ABP$ + Area of $\Delta DCP = \frac{1}{2} \times$ (Area of parallelogram $DCNM$ + Area of parallelogram $ABNM$)

$\Rightarrow$ Area of $\Delta ABP$ + Area of $\Delta DCP = \frac{1}{2} \times$ Area of parallelogram $ABCD$ ...(iii)

Now, Area of $\Delta APD$ + Area of $\Delta BPC$

= Area of parallelogram $ABCD$ – (Area of $\Delta ABP$ + Area of $\Delta DCP$)

= Area of parallelogram $ABCD - \frac{1}{2} \times$ Area of parallelogram $ABCD$

[From (iii)]

$= \frac{1}{2} \times$ Area of parallelogram $ABCD$

= Area of $\Delta ABP$ + Area of $\Delta DCP$ [From (iii)]

Hence Proved.

**Example 18.** The medians of $\Delta ABC$ intersect at point $G$. Prove that area of $\Delta AGB = \frac{1}{3} \times$ area of $\Delta ABC$.

**Solution.** Let $D$ be the mid-point of $BC$.

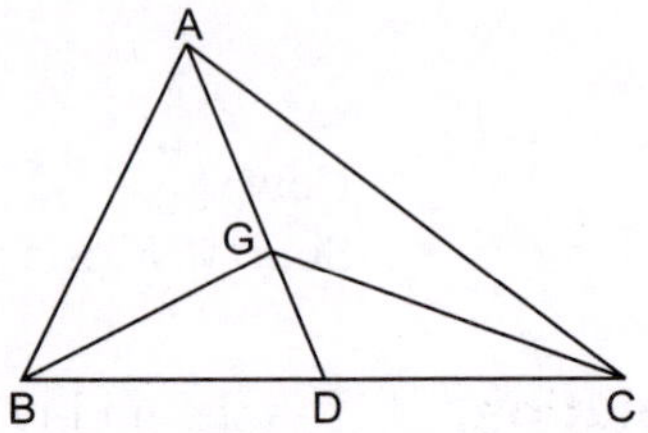


In $\Delta ABC$, $D$ is the mid-point of $BC$.

$\therefore$ Area of $\Delta ABD$ = Area of $\Delta ACD$ ...(i)

In $\Delta GBC$, $D$ is the mid-point of $BC$.

$\therefore$ Area of $\Delta GBD$ = Area of $\Delta GCD$ ...(ii)

Subtract equation (ii) from equation (i), we get

Area of $\Delta ABD$ – Area of $\Delta GBD$ = Area of $\Delta ACD$ – Area of $\Delta GCD$

$\therefore$ Area of $\Delta ABG$ = Area of $\Delta ACG$ ...(iii)

Similarly, we can prove that

Area of $\Delta ABG$ = Area of $\Delta BCG$ ...(iv)

From equations (iii) and (iv)

Area of $\Delta ABG$ = Area of $\Delta ACG$ = Area of $\Delta BCG$

$\Rightarrow$ Area of $\Delta ABG = \frac{1}{3} \times$ Area of $\Delta ABC$

Hence Proved.

**Example 19.** Prove that area of a rhombus $= \frac{1}{2} \times$ product of diagonals.

**Solution.** In thv adjoining figure,

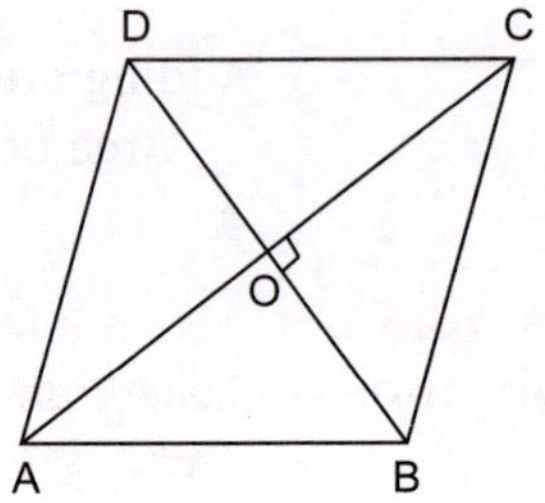


$ABCD$ be a rhombus and its diagonals $AC$ and $BD$ intersect at $O$.

Area of $\Delta ABC = \frac{1}{2} \times$ Base $\times$ Height

$= \frac{1}{2} \times AC \times OB$

and Area of $\Delta ACD = \frac{1}{2} \times AC \times OD$

$\therefore$ Area of $\Delta ABC$ + Area of $\Delta ACD = \frac{1}{2} \times AC \times OB + \frac{1}{2} \times AC \times OD$

$\Rightarrow$ Area of rhombus $ABCD = \frac{1}{2} \times AC \times (OB + OD)$

$= \frac{1}{2} \times AC \times BD$

$= \frac{1}{2} \times$ Product of diagonals.

Hence Proved.

**Example 20.** $XY$ is a line parallel to side $BC$ of a $\Delta ABC$. If $BE \parallel CA$ and $FC \parallel AB$ meet $XY$ at $E$ and $F$ respectively, show that area of $\Delta ABE$ = area of $\Delta ACF$.

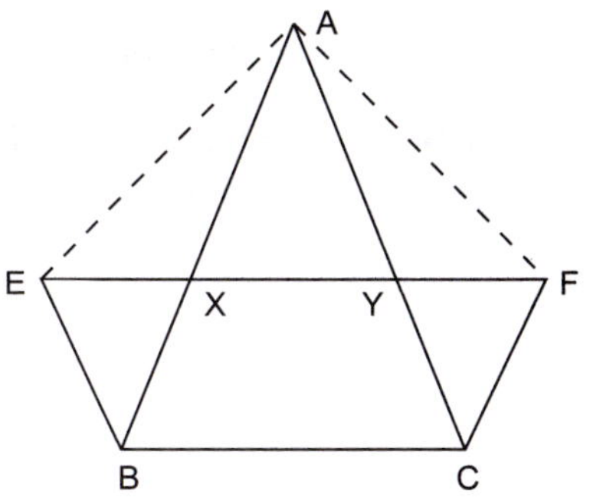


**Solution.** $\Delta ABE$ and || gm $EBCY$ are on same base $BE$ and between the same parallel lines $BE$ and $CA$.

$\therefore$ Area of $\Delta ABE = \frac{1}{2} \times$ Area of || gm $EBCY$ ...(i)

$\Delta ACF$ and || gm $CFXB$ are on same base $CF$ and between the same parallel lines $CF$ and $BA$.

$\therefore$ Area of $\Delta ACF = \frac{1}{2}$ Area of || gm $CFXB$ ...(ii)

|| gm $EBCY$ and || gm $CFXB$ are on same base $BC$ and between the same parallel lines $BC$ and $EF$.

$\therefore$ Area of || gm $EBCY$ = Area of || gm $CFXB$

$\Rightarrow$ $\frac{1}{2} \times$ Area of || gm $EBCY = \frac{1}{2} \times$ Area of || gm $CFXB$

$\Rightarrow$ Area of $\Delta ABE$ = Area of $\Delta ACF$ [From (i) and (ii)]

Hence Proved.

**Example 21.** $Q$ and $P$ are the mid-points of the sides $AB$ and $AC$ respectively of a triangle $ABC$. If $BP$ and $CQ$ meet at $O$, prove that area of $\Delta OBC$ = area of $\square AQOP$.

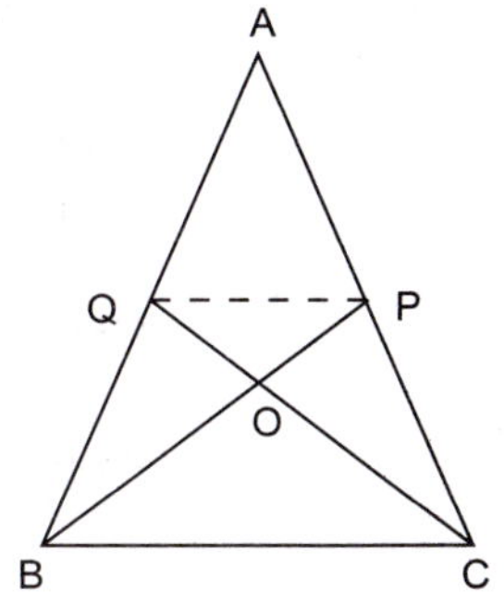


**Solution.** $E$ is the mid-point of $AB$ and $P$ is the mid-point of $AC$.

$\therefore$ $QP \parallel BC$.

$\Delta QBC$ and $\Delta PBC$ are on the same base $BC$ and between the same parallel lines $BC$ and $QP$.

$\therefore$ Area of $\Delta QBC$ = Area of $\Delta PBC$

$\Rightarrow$ Area of $\Delta QBC$ – Area of $\Delta OBC$ = Area of $\Delta PBC$ – Area of $\Delta OBC$

$\Rightarrow$ Area of $\Delta BOQ$ = Area of $\Delta COP$ ...(i)

$\because$ $P$ is the mid-point of $AC$.

$\therefore$ Area of $\Delta BCP$ = Area of $\Delta BAP$

$\Rightarrow$ Area of $\Delta BCP$ – Area of $\Delta COP$ = Area of $\Delta BAP$ – Area of $\Delta BOQ$ [From (i)]

$\Rightarrow$ Area of $\Delta OBC$ = Area of $\square AQOP$

Hence Proved.

**Example 22.** $\Delta ABC$ and $\Delta DBC$ are on the same base $BC$ such that $A$ and $D$ are on opposite sides of $BC$. If area of $\Delta ABC$ = area of $\Delta DBC$, prove that $BC$ bisects $AD$.

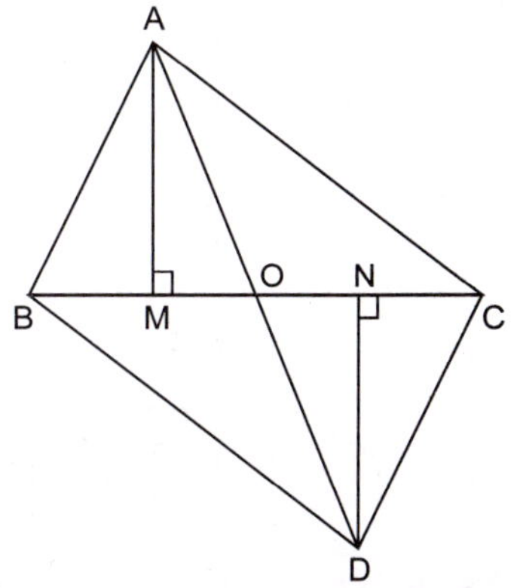


**Solution.** Let $AD$ and $BC$ intersect at $O$.

Draw $AM \perp BC$ and $DN \perp BC$.

Given,

Area of $\Delta ABC$ = Area of $\Delta DBC$

$\Rightarrow$ $\frac{1}{2} \times BC \times AM = \frac{1}{2} \times BC \times DN$

$\Rightarrow$ $AM = DN$

In $\Delta AMO$ and $\Delta DNO$

$\angle AOM = \angle DON$ (Vertically opposite angles)

$\angle AMO = \angle DNO$ (Each 90°)

$AM = DN$ (Proved above)

$\therefore$ $\Delta AMO \cong \Delta DNO$ (AAS criteria)

$\Rightarrow$ $AO = DO$ (CPCT)

Hence, $BC$ bisects $AD$.

Hence Proved.

**Example 23.** In the adjoining figure, $BC \parallel XY$, $BX \parallel CA$ and $AB \parallel YC$. Prove that ar $(\Delta ABX)$ = ar $(\Delta AYC)$.

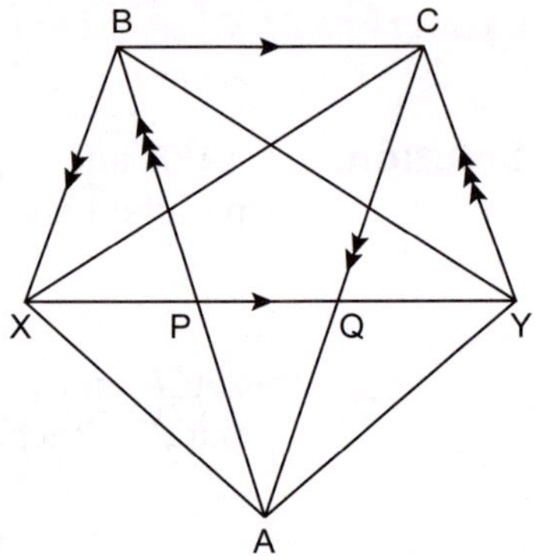


**Solution.** $\Delta BCX$ and $\Delta BCY$ are on same base $BC$ and between the same parallel lines $BC$ and $XY$.

$\therefore$ $$ar(\Delta BCX) = ar(\Delta BCY) \quad ...(i)$$

$\Delta BCX$ and $\Delta ABX$ are on same base $BX$ and between the same parallel lines $BX$ and $AC$.

$\therefore$ $$ar(\Delta BCX) = ar(\Delta ABX) \quad ...(ii)$$

$\Delta BCY$ and $\Delta AYC$ are on same base $CY$ and between the same parallel lines $CY$ and $AB$.

$\therefore$ $$ar(\Delta BCY) = ar(\Delta AYC) \quad ...(iii)$$

From equations *(i)*, *(ii)* and *(iii)*, we get

$$ar(\Delta ABX) = ar(\Delta AYC)$$

Hence Proved.

**Example 24.** In the adjoining figure, $ABCD$ is a parallelogram. Points $P$ and $Q$ are on $BC$ such that $BP = PQ = QC$. Prove that ar $(\Delta APQ)$ = ar $(\Delta DPQ)$ $= \frac{1}{6}$ ar ($\parallel$ gm $ABCD$).

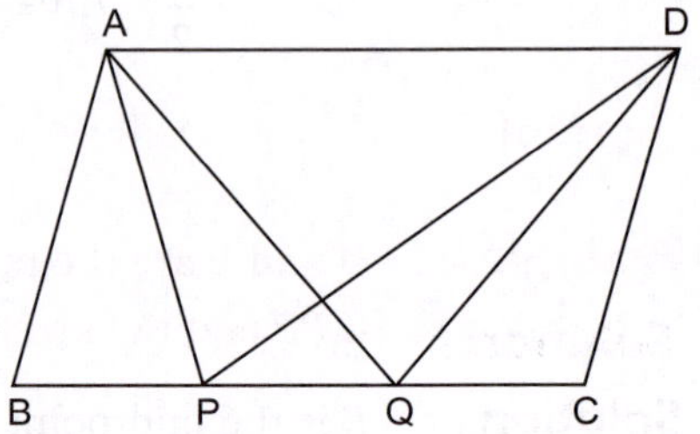


**Solution.**

$$BP = PQ = QC$$

$\Rightarrow$ $$PQ = \frac{1}{3} BC$$

Draw $AM \perp BC$ and $DN \perp BC$ produced.

$\Rightarrow$ $$AM \parallel DN$$

Now, $AM \parallel DN$ and $AD \parallel MN$

$\therefore$ $AMND$ is a parallelogram.

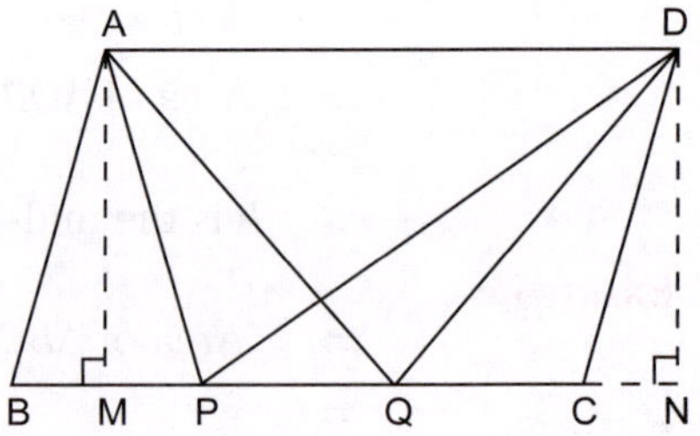


$\Rightarrow$ $$AM = DN$$

$$\text{Area of } \Delta APQ = \frac{1}{2} \times PQ \times AM$$

$$= \frac{1}{2} \times \left(\frac{1}{3} BC\right) \times AM$$

$$= \frac{1}{6} \times BC \times AM = \frac{1}{6} \times \text{ar } (\parallel \text{ gm } ABCN) \quad ...(i)$$

$$\text{Area of } \Delta DPQ = \frac{1}{2} \times PQ \times DN = \frac{1}{2} \times \left(\frac{1}{3} BC\right) \times AM$$

$$= \frac{1}{6} \times BC \times AM = \frac{1}{6} \times \text{ar } (\parallel \text{ gm } ABCD) \quad ...(ii)$$

From equations *(i)* and *(ii)*, we get

$$\text{Area of } \Delta APQ = \text{area of } \Delta DPQ = \frac{1}{6} \times \text{area of } \parallel \text{ gm } ABCD$$

Hence Proved.

**Example 25.** In the adjoining figure, $D$ is the mid-point of side $BC$ of $\Delta ABC$, $E$ is the mid-point of $BD$ and $P$ is the mid-point of $AE$, then prove that ar $(\Delta PBE) = \frac{1}{8}$ ar $(\Delta ABC)$.

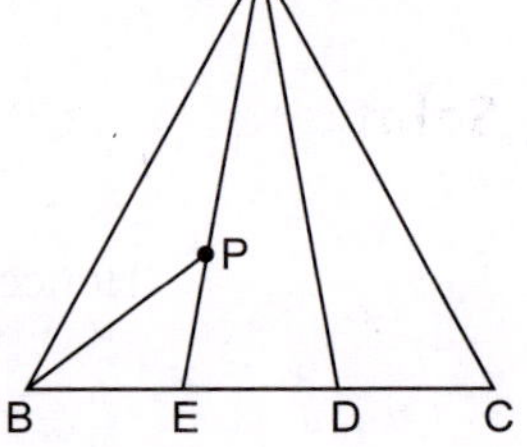


**Solution.** We know that a median of a triangle divides it into two triangles of equal area.

$D$ is mid-point of $BC \Rightarrow AD$ is a median of $\Delta ABC$.

$\therefore$ $$\text{ar } (\Delta ABD) = \frac{1}{2} \text{ ar } (\Delta ABC) \quad ...(i)$$

Again, $E$ is the mid-point of $BD \Rightarrow AE$ is the median of $\Delta ABD$.

$\therefore \quad ar(\Delta ABE) = \frac{1}{2} ar(\Delta ABD)$

$= \frac{1}{2} \cdot \frac{1}{2} ar(\Delta ABC)$ [From *(i)*]

$\Rightarrow \quad ar(\Delta ABE) = \frac{1}{4} ar(\Delta ABC)$ ...*(ii)*

Again, $P$ is the mid-point of $AE \Rightarrow BP$ is the median of $\Delta ABE$.

$\therefore \quad ar(\Delta PBE) = \frac{1}{2} ar(\Delta ABE)$

$= \frac{1}{2} \times \frac{1}{4} ar(\Delta ABC)$ [From *(ii)*]

$= \frac{1}{8} ar(\Delta ABC)$ Hence Proved.

**Example 26.** $ABCD$ is a trapezium with $AB \parallel DC$. A line parallel to $AC$ intersects $AB$ at $X$ and $BC$ at $Y$. Prove that

$ar(\Delta ADX) = ar(\Delta ACY)$

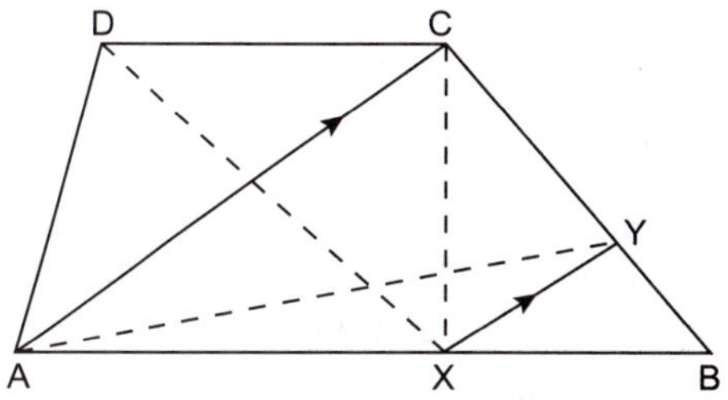


**Solution.** Join $CX$.

$\Delta ADX$ and $\Delta ACX$ are on same base $AX$ and between the same parallel lines $AX$ and $DC$.

$\therefore \quad ar(\Delta ADX) = ar(\Delta ACX)$ ...*(i)*

$\Delta ACY$ and $\Delta ACX$ are on same base $AC$ and between the same parallel lines $AC$ and $XY$.

$\therefore \quad ar(\Delta ACY) = ar(\Delta ACX)$ ...*(ii)*

From equations *(i)* and *(ii)*, we get

$ar(\Delta ADX) = ar(\Delta ACY)$ Hence Proved.

**Example 27.** In the adjoining figure, $PQRS$ and $PXYZ$ are two parallelograms of equal area. Prove that $SX \parallel YR$.

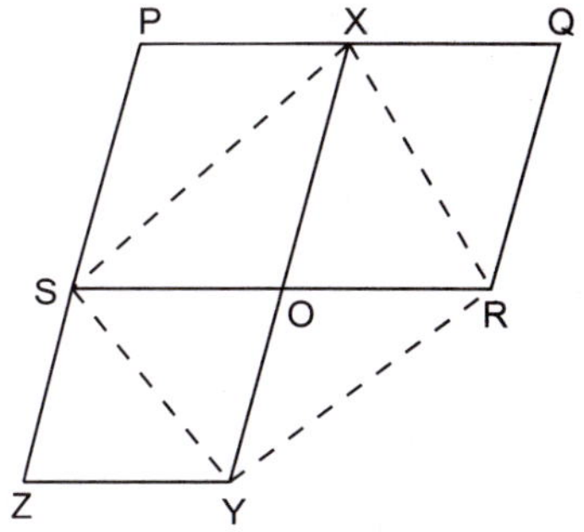


**Solution.** Join $XR$ and $SY$.

Here, $ar(\parallel gm\ PQSR) = ar(\parallel gm\ PXYZ)$

$\Rightarrow \quad ar(\parallel gm\ PQSR) - ar(\parallel gm\ PSOX)$

$= ar(\parallel gm\ PXYZ) - ar(\parallel gm\ PSOX)$

$\Rightarrow \quad ar(\parallel gm\ XORQ) = ar(\parallel gm\ SZYO)$

$\Rightarrow \quad 2 \cdot ar(\Delta XOR) = 2 \cdot ar(\Delta SOY)$

$\Rightarrow \quad ar(\Delta XOR) = ar(\Delta SOY)$

$\Rightarrow \quad ar(\Delta XOR) + ar(\Delta OYR) = ar(\Delta SOY) + ar(\Delta OYR)$

$\Rightarrow \quad ar(\Delta XYR) = ar(\Delta SRY)$

$\Delta XYR$ and $\Delta SRY$ are on same base $YR$ and have same area.

$\therefore \quad SX \parallel YR$ Hence Proved.

**Example 28.** In the adjoining figure, $ABCD$, $DCFE$ and $ABFE$ are parallelograms. Show that $ar(\Delta ADE) = ar(\Delta BCF)$.

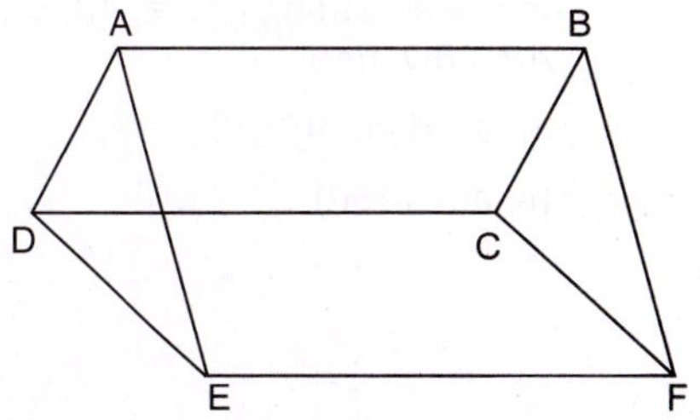


**Solution.** $ABCD$ is a parallelogram.

$\therefore \quad AD = BC$

Similarly, $\quad DE = CF$ and $AE = BF$

In $\Delta ADE$ and $\Delta BCF$,

$AD = BC$

$$DE = CF$$
$$AE = BF$$

$\therefore$ $\Delta ADE \cong \Delta BCF$ (SSS criteria)

$\Rightarrow$ ar ($\Delta ADE$) = ar ($\Delta BCF$) (Congruent figures have equal areas.)

Hence Proved.

**Example 29.** *ABCD* is a trapezium in which *AB* || *DC*. A line parallel to *AC* intersects *AB* at *P* and *BC* at *Q*. Prove that ar ($\Delta ADP$) = ar ($\Delta ACQ$).

**Solution.** Join *CP*.

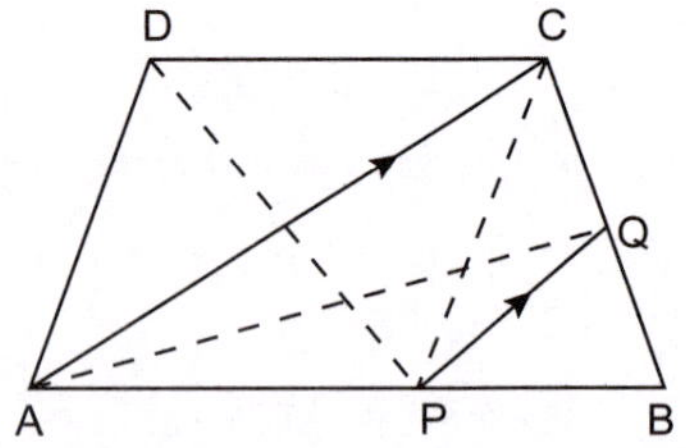


$\Delta ADP$ and $\Delta ACP$ are on same base *AP* and between the same parallel lines *AB* and *DC*.

$\therefore$ ar ($\Delta ADP$) = ar ($\Delta ACP$) ...*(i)*

$\Delta ACQ$ and $\Delta ACP$ are on same base *AC* and between the same parallel lines *AC* and *PQ*.

$\therefore$ ar ($\Delta ACQ$) = ar ($\Delta ACP$) ...*(ii)*

From equations *(i)* and *(ii)*, we get

ar ($\Delta ADP$) = ar ($\Delta ACQ$)

Hence Proved.

## Exercise 13A

**1.** In the adjoining figure; if the area of parallelogram *ABCD* is 90 cm$^2$, find :

(i) area of parallelogram *ABEF*.

(ii) area of $\Delta ABE$.

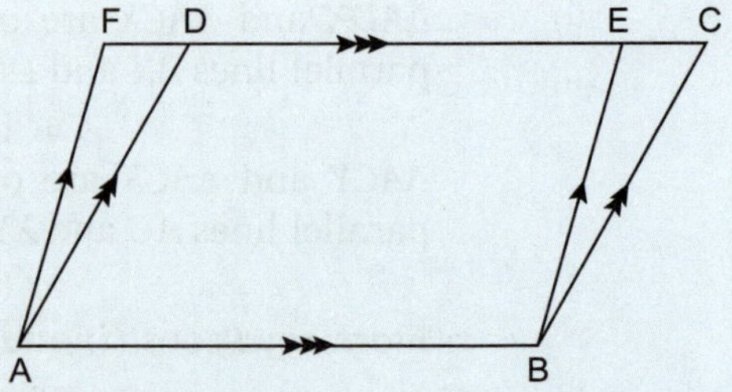


**2.** In the adjoining figure; *AB* = 16 cm, *DM* = 4 cm and *BC* = 8 cm. Find the length of *DN*.

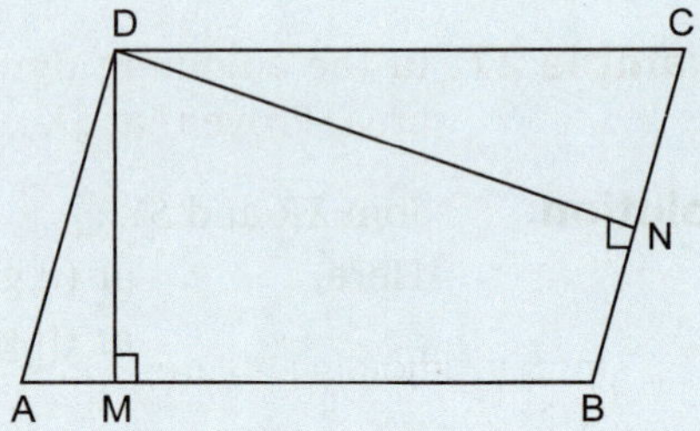


**3.** In the adjoining figure, *BD* = 2 *CD*. If area of $\Delta ABC$ = 36 cm$^2$, find the area of $\Delta ABD$.

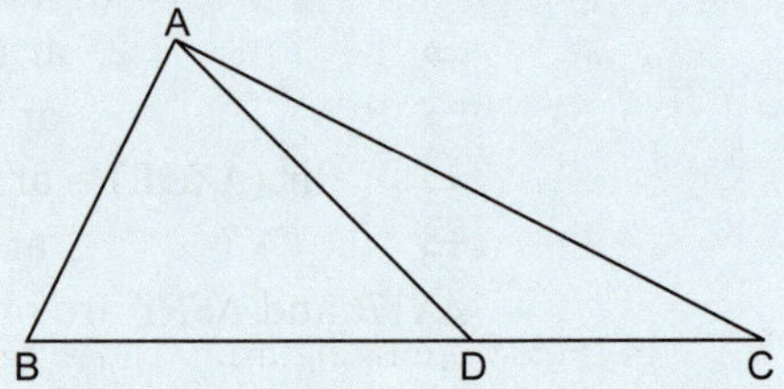


**4.** In the adjoining figure, *ABCD* is a rectangle in which *AB* = 10 cm, *AD* = 6 cm. If *AP* || *BQ*, find :

(i) ar (|| gm *ABQP*)

(ii) ar ($\Delta ABP$)

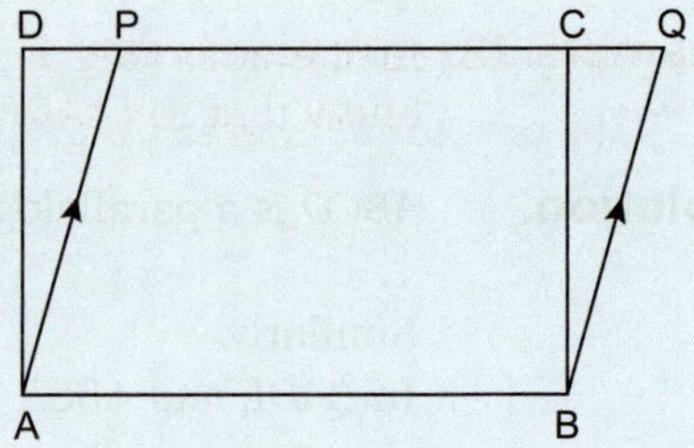

5. The area of a parallelogram is 150 $cm^2$. The ratio of its base and corresponding altitude is 3 : 2. Find the base and corresponding altitude.

6. In the adjoining figure; $AN = NB$ and $DM = MC$ in the parallelogram $ABCD$. If area ($ABCD$) $= 44$ $cm^2$,

(i) find the area of $\Delta BCE$.

(ii) find the area of parallelogram $BNMC$.

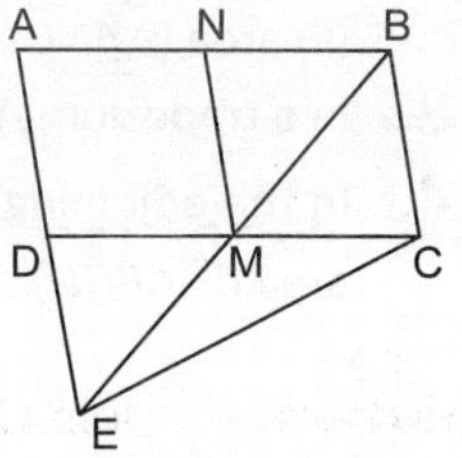


7. In the adjoining figure; $ABCD$ is a parallelogram. If $AP = BP$ and $CP$ meets the diagonal $BD$ at $Q$ and area of $\Delta BPQ = 20$ $cm^2$, find :

(i) $PQ : QC$.

(ii) Area of $\Delta PBC$.

(iii) Area of parallelogram $ABCD$.

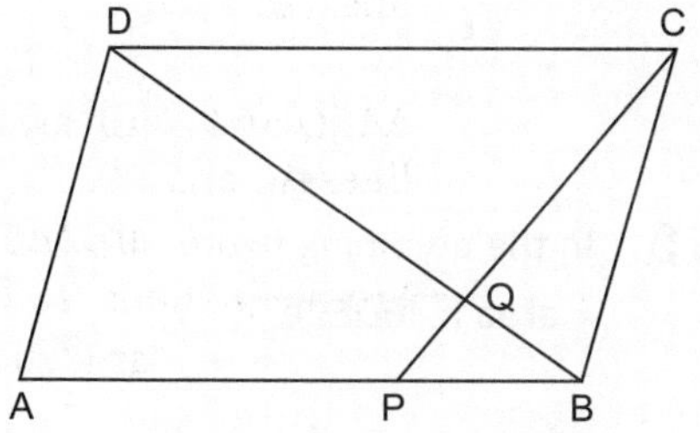


8. In the adjoining figure; $ABCD$ is a parallelogram whose area is 324 $cm^2$. If $P$ is a point on $AB$ such that $AP : PB = 1 : 2$, find :

(i) Area of $\Delta APD$.

(ii) $QP : QD$.

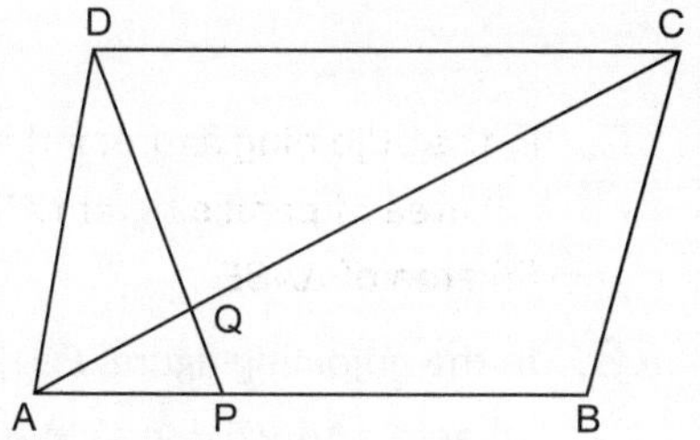


9. In a parallelogram $ABCD$, $P$ is a point on $DC$ such that $DP : PC = 2 : 3$. If area of $\Delta DPB = 40$ $cm^2$, find the area of $\square ABCD$.

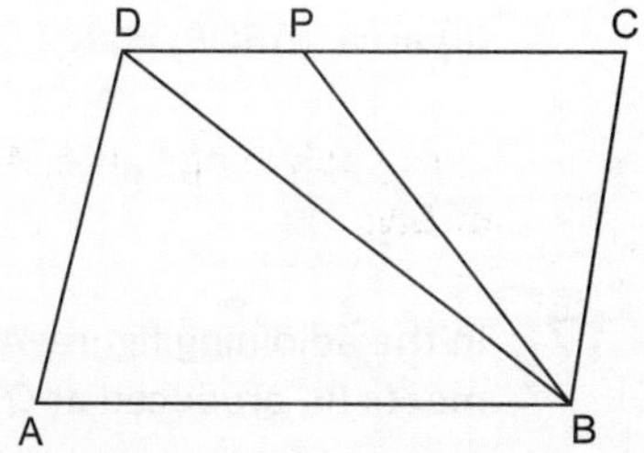


10. In the adjoining figure; $BD = DC$ and $AE = ED$. Prove that area of $\Delta ACE$ $= \frac{1}{4} \times$ area of $\Delta ABC$.

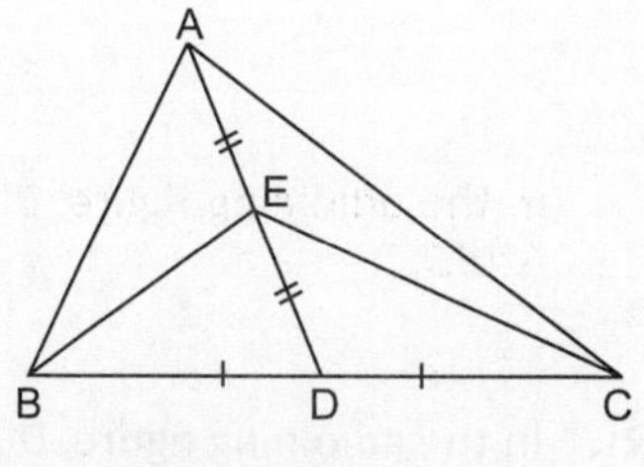


11. In the adjoining figure, $D$ is the mid-point of $BC$ and $E$ be any point on $AD$. Prove that :

(i) area ($\Delta EBD$) = area ($\Delta ECD$).

(ii) area ($\Delta ABE$) = area ($\Delta ACE$).

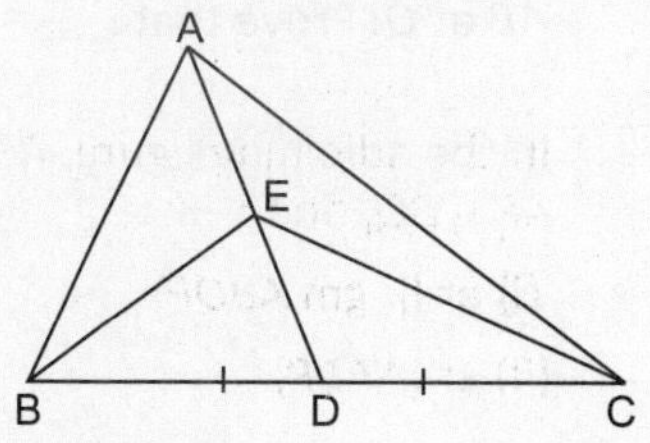

**12.** In a parallelogram *ABCD, M* and *N* are the points on *AB* and *BC* respectively. Prove that :

(i) $\Delta CMD$ and $\Delta AND$ are equal in area.

(ii) area ($\Delta AND$) = area ($\Delta AMD$) + area ($\Delta CMB$).

**13.** In a trapezium *ABCD, AB* || *DC* and the diagonals *AC* and *BD* intersect at point '*O*'. Prove that area ($\Delta AOD$) = area ($\Delta BOC$).

**14.** In the adjoining figure, *O* is the mid-point of diagonal *AC* of a quadrilateral *ABCD*. Prove that area (□*ABOD*) = area (□*BODC*).

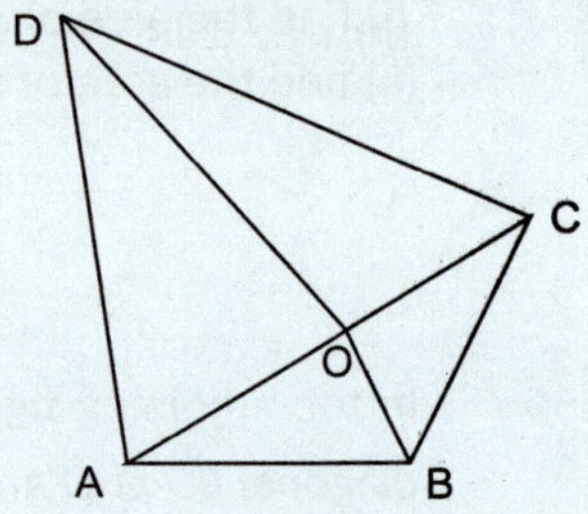


**15.** In the adjoining figure, *AD* = *BD* and □*BDEC* is a parallelogram. Prove that area ($\Delta ABC$) = area (□*BDEC*).

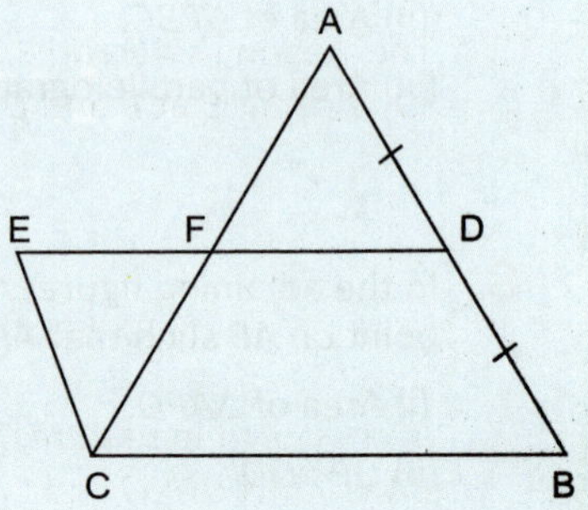


**16.** In the adjoining figure, *PQ* || *BC*. Prove that :

(i) area ($\Delta ABQ$) = area ($\Delta ACP$).

(ii) area ($\Delta BOP$) = area ($\Delta COQ$).

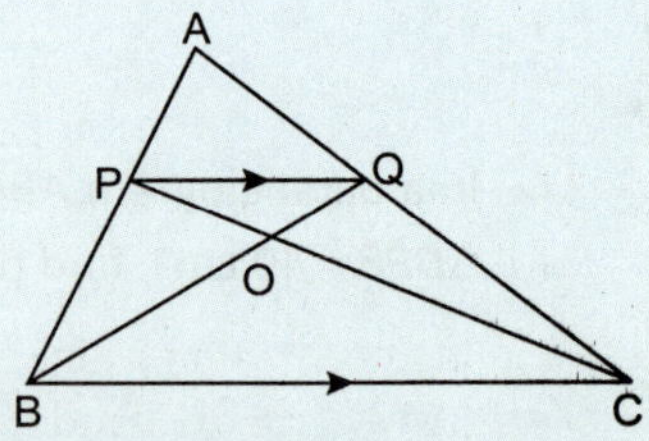


**17.** In the adjoining figure, *ABCD* is a parallelogram. A line through *A* intersects *DC* at *P* and meets *BC* produced at *Q*. Prove that :

area ($\Delta BCP$) = area ($\Delta DPQ$).

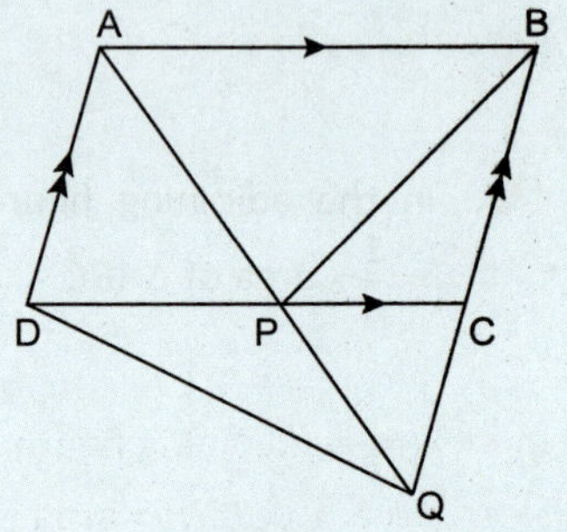


**18.** In the adjoining figure, *D* is the mid-point of *AB*. *P* is any point on *BC* and *CQ* || *PD* meets *AB* at *Q*. Prove that :

$$\text{area}(\Delta BPQ) = \frac{1}{2} \times \text{area}(\Delta ABC).$$

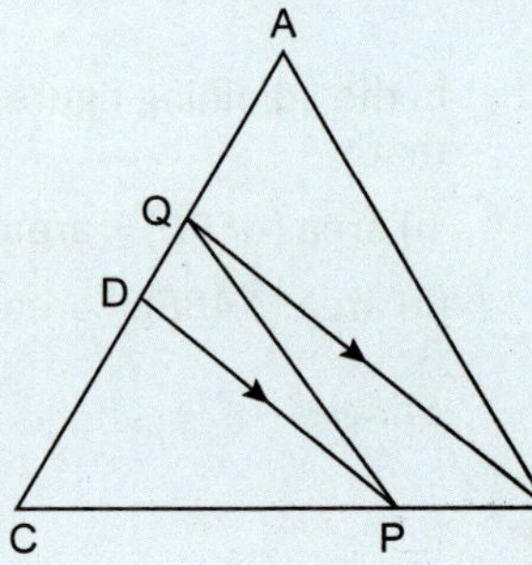

**19.** In a trapezium *ABCD*, *AB* || *DC*. A line parallel to *AC* cuts *AB* at *P* and *BC* at *Q*. Prove that area ($\Delta APD$) = area ($\Delta ACQ$).

**20.** In the adjoining figure, $\Delta ABC$ is a right-angled triangle, right angled at *B*; *ABDE* and *ACGF* are the squares. If *BH* is perpendicular to *FG*, prove that :

(i) area ($\Delta EAC$) = area ($\Delta BAF$).

(ii) area (□*ABDE*) = area (□*AIHF*).

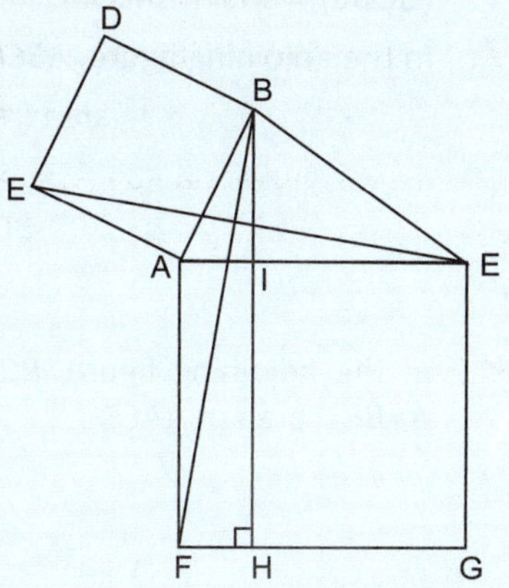


**21.** The diagonals *AC* and *BD* of a parallelogram *ABCD* intersect at '*O*'. A straight line through '*O*' meets *AB* at *P* and *DC* at *Q*. Prove that :

$$\text{area }(\square APQD) = \frac{1}{2} \times \text{area }(\square ABCD).$$

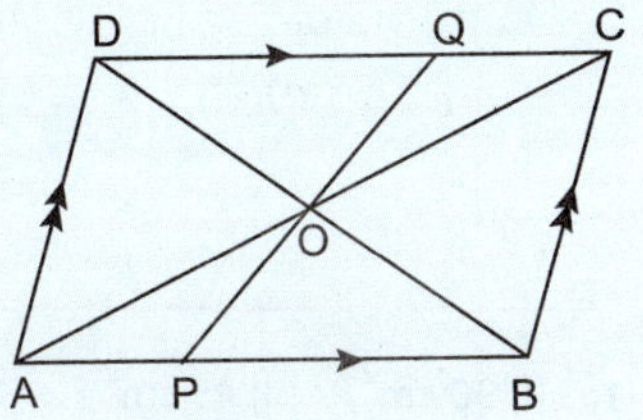


**22.** In the adjoining figure, *ABCDE* is a pentagon in which *EG* is drawn parallel to *DA* meets *BA* produced at *G* and *CF* is drawn parallel to *DB* meets *AB* produced at *F*. Prove that area of *ABCDE* = area of *GDF*.

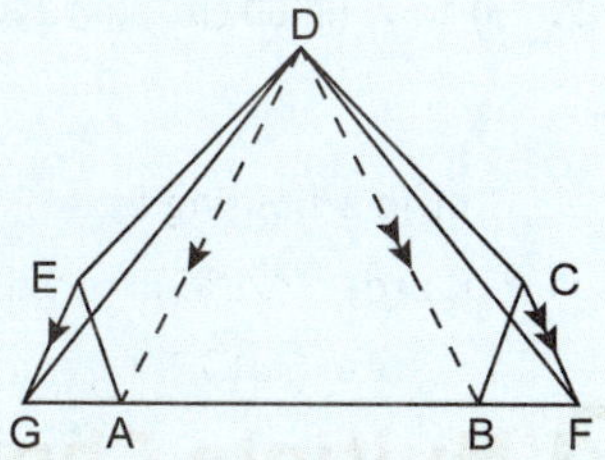


**23.** In the adjoining figure, *BD* = *CD* and *P* is a point on *AC* such that area ($\Delta APD$) : area ($\Delta ABD$) = 2 : 3. Find :

(i) *AP* : *PC*.

(ii) area ($\Delta DCP$) : area ($\Delta ABC$).

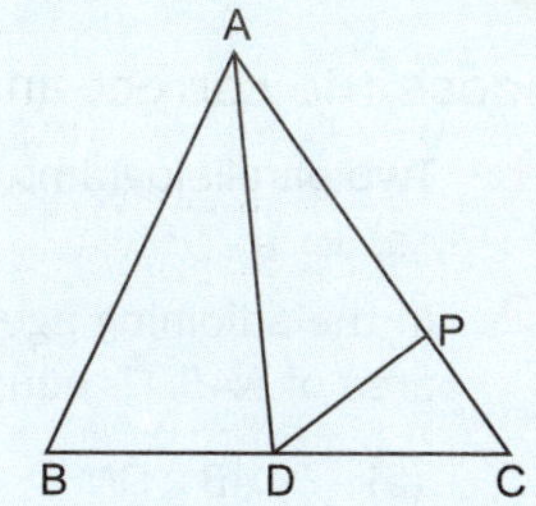


**24.** In the adjoining figure, *ABCD* and *BEFG* are two parallelograms. Prove that :
area (□*ABCD*) = area (□*BEFG*).

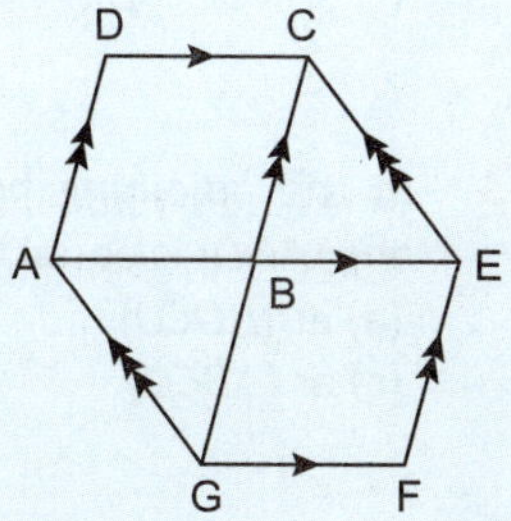


**25.** *ABCD* is a parallelogram. *E* and *F* are the mid-points of the sides *AB* and *AD* respectively. Prove that area ($\Delta AEF$) $= \frac{1}{8} \times$ area (□*ABCD*).

**26.** In $\Delta ABC$; $E$ and $F$ are the mid-points of sides $AB$ and $AC$ respectively. If $FB$ and $CE$ intersect at point '$O$', prove that area $(\Delta OBC)$ = area $(\square AEOF)$.

**27.** In the adjoining figure, $ABCD$ and $ABFE$ are two parallelograms. Prove that :

area $(ABCD)$ + area $(ABFE)$ = area $(EFCD)$.

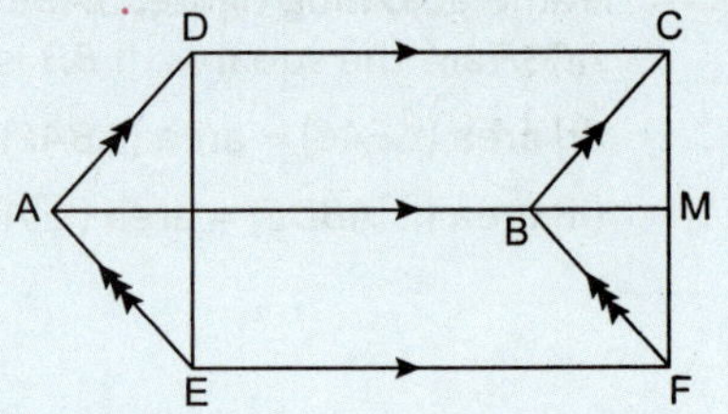


**28.** In the adjoining figure, $PQ \parallel BC$, $BE \parallel CA$ and $CF \parallel BA$. Prove that area of $\Delta ABE$ = area of $\Delta ACF$.

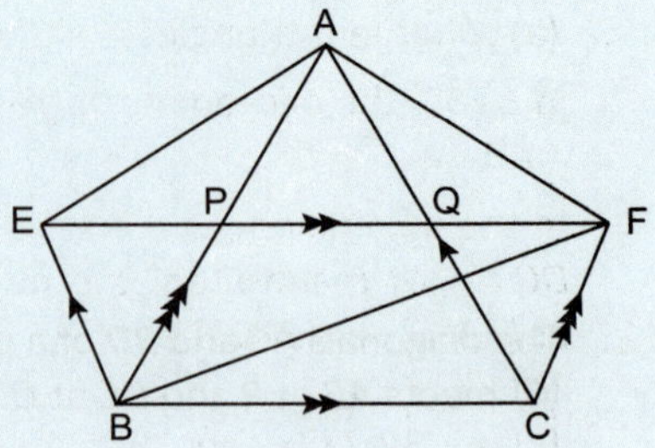


## *Answers*

**1.** (i) 90 cm$^2$, (ii) 45 cm$^2$ **2.** 8 cm **3.** 24 cm$^2$
**4.** (i) 60 cm$^2$, (ii) 30 cm$^2$ **5.** 15 cm, 10 cm **6.** (i) 22 cm$^2$, (ii) 22 cm$^2$
**7.** (i) 1 : 2, (ii) 60 cm$^2$, (iii) 240 cm$^2$ **8.** (i) 54 cm$^2$, (ii) 1 : 3 **9.** 200 cm$^2$ **23.** (i) 2 : 1, (ii) 1 : 6

# Exercise 13B

## Multiple Choice *Questions*

Choose the correct answer from the given four options in each of the following questions :

**1.** Two parallelograms are on equal bases and between the same parallel lines. The ratio of their areas is :

(a) 1 : 1 (b) 1 : 2 (c) 2 : 1 (d) 1 : 3

**2.** In the adjoining figure, a parallelogram $ABCD$ is shown. If $DM \perp AB$, $DN \perp BC$, then area of $\Delta ABD$ is equal to :

(a) $\frac{1}{2} \times AB \times DN$ (b) $\frac{1}{2} \times BC \times DN$

(c) $\frac{1}{2} \times BC \times DM$ (d) $\frac{1}{2} \times AD \times DM$

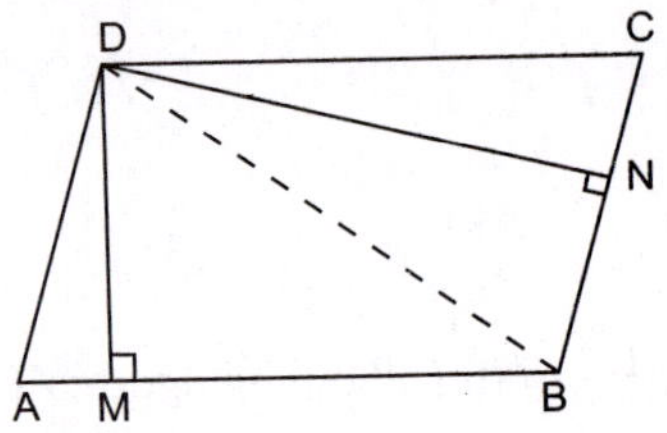


**3.** In the adjoining figure, a trapezium $ABCD$ is shown in which $AB \parallel DC$ then, ar $(\Delta AOD)$ is equal to :

(a) ar $(\Delta OCD)$ (b) ar $(\Delta AOB)$
(c) ar $(\Delta BCD)$ (d) ar $(\Delta BOC)$

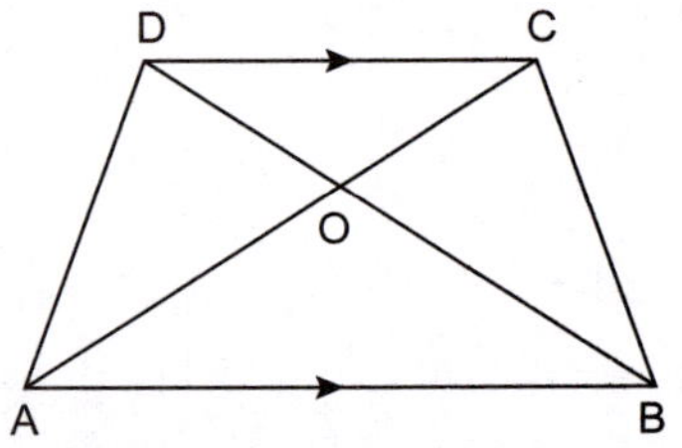


**4.** A triangle and a rectangle are on the same base and between the same parallel lines. The ratio of their areas is :

(a) 1 : 1 (b) 1 : 2 (c) 1 : 3 (d) 1 : 4

**5.** In the adjoining figure, $ABCD$ is a parallelogram and $M$ is the mid-point of $AB$. If ar (|| gm $ABCD$) = 40 cm$^2$, then ar ($\Delta ADM$) is equal to :

(a) 5 cm$^2$ (b) 20 cm$^2$
(c) 15 cm$^2$ (d) 10 cm$^2$

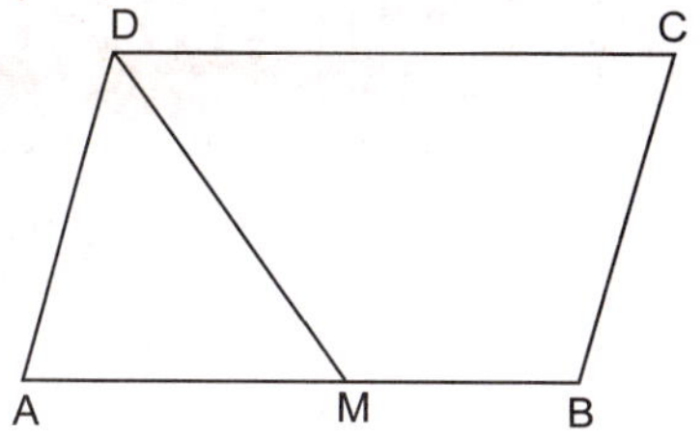


**6.** A median of a triangle divides it into two :

(a) congruent triangles (b) equilateral triangles (c) triangles of equal area (d) isosceles triangles

**7.** In $\Delta ABC$; the mid-points of the sides $BC$, $CA$ and $AB$ are $D$, $E$ and $F$ respectively. The ratio of ar ($\Delta DEF$) and ar ($\Delta ABC$) is :

(a) 1 : 4 (b) 1 : 3 (c) 1 : 2 (d) 1 : 1

**8.** In the adjoining figure, a trapezium $ABCD$ is shown in which $AB \parallel DC$, $AB = x$ and $DC = y$. If $E$ and $F$ are the mid-points of the sides $AD$ and $BC$ respectively, then ar ($ABFE$) : ar ($EFCD$) is :

(a) $x : y$ (b) $(3x + y) : (x + 3y)$
(c) $(x + 3y) : (3x + y)$ (d) $(2x + y) : (3x + y)$

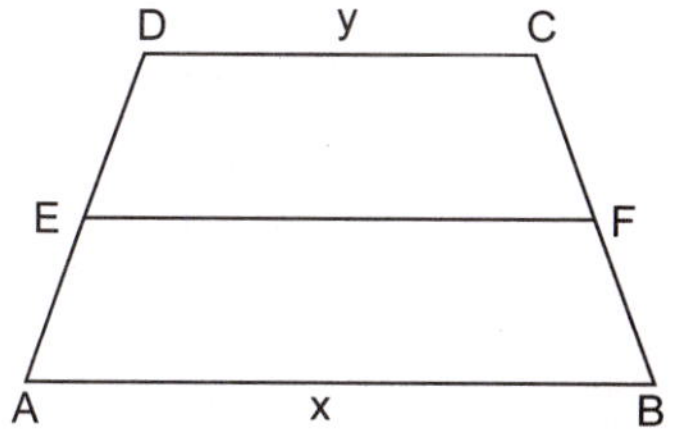


**9.** In the adjoining figure, a parallelogram $ABCD$ is shown in which $P$ divides $AB$ in the ratio 1 : 2. If the area of the parallelogram $ABCD$ is 60 cm$^2$, then area ($BPDC$) is :

(a) 20 cm$^2$ (b) 40 cm$^2$
(c) 50 cm$^2$ (d) 30 cm$^2$

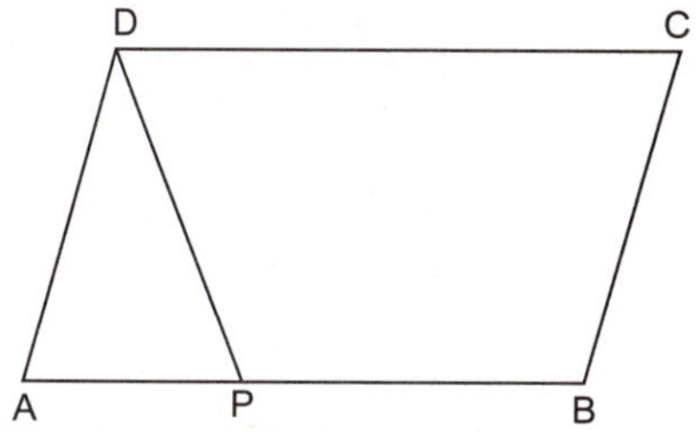


**10.** In the adjoining figure, $BM = 2$ CM. If ar ($\Delta ABC$) = 30 cm$^2$, then ar ($\Delta ABM$) is :

(a) 20 cm$^2$ (b) 15 cm$^2$
(c) 10 cm$^2$ (d) 5 cm$^2$

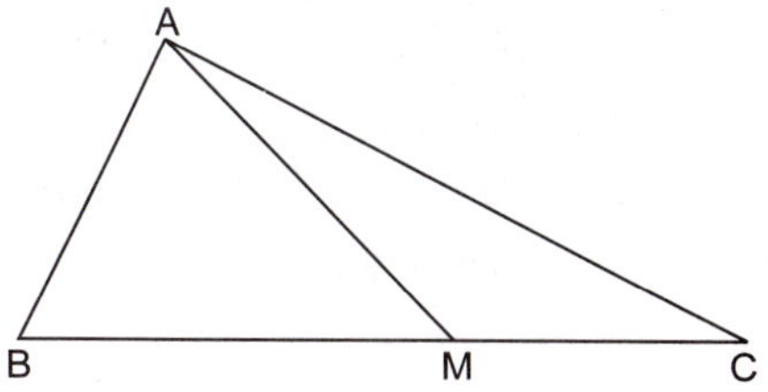


## *Answers*

| | | | | | | | | | |
|---|---|---|---|---|---|---|---|---|---|
| **1.** (a) | **2.** (b) | **3.** (d) | **4.** (b) | **5.** (d) | **6.** (c) | **7.** (a) | **8.** (b) | **9.** (c) | **10.** (a) |

## SUMMARY *of the Chapter*

- Area Axiom : Every polygon region has an area measured in square units.
- Congruent Area Axiom : If two figures are congruent then the areas enclosed by them are equal.
- If $\Delta ABC \cong \Delta DEF$ then ar $(\Delta ABC)$ = ar $(\Delta DEF)$.
- Addition Area Axiom : If a planar region $R$ consists of two non-overlapping planar regions $R_1$ and $R$ as shown in adjoining figure, then

  $$ar(R) = ar(R_1) + ar(R_2).$$

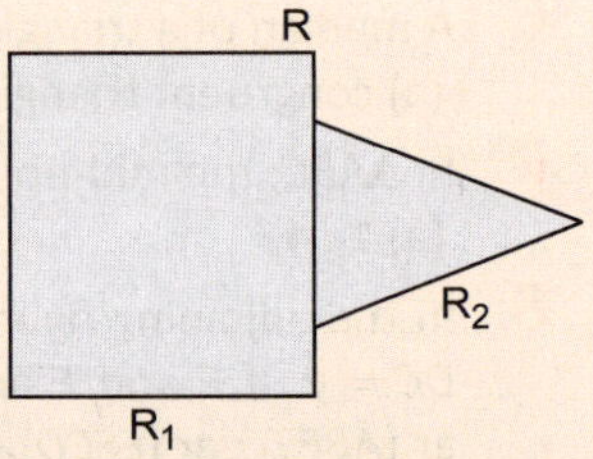


- Two congruent figures are always equal figures but equal figures may not be congruent.

**Theorem 1** A diagonal of a parallelogram divides it into two triangles of equal areas.

**Theorem 2** Parallelograms on the same base (or equal bases) and between the same parallel lines are equal in area.

**Theorem 3** Parallelograms on same base (or equal bases) and having equal areas, lie between the same parallel lines.

Corollary : The area of a parallelogram is equal to the area of the rectangle on the same base and between the same parallel lines.

**Theorem 4** The area of a triangle is half that of a parallelogram on the same base and between the same parallel lines.

**Theorem 5** Triangles on the same base and between the same parallel lines are equal in areas.

**Theorem 6** Triangles with equal areas on the same bases have equal corresponding altitudes.

# CHAPTER TEST

1. In the following figure, $ABCD$ is a parallelogram. If ar $(\Delta ABP) = 12\ cm^2$, find the area of parallelogram $ABCD$.

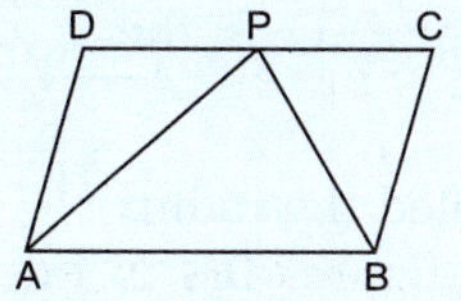


2. In the following figure, $ABCD$ is a parallelogram. $M$ is a point on side $AB$ such that $BM = 4\ AM$. If ar $(\Delta AMD) = 10\ cm^2$, find the area of parallelogram $ABCD$.

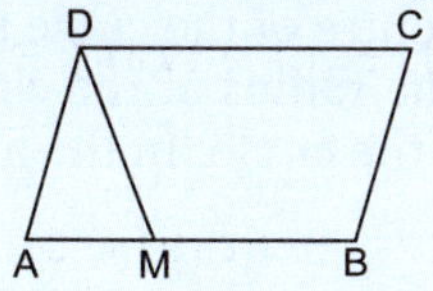


3. In the following figure $ABCD$ is a parallelogram. Prove that ar $(\Delta ABN)$ = ar $(\Delta ADM)$.

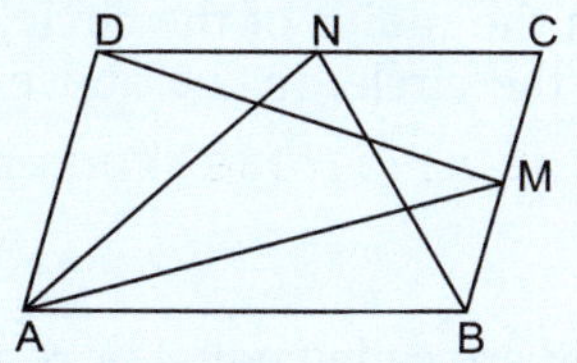


4. Prove that a median of a triangle divides it into two triangles of equal areas.

5. The diagonals of a parallelogram $ABCD$ intersect at $O$. A straight line through $O$ meets $AB$ at $P$ and $DC$ at $Q$. Prove that

$$\text{ar}(\square APQD) = \frac{1}{2}\ \text{ar}(||\text{gm } ABCD)$$

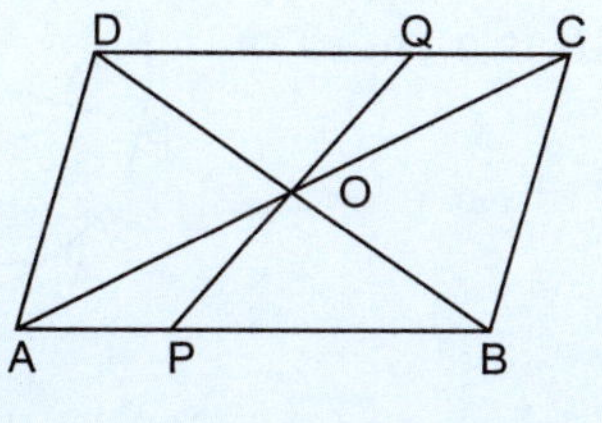


6. $\Delta ABC$ and $\Delta DBC$ are on same base $BC$ with $A$ and $D$ on opposite sides of $BC$. If ar $(\Delta ABC)$ = ar $(\Delta DBC)$, prove that $BC$ bisects $AD$.

7. Prove that the area of the quadrilateral formed by joining the mid-points of the adjacent sides of a quadrilateral is half the area of the given quadrilateral.

8. In the following figure, $ABCD$ is a parallelogram. If $M$ is any point on side $BC$, prove that

$$\text{ar}(\Delta ABM) + \text{ar}(\Delta CDM) = \frac{1}{2}\ \text{ar}(||\text{gm } ABCD)$$

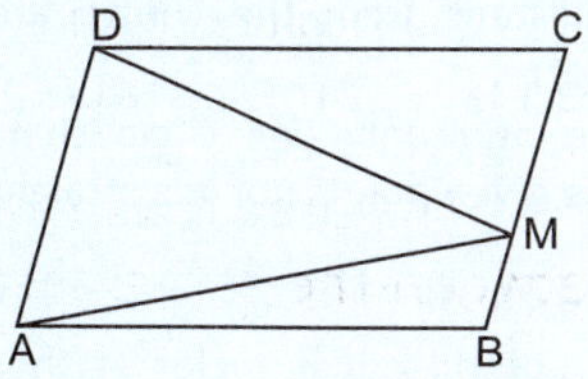


9. Any point $D$ is taken on the side $BC$ of a $\Delta ABC$ and $AD$ is produced to $E$ such that $AD = DE$. Prove that

$$\text{ar}(\Delta BCE) = \text{ar}(\Delta ABC)$$

10. In the following figure, $ABCD$ and $APQR$ are two parallelograms. Prove that

$$\text{ar}(||\text{gm } ABCD) = \text{ar}(||\text{gm } APQR)$$

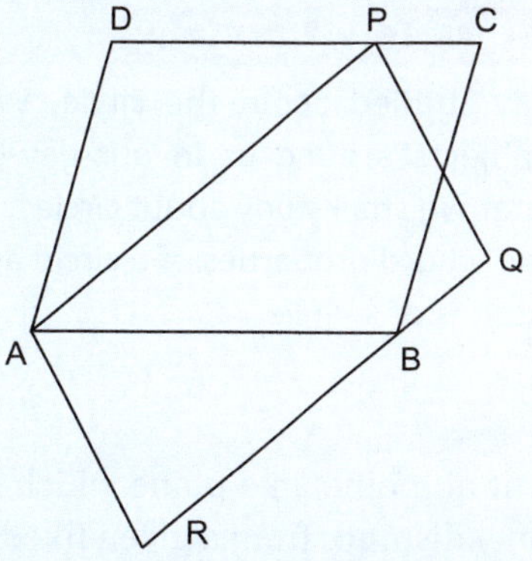


## *Answers*

**1.** $24\ cm^2$ **2.** $100\ cm^2$

Chapter 14

# CIRCLES

## Syllabus

**(a) Chord Properties:**

- A straight line drawn from the centre of a circle to bisect a chord which is not a diameter is at right angles to the chord.
- The perpendicular to a chord from the centre bisects the chord (without proof).
- Equal chords are equidistant from the centre.
- Chords equidistant from the centre are equal (without proof).
- There is one and only one circle that passes through three given points not in a straight line.

**(b) Arc and Chord Properties:**

- If two arcs subtend equal angles at the centre, they are equal, and its converse.
- If two chords are equal, they cut off equal arcs, and its converse (without proof).

**Note: Proofs of the theorems given above are to be taught unless specified otherwise.**

## INTRODUCTION

We have already studied about the circle. We see many circular objects around us in our day-to-day life. In this chapter we shall study about circles, terms related to a circle, chord properties of a circle and arc and chord properties of a circle.

## Circle

The collection of all points in a plane which are at a fixed (constant) distance from a given fixed point in that plane, is called a circle.

or

The path of a point which moves so that it is always at a constant distance from a fixed point in the plane, is called a circle.

The fixed point is called the centre of the circle. In the adjoining figure, $O$ is the centre of the circle.

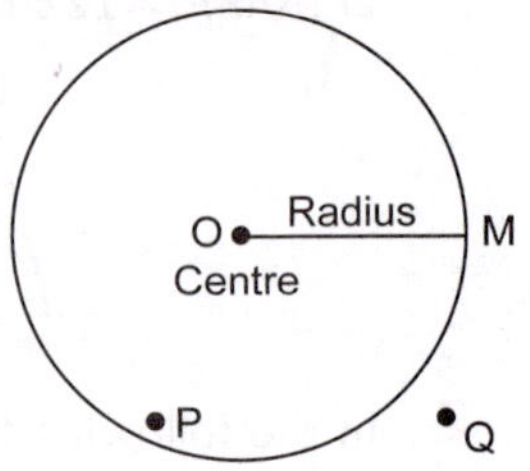


The constant distance is called the radius of the circle. In the above figure, $OM$ is the radius of the circle.

## Interior Point

If the distance between the centre of the circle and any point in the same plane is smaller than the radius of the circle, then that point is called the interior point of the circle. In the above figure, $P$ is the interior point.

## Exterior Point

If the distance between the centre of the circle and any point in the same plane is greater than the radius of the circle, then that point is called exterior point of the circle. In the above figure, $Q$ is the exterior point.

## Equal Circles

Two circles with equal radii are called equal or congruent circles.

## Concentric Circles

Two or more circles with same centre are called concentric circles.

## Chord of a Circle

A line segment joining any two points on a circle is called a chord of the circle.

In the adjoining figure, $AB$ is a chord of the circle.

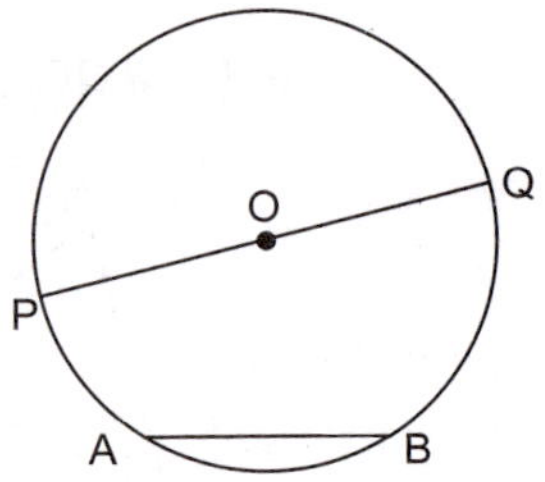


## Diameter of a Circle

A chord passes through the centre of the circle is the largest chord and is called the diameter of the circle.

Diameter = 2 × Radius.

In the above figure, $PQ$ is a diameter of the circle.

## Secant of a Circle

A line which meets a circle in two points is called a secant of the circle. In the adjoining figure, line $AB$ is a secant of the circle.

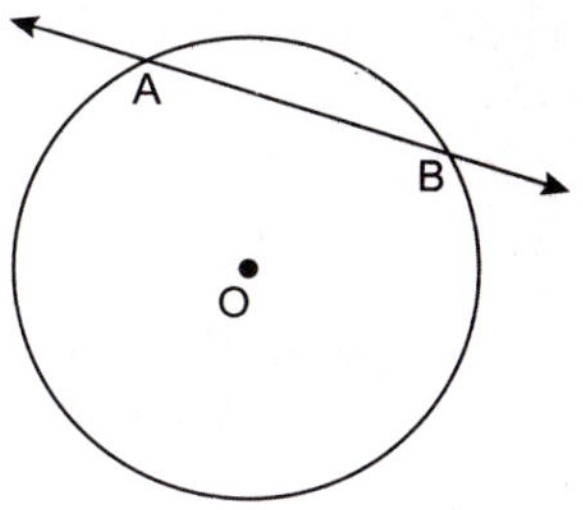


## Arc of a Circle

A continuous part of a circle is called an arc of the circle. It is denoted by the symbol '$\frown$'.

In the adjoining figure, $\overparen{AB}$ denotes the arc $AB$ of the circle.

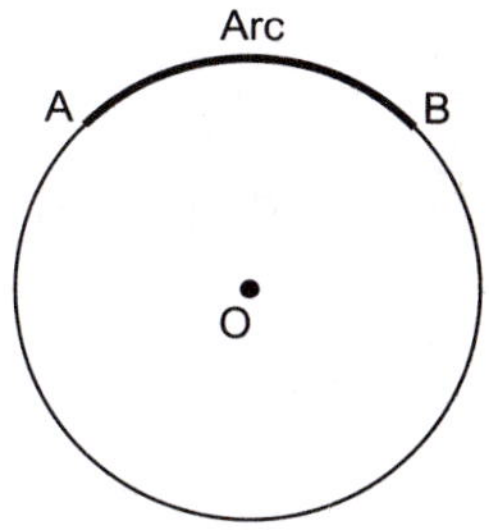


(i) Minor and Major Arcs : An arc less than one-half of the whole arc of a circle is called a minor arc and an arc greater than one-half of the whole arc of a circle is called the major arc.

In the adjoining figure, $\overparen{PQ}$ is the minor arc and $\overparen{PRQ}$ is the major arc.

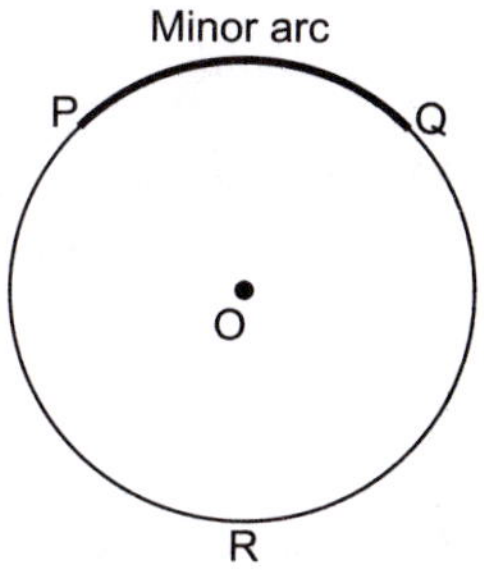


(ii) Semi-circle : When $PQ$ is a diameter then it divides the circle into two equal parts, each of them is called a semi-circle.
In the adjoining figure, $PSQ$ is a semi-circle.

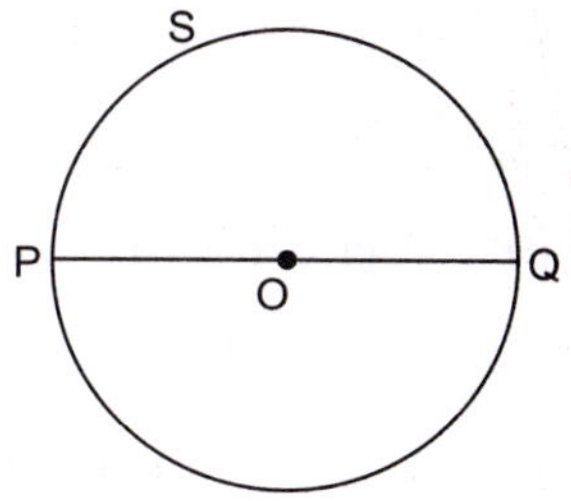


(iii) Circumference : The whole arc of a circle is called the circumference of the circle.

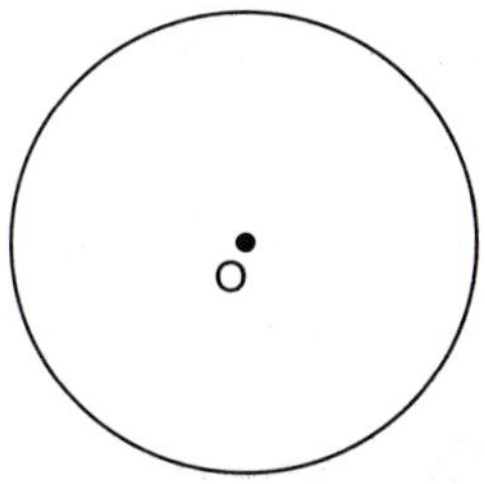


## Sector of a Circle

A part of the plane region bounded by an arc of a circle and its two bounded radii, is called a sector of the circle.

(i) Minor Sector : The part containing minor arc is called minor sector.
(ii) Major Sector : The part containing major arc is called major sector.

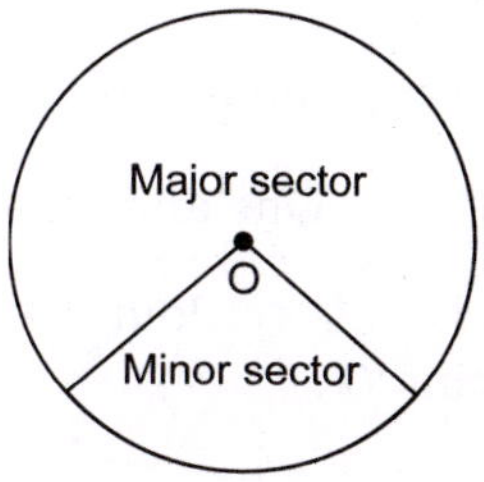

## Segment of a Circle

A chord of a circle divides the circular region into two parts, each of which is called the segment of the circle.

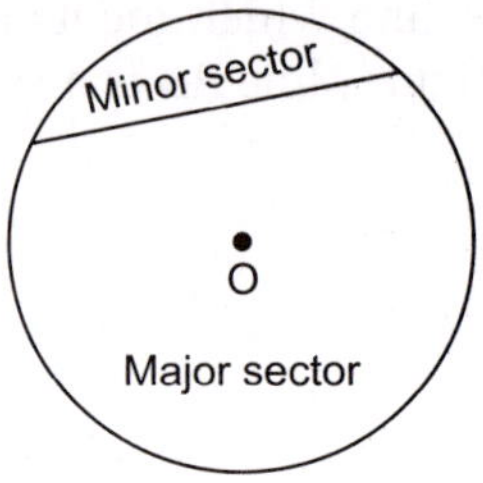


(i) Minor Segment : The part of the circular region containing minor arc is called the minor segment.

(ii) Major Segment : The part of the circular region containing major arc is called the major segment.

## Chord Properties of Circles

**Theorem 1** A straight line drawn from the centre of a circle to bisect a chord, which is not a diameter, is at right angles to the chord.

Given : A circle with centre 'O' and $OP$ bisects the chord $AB$.

To Prove : $OP$ is perpendicular to $AB$.

Construction : Join $OA$ and $OB$.

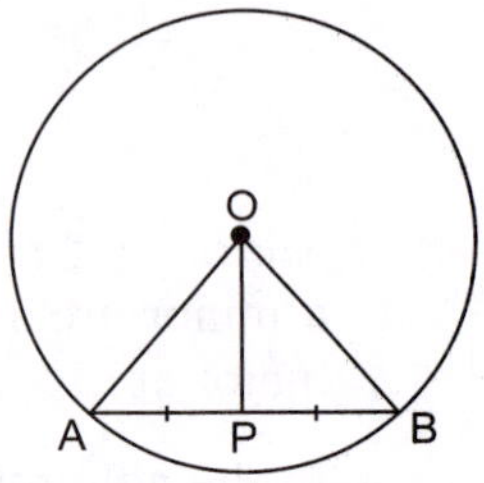


Proof :

| Statement | Reason |
|---|---|
| In $\Delta OAP$ and $\Delta OBP$, | |
| $OA = OB$ | radii of a circle |
| $OP = OP$ | common |
| $AP = BP$ | $OP$ bisects $AB$ |
| $\therefore$ $\Delta OAP \cong \Delta OBP$ | SSS axiom of congruency |
| $\Rightarrow$ $\angle OPA = \angle OPB$ | c.p.c.t. |
| But, $\angle OPA + \angle OPB = 180°$ | $APB$ is a straight line |
| $\therefore$ $\angle OPA = \angle OPB = 90°$ | |
| $\Rightarrow$ $OP$ is perpendicular to $AB$ | |

Hence Proved.

**Theorem 2 (Converse of theorem-1)** The perpendicular to a chord from the centre of the circle, bisects the chord.

Given : A circle with centre 'O' and $OP$ is perpendicular to $AB$.

To Prove : $AP = BP$

Construction : Join $OA$ and $OB$.

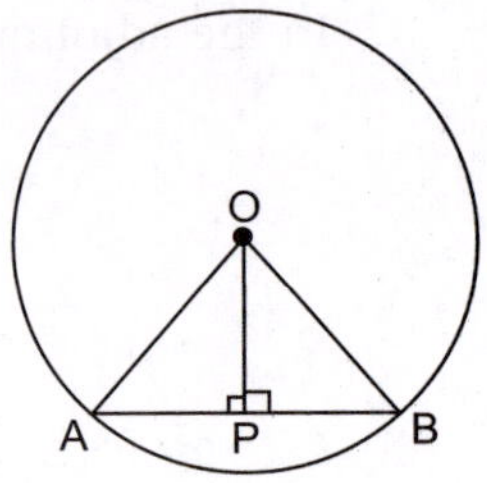


Proof :

| Statement | Reason |
|---|---|
| In $\Delta OAP$ and $\Delta OBP$ | |
| $OA = OB$ | radii of a circle |
| $\angle OPA = \angle OPB$ | each 90° |
| $OP = OP$ | common |
| $\therefore$ $\Delta OAP \cong \Delta OBP$ | SAS axiom of congruency |
| $AP = BP$ | c.p.c.t. |

Hence Proved.

**Theorem 3** There is one and only one circle, which passes through three given points, not in a straight line.

Given : Three points $P$, $Q$ and $R$, which are not in a straight line.

To Prove : One and only one circle can be drawn through points $P$, $Q$ and $R$.

Construction : Join $PQ$ and $QR$. Draw perpendicular bisectors of $PQ$ and $QR$ which intersect at point 'O'.

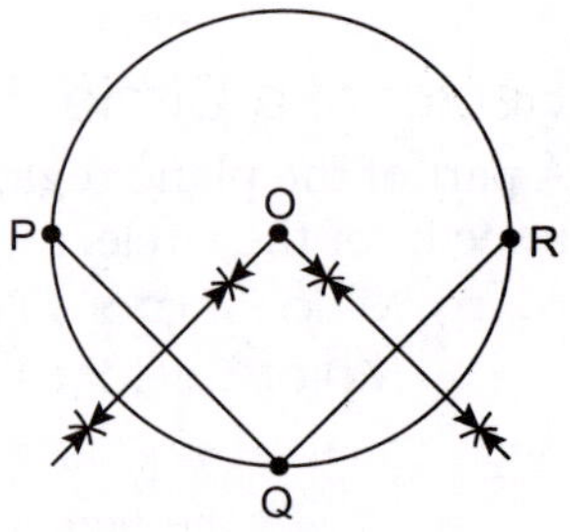

Proof : Statement — Reason

| Statement | Reason |
|---|---|
| $OP = OQ$ | each point on perpendicular bisector is equidistant from the extremities of the line segment. |
| $OQ = OR$ | each point on perpendicular bisector is equidistant from the extremities of the line segment. |

$\therefore$ $OP = OQ = OR$

$\Rightarrow$ $O$ is equidistant from $P$, $Q$ and $R$.

$\Rightarrow$ A circle drawn with centre '$O$' and radius $OP$, passes through the points $P$, $Q$ and $R$.

$\because$ The perpendicular bisectors of $PQ$ and $QR$ intersect at one point only.

$\therefore$ There can be only one circle passes through $P$, $Q$ and $R$.

Hence Proved.

**Theorem 4** Equal chords of a circle are equidistant from the centre.

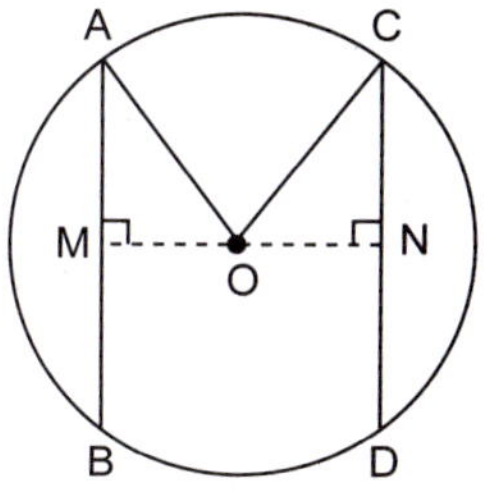


Given : Two chords $AB$ and $CD$ of a circle with centre '$O$' such that

$$AB = CD$$

To Prove : $AB$ and $CD$ are equidistant from '$O$'.

Construction : Draw $OM \perp AB$ and $ON \perp CD$. Join $AO$ and $CO$.

Proof :

| Statement | Reason |
|---|---|
| $AM = \frac{1}{2}AB$ | perpendicular from centre bisects the chord |
| $CN = \frac{1}{2}CD$ | perpendicular from centre bisects the chord |
| $AM = CN$ | $AB = CD$ (given) |
| In $\Delta AOM$ and $\Delta CON$, | |
| $AM = CN$ | proved above |
| $AO = CO$ | radii of a circle |
| $\angle AMO = \angle CNO$ | each 90° |
| $\Delta AOM \cong \Delta CON$ | R.H.S. axiom |
| $OM = ON$ | c.p.c.t. |

$\Rightarrow$ $AB$ and $CD$ are equidistant from '$O$'.

Hence Proved.

**Theorem 5 (Converse of theorem 4)** Chords of a circle, equidistant from the centre of the circle are equal.

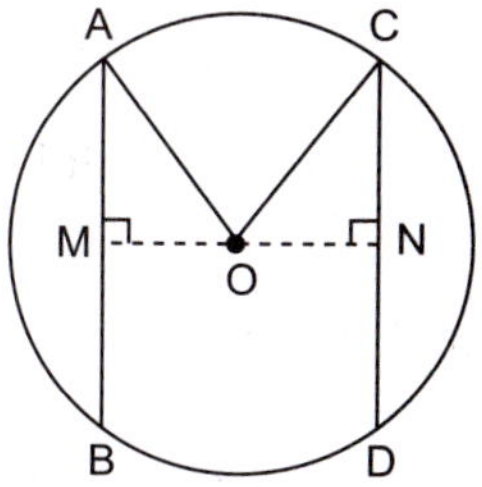


Given : A circle with centre '$O$' and two chords $AB$ and $CD$ which are equidistant from '$O$'

*i.e.,*

$$OM = ON$$
$$\angle OMA = \angle ONC = 90°$$

To Prove : $AB = CD$

Construction : Join $AO$ and $CO$.

Proof :

| Statement | Reason |
|---|---|
| In $\Delta OAM$ and $\Delta OCN$, | |
| $OA = OC$ | radii of a circle |
| $\angle OMA = \angle ONC$ | each 90° |
| $OM = ON$ | given |
| $\Delta OAM \cong \Delta OCN$ | R.H.S. axiom |
| $AM = CN$ | c.p.c.t. |
| $\frac{1}{2}AB = \frac{1}{2}CD$ | perpendicular from centre bisects the chord |

$\Rightarrow$ $AB = CD$

Hence Proved.

**NOTE**

1. The perpendicular bisector of a chord always passes through the centre of the circle.
2. The perpendicular bisectors of any two chords of a circle always intersect at the centre of the circle.

## Illustrative Examples

**Example 1.** A chord of length 8 cm is at a distance of 3 cm from the centre of the circle. Find the radius of the circle.

**Solution.** In the adjoining figure,

$AB = 8$ cm

$OM = 3$ cm

We know that the perpendicular drawn from the centre to a chord, bisects the chord.

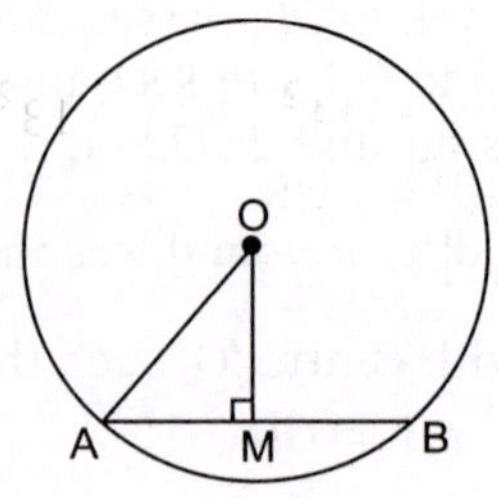


$\therefore \quad AM = \frac{1}{2} AB = \frac{1}{2} \times 8 \text{ cm} = 4 \text{ cm}$

In $\Delta OAM$,

$OA^2 = OM^2 + AM^2$ (by Pythagoras theorem)

$= 3^2 + 4^2 = 25$

$\Rightarrow \quad OA = 5$ cm

$\therefore$ Radius of circle = 5 cm **Ans.**

### Question *for* Practice

**Based on Ex. 1.**

- A chord of length 10 cm is at a distance of 12 cm from the centre of the circle. Find the radius of the circle.

**Ans.** 13 cm.

**Example 2.** A chord of length 20 cm is drawn at a distance of 24 cm from the centre of the circle. Another chord of length 48 cm is drawn in the same circle, find its distance of this chord from the centre of the circle.

**Solution.** Let chord $AB = 20$ cm, chord $CD = 48$ cm

and $OM = 24$ cm

Now, $OM$ bisects the chord $AB$.

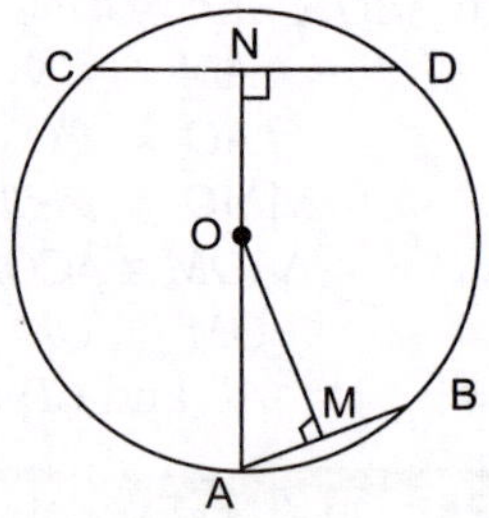


$\therefore \quad AM = \frac{AB}{2} = \frac{20}{2} \text{ cm} = 10 \text{ cm}$

In $\Delta AOM$,

$AO^2 = OM^2 + AM^2 = 24^2 + 10^2 = 676$

$\Rightarrow \quad AO = 26$ cm

Now, $DN = \frac{CD}{2} = \frac{48}{2} \text{ cm} = 24 \text{ cm}$

In $\Delta DON$,

$ON^2 + ND^2 = OD^2$

$\Rightarrow \quad ON^2 = OD^2 - ND^2 = 26^2 - 24^2 = 100$

$\Rightarrow \quad ON = 10$ cm **Ans.**

**Example 3.** In the given figure, $BD$ is the diameter of the circle which bisects the chord $AC$ at point $G$. If $AC = 8$ cm, $BG = 2$ cm, then find the radius of the circle.

**Solution.** Let $OA = OB = r$

$\therefore \quad OE = OB - BG = (r - 2)$ cm

$AG = \frac{AC}{2} = \frac{8}{2} \text{ cm} = 4 \text{ cm}$

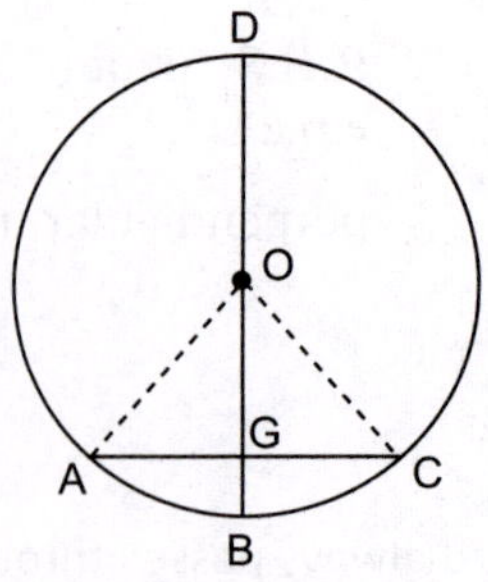


Now, $\angle OGA = 90°$

In $\Delta OAG$,

$OA^2 = OG^2 + AG^2$

$\Rightarrow \quad r^2 = (r - 2)^2 + 4^2$

$\Rightarrow \quad r^2 = r^2 - 4r + 4 + 16$

$\Rightarrow \quad r = 5$ cm

$\therefore$ Radius of circle = 5 cm **Ans.**

### Question *for* Practice

**Based on Ex. 3.**

- In the adjoining figure, $CD$ is the diameter of the circle which bisects the chord $AB$ at point $M$. If $AB = 12$ cm, $DM = 2$ cm, find the radius of the circle.

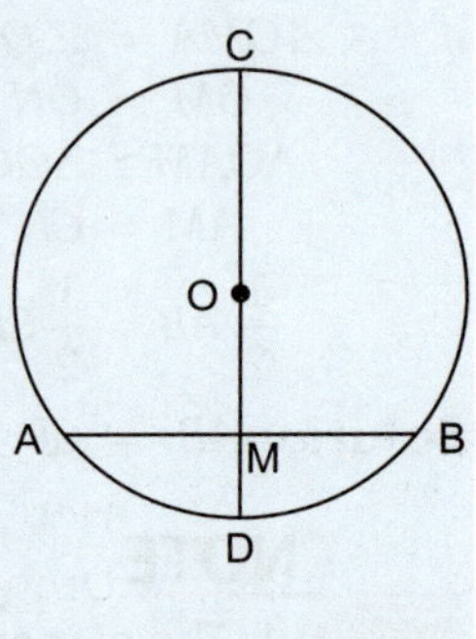


**Ans.** 10 cm.

**Example 4.** A chord of length 24 cm is drawn in a circle of radius 13 cm. Find its distance from the centre of the circle.

**Solution.** Let $AB$ be a chord of length 24 cm of a circle whose centre is $O$.

Given $OA = 13$ cm

Draw $OP \perp AB$

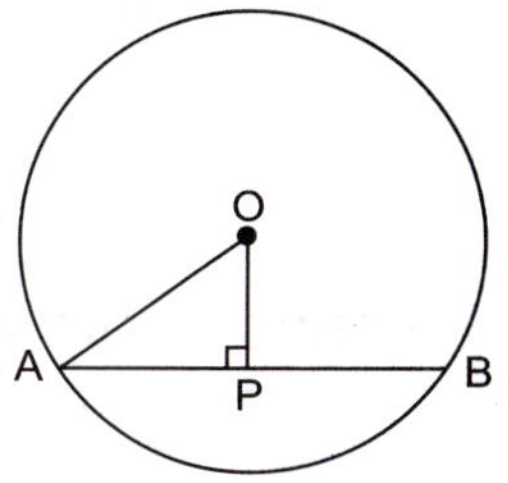


$\therefore$ $AP = \frac{1}{2} AB = \frac{1}{2} \times 24 \text{ cm} = 12 \text{ cm}$

In $\Delta OAP$,

$$OP^2 = OA^2 - AP^2 = 13^2 - 12^2 = 25$$

$\Rightarrow$ $OP = 5$ cm

$\therefore$ Required distance = 5 cm **Ans.**

**Example 5.** Two chords $AB$, $CD$ of lengths 24 cm and 10 cm, respectively, of a circle are parallel and lie on the same side of the centre. The distance between them is 7 cm, find the radius of the circle.

**Solution.** Here, $O$ is the centre of the circle.

Draw, $OP \perp AB$ and $OQ \perp CD$

Given $PQ = 7$ cm

$$AP = \frac{1}{2} AB = \frac{1}{2} \times 24 \text{ cm} = 12 \text{ cm}$$

$$CQ = \frac{1}{2} CD = \frac{1}{2} \times 10 \text{ cm} = 5 \text{ cm}$$

$\because$ $AB \parallel CD$

$\therefore$ $O, P, Q$ are collinear.

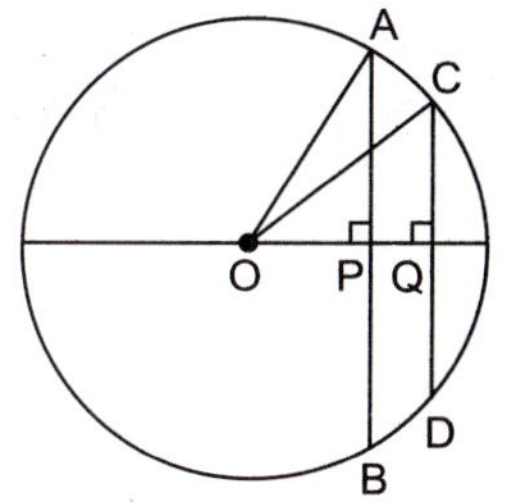


Let $OP = x$ cm, then $OQ = OP + PQ = (x + 7)$ cm

Let $OA = OC = r$

In $\Delta OAP$,

$$OA^2 = OP^2 + AP^2 \Rightarrow r^2 = x^2 + 12^2 \quad ...(i)$$

In $\Delta OCQ$,

$$OC^2 = OQ^2 + CQ^2 \Rightarrow r^2 = (x+7)^2 + 5^2 \quad ...(ii)$$

From equations *(i)* and *(ii)*, we get

$$(x+7)^2 + 5^2 = x^2 + 12^2 \Rightarrow x^2 + 14x + 49 + 25 = x^2 + 144$$

$$\Rightarrow 14x = 70 \Rightarrow x = 5$$

From equation *(i)*, we get

$$r^2 = 5^2 + 12^2 = 169 \Rightarrow r = 13$$

$\therefore$ Radius of circle = 13 cm **Ans.**

## Question *for* Practice

**Based on Ex. 5.**

- Two chords $AB$ and $CD$ of lengths 32 cm and 24 cm, respectively, of a circle are parallel and lie on the same side of the centre. The distance between them is 4 cm. Find the radius of the circle.

  **Ans.** 20 cm.

**Example 6.** $AB$ and $CD$ are two parallel chords of a circle, which are on opposite sides of the centre such that $AB = 10$ cm, $CD = 24$ cm and the distance between them is 17 cm. Find the radius of the circle.

**Solution.** Let '$O$' be the centre of the circle.

Here, $AB = 10$ cm, $CD = 24$ cm

Draw $OP \perp AB$ and $OQ \perp CD$.

$$AP = \frac{AB}{2} = \frac{10}{2} \text{ cm} = 5 \text{ cm}$$

## Question *for* Practice

**Based on Ex. 6.**

- $AB$ and $CD$ are two parallel chords of a circle, which are on opposite sides of the centre such that $AB = 6$ cm, $CD = 8$ cm and the distance between them is 7 cm. Find the radius of the circle.

  **Ans.** 5 cm.

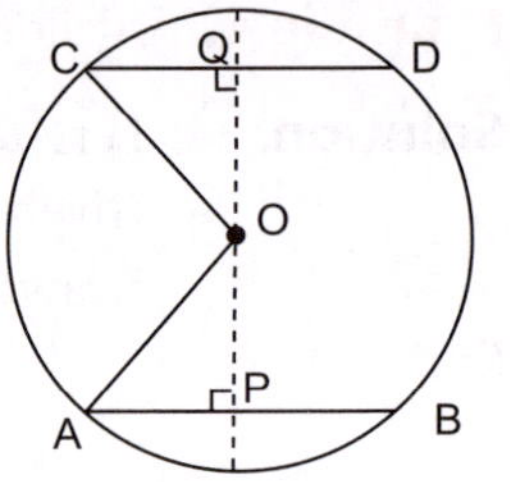


$$CQ = \frac{CD}{2} = \frac{24}{2}\text{ cm} = 12\text{ cm}$$

Let $OP = x$

$\therefore$ $OQ = 17 - x$ $(\because PQ = 17\text{ cm})$

Let $OA = OC = r$

In $\Delta OAP$,

$$OA^2 = OP^2 + AP^2$$

$\Rightarrow$ $r^2 = x^2 + 5^2$ ...(i)

In $\Delta OCQ$,

$$OC^2 = OQ^2 + CQ^2$$

$\Rightarrow$ $r^2 = (17 - x)^2 + 12^2$ ...(ii)

From equations (i) and (ii), we get

$$x^2 + 5^2 = (17 - x)^2 + 12^2 \Rightarrow x^2 + 25 = 289 - 34x + x^2 + 144$$

$\Rightarrow$ $34x = 408$ $\Rightarrow$ $x = 12$

Put $x = 12$ in equation (i), we get

$$r^2 = 5^2 + 12^2 = 169 \Rightarrow r = 13\text{ cm}$$

$\therefore$ Radius of circle $= 13$ cm **Ans.**

**Example 7.** Prove that, out of two unequal chords of a circle, the bigger chord is closer to the centre of the circle.

**Solution.** Let $AB$ and $CD$ be two chords of a circle with centre '$O$' and radius '$r$' such that

$$AB > CD$$

Draw $OP \perp AB$ and $OQ \perp CD$

We will prove that

$$OP < OQ$$

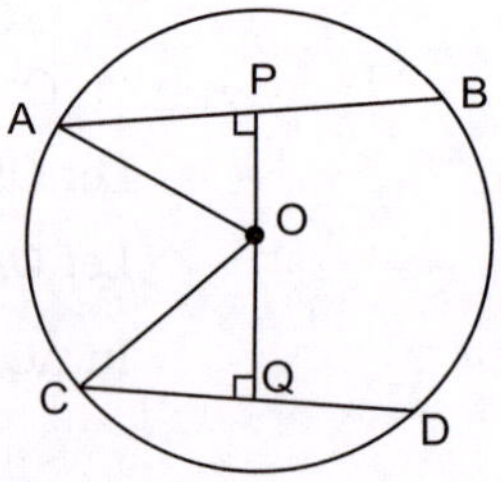


In $\Delta AOP$,

$$AP^2 = AO^2 - OP^2 = r^2 - OP^2 \quad ...(i)$$

And, in $\Delta OCQ$,

$$CQ^2 = OC^2 - OQ^2 = r^2 - OQ^2 \quad ...(ii)$$

Now, $AP = \frac{1}{2}AB$ and $CQ = \frac{1}{2}CD$

Now, $AB > CD$ (given)

$\Rightarrow$ $\frac{1}{2}AB > \frac{1}{2}CD$ $\Rightarrow$ $AP > CQ$

$\Rightarrow$ $AP^2 > CQ^2$ $\Rightarrow$ $r^2 - OP^2 > r^2 - OQ^2$ [from eqs. (i) and (ii)]

$\Rightarrow$ $-OP^2 > -OQ^2$ $\Rightarrow$ $OP^2 < OQ^2$

$\Rightarrow$ $OP < OQ$ **Hence proved.**

**Example 8.** In the adjoining figure, $AB$ and $CD$ are two chords of a circle with centre $O$ such that $OP = 6$ cm and $OQ = 8$ cm, where $OP \perp AB$ and $OQ \perp CD$. If the radius of the circle is 10 cm, find the length of the chords.

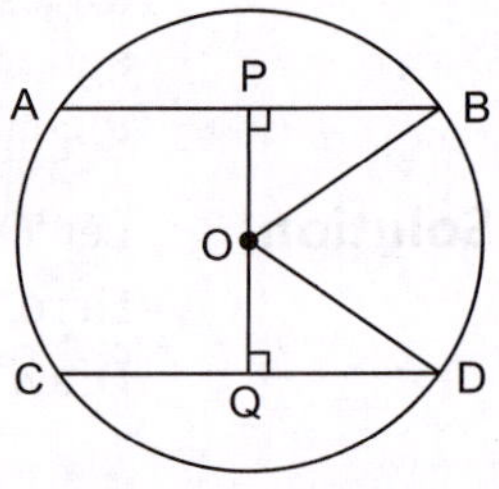


**Solution.** In $\Delta OBP$,

$$\angle OPB = 90°$$

$\therefore$ $BP^2 = OB^2 - OP^2 = 10^2 - 6^2 = 64 \Rightarrow BP = 8\text{ cm}$

and $AB = 2 \times BP = 2 \times 8 = 16$ cm **Ans.**

In $\Delta ODQ$,

$$\angle OQD = 90°$$

$\therefore$ $$QD^2 = OD^2 - OQ^2 = 10^2 - 8^2 = 36 \Rightarrow QD = 6$$

and $$CD = 2 \times QD = 2 \times 6 = 12 \text{ cm}$$ Ans.

**Example 9.** In a circle of radius 5 cm, $AB$ and $AC$ are two chords such that $AB = AC = 6$ cm, find the length of chord $BC$.

**Solution.** Here, the centre of the circle is $O$.

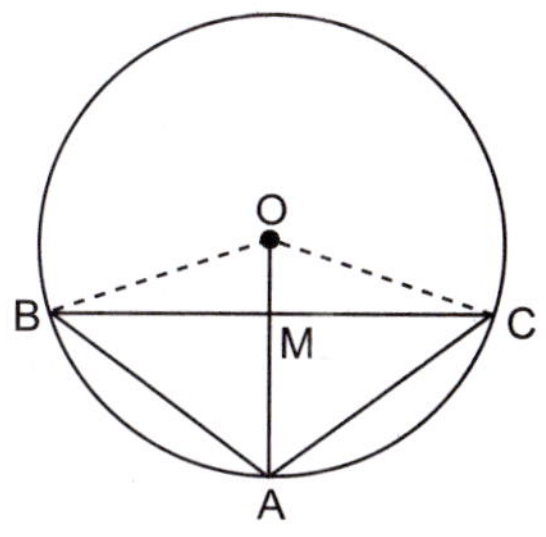


The bisector of $\angle BAC$ meet $BC$ at $M$.

In $\Delta BAM$ and $\Delta CAM$,

$AB = AC$ (given)

$\angle BAM = \angle CAM$ (by construction)

$AM = AM$ (common)

$\therefore$ $\Delta BAM \cong \Delta CAM$ (*SAS* criteria)

$\Rightarrow$ $BM = CM$ and $\angle BMA = \angle CMA$ (c.p.c.t.)

But $\angle BMA + \angle CMA = 180°$

$\therefore$ $\angle BMA = 90°$

So, $AM$ is perpendicular bisector of $BC$.

We know that the perpendicular bisector of a chord passes through the centre of the circle.

So, $AM$ passes through the centre $O$ of the circle.

Let $BM = y$ and $OM = x$

$\therefore$ $$MA = OA - OM = (5 - x) \text{ cm}$$

In $\Delta OBM$,

$$BM^2 + OM^2 = OB^2 \Rightarrow y^2 + x^2 = 5^2 \quad ...(i)$$

In $\Delta ABM$,

$$AM^2 + BM^2 = AB^2 \Rightarrow (5 - x)^2 + y^2 = 6^2 \quad ...(ii)$$

Subtracting equation *(i)* from *(ii)*, we get

$$(5 - x)^2 - x^2 = 36 - 25$$

$$-10x + 25 = 11 \Rightarrow 10x = 14 \Rightarrow x = \frac{7}{5}$$

From equation *(i)*,

$$y^2 = 5^2 - x^2 = 25 - \frac{49}{25} = \frac{576}{25} \Rightarrow y = \frac{24}{5} = 4.8$$

$$BC = 2\,BM = 2y = 2 \times 4.8 = 9.6 \text{ cm}$$

$\therefore$ Length of chord $BC = 9.6$ cm. Ans.

**Example 10.** If the line joining the mid-points of two chords of a circle passes through the centre of the circle, then prove that the chords are parallel.

**Solution.** Let $AB$ and $CD$ be two chords in a circle of centre '$O$'. $M$ and $N$ are the mid-points of $AB$ and $CD$, respectively. The line $MN$ passes through the point '$O$'.

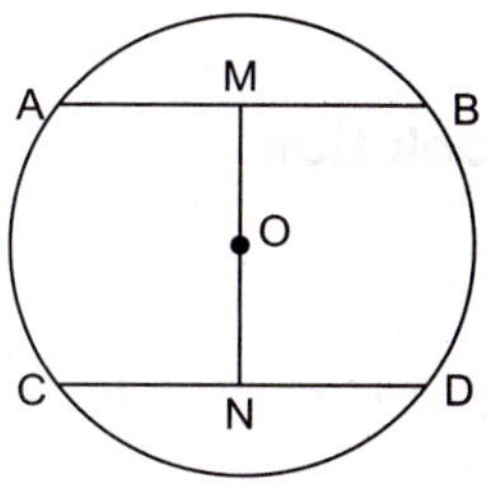


Now, $M$ is the mid-point of chord $AB$.

$\therefore$ $\angle AMO = 90°$

Similarly $\angle CNO = 90°$

Now, $\angle AMO + \angle CNO = 90° + 90°$

$\Rightarrow$ $\angle AMN + \angle CNM = 180°$

But these are the interior angles.

$\therefore$ $AM \parallel CN$

$\Rightarrow$ $AB \parallel CD$ Hence Proved.

**Example 11.** Two circles with centres $A$ and $B$ intersect each other at points $P$ and $Q$. Prove that the line joining $AB$ bisects the common chord $PQ$ at right angle.

**Solution.** Let $M$ be the point of intersection of $AB$ and $PQ$.

Join $AP$, $AQ$, $BP$ and $BQ$,

In $\Delta PAB$ and $\Delta QAB$,

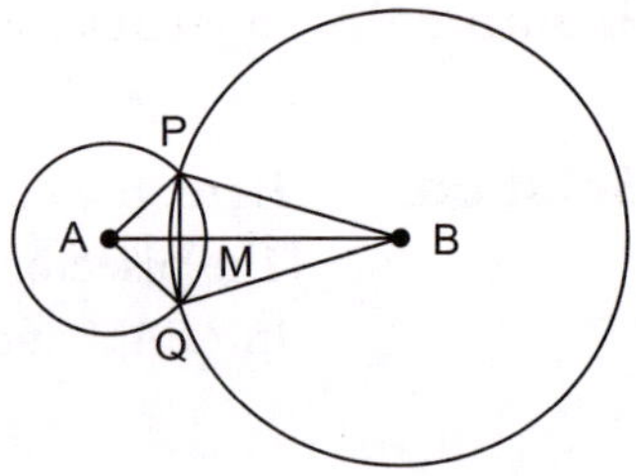


$PA = QA$ (radii of a circle)

$AB = AB$ (common)

$PB = QB$ (radii of a circle)

$\therefore$ $\Delta PAB \cong \Delta QAB$ (SSS axiom of congruency)

$\Rightarrow$ $\angle PAB = \angle QAB$ (c.p.c.t.)

$\Rightarrow$ $\angle PAM = \angle QAM$ ...(i)

In $\Delta PAM$ and $\Delta QAM$,

$\angle PAM = \angle QAM$ [from eq. (i)]

$PA = QA$ (radii of a circle)

$AM = AM$ (common)

$\therefore$ $\Delta PAM \cong \Delta QAM$ (SAS axiom of congruency)

$\Rightarrow$ $PM = QM$

And, $\angle AMP = \angle AMQ$

But, $\angle AMP + \angle AMQ = 180°$

$\therefore$ $\angle AMP = \angle AMQ = 90°$

Hence, $AB$ bisects $PQ$ at right angle. Hence Proved.

**Example 12.** In the following figure, 'O' is the centre of two concentric circles. Prove that $AB = CD$.

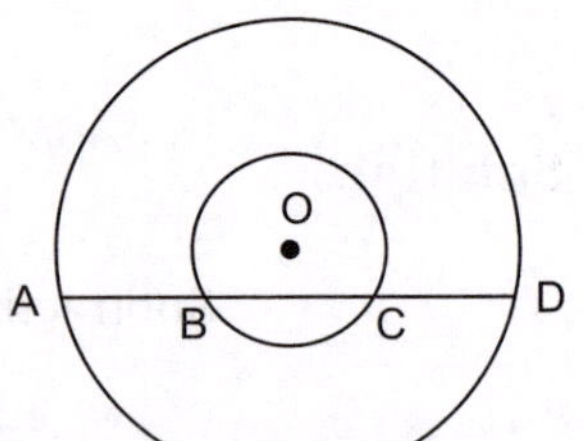


**Solution.** Draw $OE$ perpendicular to $AD$.

We know that the perpendicular drawn from centre to the chord bisects it.

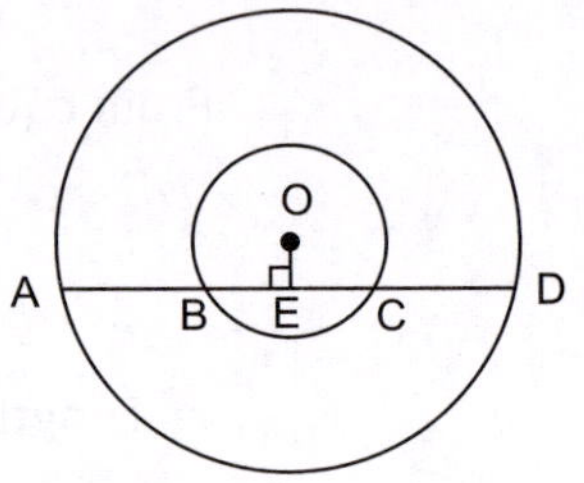


For smaller circle, $OE$ is perpendicular to the chord $BC$.

$\therefore$ $BE = CE$ ...(i)

For larger circle, $OE$ is perpendicular to the chord $AD$.

$\therefore$ $AE = DE$ ...(ii)

Subtracting equation (i) from equation (ii), we get

$AE - BE = DE - CE$

$\Rightarrow$ $AB = CD$ Hence Proved.

**Example 13.** In the adjoining figure, $AD$ is a straight line, $OM \perp AD$ and 'O' is the centre of both the circles. If $OA = 34$ cm, $OM = 16$ cm and $OB = 20$ cm, find the length of $AB$.

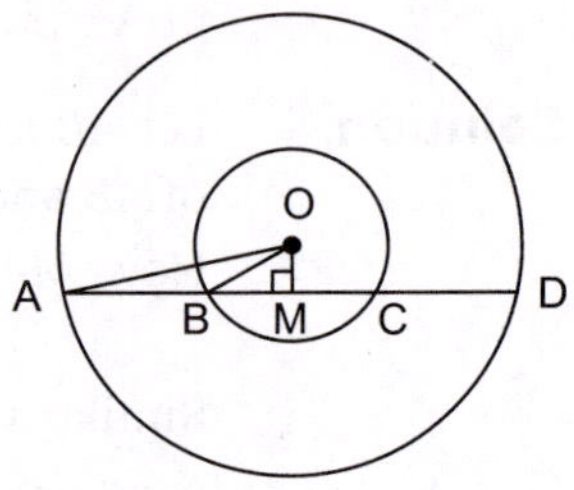


**Solution.** In $\Delta OBM$,

$$BM^2 = OB^2 - OM^2 = 20^2 - 16^2 = 144$$

$\Rightarrow$ $BM = 12$ cm

In $\Delta OAM$,

$$AM^2 = AO^2 - OM^2 = 34^2 - 16^2 = 1156 - 256 = 900$$

$\Rightarrow$ $AM = 30$ cm

$\therefore$ $AB = AM - BM = (30 - 12)$ cm $= 18$ cm Ans.

**Example 14.** $AB$ and $AC$ are two chords of a circle of radius $r$ such that $AB = 2AC$. If $p$ and $q$ are perpendicular distances from centre to $AB$ and $AC$, respectively, prove that $4q^2 = p^2 + 3r^2$.

**Solution.** Let $O$ be the centre of the circle.

Let $OM \perp AB$ and $ON \perp AC$

Then, $OM = p$, $ON = q$ and $OA = r$

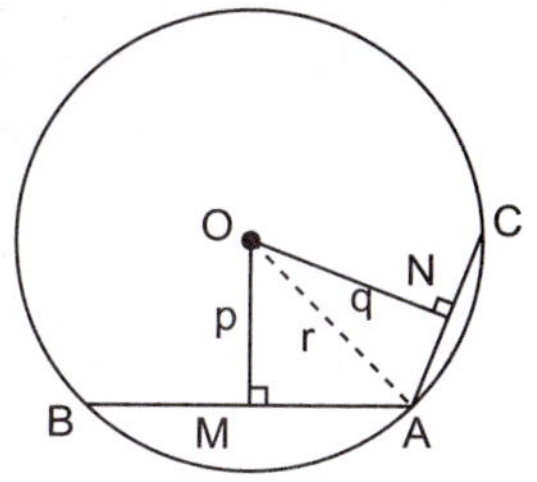


$$\therefore \quad AM = \frac{AB}{2} \text{ and } AN = \frac{AC}{2}$$

In $\Delta OAM$,

$$OA^2 = AM^2 + OM^2 \quad \Rightarrow \quad r^2 = \left(\frac{AB}{2}\right)^2 + p^2$$

$$\Rightarrow \quad r^2 - p^2 = \left(\frac{2AC}{2}\right)^2 \quad \Rightarrow \quad AC^2 = r^2 - p^2 \qquad \ldots(i)$$

In $\Delta OAN$,

$$OA^2 = ON^2 + AN^2$$

$$\Rightarrow \quad r^2 = q^2 + \left(\frac{AC}{2}\right)^2 \quad \Rightarrow \quad 4r^2 = 4q^2 + AC^2$$

$$\Rightarrow \quad 4r^2 = 4q^2 + r^2 - p^2 \qquad \text{[from } (i)\text{]}$$

$$\Rightarrow \quad p^2 + 3r^2 = 4q^2$$

Hence Proved.

**Example 15.** If two circles intersect at two points, then prove that the line through their centres is perpendicular bisector of the common chord.

**Solution.** Given : Two circles with centres $C$ and $D$, intersect at points $A$ and $B$. $AB$ is their common chord.

To prove : $CD$ is perpendicular bisector of $AB$.

Construction : Join $CB$, $CA$, $DB$, $DA$.

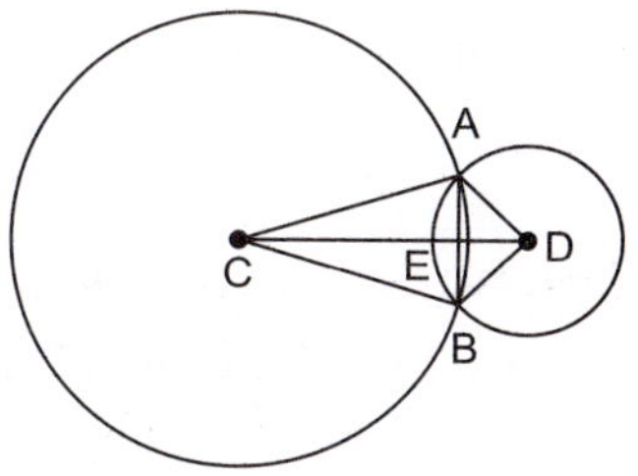


Proof :

| | Statement | Reason |
|---|---|---|
| 1. | $AC = BC$ | radii of a circle |
| 2. | $AD = BD$ | radii of a circle |
| 3. | $CD = CD$ | common |
| 4. | $\Delta ACD \cong \Delta BCD$ | SSS axiom of congruency |
| 5. | $\angle ACD = \angle BCD$ | (c.p.c.t.) |
| | $\Rightarrow \angle ACE = \angle BCE$ | |
| 6. | $AC = BC$ | radii of a circle |
| 7. | $\angle ACE = \angle BCE$ | from (5) |
| 8. | $CE = CE$ | common |
| 9. | $\Delta ACE \cong \Delta BCE$ | SAS axiom of congruency |
| 10. | $AE = BE$ and | |
| | $\angle CEA = \angle CEB$ | c.p.c.t. |
| 11. | $\angle CEA + \angle CEB = 180°$ | $AEB$ is a straight line |
| 12. | $\angle CEA = 90°$ | From 9 and 10. |

Hence, $CD$ is perpendicular bisector of $AB$.

Hence Proved.

# Exercise 14A

**1.** In the adjoining figure, 'O' is the centre of the circle. If $AC = 10$ cm and chord $AB = 6$ cm, find the distance of this chord from the centre of the circle.

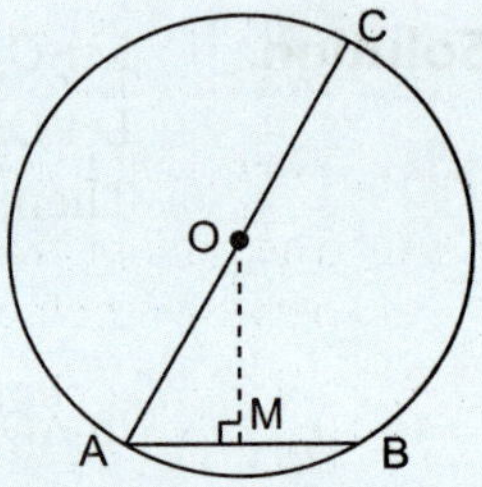


**2.** A chord of length 10 cm, is at a distance of 12 cm from the centre of the circle. Find the radius of the circle.

**3.** A chord of length 10 cm is drawn in a circle of diameter 26 cm. Find its distance from the centre of the circle.

**4.** The radius of a circle is 17 cm and the length of perpendicular from centre to a chord is 8 cm. Find the length of the chord.

**5.** In the adjoining figure, $AB$ and $CD$ are two parallel chords and 'O' is the centre. If the radius of the circle is 15 cm, find the distance $MN$ between the two chords of lengths 24 cm and 18 cm, respectively.

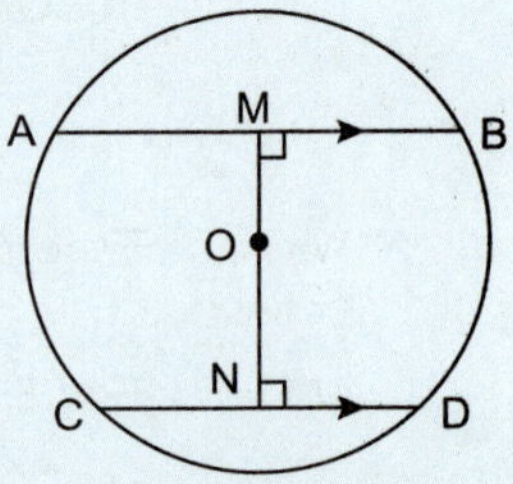


**6.** In the adjoining figure, $O$ is the centre of the circle. $AB$ and $CD$ are two chords of the circle and $OQ \perp CD$, $OP \perp AB$. If $AB = 24$ cm, $OQ = 12$ cm, $CD = 10$ cm. Find

(i) radius of the circle

(ii) length of $OP$.

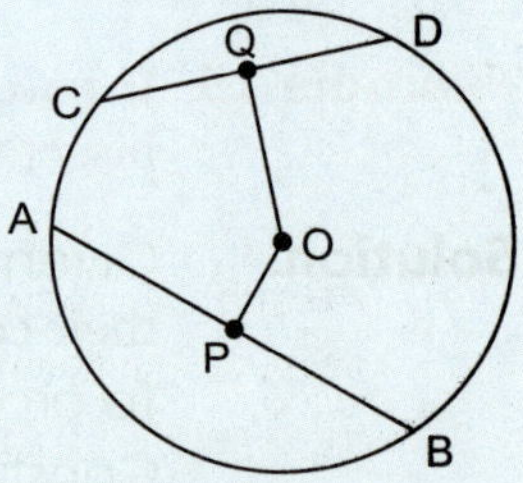


**7.** In the adjoining figure, a circle with centre $O$ is shown in which $AB$ is the diameter which bisects the chord $CD$ at point $M$. If $CD = 16$ cm, $BM = 4$ cm, find the diameter of the circle.

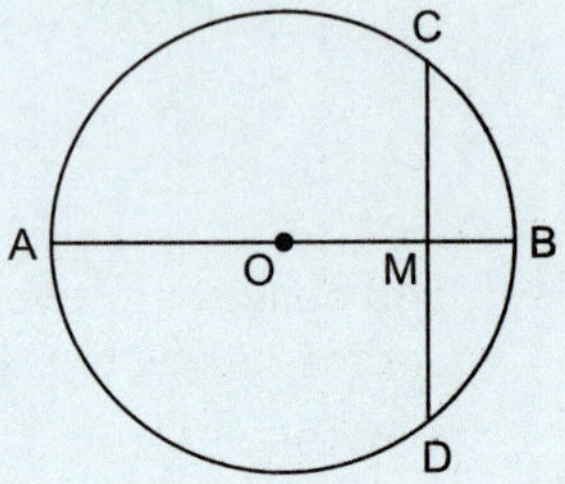


**8.** In the adjoining figure, $O$ is the centre of a circle with a diameter $AB$. If $\angle OMC = 90°$, $CD = 6$ cm, $BM = 1$ cm, find the radius of the circle.

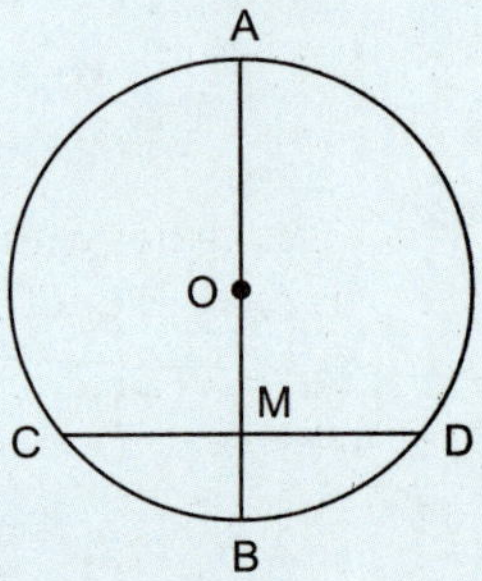


**9.** In a circle of radius 13 cm, two parallel chords of lengths 24 cm and 10 cm are drawn. Find the distance between the chords, if both the chords are

(i) on the same side of the centre.

(ii) on the opposite side of the centre.

**10.** Chords $AB$ and $CD$ of a circle are parallel to each other and lie on the opposite sides of the centre of the circle. If $AB = 48$ cm, $CD = 36$ cm and the distance between the chords is 42 cm, find the radius of the circle.

**11.** Two parallel chords are drawn in a circle of radius 15 cm. The length of one chord is 18 cm and the distance between the two chords is 21 cm. Find the length of another chord.

**12.** Prove that the line segments joining the mid-points of two parallel chords of a circle passes through the centre of the circle.

**13.** The radii of two intersecting circles are 17 cm and 25 cm. If the length of the common chord is 30 cm, find the distance between their centres.

**14.** Two equal chords $AB$ and $CD$ of a circle with centre $O$ intersect each other at right angle at point $P$. If $OM \perp AB$ and $ON \perp CD$, prove that $OMPN$ is a square.

**15.** Two chords $AB$ and $CD$ of a circle with centre $O$ intersect at point $M$ such that $\angle OMD = \angle OMA$. Prove that $AB = CD$.

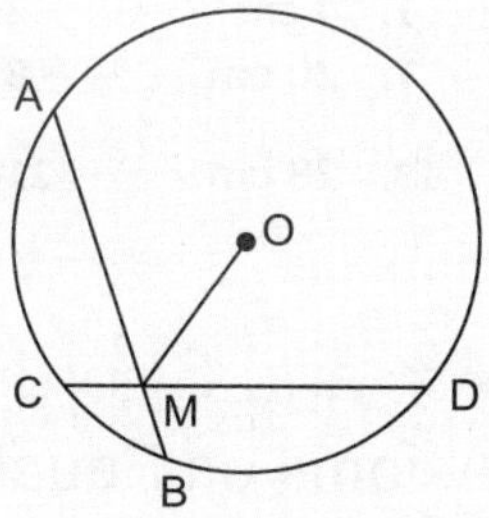


**16.** Two equal chords $AB$ and $CD$ of a circle with centre $O$ intersect at point $M$ inside the circle. Prove that

$AM = DM$ and $BM = CM$

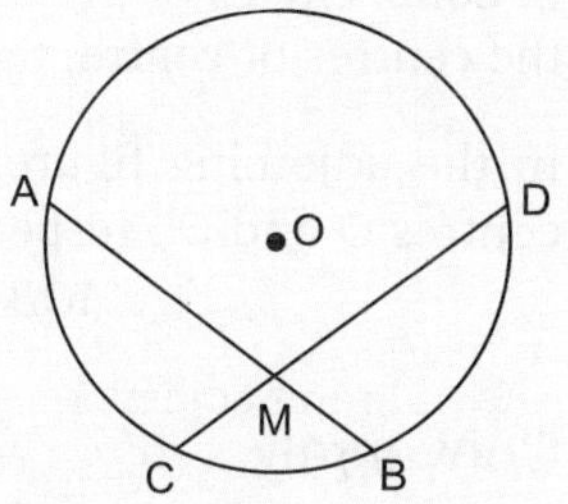


**17.** $AB$ and $CD$ are two equal chords of a circle with centre $O$. If $P$ and $Q$ are mid-points of $AB$ and $CD$, respectively, prove that

(i) $\angle BPQ = \angle DQP$ (ii) $\angle APQ = \angle CQP$

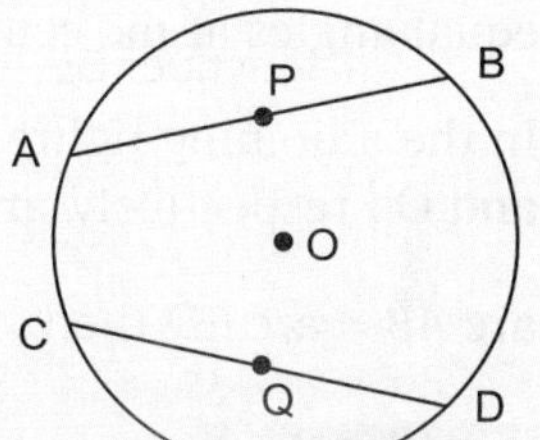


**18.** $AB$ and $CD$ are two equal chords of a circle with centre $O$, intersecting each other outside the circle at point $M$. Prove that

(i) $AM = CM$ (ii) $BM = DM$

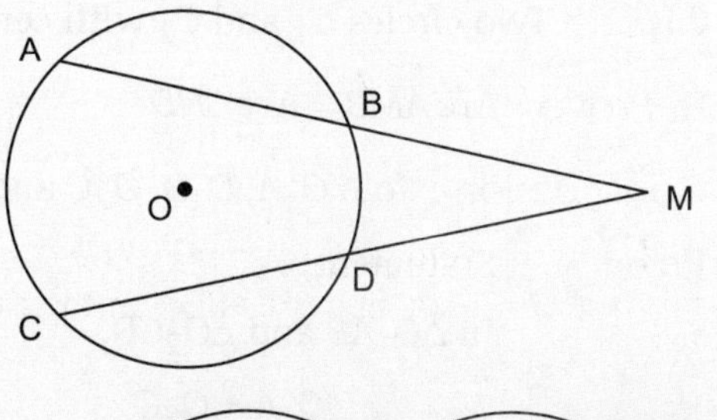


**19.** Two circles with centres $C$ and $D$, intersect each other at points $P$ and $Q$. If $APB$ is parallel to $CD$, prove that

$AB = 2 \cdot CD$

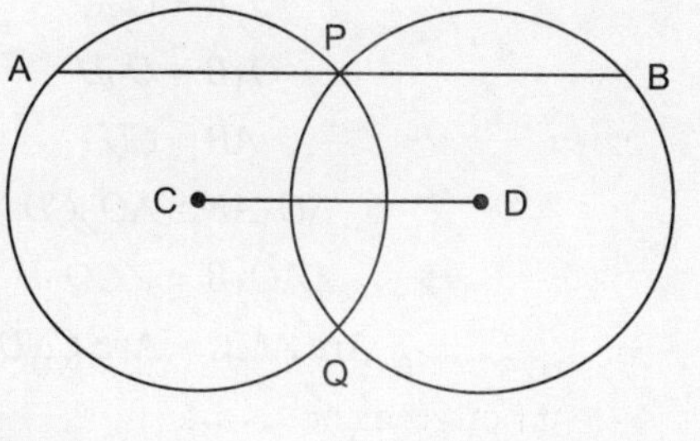


**20.** In an equilateral triangle, prove that the centroid and circumcentre of triangle coincide.

**21.** In $\Delta ABC$, $AB = AC = 25$ cm and $BC = 14$ cm. Find the radius of the circle circumscribing the triangle.

**22.** In the adjoining figure, $AD$ is the diameter of the circle whose centre is $O$. If $AB \parallel CD$, prove that $AB = CD$.

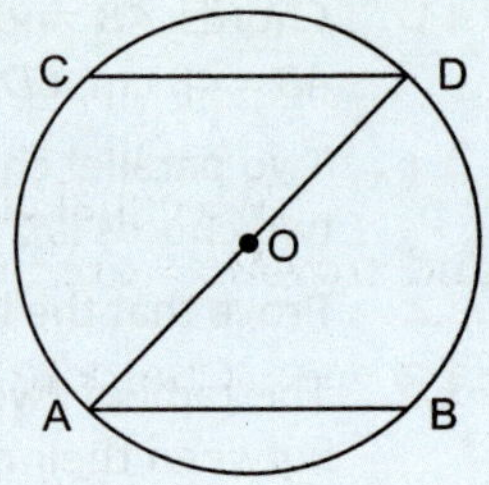


## *Answers*

| | | | | | |
|---|---|---|---|---|---|
| **1.** 4 cm | **2.** 13 cm | **3.** 12 cm | **4.** 30 cm | **5.** 21 cm | **6.** (i) 13 cm (ii) 5 cm |
| **7.** 20 cm | **8.** 5 cm | **9.** (i) 7 cm (ii) 17 cm | | **10.** 30 cm | **11.** 24 cm |
| **13.** 28 cm | **21.** $13\frac{1}{48}$ cm | | | | |

# Arc and Chord Properties

## Axioms on Equal Arcs

In equal circles or in the same circle, if two arcs subtend equal angles at the centres or centre, then they are equal.

In the adjoining figure, arc $AB$ and arc $CD$ of two equal circles with centres $O$ and $O'$, respectively, make equal angles at the centres.

$\angle AOB = \angle CO'D$ then arc $AB$ = arc $CD$

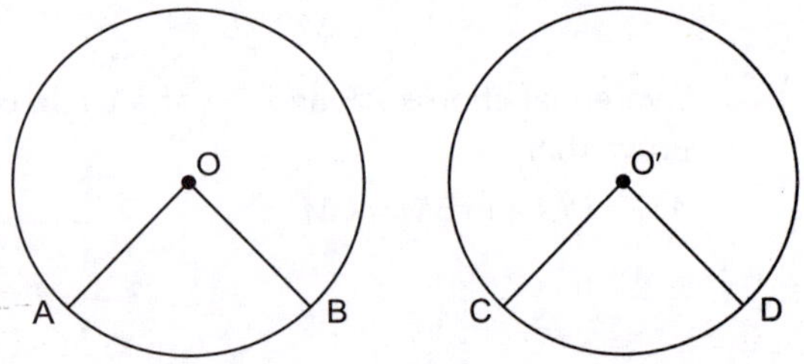


### Conversely

In equal circles or in same circle, if two arcs are equal then they subtend equal angles at the centres or centre.

In the adjoining figure, arc $AB$ and arc $CD$ of equal circles with centre $O$ and $O'$, respectively, are equal.

arc $AB$ = arc $CD$ then $\angle AOB = \angle CO'D$.

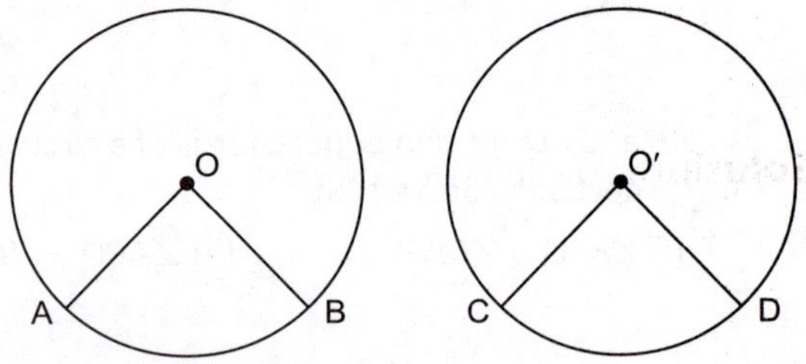


**Theorem 6** In equal circles or in the same circle, if two chords are equal, they cut off equal arcs.

Given : Two circles $C_1$ and $C_2$ with centres $O_1$ and $O_2$, respectively, and chord $AB$ = chord $CD$.

To Prove : Arc $AMB$ = Arc $CND$

Construction : Join $O_1A$, $O_1B$, $O_2C$ and $O_2D$.

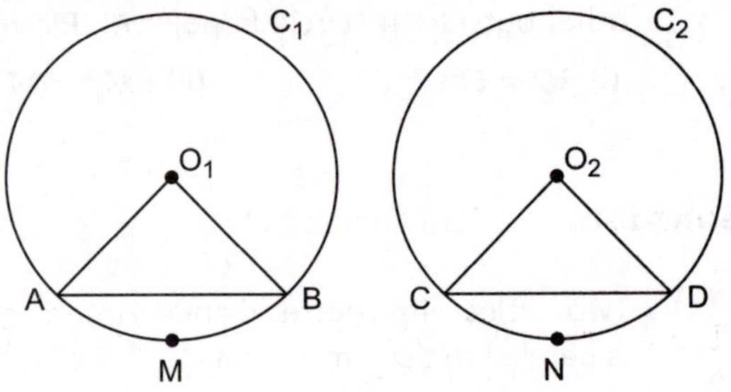


Proof :

| Statement | Reason |
|---|---|
| In $\Delta O_1AB$ and $\Delta O_2CD$, | |
| $O_1A = O_2C$ | radii of equal circles |
| $O_1B = O_2D$ | radii of equal circles |
| $AB = CD$ | given |
| $\therefore$ $\Delta O_1AB \cong \Delta O_2CD$ | SSS axiom of congruency |
| $\Rightarrow$ $\angle AO_1B = \angle CO_2D$ | c.p.c.t. |
| $\Rightarrow$ Arc $AMC$ = Arc $CND$ | arcs of equal circles subtend equal angles at centre, hence, the arcs are equal. |

Hence Proved.

**Theorem 7 (Converse of theorem 6)** In equal circles or in the same circle, if two arcs are equal, the chords of the arcs are also equal.

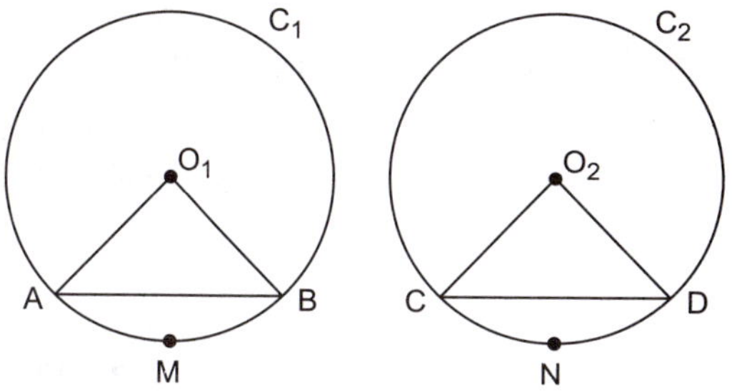


**Given :** Two equal circles $C_1$ and $C_2$ with centres $O_1$ and $O_2$, respectively, and arc $AMB$ = arc $CND$.

**To Prove :** Chord $AB$ = Chord $CD$

**Construction :** Join $O_1A$, $O_1B$, $O_2C$ and $O_2D$.

**Proof :**

| Statement | Reason |
|---|---|
| Arc $AMB$ = Arc $CND$ | given |
| $\Rightarrow$ $\angle AO_1B = \angle CO_2D$ | equal arcs of equal circles subtend equal angles at the centre |
| In $\Delta AO_1B$ and $\Delta CO_2D$, | |
| $AO_1 = CO_2$ | radii of equal circles |
| $\angle AO_1B = \angle CO_2D$ | proved above |
| $O_1B = O_2D$ | radii of equal circles |
| $\therefore$ $\Delta AO_1B \cong \Delta CO_2D$ | SAS axiom of congruency |
| chord $AB$ = chord $CD$ | c.p.c.t. |

Hence Proved.

# Illustrative Examples

**Example 1.** In a circle with centre $O$, two equal chords $PQ$ and $PR$ are drawn. Prove that $OP$ bisects $\angle QPR$.

**Solution.** Join $OP$, $OQ$ and $OR$.

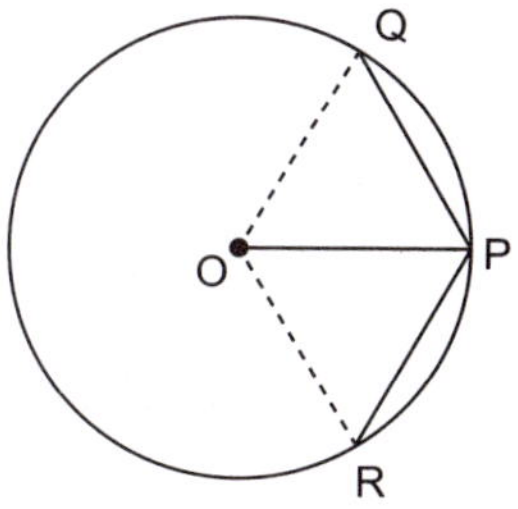


| | Statement | Reason |
|---|---|---|
| 1. | $PQ = PR$ | equal chords given |
| 2. | $OQ = OR$ | radii of a circle |
| 3. | $OP = OP$ | common |
| 4. | $\Delta OPQ \cong \Delta OPR$ | SSS axiom of congruency |
| 5. | $\angle OPQ = \angle OPR$ | c.p.c.t. |

$\therefore$ $OP$ bisects $\angle QPR$.

Hence Proved.

**Example 2.** If two chords $PQ$ and $PR$ of a circle with centre $O$ are such that the centre $O$ lies on the bisector of $\angle QPR$, then prove that chords are equal.

**Solution.** Join $OQ$ and $OR$.

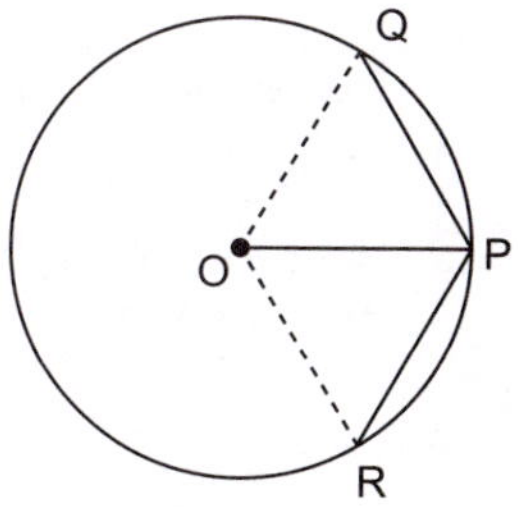


| | Statement | Reason |
|---|---|---|
| 1. | $OP = OQ$ | radii of a circle |
| 2. | $\angle OQP = \angle OPQ$ | angles opposite to equal sides in $\Delta OPQ$ |
| 3. | $OP = OR$ | radii of a circle |
| 4. | $\angle ORP = \angle OPR$ | angles opposite to equal sides in $\Delta OPR$ |
| 5. | $\angle OPQ = \angle OPR$ | $O$ lies on the bisector of $\angle QPR$ |
| 6. | $\angle OQP = \angle ORP$ | from (2), (4) and (5) |
| 7. | $OP = OP$ | common |
| 8. | $\Delta POQ \cong \Delta POR$ | AAS axiom of congruency from (5), (6) and (7) |
| 9. | chord $PQ$ = chord $PR$ | c.p.c.t. |

Hence Proved.

**Example 3.** In the adjoining figure, $AOC$ is a diameter of the circle and $2 \cdot \text{arc } AXB = \text{arc } BYC$. Find $\angle AOB$ and $\angle BOC$.

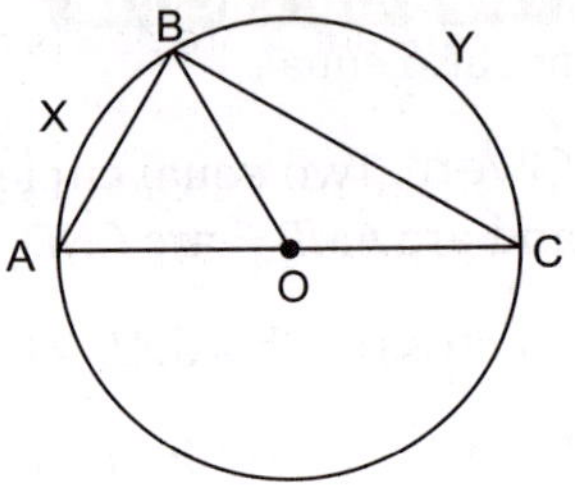


**Solution.** $2 \cdot \text{arc } AXB = \text{arc } BYC$

$\Rightarrow \quad 2\angle AOB = \angle BOC$

$\Rightarrow \quad 2\angle AOB + \angle AOB = \angle BOC + \angle AOB$

$\Rightarrow \quad 3\angle AOB = \angle AOC = 180°$

$\Rightarrow \quad \angle AOB = 60°$ **Ans.**

and $\angle BOC = 2\angle AOB = 2 \times 60° = 120°$ **Ans.**

**Example 4.** In the adjoining figure, the chords $AB$ and $CD$ of a circle are equal. Prove that $AD = CB$.

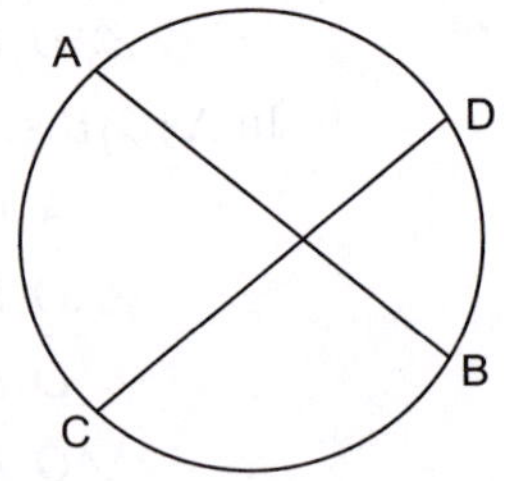


**Solution.** chord $AB$ = chord $CD$

$\Rightarrow$ minor arc $AB$ = minor arc $CD$

$\Rightarrow \quad \overset{\frown}{AB} = \overset{\frown}{CD} \quad \Rightarrow \quad \overset{\frown}{AD} + \overset{\frown}{BD} = \overset{\frown}{BC} + \overset{\frown}{BD}$

$\Rightarrow \quad \overset{\frown}{AD} = \overset{\frown}{BC} \quad \Rightarrow \quad$ chord $AD$ = chord $BC$

$\Rightarrow \quad AD = BC$ **Hence Proved.**

**Example 5.** In the adjoining figure, chord $AB$ is parallel to chord $CD$ in a circle with centre 'O' and $BC$ is a diameter. Prove that arc $AC$ = arc $BD$.

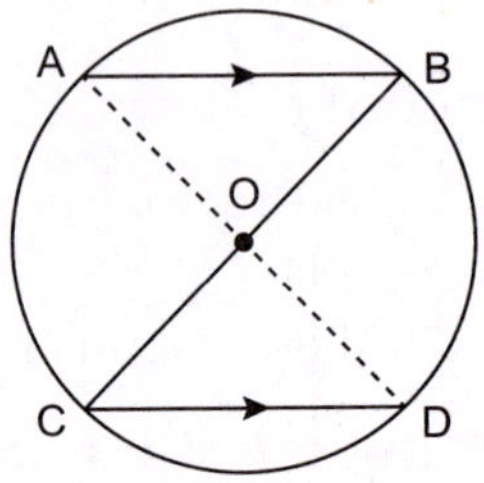


**Solution.** $AB \parallel CD$ and $BC$ is a transversal.

$\therefore \quad \angle ABO = \angle OCD$ (alternate angles)

Similarly, $AB \parallel CD$ and $AD$ is a transversal.

$\therefore \quad \angle OAB = \angle ODC$

Now, $\angle ABO + \angle OAB = \angle OCD + \angle ODC$

$\Rightarrow \quad 180° - \angle AOB = 180° - \angle COD \quad \Rightarrow \quad \angle AOB = \angle COD$

In $\Delta AOB$ and $\Delta COD$,

$AO = CO$ (radii of a circle)

$\angle AOB = \angle COD$ (proved above)

$OB = OD$ (radii of a circle)

$\therefore \quad \Delta AOB \cong \Delta COD$ (SAS axiom of congruency)

$\Rightarrow \quad AB = CD$ (c.p.c.t.)

Now, chord $AB$ = chord $CD$

$\Rightarrow$ Arc $AB$ = Arc $CD$

But $BC$ is the diameter of the circle

$\therefore$ Arc $CAB$ = Arc $CDB$

$\Rightarrow$ Arc $CA$ + Arc $AB$ = Arc $CD$ + Arc $BD$

$\Rightarrow$ Arc $AC$ = Arc $BD$ ($\because$ Arc $AB$ = Arc $CD$) **Hence Proved.**

## Exercise 14B

1. Two chords $PQ$ and $PR$ of a circle with centre $O$ are equal. Prove that the centre of the circle lies on the bisector of $\angle QPR$.
2. Prove that the line of centres of two intersecting circles subtend equal angles at the two points of intersection.
3. In the adjoining figure, $AB$ is a diameter of a circle with centre $O$. If chord $AM$ = chord $AN$, prove that arc $BM$ = arc $BN$.

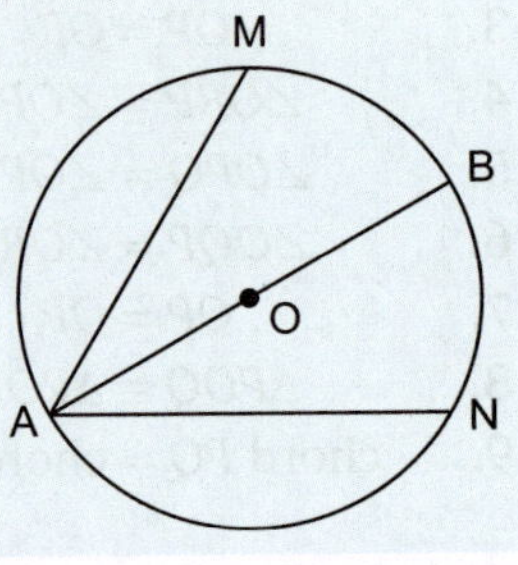

4. $A$ and $B$ are points on a circle with centre $O$. $C$ is a point on the circle such that $OC$ bisects $\angle AOB$. Prove that $OC$ bisects the arc $AB$.

5. In the adjoining figure, two chords $AB$ and $CD$ of a circle intersect at $M$. If $AB = CD$, prove that arc $AD$ = arc $CB$.

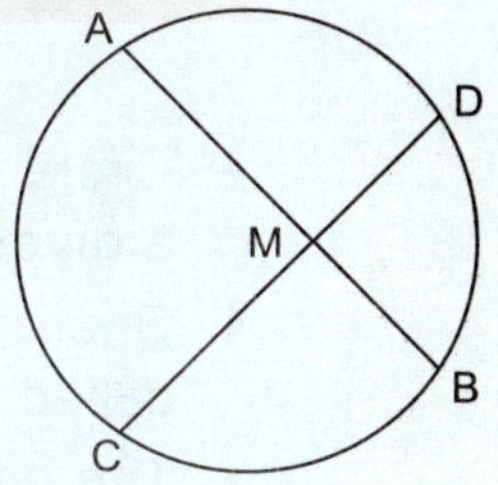


6. In a circle with centre $O$, chord $SR$ = chord $SM$. The radius $OS$ intersects the chord $RM$ at $P$. Prove that $PR = PM$.

7. Prove that the angle subtended by an arc at the centre of a circle is bisected by the radius passing through the mid-point of the arc.

# Exercise 14C

## Multiple Choice Questions

Choose the correct answer from the given four options in each of the following questions :

1. The largest chord of a circle is called :
   (a) radius (b) diameter (c) circumference (d) arc
2. The line segment joining any two points lying on the circumference of a circle is called :
   (a) radius (b) arc (c) secant (d) chord
3. If $P$ is any point in the interior of a circle with centre $O$ and radius '$r$', then :
   (a) $OP = r$ (b) $OP > r$ (c) $OP < r$ (d) $OP = 2r$
4. Two arcs of a circle are congruent, the ratio of their corresponding chords is :
   (a) 1 : 1 (b) 1 : 2 (c) 1 : 3 (d) 1 : 4
5. The radius of a circle is 5 cm. The length of its largest chord is :
   (a) 2.5 cm (b) 5 cm (c) 7.5 cm (d) 10 cm
6. A chord of length 6 cm is drawn in a circle of diameter 10 cm. Its distance from the centre of the circle is :
   (a) 3 cm (b) 4 cm (c) 5 cm (d) 8 cm
7. In the adjoining figure, $C$ and $D$ are the centres of two circles which intersect at points $M$ and $N$. If $AMB \parallel CD$, then $AB$ is equal to :
   (a) $4CD$ (b) $CD$
   (c) $2CD$ (d) $3CD$

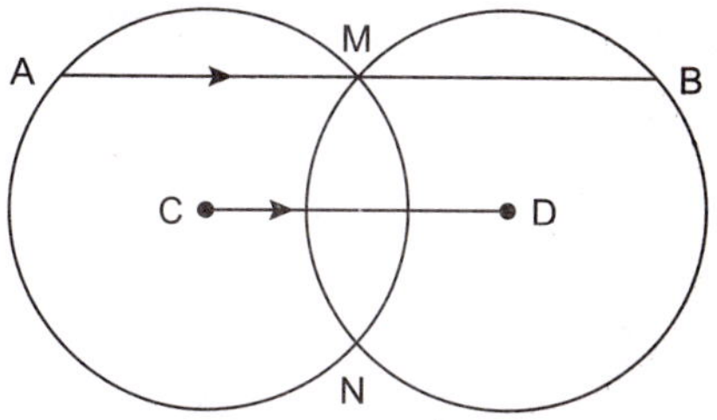


### Answers

| | | | | | | |
|---|---|---|---|---|---|---|
| 1. (b) | 2. (d) | 3. (c) | 4. (a) | 5. (d) | 6. (b) | 7. (c) |

## SUMMARY *of the Chapter*

- Circle : The collection of all points in a plane which are at a fixed (constant) distance from a given fixed point in that plane, is called a circle.
- Chord : A line segment joining any two points lying on the circumference of the circle is called the chord of the circle.
- The largest chord of the circle is called the diameter of the circle.
- Diameter = 2 × Radius
- Arc : A continuous part of a circle is called an arc of the circle. It is denoted by the symbol '⌒'.
- Circumference : The whole arc of a circle is called the circumference of the circle.
- Semi-circle : One-half of the circumference of a circle is called the semi-circle.

### Theorem

1. A straight line drawn from the centre of a circle to 'bisect a chord, which is not a diameter, is at right angles to the chord.
2. The perpendicular to a chord from the centre of the circle, bisects the chord.
3. There is one and only one circle, which passes through three given non-collinear points.
4. Equal chords of a circle are equidistant from the centre.
5. Chords of a circle, equidistant from the centre of the circle are equal.
6. In equal circles or in the same circle, if two chords are equal, they cut off equal arcs.
7. In equal circles or in the same circle, if two arcs are equal, the chords of the arcs are also equal.

# CHAPTER TEST

1. A chord of length 48 cm is at a distance of 10 cm from the centre of the circle. If another chord of length 20 cm is drawn in the same circle, find its distance from the centre of the circle.

2. In the adjoining figure, two equal chords $AB$ and $CD$ of a circle with centre $O$ intersect at right angles at $P$. If $M$ and $N$ are mid-points of the chords $AB$ and $CD$, respectively, prove that $NOMP$ is a square.

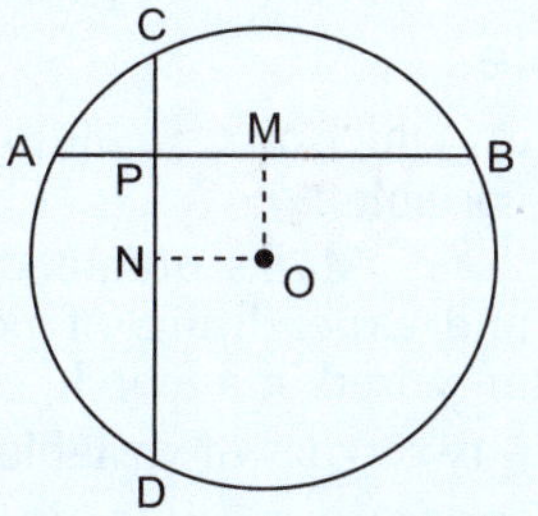


3. Prove that equal chords of a circle are equidistant from the centre.

4. A chord of length 8 cm is drawn in a circle of radius 5 cm. Find its distance from the centre of the circle.

5. In the adjoining figure, $AB$ is diameter of a circle. If chords $AC$ and $AD$ are equidistant from the centre $O$, prove that $AB$ bisects $\angle CAD$ and $\angle CBD$.

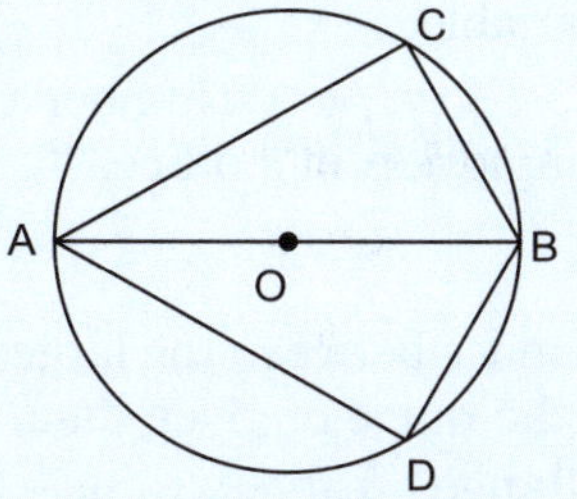


6. In the adjoining figure, $O$ is the centre of the circle. If $OA = 5$ cm, $AB = 8$ cm and $OM \perp AB$, find the length of $CM$.

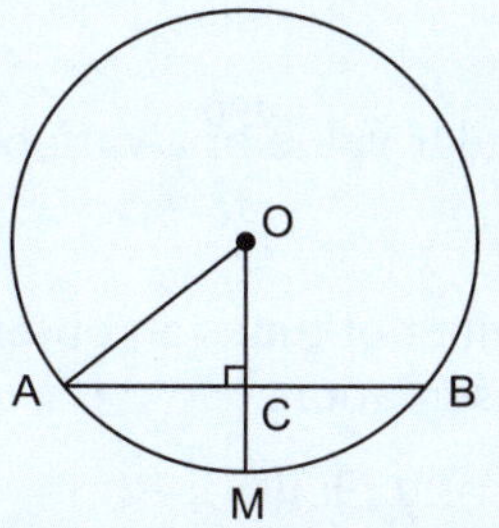


7. In the adjoining figure, arc $AB$ = arc $CD$. Prove that $\angle A = \angle B$.

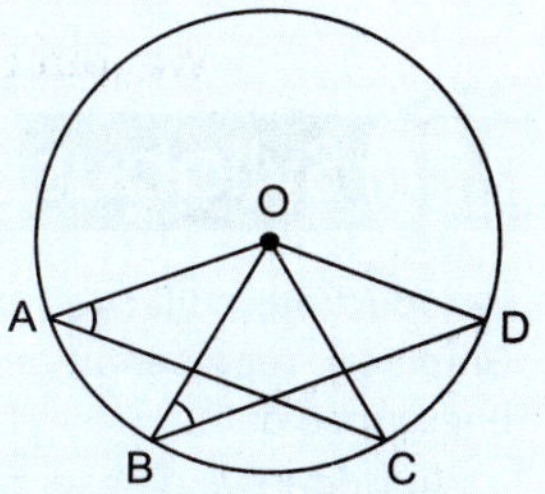


8. Of two unequal chords of a circle, prove that greater chord is nearer to the centre of the circle.

9. In a circle of radius 5 cm, $AB$ and $AC$ are two equal chords such that $AB = AC = 6$ cm. Find the length of chord $CD$.

10. In the adjoining figure $OD$ is perpendicular to the chord $AB$ of a circle where '$O$' is the centre of the circle. If $BC$ is the diameter, prove that $CA = 2 \cdot OD$.

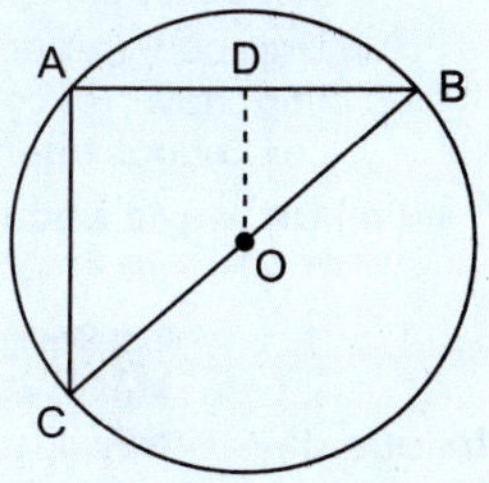


## Answers

**1.** 24 cm **4.** 3 cm **6.** 2 cm **9.** 9.6 cm

# Chapter 15

# STATISTICS

## Syllabus

Introduction, collection of data, presentation of data, Graphical representation of data, Mean, Median of ungrouped data.

(i) Understanding and recognition of raw, arrayed and grouped data.
(ii) Tabulation of raw data using tally-marks.
(iii) Understanding and recognition of discrete and continuous variables.
(iv) Mean, median of ungrouped data.
(v) Class intervals, class boundaries and limits, frequency, frequency table, class size for grouped data.
(vi) Grouped frequency distributions : The need to and how to convert discontinuous intervals to continuous intervals.
(vii) Drawing a frequency polygon.

## INTRODUCTION

In our day-to-day life, we need informations in the numerical figures which are called data. These data can be marks obtained by the students of a class in a test, monthly wages earned by workers of a factory, profit of a company in previous years. In this chapter, we shall study presentation of data in tabular form, graphical representation of data, mean and median of ungrouped data.

The word statistics come into existence in the middle of the 18th century. It seems to have derived from the Latin word '*status*' which means a 'political state'. Initially, the study of statistics was confined only to the collection of data, but now-a-days, its scope is quite wider.

## Terms Related to Statistics

### Primary Data

The data or information collected by the investigator himself with a given purpose, is called primary data.

### Secondary Data

The data or information collected from sources which already had the data stored, is called the secondary data.

### Raw Data

The numerical data collected in original form, is called raw data.

### Variable

A quantity which is capable of taking several different values, is called a variable.

*For example :* Marks obtained by students in a test, height, age, income and expenditure of people, number of employees in an office, run scored in a match, etc.

There are two types of variable :

(i) **Continuous variable :** A variable which can take any numerical value within a range of real numbers is called a continuous variable.

*For example :* Heights of students, wages of workers, etc.

(ii) **Discrete or discontinuous variable :** A variable which takes values from the set of integers is called a discrete variable.

*For example :* Number of students in a class, number of employees in a office.

### Range

The difference between the largest and smallest values of a variable is called the range of given data.

Range = Largest value − Smallest value

### Variate

A particular value of a variable is called variate of observation.

### Frequency

The number of times an observation occurs, is called the frequency of an observation.

### Frequency Distribution

A frequency distribution in a tabular form of data represents the frequency of each observation.

### Array

An arrangement of raw data in ascending or descending order of magnitude, is called an array.

*For example :*

Raw data : 5, 11, 17, 9, 6, 23, 18

Array data : 5, 6, 9, 11, 17, 18, 23

or

23, 18, 17, 11, 9, 6, 5

Tabulation of raw data : Suppose the following data gives the number of children in 20 families:

5, 2, 3, 3, 1, 2, 2, 4, 2, 5, 4, 1, 1, 2, 3, 4, 1, 1, 2, 3

We have to construct a frequency table from these data.

First we arrange the given raw data in array:

1, 1, 1, 1, 1, 2, 2 ,2, 2, 2, 2, 3, 3, 3, 3, 4, 4, 4, 5, 5

Now frequency table is :

| Number of children | Tally marks | Frequency |
|---|---|---|
| 1 |卌 | 5 |
| 2 | 卌 \| | 6 |
| 3 | \|\|\|\| | 4 |
| 4 | \|\|\| | 3 |
| 5 | \|\| | 2 |
| | Total | 20 |

## Working Method

(i) In first column, write the number of children in ascending (or descending) order.

(ii) The number of children are recorded in second column (tally marks) by marking a short vertical line called a stroke.

(iii) The first number of children is 1, so make a stroke in the tally marks column opposite to 1.

(iv) Similarly we make a stroke in tally marks columns opposite to variate for every number of children.

(v) When four strokes have been made, opposite to any variate, we make a stroke across the first four for the fifth stroke which gives a pack of five strokes. The next stroke starts a new pack.

(vi) When marking of strokes is completed, we count the strokes against each variate and write it in third column headed as frequency.

* This table is called ungrouped frequency distribution table.

## Grouped or Classified Data

We may condense the large number of data into classes or groups. Such a presentation is called grouped or classified data.

Suppose the following data gives the marks of 30 students out of 50 marks in a class test :

| | | | | | | | | | |
|---|---|---|---|---|---|---|---|---|---|
| 40, | 12, | 46, | 37, | 17, | 27, | 30, | 6, | 2, | 23, |
| 19, | 39, | 25, | 5, | 33, | 19, | 21, | 12, | 41, | 17, |
| 19, | 17, | 12, | 8, | 10, | 1, | 9, | 21, | 13, | 48 |

We have to arrange them into grouped data. There are two types of grouped data :

### (i) Inclusive Form

| Marks (class-intervals) | Tally marks | Number of students (frequency) |
|---|---|---|
| 1–10 | 卌 \|\| | 7 |
| 11–20 | 卌 卌 | 10 |
| 21–30 | 卌 \| | 6 |
| 31–40 | \|\|\|\| | 4 |
| 41–50 | \|\|\| | 3 |
| | Total | 30 |

Here the marks are divided into classes : 1–10, 11–20, 21–30, ....... .

For class 1–10, the lower limit is 1 and upper limit is 10.

For mark $x$, if it is a member of class 1–10, then

$$1 \leq x \leq 10.$$

Here, the classes are non-overlapping. These classes are called discontinuous and frequency distribution is called inclusive or discrete distribution.

**NOTE**

In the inclusive form of frequency table, the upper limit of a class does not coincide with the lower limit of the next class.

### (ii) Exclusive Form

| Marks (class-intervals) | Tally marks | Number of students (frequency) |
|---|---|---|
| 1–10 | 卌 \| | 6 |
| 10–20 | \|卌 卌 \| | 11 |
| 20–30 | 卌 | 5 |
| 30–40 | \|\|\|\| | 4 |
| 40–50 | \|\|\|\| | 4 |
| | Total | 30 |

Here the marks are divided into classes : 0–10, 10–20, 20–30, ....... .
For class 10–20, the lower limit is 10 and upper limit is 20.

The upper limit of a class coincides with the lower limit of the next class. Here, the marks 10 are included in the class 10–20.

Similarly, marks 20 are included is the class 20–30. So marks $x$, is a member of class 10–20 if

$$10 \leq x < 20.$$

This distribution is called continuous or exclusive form of the frequency distribution.

### Class Intervals

Each group into which the raw data is condensed is called a class-interval. Each class is bounded by two numbers which are called the class-limits. For class 10–20, 10 is called the lower limit and 20 is called the upper limit.

True upper and True lower limits : The upper and lower limits of the frequency table of exclusive form are called the true upper limit and true lower limit.

The upper and lower limits of inclusive form frequency table can be converted into true limits by adjusting factor.

$$\text{Adjusting factor} = \frac{\text{Lower limit of a class} - \text{Upper limit of previous class}}{2}$$

Now, True lower limit = Lower limit – Adjusting factor

and True upper limit = Upper limit + Adjusting factor

### Class Size

The difference between the true upper limit and true lower limit of a class is called class-size.

For class-interval 10–20

class-size = 20–10 = 10

### Class-mark or Mid-value

It is defined as

$$\text{Class-mark} = \frac{\text{Upper limit} + \text{Lower limit}}{2}$$

### Range

The difference between the maximum and minimum values of the variate is called the range.

### Cumulative Frequency and Cumulative Frequency Table

Cumulative frequency of a class is the sum of all frequencies upto and including that class.

A table which shows the manner in which cumulative frequencies are distributed over different classes, is called a cumulative frequency table.

*For example :* Given in exclusive form, the cumulative frequency table is as follows :

| Marks (class-intervals) | Frequency | Cumulative frequency |
|---|---|---|
| 0–10 | 6 | 6 |
| 10–20 | 11 | $6+11=17$ |
| 20–30 | 5 | $17+5=22$ |
| 30–40 | 4 | $22+4=26$ |
| 40–50 | 4 | $26+4=30$ |
| Total | 30 | 30 |

## Illustrative Examples

**Example 1.** The marks obtained by 40 students of class IX in an examination are given below :

18, 8, 12, 6, 8, 16, 12, 5, 23, 2, 16, 23, 2, 10
20, 12, 9, 7, 0, 5, 3, 5, 13, 21, 13, 15, 20,
24, 1, 7, 21, 10, 13, 18, 23, 7, 3, 18, 17, 16.

Present the data in the form of a frequency distribution using the same class size, one such class being 15–20 (where 20 not included).

**Solution.** Minimum observation is 0 and maximum observation is 24. The classes of equal size covering the given data are :

0–5, 5–10, 10–15, 15–20 and 20–25.

Thus, the frequency distribution may be given as under :

| Marks | Tally marks | Frequency |
|---|---|---|
| 0–5 | ₩ I | 6 |
| 5–10 | ₩ ₩ | 10 |
| 10–15 | ₩ III | 8 |
| 15–20 | ₩ III | 8 |
| 20–25 | ₩ III | 8 |
| Total | | 40 |

**Example 2.** The water tax bills (in rupees) of 30 houses in a locality are given below :

95, 32, 44, 84, 30, 34, 96, 110, 102, 45, 75, 54
74, 14, 112, 74, 88, 20, 14, 40, 88, 76, 66,
112, 108, 78, 66, 44, 35, 15.

Construct a frequency distribution table with a class-size of 10.

**Solution.** The minimum and maximum observations are 14 and 112 respectively. So, the classes of equal size covering the above data are :

14–24, 24–34, 34–44, 44–54, 54–64, 64–74, 74–84, 84–94, 94–104, 104–114

And, the frequency distribution table may be presented as given below :

| Bill (in ₹) | Tally marks | Frequency |
|---|---|---|
| 14–24 | IIII | 4 |
| 24–34 | II | 2 |
| 34–44 | III | 3 |
| 44–54 | III | 3 |

| | | |
|---|---|---|
| 54–64 | \| | 1 |
| 64–74 | \|\| | 2 |
| 74–84 | ~~\|\|\|\|~~ | 5 |
| 84–94 | \|\|\| | 3 |
| 94–104 | \|\|\| | 3 |
| 104–114 | \|\|\|\| | 4 |
| Total | | 30 |

**Example 3.** The weights in grams of 50 oranges picked at random from a consignment are as follows :
131, 113, 82, 75, 204, 81, 84, 111, 141, 136
118, 104, 110, 80, 107, 115, 110, 98, 106, 82
100, 109, 123, 90, 78, 90, 99, 107, 84, 76, 186,
119, 93, 187, 139, 195, 123, 125, 129, 130,
68, 128, 115, 107, 115, 126, 70, 86, 92, 111.

Form the grouped frequency table by dividing the variable range into intervals of equal width, each corresponding to 20 gms in such a way that the mid-value of the first class corresponding to 70 gms.

**Solution.** The mid-value of the first class = 70. Size of each class = 20
So, the lower limit of first class interval is (70 – 10) = 60,
And, the upper limit of this class interval is (70 + 10) = 80.
∴ First class interval is 60–80.
So, the frequency distribution table is given as under.

| Weights (in gms) | Tally marks | Frequency |
|---|---|---|
| 60–80 | ~~\|\|\|\|~~ | 5 |
| 80–100 | ~~\|\|\|\|~~ ~~\|\|\|\|~~ \|\|\| | 13 |
| 100–120 | ~~\|\|\|\|~~ ~~\|\|\|\|~~ ~~\|\|\|\|~~ \|\| | 17 |
| 120–140 | ~~\|\|\|\|~~ ~~\|\|\|\|~~ | 10 |
| 140–160 | \| | 1 |
| 160–180 | | 0 |
| 180–200 | \|\|\| | 3 |
| 200–220 | \| | 1 |
| Total | | 50 |

**Example 4.** The marks obtained by 35 students in an examination are given below :
405, 378, 410, 170, 275, 325, 305, 380, 375, 315
370, 290, 318, 175, 405, 154, 175, 355, 261,
288, 241, 402, 380, 178, 253, 428, 240, 210,
425, 440, 328, 460, 380, 370, 360.

Form a cumulative frequency table with class intervals of length 50.

**Solution.** We may form the table as under :
so, the lower limit of first class interval is (70 – 10) = 60

| Class interval | Tally marks | Frequency | Cumulative frequency |
|---|---|---|---|
| 150–200 | ~~\|\|\|\|~~ | 5 | 5 |
| 200–250 | \|\|\| | 3 | 8 |
| 250–300 | ~~\|\|\|\|~~ | 5 | 13 |
| 300–350 | ~~\|\|\|\|~~ \| | 6 | 19 |
| 350–400 | ~~\|\|\|\|~~ \|\|\| | 8 | 27 |
| 400–450 | ~~\|\|\|\|~~ \|\| | 7 | 34 |
| 450–500 | \| | 1 | 35 |

**Example 5.** The frequency distribution of the maks obtained by 100 students of a class is given below :

| Marks obtained | 20–30 | 30–40 | 40–50 | 50–60 | 60–70 | 70–80 | Total |
|---|---|---|---|---|---|---|---|
| Number of students | 6 | 18 | 25 | 22 | 17 | 12 | 100 |

From this table form : (i) the less than series, and (ii) the more than series.

**Solution.** (i) Less than Cumulative Frequency Table :

| Marks obtained | Less than 30 | Less than 40 | Less than 50 | Less than 60 | Less than 70 | Less than 80 |
|---|---|---|---|---|---|---|
| Number of students (Cumulative frequency) | 6 | 24 | 49 | 71 | 88 | 100 |

(ii) More than Cumulative Frequency Table :

| Marks obtained | More than 19 | More than 29 | More than 39 | More than 49 | More than 59 | More than 69 |
|---|---|---|---|---|---|---|
| Cumulative frequency | 100 | 94 | 76 | 51 | 29 | 12 |

**Example 6.** Then class marks of a distribution are 10, 14, 18, 22, 26. Find the class size and the class limits.

**Solution.** Class size = difference of two consecutive class marks

$= 14 - 10 = 18 - 14 = 22 - 18 = 26 - 22 = \mathbf{4}$ Ans.

$\therefore$ Half of the class size $= \frac{4}{2} = 2$

Now, the class limits of first class are $10 - 2$ and $10 + 2$, *i.e.*, 8 and 12. Similarly the class limits of second class are $14 - 2$ and $14 + 2$, *i.e.*, 12 and 16. Similarly we can find the class limits of other classes.

$\therefore$ The class limits are 8–12, 12–16, 16–20, 20–24, 24–28. Ans.

**Example 7.** The table given below shows a frequency distribution table :

| Class interval | 0–5 | 5–10 | 10–15 | 15–20 | 20–25 | 25–30 |
|---|---|---|---|---|---|---|
| Frequency | 11 | 18 | 25 | 32 | 19 | 8 |

Find :

(i) lower limit of second class interval

(ii) upper limit of fourth class interval

(iii) class size

(iv) class mark of third class.

**Solution.**

(i) Second class interval : 5 – 10

lower limit of second class interval = 5 Ans.

(ii) Fourth class interval : 15 – 20

upper limit of fourth class interval = 20 Ans.

(iii) Class size $= 5 - 0 = 10 - 5 = 15 - 10 = 20 - 15 = 25 - 20 = 30 - 25 = 5$ Ans.

(iv) Third class : 10 – 15

Class mark of third class $= \frac{10 + 15}{2} = 12.5$ Ans.

**Example 8.** The marks obtained by 60 students of a class in class test out of 50 are given in the following frequency table

| Marks | 0–10 | 10–20 | 20–30 | 30–40 | 40–50 |
|---|---|---|---|---|---|
| No. of students | 4 | 14 | 22 | 14 | 6 |

Find :

(i) how many students get at least 30 marks?

(ii) how many students get passing marks if the pass marks are 20?

**Solution.** (i) Number of students getting at least 30 marks.

$= 14 + 6 = 20$ **Ans.**

(ii) No. of students getting passing marks $= 22 + 14 + 6$

$= 42$ **Ans.**

**Example 9.** Construct a continuous grouped frequency table from the following data :

| Class marks | 4 | 12 | 20 | 28 | 36 |
|---|---|---|---|---|---|
| Frequency | 5 | 11 | 15 | 12 | 3 |

**Solution.** Class size $= 12 - 4 = 8$

Half of class size $= \frac{8}{2} = 4$

Now, Lower limit = Class mark – Half of class size

$\Rightarrow$ Lower limits $= 4–4, 12–4, 20–4, 28–4, 36–4$

$= 0, 8, 16, 24, 32$

and Upper limit = Class mark + Half of class size

$= 4 + 4, 12 + 4, 20 + 4, 28 + 4, 36 + 4$

$= 8, 16, 24, 32, 40$

$\therefore$ Continuous frequency table is

| Class interval | 0–8 | 8–16 | 16–24 | 24–32 | 32–40 |
|---|---|---|---|---|---|
| Frequency | 5 | 11 | 15 | 12 | 3 |

## Exercise 15A

1. Following data gives the number of children in 40 families. Represent them in the form of a frequency table.

   1, 2, 6, 5, 1, 5, 1, 3, 2, 6, 2, 3, 4, 2, 0, 4, 4,
   3, 2, 2, 0, 0, 1, 2, 2, 4, 3, 2, 1, 0, 5, 1,
   2, 4, 3, 4, 1, 6, 2, 2

2. The marks obtained by 40 students of a class in an examination are given below. Present the data in the form of a frequency distribution using equal class-size, one such class being 10–15 (15 not included).

   15, 23, 6, 23, 8, 17, 16, 8, 16, 10, 7, 5, 2, 18, 7,
   12, 10, 3, 20, 3, 20, 13, 1, 21, 13, 3, 23, 16, 13,
   18, 12, 5, 24, 9, 2, 7, 18, 23, 4, 12

3. Construct a frequency table for the following ages (in years) of 30 students using equal class-intervals, one of them being 9–12, where 12 is not included.

   18, 12, 7, 6, 11, 15, 21, 9, 8, 13, 15, 17, 22, 19, 14,
   21, 23, 8, 12, 16, 11, 21, 9, 16, 22, 23, 18, 6,
   15, 17.

4. The weights (in grams) of 40 bananas picked at random from a basket are as follows :

   84, 45, 30, 110, 75, 100, 40, 70, 60, 70, 75,
   40, 100, 65, 60, 95, 85, 80, 70, 45, 35, 30, 55,
   70, 110, 80, 75, 85, 70, 85, 75, 90, 30, 100,
   55, 45, 65, 60, 50, 40.

   Construct a cumulative frequency distribution table.

5. The monthly wages of 30 workers in a factory are given below :

   832, 860, 820, 890, 898, 845, 869, 836,
   835, 810, 890, 835, 830, 833, 855, 845, 804,
   808, 812, 840, 885, 835, 836, 878, 840, 868,
   890, 840, 806, 890.

   Represent the data in the form of a frequency distribution with class interval 10.

6. The water bills (in ₹) of 25 houses in a certain locality for the period from January 1998 to March 1998 are given below :

56, 8, 5, 18, 10, 44, 50, 30, 47, 36, 25, 16
14, 22, 20, 22, 30, 24, 15, 12, 27, 42, 45, 25
24.

Construct a frequency table and cumulative frequency table.

7. Construct a frequency table with equal class intervals from the following data on the monthly wages (in rupees) of 28 labourers working in a factory, taking one of the class intervals as 210-230 (230 not included)

319, 320, 300, 290, 311, 242, 272, 220, 268,
258, 242, 210, 268, 215, 306, 316, 280, 240,
210, 278, 254, 304, 302, 318, 306, 292, 236, 256.

8. Following are the ages of 360 patients getting medical treatment in a nursing home on a day

| Ages (in years) | 10–20 | 20–30 | 30–40 | 40–50 | 50–60 | 60–70 |
|---|---|---|---|---|---|---|
| No. of patients | 90 | 50 | 60 | 80 | 50 | 30 |

Construct the cumulative frequency distribution table.

9. From the following frequency distribution, obtain the (i) 'less than' series and (ii) 'more than' series.

| Marks obtained | 0–10 | 10–20 | 20–30 | 30–40 | 40–50 |
|---|---|---|---|---|---|
| Number of students | 7 | 11 | 9 | 25 | 8 |

10. Make a frequency table from the following :

| Marks obtained | More than 100 | More than 90 | More than 80 | More than 70 | More than 60 | More than 50 | More than 40 | More than 30 | More than 20 | More than 10 | More than 0 |
|---|---|---|---|---|---|---|---|---|---|---|---|
| Number of students | 0 | 2 | 15 | 30 | 48 | 59 | 71 | 78 | 82 | 88 | 90 |

11. The table given below shows the frequency distribution of the monthly wages of the employees of a company :

| Wages (in ₹) | 400–499 | 500–599 | 600–699 | 700–799 | 800–899 |
|---|---|---|---|---|---|
| No. of employees | 12 | 17 | 13 | 8 | 5 |

Use this table and find :

(i) The lower limit of the fourth class;
(ii) The upper limit of the fifth class;
(iii) The class boundaries of second class;
(iv) The class mark of first class;
(v) The class-size of third class.

12. Given below is a cumulative frequency distribution table :

| Marks | Below 10 | Below 20 | Below 30 | Below 40 | Below 50 | Below 60 |
|---|---|---|---|---|---|---|
| Number of students | 17 | 22 | 29 | 37 | 50 | 60 |

Extract a frequency table from the above.

13. The class marks of a frequency distribution are 5, 10, 15, 20, 25, 30; find the class intervals.

14. The class marks of a frequency distribution are 10, 20, 30, 40, 50; find the class-size and class intervals.

15. Construct the grouped frequency table from the following :

| Class marks | 15 | 25 | 35 | 45 | 55 | 65 |
|---|---|---|---|---|---|---|
| Frequency | 7 | 12 | 18 | 22 | 16 | 5 |

16. The ages of 80 students (above 8 years) of a school are measured and tabulated as below :

| Age (in years) | 8–10 | below 12 | below 14 | below 16 | below 18 |
|---|---|---|---|---|---|
| Number of students | 7 | 15 | 29 | 68 | 80 |

Construct a frequency distribution table for the above data. Also answer the following questions :

(i) How many students have at least 16 years age but less than 18 years?
(ii) How many students have at most 14 years age?

## Answers

**1.**

| No. of children | 0 | 1 | 2 | 3 | 4 | 5 | 6 |
|---|---|---|---|---|---|---|---|
| No. of families | 4 | 7 | 12 | 5 | 6 | 3 | 3 |

**2.**

| Class | 0–5 | 5–10 | 10–15 | 15–20 | 20–25 |
|---|---|---|---|---|---|
| No. of students | 7 | 9 | 8 | 8 | 8 |

**3.**

| Class | 6–9 | 9–12 | 12–15 | 15–18 | 18–21 | 21–24 |
|---|---|---|---|---|---|---|
| No. of students | 5 | 4 | 4 | 7 | 3 | 7 |

**4.**

| Class | 20–40 | 40–60 | 60–80 | 80–100 | 100–120 |
|---|---|---|---|---|---|
| Frequency | 4 | 7 | 16 | 9 | 4 |
| Cumulative frequency | 4 | 11 | 27 | 36 | 40 |

**5.**

| Class | 800–810 | 810–820 | 820–830 | 830–840 | 840–850 | 850–860 | 860–870 | 870–880 | 880–890 | 890–900 |
|---|---|---|---|---|---|---|---|---|---|---|
| Frequency | 3 | 2 | 1 | 8 | 5 | 1 | 3 | 1 | 1 | 5 |

**6.**

| Class | 0–10 | 10–20 | 20–30 | 30–40 | 40–50 | 50–60 |
|---|---|---|---|---|---|---|
| Frequency | 2 | 6 | 8 | 3 | 4 | 2 |
| Cumulative frequency | 2 | 8 | 16 | 19 | 23 | 25 |

**7.**

| Class | 210–230 | 230–250 | 250–270 | 270–290 | 290–310 | 310–330 |
|---|---|---|---|---|---|---|
| Frequency | 4 | 4 | 5 | 3 | 7 | 5 |

**8.**

| Age (in years) | 10–20 | 20–30 | 30–40 | 40–50 | 50–60 | 60–70 |
|---|---|---|---|---|---|---|
| No. of patients | 90 | 50 | 60 | 80 | 50 | 30 |
| Cumulative frequency | 90 | 140 | 200 | 280 | 330 | 360 |

**9.** (i)

| Marks (less than) | 10 | 20 | 30 | 40 | 50 |
|---|---|---|---|---|---|
| No. of students | 7 | 18 | 27 | 52 | 60 |

(ii)

| Marks (more than) | 0 | 10 | 20 | 30 | 40 |
|---|---|---|---|---|---|
| No. of students | 60 | 53 | 42 | 33 | 8 |

**10.**

| Marks | 0–10 | 10–20 | 20–30 | 30–40 | 40–50 | 50–60 | 60–70 | 70–80 | 80–90 | 90–100 |
|---|---|---|---|---|---|---|---|---|---|---|
| No. of students | 2 | 6 | 4 | 7 | 12 | 11 | 18 | 15 | 13 | 2 |

**11.** (i) 700 (ii) 899 (iii) 499.5–599.5 (iv) 499.5 (v) 100

**12.**

| Marks | 0–10 | 10–20 | 20–30 | 30–40 | 40–50 | 50–60 |
|---|---|---|---|---|---|---|
| No. of students | 17 | 5 | 7 | 8 | 13 | 10 |

**13.** 7.5–12.5, 12.5–17.5, 17.5–22.5, 22.5–27.5, 27.5–32.5

**14.** Class size = 10, class-limits : 5–15, 15–25, 25–35, 35–45, 45–55

**15.**

| Class intervals | 10–20 | 20–30 | 30–40 | 40–50 | 50–60 | 60–70 |
|---|---|---|---|---|---|---|
| Frequency | 7 | 12 | 18 | 22 | 16 | 5 |

**16.** (i) 12 (ii) 51

## Graphical Representation of Statistical Data

One of the most convincing and appealing ways in which statistical results may be presented is through diagrams and graphs. Evidence of this can be found in newspapers, magazines, journals, advertisements, etc. There are numerous ways in which statistical data may be displayed pictorially such as different types of diagrams, graphs and maps. Some of these are given below :

### Bar Chart (or Bar Graph)

Bar diagrams are the most common type of diagrams used in practice. The special merits of bar charts are the following :

(i) They are readily understood.
(ii) They possess the outstanding advantage that they are the simplest and the easiest to make.
(iii) When a large number of items are to be compared they are the only form that can be used effectively.

While constructing bar charts the following points should be kept in mind :

(i) The width of the bar should be uniform throughout the diagram.
(ii) The gap between one bar and another should be uniform throughout.
(iii) Bars may be either horizontal or vertical. The vertical bars should be preferred because they give a better look and also facilitate comparison.
(iv) While constructing the bar diagram, it is desirable to write the respective figures at the end of each bar so that the reader can know the precise value without looking at the scale.

## Illustrative Examples

**Example 1.** The following table shows the marks obtained by Aarushi in the annual examination :

| English | Maths | Hindi | Sanskrit | Science | Social Studies |
|---|---|---|---|---|---|
| 50 | 40 | 60 | 70 | 50 | 54 |

Draw a bar graph to show the above information.

**Solution.** (i) Set up the scale on the vertical line. Let 1 cm represent 10 marks. Suppose width of each bar is $\frac{1}{2}$ cm and the space between any two consecutive bars 1 cm.

(ii) Determine the length of the bar corresponding to marks in each subject according to the scale chosen.

(iii) Draw the bars as shown in the graph.

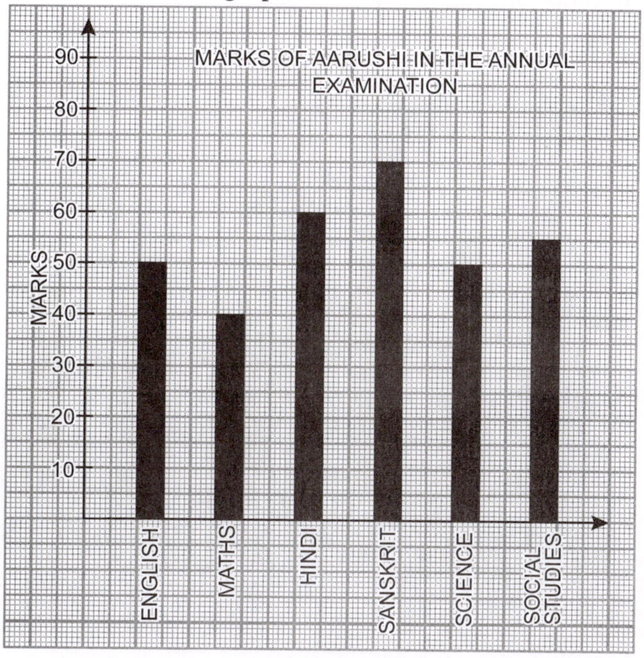

**Example 2.** The area under rice cultivation in the following countries in a year, correct to nearest million hectares was given

| Country | India | Bangladesh | Japan | Burma | Brazil | USA |
|---|---|---|---|---|---|---|
| Cultivated area | 78 | 19 | 16 | 11 | 7 | 6 |

Represent this information by a bar graph.

**Solution.**

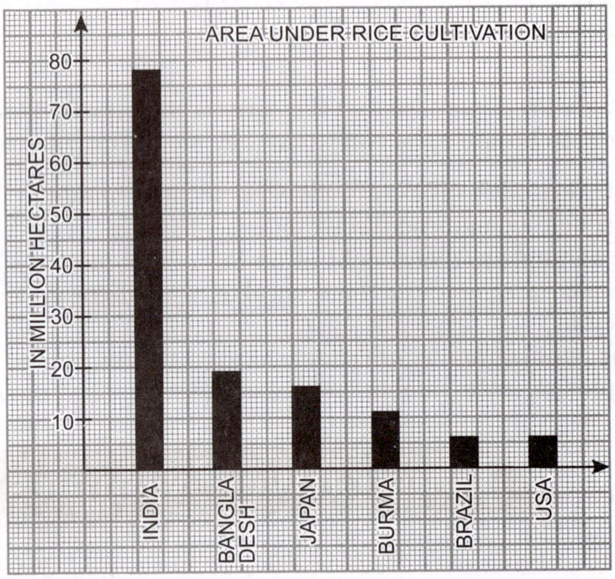


Let 1 cm represent 10 million hectares, width of each bar be $\frac{1}{2}$ cm and the space between any two consecutive bars be 1 cm.

**Example 3.** Given table shows the number of boys and girls going in the different classes of a school :

| Class | 6 | 7 | 8 | 9 | 10 |
|---|---|---|---|---|---|
| No. of boys | 50 | 45 | 60 | 30 | 40 |
| No. of girls | 30 | 40 | 50 | 45 | 50 |

Draw a bar graph to represent the above data.

**Solution.** The required bar graph is as follows :

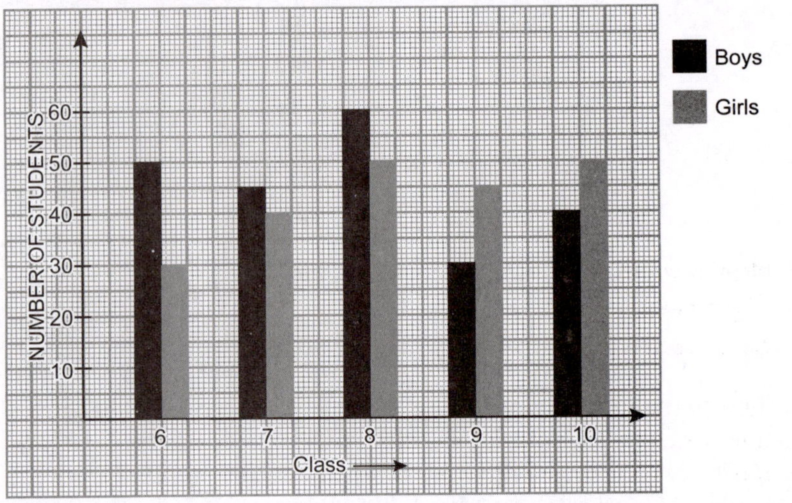

## Histogram

It is a graphical representation of a frequency distribution in the form of rectangles with class-intervals as bases and the corresponding frequencies as heights, there being no gap between any two successive rectangles.

### NOTE

1. If a frequency table is in the inclusive form, we first convert it into an exclusive form and then draw the histogram.
2. In a bar chart, the height of each bar matters and not its width. Whereas, in histogram, the height as well as width of each rectangle matters.

## Frequency Polygon

When a grouped frequency distribution is given then if the frequencies are taken along $y$-axis with the corresponding mid-values of the class intervals on the $x$-axis, we can plot a number of points corresponding to the number of class-intervals. If these points are joined by lines, then we get the *frequency graph*. If the end points of the frequency graph are joined to the mid-values of the adjacent class intervals outside the range, then we get a closed figure, called the *frequency polygon*.

In other words, when the mid-points of the adjacent tops of the rectangles of a histogram are joined by straight lines, the figure so obtained is called a *frequency polygon*.

**Example 4.** Represent the following distribution by means of a histogram :

| Marks | 10–15 | 15–20 | 20–25 | 25–30 | 30–35 |
|---|---|---|---|---|---|
| Number of students | 6 | 9 | 13 | 7 | 3 |

**Solution.** We represent the class limit along $x$-axis on a suitable scale and the frequencies along $y$-axis on a suitable scale.

We construct rectangles with class-intervals as bases and respective frequencies as heights. Thus, we obtain the histogram, shown in fig.

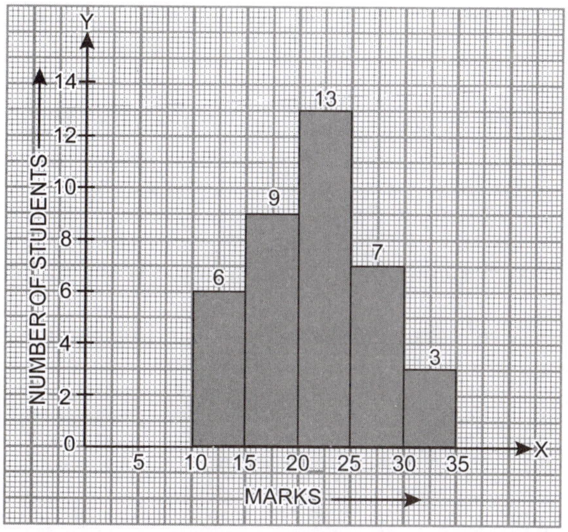


**Example 5.** Depict the following frequency distribution by histogram :

| Monthly wages (in rupees) | 725–750 | 750–775 | 775–800 | 800–825 | 825–850 |
|---|---|---|---|---|---|
| No. of workers | 30 | 45 | 75 | 60 | 35 |

**Solution.** We represent along $x$-axis the class limits on a suitable scale and mark frequencies along the $y$-axis on a suitable scale.

We construct rectangles with class-intervals as bases and respective frequencies as heights.

Since, the scale on the $x$-axis starts at 725, a kink (*i.e.*, break) is indicated near the origin to signify that the graph is drawn to a scale beginning at 725, and not at the origin.

Thus, we get the histogram, as shown in fig.

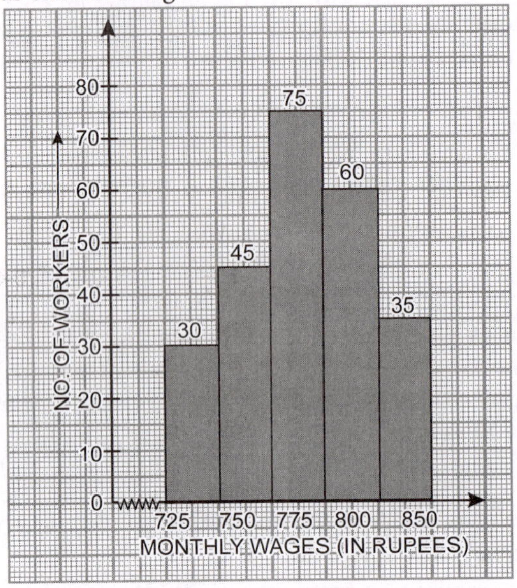


**Example 6.** Draw a histogram for the following frequency distribution showing the daily earnings of 50 physicians of a town :

| **Daily earnings (in ₹) :** | 101–150 | 151–200 | 201–250 | 251–300 | 301–350 | 351–400 | 401–450 | Total |
|---|---|---|---|---|---|---|---|---|
| **Number of physicians :** | 6 | 9 | 13 | 4 | 7 | 9 | 2 | 50 |

Draw a histogram for the above data.

**Solution.** The given frequency distribution is not continuous. If we try to represent the data by a histogram, we will get only a bar diagram as there will be gaps between the classes whereas in a histogram the bars are continuous without any gaps. Therefore, we will have to make the classes continuous by taking the actual class limits, *i.e.*, 100.5–150.5, 150.5–200.5, etc. Thus, the continuous distribution table will be as follows :

| **Daily earnings (in ₹)** | 100.5–150.5 | 150.5–200.5 | 200.5–250.5 | 250.5–300.5 | 300.5–350.5 | 350.5–400.5 | 400.5–450.5 | Total |
|---|---|---|---|---|---|---|---|---|
| **Number of physicians** | 6 | 9 | 13 | 4 | 7 | 9 | 2 | 50 |

We represent along $x$-axis the class limits on a suitable scale and mark frequencies along the $y$-axis on another suitable scale.

We construct rectangles with class-intervals as bases and respective frequencies as heights.

Thus, the required histogram will be as shown in fig.

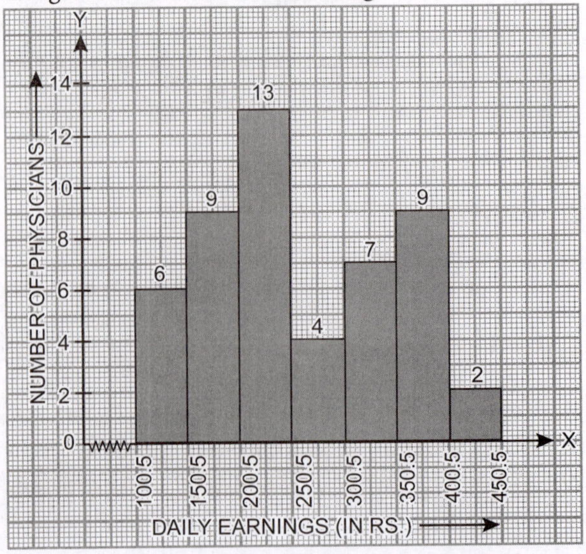

**Example 7.** The weekly pocket expenses of 206 students have been given below :

| Pocket expenses (in rupees) | 0–5 | 5–10 | 10–15 | 15–20 | 20–25 | 25–30 | 30–35 | 35–40 | Total |
|---|---|---|---|---|---|---|---|---|---|
| Number of students | 10 | 16 | 30 | 42 | 50 | 30 | 16 | 12 | 206 |

Construct a frequency polygon from the data given above.

**Solution.** We know that to complete the polygon, the mid-points at each end are joined to the immediately lower or higher mid-points at zero frequency. Hence, we have the following frequency distribution table :

| Pocket expenses (in rupess) | −5–0 | 0–5 | 5–10 | 10–15 | 15–20 | 20–25 | 25–30 | 30–35 | 35–40 | 40–45 |
|---|---|---|---|---|---|---|---|---|---|---|
| Mid-value | −2.5 | 2.5 | 7.5 | 12.5 | 17.5 | 22.5 | 27.5 | 32.5 | 37.5 | 42.5 |
| Frequency (No. of students) | 0 | 10 | 16 | 30 | 42 | 50 | 30 | 16 | 12 | 0 |

**NOTE**

Observe carefully the first and last entries in the above table.

Taking mid-values on $x$-axis and frequencies on $y$-axis, we get the frequency polygon as shown in Fig.

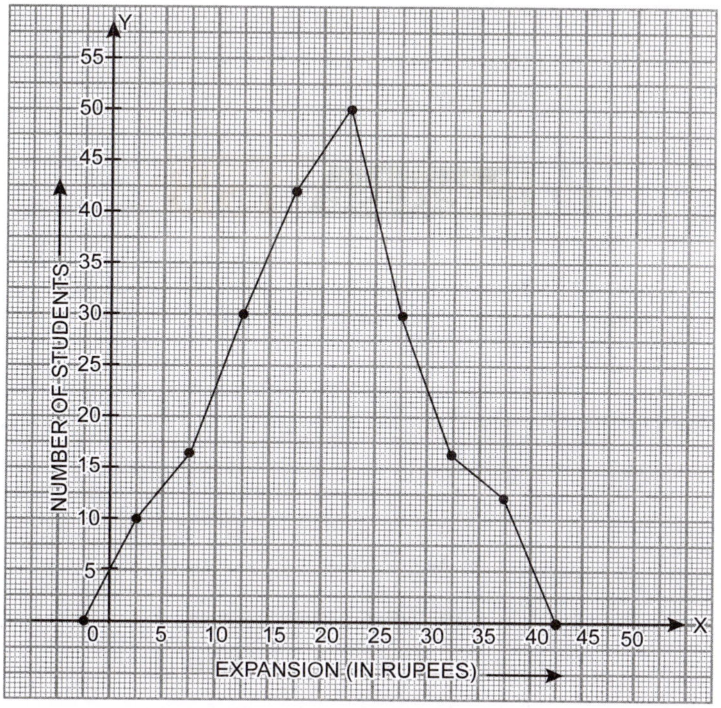


**Example 8.** In a study on cost of living index for a particular year in a city, the following weekly observations were made.

| Cost of living index : (in Rupees) | 140–150 | 150–160 | 160–170 | 170–180 | 180–190 | 190–200 |
|---|---|---|---|---|---|---|
| Number of weeks | 5 | 10 | 20 | 9 | 6 | 2 |

Draw a histogram and a frequency polygon on the same scale.

**Solution.** We represent the class-limits along $x$-axis on a scale and the corresponding frequencies along $y$-axis on another scale.

We construct rectangles with class-intervals as the bases and respective frequencies as heights.

Thus, we obtain the histogram given in Fig.

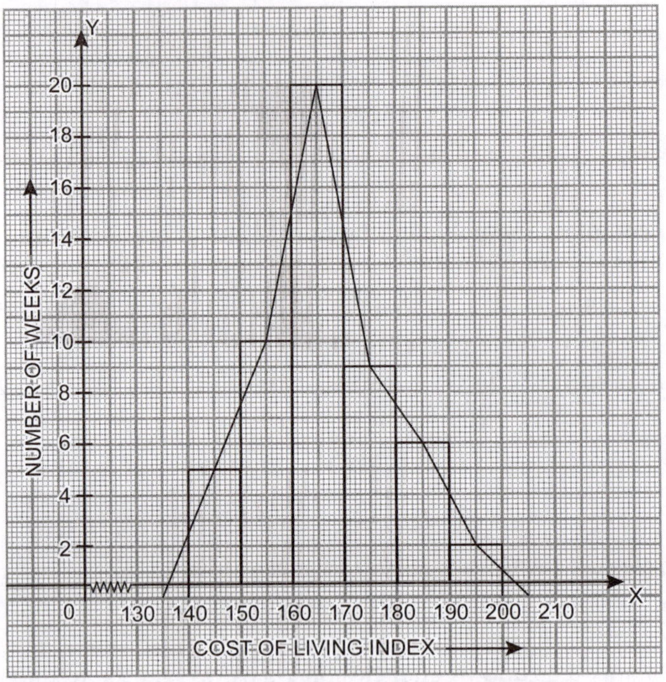


We join the mid-points of the tops of the adjacent rectangle by straight lines.

In order to complete the frequency polygon we take the mid-point of the class interval 130–140 with frequency 0 and join it with the mid-point of the top of the adjoining rectangle, as shown in the figure,

## Exercise 15B

**1.** Draw a bar graph to illustrate the following :

| **Transport to school** | Walk | Bus | Bicycle | Car |
|---|---|---|---|---|
| **Number of children** | 10 | 12 | 18 | 8 |

**2.** Percentage of passes of a certain school at the I.C.S.E. examination for five consecutive years.

| **Year** | 1994 | 1995 | 1996 | 1997 | 1998 |
|---|---|---|---|---|---|
| **% on passes** | 96 | 100 | 98 | 85 | 92 |

Draw bar graph to represent the data.

**3.** Draw bar graph to represent the survey of favourite colours among 32 girls :

| **Colour** | Red | Orange | Yellow | Green | Blue | Indigo | Violet |
|---|---|---|---|---|---|---|---|
| **Number of girls** | 7 | 5 | 3 | 5 | 7 | 1 | 4 |

**4.** The number of visitors to an exhibition organised by a school are :

| **Day** | 1st | 2nd | 3rd | 4th | 5th | 6th | 7th |
|---|---|---|---|---|---|---|---|
| **Number of visitors** | 600 | 480 | 510 | 630 | 560 | 580 | 500 |

Represent the data by a bar graph.

**5.** Fig. illustrates the information collected about the number of brothers of the boys in a certain group. What is the total number of boys in this group.

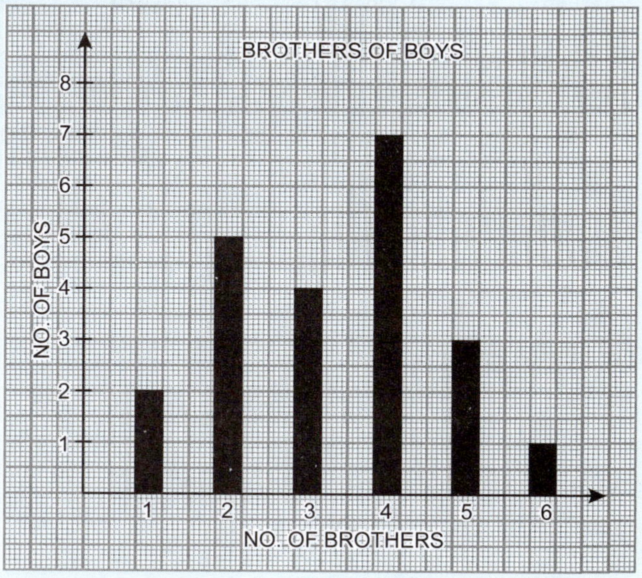


**6.** Draw a bar-chart to represent the following data :

| Name of the animals | Goat | Horse | Cow | Camel | Elephant |
|---|---|---|---|---|---|
| Age (in years) | 12 | 15 | 15 | 26 | 60 |

**7.** The following table shows the market position of different brands of Talcum Powders.

| Brand | *A* | *B* | *C* | Others |
|---|---|---|---|---|
| % Buyers | 50 | 25 | 15 | 10 |

Draw a bar-graph.

**8.** The number of bags of rice sold by a shop on a certain week was as follows :

| Week days | Monday | Tuesday | Wednesday | Thursday | Friday | Saturday |
|---|---|---|---|---|---|---|
| Rice bags sold | 74 | 86 | 78 | 61 | 72 | 97 |

Draw a bar chart for this data.

**9.** Following table shows the number of boys and girls in four sections of class IX in a school. Represent them by a bar graph.

| Section | *A* | *B* | *C* | *D* |
|---|---|---|---|---|
| No. of boys | 30 | 40 | 35 | 40 |
| No. of girls | 25 | 30 | 50 | 45 |

**10.** The following table gives the number of first divisions obtained in various years by the students of a particular school. Illustrate them by a broken line graph.

| Year | 92-93 | 93-94 | 94-95 | 95-96 | 96-97 | 97-98 |
|---|---|---|---|---|---|---|
| No. of first divisions | 35 | 30 | 45 | 40 | 27 | 50 |

**11.** The following table gives the relation (obtained experimentally) between the time-period and the effective length of a pendulum. Illustrate the result by a broken line graph.

| Time-period (in sec) | 0.6 | 0.8 | 1.2 | 1.4 | 1.6 | 2.0 |
|---|---|---|---|---|---|---|
| Effective length (in cm) | 10 | 15 | 235 | 50 | 70 | 90 |

**12.** Illustrate the following results (representing the average weight of a boy at different heights) by a broken line graph.

| Height (in cm) | 70 | 75 | 80 | 85 | 90 | 95 | 100 | 105 |
|---|---|---|---|---|---|---|---|---|
| Weight in kg | 37 | 40 | 42 | 46 | 52 | 55 | 56 | 60 |

**13.** Represent the following distribution of ages (in years) of 35 teachers in a school by means of a histogram :

| Age (in years) | 25–30 | 30–35 | 35–40 | 40–45 | 45–50 |
|---|---|---|---|---|---|
| Number of teachers | 12 | 11 | 8 | 1 | 3 |

**14.** Draw a histogram for daily earnings of 20 drug stores given in the following data :

| Daily earnings : (in ₹) | 150–200 | 200–250 | 250–300 | 300–350 |
|---|---|---|---|---|
| Number of stores | 14 | 9 | 3 | 4 |

**15.** Draw histogram, for the following distribution :

| Money earned (in ₹) | 0–20 | 20–40 | 40–60 | 60–80 | 80–100 | 100–120 | 120–140 |
|---|---|---|---|---|---|---|---|
| No. of students | 4 | 18 | 22 | 14 | 10 | 8 | 4 |

**16.** For following distribution, draw a histogram :

| Class | 1–10 | 11–20 | 21–30 | 31–40 | 41–50 | 51–60 |
|---|---|---|---|---|---|---|
| Frequency | 7 | 3 | 5 | 2 | 6 | 4 |

**17.** Given below are the marks obtained by 40 students in an examination :

| | | | | | | | | | |
|---|---|---|---|---|---|---|---|---|---|
| 29 | 45 | 23 | 30 | 40 | 11 | 48 | 01 | 15 | 35 |
| 40 | 03 | 12 | 48 | 49 | 18 | 30 | 24 | 25 | 29 |
| 31 | 32 | 25 | 22 | 27 | 41 | 12 | 13 | 02 | 44 |
| 07 | 43 | 09 | 49 | 19 | 13 | 32 | 39 | 25 | 03 |

Taking class intervals 1–10, 11–20, ... , 41–50, make a frequency table for the above distributions and draw a histogram to represent it.

**18.** In a class of 60 boys, the marks obtained in a monthly test were as under :

| Marks | 10–20 | 20–30 | 30–40 | 40–50 | 50–60 |
|---|---|---|---|---|---|
| Students | 10 | 25 | 12 | 08 | 05 |

Draw a frequency polygon to represent the above data.

**19.** Draw a frequency polygon for the following frequency distribution :

| Class interval | 0–10 | 10–20 | 20–30 | 30–40 | 40–50 | 50–60 | 60–70 | 70–80 |
|---|---|---|---|---|---|---|---|---|
| Frequency | 5 | 7 | 7 | 8 | 10 | 11 | 12 | 8 |

**20.** Draw a histogram and frequency polygon from the following data :

| Class interval | 20–25 | 25–30 | 30–35 | 35–40 | 40–45 | 45–50 |
|---|---|---|---|---|---|---|
| Frequency | 24 | 30 | 52 | 46 | 28 | 10 |

**21.** Represent the following frequency distribution by a frequency polygon :

| Scores | 20–29 | 30–39 | 40–49 | 50–59 | 60–69 | 70–79 | 80–89 | 90–99 |
|---|---|---|---|---|---|---|---|---|
| Frequency | 1 | 1 | 3 | 14 | 29 | 22 | 12 | 2 |

**22.** Construct a frequency polygon from the following data :

| Scores | 32–34 | 35–37 | 38–40 | 41–43 | 44–46 | 47–49 |
|---|---|---|---|---|---|---|
| Frequency | 13 | 12 | 20 | 18 | 15 | 10 |

**23.** The data given below represent the marks obtained by 35 students.

| | | | | | | | | |
|---|---|---|---|---|---|---|---|---|
| 21 | 26 | 21 | 20 | 23 | 24 | 22 | 19 | 24 |
| 26 | 25 | 23 | 26 | 29 | 21 | 24 | 19 | 25 |
| 26 | 25 | 22 | 25 | 23 | 27 | 26 | 24 | 25 |
| 30 | 25 | 23 | 27 | 28 | 24 | 28 | 28. | |

Taking class intervals 19–20, 21–22, etc., make a frequency distribution for the above data. Then construct a combined histogram and frequency polygon for the distribution.

**24.** The number of match sticks in 40 boxes, on counting was found as given below :

| | | | | | | | | | |
|---|---|---|---|---|---|---|---|---|---|
| 44 | 41 | 42 | 43 | 47 | 50 | 51 | 49 | 43 | 42 |
| 40 | 42 | 44 | 45 | 49 | 42 | 46 | 49 | 45 | 49 |
| 45 | 47 | 48 | 43 | 43 | 44 | 48 | 43 | 46 | 50 |
| 43 | 52 | 46 | 49 | 52 | 51 | 47 | 43 | 43 | 45. |

Taking classes 40–41, 42–43 etc., construct the frequency distribution table for the above data. Draw a histogram to represent the above distribution.

## Mean of Ungrouped Data

We are familiar with the word average. In statistics it is also called the mean.

The mean of a number of observations is the sum of all observations divided by the total number of observations.

Consider the '$n$' observations : $x_1, x_2, x_3, \ldots\ldots\ldots\ldots, x_n$

$$\text{Their mean } \bar{x} = \frac{x_1 + x_2 + x_3 \ldots + x_n}{n} \Rightarrow \frac{\sum_{i=1}^{n} x_i}{n}$$

or

$$\text{Mean} = \frac{\text{Sum of observations}}{\text{Number of observations}}$$

Here, the symbol $\Sigma$, called **sigma** means the summation of the given observations.

## Median of Ungrouped Data

It is the value of the middle-most observation when the given data are arranged in ascending or descending order.

### Method of Finding the Median

1. Arrange the given data in ascending or descending order.
2. Count the number of observations, say it is '$n$'.
3. (a) If '$n$' is odd, then

$$\text{Median} = \left(\frac{n+1}{2}\right)\text{th term}$$

(b) If '$n$' is even, then

$$\text{Median} = \frac{\left(\frac{n}{2}\right)\text{th term} + \left(\frac{n}{2}+1\right)\text{th term}}{2}$$

## Illustrative Examples

**Example 1.** Find the mean of first 7 natural numbers.

**Solution.** Sum of first of natural numbers $= 1 + 2 + 3 + 4 + 5 + 6 + 7$

$= 28$

$$\text{Mean} = \frac{\text{sum of 7 numbers}}{7}$$

$$= \frac{28}{7} = 4$$ Ans.

**Example 2.** The marks obtained by 6 students in a class test are 15, 17, 18, 18, 16, 12, Find the mean.

**Solution.** Total marks obtained by 6 students $= 15 + 17 + 18 + 18 + 16 + 12$

$= 96$

$$\text{Mean marks} = \frac{\text{total marks}}{\text{no. of students}}$$

$$= \frac{96}{6} = 16$$ Ans.

**Example 3.** Find the mean of first 5 prime numbers.

**Solution.** First 5 prime numbers = 2, 3, 5, 7, 11

Sum of first 5 prime numbers = 2 + 3 + 5 + 7 + 11 = 28

$$\text{Mean} = \frac{\text{sum of first 5 prime numbers}}{5}$$

$$= \frac{28}{5} = 5.6$$ Ans.

**Example 4.** (i) Find the mean of 7, 9, 11, 15, 15, 16, 18, 21.

(ii) Also find the resulting mean if each observation is

(a) increased by 5 (b) decreased by 5 (c) multiplied by 5 (d) divided by 5

**Solution.** (i)

$$\text{Mean } \bar{x} = \frac{\text{sum of observations}}{\text{number of observations}}$$

$$= \frac{7 + 9 + 11 + 15 + 15 + 16 + 18 + 21}{8}$$

$$= \frac{112}{8} = 14$$ Ans.

(ii) (a) If each observation is increased by 5, then

$$\text{new mean} = \bar{x} + 5$$

$$= 14 + 5 = 19$$ Ans.

(b) If each observation is decreased by 5, then

$$\text{new mean} = \bar{x} - 5$$

$$= 14 - 5 = 9$$ Ans.

(c) If each observation is multiplied by 5, then

$$\text{new mean} = 5\bar{x}$$

$$= 5 \times 14 = 70$$ Ans.

(d) If each observation is divided by 5, then

$$\text{new mean} = \frac{\bar{x}}{5}$$

$$= \frac{14}{5} = 2.8$$ Ans.

**Example 5.** For the data 17, 29, $x + 3$, 28, 26, $x - 2$, 13, 20 mean is 25. Find the value of $x$.

**Solution.**

$$\text{Mean} = \frac{\text{sum of observations}}{\text{number of observations}}$$

$$\Rightarrow \quad 25 = \frac{17 + 29 + (x + 3) + 28 + 26 + (x - 2) + 13 + 20}{8}$$

$$200 = 2x + 134$$

$$\Rightarrow \quad 2x = 66$$

$$\Rightarrow \quad x = 33$$ Ans.

**Example 6.** Find the mean of the positive factors of 28.

**Solution.** Factors of 28 = 1, 2, 4, 7, 14, 28

$$\text{Mean} = \frac{\text{sum of factors}}{\text{number of factors}}$$

$$= \frac{1 + 2 + 4 + 7 + 14 + 28}{6} = \frac{56}{6} = 9\frac{1}{3}$$ Ans.

**Example 7.** If mean of 10 observations is 14. If mean of first 6 observations is 13. Find the mean of the remaining 4 observations.

**Solution.** The mean of 10 observations =14

$\therefore$ Total sum of 10 observations = 14 × 10 = 140

The mean of first 6 observations = 13

$\therefore$ Total sum of first 6 observations = 13 × 6 = 78

Now total sum of last 4 observations = 140 – 78 = 62

$\therefore$ The mean of last 4 observations $= \frac{62}{4} - 15.5$ **Ans.**

**Example 8.** The mean of 11 observations is 15. If the mean of first 6 observations is 14 and that of the last 6 observations is 17. Find the 6th observation.

**Solution.** The mean of 11 observations = 15

$\therefore$ The total sum of 11 observations = 15 × 11 = 165

The mean of first 6 observations =14

$\therefore$ The total sum of 6 observations = 14 × 6 = 84

The mean of last 6 observations = 17

$\therefore$ The total sum of last 6 observations = 17 × 6 = 102

Now, the 6th observations = 102 + 84 – 165

= 21 **Ans.**

**Example 9.** The mean of 7 observations is 22. The six of them are 20, 25, 21, 24, 19, 23. Find the 7th observations.

**Solution.** Let the 7th observations be $x$

Now, $$\text{Mean} = \frac{\text{sum of observations}}{\text{number of observations}}$$

$$\Rightarrow \quad 22 = \frac{20 + 25 + 21 + 24 + 19 + 23 + x}{7}$$

$$\Rightarrow \quad 154 = 142 + x \quad \Rightarrow \quad x = 12$$

$\therefore$ 7th observation = 12 **Ans.**

**Example 10.** The mean of weight of 10 students is 44 kg. Two more students of weights 40 kg and 36 kg join the group. Find the new mean weight.

**Solution.**
$$\text{Mean} = \frac{\text{sum of weight of 10 students}}{10}$$

$$\Rightarrow \quad 44 = \frac{\text{sum of weight of 10 students}}{10}$$

$\Rightarrow$ Sum of weight of 10 students = 44 × 10 kg = 440 kg

Now, sum of weight of 12 students = 440 kg + 40 kg + 36 kg

= 516 kg

$$\text{New mean weight} = \frac{\text{sum of weight of 12 students}}{12}$$

$$= \frac{516}{12}\text{ kg} = 43\text{ kg}$$ **Ans.**

**Example 11.** The mean of 20 observations is 112. It was detected that one observations 137 was wrongly copied as 117. Find the correct mean.

**Solution.** Mean of 20 observations = 112

Total incorrect sum of 20 observations = 112 × 20 = 2240

Now correct sum of 20 observations = 2240 – 117 + 137 = 2260

$\therefore$ Correct mean $= \frac{2260}{20} = 113$ **Ans.**

**Example 12.** The mean of 10 observations is 22. One observation is excluded. The mean of remaining observations is 20. Find the excluded observation.

**Solution.** Mean of 10 observations = 22

Total sum of 10 observations = 22 × 10 = 220

When one observation is excluded

The mean of 9 observations = 20

The total sum of 9 observations = 20 × 9 = 180

∴ Excluded observation = 220 – 180 = **40** Ans.

**Example 13.** Find the median : 5, 11, 18, 7, 12, 14, 10.

**Solution.** Arranging the given data in ascending order.

5, 7, 10, 11, 12, 14, 18

$n = 7$ (number of observations)

which is odd

$$\therefore \quad \text{Median} = \frac{n+1}{2}\text{th term} = \frac{7+1}{2}\text{th term} = 4\text{th term} = \mathbf{11}$$ Ans.

**Example 14.** Find the median :

3, 3, 4, 3, 0, 5, 2, 1, 3, 1

**Solution.** Arranging the data in ascending order

0, 1, 1, 2, 3, 3, 3, 3, 4, 5

Here $n = 10$

Which is even

$$\therefore \quad \text{Median} = \frac{\frac{n}{2}\text{th observation} + \left(\frac{n}{2}+1\right)\text{th observation}}{2}$$

$$= \frac{\frac{10}{2}\text{th observation} + \left(\frac{10}{2}+1\right)\text{th observation}}{2}$$

$$= \frac{5\text{th observation} + 6\text{th observation}}{2}$$

$$= \frac{3+3}{2} = \mathbf{3}$$ Ans.

**Example 15.** The numbers 10, 12, 23, 29, $x$, $x + 4$, 37, 38, 40, 58 are in ascending order. Their median is 33. Find the value of $x$.

**Solution.** Here, $n = 10$ (even)

$$\therefore \quad \text{Median} = \frac{\frac{n}{2}\text{th term} + \left(\frac{n}{2}+1\right)\text{th term}}{2}$$

$$\Rightarrow \quad 33 = \frac{\left(\frac{10}{2}\right)\text{th term} + \left(\frac{10}{2}+1\right)\text{th term}}{2}$$

$$\Rightarrow \quad 66 = 5\text{th term} + 6\text{th term} \quad \Rightarrow \quad 66 = x + x + 4$$

$$\Rightarrow \quad 2x = 62 \quad \Rightarrow \quad x = \mathbf{31}$$ Ans.

# Exercise 15C

1. Find the mean of the following :
   (i) 22, 26, 35, 42, 45
   (ii) First 8 odd prime numbers
   (iii) Factors of 48
   (iv) odd numbers lying between 20 and 30.
   (v) even numbers lying between 11 and 31.
2. (i) The mean of 13, 17, $x$, 16, 20, 26, is 23. Find the value of $x$.
   (ii) The mean of 72, 78, 82, $x$, 75, 80, 72 is 77. Find the value of $x$.
3. The mean of 6 observations is 25 and the mean of other 4 observations is 20. Find the mean of all observations.
4. The mean of 30 observations is 60. The mean of first 20 observations is 65. Find the mean of last 10 observations.
5. Find the mean of 12, 17, 31, 25, 15.
   Find the resulting mean if each observations is :
   (i) increased by 2 (ii) decreased by 2 (iii) multiplied by 2 (iv) divided by 2
6. The mean of 9 observations is 15. The mean of first 5 observations is 16 and the mean of last 5 observations is 14. Find the 5th observation.
7. The mean of 11 observations is 12. The mean of first 6 observations is 14 and the mean of last 6 observations is 11. Find the 6th observation.
8. The mean of 15 observations is 40. It was detected that one observation 47 was misread as 77. Find the correct mean.
9. The mean of 20 observations is 32. It was detected that one observation 43 was wrongly copied as 33. Find the correct mean.
10. The mean of 10 observations is 72. It was found that two observations 65 and 85 were misread as 56 and 58. Find the correct mean.
11. The mean of 12 observations is45. It was found that two observations 38 and 52 were misread as 28 and 32. Find the correct mean.
12. A batsman has a mean score of 73 in 19 innings. Find how many runs are to be scored by him in 20th inning so that his mean score becomes 75?
13. The mean monthly salary of 9 employees of an office is ₹ 72,000. When the salary of the manager is included, their mean becomes ₹ 80,000. Find the salary of the manager.
14. The mean of 11 observations is 28. It was found that one observation 34 was misread as 23. Find the mean if :
    (a) this observation is excluded. (b) correct observation is included.
15. The mean of 9 observations is 32. It was found that one observation 36 was misread as 63. Find the mean if :
    (a) this observation is excluded. (b) correct observation is included.
16. If $x$ is the mean of $n$ observations $x_1, x_2, x_3, \ldots x_n$, then prove that
$$\sum_{i=1}^{n}(x_1 - \bar{x}) = 0$$
17. Find the mediam :
    (i) 27, 32, 24, 26, 11, 14, 19
    (ii) 7, 14, 21, 15, 19, 18, 6, 10, 14
    (iii) 3, 4, 12, 13, 18, 20, 7, 8
    (iv) 28, 30, 35, 31, 27, 46, 32, 44, 33, 25
18. Find the median of first 7 even natural numbers.
19. Find the median of first 10 prime numbers.
20. If 12, 16, 18, $x+2$, $x+4$, 45, 48, 52 are arranged in ascending order and their median is 31, find the value of $x$.

## Answers

| | | | | | | |
|---|---|---|---|---|---|---|
| **1.** (i) 34 | (ii) 10.125 | (iii) 12.4 | (iv) 25 | (v) 21 | **2.** (i) 46 | (ii) 80 |
| **3.** 23 | **4.** 50 | **5.** 20 | (i) 22 | (ii) 18 | (iii) 40 | (iv) 10 |
| **6.** 15 | **7.** 18 | **8.** 38 | **9.** 32.5 | **10.** 75.6 | **11.** 47.5 | **12.** 113 |
| **13.** 1,52,000 | **14.** (a) 28.5 | (b) 29 | **15.** (a) 25 | (b) 29 | **17.** (i) 24 | (ii) 14 |
| (iii) 10 | (iv) 32.5 | **18.** 8 | **19.** 12 | **20.** 29. | | |

# Exercise 15D

## Multiple Choice Questions

Choose the correct answer from the given four options in each of the following questions :

1. The class-mark of the class-interval 40–48 is :
(a) 40 (b) 42 (c) 44 (d) 48

2. For the data 30, 36, 26, 42, 31, 49, 33, 42, 38, the range is :
(a) 19 (b) 23 (c) 26 (d) 49

3. Which of the following is not the graphical representation of data?
(a) Bar graph (b) Histogram (c) Frequency polygon (d) Median

4. In a frequency distribution, the mid-value of a class is 12 and the class-size is 20. The lower limit of the class is :
(a) 2 (b) 8 (c) 10 (d) 12

5. The mean of first 7 odd natural numbers is :
(a) 5 (b) 7 (c) 8 (d) 10

6. In the class intervals 20–25, 25–30, 30–35, the number 30 is included in the class :
(a) 20-25 (b) 25-30 (c) 30-35 (d) none of these

7. The mean of first 8 odd prime number is :
(a) 11.75 (b) 12 (c) 12.25 (d) 12.50

8. The mean of 25 observations is 32. If each observation is increased by 5, the new mean will be :
(a) 27 (b) 37 (c) 32 (d) 30

9. The median of the data 17, 19, 32, 24, 18, 8, 12 is :
(a) 12 (b) 17 (c) 19 (d) 18

10. The median of the data 6, 12, 25, 16, 4, 19, 10, 27 is :
(a) 12 (b) 14 (c) 16 (d) 19

11. The mean of 20 observations is 30. If the mean of 15 observations is 32, then the mean of last 5 observations is :
(a) 24 (b) 23 (c) 22 (d) 20

12. A cricketer has a mean score of 48 runs in 5 innings. The run scored by him in 6th inning to raise his mean score to 50, will be :
(a) 42 (b) 50 (c) 56 (d) 60

13. The numbers 12, 14, 22, 26, $x$, $x + 2$, 38, 45, 49, 51 are in ascending order. Their median is 34. The value of $x$ is :
(a) 31 (b) 33 (c) 34 (d) 36

14. The class marks of a frequency distribution are 5, 10, 15, 20, 25, 30. The class corresponding to class mark 20 is :
(a) 17.5–22.5 (b) 17–23 (c) 15–25 (d) none of these

### Answers

| | | | | | | |
|---|---|---|---|---|---|---|
| **1.** (c) | **2.** (b) | **3.** (d) | **4.** (a) | **5.** (b) | **6.** (c) | **7.** (c) |
| **8.** (b) | **9.** (d) | **10.** (b) | **11.** (a) | **12.** (d) | **13.** (b) | **14.** (a) |

## SUMMARY of the Chapter

- Statistics is the study of collection of date, their presentation, analysis and interpretation.
- The numerical informations collected for definite purpose are called data.
- A quantity which is capable of taking several different values, is called a variable.
- The difference between the maximum and minimum value of a variable is called its range.
- The number of times a particular observation occurs is called its frequency.
- A table which represents the frequency of various observations is called frequency distribution table.
- There are two types of frequency distribution :
  1. Ungrouped frequency distribution
  2. Grouped frequency distribution
     (a) Inclusive frequency table.
     (b) Exclusive frequency table.
- Class Interval. In a frequency distribution, a group bounded by two numbers is called a class-interval. The first number of this group is called lower limit and the last number is called the upper limit.
- Class Size. The difference between the true upper limit and true lower limit of a class interval is called its class size.
- Class Mark. It is the value, midway between the actual lower limit and actual upper limit of a class interval.
- Cumulative Frequency. The total frequency of all values upto and inclusive of a particular class is called the cumulative frequency of that class.
- The numerical data can be represented graphically.
- Bar Graph. In bar graphs, bar of equal width are drawn with equal gap (space) between them. The height of a bar shows the frequency of the corresponding observation.
- Histogram. Histogram can be formed for continuous grouped data. It consists of adjacent rectangles whose breadth corresponds to the class size and length corresponds to the frequency of the class.
- Frequency Polygon. First we draw a histogram, then we join the mid-points of the adjacent tops of the rectangles by the straight lines. The mid-point of each end are joined to the adjacent lower or higher mid-point at zero frequency on the $x$-axis.
- Mean. $$\text{Mean } \bar{x} = \frac{\text{Sum of observations}}{\text{Number of observations}} = \frac{\sum_{i=1}^{n} x_i}{n}$$
- Median. The value of the middle most term is called median when the data are arranged in ascending or descending order.
  1. If number of observations '$n$' are odd, then
  $$\text{Median} = \left(\frac{n+1}{2}\right)\text{th term}$$
  2. If number of observations '$n$' are even, then
  $$\text{Median} = \frac{\left(\frac{n}{2}\right)\text{th term} + \left(\frac{n}{2}+1\right)\text{th term}}{2}$$

# CHAPTER TEST

**1.** Prepare a frequency table from the following data using class intervals 0–5, 5–10, 10–15, ... etc.

11, 16, 12, 22, 9, 4, 13, 10, 5, 21,

3, 9, 15, 20, 11, 24, 7, 9, 18, 23

**2.** Prepare a frequency table from the following data using class intervals 0–9, 10–19, 20–29, ... etc.

30, 48, 36, 11, 26, 3, 40, 7, 13, 21

28, 45, 16, 29, 49, 42, 39, 17, 8, 32

**3.** Construct a cumulative frequency table from the following frequency table :

| Class interval | 0–4 | 4–8 | 8–12 | 12–16 | 16–20 | 20–24 |
|---|---|---|---|---|---|---|
| Frequency | 5 | 12 | 18 | 15 | 10 | 4 |

**4.** Construct (i) more than frequency table (ii) less than frequency table from the following data :

| Class | 0–10 | 10–20 | 20–30 | 30–40 | 40–50 |
|---|---|---|---|---|---|
| Frequency | 3 | 8 | 15 | 9 | 4 |

**5.** Construct a continuous frequency table from the following :

(i)

| Age (less than in years) | 10 | 12 | 14 | 16 | 18 | 20 |
|---|---|---|---|---|---|---|
| No. of students | 3 | 6 | 12 | 28 | 38 | 40 |

(ii)

| Marks (Mroe than) | 0 | 5 | 10 | 15 | 20 |
|---|---|---|---|---|---|
| No. of students | 50 | 46 | 35 | 11 | 4 |

**6.** The class marks of a distribution are 20, 25, 30, 35, 40. Find the class intervals.

**7.** Draw a bar graph to represent the following data :

| Subject | Hindi | English | Maths | Science | Social Science |
|---|---|---|---|---|---|
| Marks | 25 | 40 | 45 | 35 | 30 |

**8.** Draw a histogram and frequency polygon to represent the following data :

| Class | 0–10 | 10–20 | 20–30 | 30–40 | 40–50 | 50–60 |
|---|---|---|---|---|---|---|
| Frequency | 3 | 7 | 9 | 8 | 6 | 2 |

**9.** Find the mean of prime numbers lying between 20 and 40.

**10.** The mean of 100 observations is 126. It is found that one observation 183 was misread as 138. Find the correct mean.

**11.** The mean of 10 observations is 27 and mean of first 9 observations is 28. Find the 10th observations.

**12.** Find the median :

16, 28, 35, 11, 19, 25, 39, 21

# Answers

**1.**

| Class | Tally Marks | Frequency |
|---|---|---|
| 0–5 | \|\| | 2 |
| 5–10 | 卌 | 5 |
| 10–15 | 卌 | 5 |
| 15–20 | \|\|\| | 3 |
| 20–25 | 卌 | 5 |
| | Total | 20 |

**2.**

| Class | Tally marks | Frequency |
|---|---|---|
| 0–9 | \|\|\| | 3 |
| 10–19 | \|\|\|\| | 4 |
| 20–29 | \|\|\|\| | 4 |
| 30–39 | \|\|\|\| | 4 |
| 40–49 | 卌 | 5 |
| | Total | 20 |

**3.**

| Class interval | Frequency | Cumulative frequency |
|---|---|---|
| 0–4 | 5 | 5 |
| 4–18 | 12 | 17 |
| 8–12 | 18 | 35 |
| 12–16 | 15 | 50 |
| 16–20 | 10 | 60 |
| 20–24 | 4 | 64 |

**4.** (i)

| More than | 0 | 10 | 20 | 30 | 40 |
|---|---|---|---|---|---|
| Frequency | 39 | 36 | 28 | 13 | 4 |

(ii)

| Less than | 10 | 20 | 30 | 40 | 50 |
|---|---|---|---|---|---|
| Frequency | 3 | 11 | 26 | 35 | 39 |

**5.** (i)

| Age (in years) | 0–10 | 10–12 | 12–14 | 14–16 | 16–18 | 18–20 |
|---|---|---|---|---|---|---|
| No. of students | 3 | 3 | 6 | 16 | 10 | 2 |

(ii)

| Marks | 0–5 | 5–10 | 10–15 | 15–20 | 20 and more |
|---|---|---|---|---|---|
| No. of students | 4 | 11 | 24 | 7 | 4 |

**6.** 17.5–22.5, 22.5–27.5–27.5–32.5, 32.5–37.5, 37.5–42.5

**9.** 30 **10.** 126.45 **11.** 18 **12.** 23

UNIT VI : MENSURATION

Chapter

16

# MENSURATION

## Syllabus

Area and perimeter of a triangle and a quadrilateral. Area and circumference of circle. Surface area and volume of cube and cuboids.

(a) Area and perimeter of triangle (including Heron's formula), all types of quadrilaterals.

(b) Circle: Area and circumference. Direct application problems including inner and outer area.

Areas of sectors of circles other than quarter-circle and semicircle are not included.

(c) Surface area and volume of 3-D solids: cube and cuboid including problems of type involving:

- Different internal and external dimensions of the solid.
- Cost.
- Concept of volume being equal to area of cross-section × height.
- Open/closed cubes/cuboids.

## INTRODUCTION

In previous classes, you have studied about the perimeter and area of closed plane figures, like triangles, quadrilaterals and circles. You have already studied about the surface area and volume of cube and cuboid. Now, we shall review the perimeter and area of triangles, quadrilaterals and the surface area and volume of cube and cuboid.

## Perimeter

The perimeter of a plane figure is the length of its boundary.

Its unit is same as the unit of length, *i.e.*, m, cm, km, etc.

## Area

The area of a plane figure is the surface enclosed by its boundary.

It is measured in square units, *i.e.*, square meter ($m^2$), square centimeter ($cm^2$), etc.

## Area of Triangles

1. Area $= \frac{1}{2}$ base × corresponding height.

Corresponding height or altitude of a triangle means length of perpendicular from the opposite vertex to the base.

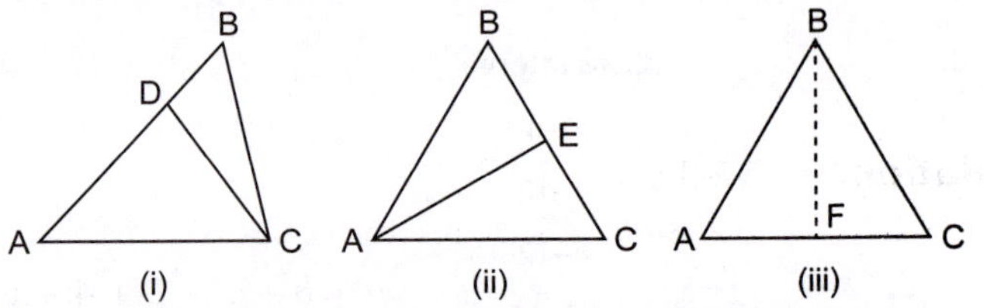


In a triangle, any of its sides can be considered as base, *e.g.*,

(i) If side $AB$ is taken as the base then the length of perpendicular $CD$ is the corresponding height.

$\therefore$ Area $= \frac{1}{2}$ base × height $= \frac{1}{2} AB \times CD.$

(ii) If side $BC$ is taken as base then the length of perpendicular $AE$ is the corresponding height.

$\therefore$ Area $= \frac{1}{2} BC \times AE.$

(iii) If side $AC$ is taken as base then the length of perpendicular $BF$ is the corresponding height.

$\therefore$ Area $= \frac{1}{2} AC \times BF.$

2. If $a$, $b$ and $c$ are three sides of a triangle, then its perimeter $= a + b + c.$

and area $= \sqrt{s(s-a)(s-b)(s-c)}$;

where $s = \frac{a+b+c}{2}$ = semi-perimeter of the triangle.

## Area of Special Types of Triangles

1. Equilateral Triangle

Let the length of each side of an equilateral triangle be a units; then its perimeter

$= 3 \times$ its sides $= 3a$

and its area $= \frac{\sqrt{3}}{4} \times (\text{side})^2 = \frac{\sqrt{3}}{4} a^2.$

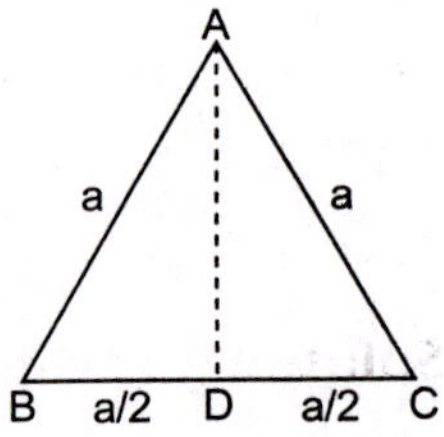

2. Isosceles Triangle

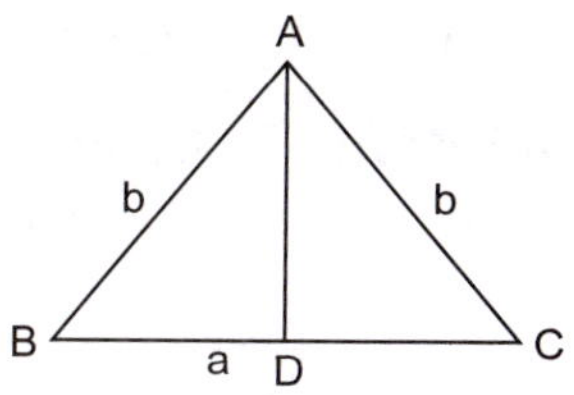


Let $BC = a$ and each of the equal sides be $b$.

$$\text{Perimeter} = a + 2b$$

$$\text{Area} = \frac{1}{4} a\sqrt{4b^2 - a^2}$$

3. Right-angled Triangle

The area of a right-angled triangle is equal to half the product of the sides containing the right angle.

In adjoining figure,

$$\text{area of } \Delta ABC = \frac{1}{2} AB \times BC.$$

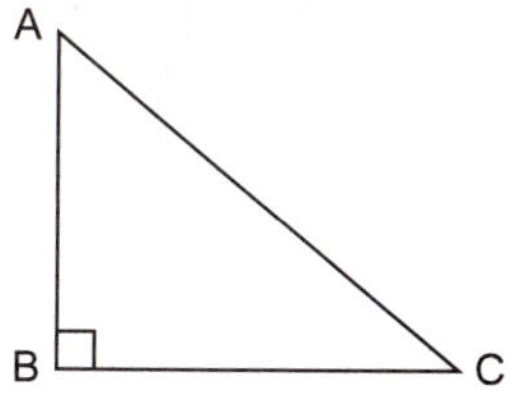


## Illustrative Examples

**Example 1.** The sides of a triangle area 3 cm, 4 cm and 5 cm. Find its area.

**Solution.** We have,

$a = 3$ cm, $b = 4$ cm and $c = 5$ cm.

$$\therefore \quad s = \frac{a+b+c}{2} = \frac{3+4+5}{2} = 6 \text{ cm}.$$

$$\therefore \quad \text{Area} = \sqrt{s(s-a)(s-b)(s-c)}$$

$$= \sqrt{6(6-3)(6-4)(6-5)}$$

$$= \sqrt{6 \times 3 \times 2 \times 1} = \sqrt{36} = 6 \text{ cm}^2$$

Ans.

**Example 2.** The sides of a triangle are 25 cm, 17 cm and 12 cm. Find the area and the length of the altitude on the longest side.

**Solution.** We have,

$$s = \frac{25+17+12}{2} = \frac{54}{2} = 27 \text{ cm}$$

$$\therefore \quad \text{Area} = \sqrt{s(s-a)(s-b)(s-c)}$$

$$= \sqrt{27(27-25)(27-17)(27-12)}$$

$$= \sqrt{27 \times 2 \times 10 \times 15}$$

$$= \sqrt{3 \times 3 \times 3 \times 2 \times 2 \times 5 \times 3 \times 5}$$

$$= 3 \times 3 \times 2 \times 5 = 90 \text{ cm}^2$$

Ans.

Let $h$ be the altitude on the longest side (25 cm). Then

$$\text{Area} = \frac{1}{2} \times 25 \times h$$

$$\therefore \quad \frac{1}{2} \times 25h = 90 \quad \Rightarrow \quad h = 90 \times \frac{2}{25} = 7.2 \text{ cm}$$

Ans.

**Example 3.** Find the area of an equilateral triangle of side 4 cm, correct to three significant figures.

**Solution.** Area of an equilateral triangle

$$= \frac{\sqrt{3}}{4} \times a^2 = \frac{\sqrt{3}}{4} \times 4 \times 4 = 1.732 \times 4 = 6.93 \text{ cm}^2$$

Ans.

**Example 4.** Calculate the area of an equilateral triangle, whose height is 20 cm.

**Solution.** Let $ABC$ be the given equilateral triangle and $AD$ is perpendicular to base $BC$, then $AD = 20$ cm. Let each side of the given triangle be $a$ cm then $BD = a/2$. In right-angled triangle $ABC$:

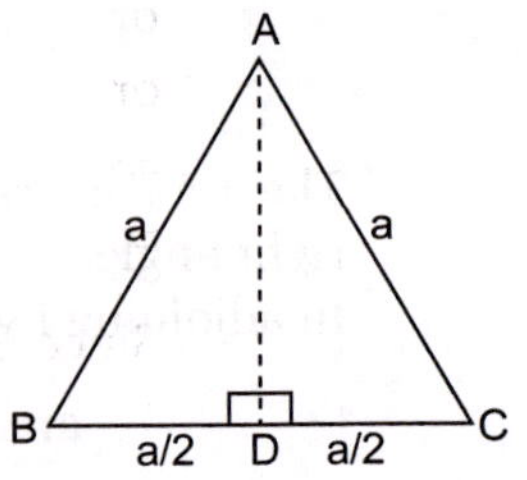


$$AD^2 + BD^2 = AB^2 \quad \text{(Pythagoras Theorem)}$$

$$\Rightarrow \quad (20)^2 + \left(\frac{a}{2}\right)^2 = a^2$$

$$\Rightarrow \quad a^2 - \frac{a^2}{4} = \frac{3a^2}{4} = 400 \quad \Rightarrow \quad a^2 = \frac{4 \times 400}{3} = \frac{1600}{3}$$

$$\therefore \quad \text{Area of the triangle} = \frac{\sqrt{3}}{4}a^2 = \frac{\sqrt{3}}{4} \times \frac{1600}{3} \text{ cm}^2$$

$$= \frac{400}{\sqrt{3}} = \frac{400}{1.732} = 230.9 \text{ cm}^2$$

Ans.

**Example 5.** Find the area of an isosceles triangle whose equal sides are 5 cm each and base is 6 cm.

**Solution.** Area of an isosceles triangle $= \frac{1}{4}a\sqrt{(4b^2 - a^2)}$

where $b$ is the length of equal sides and $a$ is the base.

$$\therefore \quad \text{Required area} = \frac{1}{4} \times 6\sqrt{4 \times 5^2 - 6^2} = \frac{3}{2}\sqrt{100 - 36} = \frac{3}{2}\sqrt{64} = \frac{3 \times 8}{2} = 12 \text{ cm}^2$$

Ans.

**Example 6.** The base of a right-angled triangle is 5 units and hypotenuse is 13 units. Find its area.

**Solution.** Let $ABC$ is a right-angled triangle. Then $BC = 5$ and $AC = 13$, we know from Pythagoras Theorem,

$$AC^2 = AB^2 + BC^2 \quad \Rightarrow \quad AB^2 = AC^2 - BC^2$$

$$= 13^2 - 5^2 = 169 - 25 = 144$$

$$\therefore \quad AB = 12 \text{ units}$$

Hence, $\quad \text{Area} = \frac{1}{2} \times \text{base} \times \text{height} = \frac{1}{2} \times BC \times AB$

$$= \frac{1}{2} \times 5 \times 12 = 30 \text{ sq.units}$$

Ans.

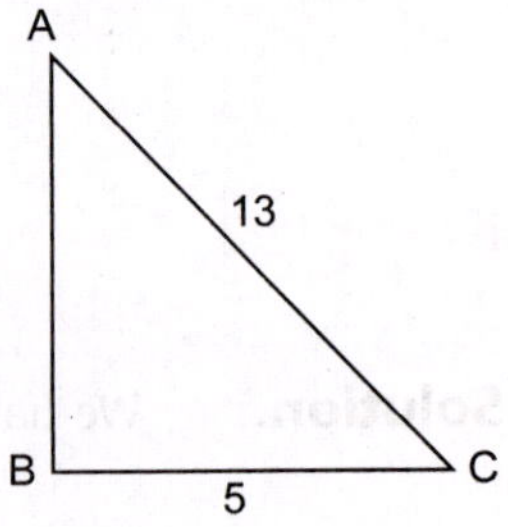


**Example 7.** Find the area of the isosceles triangle whose base is 3 cm and perimeter 8 cm.

**Solution.** The sum of two equal sides = 8 cm – 3 cm = 5 cm

$$\therefore \quad \text{Each of the equal sides} = \frac{5}{2} = 2.5 \text{ cm}$$

Now, $\quad a = 2.5$ cm, $b = 2.5$ cm, $c = 3$ cm

$$\therefore \quad s = \frac{a + b + c}{2} = \frac{2.5 + 2.5 + 3}{2} = 4 \text{ cm}$$

$$\therefore \quad \text{Area} = \sqrt{s(s-a)(s-b)(s-c)}$$

$$= \sqrt{4 \times (4 - 2.5)(4 - 2.5)(4 - 3)}$$

$$= \sqrt{4 \times 1.5 \times 1.5 \times 1} = 2 \times 1.5 = 3 \text{ cm}^2$$

Ans.

**Example 8.** The sides of a triangle containing the right angle are $5x$ cm and $(3x - 1)$ cm. If the area of the triangle is 60 cm$^2$, calculate the length of the sides of the triangle.

**Solution.** Area of a right-angled triangle $= \frac{1}{2} \times$ product of sides containing the right angle

$$\therefore \quad 60 = \frac{1}{2} \times 5x \times (3x - 1)$$

$$\Rightarrow \quad 120 = 15x^2 - 5x$$

or $$3x^2 - x - 24 = 0$$

or $$3x^2 - 9x + 8x - 24 = 0$$

$$\Rightarrow \quad (3x + 8)(x - 3) = 0$$

$$\Rightarrow \quad x = 3 \text{ and } x = -8/3$$

Since $x = -\frac{8}{3}$ will give negative values of the sides of the triangle, which is impossible. Hence $x = 3$.

$\therefore$ Lengths of the sides = $5x$ cm and $(3x - 1)$ cm

$= 5 \times 3$ cm and $(3 \times 3 - 1)$ cm

$= 15$ cm and 8 cm. **Ans.**

**Example 9.** Find the base of an isosceles triangle whose area is 60 sq. cm and the length of one of its equal sides is 13 cm.

**Solution.** We have,

$$\text{Area of an isosceles triangle} = \frac{a}{4}\sqrt{(4b^2 - a^2)},$$

where $a$ is the base and $b$ is one of the equal sides.

$$\therefore \quad \frac{a}{4}\sqrt{(4b^2 - a^2)} = 60 \text{ or } \frac{a}{4}\sqrt{(4 \times 13^2 - a^2)} = 60$$

$$\Rightarrow \quad a\sqrt{(676 - a^2)} = 60 \times 4$$

$$\Rightarrow \quad a^2(676 - a^2) = 57600$$

$$\Rightarrow \quad 676a^2 - a^4 = 57600$$

$$\Rightarrow \quad a^4 - 676a^2 + 57600 = 0$$

$$\Rightarrow \quad a^4 - 576a^2 - 100a^2 + 57600 = 0$$

$$\Rightarrow \quad a^2(a^2 - 576) - 100(a^2 - 576) = 0$$

$$\Rightarrow \quad (a^2 - 576)(a^2 - 100) = 0$$

$$\Rightarrow \quad a^2 = 576 \text{ or } a^2 = 100$$

If $a^2 = 576$, then $a = 24$ (neglecting it)

If $a^2 = 100$, then $a = 10$

$\therefore$ The length of base = 10 cm. **Ans.**

**Example 10.** The area of an equilateral triangle is as many square meters as the perimeter of the equilateral triangle is in meters. Find the length of its side correct to three, decimal places.

**Solution.** Let the side of equilateral triangle be $a$ meter.

$$\text{Area of equilateral triangle} = \frac{\sqrt{3}}{4} \times a^2$$

Perimeter of equilateral triangle = $3a$

$$\therefore \quad \text{According to question } \frac{\sqrt{3}}{4}a^2 = 3a$$

$$\therefore \quad a = \frac{4 \times 3}{\sqrt{3}} = 4\sqrt{3} = 4 \times 1.732$$

$= 6.928$ meter **Ans.**

**Example 11.** In the following figure *ABC* is a right-angled triangle, right-angled at *B* and *BCD* is an equilateral triangle. If *BC* = 5 cm and *AC* = 10 cm, find the area of $\Delta ABD$.

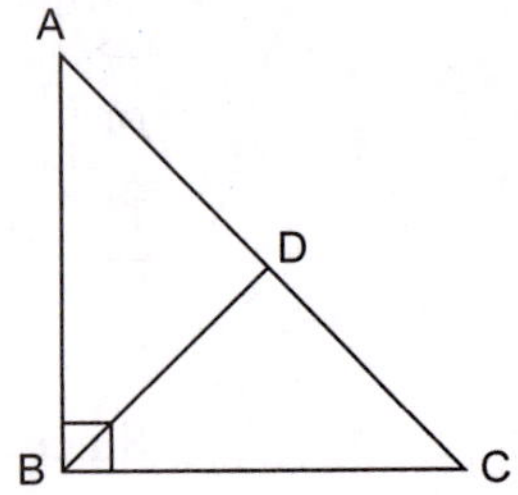


**Solution.**

$$\text{Area of } \Delta BCD = \frac{\sqrt{3}}{4}(BC)^2$$

$$= \frac{\sqrt{3}}{4}(5)^2 \text{ cm}^2 = \frac{25 \times 1.732}{4} \text{ cm}^2$$

$$= 10.825 \text{ cm}^2$$

In $\Delta ABC$, from Pythagoras theorem

$$AB^2 = AC^2 - BC^2 = 10^2 - 5^2 = 75$$

$$\Rightarrow \quad AB = 5\sqrt{3} \text{ cm}$$

$$\therefore \quad \text{Area of } \Delta ABC = \frac{1}{2} \times BC \times AB = \frac{1}{2} \times 5 \times 5\sqrt{3} = 21.65 \text{ cm}^2$$

Now,

$$\text{Area of } \Delta ABD = \text{Area of } \Delta ABC - \text{Area of } \Delta BCD$$

$$= (21.65 - 10.825) \text{ cm}^2 = 10.825 \text{ cm}^2$$

Ans.

**Example 12.** The perimeter of an isosceles triangle is 42 cm and base is $1\frac{1}{2}$ times each of the equal sides. Find :

(a) the length of each side of the triangle,
(b) the area of the triangle.

**Solution.** (a) Let the sides of the triangle be $a$, $a$ and $\frac{3a}{2}$.

Given that,

$$\text{perimeter of triangle} = 42 \text{ cm}$$

$$\Rightarrow \quad a + a + \frac{3a}{2} = 42 \quad \Rightarrow \quad a = 12 \text{ cm}$$

$$\therefore \quad \frac{3a}{2} = 18 \text{ cm}$$

Hence sides of the triangle = 12 cm, 12 cm and 18 cm

Ans.

(b) Here $a$ = 12 cm and $b$ = 18 cm

$$\therefore \quad \text{Area of triangle} = \frac{1}{4} \cdot b \cdot \sqrt{4a^2 - b^2}$$

$$= \frac{1}{4} \times 18 \times \sqrt{4 \times 12^2 - 18^2}$$

$$= \frac{1}{4} \times 18 \times 6 \times \sqrt{16 - 9}$$

$$= 27 \times \sqrt{7} = 27 \times 2.64$$

$$= 71.28 \text{ cm}^2$$

Ans.

**Example 13.** The difference between the sides of a right-angled triangle containing the right-angle is 7 cm and its area is 60 cm$^2$. Find the perimeter of the triangle.

**Solution.** Let the sides containing the right angle be $x$ cm and $(x + 7)$ cm.

$$\therefore \quad \text{Area of } \Delta = \frac{1}{2} \cdot x \cdot (x + 7)$$

$$\therefore \quad \frac{1}{2} \cdot x \cdot (x + 7) = 60$$

$\Rightarrow \quad x^2 + 7x = 120 \qquad \Rightarrow \qquad x^2 + 7x - 120 = 0 \qquad \Rightarrow \qquad x^2 + 15x - 8x - 120 = 0$

$\Rightarrow \quad x(x + 15) - 8(x + 15) = 0 \qquad \Rightarrow \qquad (x + 15)(x - 8) = 0 \qquad \Rightarrow \qquad x + 15 = 0 \text{ or } x - 8 = 0$

$\Rightarrow \quad x = -15 \text{ or } x = 8$

but $x$ cannot be negative.

$\therefore \qquad x = 8$

Now, $\qquad x + 7 = 8 + 7 = 15$

and $\qquad \text{hypotenuse} = \sqrt{8^2 + 15^2} = \sqrt{64 + 225} = 17\text{cm}$

so, $\qquad$ sides of triangle = 8 cm, 15 cm and 17 cm.

Hence, $\qquad$ perimeter of triangle = (8 + 15 + 17) cm.

$= 40$ cm **Ans.**

**Example 14.** Sides of a triangle are in the ratio 12 : 17 : 25 and its perimeter is 270 cm. Find its area.

**Solution.** Since the sides of the triangle are in the ratio 12 : 17 : 25, let the sides be $12x$, $17x$ and $25x$ (in centimetres).

Since the perimeter of the triangle is 270 cm, therefore,

$$12x + 17x + 25x = 270 \quad \Rightarrow \quad 54x = 270 \quad \Rightarrow \quad x = 5$$

$\therefore$ The sides of the triangle are $(12 \times 5)$ cm, $(17 \times 5)$ cm and $(25 \times 5)$ cm

*i.e.,* 60 cm, 85 cm and 125 cm.

$$s = \text{semi-perimeter} = \frac{270}{2} \text{ cm} = 135 \text{ cm}$$

Using Heron's formula,

$$\text{area of the triangle} = \sqrt{s(s-a)(s-b)(s-c)}$$

$$= \sqrt{135(135-60)(135-85)(135-125)} \text{ cm}^2$$

$$= \sqrt{135 \times 75 \times 50 \times 10} \text{ cm}^2 = 4500 \text{ cm}^2$$ **Ans.**

**Example 15.** The triangular side walls of a flyover have been used for advertisements. The sides of the walls are 122 m, 22 m and 120 m (shown in the adjoining figure). The advertisements yield an earning of ₹ 5000 per m$^2$ per year. A company hired one of its walls for 3 months. How much rent did it pay?

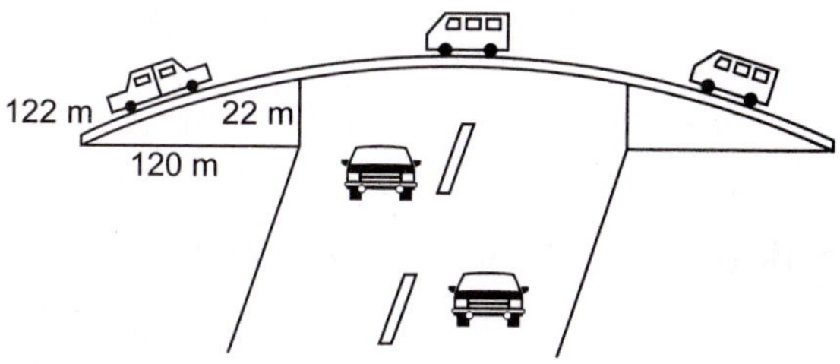


**Solution.** Here, $s = \dfrac{122 + 22 + 120}{2} \text{ m} = 132 \text{ m}$.

Using Heron's formula,

$$\text{area of one triangular wall} = \sqrt{s(s-a)(s-b)(s-c)}$$

$$= \sqrt{132(132-122)(132-22)(132-120)} \text{ m}^2$$

$$= \sqrt{132 \times 10 \times 110 \times 12} \text{ m}^2 = 1320 \text{ m}^2$$

Rent = ₹ 5000 per m$^2$ per year.

$\therefore$ Rent of one wall for 3 months = ₹ $\dfrac{1320 \times 5000 \times 3}{12}$ = ₹ 1650000 **Ans.**

**Example 16.** The perimeter of a triangle is 50 cm. One side of a triangle is 4 cm longer than the smallest side and the third side is 6 cm less than twice the smallest side. Find the area of the triangle.

**Solution.** Let the smallest side of the triangle be $x$ cm, then the other two sides are $(x + 4)$ cm and $(2x - 6)$ cm.

Given, perimeter of the triangle = 50 cm

$\Rightarrow \quad x + (x + 4) + (2x - 6) = 50 \quad \Rightarrow \quad 4x = 52 \quad \Rightarrow \quad x = 13$

$\therefore$ The lengths of three sides of the triangle are 13 cm, $(13 + 4)$ cm and $(2 \times 13 - 6)$ cm *i.e.,* 13 cm, 17 cm and 20 cm.

Here, $s$ = semi-perimeter $= \frac{50}{2}$ cm = 25 cm.

Using Heron's formula,

$$\text{area of the triangle} = \sqrt{s(s-a)(s-b)(s-c)}$$
$$= \sqrt{25(25-13)(25-17)(25-20)}\ \text{cm}^2$$
$$= \sqrt{25 \times 12 \times 8 \times 5}\ \text{cm}^2 = 20\sqrt{30}\ \text{cm}^2$$ Ans.

**Example 17.** From a point in the interior of an equilateral triangle, perpendiculars are drawn on the three sides. If the lengths of the perpendiculars are 14 cm, 10 cm and 6 cm, find the area of the triangle.

**Solution.** Let $ABC$ be an equilateral triangle with length of each side = $a$ cm.
$O$ is a point in the interior of $\Delta ABC$, $OD \perp BC$, $OE \perp CA$ and $OF \perp AB$ such that $OD$ = 14 cm, $OE$ = 10 cm and $OF$ = 6 cm.

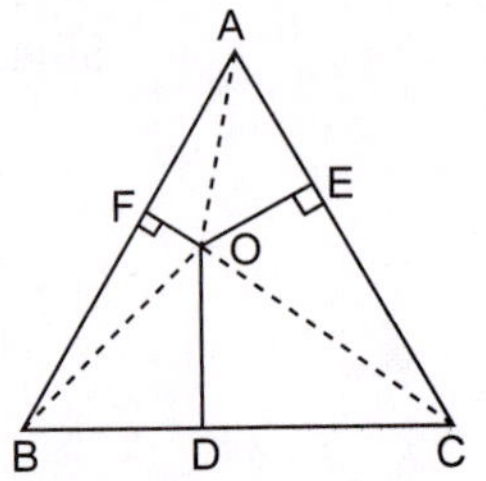


Area of equilateral triangle $ABC = \frac{\sqrt{3}}{4} a^2\ \text{cm}^2$

Also area of $\Delta ABC$ = area of $\Delta OBD$ + area of $\Delta OCA$ + area of $\Delta OAB$

$$= \frac{1}{2} BC \times OD + \frac{1}{2} CA \times OE + \frac{1}{2} AB \times OF$$

$$\Rightarrow \quad \frac{\sqrt{3}}{4} a^2\ \text{cm}^2 = \frac{1}{2}(a \times 14 + a \times 10 + a \times 6)\ \text{cm}^2$$

$$\Rightarrow \quad \frac{\sqrt{3}}{2} a^2 = 30a \quad \Rightarrow \quad \sqrt{3}\,a = 60 \qquad (\because a \neq 0)$$

$$\Rightarrow \quad a = 20\sqrt{3}$$

$$\therefore \quad \text{Area of } \Delta ABC = \frac{\sqrt{3}}{4} \times (20\sqrt{3})^2\ \text{cm}^2 = 300\sqrt{3}\ \text{cm}^2$$ Ans.

**Example 18.** In the adjoining figure, $ABC$ is an isosceles triangle with base $BC$ = 8 cm and $AB = AC$ = 12 cm. $AD$ is perpendicular to $BC$ and $O$ is a point on $AD$ such that $\angle BOC = 90°$. Find the area of the shaded region.

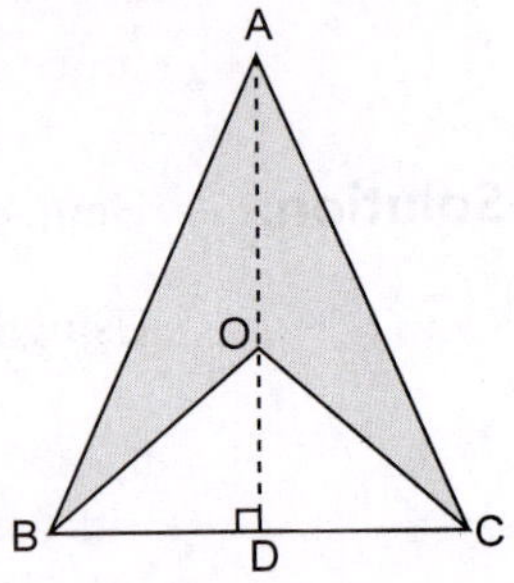


**Solution.** As $AD \perp BC$, $D$ is mid-point of $BC$.

$$\therefore \quad BD = \frac{1}{2} \times 8\ \text{cm} = 4\ \text{cm}.$$

From $\Delta ABD$, by Pythagoras theorem,

$$AD^2 = AB^2 - BD^2 = 12^2 - 4^2 = 144 - 16$$

$$\Rightarrow \quad AD = \sqrt{128}\ \text{cm} = 8\sqrt{2}\ \text{cm}$$

$$\therefore \quad \text{Area of } \Delta ABC = \frac{1}{2} BC \times AD = \frac{1}{2} \times 8 \times 8\sqrt{2}\ \text{cm}^2 = 32\sqrt{2}\ \text{cm}^2$$ Ans.

**Example 19.** If each side of a triangle is doubled, then find the percentage increase in the area of the triangle.

**Solution.** Let $a$, $b$, $c$ be the sides of given triangle and $s$ be its semi-perimeter, then

$$s = \frac{a+b+c}{2} \quad \Rightarrow \quad 2s = a + b + c$$

$$\text{Area of the given triangle} = \sqrt{s(s-a)(s-b)(s-c)} \qquad \ldots(i)$$

As the sides of the given triangle are doubled, the sides of new triangle are $2a$, $2b$ and $2c$.
Let $S$ be the semi-perimeter of new triangle, then

$$S = \frac{2a + 2b + 2c}{2} = a + b + c = 2s \qquad \ldots(ii)$$

$$
\begin{aligned}
\text{Area of new triangle} &= \sqrt{S(S-2a)(S-2b)(S-2c)} \\
&= \sqrt{2s(2s-2a)(2s-2b)(2s-2c)} && \text{[Using (ii)]} \\
&= \sqrt{16s(s-a)(s-b)(s-c)} \\
&= 4\sqrt{s(s-a)(s-b)(s-c)} \\
&= 4 \times \text{area of given triangle} && \text{[Using (i)]}
\end{aligned}
$$

$$
\begin{aligned}
\text{Increase in area} &= \text{area of new triangle} - \text{area of given triangle} \\
&= 4 \times \text{area of given triangle} - \text{area of given triangle} \\
&= 3 \times \text{area of given triangle}
\end{aligned}
$$

The percentage increase in the area of given triangle

$$= \left(\frac{\text{increase in area}}{\text{area of given triangle}} \times 100\right)\%$$

$$= \left(\frac{3 \times \text{ area of given triangle}}{\text{area of given triangle}} \times 100\right)\% = 300\%$$ Ans.

## Exercise 16A

1. Calculate the area of the triangle with the following sides :
   (i) 42 cm, 34 cm and 20 cm
   (ii) 33 cm, 44 cm and 55 cm
   (iii) 39 m, 42 m and 45 m
   (iv) 29 cm, 20 cm and 21 cm
2. Find the area of a triangle whose base is 15 cm and height is 18 cm.
3. Find the area of an isosceles right triangle, the lengths of whose each side containing the right angle is 15 cm.
4. The sides of an equilateral triangle is 8 cm. Find its area and height.
5. $ABC$ is a triangle in which $AB = AC = 4$ cm and $\angle A = 90°$. Calculate the area of $\Delta ABC$.
6. Find the area of a triangle whose sides are 20 cm, 34 cm and 42 cm. Hence find the height corresponding to the side 42 cm.
7. Find the area of an isosceles triangle in which base is 24 cm and each of equal sides is 13 cm.
8. Find the area of an isosceles triangle in which base is 12 cm and each of equal sides is 10 cm.
9. Find the area of an equilateral triangle whose height is 8 cm.
10. Find the perimeter of an equilateral triangle whose area is $36\sqrt{3}\ \text{cm}^2$.
11. The sides of a triangular field are 975 m, 1050 m and 1125 m. If this field is sold at the rate of ₹ 100 per hectare, find its selling price. [Note : 1 hectare = 10000 $m^2$]
12. The base of an isosceles triangle is 24 cm and its area is 192 sq. cm. Find its perimeter.
13. The base of a triangular field is $2\frac{1}{2}$ times its height. If the cost of turfing it at ₹ 48 per 100 sq. m is ₹ 960, find its base.
14. A plot of ground in the form of an isosceles triangle is turfed for ₹ 15 at 25 paise per sq. meter. Find the length of each of the equal sides if its base is 24 metres.
15. The base of an isosceles triangle is 6 cm and its area is 12 sq. cm. Find its perimeter.
16. Fig. shows an equilateral triangle $ABC$ whose each side is 10 cm and a right-angled triangle $BDC$ whose side $BD = 8$ cm and $\angle D = 90°$. Find the area of the shaded portion.

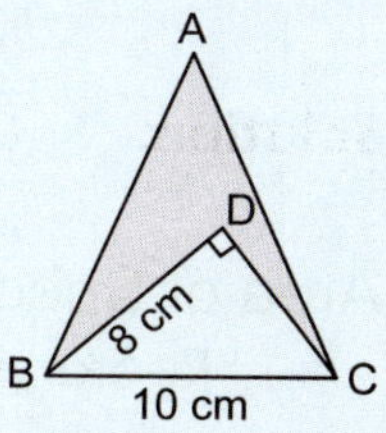


17. Each of equal sides of an isosceles triangle is 4 cm greater than its height. If the base of the triangle is 24 cm. Calculate the perimeter and area of the triangle.
18. Calculate the area and the height of an equilateral triangle whose perimeter is 60 cm.

**19.** The perimeter of a triangle is 540 m and its sides are in the ratio 25 : 17 : 12. Find the area of the triangle.

**20.** In the adjoining figure, *ABC* is an equilateral triangle in which *BC* = 10 cm and *BCD* is a right-angled triangle in which *BD* = *CD*. Find the area of the shaded region.

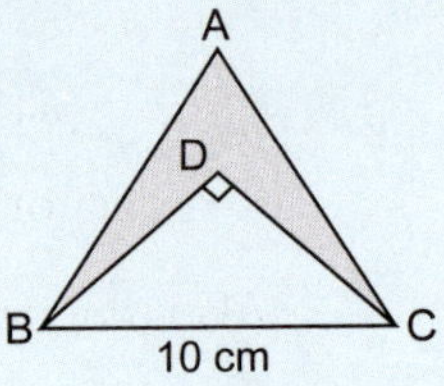


**21.** $\Delta ABC$ and $\Delta ADE$ are two equilateral triangles is which *AB* = 12 cm and *AD* = 6 cm. Find the area of the shaded region. (Use $\sqrt{3} = 1.73$ )

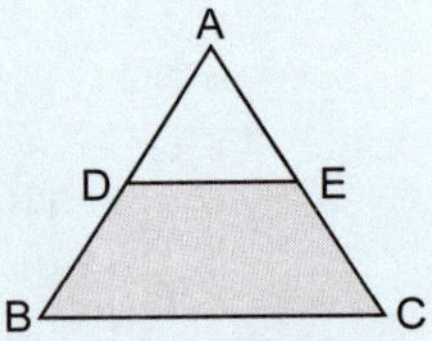


**22.** Find the side of an equilateral triangle whose area is equal to the area of that triangle whose sides are 12 cm, 15 cm and 21 cm.

## *Answers*

| | | | |
|---|---|---|---|
| **1.** (i) 336 $cm^2$ | (ii) 726 $cm^2$ | (iii) 756 $m^2$ | (iv) 210 $cm^2$ |
| **2.** 135 $cm^2$ | **3.** 112.5 $cm^2$ | **4.** 27.712 $cm^2$, 6. 928 cm | **5.** 8 $cm^2$ |
| **6.** 336 $cm^2$, 16 cm, | **7.** 60 $cm^2$ | **8.** 48 $cm^2$ | **9.** 36.95 $cm^2$ |
| **10.** 36 cm | **11.** ₹ 4725 | **12.** 64 cm | **13.** 100 m |
| **14.** 13 m | **15.** 16 cm | **16.** 19.3 $cm^2$ | **17.** 64 cm, 192 $cm^2$ |
| **18.** 173.2 $cm^2$, 17.32 cm | **19.** 9000 $m^2$ | **20.** 18.3 $cm^2$ | **21.** 46.71 $cm^2$ |
| **22.** 14.27 cm | | | |

## Area and Perimeter of Quadrilaterals

1. *When one diagonal and perpendiculars to this diagonal from the remaining vertices are given.*

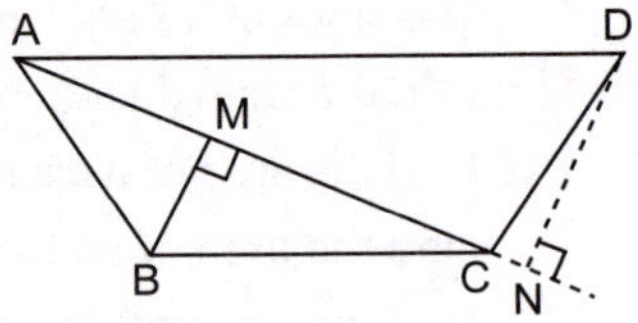


Let in quadrilateral *ABCD*, the diagonal *AC* and perpendicular *BM* and *DN* to *AC* from the remaining vertices *B* and *D* respectively are given, then area of quadrilateral *ABCD*

$$= \Delta ABC + \Delta ADC,$$

$$= \frac{1}{2} AC \times BM + \frac{1}{2} AC \times DN = \frac{1}{2} AC\,(BM + DN)$$

$\therefore$ Area of quadrilateral

$= \frac{1}{2} \times$ one diagonal $\times$ sum of the lengths of the perpendiculars drawn on it from the remaining two vertices.

2. *When two diagonals of a quadrilateral cut each other at right angle.*

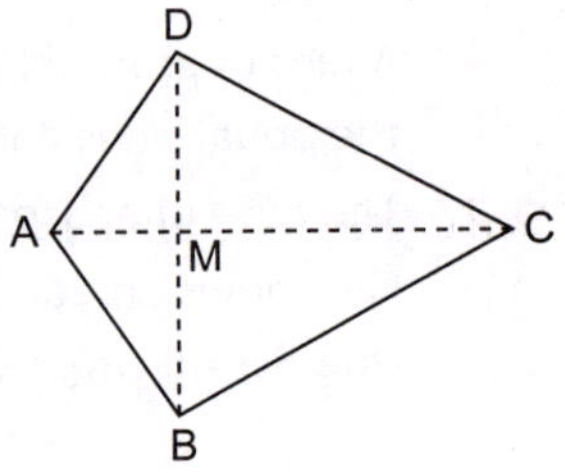


The area of quadrilateral *ABCD*

$$= \Delta ABC + \Delta ADC$$

$$= \frac{1}{2} AC \times BM + \frac{1}{2} AC \times DM = \frac{1}{2} AC\,(BM + DM) = \frac{1}{2} AC \times BD$$

$= \frac{1}{2} \times$ product of the diagonals.

## Area of Special Types of Quadrilaterals

1. Rectangle

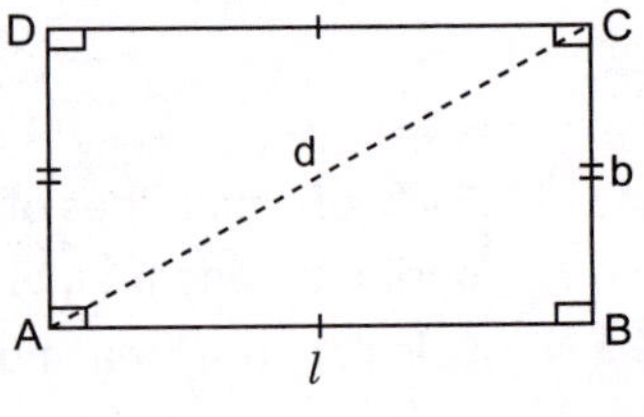


Area = length × breadth = $l \times b$

Perimeter = 2 (length + breadth) = $2(l + b)$

Length of diagonal ($d$) = $\sqrt{(l^2 + b^2)}$

2. Square

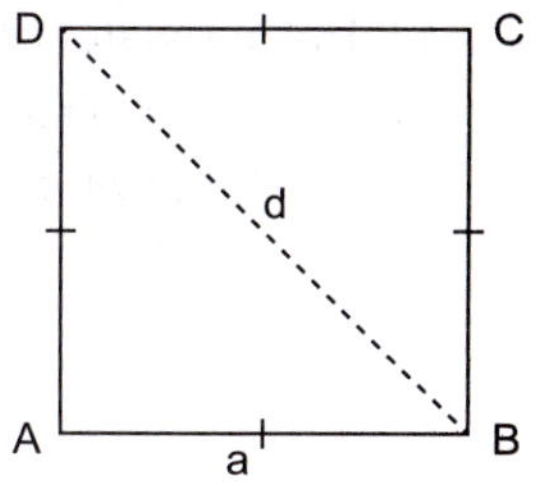


$$\text{Area} = (\text{side})^2 = a^2$$

$$\text{Perimeter} = 4 \times \text{side} = 4a.$$

$$\text{Diagonal } (d) = \sqrt{(a^2 + a^2)} = a\sqrt{2}$$

$$\text{Also diagonal } (d) = \sqrt{a^2 + a^2}$$

$$= \sqrt{2a^2} = \sqrt{2 \times \text{Area}}$$

3. Parallelogram

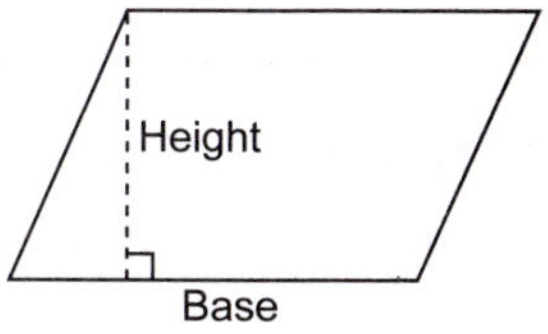


$$\text{Area} = \text{base} \times \text{height}$$

(The height of a parallelogram is the distance between its base and side opposite to the base).

4. Rhombus

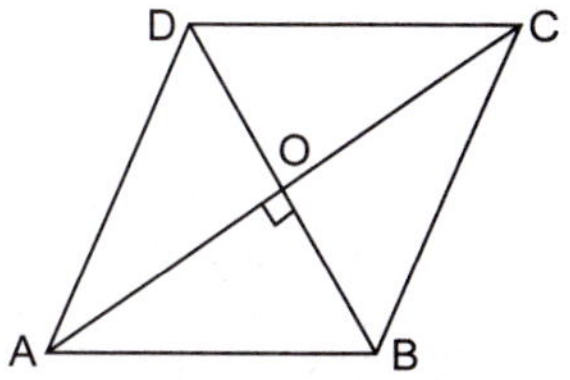


$$\text{Perimeter} = 4 \times \text{side} = 4a$$

$$\text{Area} = \frac{1}{2} \times (\text{the product of diagonals})$$

$$= \frac{1}{2}\ AC \times BD \text{ and } (\text{side})^2 = \left(\frac{AC}{2}\right)^2 + \left(\frac{BD}{2}\right)^2$$

5. Trapezium

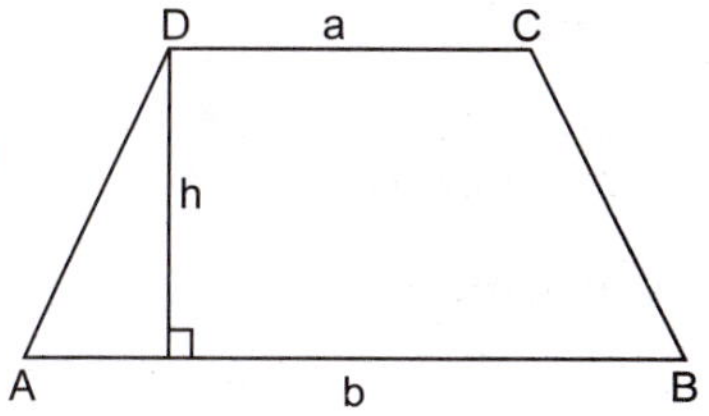


$$\text{Area} = \frac{1}{2} \times (\text{sum of parallel sides}) \times (\text{distance between parallel sides})$$

$$= \frac{1}{2}(a + b)\,h.$$

## Illustrative Examples

**Example 1.** Find the area of a quadrilateral $ABCD$ in which $AC = 16$ cm and the length of perpendiculars $BP$ and $DQ$ drawn from $B$ and $D$ respectively to $AC$ are 6 cm and 4 cm.

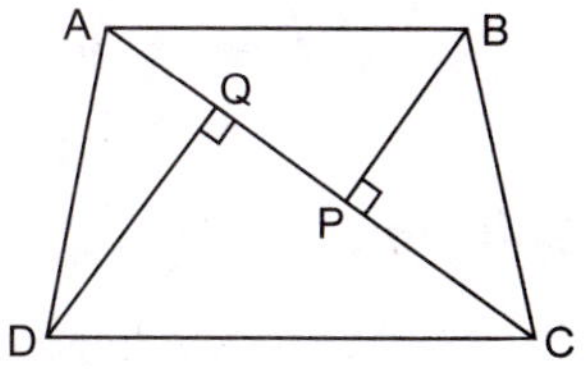


**Solution.** $\text{Area of } \square ABCD = \frac{1}{2} \times AC \times (BP + DQ) = \frac{1}{2} \times 16 \times (6 + 4) \text{ cm}^2$

$= 80 \text{ cm}^2$ Ans.

**Example 2.** Find the area of $\square ABCD$ in which $\angle B = 90°$, $AB = 9$ cm, $BC = 12$ cm and $AD = CD = 12.5$ cm.

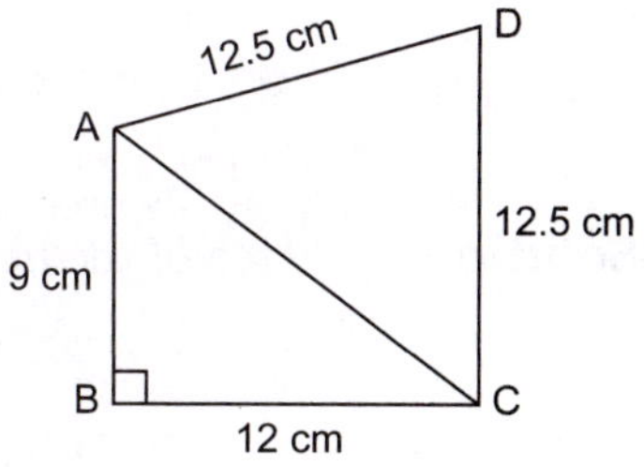


**Solution.** In $\Delta ABC$,

$$\angle B = 90°$$

Using Pythagoras theorem,

$$AC^2 = AB^2 + BC^2 = 9^2 + 12^2 = 81 + 144 = 225$$

$\Rightarrow$ $AC = 15$ cm

$$ar\ (\Delta ABC) = \frac{1}{2} \times BC \times AB = \frac{1}{2} \times 12 \text{ cm} \times 9 \text{ cm} = 54 \text{ cm}^2$$

In $\Delta ADC$

Let $a = AC = 15$ cm, $b = CD = 12.5$ cm, $C = AD = 12.5$ cm

$\therefore$ $s = \frac{a + b + c}{2} = \frac{15 + 12.5 + 12.5}{2} \text{ cm} = 20 \text{ cm}$

$$s - a = (20 - 15) \text{ cm} = 5 \text{ cm}$$

$$s - b = s - c = (20 - 12.5) \text{ cm} = 7.5 \text{ cm}$$

$$\text{ar}(\Delta ADC) = \sqrt{s(s-a)(s-b)(s-c)}$$

$$= \sqrt{20 \times 5 \times 7.5 \times 7.5} = 75 \text{ cm}^2$$

Now, $\text{ar}(\square ABCD) = \text{ar}(\Delta ABC) + \text{ar}(\Delta ADC)$

$$= 54 \text{ cm}^2 + 75 \text{ cm}^2 = 129 \text{ cm}^2$$ **Ans.**

**Example 3.** Find the area of a rectangle whose perimeter is 40 cm and length is 15 cm.

**Solution.** Here $l = 15$ cm

Let breadth of rectangle = $b$ cm

$\therefore$ Perimeter of rectangle = $2(l + b)$

$\Rightarrow$ $2(15 + b) = 40$

$\Rightarrow$ $15 + b = 20$

$\Rightarrow$ $b = 5$ cm

and area of rectangle = $l \times b$

$= 15 \times 5 = 75 \text{ cm}^2$ **Ans.**

**Example 4.** The area of a square field is 625 $\text{m}^2$. Find :

(a) the length of its one side

(b) the perimeter of the square

**Solution.** Let the side of square be '$a$' m.

(a) area = $a^2$

$\Rightarrow$ $a^2 = 625 = 25^2$

$\Rightarrow$ $a = 25$

$\therefore$ side of square = 25 m **Ans.**

(b) perimeter of square = $4a$

$= 4 \times 25$ m

$= 100$ m **Ans.**

**Example 5.** The diagonals of a rectangle intersect each other at right angles and are 25 cm and 20 cm respectively. Find the area of rectangle.

**Solution.** Area of the given quadrilateral

$$= \frac{1}{2} \times (\text{product of the lengths of two mutually perpendicular diagonals})$$

$$= \frac{1}{2} \times 25 \times 20 \text{ cm}^2 = 250 \text{ cm}^2$$ **Ans.**

**Example 6.** One of the diagonals of a field, in the form of a quadrilateral, is 70 m and its offsets are 50 m and 30 m respectively. Find the area of the field.

**Solution.** Area of the field

$$= \frac{1}{2} \times \text{length of the diagonal} \times (\text{sum of the length of its offsets})$$

$$= \frac{1}{2} \times 70 \times (50 + 30) \text{ m}^2 = 35 \times 80 \text{ m}^2 = 2800 \text{ m}^2$$ **Ans.**

**Example 7.** The sides of a parallelogram are 40 m and 30 m respectively and its diagonal is 50 m. Find its area.

**Solution.** Area of parallelogram $ABCD$ = Area of $\Delta ABC$ + Area of $\Delta ACD$

$= 2 \times$ area of $\Delta ABC$

($\because$ Each diagonal of a parallelogram bisects it)

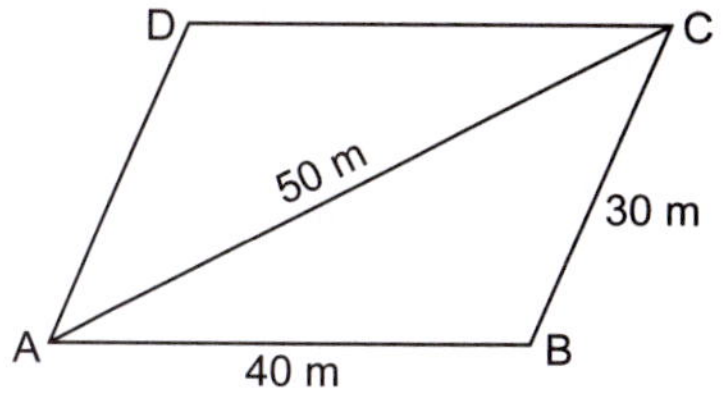


Semi-perimeter ($s$) of $\Delta ABC = \dfrac{50 + 40 + 30}{2} = 60$ m

$\therefore$ Area of $\Delta ABC = \sqrt{s(s-a)(s-b)(s-c)}$

$= \sqrt{60 \times (60-40)(60-30)(60-50)}$

$= \sqrt{60 \times 20 \times 30 \times 10} = \sqrt{360000}$

$= 600 \text{ m}^2$

$\therefore$ Area of parallelogram $ABCD$

$= 2 \times 600 \text{ m}^2 = 1200 \text{ m}^2$ Ans.

**Example 8.** The base and height of a parallelogram are 45 cm and 22 cm respectively. Find its area.

**Solution.** Area of a parallelogram = base × height = $45 \times 22 \text{ cm}^2 = 990 \text{ cm}^2$ Ans.

**Example 9.** The diagonals of a rhombus are 10 cm and 8 cm. Find its area and the length of its side.

**Solution.** The diagonals of a rhombus bisect each other at right angles. Therefore,

Area of rhombus $ABCD$

$= \dfrac{1}{2} \times$ (product of the length of its diagonals)

$= \dfrac{1}{2} \times 10 \times 8 = 40 \text{ cm}^2$ Ans.

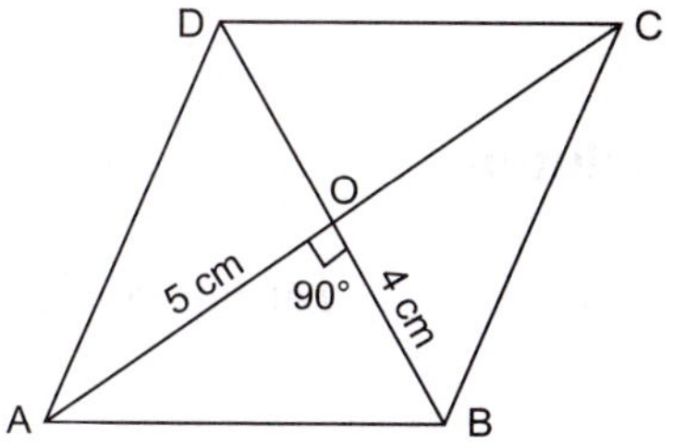


Again, from fig., $\Delta AOB$ is a right-angled triangle and

$AO = \dfrac{1}{2} AC = \dfrac{1}{2} \times 10 = 5$ cm

and $BO = \dfrac{1}{2} BD = \dfrac{1}{2} \times 8 = 4$ cm

$\therefore$ $AB^2 = AO^2 + BO^2$

$= 5^2 + 4^2 = 25 + 16 = 41$

$\therefore$ $AB = \sqrt{41}$ cm $= 6.403$ cm Ans.

**Example 10.** The parallel sides of a trapezium are 60 cm and 99 cm and its non-parallel sides are 42 cm and 45 cm. Find its area.

**Solution.** Let $ABCD$ be the given trapezium. From $C$ draw $CE$ parallel to $DA$. Then $AECD$ is a parallelogram and $AE = 60$ cm. Draw a perpendicular $CP$ from $C$ on $AB$. Let $CP = h$.

Now, in $\Delta CEB$, $CE = 45$ cm, $CB = 42$ cm and $BE = 39$ cm.

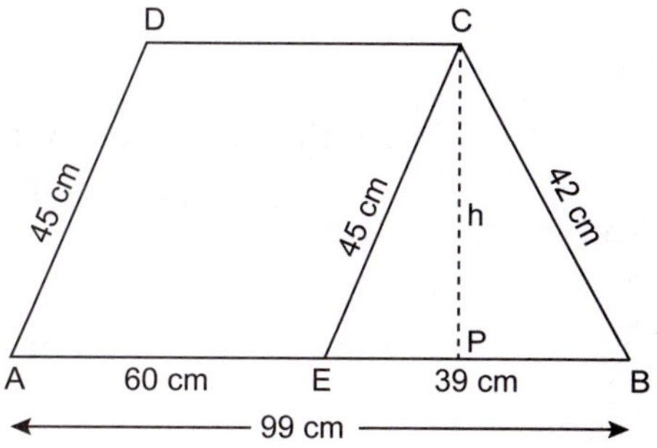


$\therefore$ Semi-perimeter ($s$) $= \dfrac{45 + 42 + 39}{2} = 63$ cm

$\therefore$ Area of $\Delta CEB = \sqrt{63 \times (63-45)(63-42)(63-39)}$

$= \sqrt{63 \times 18 \times 21 \times 24} = 756 \text{ cm}^2$

But area of $\Delta CEB = \frac{1}{2}$ base × height

$\therefore$ $\frac{1}{2} \times 39 \times h = 756$

or $h = \frac{756 \times 2}{39} = \frac{504}{13}$ cm

$\therefore$ Height of trapezium $= \frac{504}{13}$ cm

$\therefore$ Area of trapezium $ABCD = \frac{1}{2}$ height (sum of the lengths of its parallel sides)

$= \frac{1}{2} \times \frac{504}{13} \times (60 + 99)\text{ cm}^2 = \frac{252}{13} \times 159\text{ cm}^2 = 3082.15\text{ cm}^2$ **Ans.**

**Example 11.** Find the area of a square field which is double the area of a rectangular field with length 60 m and breadth 40 m.

**Solution.** Area of the rectangular field = $60 \times 40 = 2400\text{ m}^2$

$\therefore$ Area of the square field = $2 \times 2400 = 4800\text{ m}^2$ **Ans.**

**Example 12.** Find the perimeter of a square field which has the same area of a rectangular field with length 90 m and breadth 40 m.

**Solution.** The area of the rectangular field = $90 \times 40 = 3600\text{ m}^2$

$\therefore$ Area of square field = $3600\text{ m}^2$

Let side of the square field = $a$ meter

$\therefore$ $a^2 = 3600$

$\Rightarrow$ $a = \sqrt{3600} = 60$ m

Hence, the perimeter of the square field = $4 \times 60 = 240$ m. **Ans.**

**Example 13.** A wire is bent in the form of an equilateral triangle and enclosed an area of $16\sqrt{3}\text{ m}^2$. If the same wire is bent in the form of a square, find the area enclosed.

**Solution.** Let side of equilateral triangle be $x$.

$\therefore$ area of triangle $= \frac{\sqrt{3}}{4}x^2$

$\Rightarrow$ $\frac{\sqrt{3}}{4}x^2 = 16\sqrt{3}$

$\Rightarrow$ $x^2 = 64 = 8^2$

$\Rightarrow$ $x = 8$ m

length of wire = perimeter of equilateral triangle

$= 3x = 3 \times 8\text{ m} = 24$ m

Let the side of square be $y$.

$\therefore$ perimeter of square = length of wire

$\Rightarrow$ $4y = 24$ m

$\Rightarrow$ $y = 6$ m

Now, area enclosed = area of square = $y^2 = 6^2\text{ m}^2 = 36\text{ m}^2$ **Ans.**

**Example 14.** A rhombus shaped field has green grass for 12 cows to graze. If each side of the rhombus is 30 m and its longer diagonal is 48 m, how much area of the grass field will each cow be getting?

**Solution.** Diagonal *AC* divides the rhombus *ABCD* into two congruent triangles of equal area.

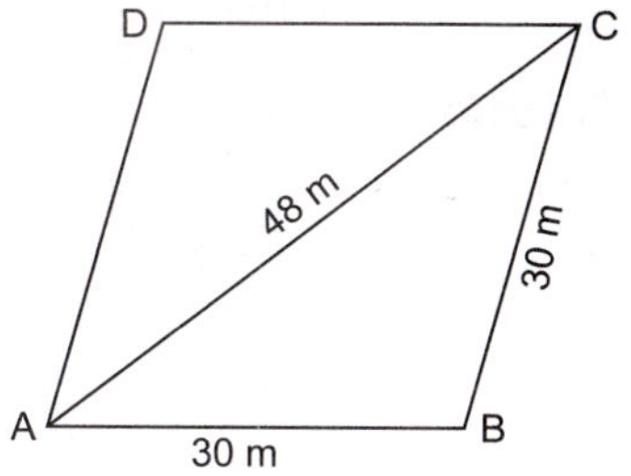


For $\Delta ABC$, $\quad s = \dfrac{30 + 30 + 48}{2}$ m $= 54$ m,

$$\text{Area of } \Delta ABC = \sqrt{54(54-30)(54-30)(54-48)}\ \text{m}^2$$

$$= \sqrt{54 \times 24 \times 24 \times 6}\ \text{m}^2 = 432\ \text{m}^2.$$

$\therefore$ Area of field = 2 × area of $\Delta ABC$ = $(2 \times 432)$ m$^2$ = 864 m$^2$.

$\therefore$ Area of grass field which each cow will be getting

$$= \frac{864}{12}\ \text{m}^2 = 72\ \text{m}^2$$

Ans.

**Example 15.** Kamla has a triangular field with sides 240 m, 200 m and 300 m, where she grew wheat. In another triangular field with sides 240 m, 320 m and 400 m adjacent to the previous field, she wanted to grow potatoes and onions. She divided the field into two parts by joining the mid-point of the longest side to the opposite vertex and grew potatoes in one part and onions in the other part. How much area (in hectares) has been used for wheat, potatoes and onions? (1 hectare = 10000 m$^2$).

**Solution.** Let *ABC* be the triangular field where wheat is grown and *ACD* be the adjacent triangular field which has been divided into two parts by joining vertex *C* to the mid-point *E* of the longest side *AD*.

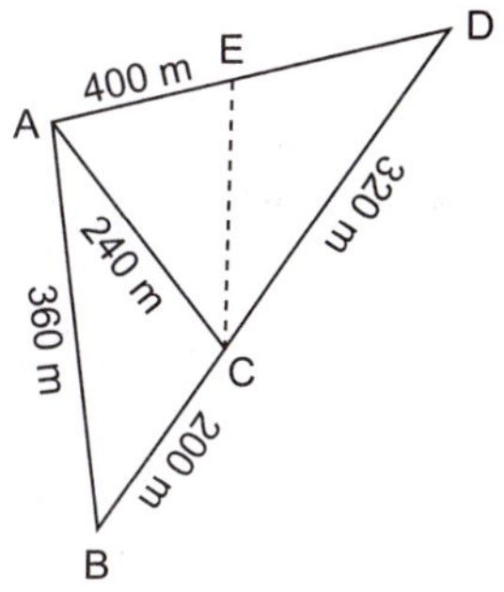


For $\Delta ABC$, $\quad s = \dfrac{240 + 200 + 360}{2}$ m $= 400$ m

$\therefore$ Area for growing wheat = area of $\Delta ABC$

$$= \sqrt{400(400-240)(400-200)(400-360)}\ \text{m}^2$$

$$= \sqrt{400 \times 160 \times 200 \times 40}\ \text{m}$$

$$= 16000\sqrt{2}\ \text{m}^2 = \frac{16000\sqrt{2}}{10000}\ \text{hectares}$$

$$= 2.26 \text{ hectares (approx.)}$$

For $\Delta ACD$, $\quad s = \dfrac{240 + 400 + 320}{2}$ m $= 480$ m

$$\text{Area of } \Delta ACD = \sqrt{480(480-240)(480-400)(480-320)}\ \text{m}^2$$

$$= \sqrt{480 \times 240 \times 80 \times 160}\ \text{m}^2 = 38400\ \text{m}^2 = 3.84 \text{ hectares}$$

Note that the line segment *EC* divides $\Delta ACD$ into two triangles of equal area because $\Delta ACE$ and $\Delta DCE$ have equal bases *AE*, *DE* and have equal heights.

$\therefore$ Area for growing potatoes = area for growing onions $= \dfrac{1}{2}$ of 3.84 hectares = 1.92 hectares. Ans.

**Example 16.** How many square tiles of side 20 cm will be needed to pave a footpath which is 2 metres wide and surrounds a rectangular plot 40 m long and 22 m wide?

**Solution.** Since the footpath is 2 m wide, length of the outer plot = 44 m and its breadth = 26 m.

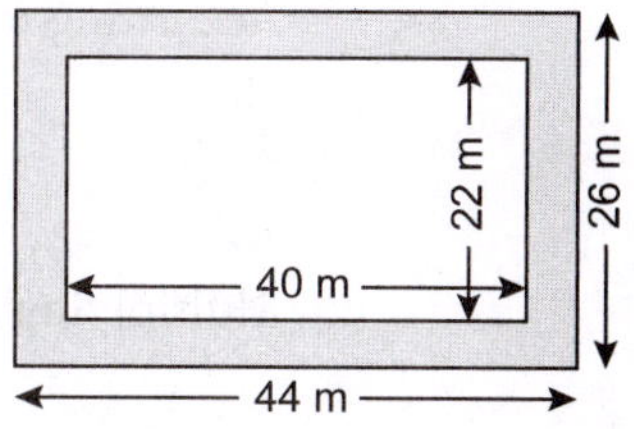


$\therefore$ Area of outer plot = $(44 \times 26)$ m$^2$ = 1144 m$^2$

Area of inner plot = $(40 \times 22)$ m$^2$ = 880 m$^2$

$\therefore$ Area to be covered with tiles

$= (1144 - 880)$ m$^2$ = 264 m$^2$

$= (264 \times 100 \times 100)$ cm$^2$

Area of one tile = $(20 \times 20)$ cm$^2$ = 400 cm$^2$

$\therefore$ The number of tiles required to pave the footpath $= \dfrac{264 \times 100 \times 100}{400} = 6600$ Ans.

**Example 17.** In the adjoining diagram, two paths are drawn inside a rectangular field. Find the area of two paths.

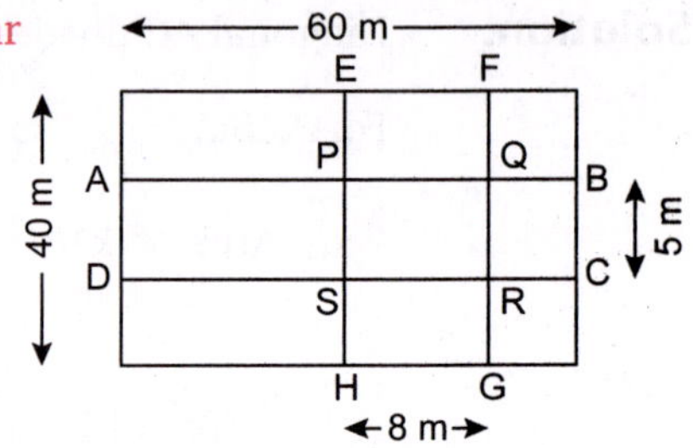


**Solution.** For path *ABCD*, $AB = 60$ m and $BC = 5$ m

$\therefore$ Area of path $ABCD = AB \times BC = 60 \times 5 = 300 \text{ m}^2$

For path *EFGH*, $EF = 8$ m and $EH = 40$ m

$\therefore$ Area of path $EFGH = EF \times EH = 8 \times 40 = 320 \text{ m}^2$

But the area *PQRS* is common in two paths *ABCD* and *EFGH*.

For path *PQRS*

$$PQ = 8 \text{ m and } QR = 5 \text{ m}$$

$\therefore$ Area of path $PQRS = PQ \times QR = 8 \times 5 = 40 \text{ m}^2$

Now, the total area of two paths.

$$= \text{Area of } ABCD + \text{Area of } EFGH - \text{Area of } PQRS$$
$$= 300 + 320 - 40 = 580 \text{ m}^2$$ Ans.

**Example 18.** A kite in the shape of a square with diagonal 32 cm and an isosceles triangle of base 8 cm and sides 6 cm each is to be made of three different shades as shown in the adjoining figure. How much paper of each shade has been used in it?

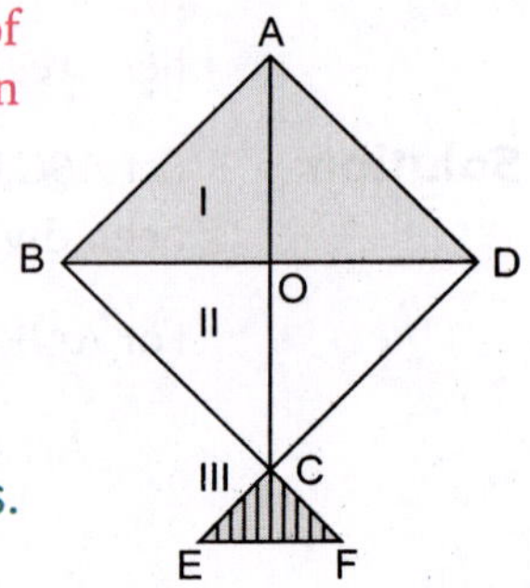


**Solution.** As the diagonals of a square bisect each other at right angles,

$$AO = OC = \frac{1}{2} \times 32 \text{ cm} = 16 \text{ cm}$$

Area of shade I $= \frac{1}{2} \times BD \times AO = \frac{1}{2} \times 32 \times 16 \text{ cm}^2 = 256 \text{ cm}^2$ Ans.

Area of shade II $= \frac{1}{2} \times BD \times OC = \frac{1}{2} \times 32 \times 16 \text{ cm}^2 = 256 \text{ cm}^2$ Ans.

For $\Delta CEF$, $s = \frac{6 + 8 + 6}{2} = 10$ cm

$$\text{ar}(\Delta CEF) = \sqrt{10(10-6)(10-8)(10-6)} \text{ cm}^2 = \sqrt{10 \times 4 \times 2 \times 4} \text{ cm}^2 = 17.9 \text{ cm}^2$$

area of shade III $= 17.9 \text{ cm}^2$ Ans.

**Example 19.** If the length of a rectangle is increased by 10 cm and the breadth is decreased by 5 cm, the area is unaltered. If the length is decreased by 5 cm and the breadth is increased by 4 cm, even then the area is unaltered. Find the dimensions of the rectangle.

**Solution.** Let the length and the breadth of the rectangle be $x$ cm and $y$ cm respectively, then its area $= xy \text{ cm}^2$.
According to the first condition, when length is increased by 10 cm and breadth decreased by 5 cm, area of the rectangle remains unaltered.

$\therefore$ $(x + 10)(y - 5) = xy$

$\Rightarrow$ $xy - 5x + 10y - 50 = xy$

$\Rightarrow$ $-5x + 10y - 50 = 0$

$\Rightarrow$ $x - 2y + 10 = 0$ ...(*i*)

According to the second condition, we get

$(x - 5)(y + 4) = xy$

$\Rightarrow$ $xy + 4x - 5y - 20 = xy$

$\Rightarrow$ $4x - 5y - 20 = 0$ ...(*ii*)

Multiplying (*i*) by 4, we get

$4x - 8y + 40 = 0$ ...(*iii*)

Subtracting (*iii*) from (*ii*), we get

$$3y - 60 = 0 \Rightarrow 3y = 60 \Rightarrow y = 20$$

From *(i)*, we get

$$x - 2 \times 20 + 10 = 0 \quad \Rightarrow \quad x - 40 + 10 = 0 \quad \Rightarrow \quad x = 30.$$

Hence, the length of the rectangle = 30 cm and its breadth = 20 cm **Ans.**

**Example 20.** The side of a square exceeds the side of another square by 4 cm and the sum of the areas of the two squares is 520 $cm^2$. Find the perimeters of the squares.

**Solution.** Let the side of one square be $x$ cm then the side of the other square is $(x + 4)$ cm.

Then the area of the two squares are $x^2$ $cm^2$ and $(x + 4)^2$ $cm^2$

According to given,

$$x^2 + (x + 4)^2 = 520$$

$$\Rightarrow \quad x^2 + x^2 + 8x + 16 = 520$$

$$\Rightarrow \quad 2x^2 + 8x - 504 = 0 \quad \Rightarrow \quad x^2 + 4x - 252 = 0$$

$$\Rightarrow \quad (x - 14)(x + 18) = 0$$

$$\Rightarrow \quad x = 14, -18$$

$$\Rightarrow \quad x = 14 \qquad (\because x \text{ cannot be negative})$$

$\therefore$ The sides of two squares are 14 cm and 18 cm.

$\therefore$ Perimeters of the two squares are 56 cm and 72 cm. **Ans.**

**Example 21.** Find the area and the perimeter of the figure given in fig. (1).

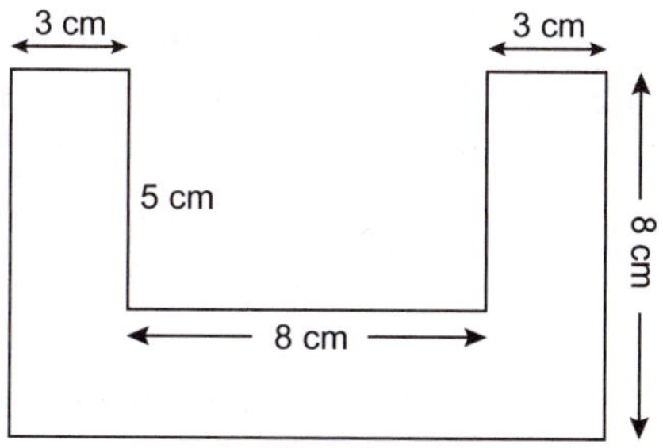


Fig.(1)

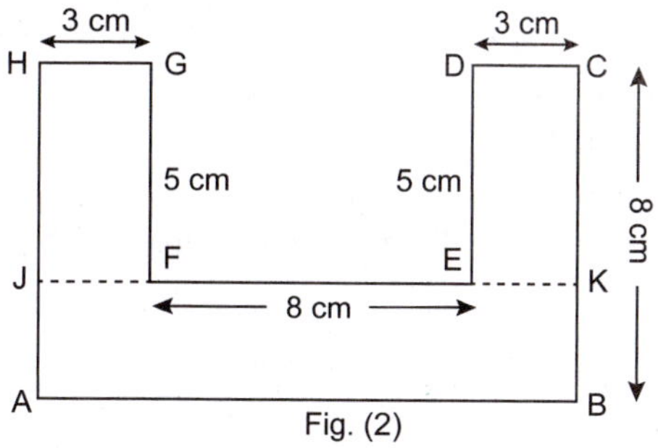


Fig. (2)

**Solution.** The figure can be named as shown in fig. (2). The figure is cut into three rectangles.

The area of $JFGH = 5 \times 3 = 15$ $cm^2$

The area of $EKCD = 5 \times 3 = 15$ $cm^2$

The area of $ABKJ = AB \times AJ$

$$= (JF + FE + EK)(AH - JH) = (3 + 8 + 3)(8 - 5)$$

$$= 14 \times 3 = 42 \text{ cm}^2$$

$\therefore$ The total area of figure $= 15 + 15 + 42 = 72$ $cm^2$

Perimeter of the figure $= 8 + 3 + 5 + 8 + 5 + 3 + 8 + 3 + 8 + 3$

$= 54$ cm **Ans.**

**Example 22.** In the trapezium *ABCD*, $AB = 8$ cm, $DC = BC = 13$ cm and *AB* is parallel to *DC*. Find area of the trapezium.

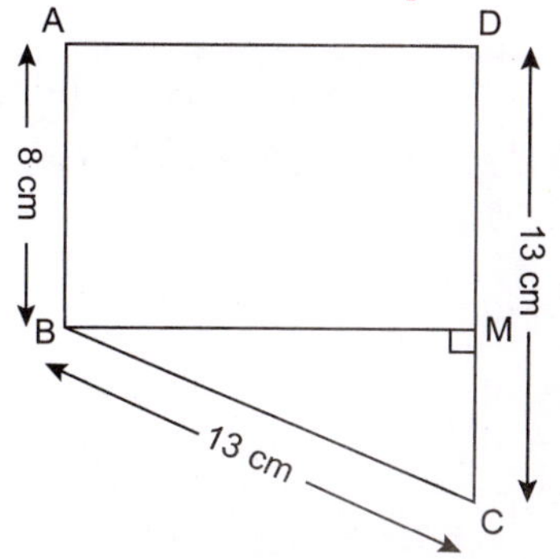


**Solution.** Given $AB = 8$ cm and $DC = 13$ cm

$$\therefore \quad MC = 13 - 8 = 5 \text{ cm}$$

Now in right angled triangle *BMC*,

$$BM^2 = BC^2 - MC^2 = 13^2 - 5^2 = 169 - 25 = 144$$

$$\therefore \quad BM = 12 \text{ cm}$$

$$\therefore \quad \text{Area of the trapezium} = \frac{1}{2}(AB + DC) \times AD = \frac{1}{2}(8 + 13) \times 12$$

$$= 126 \text{ cm}^2$$

**Ans.**

# Exercise 16B

1. Find the area of a quadrilateral, the length of one of its diagonals being 80 m and the lengths of the perpendiculars upon it from the opposite corners are 16 m and 24 m.
2. Find the area of a quadrilateral the length of whose diagonals are 120 m and 80 m respectively, and are at the right angles to each other.
3. Find the area of a quadrilateral plot of ground whose diagonals are 140 m and 130 m and intersect each other at right angles. Find also the cost of the land at ₹ 10 per $m^2$.
4. Find the cost of cultivating a quadrilateral field at 50 paise per square meter whose one diagonal is 40 m and its offsets are 25 m and 20 m respectively.
5. Find the area of the parallelogram whose base is 25 cm and height is 16 cm.
6. The lengths of the adjacent sides of a plot of land in the form of a parallelogram are 15 m and 13 m. If a diagonal is 14 m, find its area.
7. The perimeter of a rectangle is 32 cm and its length is 6 cm. Find the area of the rectangle.
8. The area of a rectangle is 72 $cm^2$ and length is 9 cm. Find its perimeter.
9. The area of a square is 576 $cm^2$. Find its perimeter.
10. A field, in the form of a rhombus, has its diagonals as 40 m and 25 m long respectively. Find the cost of watering the field at 12 paise per $m^2$.
11. The perimeter of a rhombus is 100 m and one of its diagonals is 40 m. Find its other diagonal and area.
12. Calculate the area of a trapezium, the sides of which, taken in order, are 50, 17, 25 and 12 cm, respectively and the first being parallel to the third.
13. A field, in the form of a trapezium, has its parallel sides 45.2 m and 22.8 m long and the distance between them is 12 m. Find the cost of turfing it at 20 paise per sq. m.
14. Find the area of the rhombus whose diagonals are 5 cm and 6 cm.
15. The area of a rhombus is 98 $cm^2$. If one of its diagonals is 14 cm, what is the length of the other diagonal?
16. The sides of a rhombus are 5 cm each and one diagonal is 8 cm, calculate
    (i) The length of the other diagonal,
    (ii) The area of the rhombus.
17. The perimeter of a rhombus is 20 cm. If one diagonal of the rhombus is 8 cm, find
    (i) the length of the other diagonal,
    (ii) the area of the rhombus.
18. The area of a rhombus is 120 $m^2$. If one of the diagonals is 24 m, find the perimeter of the rhombus.
19. Find the area of the following figure:

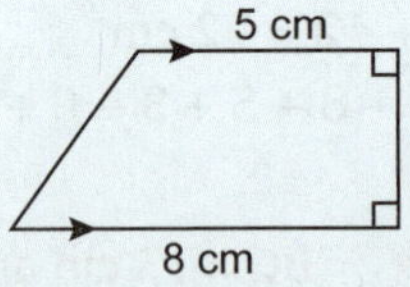


20. The area of a trapezium is 540 $cm^2$. If the ratio of its parallel sides is 5 : 7 and the distance between the parallel sides 18 cm, find the length of the parallel sides.
21. In the following figure, two paths are shown in a rectangular field. Find the area of the path.

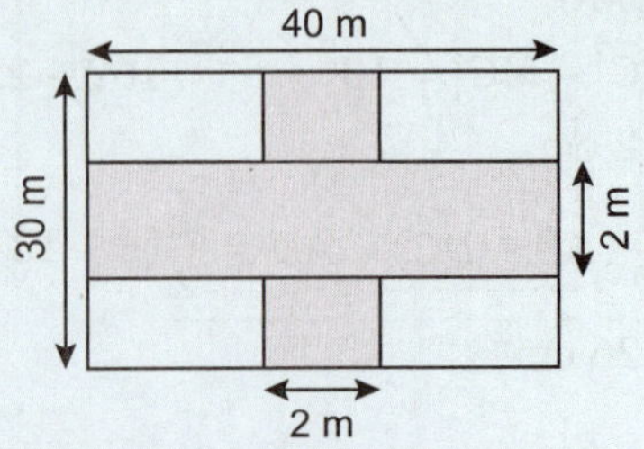

**22.** A footpath of uniform width of 2 m runs all around outside of a rectangular field 30 m long and 20 m wide. Find the area of the footpath.

**23.** A rectangular carpet has an area 60 $m^2$. If the sum of its diagonal and longer side is equal to 5 times the shorter side, find the breadth of the carpet.

**24.** A rectangular plot 32 m long and 20 m wide is to be covered with grass leaving 1.5 m all around it. Find the area covered with grass.

**25.** A room is 16 m long and 12 m wide. Find the cost of carpeting the room with a carpet 75 cm wide at ₹ 22.50 per metre.

**26.** A floor is 20 m long and 8 m wide. How many tiles measuring 50 cm × 25 cm are required to cover the floor?

**27.** A rectangular hall 27 m long and 15 m wide, is to be covered with a carpet of width 60 cm. Find the cost of carpeting at ₹ 12 per metre.

**28.** A wire when bent in the form of a square encloses an area of 900 $cm^2$. Find the largest area enclosed by the same wire when bent to form an equilateral triangle.

**29.** A wire when bent in the form of a square encloses an area of 225 $cm^2$. Find the largest area enclosed by the same wire when bent to form a rectangle of breadth 12 cm.

**30.** The length and breadth of a rectangle are 6 cm and 4 cm respectively. Find the height of a triangle whose base is 8 cm and whose area is 2 times that of the rectangle.

**31.** A rectangle has twice the area of a square. The length of the rectangle is 12 cm greater and the width is 8 cm greater than a side of the square. Find the side of the square.

**32.** In the figure, *ABCD*, it is given that $BC \parallel AD$. $BC = 10$ cm, $AD = 6$ cm, $AB = 5$ cm and $BE = 3$ cm. Find the area of the figure *ABCD*.

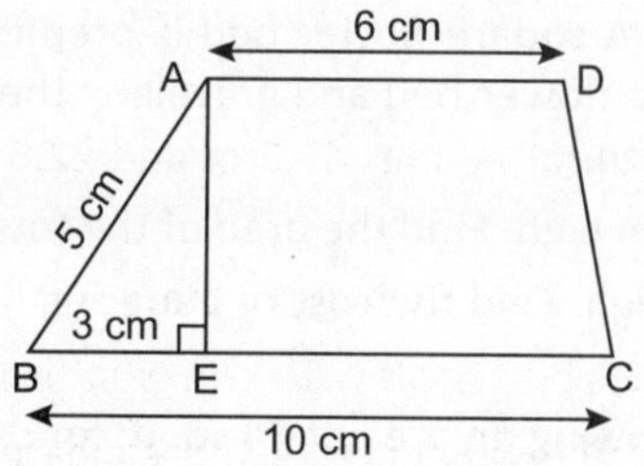


**33.** Find the area and perimeter of the following trapeziums:

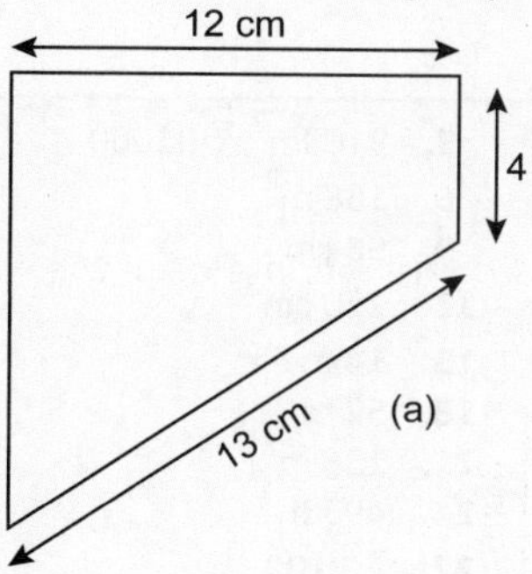


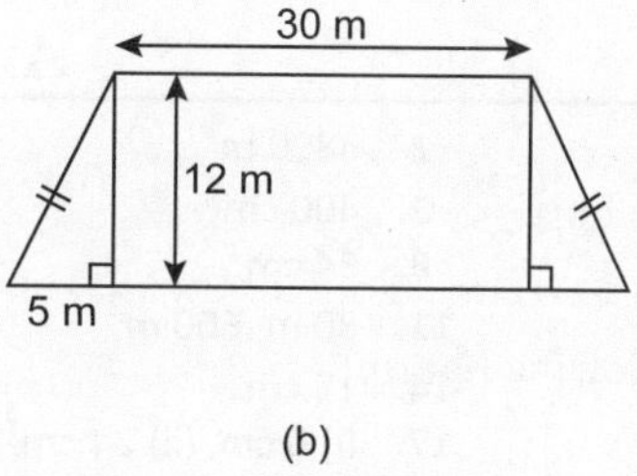


**34.** Find the area and perimeter of the given frame work, *ABCDEFGHI*. Given $GH = GF$.

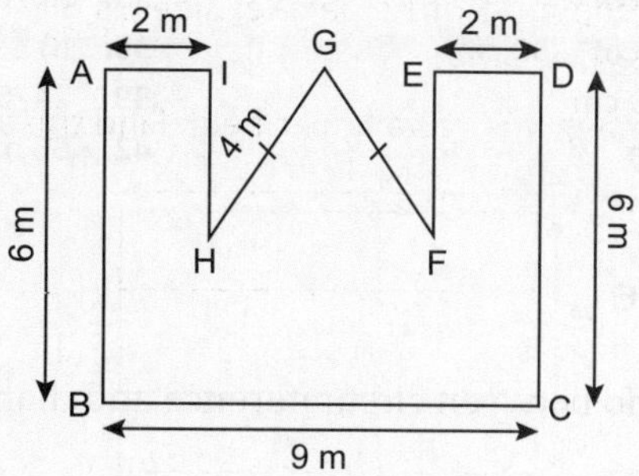

**35.** Find the area and perimeter of the following figure.

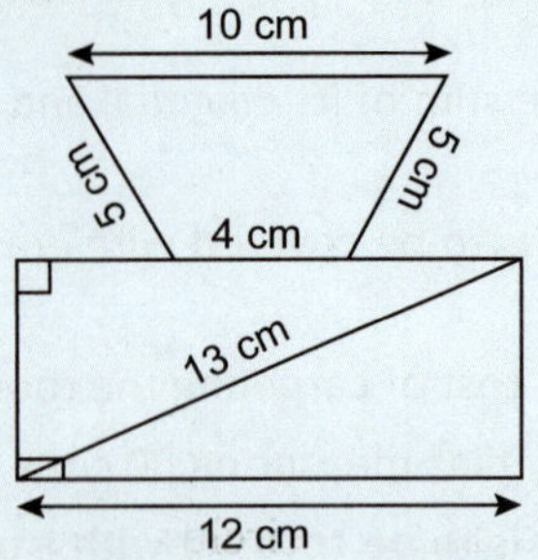


**36.** A rectangular garden is 276 m long and 180 m wide. It has an inside path of uniform width of 3 m all around it. Find the cost of
(i) repairing the path at 10 paise per sq. m and
(ii) watering the remaining portion of the garden at ₹ 3 per 100 sq. meters.

**37.** A hall room 25 m long and 20 m wide is surrounded by a verandah 2.5 m wide. Find the cost of the flooring the verandah at ₹ 1.65 per sq. m.

**38.** A marginal walk all round the inside of a rectangular field 30 m long and 28 m wide costs ₹ 56.00 at 50 paise per $m^2$ to construct it. Find the width of the walk.

**39.** A rectangular field 250 m by 250 m has two roads each 5 m wide in the middle of the field, one parallel to the length and the other parallel to the breadth. Find the area of the roads.

**40.** A carpet is spread in a square room leaving a margin of 5 dm all round the carpet. Find the cost of the carpet at ₹ 2.20 per sq. m, if the margin occupies an area of 13 $m^2$.

**41.** There is a field whose each side is 40 m. A square flower bed is prepared in its centre leaving a gravel path all around the flower bed. The total cost of laying the flower bed and gravelling the path at ₹ 1.50 and 60 paise per square meter is ₹ 2126.40. Find the length of the gravel path.

**42.** A room is 5.5 m long, 2.5 m wide and 3.5 m high. Find the area of the four walls of the room.

**43.** A room is 6 m long, 4.5 m wide and 5 m high. Find the cost of papering its walls with paper 1 m wide which is available at 40 paise per meter.

**44.** A room is 5.2 m long and 3.8 m broad. Allowing an area of 14 sq. m for doors and windows, the cost of papering the walls with paper 75 cm wide at 45 paise per meter is ₹ 24. Find the height of the room.

## Answers

| | | |
|---|---|---|
| **1.** 1600 $m^2$ | **2.** 4800 $m^2$ | **3.** 9100$m^2$, ₹ 91000 |
| **4.** ₹ 450 | **5.** 400 $cm^2$ | **6.** 168 $m^2$ |
| **7.** 60 $cm^2$ | **8.** 34 cm | **9.** 96 cm |
| **10.** ₹ 60 | **11.** 30 m, 600 $m^2$ | **12.** 270 $cm^2$ |
| **13.** ₹ 81.60 | **14.** 15 $cm^2$ | **15.** 14 m |
| **16.** (i) 6 cm, (ii) 24 $cm^2$ | **17.** (i) 6 cm, (ii) 24 $cm^2$ | **18.** 52 m |
| **19.** 19.5 $cm^2$ | **20.** 25 cm, 35 cm | **21.** 136 $m^2$ |
| **22.** 216 $m^2$ | **23.** 5 m | **24.** 493 $m^2$ |
| **25.** ₹ 5760 | **26.** 1280 | **27.** ₹ 8100 |
| **28.** 692.8 $cm^2$ | **29.** 216 $cm^2$ | **30.** 12 cm |
| **31.** 24 cm | **32.** 32 $cm^2$ | **33.** (i) 78 $cm^2$, 38 cm (ii) 420 $m^2$, 96m |
| **34.** 44 $m^2$, 42.43 m | **35.** 88 $cm^2$ , 50 cm | **36.** (i) ₹ 270, (ii) ₹ 1409.40 |
| **37.** ₹ 412.50 | **38.** 100 cm | **39.** 2475 $m^2$ |
| **40.** ₹ 79.20 | **41.** 2 m | **42.** 56 $m^2$ |
| **43.** ₹ 42 | **44.** 3 m | |

## Circumference and Area of a Circle

### 1. Circumference

It is the perimeter of a circle. The ratio between circumference and diameter of a circle is represented by the Greek letter $\pi$ (Pi), *i.e.*,

$$\frac{\text{circumference}}{\text{diameter}} = \pi$$

or circumference $(C) = \pi \times \text{diameter} = \pi \times 2 \times \text{radius}$

$\therefore$ $C = 2\pi r$.

**NOTE**

Approximate value of $\pi$ is $\frac{22}{7}$ or 3.1416.

2. Area of a circle $= \pi r^2$
3. Area of a circular ring

   If $R$ and $r$ are the radii of the bigger and smaller circles, then area of ring (shaded portion) $= \pi (R^2 - r^2)$.

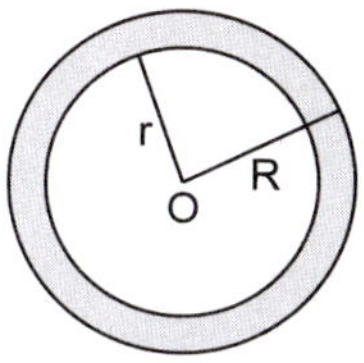


4. Area of semi-circle $= \frac{1}{2} \pi r^2$

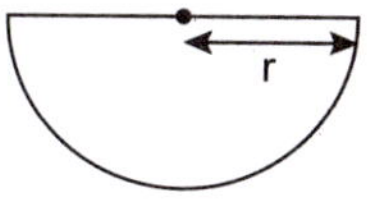


5. Perimeter of semi-circle $= \pi r + 2r = (\pi + 2)r$
6. Area of a quadrant $= \frac{1}{4} \pi r^2$

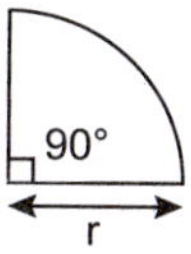


7. Perimeter of a quadrant $= \frac{\pi r}{2} + r + r = \frac{r}{2}(\pi + 4)$

## Illustrative Examples

**Example 1.** Find the circumference and area of a circle of radius 4.2 cm.

**Solution.**

$$\text{Circumference} = 2\pi r = \left(2 \times \frac{22}{7} \times 4.2\right) \text{cm} = 26.4 \text{ cm}$$ Ans.

$$\text{Area of the circle} = \pi r^2 = \left(\frac{22}{7} \times 4.2 \times 4.2\right) \text{cm}^2 = 55.44 \text{ cm}^2$$ Ans.

**Example 2.** Find the area of a circle whose circumference is 22 cm.

**Solution.** Let the radius of the circle be $r$ cm.

Then, its circumference $= 2\pi r$

$$\therefore \quad 2\pi r = 22 \Rightarrow 2 \times \frac{22}{7} r = 22 \Rightarrow r = \frac{7}{2}$$

$$\therefore \quad \text{Area of the circle} = \pi r^2 = \left(\frac{22}{7} \times \frac{7}{2} \times \frac{7}{2}\right) \text{cm}^2 = 38.5 \text{ cm}^2$$ Ans.

**Example 3.** A steel wire when bent in the form of a square encloses an area of 121 sq. cm. If the same wire is bent in the form of a circle, find the area of the circle.

**Solution.**

$$\text{Side of the square} = \sqrt{(121)} \text{ cm} = 11 \text{ cm}$$

$$\text{Perimeter of the square} = (4 \times 11) \text{ cm} = 44 \text{ cm}$$

$\therefore$ length of the wire $= 44$ cm

$\therefore$ circumference of the circle $=$ length of the wire $= 44$ cm

Let the radius of the circle $= r$ cm.

Then, $2\pi r = 44 \Rightarrow 2 \times \frac{22}{7} r = 44$

$\therefore$ $r = 7$ cm.

$$\therefore \quad \text{Area of the circle} = \pi r^2 = \left(\frac{22}{7} \times 7 \times 7\right) \text{cm}^2 = 154 \text{ cm}^2$$ Ans.

**Example 4.** The circumference of a circle is 123. 2 cm. Taking $\pi = \frac{22}{7}$, calculate:

(a) the radius of the circle in cm,
(b) the area of the circle in $cm^2$, correct to the nearest $cm^2$,
(c) the effect on the area of the circle if the radius is doubled.

**Solution.** (a) Let radius of the circle = $r$ cm

Then, $2\pi r = 123.2$

or $2 \times \frac{22}{7} \times r = 123.2$

$\therefore \quad r = \frac{123.2 \times 7}{2 \times 22} = 19.6$ cm **Ans.**

(b) Area of the circle = $\pi r^2 = \frac{22}{7} \times 19.6 \times 19.6 = 22 \times 2.8 \times 19.6 = 1207$ $cm^2$ (approx.) **Ans.**

(c) The area of circle, when radius is $r = \pi r^2$

The area when radius is $2r = \pi\ (2r)^2 = 4\pi r^2$

= 4 times the original area. **Ans.**

**Example 5.** A wire is looped in the form of a circle of radius 28 cm. It is re-bent into a square form. Determine the length of the side of the square.

**Solution.** Length of the wire = circumference of the circle = $\left(2 \times \frac{22}{7} \times 28\right)$ cm = 176 cm

$\therefore$ Perimeter of the square = length of the wire = 176 cm

Hence, the side of the square = $\left(\frac{176}{4}\right)$ cm = 44 cm **Ans.**

**Example 6.** A bicycle wheel makes 5000 revolutions in moving 11 km. Find the diameter of the wheel.

**Solution.** Distance covered by the wheel in 1 revolution

$= \left(\frac{11 \times 1000 \times 100}{5000}\right)$ cm = 220 cm

$\therefore$ Circumference of the wheel = 220 cm

Let the radius of the wheel = $r$ cm

Then, $2\pi r = 220 \Rightarrow 2 \times \frac{22}{7} \times r = 220 \Rightarrow r = \frac{7 \times 220}{2 \times 22} = 35$ cm

$\therefore$ Diameter of the wheel = $2r$

$= 2 \times 35 = 70$ cm **Ans.**

**Example 7.** A tonga is being driven at 11 km\hr. If each wheel of the tonga is 140 cm in diameter, find the number of revolutions made by each wheel per minute.

**Solution.** Radius of the wheel of the tonga = $\frac{1}{2} \times 140$ cm = 70 cm

Hence, distance travelled by wheel in one revolution = circumference of the wheel

$= 2\pi r = 2 \times \frac{22}{7} \times 70$ cm = 440 cm.

Speed of tonga = 11 km/hr = $11 \times 1000 \times 100$ cm /hr

$\therefore$ Distance travelled by the tonga in 1 minute = $\frac{11 \times 1000 \times 100}{60}$ cm

Number of revolutions made by the wheel in one minute

$$= \frac{\text{Total distance travelled in 1 minute}}{\text{circumference}} = \frac{11 \times 1000 \times 100}{60 \times 440} = 41\frac{2}{3}$$ **Ans.**

**Example 8.** The shaded area in adjacent fig. between the circumferences of two concentric circles is 346.5 $cm^2$. The circumference of the inner circle is 88 cm. Calculate the radius of the outer circle.

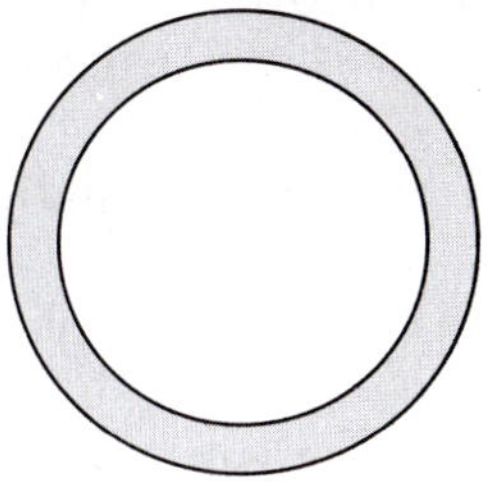

**Solution.** Let the radius of inner circle be $r$, then

$$2\pi r = 88 \Rightarrow 2 \times \frac{22}{7} r = 88 \Rightarrow r = \frac{7 \times 88}{22 \times 2} = 14 \text{ cm}$$

Let the radius of outer circle be $R$. Then area of the shaded portion

$$= \pi(R^2 - r^2) = \frac{22}{7}\{R^2 - (14)^2\}$$

Hence, according to the question

$$\frac{22}{7}\{R^2 - (14)^2\} = 346.5 \Rightarrow R^2 - (14)^2 = \frac{7 \times 346.5}{22} = 110.25$$

$$\Rightarrow \quad R^2 = 110.25 + 196 = 306.25$$

$$\therefore \quad R = \sqrt{(366.25)} = 17.5 \text{ cm}$$ **Ans.**

**Example 9.** If the perimeter of a semicircular protractor is 36 cm, find its diameter.

**Solution.** Let the radius of the protractor be $r$ cm.

Then, $\quad \text{perimeter} = (\pi r + 2r) = (\pi + 2)\,r = \left(\frac{22}{7} + 2\right) r = \frac{36}{7} r$

$$\therefore \quad \frac{36}{7} r = 36, \text{ i.e., } r = 7 \text{ cm}$$

$\therefore$ Diameter of the protractor $= 2r = 14$ cm **Ans.**

**Example 10.** A road which is 7 m wide surrounds a circular park whose circumference is 352 m. Find the area of the road.

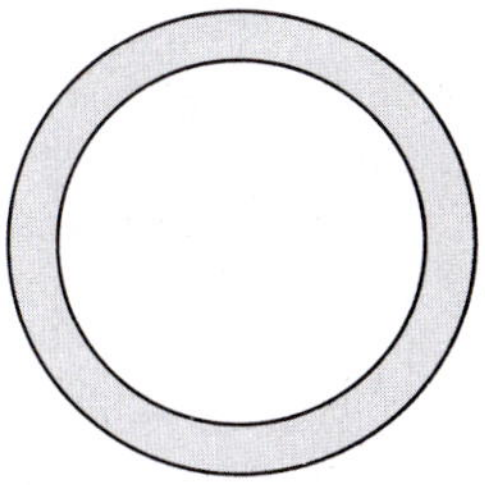

**Solution.** Let the radius of the park be $r$ m. Hence, its circumference $= 2\pi r$

$$\therefore \quad 2\pi r = 352$$

$$\Rightarrow \quad 2 \times \frac{22}{7} \times r = 352 \Rightarrow r = \frac{7 \times 352}{44} \text{ m} = 56 \text{ m}$$

Thus, inner radius = 56m

and outer radius = (56 + 7)m = 63 m

$$\text{Area of the road} = \pi[(63)^2 - (56)^2]\text{m}^2 = \frac{22}{7} \times (63 - 56)(63 + 56)\text{ m}^2$$

$$= \left(\frac{22}{7} \times 7 \times 119\right)\text{m}^2 = 2618 \text{ m}^2$$ **Ans.**

**Example 11.** The area of a circle is numerically equal to its circumference. Find its circumference in terms of 'π'.

**Solution.** Let radius of the circle be '$r$'.

It is given that 'numerically'

Area of circle = Circumference of the circle

$$\Rightarrow \quad \pi r^2 = 2\pi r$$

$$\Rightarrow \quad r = 2 \text{ units}$$

$\therefore$ Area of circle $= \pi r^2 = \pi (2)^2 = 4\pi$ square units **Ans.**

**Example 12.** The sum of the diameters of two circles is 35 cm and the difference of their circumferences is 66 cm. Find the areas of the two circles.

**Solution.** Let the radii of two circles are $R$ and $r$.

Then, $2R + 2r = 35$

$$R + r = 17.5 \quad \ldots(i)$$

and $2\pi R - 2\pi r = 66 \Rightarrow 2\pi(R - r) = 66$

$$\Rightarrow 2 \times \frac{22}{7} \times (R - r) = 66$$

$$\Rightarrow R - r = 10.5 \quad \ldots(ii)$$

From equations *(i)* and *(ii)*, we get

$R = 14$ cm and $r = 3.5$ cm

$\therefore$ Area of first circle $= \pi R^2 = \frac{22}{7} \times 14 \times 14 \text{ cm}^2 = 616 \text{ cm}^2$ Ans.

and area of second circle $= \pi r^2 = \frac{22}{7} \times 3.5 \times 3.5 \text{ cm}^2 = 38.5 \text{ cm}^2$ Ans.

**Example 13.** The area of an equilateral triangle is $49\sqrt{3}\text{ cm}^2$. With each vertex of the triangle as centre, a circle is described with radius equal to half the length of the side of the triangle as shown in the adjoining figure. Find the area of the shaded region.

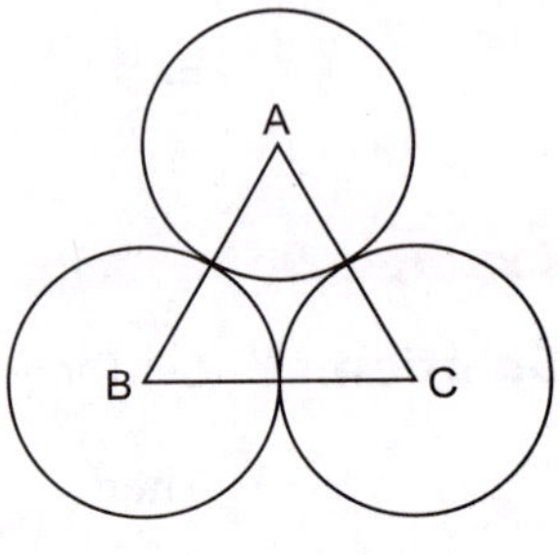


**Solution.** Let $a$ cm be the side of equilateral triangle, then

$$\text{area of } \Delta ABC = \frac{\sqrt{3}}{4}a^2 = 49\sqrt{3} \text{ (given)}$$

$$\Rightarrow a^2 = 196 \Rightarrow a = 14.$$

$\therefore$ Each side of triangle = 14 cm,

so, radius of each circle $= \left(\frac{1}{2} \times 14\right)$ cm $= 7$ cm.

$\therefore$ Required area = area of $\Delta ABC$ – sum of areas of three sectors each of central angle 60° and radius of circle 7 cm

= area of $\Delta ABC$ – area of a sector of radius 7 cm and central angle as 60° + 60° + 60°, *i.e.*, 180°

= area of $\Delta ABC$ – area of semicircle of radius 7 cm

$$= \left(49\sqrt{3} - \frac{1}{2} \times \frac{22}{7} \times 7^2\right) \text{cm}^2 = (49\sqrt{3} - 77) \text{ cm}^2$$ Ans.

**Example 14.** Four equal circles are described about the four corners of a square so that each touches two of the others as shown in the fig. Find the area of the shaded region, each side of the square measuring 14 cm.

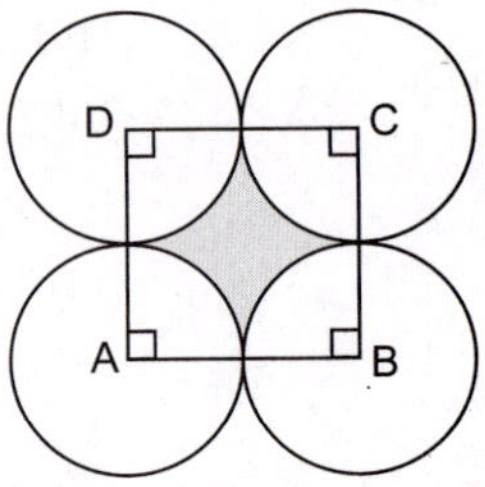


**Solution.** Clearly, the radius of each circle is 7 cm.

$\therefore$ Area of the shaded region = (area of square $ABCD$)

– 4 × (area of a sector with $r = 7$ cm and $\theta = 90°$)

$$= \left[(14 \times 14) - 4 \times \frac{22}{7} \times 7 \times 7 \times \frac{90}{360}\right] \text{cm}^2 = 42 \text{ cm}^2$$ Ans.

**Example 15.** Calculate the area of the shaded portion. The quadrants shown in the given figure are each of radius 7 cm. Take $\pi = \frac{22}{7}$.

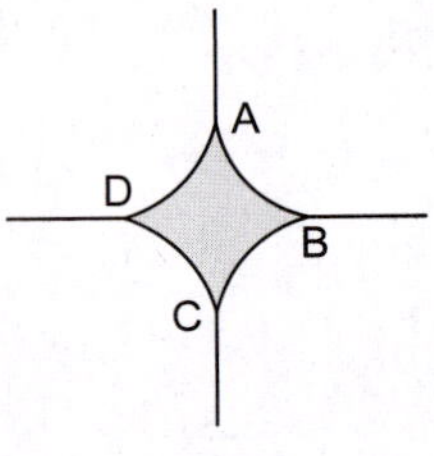


**Solution.** By drawing vertical lines from $B$ and $D$ and horizontal lines from $A$ and $C$, complete a square as shown in the fig. of example 14. Then this example becomes similar to ex. 14. Thus the area of shaded portion = 42 cm. Ans.

**Example 16.** In fig., *ABCD* is a square inscribed in a circle of radius 7 cm. Calculate :
(a) the area of the circle,
(b) the area of the shaded portion.

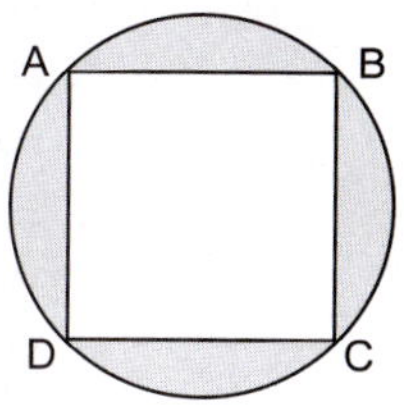


**Solution.** (a) Area of the circle $= \pi r^2 = \frac{22}{7} \times 7 \times 7 \text{ cm}^2 = 154 \text{ cm}^2$ **Ans.**

(b) Let $x$ cm be the side of the square *ABCD* inscribed in the given circle.
Join *BD*, then $BD$ = diameter of circle $= 2 \times 7$ cm $= 14$ cm
From right-angled triangle *BCD*, we get

$$BC^2 + CD^2 = BD^2$$

or $\quad x^2 + x^2 = (14)^2 \quad \Rightarrow \quad 2x^2 = 196$

$\Rightarrow \quad x^2 = 98.$

$\therefore$ Area of the square $ABCD = x^2 \text{ cm}^2 = 98 \text{ cm}^2$

$\therefore$ The area of the shaded portion

= area of circle–area of square *ABCD*

$= 154 \text{ cm}^2 - 98 \text{ cm}^2 = 56 \text{ cm}^2.$ **Ans.**

**Example 17.** In fig., the points *A*, *B* and *C* are the centres of arcs of circles of radii 5 cm, 3 cm and 2 cm respectively. Find the perimeter and the area of the shaded region. (Leave the answer as a multiple of π).

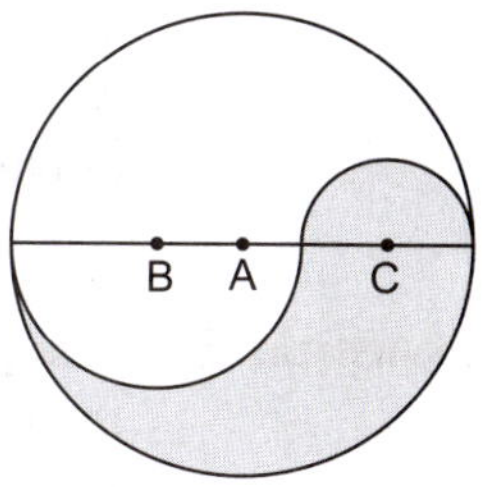


**Solution.** Perimeter of the shaded region

$$= \left(\frac{1}{2} \cdot 2\pi \cdot 5 + \frac{1}{2} \cdot 2\pi \cdot 3 + \frac{1}{2} \cdot 2\pi \cdot 2\right) \text{cm}$$

$= \pi (5 + 3 + 2) = 10\pi$ cm. **Ans.**

Area of the shaded portion

$$= \left(\frac{1}{2} \cdot \pi \cdot 5^2 - \frac{1}{2} \cdot \pi \cdot 3^2 + \frac{1}{2} \cdot \pi \cdot 2^2\right) \text{cm}^2$$

$$= \frac{\pi}{2}(25 - 9 + 4) \text{ cm}^2 = 10\pi \text{ cm}^2$$ **Ans.**

**Example 18.** *AOBC* is a quadrant of a circle of radius 10 m. Calculate the area of the shaded portion. Take π = 3.14 and give your answer correct to two significant figures.

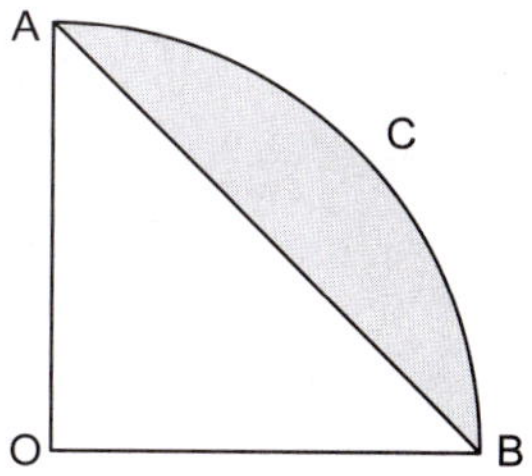


**Solution.** Area of the quadrant of the circle

$$= \frac{1}{4}\pi r^2 = \frac{1}{4} \times 3.14 \times 10^2 \text{ m}^2$$

$$= 25 \times 3.14 \text{ m}^2 = 78.5 \text{ m}^2$$

In right-angled triangle *OAB*, $OA = OB = 10$ m.

$\therefore \quad$ Area of $\Delta OAB = \frac{1}{2} \times 10 \times 10 \text{ m}^2 = 50 \text{ m}^2$

$\therefore$ Area of the shaded region

= Area of the quadrant – Area of $\Delta OAB$

$= 78.5 \text{ m}^2 - 50 \text{ m}^2$

$= 28.5 \text{ m}^2 = 29 \text{ m}^2$ (upto two significant figures) **Ans.**

**Example 19.** Two circles touch externally. The sum of their areas is $58\pi \text{ cm}^2$ and the distance between their centres is 10 cm. Find the radii of the two circles.

**Solution.** Let $R$ cm and $r$ cm be the radii of two circles, then

$$R + r = 10$$

$\Rightarrow \quad r = 10 - R \quad \ldots(i)$

Also $\quad \pi R^2 + \pi r^2 = 58\pi$

$\Rightarrow \quad R^2 + r^2 = 58$

$\Rightarrow \quad R^2 + (10 - R)^2 = 58 \quad$ [Using *(i)*]

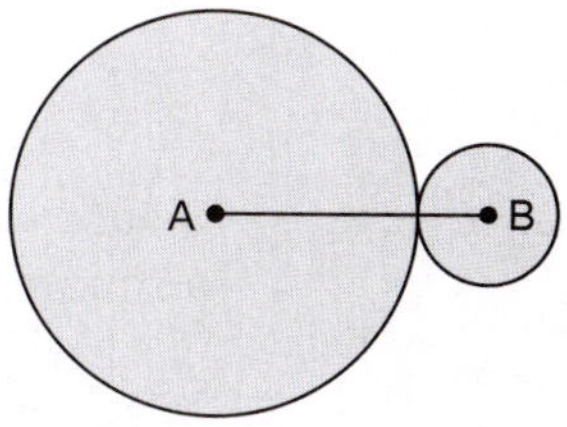

$$\Rightarrow \quad R^2 + 100 + R^2 - 20R - 58 = 0$$
$$\Rightarrow \quad 2R^2 - 20R + 42 = 0$$
$$\Rightarrow \quad R^2 - 10R + 21 = 0 \quad \Rightarrow (R-7)(R-3) = 0$$
$$\Rightarrow \quad R - 7 = 0 \text{ or } R - 3 = 0 \quad \Rightarrow R = 7 \text{ or } R = 3$$

When $R = 7$, then $r = 10 - 7 = 3$ and when $R = 3$, $r = 10 - 3 = 7$.

Hence, the radii of the two circles are 7 cm and 3 cm. **Ans.**

**Example 20.** Two circles touch internally. The sum of their areas is $116\pi$ cm$^2$ and distance between their centres is 6 cm. Find the radii of the circles.

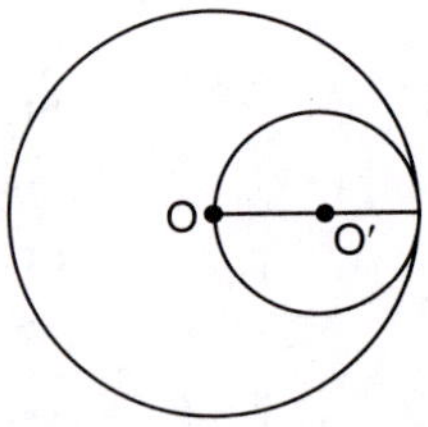


**Solution.** Let the radii of the given circles be $R$ and $r$ respectively. Then,

$$\pi R^2 + \pi r^2 = 116\pi$$

or
$$R^2 + r^2 = 116 \quad \text{...(i)}$$

Now, if $O$ and $O'$ be the centres of these circles then

$$OO' = R - r$$

So,
$$R - r = 6 \quad \text{...(ii)}$$

Now,
$$(R+r)^2 + (R-r)^2 = 2(R^2 + r^2)$$

or
$$(R+r)^2 = 2 \times 116 - 36 = 196 \quad \text{[From (i) and (ii)]}$$

or
$$R + r = 14 \quad \text{...(iii)}$$

Solving eqs. *(ii)* and *(iii)*, we get

$$R = 10 \text{ cm} \quad \text{and} \quad r = 4 \text{ cm}.$$ **Ans.**

**Example 21.** It is proposed to add to a square lawn with each side 58 m, two circular ends, the centre of each circle being the point of intersection of the diagonals of the square. Find the area of the whole lawn (Take $\pi = 22/7$).

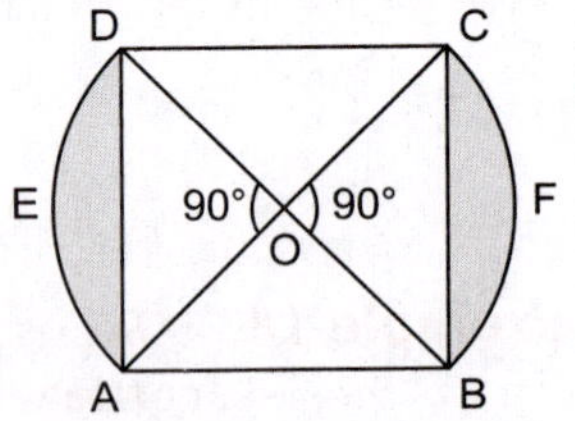


**Solution.** Let $ABCD$ be a square with side 58 m. Let its diagonals intersect at $O$. Then,

$$OA = OB = OC = OD \quad \text{and} \quad \angle AOD = \angle BOC = 90°$$

With $O$ as centre and radius equal to $OC = \frac{1}{2}AC$, arcs $AED$ and $BFC$ are drawn.

$\therefore$ Radius of each arc $= \frac{1}{2}$ (diagonal) $= \frac{1}{2} \times \sqrt{2} \times 58 = (1.4142 \times 29)$ m

$$= 41.01 \text{ m}.$$

$\therefore$ Area of whole lawn = area (sq. $ABCD$) + 2 (area of sector with $r = 41.01$ m and $\theta = 90° - 2 \times$ area of $\Delta AOD$)

$$= (58 \times 58) + 2 \times \left[\frac{22}{7} \times (41.01)^2 \times \frac{90}{360} - \frac{1}{2} \times (41.01)^2 \sin 90°\right]$$

$$= 3364 + \frac{11 \times (41.01)^2}{7} - (41.01)^2 = 3364 + \left(\frac{11}{7} - 1\right)(41.01)^2$$

$$= 3364 + \frac{4}{7} \times (41.01)^2 = 961.04 \text{ m}^2$$

$\therefore$ Area of the whole lawn = 4325.04 m$^2$ **Ans.**

**Example 22.** Figure shows a running track surrounding a grassed enclosure $PQRSTU$. The enclosure consists of a rectangle $PQST$ with a semicircular region at each end $PQ = 200$ m; $PT = 70$ m.

(a) Calculate the area of the grassed enclosure in m$^2$.

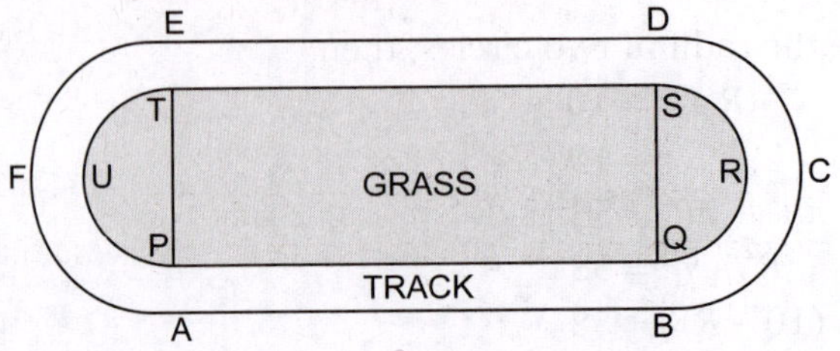

(b) Given that the track is of constant width, 7 m, calculate the outer perimeter *ABCDEF* of the track (Take $\pi$ to be 22/7).

**Solution.** (a) Grassed enclosure consists of a rectangle *PQST* and two semicircles *TUP* and *SRQ*.

Given: $PQ = 200$ m, $PT = 70$ m.

$\therefore$ Area of rectangle $PQST = 200 \times 70 \text{ m}^2 = 14000 \text{ m}^2$

Radius of semicircle *TUP* or *SRQ*

$$= \frac{1}{2} PT = 35 \text{ m}$$

$\therefore$ Area of semicircles *TUP* and *SRQ*

$$= 2 \times \frac{1}{2} \pi (35)^2 = \frac{22}{7} \times 35 \times 35 = 3850 \text{ m}^2$$

$\therefore$ Area of grassed enclosure $= (14000 + 3850) \text{ m}^2 = 17850 \text{ m}^2$ Ans.

(b) Perimeter $ABCDEF = DE + DCB + AB + AFE = 2AB + 2AFE$

$$= 2 \times 200 + 2 \times \frac{1}{2} \times 2\pi (35 + 7)$$

$$= \left(400 + 2 \times \frac{22}{7} \times 42\right) \text{m}$$

$$= (400 + 264) \text{ m} = 664 \text{ m}$$ Ans.

## Exercise 16C

1. Find the circumference and area of a circle whose radius is 6 cm. (Leave the answer in $\pi$).
2. Find the length of the circumference of a circle whose diameter is 7 cm.
3. Find the radius and the area of a circle if its circumference is $18\pi$ cm.
4. Find the perimeter of semi-circular plate of radius 3.85 cm.
5. A garden roller has a circumference of 3 meters. How many revolutions does it makes in moving a distance of 21 meters?
6. A wire when bent in the form of a square, encloses an area of 121 cm$^2$. The same wire is bent in the form of a circle. Find the area enclosed by the circle.
7. The wheel of a cart is making 5 revolutions per second. If the diameter of the wheel is 84 cm, find its speed in km/hr. Give your answer, correct to the nearest km.
8. Find the radius of a circular field if its area is 1386 cm$^2$.
9. In the figure the diameter of the inner circle is 3 m and that of outer circle is 11 m. Taking $\pi$ to be $\frac{22}{7}$, find the area of the shaded region.

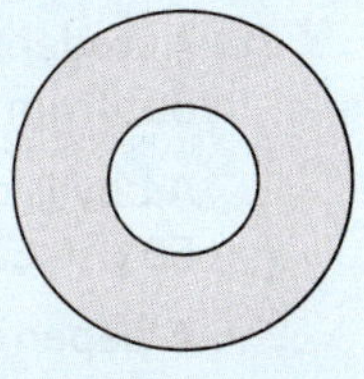

10. In figure, the area enclosed between the concentric circles is 770 cm$^2$. Given that the radius of the outer circle is 21 cm, calculate the radius of the inner circle ($\pi = 22/7$).

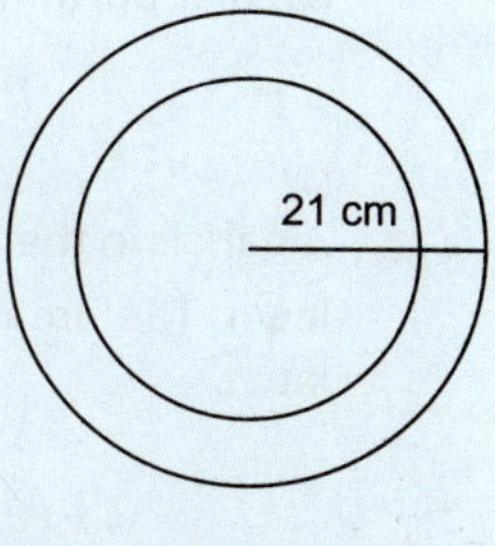


11. A road which is 7 m wide surrounds a circular park whose circumference is 352 m. Find the surface area of the road.
12. A road 3.5 m wide surrounds a circular plot whose circumference is 44 m. Find the cost of paving the road at ₹ 10 per m$^2$.

**13.** The sum of radii of two circles is 7 cm and the difference of their circumference is 8 cm. Find the circumferences of the two circles.

**14.** A lawn is in the shape of a semi- circle of diameter 35 dm. The lawn is surrounded by a flower bed of width 3.5 dm all round. Find the area of the flower bed in $dm^2$

**15.** A wire is in the form of a circle of radius 28 cm. Find the area of the square into which it can be bent.

**16.** A copper wire when bent in the form of a square encloses an area of 484 $cm^2$. If the same wire is bent in the form of a circle, find the area enclosed by it.

**17.** How long will a man take to walk round once round a circular park of radius 84 m at the rate of 4.8 km per hour?

**18.** The length of a wire which is tied as a boundary of a semicircular park is 72 m. Find the radius of the semi-circular park and its area. [**Hint :** $(\pi r + 2r) = 72$]

**19.** In the figure, *A* is the centre of the arc of the circle. Find the perimeter and the area of the shaded region, where length and breadth are 12 cm and 7 cm respectively.

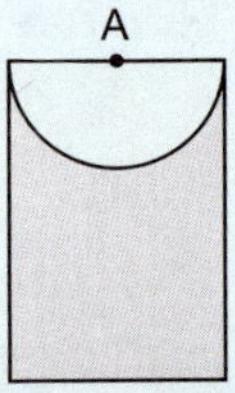


**20.** In the fig., *A* is the centre of the arc of the circle. Find the perimeter and the area of the shaded region and the side of square is 10 cm.

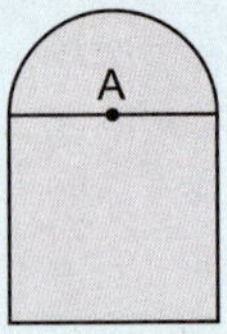


**21.** Find the area of the figure in square cm correct to one place of decimal $\left(\text{take } \pi = \dfrac{22}{7}\right)$.

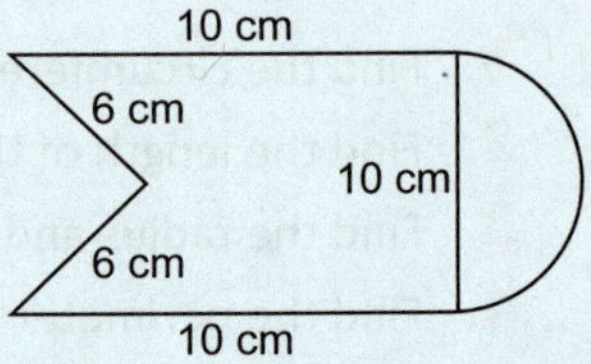


**22.** Fig. represents a quadrant of a circle of radius 3.5 cm with centre *O*.

(i) Calculate the area of the quadrant *OACB*.

(ii) Given $OD = 2$ cm, calculate the area of the shaded region (Take $\pi = 22/7$).

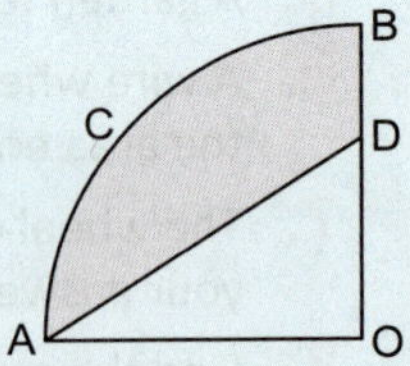


**23.** A student takes a rectangular piece of paper 30 cm long and 21 cm wide. Find the area of the biggest circle that can be cut out from the paper. Also find the area of the paper left after cutting out the circle (Take $\pi = 22/7$).

**24.** A boy is cycling such that the wheels of the cycle are making 140 revolutions per minute. If the diameter of each wheel is 60 cm. Calculate the speed which the boy is cycling.

**25.** A paper is in the form of a rectangle *ABCD* in which $AB = 20$ cm and $BC = 14$ cm. A semi-circular portion with *BC* as diameter is cut off. Find the area of the remaining part.

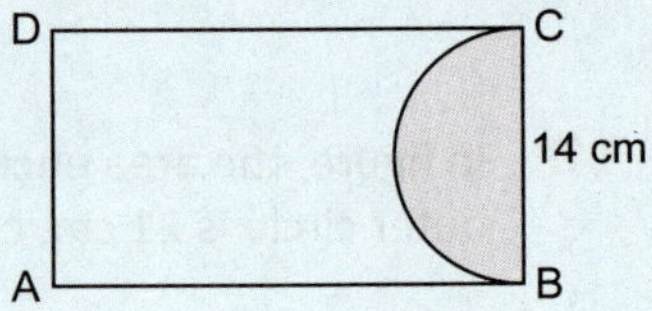


**26.** A park is in the form of a rectangle 100 m × 80 m. At the centre of the park there is a circular lawn. The area of the park excluding the lawn is 4150 $m^2$. Find the radius of the circular lawn.

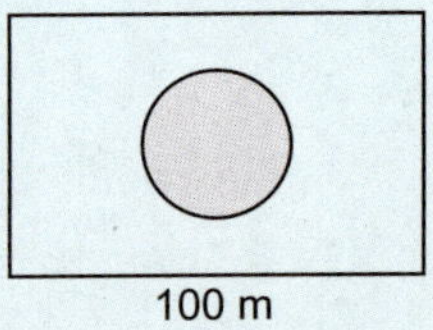


**27.** The short and long hands of a clock are 4 cm and 6 cm long respectively. Find the sum of distances travelled by their tips in 2 days (Take $\pi = 3.14$).

**28.** A square park has each side of 100 m. At each corner of the park, there is a flowerbed in the form of a quadrant of radius 14 m as shown in the figure. Find the area of the remaining part of the park.

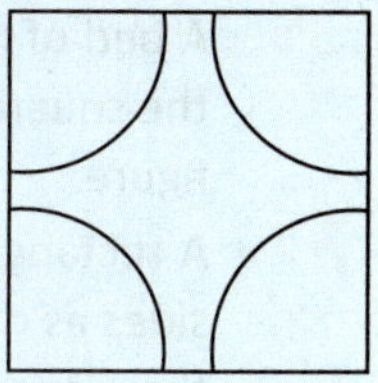

**29.** The inside perimeter of a running track (shown in fig.) is 400 m. The length of each of the straight portion is 90 m and the ends are semicircles. If the track is everywhere 14 m wide, find the area of the track. Also, find the length of the outer running track.

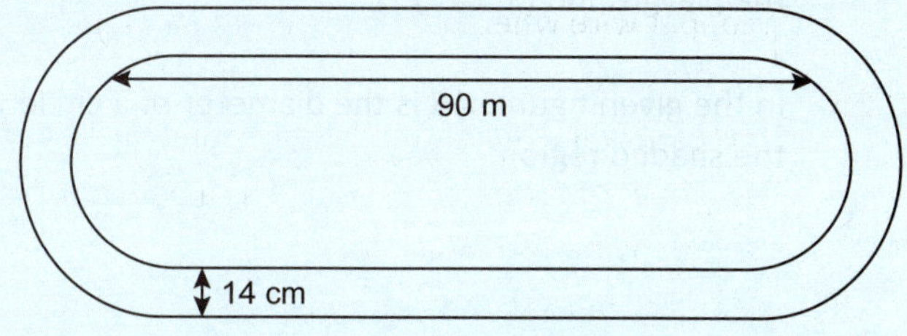


**30.** In fig, the inside perimeter of a practice running track with semi-circular ends and straight parallel sides is 312 m. The length of the straight portion of the track has a uniform width of 2 m through out, find its area.

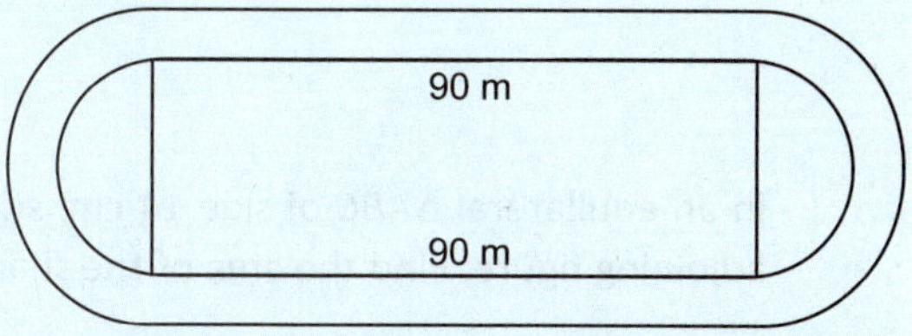


**31.** In the figure, two circles with centres $A$ and $B$ touch each other at the point $C$. If $AC = 8$ cm and $AB = 3$ cm, find the area of the shaded region (Take $\pi = 22/7$).

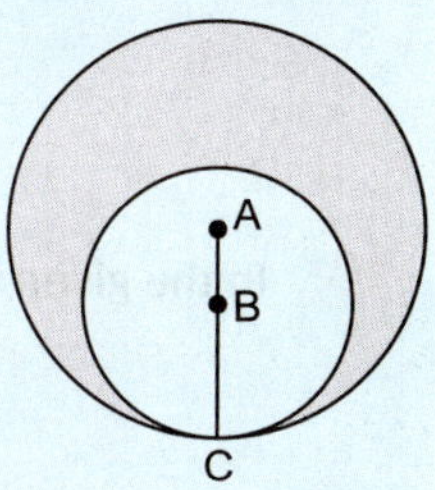


**32.** In fig., $O$ is the centre of a circular arc and $AOB$ is a straight line. Find the perimeter and area of the shaded region correct to one decimal place (Take $\pi = 3.14$).

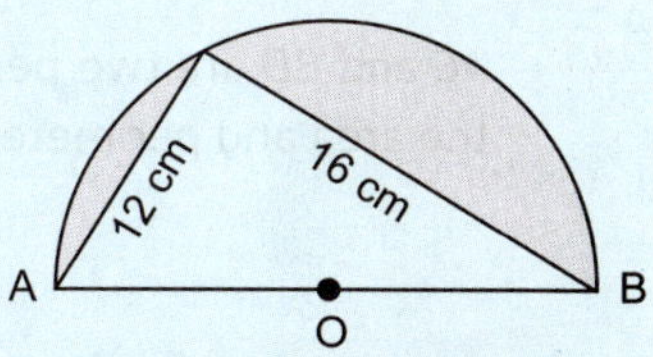


**33.** In fig., the boundary of the shaded region in the given diagram consists of four semi-circular arcs, the smallest two being equal. If the diameter of the largest is 14 cm and of the smallest is 3.5 cm, calculate :

(i) the length of the boundary,

(ii) the area of the shaded region ( Take $\pi = 22/7$).

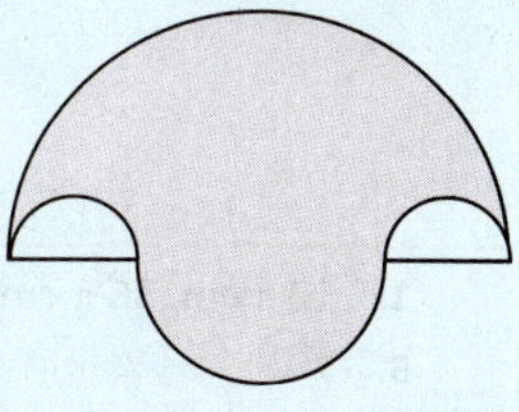

**34.** In the fig., a piece of cardboard, in the shape of a trapezium $ABCD$, and $AB \parallel DC$ and $\angle BCD = 90°$, quarter circle $BFEC$ is removed. Given $AB = BC = 3.5$ cm and $DE = 2$ cm. Calculate the area of the remaining piece of the cardboard (Take $\pi = 22/7$).

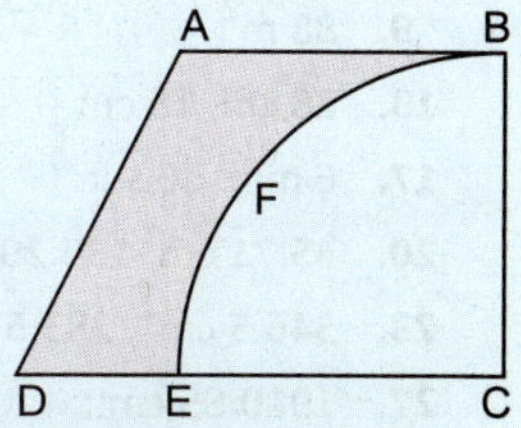


**35.** The boundary of the shaded region in fig. (a) consists of three semi-circular arcs, the smaller ones being equal. If the diameter of the larger arc is 10 cm, calculate :

(i) the length of the boundary,

(ii) the area of the shaded region (Take $\pi = 3.14$).

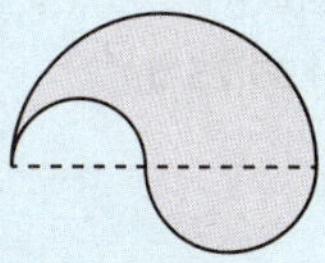
(a)

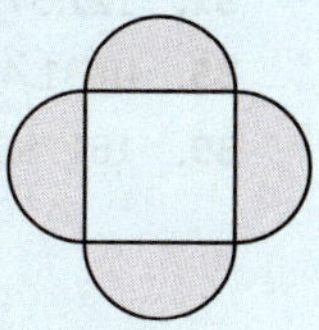
(b)

**36.** A bed of roses is like the adjoining diagram (fig. b). In the centre is a square and on each side there is semi-circle. Side of the square is 21 m. If each rose-plant needs 6 $m^2$ of space, find out the number of plants which can be planted in the whole figure.

**37.** A rectangular playground has two semi-circles added to its outside with its smaller sides as diameters. If the sides of the rectangle are 120 m and 21 m, find the area of the playground ($\pi = 22/7$).

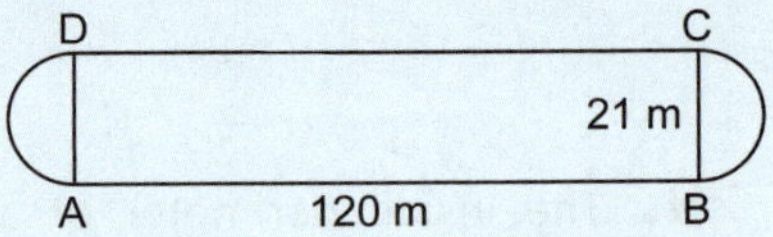


**38.** In the given figure, *AB* is the diameter of a circle with centre *O* and *OA* = 7 cm. Find the area of the shaded region.

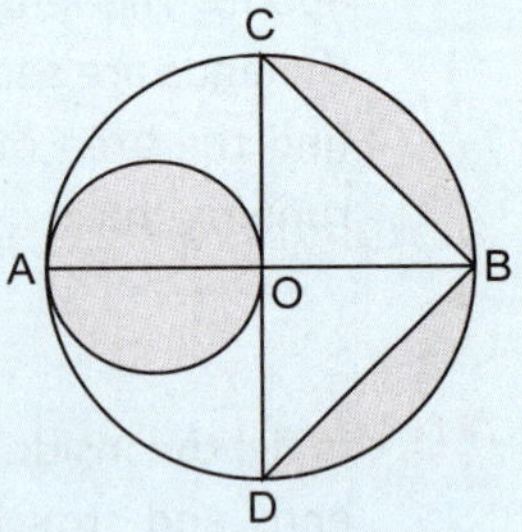


**39.** In an equilateral $\Delta ABC$ of side 14 cm, side *BC* is the diameter of a semi-circle as shown in the adjoining figure. Find the area of the shaded region (Take $\pi = 22/7$ and ($\sqrt{3} = 1.732$).

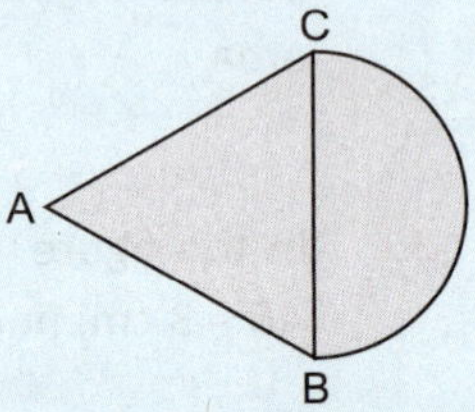


**40.** In the given figure, find the area of the unshaded portion within the rectangle (Take $\pi = 3.14$).

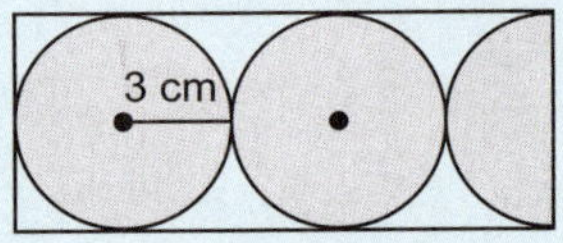


**41.** *AC* and *BD* are two perpendicular diameters of a circle with centre *O*. If *AC* = 16 cm, calculate the area and perimeter of the shaded part (Take $\pi = 3.14$).

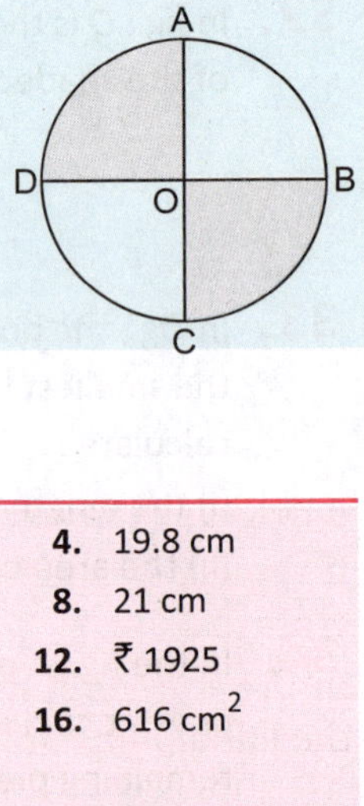


## *Answers*

| | | | |
|---|---|---|---|
| **1.** $12\pi$ cm, $36\pi$ $cm^2$ | **2.** 22 cm | **3.** 9 cm, $81\pi$ $cm^2$ | **4.** 19.8 cm |
| **5.** 7 | **6.** 154 $cm^2$ | **7.** 4 km/hr | **8.** 21 cm |
| **9.** 88 $m^2$ | **10.** 14 cm | **11.** 2618 $m^2$ | **12.** ₹ 1925 |
| **13.** 26 cm, 18 cm | **14.** 211.75 $dm^2$ | **15.** 1936 $cm^2$ | **16.** 616 $cm^2$ |
| **17.** 6 min. 36 sec. | **18.** 14 m, 308 $m^2$ | **19.** 42 cm, 64.75 $cm^2$ | |
| **20.** 45.71 cm, 139.29 $cm^2$ | **21.** 122.7 $cm^2$ | **22.** (i) 9.625 $cm^2$, (ii) 6.125 $cm^2$ | |
| **23.** 346.5 $cm^2$, 283.5 $cm^2$ | **24.** 15.84 km/hr | **25.** 203 sq. cm | **26.** 35 m |
| **27.** 1910.85 cm | **28.** 9384 $m^2$ | **29.** 6216 $m^2$, 488 m | **30.** 636.57 $m^2$ |
| **31.** 122.57 $cm^2$ | **32.** 59.4 cm, 61 $cm^2$ | **33.** (i) 44 cm, (ii) 86.625 $cm^2$ | **34.** 6.125 $cm^2$ |
| **35.** (i) 31.4 cm, (ii) 39.25 $cm^2$ | **36.** 189 plants | **37.** 2866.5 $m^2$ | **38.** 66.5 $cm^2$ |
| **39.** 161. 868 $cm^2$ | **40.** 19.35 $cm^2$ | **41.** Area = 100.48 $cm^2$, Perimeter = 57.12 cm | |

## Surface Area and Volumes of Cubes and Cuboids

### Solid

Any thing which occupies space is called a ***solid.*** It has three dimensions *viz., length, breadth* and *height*.

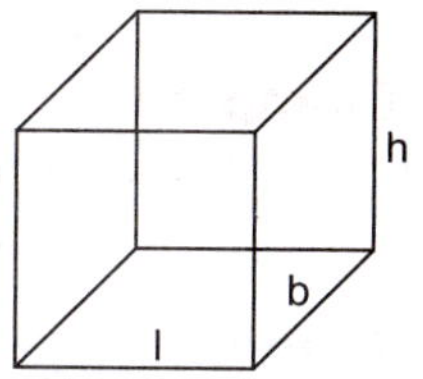


### Cuboid

A ***cuboid*** is a rectangular solid having six faces.

### Cube

A rectangular solid whose every face is a square, is called a ***cube***.

## Volume and Areas

### Cuboid

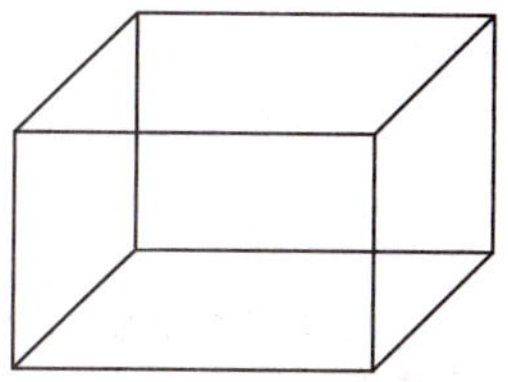

(i) Volume of a cuboid = $l \times b \times h$;
where $l$, $b$ and $h$ denote length, breadth and height respectively.

(ii) Area of four walls of a cuboid = $2(l + b) \times h$.

(iii) Total surface of a cuboid = $2(lb + bh + lh)$.

(iv) Diagonal of a cuboid $= \sqrt{(l^2 + b^2 + h^2)}$.

### Cube

(i) Volume of a cube = $a^3$, where $a$ is the edge of the cube.

(ii) Total surface of a cube= $6a^2$.

**NOTE**

**1.** If $l$, $b$ and $h$ are the external dimensions of a closed cuboid of thickness $x$, then internal dimensions are $(l - 2x)$, $(b - 2x)$ and $(h - 2x)$.

**2.** If the cuboid is an open cuboid, then internal dimensions are $(l - 2x)$, $(b - 2x)$ and $(h - x)$.

**3.** Volume of material = External Volume – Internal Volume.

## Cross-Section

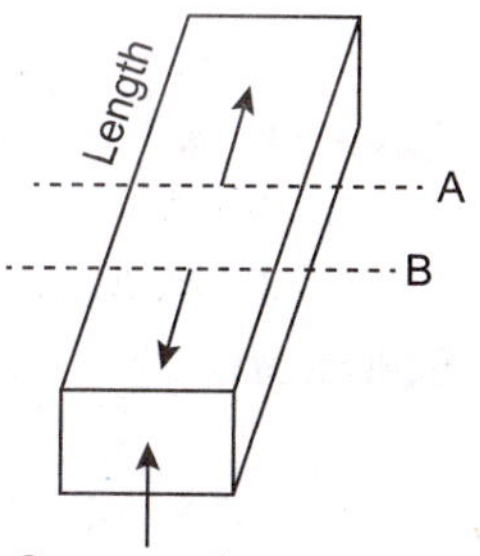

Cross-section

A cut which is made through a solid perpendicular to its length, is called its cross-section.

If the cut has the same shape and size at each point of its length, then it is called the uniform cross-section.

In the adjoining figure, a cuboid is cut through points $A$ and $B$ perpendicular to its length, then the cuboid has uniform cross-section.

1. Volume of a solid with uniform cross-section = area of its cross-section × length.
2. Lateral surface area of a solid with uniform cross-section
= perimeter of its cross-section × length.

## Flow of Liquid

If a liquid is flowing through a pipe of uniform cross-section, then the volume of liquid flow in unit time
= area of cross-section × speed of flow of liquid.

## Illustrative Examples

**Example 1.** A closed rectangular box has inner dimensions 24 cm by 12 cm by 10 cm. Calculate :
(a) its capacity,
(b) area of tin-foil needed to line its inner surface.

**Solution.** (a) Capacity = Volume = $24 \times 12 \times 10 = 2880 \text{ cm}^3$ Ans.

(b) Area of tin-foil = Total Surface = $2(24 \times 12 + 12 \times 10 + 24 \times 10)$

$= 2(228 + 120 + 240) = 2 \times 648 = 1296 \text{ cm}^2$ Ans.

**Example 2.** Three sides of a cuboid are 18, 37.7 and 40 cm. Find the edge of that cube whose volume is equal to this cuboid. Also find diagonal of the cube correct to the nearest integer.

**Solution.** Volume of the cuboid $= l \times b \times h$

$= 18 \times 37.5 \times 40$

$= 27000 \text{ cm}^3$

From the question, volume of the cuboid = Volume of the cube

$\therefore$ Volume of the cube = 27000

$\therefore$ $a^3 = 30^3 \Rightarrow a = 30$ cm

$\therefore$ Edge of the cube = 30 cm Ans.

Now, diagonal of a cube $= \sqrt{3a^2} = \sqrt{3} \times 30 = 52$ cm Ans.

**Example 3.** The external dimensions of a wooden box are 18 cm, 10 cm and 6 cm respectively and thickness of the wood is 5 mm. If the empty box weights 3.15 kg, find the weight of 1 c.c. of wood.

**Solution.** External volume = $18 \times 10 \times 6 = 1080$ c.c.

Internal volume = $17 \times 9 \times 5 = 765$ c.c.

Since thickness = 5 m.m. $= \frac{1}{2}$ cm

$\therefore$ $l = 18 - 1, b = 10 - 1, h = 6 - 1$

Now, volume of wood = external volume – internal volume

$= 1080 - 765$

$= 315$ c.c.

$\therefore$ Weight of 1 c.c. of wood $= \frac{3.15}{315} \text{ kg} = \frac{3150}{315} \text{ gm} = 10 \text{ gm}$ Ans.

**Example 4.** A trench is 10 m long, 5 m broad and $3\frac{1}{3}$ m deep. The earth dug out from this trench is evenly spread on a road which is 200 m long and 5 m broad. Find the height of the earth on the road.

**Solution.** Volume of the trench = length × breadth × depth

$= 10 \times 5 \times \frac{10}{3} \text{ cu. m.} = \frac{500}{3} \text{ cu. m.}$

The area of the road on which the earth is spread $= 200 \times 5 = 1000 \text{ m}^2$

Let height of the earth spread on the road = $x$ m.

$\therefore$ $1000 \times x = \frac{500}{3}$

$\therefore$ $x = \frac{500}{3} \times \frac{1}{1000} = \frac{1}{6} \text{ m} = 16\frac{2}{3}$ cm Ans.

**Example 5.** Three cubes each of side 5 cm are joined together side by side as shown in the adjoining figure, to form a cuboid. Find the volume and surface area of the cuboid.

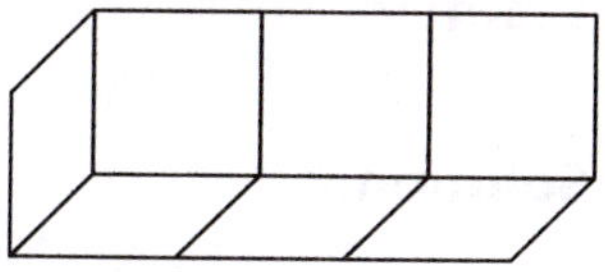

**Solution.** For cuboid,

$$l = (5 + 5 + 5) \text{ cm} = 15 \text{ cm}$$
$$b = h = 5 \text{ cm}$$

$\therefore$ Volume $= l \times b \times h$

$= 15 \times 5 \times 5 \text{ cm} = 375 \text{ cm}^3$ **Ans.**

and surface area $= 2\,(l \cdot b + b \cdot h + l \cdot h)$

$= 2\,(15 \times 5 + 5 \times 5 + 15 \times 5) \text{ cm}^2$

$= 2\,(75 + 25 + 75) \text{ cm}^2 = 350 \text{ cm}^2$ **Ans.**

**Example 6.** The floor of a rectangular hall has a perimeter 250 m. If the cost of painting the four walls at the rate of ₹ 10 per m$^2$ is ₹ 25000, find the height of the hall.

**Solution.** As the cost of painting the walls at the rate of ₹ 10 per m$^2$ is ₹ 15000, the painted area

$$= \frac{25000}{10} \text{ m}^2 = 2500 \text{ m}^2$$

Let $h$ metres be the height of the hall.

Area of four walls = perimeter × height.

$\therefore$ $250 \times h = 2500 \Rightarrow h = 10$

Hence, the height of the hall = 10 metres **Ans.**

**Example 7.** There is a cubical room whose length is 10 m. How many students can it accommodate if each student requires 5 m$^3$ of space? Find also the surface of the room.

**Solution.** Volume of the room $= (10)^3 \text{ m}^3 = 1000 \text{ m}^3$

Space required for a student $= 5 \text{ m}^3$

$\therefore$ Required number of students $= \dfrac{1000}{5} = 200$ **Ans.**

Surface of the room $= 6 \times (\text{length})^2$

$= 6 \times (10)^2 \text{ m}^2$

$= 6 \times 100 = 600 \text{ m}^2$ **Ans.**

**Example 8.** Three cubes whose edges are 3 cm, 4 cm and 5 cm respectively are melted to form a single cube. Find the surface of the new cube, supposing that there is no waste in the process.

**Solution.** Volume of the first cube $= (3)^3 \text{ cm}^3 = 27 \text{ cm}^3$

Volume of the second cube $= (4)^3 \text{ cm}^3 = 64 \text{ cm}^3$

Volume of third cube $= (5)^3 \text{ cm}^3 = 125 \text{ cm}^3$

$\therefore$ Total volume of three cubes $= 27 + 64 + 125 = 216 \text{ cm}^3$

$\therefore$ Volume of the new cube $= 216 \text{ cm}^3$

$\therefore$ Edge of the new cube $= \sqrt[3]{216} = 6 \text{ cm}$

Surface of the new cube $= 6 \times (6)^2 \text{ cm}^2$

$= 216 \text{ cm}^2$ **Ans.**

**Example 9.** Find the length of the longest rod that can be placed in a room 12 m long, 9 m broad and 8 m high.

**Solution.** The longest rod that can be placed in the room is equal to the length of its diagonal.

$\therefore$ Length of the longest rod $= \sqrt{12^2 + 9^2 + 8^2}$

$= \sqrt{(144 + 81 + 64)}$

$= \sqrt{289} = 17 \text{ m}$ **Ans.**

**Example 10.** The cost of wood is ₹ 1500 per m$^3$. A certain cube of that wood was bought for ₹ 768. Find the side of the cube.

**Solution.** $1 \text{ m}^3 = 100 \times 100 \times 100 \text{ cm}^3$

For ₹ 1500 the volume of wood

$= 100 \times 100 \times 100 \text{ cm}^3$

For ₹ 768 the volume of the wood

$$= \frac{100 \times 100 \times 100 \times 768}{1500} = 512000 \text{ cm}^3$$

The side of the cube $= \sqrt[3]{512000} = 80$ cm **Ans.**

**Example 11.** The length, breadth and height of a room are 9 m, 7 m and 4 m respectively. There are two doors measuring 2 m × 1.5 m and four windows measuring 1.5 m × 1 m. Find the area of the remaining walls.

**Solution.**

Area of 4 walls $= 2\,(l + b).\,h = 2\,(9 + 7) \times 4 = 128 \text{ m}^2$

Area of 1 door $= 2 \times 1.5 = 3 \text{ m}^2$

$\therefore$ Area of 2 doors $= 2 \times 3 \text{ m}^2 = 6 \text{ m}^2$

Area of 1 window $= 1.5 \times 1 = 1.5 \text{ m}^2$

$\therefore$ Area of 4 windows $= 4 \times 1.5 \text{ m}^2 = 6 \text{ m}^2$

Area of remaining walls = Area of four walls – Area of doors – Area of windows

$= 128 \text{ m}^2 - 6\text{m}^2 - 6\text{m}^2 = 116 \text{ m}^2$ **Ans.**

**Example 12.** The length, breadth and height of a rectangular solid are in the ratio 6 : 4 : 5. If the total surface area is 21312 cm$^2$, find the dimensions of the solid.

**Solution.** Let $l = 6x$, $b = 4x$ and $h = 5x$

$\therefore$ Total surface area $= 2\,[l \cdot b + b \cdot h + h \cdot l]$

$= 2\,[6x \cdot 4x + 4x \cdot 5x + 5x \cdot 6x]$

$= 2\,(74x^2) = 148x^2$

Now, $148x^2 = 21312 \quad \Rightarrow \quad x^2 = 144$

$\Rightarrow \quad x = 12$

$\therefore \quad l = 72$ cm, $b = 48$ cm and $h = 60$ cm **Ans.**

**Example 13.** In a rectangular plot 80 m × 60 m, a square pond of side 20 m is dug to a depth of 5.5 m and the earth taken out is spread evenly to cover the remaining area. Find the rise in the level of the plot.

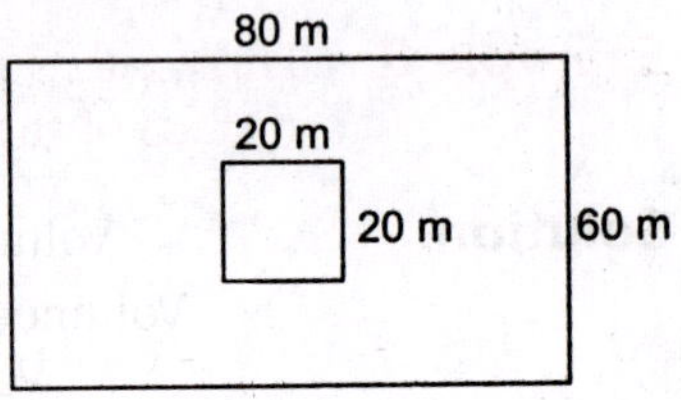


**Solution.** For pond : $l = 20$ m, $b = 20$ m and $h = 5.5$ m

$\therefore$ Volum of earth taken out $= 20 \times 20 \times 5.5 \text{ m}^3 = 2200 \text{ m}^3$

Area of plot $= 80 \times 60 \text{ m}^2 = 4800 \text{ m}^2$

Area of pond $= 20 \times 20 \text{ m}^2 = 400 \text{ m}^2$

Area of remaining pond $= (4800 - 400) \text{ m}^2 = 4400 \text{ m}^2$

$$\therefore \text{Rise in the level of plot} = \frac{\text{Volume of earth taken out}}{\text{Area of remaining plot}} = \frac{2200}{4400} = 0.5 \text{ m}$$ **Ans.**

**Example 14.** The cost of preparing the walls of a room 12 m long at the rate of ₹ 13.50 per square metre is ₹ 3402 and the cost of matting the floor at ₹ 9.50 per square metre is ₹ 1026. Find the height of the room.

**Solution.**

$$\text{Area of floor} = \frac{\text{Cost of matting}}{\text{Rate per square metre}} = \frac{1026}{9.50} = 108 \text{ m}^2$$

$\Rightarrow \quad l \times b = 108$

$\Rightarrow \quad b = \dfrac{108}{12} = 9 \text{ m} \qquad (\because l = 12 \text{ m})$

Now, area of 4 walls $= 2(l + b) \times h = 2(12 + 9) \times h = 42h$

Cost of preparing the walls $= 42h \times ₹\,13.50$

$\therefore \quad 42h \times ₹\,13.50 = ₹\,3402$

$\Rightarrow \quad h = \dfrac{3402}{42 \times 13.50} = 6 \text{ m}$

$\therefore$ Height of the room = 6 m **Ans.**

**Example 15.** Find the volume of wood required for a closed wooden box with external dimensions 15 cm × 12 cm × 8 cm if the wood is 0.5 cm thick.

**Solution.** Here, external dimensions are $L = 15$ cm, $B = 12$ cm and $H = 8$ cm

Thickness of wood $d = 0.5$ cm

$\therefore$ Internal dimensions are

$$l = L - 2d = 15 - 2 \times 0.5 = 14 \text{ cm}$$
$$b = B - 2d = 12 - 2 \times 0.5 = 11 \text{ cm}$$
$$h = H - 2d = 8 - 2 \times 0.5 = 7 \text{ cm}$$

Now, volume of wood used = External volume – Internal volume

$$= L \times B \times H - l \times b \times h$$
$$= 15 \times 12 \times 8 - 14 \times 11 \times 7$$
$$= 1440 - 1078 = 362 \text{ cm}^3$$

**Ans.**

**Example 16.** A rectangular tank is 25 m long and 8.5 m deep. If 255 cubic metres of water be drawn off the tank, the level of water in the tank goes down by 1.5 m. Find :

(a) The width of the tank,

(b) The total volume of water which the tank can hold.

**Solution.** (a) Volume of water drawn off the tank $= l \times b \times$ fall in the level of water

$\Rightarrow \quad 255 = 25 \times b \times 1.5$

$\Rightarrow \quad b = \dfrac{255}{25 \times 1.5} = 6.8 \text{ m}$

$\therefore$ Width of the tank = 6.8 m **Ans.**

(b) Capacity of the tank $= l \times b \times h$

$$= 25 \times 6.8 \times 8.5 \text{ m}^3 = 1445 \text{ m}^3$$

**Ans.**

**Example 17.** How many bricks will be required to build a wall 30 m long, 30 cm thick and 5 m high with a provision of 2 doors, each 2.5 m × 1.2 m; each brick being 20 cm × 16 cm × 8 cm when 1/9 of the wall is filled with lime?

**Solution.** Area of the wall $= 30 \times 5 = 150 \text{ m}^2$

Area of 2 doors $= 2 \times 2.5 \times 1.2 = 6 \text{ m}^2$

Remaining area of the wall $= 150 - 6 = 144 \text{ m}^2$

Volume of the wall $= 144 \times \dfrac{30}{100} \text{ m}^3 = \dfrac{216}{5} \text{ m}^3$

Lime used in the wall $= \dfrac{216}{5} \times \dfrac{1}{9} = \dfrac{24}{5} \text{ m}^3$

Volume of the bricks used in the wall

$$= \frac{216}{5} - \frac{24}{5} = \frac{192}{5} \text{ m}^3$$

Volume of 1 brick $= \frac{20}{100} \times \frac{16}{100} \times \frac{8}{100}\ m^3 = \frac{8}{3125}\ m^3$

$\therefore$ Number of bricks used in the wall

$= \frac{192}{5} \div \frac{8}{3125} = \frac{192}{5} \times \frac{3125}{8} = 24 \times 625 = 15000$ **Ans.**

**Example 18.** Shanti Sweets wants to place an order for cardboard boxes for packing sweets. They need two types of boxes, one with dimensions 25 cm × 20 cm × 5 cm and another with dimensions 15 cm × 12 cm × 5 cm. For all the overlaps, 5% of the total surface is required extra. If the cost of the cardboard is ₹ 4 for 1000 $cm^2$, find the cost of cardboard required for supplying 250 boxes of each type.

**Solution.** Surface area of 1 big box $= 2(25 \times 20 + 20 \times 5 + 25 \times 5)\ cm^2 = 1450\ cm^2$.

As 5% of total surface is required extra for overlaps,

$\therefore$ area of cardboard required for making one big box

$= \left(1 + \frac{5}{100}\right) \times 1450\ cm^2 = \frac{21}{20} \times 1450\ cm^2 = 1522.5\ cm^2$

$\therefore$ Area of cardboard required for making 250 big boxes

$= 1522.5 \times 250\ cm^2 = 380625\ cm^2$.

Surface area of 1 small box $= 2(15 \times 12 + 12 \times 5 + 15 \times 5)\ cm^2 = 630\ cm^2$.

As 5% of total surface area is required for overlaps,

$\therefore$ area of cardboard required for making one small box

$= \left(1 + \frac{5}{100}\right) \times 630\ cm^2 = \frac{21}{20} \times 630\ cm^2 = 661.5\ cm^2$

$\therefore$ Area of cardboard required for making 250 small boxes

$= 661.5 \times 250\ cm^2 = 165375\ cm^2$.

$\therefore$ Total area of cardboard required for supplying 250 big boxes and 250 small boxes

$= (380625 + 165375)\ cm^2 = 546000\ cm^2$.

As cost of 1000 $cm^2$ of cardboard is ₹ 4,

$\therefore$ cost of 546000 $cm^2$ of cardboard $=$ ₹ $\frac{546000 \times 4}{1000} =$ ₹ 2184 **Ans.**

**Example 19.** Given figure shows the vertical cross-section of a trench which is 150 m long. Find :

(a) the total area of walls and floor,

(b) its cubic contents.

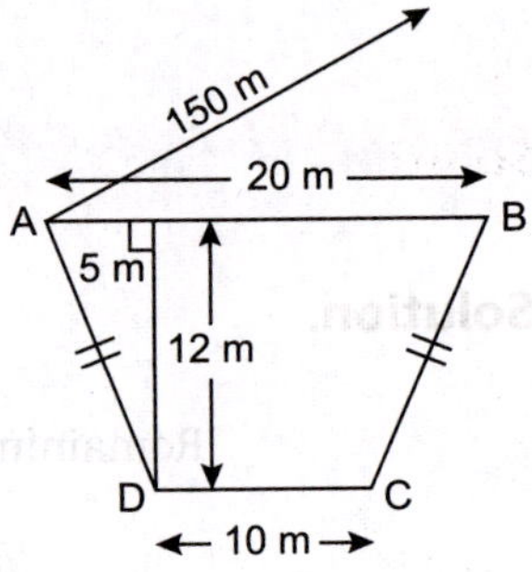


**Solution.** (a) From given fig., we have

$AD = \sqrt{5^2 + 12^2} = \sqrt{169} = 13$ m

$\therefore$ $BC = AD$ (given) $= 13$ m

Hence perimeter of the cross-section, excluding the top

$= AD + DC + BC = 13 + 10 + 13 = 36$ m

$\therefore$ The area of the walls and floor

= Perimeter of the cross-section × length of the trench

$= 36 \times 150 = 5400\ cm^2$ **Ans.**

(b) Volume = Area of the cross-section × length

$= \left[\frac{1}{2}(20 + 10) \times 12\right] \times 150$

$= 180 \times 150 = 27000\ m^3$ **Ans.**

**Example 20.** The horizontal cross-section of a water tank is in the shape of a rectangle with a semi-circle at one end, as shown in given fig. The water is 4 metres deep in the tank. Calculate the volume of water in the tank.

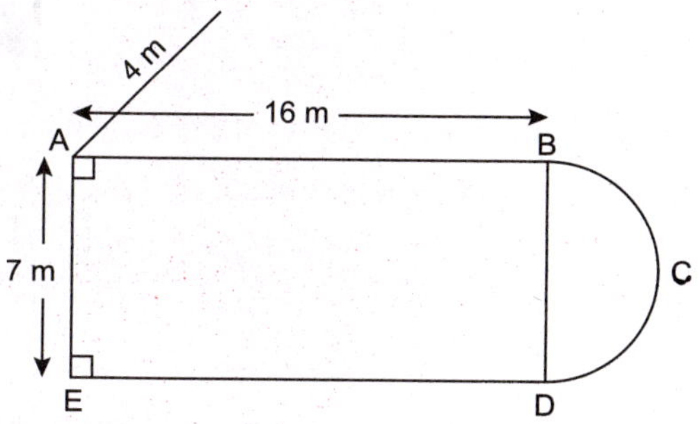


**Solution.** Area of cross-section = (Area of the rectangle *ABDE* + Area of the semi-circle *BCD*)

$$= 16 \times 7 + \frac{1}{2} \times \frac{22}{7} \times \frac{7}{2} \times \frac{7}{2}$$

$$= 122 + \frac{77}{4} = \frac{525}{4} \text{ m}^2$$

$\therefore$ Volume of water in the tank = Area of cross-section × depth

$$= \frac{525}{4} \times 4 \text{ m}^3 = 525 \text{ m}^3$$

Ans.

**Example 21.** A swimming bath is 300 m long, 30 m wide. It is 1 m deep at the shallow end and 4 m deep at the other end. Find the volume of water when it is full.

**Solution.** The side wall of the wall forms the cross-area, which is a trapezium as shown in fig.

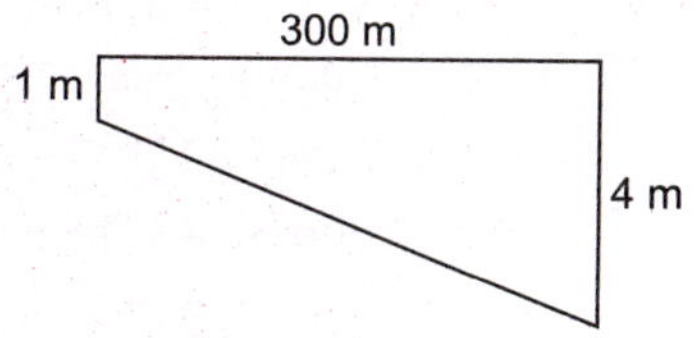


Area of the trapezium

$$= \frac{1}{2} \times 300 \times (1 + 4) \text{ m}^2 = 750 \text{ m}^2$$

Volume of water = Area of cross-section × width of the path

$$= 750 \times 30 \text{ m}^3 = 22500 \text{ m}^3$$

Ans.

**Example 22.** Find the volume of solid drawn in fig. (a).

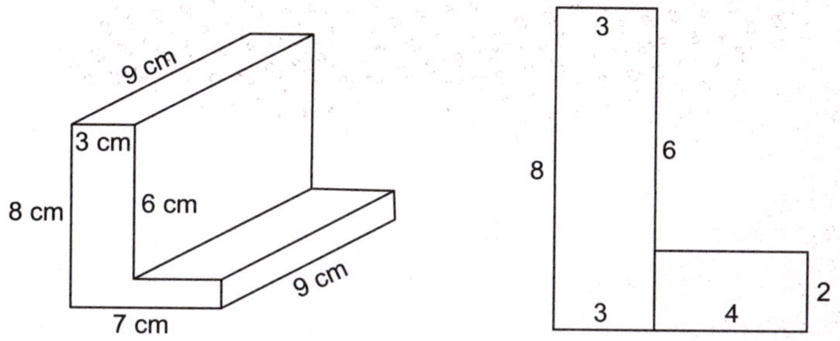


(a) (b)

**Solution.** The solid is 9 cm long. The cross-section of the front face is, as drawn in fig. (b). Its area can be found by dividing it into two rectangles. Thus,

Area of cross-section = $(8 \times 3) + (4 \times 2)$

$= 24 + 8 = 32 \text{ cm}^2$

$\therefore$ Volume of solid = cross-area × length

$= (32 \times 9) \text{ cm}^3 = 288 \text{ cm}^3$

Ans.

**Example 23.** How many litres of water flows out of a pipe of cross-section area 5 $\text{cm}^2$ in 1 minute, if the speed of the water in the pipe is 30 cm/sec?

**Solution.** Volume of water flowing in 1 sec.

$= 5 \times 30 \text{ cm}^3 = 150 \text{ cm}^3$

$\therefore$ Volume of water flowing in 1 min.

$= 150 \times 60 \text{ cm}^3 = 9000 \text{ cm}^3$

$= 9$ litre ($\because$ one litre $= 1000 \text{ cm}^3$) Ans.

# Exercise 16D

1. Find the surface area of the cube whose dimensions are (a) 7 cm, (b) 10 m.
2. The total surface area of a cube is 726 $cm^2$. Find its volume.
3. The volume of a rectangular solid is 3600 $cm^3$. If it is 20 cm long and 9 cm high, find the width.
4. The length and breadth of a rectangular solid are respectively 25 cm and 20 cm. If the volume is 7000 $cm^3$, find its height.
5. The perimeter of one face of a cube is 20 cm. Find (i) the total area of the 6 faces, (ii) the volume of the cube.
6. The area of a playground is 4800 $m^2$. Find the cost of covering it with gravel 1 cm deep, if the gravel costs ₹ 4.80 per cubic meter.
7. A rectangular water tank of base 7 m × 6 m contains water up to a depth of 5 m. How many cubic meters of water are there in the tank?
8. The internal measurements of a box are 20 cm long, 16 cm wide, and 24 cm high. How many 4 cm cubes could be put into the box?
9. The length, breadth and height of a rectangular solid are in the ratio of 5 : 4 : 2. If the total surface area is 1216 $cm^2$, find the length, breadth and height of the solid.
10. There is a cubical room whose length is 5 m. How many students can it accommodate if each student requires 5 $m^3$ of space.
11. Three cubes whose lengths are 2 cm, 3 cm and 4 cm respectively are melted to form a single cube. Find the edge of the new cube, supposing there is no waste in the process.
12. A rectangular water reservoir is 5 m by 4 m at the base. Water flows into it through a pipe whose cross-section is 5 cm × 3 cm at the rate of 2/3 m/sec. Find the height to which the water will rise in the reservoir in 25 minutes.
13. Find the length of the longest rod that can be placed in a room of 12 ft. long, 9 ft broad and 8 ft. high.
14. A field is 30 m long and 18 m broad. A pit 6 m long, 5 m wide and 3 m deep, is dug out from the middle of the field and the earth removed in evenly spread over the remaining area of the field. Find the rise in the level of the remaining part of the field in centimeters correct to one decimal place.
15. The rain water from a flat roof 5 m by 7 m drains into a tank which has dimensions 42 cm, 20 cm and 50 m. What depth of rainfall will fill the tank?
16. A rectangular container, whose base is a square of side 5 cm, stands on a horizontal table and holds water upto 1 cm from the top. When a cube is placed in the water and is completely submerged, the water rises to the top and 2 $cm^3$ of water overflows. Calculate the volume of the cube and the length of its edge.
17. A certain quality of wood costs ₹ 250 per $m^3$. A solid cubical block of such wood is bought for ₹ 182.25. Calculate the volume of the block and use the method of factors to find the length of one edge of the block.
18. A swimming pool is 50 meter long and 15 meters wide. Its shallow and deep ends are $1\frac{1}{2}$ meters and $4\frac{1}{2}$ meters deep respectively. If the bottom of the pool slopes uniformly, find the amount of water required to fill the pool.
19. When each side of a cube was increased by 2 cm the volume increased by 1016 $cm^3$. Find the side of the cube. If each side is decreased by 2 cm, by how much will the volume decrease?
20. A cube of 11 cm edge is immersed completely in a rectangular vessel containing water. If the dimensions of base are 15 cm and 12 cm, find the rise in water level in the vessel.
21. Find the area of the cross-section, assuming it to be uniform, of a solid, given that its volume is 92.8 $cm^3$ and length is 6.4 m.
22. Find the volume of a rail of uniform cross-section given area of cross-section 12.8 $cm^2$ and length 1.26 cm.
23. The cross-section of a pipe is 42 $cm^2$, and water is pouring out of it at the rate of 1.25 m per sec. If the pipe remains full, find the number of litres discharged per minute.

**24.** Fig. (a) shows a solid of uniform cross-section which is trapezium in shape. If length of the solid is 1 m, find its volume.

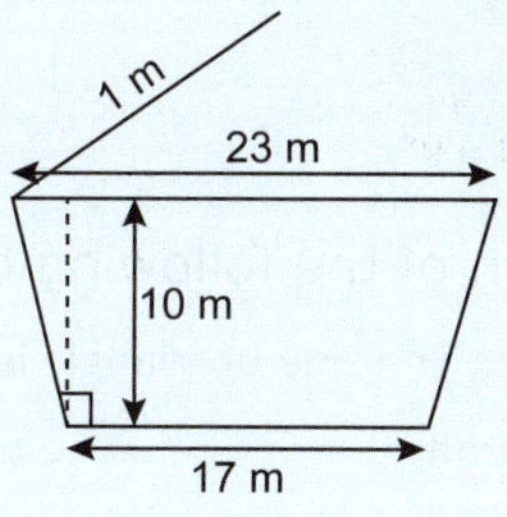


(a)

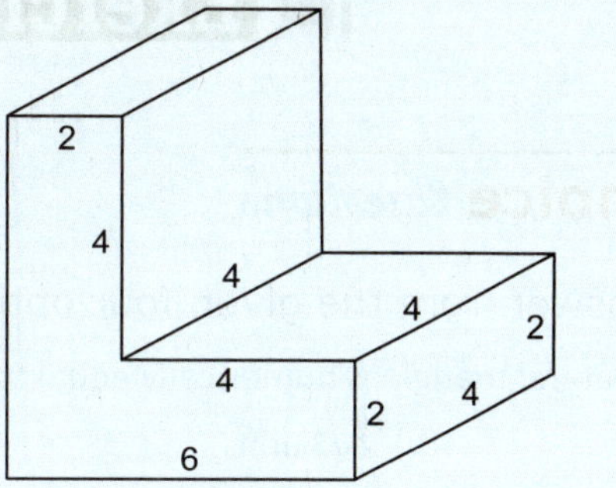


(b)

**25.** Fig. (b) shows a solid of uniform cross-section. Find its volume.

**26.** The area of cross-section of a pipe is 5.4 cm $^2$ and water is pumped out of it at the rate of 27 km/hr. Find in litres the volume of water which flows out of the pipe in one minute.

**27.** The cross-section of a railway tunnel is a rectangle 6 m broad and 8 m high surmounted by a semi-circle as shown in fig. (a).The tunnel is 35 m long. Find the cost of plastering the internal surface of the tunnel (excluding the floor) at the rate of ₹ 2.25 per m$^2$.

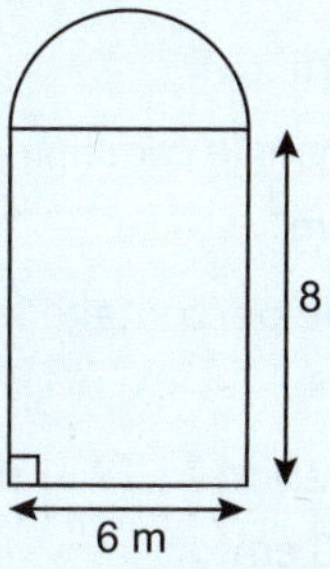


(a)

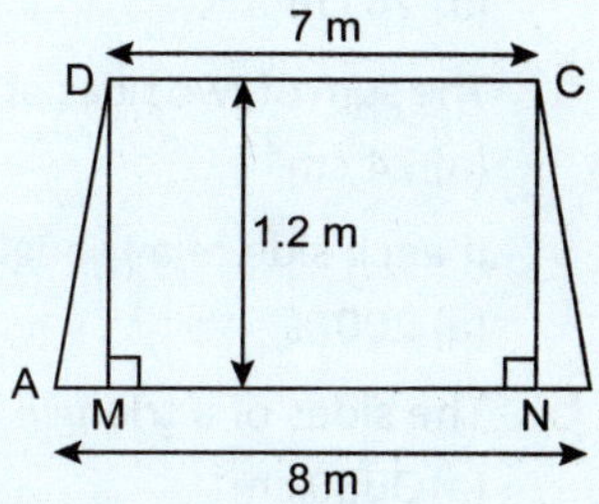


(b)

**28.** The cross-section of a tunnel perpendicular to its length is an isosceles trapezium as shown in the fig. (b). If $AB = 8$ m, $DC = 7$ m, $AD = BC$ and $DM = 1.2$ m and the tunnel is 100 m long, then calculate:

(i) the cost of painting the internal surface of the tunnel (excluding the floor) at the rate of ₹ 6 per m$^2$.

(ii) the cost of paving the floor at the rate of ₹ 20 per m$^2$.

(iii) the cubic content of the tunnel.

**29.** A solid copper piece has the shape shown in fig. (All measurements are in cm). The face *ABCDEFA* is the uniform cross-section. Assume that the angles at *A, B, C, D, E* and *F* are right angles.

(i) Calculate the area of the uniform cross-section.

(ii) Calculate the volume of the above piece.

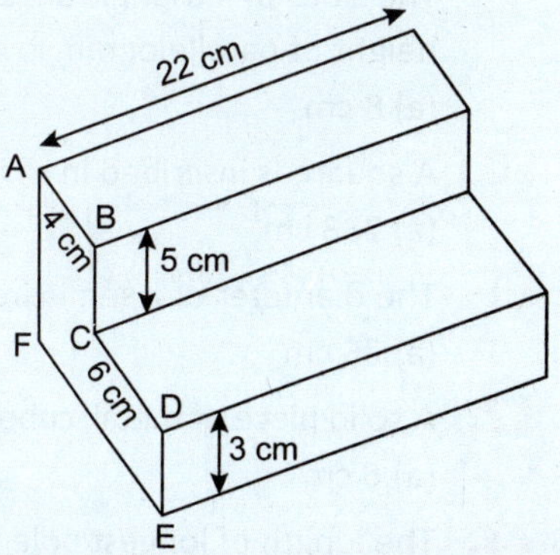


## *Answers*

| | | | |
|---|---|---|---|
| **1.** (a) 294 cm$^2$, (b) 600 m$^2$ | **2.** 1331 cm$^3$ | **3.** 20 cm | **4.** 14 cm |
| **5.** (i) 150 cm$^2$, (ii) 125 cm$^3$ | **6.** ₹ 230.40 | **7.** 210 m$^3$ | **8.** 120 |
| **9.** 20 cm, 16 cm, 8 cm | **10.** 25 | **11.** 4.626 cm | **12.** 7.5 |
| **13.** 17 ft | **14.** 17.65 cm | **15.** 12 cm | **16.** 27 cm$^3$, 3 cm |
| **17.** 0.729 m$^3$; $l = .9$ m | **18.** 2250 m$^3$ | **19.** 12 cm, 728 cm$^3$ | **20.** 2000 m$^3$ |
| **21.** 0.145 cm$^2$ | **22.** 16.128 cm$^3$ | **23.** 315 litres | **24.** 200 m$^3$ |
| **25.** 80 cm$^3$ | **26.** 243 litres | **27.** ₹ 2002.50 | |
| **28.** (i) ₹ 5760, (ii) ₹ 16000, (iii) 900 m$^3$ | | **29.** (i) 50 cm $^2$, (ii) 1100 cm$^3$ | |

# Exercise 16E

## Multiple Choice Questions

Choose the correct answer from the given four options in each of the following questions :

1. The area of an equilateral triangle is numerically equal to its perimeter. The side of triangle is :
(a) $\sqrt{3}$ unit (b) $2\sqrt{3}$ unit (c) $3\sqrt{3}$ unit (d) $4\sqrt{3}$ unit

2. The area of an isosceles triangle whose equal sides are 5 cm each and base is 8 cm, is :
(a) 12 $cm^2$ (b) 18 $cm^2$ (c) 6 $cm^2$ (d) 9 $cm^2$

3. Each of the equal sides of an isosceles triangle is 2 cm more than its height. If the base of triangle is 12 cm, then the area of triangle is :
(a) 24 $cm^2$ (b) 36 $cm^2$ (c) 48 $cm^2$ (d) 72 $cm^2$

4. The sum of two sides of a right-angled triangle containing right angle is 17 cm and its hypotenuse is 13 cm. The area of triangle is :
(a) 24 $cm^2$ (b) 30 $cm^2$ (c) 36 $cm^2$ (d) 40 $cm^2$

5. If each side of a triangle is doubled, the percentage increase in the area of triangle is :
(a) 200 % (b) 300 % (c) 100 % (d) 400 %

6. The sides of a triangle are in the ratio 25 : 17 : 12 and its perimeter is 540 cm. Its area is :
(a) 3600 $cm^2$ (b) 4500 $cm^2$ (c) 7200 $cm^2$ (d) 9000 $cm^2$

7. The diagonals of a rhombus are 20 cm and 12 cm. Its area is :
(a) 60 $cm^2$ (b) 90 $cm^2$ (c) 120 $cm^2$ (d) 240 $cm^2$

8. A wire when bent in the form of a square, encloses an area of 900 $cm^2$. When this wire is bent in the form of equilateral triangle, its area becomes :
(a) $400\sqrt{3}$ $cm^2$ (b) $300\sqrt{3}$ $cm^2$ (c) $200\sqrt{3}$ $cm^2$ (d) $100\sqrt{3}$ $cm^2$

9. The sides of a triangle are 26 cm, 28 cm and 30 cm. Its area is equal to the area of a parallelogram whose base is 28 cm. The height of parallelogram is :
(a) 8 cm (b) 12 cm (c) 15 cm (d) 30 cm

10. A square is inscribed in a circle of radius 14 cm. The area of square is :
(a) 288 $cm^2$ (b) 98 $cm^2$ (c) 196 $cm^2$ (d) 392 $cm^2$

11. The diameter of a semi-circular protractor is 21 cm. Its perimeter is :
(a) 36 cm (b) 54 cm (c) 72 cm (d) 108 cm

12. A solid piece of metal, cuboidal in shape, with dimensions 24 cm, 18 cm and 4 cm is recast into a cube. The side of cube is :
(a) 6 cm (b) 8 cm (c) 12 cm (d) 16 cm

13. The length of longest pole that can be put in a room of dimensions 10 m $\times$ 6 m $\times$ 8 m is :
(a) $10\sqrt{2}$ m (b) 20 m (c) $20\sqrt{2}$ m (d) 10 m

14. The length, breadth and height of a room are 10 m, 6 m and 4 m, respectively. If each child requires 2 $m^2$ area on floor, the number of children that can accommodate in the room are :
(a) 30 (b) 15 (c) 10 (d) 5

### Answers

**1.** (d) **2.** (a) **3.** (c) **4.** (b) **5.** (b) **6.** (d) **7.** (c) **8.** (a) **9.** (b) **10.** (d)
**11.** (b) **12.** (c) **13.** (a) **14.** (a)

## Valid Statements *Questions*

In the following questions, two statements (i) and (ii) are given. Choose the valid statement.

(a) Only (i) (b) Only (ii) (c) Both (i) and (ii) (d) Neither (i) nor (ii)

1. (i) Area of a parallelogram = base × corresponding height.

   (ii) Each of equal sides of an isosceles triangle is 5 cm and base is 8 cm. Its area will be 12 $cm^2$.

2. (i) The diagonals of a rhombus are 20 cm and 12 cm. Its area will be 240 $cm^2$.

   (ii) Circumference of a circle of radius $r$ is $\pi r^2$.

3. (i) The length of the longest pole that can be put in a room of dimensions 6 m × 8 m × 10 m is 12 m.

   (ii) Perimeter of a semi-circle of radius $r$ is $(\pi + 2)r$.

4. (i) Area of a trapezium $= \frac{1}{2} \times$ sum of parallel sides × distance between parallel sides.

   (ii) A square is inscribed in a circle of radius 14 cm. The area of square is 196 $cm^2$.

### *Answers*

**1.** (c) **2.** (d) **3.** (b) **4.** (a)

## SUMMARY *of the Chapter*

### For Plane Figures

- Area of triangle $= \frac{1}{2} \times$ base × corresponding height.
- Heron's formula : If the sides of a triangle are $a$, $b$ and $c$ then area of triangle $= \sqrt{s(s-a)(s-b)(s-c)}$, where $2s = a + b + c$ is the perimeter of the triangle.
- Area of a right-angled triangle $= \frac{1}{2} \times$product of sides containing right angle.
- Area of an equilateral triangle $= \frac{\sqrt{3}}{4} \times (\text{side})^2$.
- Area of an isosceles triangle $= \frac{1}{4} b\sqrt{4a^2 - b^2}$, where $b$ = base and $a$ = each of the equal sides.
- When two diagonals of a quadrilateral cut at right angles, then area of quadrilateral $= \frac{1}{2} \times$product of two diagonals.
- When one diagonal and perpendiculars to this diagonal from the remaining two vertices are given, then area of quadrilateral $ABCD = \frac{1}{2} \times AC \times (BM \times DN)$.

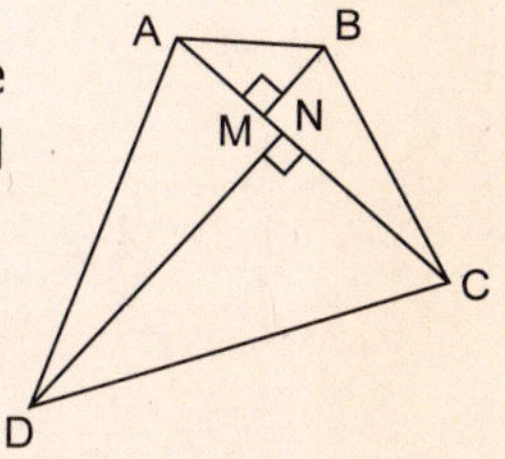

- Rectangle : Area = $l \times b$; Perimeter = $2(l + b)$; Diagonal $= \sqrt{l^2 + b^2}$
- Square : Area = $(\text{side})^2$ ; Perimeter = $4 \times$ side; Diagonal $=$ side $\times \sqrt{2}$
- Area of parallelogram = base $\times$ corresponding height.
- Area of rhombus $= \frac{1}{2} \times$ product of two diagonals.
- Area of trapezium $= \frac{1}{2} \times$ sum of parallel sides $\times$ distance between parallel sides.
- Circumference of circle = $2\pi r$.
- Area of circle = $\pi r^2$.
- Perimeter of semicircle = $(\pi + 2)\, r$
- Area of circular ring = $\pi (R^2 - r^2)$, where $R$ = radius of external circle and $r$ = radius of internal circle.

## For 3D Figures

- Cuboid : If $l$, $b$ and $h$ be the length, breadth and height respectively, then :
  1. Volume = $l \times b \times h$.
  2. Total surface area = $2(l \cdot b + b \cdot h + h \cdot l)$.
  3. Area of four walls = $2(l + b) \cdot h$.
  4. Diagonal $= \sqrt{l^2 + b^2 + h^2}$.
  5. If the external length, breadth and height of a cuboid are $L$, $B$ and $H$ respectively and the thickness of its sides be '$x$', then:

     (a) For closed cuboid

     Internal length = $l = L - 2x$

     Internal breadth = $b = B - 2x$

     Internal height = $h = H - 2x$

     (b) For open cuboid

     Internal length = $l = L - 2x$

     Internal breadth = $b = B - 2x$

     Internal height = $h = H - x$
- Cube : If the edge of a cube is '$a$', then :
  1. Volume = $a^3$
  2. Total surface area = $6a^2$
  3. Area of four walls = $4a^2$
  4. Diagonal $= a\sqrt{3}$
- For a solid of uniform cross-section :
  1. Volume of solid = area of cross-section $\times$ length
  2. Lateral surface of solid = perimeter of its cross-section $\times$ length.

# CHAPTER TEST

1. The sides of a triangle are 20 cm, 39 cm and 51 cm respectively. Find its area.
2. The area of a triangle equals the area of a square whose side is 45 m. Find the length of the side of the triangle which is 75 m from the opposite vertex.
3. The base of an isosceles triangle is 24 cm and its area is 192 $cm^2$. Find its perimeter.
4. A hall of length 15 m requires 7500 tiles of area 180 $cm^2$ each, to cover the entire floor. Find the breadth of the hall.
5. The area of a right angled triangle is 240 $mm^2$. If the difference between the sides containing the right angle is 14 mm, find the length of the hypotenuse.
6. The length and breadth of an open box are 50 cm and 45 cm. If the depth is 10 cm, find the area of the tinfoil required to line the box completely inside.
7. A footpath of uniform width runs round the inside of a rectangular field 38 meters long and 32 meters wide. If the path occupies 600 $m^2$ , find its width.
8. A rectangular plot of land measures 41 meters in length and 22.5 meters in width. A boundary wall 2 meters high is built all around the plot at a distance of 1.5 m from the plot. Find the inner surface area of the boundary wall.
9. How many $cm^3$ of iron are there is an open box, whose external dimensions are 30 cm, 24 cm and 330 cm, the iron being 2 cm thick throughout?
10. A room 6 m by 4 m by 5 m high, is to be papered with wallpaper 75 cm wide. What lengths of the wallpaper is required? Also find the cost of the paper at the rate of ₹ 3 per meter.
11. A hall is 14.50 m long, 9.50 m wide and 10 m high. There is a door 8 m by 3 m and two windows each 4 m by 3 m. Find the cost of distempering the walls at 25 paise $m^2$.
12. The cross-section of a tunnel perpendicular to its length is a trapezium *ABCD* as shown in fig. $AM = BN$; $AB = 4.4$ m; $CD = 3$ m. The height of the tunnel is 2.4 m. The tunnel is 50 m long. Calculate :

    (i) the cost of painting the internal surface of the tunnel (excluding the floor) at the rate of ₹ 5 per $m^2$,

    (ii) the cost of paving the floor at the rate of ₹ 18 per $m^2$.

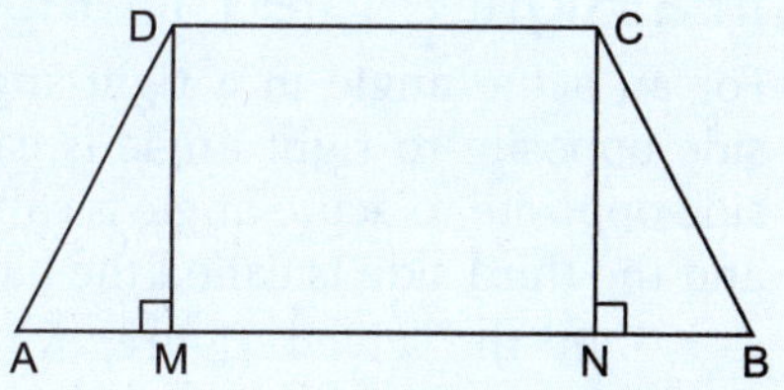


## *Answers*

1. 350.99 $cm^2$
2. 54 m
3. 64 cm
4. 9 m
5. 34 mm
6. 4150 $cm^2$
7. 5 m
8. 278 $m^2$
9. 67040 $cm^3$
10. 133.33 m, ₹ 400
11. ₹ 108
12. (i) ₹ 2000, (ii) ₹ 3960

UNIT VII : TRIGONOMETRY

Chapter

# 17 TRIGONOMETRIC RATIOS

## Syllabus

- Trigonometric Ratios: sine, cosine, tangent of an angle and their reciprocals.

## INTRODUCTION

Trigonometry is a branch of mathematics which was first developed by the astronomers to study the spherical triangles. The name trigonometry is derived from two Greek words '*trigonon*' means triangle and '*metron*' means measure, which gives the measurement of triangle. So, we deal with the measure of the sides and the angles of a triangle in trigonometry. In this chapter, we shall study some ratios of the sides of a right-angled triangle with respect to acute angles which are called trigonometrical ratios of the angle and establish some relations between the trigonometrical ratios.

## Base, Perpendicular and Hypotenuse in a Right-angled Triangle

For an acute angle in a right-angled triangle, the side opposite to right angle is called hypotenuse, side opposite to acute angle is called perpendicular and the third side is called the base.

(i) In the given figure, for angle $C$,

Hypotenuse $= AC$,
Perpendicular $= AB$ and
Base $= BC$

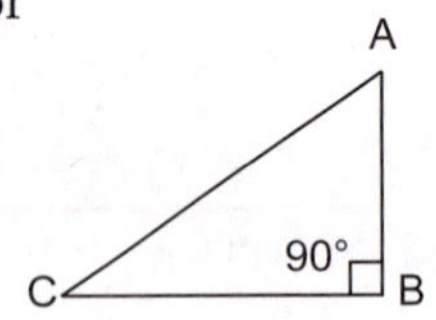


(ii) In the given figure, for angle $A$,

Hypotenuse $= AB$,
Perpendicular $= BC$ and
Base $= AC$

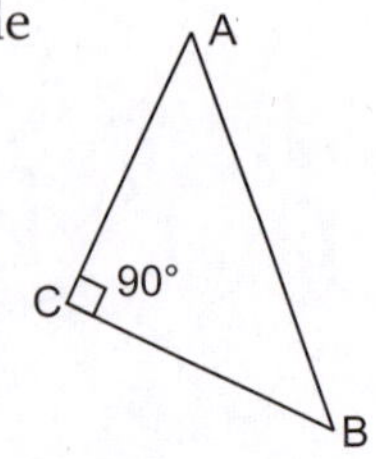


## Trigonometric Ratio

In a right-angled triangle, the ratio of the lengths of two sides is called a trigonometric ratio. There are six trigonometric ratios. Consider a right-angled triangle $ABC$, in which

$\angle A = 90°$
$\angle B = \theta$ (acute angle)
Hypotenuse $= BC$
Perpendicular $= AC$
Base $= AB$

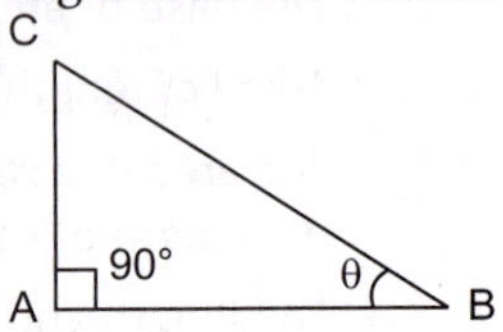


1. The ratio of the length of perpendicular to the length of hypotenuse is called the sine of the angle θ. It is written as

$$\sin\theta = \frac{\text{Perpendicular}}{\text{Hypotenuse}} = \frac{AC}{BC}$$

2. The ratio of the length of base to the length of hypotenuse is called the cosine of the angle θ. It is written as

$$\cos\theta = \frac{\text{Base}}{\text{Hypotenuse}} = \frac{AB}{BC}$$

3. The ratio of the length of perpendicular to the length of base is called the tangent of the angle θ. It is written as

$$\tan\theta = \frac{\text{Perpendicular}}{\text{Base}} = \frac{AC}{AB}$$

4. The ratio of the length of base to the length of perpendicular is called the cotangent of the angle θ. It is written as

$$\cot\theta = \frac{\text{Base}}{\text{Perpendicular}} = \frac{AB}{AC}$$

5. The ratio of the length of hypotenuse to the length of base is called the secant of the angle θ. It is written as

$$\sec\theta = \frac{\text{Hypotenuse}}{\text{Base}} = \frac{BC}{AC}$$

6. The ratio of the length of hypotenuse to the length of perpendicular is called the cosecant of the angle θ. It is written as

$$\text{cosec}\,\theta = \frac{\text{Hypotenuse}}{\text{Perpendicular}} = \frac{BC}{AC}$$

**Remember**

1. $\sin\theta \neq \sin \times \theta$
2. For acute angle $\theta$, all six trigonometric ratios are positive.
3. Since all trigonometric ratios are the ratio of two sides of a right-angled triangle, so they have no unit.

## Reciprocal Relations

1. We know that

$$\sin\theta = \frac{\text{Perpendicular}}{\text{Hypotenuse}} = \text{ and } \operatorname{cosec}\theta = \frac{\text{Hypotenuse}}{\text{Perpendicular}}$$

$$\therefore \quad \sin\theta = \frac{1}{\operatorname{cosec}\theta} \text{ and } \operatorname{cosec}\theta = \frac{1}{\sin\theta}$$

2. Again,

$$\cos\theta = \frac{\text{Base}}{\text{Hypotenuse}} \text{ and } \sec\theta = \frac{\text{Hypotenuse}}{\text{Base}}$$

$$\therefore \quad \cos\theta = \frac{1}{\sec\theta} \text{ and } \sec\theta = \frac{1}{\cos\theta}$$

3. Similarly,

$$\tan\theta = \frac{\text{Perpendicular}}{\text{Base}} \text{ and } \cot\theta = \frac{\text{Base}}{\text{Perpendicular}}$$

$$\therefore \quad \tan\theta = \frac{1}{\cot\theta} \text{ and } \cot\theta = \frac{1}{\tan\theta}$$

4. Now,

$$\frac{\sin\theta}{\cos\theta} = \frac{\text{Perpendicular/Hypotenuse}}{\text{Base/Hypotenuse}} = \frac{\text{Perpendicular}}{\text{Base}} = \tan\theta$$

$$\therefore \quad \tan\theta = \frac{\sin\theta}{\cos\theta} \text{ and } \cot\theta = \frac{\cos\theta}{\sin\theta}$$

## Square Relations

Let $\Delta ABC$ be right-angled triangle, right-angle at $A$ and $\angle ABC = \theta$

By Pythagoras theorem

$$AB^2 + AC^2 = BC^2 \qquad \ldots(i)$$

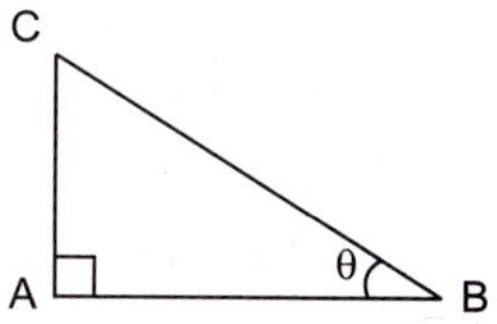


1. Dividing both sides by $BC^2$,

$$\frac{AB^2}{BC^2} + \frac{AC^2}{BC^2} = 1 \quad \Rightarrow \quad \left(\frac{AB}{BC}\right)^2 + \left(\frac{AC}{BC}\right)^2 = 1 \quad \Rightarrow \quad \mathbf{\cos^2\theta + \sin^2\theta = 1}$$

2. Dividing both sides of equation *(i)* by $AB^2$,

$$1 + \left(\frac{AC}{AB}\right)^2 = \left(\frac{BC}{AB}\right)^2 \quad \Rightarrow \quad \mathbf{1 + \tan^2\theta = \sec^2\theta}$$

3. Dividing both sides of equation *(i)* by $AC^2$,

$$\left(\frac{AB}{AC}\right)^2 + 1 = \left(\frac{BC}{AC}\right)^2 \quad \Rightarrow \quad \mathbf{\cot^2\theta + 1 = \operatorname{cosec}^2\theta}$$

**NOTE**

$\sin^2\theta = (\sin\theta)^2$

# Illustrative Examples

**Example 1.** In a $\Delta ABC$, right angled at $B$, if $AB = 12$ and $BC = 5$, find :
(i) $\sin A$ and $\tan A$, (ii) $\cos C$ and $\cot C$.

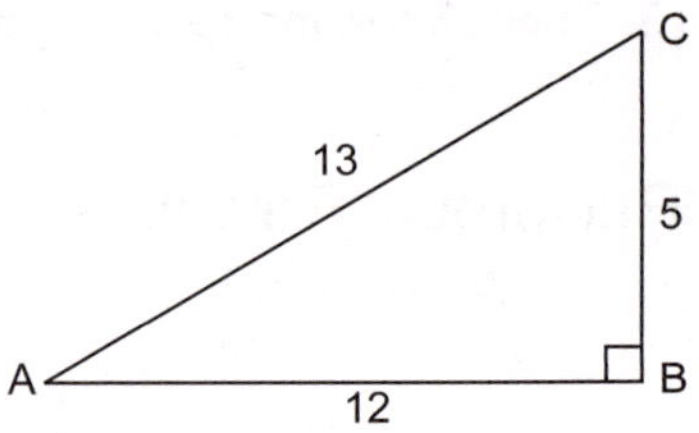


**Solution.** (i) For $\angle A$, we have

Base $= AB = 12$ and

Perpendicular $= BC = 5$

$\therefore$ Hypotenuse $= AC = \sqrt{(AB^2 + BC^2)} = \sqrt{(12)^2 + 5^2}$ (By Pythagoras Theorem)

$= \sqrt{169} = 13$

$\therefore$ $\sin A = \dfrac{BC}{AC} = \dfrac{5}{13}$ and $\tan A = \dfrac{BC}{AB} = \dfrac{5}{12}$ **Ans.**

(ii) For $\angle C$, we have

Base $= BC = 5$, Perpendicular $= AB = 12$

$\therefore$ Hypotenuse $= AC = 13$

Thus, $\cos C = \dfrac{BC}{AC} = \dfrac{5}{13}$ and $\cot C = \dfrac{BC}{AB} = \dfrac{5}{12}$ **Ans.**

**Example 2.** In a $\Delta ABC$, right angled at $B$, if $AB = 4$ and $BC = 3$, find all the six $t$-ratios of $\angle A$.

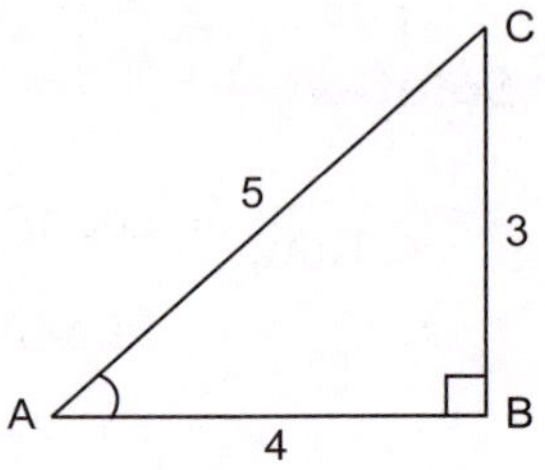


**Solution.** By Pythagoras theorem, we have

$$AC = \sqrt{(AB^2 + BC^2)} = \sqrt{(4^2 + 3^2)} = 5$$

Now, for $\angle A$, we have

Base $= AB = 4$, Perpendicular $= BC = 3$ and Hypotenuse $= AC = 5$

$\therefore$ $\sin A = \dfrac{BC}{AC} = \dfrac{3}{5}$; $\cos A = \dfrac{AB}{AC} = \dfrac{4}{5}$;

$\tan A = \dfrac{BC}{AB} = \dfrac{3}{4}$; $\operatorname{cosec} A = \dfrac{1}{\sin A} = \dfrac{5}{3}$;

$\sec A = \dfrac{1}{\cos A} = \dfrac{5}{4}$; $\cot A = \dfrac{1}{\tan A} = \dfrac{4}{3}$.

**Example 3.** From the following figure, find:
(i) $\sin A$ (ii) $\cos A$
(iii) $\tan C$ (iv) $\sec C$
(v) $\operatorname{cosec}^2 A - \cot^2 A$ (vi) $\sin^2 C + \cos^2 C$

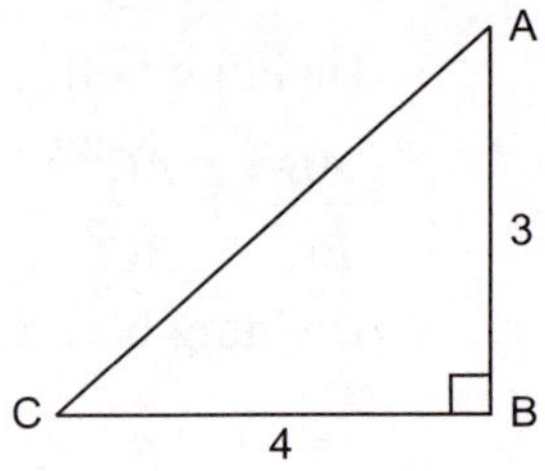


**Solution.** In $\Delta ABC$,

$\angle B = 90°$

$\therefore$ $AC^2 = AB^2 + BC^2$ (From Pythagoras theorem)

$= 3^2 + 4^2 = 9 + 16 = 25$

$\Rightarrow$ $AC = 5$

(i) $\sin A = \dfrac{\text{Perpendicular}}{\text{Hypotenuse}} = \dfrac{BC}{AC} = \dfrac{4}{5}$ **Ans.**

(ii) $\cos A = \dfrac{\text{Base}}{\text{Hypotenuse}} = \dfrac{AB}{AC} = \dfrac{3}{5}$ **Ans.**

(iii) $\tan C = \dfrac{\text{Perpendicular}}{\text{Base}} = \dfrac{AB}{BC} = \dfrac{3}{4}$ **Ans.**

(iv) $\sec C = \dfrac{\text{Hypotenuse}}{\text{Base}} = \dfrac{AC}{BC} = \dfrac{5}{4}$ **Ans.**

(v) $\text{cosec } A = \dfrac{\text{Hypotenuse}}{\text{Perpendicular}} = \dfrac{AC}{BC} = \dfrac{5}{4}$

and $\cot A = \dfrac{\text{Base}}{\text{Perpendicular}} = \dfrac{AB}{BC} = \dfrac{3}{4}$

$\therefore \quad \text{cosec}^2 A - \cot^2 A = \left(\dfrac{5}{4}\right)^2 - \left(\dfrac{3}{4}\right)^2 = \dfrac{25}{16} - \dfrac{9}{16} = \dfrac{25-9}{16} = 1$ **Ans.**

(vi) $\sin C = \dfrac{\text{Perpendicular}}{\text{Hypotenuse}} = \dfrac{AB}{AC} = \dfrac{3}{5}$

$\cos C = \dfrac{\text{Base}}{\text{Hypotenuse}} = \dfrac{BC}{AC} = \dfrac{4}{5}$

$\therefore \quad \sin^2 C + \cos^2 C = \left(\dfrac{3}{5}\right)^2 + \left(\dfrac{4}{5}\right)^2 = \dfrac{9+16}{25} = \dfrac{25}{25} = 1$ **Ans.**

**Example 4.** If $\cos B = \dfrac{15}{17}$ in right-angled $\Delta ABC$ in which $\angle A = 90°$, find all other $t$-ratios.

**Solution.** $\cos B = \dfrac{15}{17} \Rightarrow \dfrac{\text{Base}}{\text{Hypotenuse}} = \dfrac{15}{17} \Rightarrow \dfrac{AB}{BC} = \dfrac{15}{17}$

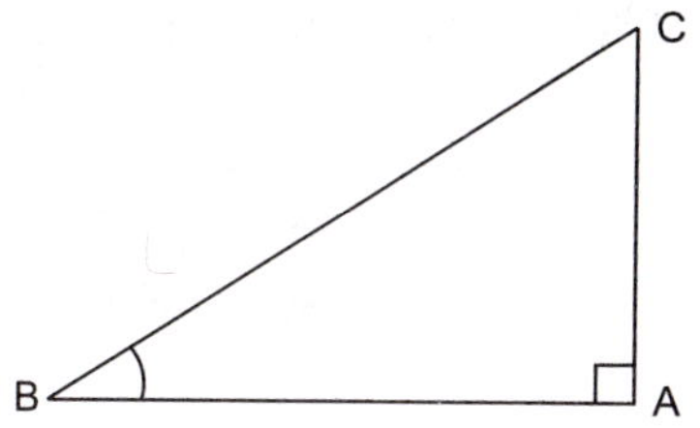


Let $AB = 15k$, $BC = 17k$

In $\Delta ABC$,

By pythagoras theorem,

$$BC^2 = AB^2 + AC^2$$

$$\Rightarrow \quad (17k)^2 = (15k)^2 + AC^2$$

$$\Rightarrow \quad AC^2 = 289k^2 - 225k^2 = 64k^2$$

$$\Rightarrow \quad AC = 8k$$

Now, $\sin B = \dfrac{AC}{BC} = \dfrac{8k}{17k} = \dfrac{8}{17}$ **Ans.**

$\tan B = \dfrac{AC}{AB} = \dfrac{8k}{15k} = \dfrac{8}{15}$ **Ans.**

$\cot B = \dfrac{AB}{AC} = \dfrac{15k}{8k} = \dfrac{15}{8}$ **Ans.**

$\sec B = \dfrac{BC}{AB} = \dfrac{17k}{15k} = \dfrac{17}{15}$ **Ans.**

$\text{cosec } B = \dfrac{BC}{AC} = \dfrac{17k}{8k} = \dfrac{17}{8}$ **Ans.**

**Example 5.** If $\tan\theta = \frac{12}{5}$, find the value of $\sin\theta + \frac{1}{\sec\theta}$, where θ is an acute angle.

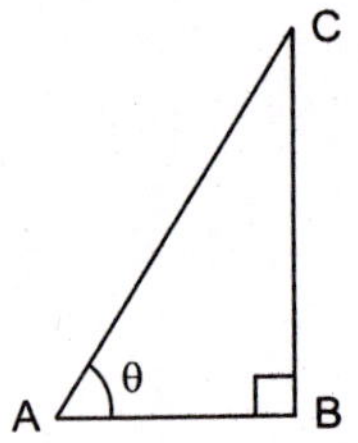


**Solution.** Draw $\Delta ABC$ in which $\angle B = 90°$ and $\angle A = \theta$

$$\tan\theta = \frac{12}{5} \Rightarrow \frac{\text{Perpendicular}}{\text{Base}} = \frac{12}{5} \Rightarrow \frac{BC}{AB} = \frac{12}{5}$$

Let $BC = 12\,k$, $AB = 5k$

In $\Delta ABC$,

By Pythagoras theorem,

$$AC^2 = AB^2 + BC^2 = (5k)^2 + (12k)^2 = 25k^2 + 144k^2 = 169k^2$$

$$\Rightarrow \quad AC = 13k$$

$$\therefore \quad \sin\theta = \frac{BC}{AC} = \frac{12k}{13k} = \frac{12}{13}$$

$$\sec\theta = \frac{AC}{AB} = \frac{13k}{5k} = \frac{13}{5}$$

Now, $\sin\theta + \frac{1}{\sec\theta} = \frac{12}{13} + \frac{1}{13/5} = \frac{12}{13} + \frac{5}{13} = \frac{17}{13}$ **Ans.**

**Example 6.** If $\sec\theta = \frac{5}{4}$, find $\sin\theta$ and $\tan\theta + \cot\theta$, where θ is an acute angle.

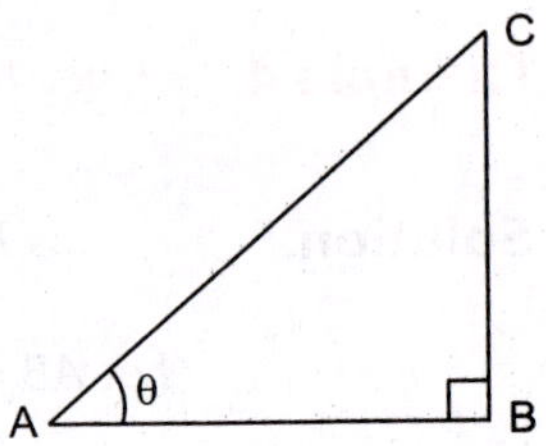


**Solution.** Draw $\Delta ABC$ in which $\angle B = 90°$, $\angle A = \theta$

$$\sec\theta = \frac{5}{4}$$

$$\Rightarrow \quad \frac{\text{Hypotenuse}}{\text{Base}} = \frac{5}{4} \Rightarrow \frac{AC}{AB} = \frac{5}{4}$$

Let $AC = 5k$, $AB = 4k$

In $\Delta ABC$,

By Pythagoras theorem,

$$BC^2 = AC^2 - AB^2 = (5k)^2 - (4k)^2 = 9k^2$$

$$\Rightarrow \quad BC = 3k$$

$$\therefore \quad \sin\theta = \frac{BC}{AC} = \frac{3k}{5k} = \frac{3}{5}$$ **Ans**

and $\tan\theta + \cot\theta = \frac{BC}{AB} + \frac{AB}{BC} = \frac{3k}{4k} + \frac{4k}{3k} = \frac{3}{4} + \frac{4}{3} = \frac{9+16}{12} = \frac{25}{12}$ **Ans.**

**Example 7.** In $\Delta ABC$, $\angle B = 90°$ and $\tan A = 1$. Prove that $2\sin A \cdot \cos A = 1$.

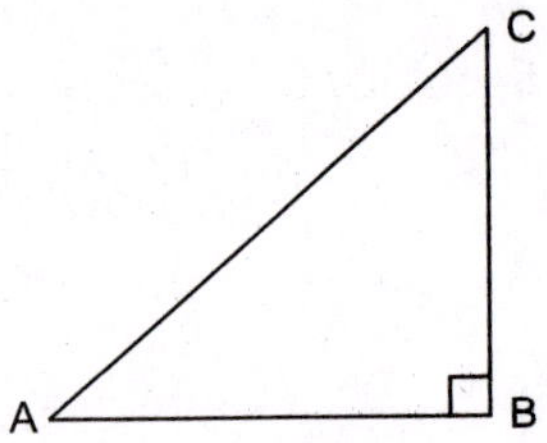


**Solution.** In $\Delta ABC$, $\angle B = 90°$

$$\tan A = 1 \Rightarrow \frac{BC}{AB} = 1 \Rightarrow BC = AB$$

Let $BC = AB = k$

By Pythagoras theorem,

$$AC^2 = AB^2 + BC^2 = k^2 + k^2 = 2k^2$$

$$\Rightarrow \quad AC = k\sqrt{2}$$

Now, $2\sin A \cdot \cos A = 2 \cdot \frac{BC}{AC} \cdot \frac{AB}{AC} = 2 \cdot \frac{k}{k\sqrt{2}} \cdot \frac{k}{k\sqrt{2}} = 1$ **Hence Proved**

**Example 8.** If θ is acute angle and $5\cos\theta = 12\sin\theta$, find the value of $9\sin^2\theta - 4\cos^2\theta + 1$

**Solution.** $5\cos\theta = 12\sin\theta$

$$\Rightarrow \quad \frac{\sin\theta}{\cos\theta} = \frac{5}{12} \Rightarrow \tan\theta = \frac{5}{12}$$

Draw $\Delta ABC$ in which

$$\angle B = 90°, \angle C = \theta$$

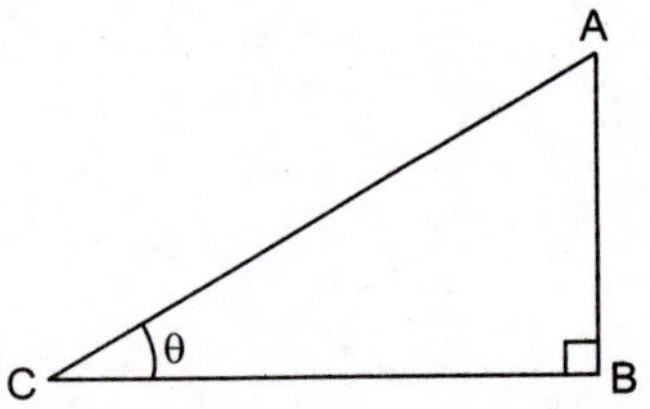

$AB = 5k, BC = 12k$ $\left(\because \tan\theta = \dfrac{AB}{BC}\right)$

By Pythagoras theorem,

$$AC^2 = AB^2 + BC^2 = (5k)^2 + (12k)^2 = 169\,k^2$$

$\Rightarrow$ $AC = 13k$

$\therefore$ $\sin\theta = \dfrac{AB}{AC} = \dfrac{5k}{13k} = \dfrac{5}{13}$

$\cos\theta = \dfrac{BC}{AC} = \dfrac{12k}{13k} = \dfrac{12}{13}$

Now, $9\sin^2\theta - 4\cos^2\theta + 1$

$$= 9 \times \left(\frac{5}{13}\right)^2 - 4 \times \left(\frac{12}{13}\right)^2 + 1 = \frac{225 - 576 + 169}{169} = \frac{-182}{169} = -\frac{14}{13}$$ Ans.

**Example 9.** If $\cot A = \dfrac{12}{5}$, prove that $\tan^2 A - \sin^2 A = \sin^4 A\ \sec^2 A$

**Solution.** Draw $\Delta ABC$ in which $\angle B = 90°$

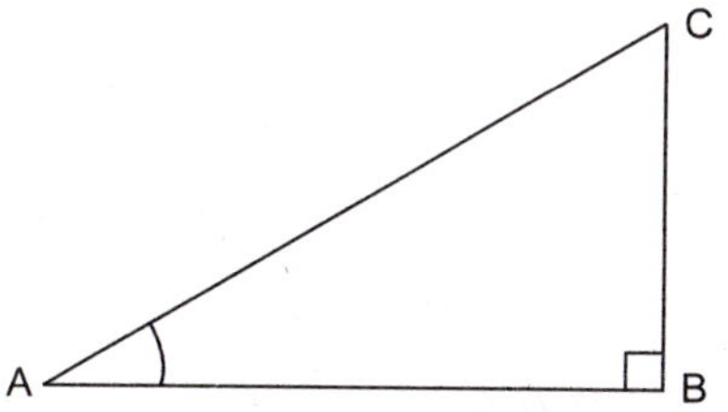


$\cot A = \dfrac{12}{5} \quad \Rightarrow \quad \dfrac{AB}{BC} = \dfrac{12}{5}$

Let $AB = 12k$, $BC = 5k$

From Pythagoras theorem,

$$AC^2 = AB^2 + BC^2 = (12k)^2 + (5k)^2 = 169k^2$$

$\Rightarrow$ $AC = 13k$

Now, $\tan A = \dfrac{BC}{AB} = \dfrac{5k}{12k} = \dfrac{5}{12}$; $\sin A = \dfrac{BC}{AC} = \dfrac{5k}{13k} = \dfrac{5}{13}$; $\sec A = \dfrac{AC}{AB} = \dfrac{13k}{12k} = \dfrac{13}{12}$

L.H.S. $= \tan^2 A - \sin^2 A$

$$= \left(\frac{5}{12}\right)^2 - \left(\frac{5}{13}\right)^2 = 25\left(\frac{1}{144} - \frac{1}{169}\right) = \frac{25 \times (169 - 144)}{144 \times 169} = \frac{25 \times 25}{144 \times 169}$$

and R.H.S. $= \sin^4 A\ \sec^2 A = \left(\dfrac{5}{13}\right)^4 \times \left(\dfrac{13}{12}\right)^2 = \dfrac{25 \times 25}{169 \times 144}$

$\therefore$ L.H.S. = R.H.S. Hence Proved

**Example 10.** In $\Delta ABC$, $\angle B = 90°$, $AB = 5$ cm, $AC + BC = 25$ cm. Find (i) $\sin A$, (ii) $\cos A$ (iii) $\tan A$

**Solution.** Let $BC = x$

Given that

$AC + BC = 25 \quad \Rightarrow \quad AC = 25 - x$

In $\Delta ABC$,

$\angle B = 90°$

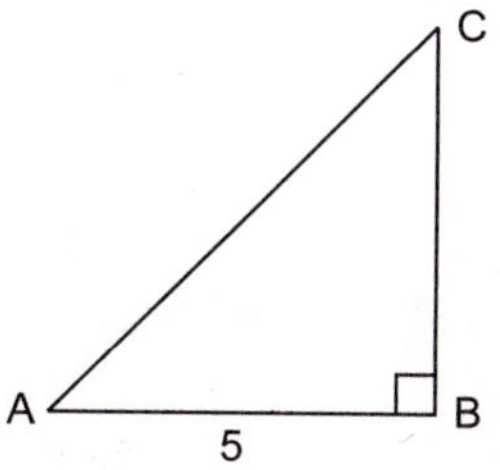


By Pythagoras theorem,

$AC^2 = AB^2 + BC^2 \quad \Rightarrow \quad (25 - x)^2 = 5^2 + x^2$

$\Rightarrow$ $625 - 50x + x^2 = 25 + x^2 \quad \Rightarrow \quad 50x = 600 \Rightarrow x = 12$

$\therefore$ $BC = 12$ cm and $AC = 25 - 12 = 13$ cm

(i) $\sin A = \dfrac{BC}{AC} = \dfrac{12}{13}$ Ans.

(ii) $\cos A = \dfrac{AB}{AC} = \dfrac{5}{13}$ Ans.

(iii) $\tan A = \dfrac{BC}{AB} = \dfrac{12}{5}$ Ans.

**Example 11.** In the adjoining figure, $\angle A = 90°$, $AB = 3$ cm, $BC - AC = 1$ cm, find the values of
(i) $\cos B$, (ii) $\tan B$

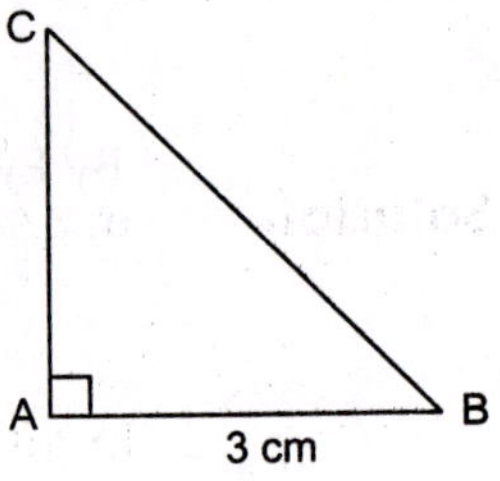


**Solution.** Let $AC = x$ cm

Given that

$$BC - AC = 1 \quad \Rightarrow \quad BC = (x + 1) \text{ cm}$$

In $\Delta ABC$,

$$\angle A = 90°$$

By Pythagoras theorem,

$$BC^2 = AC^2 + AB^2 \quad \Rightarrow \quad (x+1)^2 = x^2 + 3^2$$

$$\Rightarrow \quad x^2 + 2x + 1 = x^2 + 9 \quad \Rightarrow \quad 2x = 8 \quad \Rightarrow \quad x = 4$$

$\therefore$ $AC = 4$ cm and $BC = 4 + 1 = 5$ cm

(i) $\cos B = \dfrac{AB}{BC} = \dfrac{3}{5}$ **Ans.**

(ii) $\tan B = \dfrac{AC}{AB} = \dfrac{4}{3}$ **Ans.**

**Example 12.** From the adjoining figure, find :
(i) $\sin A$ (ii) $\cos C$
(iii) $\sin^2 A + \cos^2 A$ (iv) $\text{cosec}^2\, C - \cot^2 C$
(v) $\tan A + \sec A$

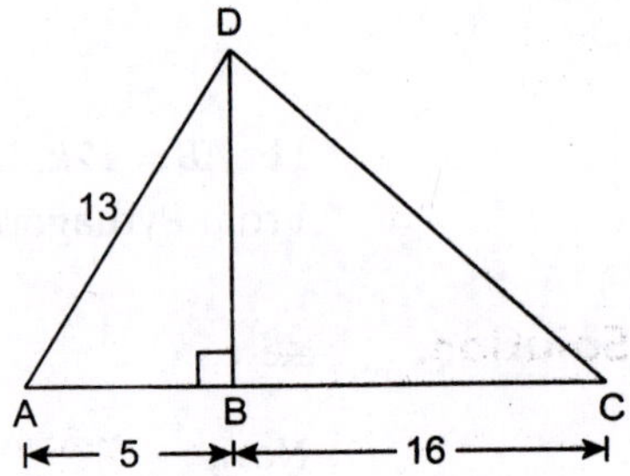


**Solution.** In $\Delta ABD$, $\angle B = 90°$, from Pythagoras theorem

$\therefore$ $BD^2 = AD^2 - AB^2 \Rightarrow 13^2 - 5^2 = 144 \Rightarrow BD = 12$

In $\Delta BCD$, $\angle B = 90°$, from Pythagoras theorem

$\therefore$ $DC^2 = BD^2 + BC^2 \Rightarrow 12^2 + 16^2 = 400 \Rightarrow DC = 20$

(i) $\sin A = \dfrac{\text{Perpendicular}}{\text{Hypotenuse}} = \dfrac{BD}{AD} = \dfrac{12}{13}$ **Ans.**

(ii) $\cos C = \dfrac{\text{Base}}{\text{Hypotenuse}} = \dfrac{BC}{CD} = \dfrac{16}{20} = \dfrac{4}{5}$ **Ans.**

(iii) $\cos A = \dfrac{\text{Base}}{\text{Hypotenuse}} = \dfrac{AB}{AD} = \dfrac{5}{13}$

$\therefore$ $\sin^2 A + \cos^2 A = \left(\dfrac{12}{13}\right)^2 + \left(\dfrac{5}{13}\right)^2 = \dfrac{144}{169} + \dfrac{25}{169} = 1$ **Ans.**

(iv) $\text{cosec}\, C = \dfrac{\text{Hypotenuse}}{\text{Perpendicular}} = \dfrac{DC}{BD} = \dfrac{20}{12} = \dfrac{5}{3}$

$\cot C = \dfrac{\text{Base}}{\text{Perpendicular}} = \dfrac{BC}{BD} = \dfrac{16}{12} = \dfrac{4}{3}$

$\therefore$ $\text{cosec}^2\, C - \cot^2 C = \left(\dfrac{5}{3}\right)^2 - \left(\dfrac{4}{3}\right)^2 = \dfrac{25}{9} - \dfrac{16}{9} = 1$ **Ans.**

(v) $\tan A = \dfrac{\text{Perpendicular}}{\text{Base}} = \dfrac{BD}{AB} = \dfrac{12}{5}$

$\sec A = \dfrac{\text{Hypotenuse}}{\text{Base}} = \dfrac{AD}{AB} = \dfrac{13}{5}$

$\therefore$ $\tan A + \sec A = \dfrac{12}{5} + \dfrac{13}{5} = 5$ **Ans.**

**Example 13.** From the adjoining figure, find:
(a) $\cos x$ (b) $\cot x$ (c) $\sin y$ (d) $\tan y$

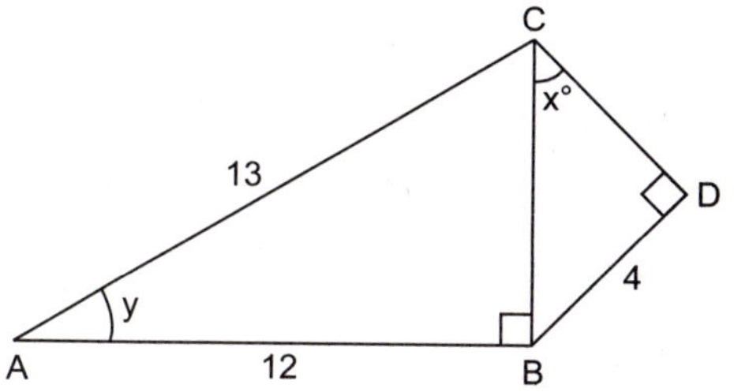


**Solution.** In $\Delta ABC$,

$$\angle ABC = 90°$$

$$\therefore \quad BC^2 = AC^2 - AB^2 = 13^2 - 12^2 = 25 \quad \Rightarrow \quad BC = 5$$

In $\Delta BDC$,

$$\angle BDC = 90°$$

$$\therefore \quad CD^2 = BC^2 - BD^2 = 5^2 - 4^2 = 9$$

$$\Rightarrow \quad CD = 3$$

(a) $$\cos x = \frac{\text{Base}}{\text{Hypotenuse}} = \frac{CD}{BC} = \frac{3}{5}$$ **Ans.**

(b) $$\cot x = \frac{\text{Base}}{\text{Perpendicular}} = \frac{CD}{BD} = \frac{3}{4}$$ **Ans.**

(c) $$\sin y = \frac{\text{Perpendicular}}{\text{Hypotenuse}} = \frac{BC}{AC} = \frac{5}{13}$$ **Ans.**

(d) $$\tan y = \frac{\text{Perpendicular}}{\text{Base}} = \frac{BC}{AB} = \frac{5}{12}$$ **Ans.**

**Example 14.** In $\Delta ABC$, $\angle B = 90°$, $\tan A = \frac{1}{\sqrt{3}}$, find the value of $\sin A \cos C - \cos A \sin C$.

**Solution.** Here,

$$\tan A = \frac{1}{\sqrt{3}} = \frac{BC}{AB}$$

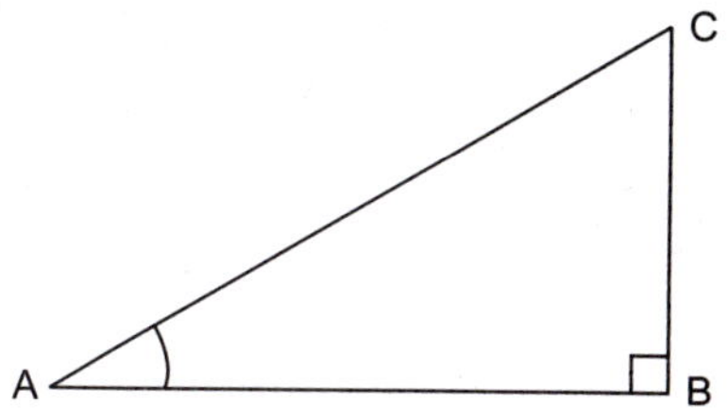


Let $BC = k$

$$\therefore \quad AB = k\sqrt{3}$$

By Pythagoras theorem,

$$AC^2 = AB^2 + BC^2 = (k\sqrt{3})^2 + k^2 = 4k^2$$

$$AC = 2k$$

Now, $$\sin A = \frac{BC}{AC} = \frac{k}{2k} = \frac{1}{2}; \quad \cos A = \frac{AB}{AC} = \frac{\sqrt{3}k}{2k} = \frac{\sqrt{3}}{2};$$

$$\sin C = \frac{AB}{AC} = \frac{\sqrt{3}k}{2k} = \frac{\sqrt{3}}{2}; \quad \cos C = \frac{BC}{AC} = \frac{k}{2k} = \frac{1}{2}$$

Now, $$\sin A \cos C - \cos A \sin C = \frac{1}{2} \times \frac{1}{2} - \frac{\sqrt{3}}{2} \times \frac{\sqrt{3}}{2} = \frac{1}{4} - \frac{3}{4} = -\frac{1}{2}$$ **Ans.**

**Example 15.** In a rhombus $ABCD$, $\angle CAB = \theta$. If $\cos\theta = \frac{2}{3}$ and $OB = 3$ cm, find $AB$ and $AC$.

**Solution.** We know that the diagonals of a rhombus bisect each other at right-angles.

$$\therefore \quad \angle AOB = 90°$$

$$\cos\theta = \frac{2}{3} = \frac{OA}{AB}$$

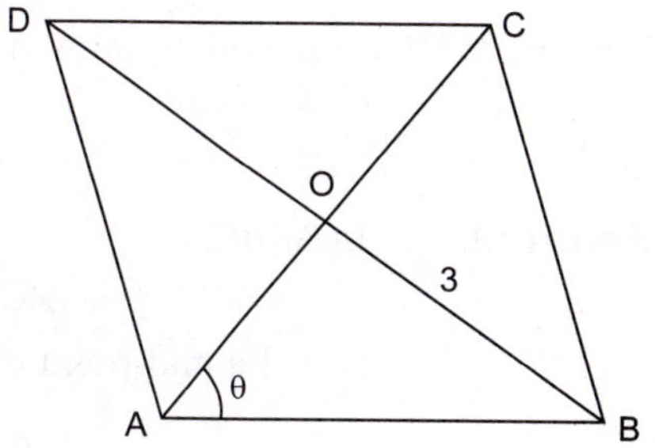


Let $OA = 2k$

$$\therefore \quad AB = 3k$$

By Pythagoras theorem

$$AB^2 = OA^2 + OB^2 \quad \Rightarrow \quad (3k)^2 = (2k)^2 + 3^2$$

$$\Rightarrow \quad 5k^2 = 9 \quad \Rightarrow \quad k = \frac{3}{\sqrt{5}}$$

$\therefore \quad OA = \dfrac{6}{\sqrt{5}}$ and $AB = \dfrac{9}{\sqrt{5}}$

Now, $\quad AC = 2.OA = 2 \times \dfrac{6}{\sqrt{5}} = \dfrac{12}{\sqrt{5}}$ cm **Ans.**

$AB = \dfrac{9}{\sqrt{5}}$ cm **Ans.**

**Example 16.** If $\tan\theta = \dfrac{3}{8}$, find the value of $\dfrac{3\sin\theta - 2\cos\theta}{3\sin\theta + 2\cos\theta}$.

**Solution.** Here, $\tan\theta = \dfrac{3}{8}$

$$\therefore \quad \frac{3\sin\theta - 2\cos\theta}{3\sin\theta + 2\cos\theta} = \frac{\dfrac{3\sin\theta}{\cos\theta} - \dfrac{2\cos\theta}{\cos\theta}}{\dfrac{3\sin\theta}{\cos\theta} + \dfrac{2\cos\theta}{\cos\theta}} = \frac{3\tan\theta - 2}{3\tan\theta + 2} = \frac{3 \times \dfrac{3}{8} - 2}{3 \times \dfrac{3}{8} + 2} = \frac{9-16}{9+16} = \frac{-7}{25}$$ **Ans.**

**Example 17.** If $\theta$ and $\phi$ are acute angles and $\sin\theta = \dfrac{\sqrt{3}}{2}$ and $\sec\phi = \sqrt{2}$, find the value of $\dfrac{\tan\theta + \tan\phi}{1 - \tan\theta\tan\phi}$

**Solution.** Draw $\Delta ABC$ in which $\angle A = \theta$.

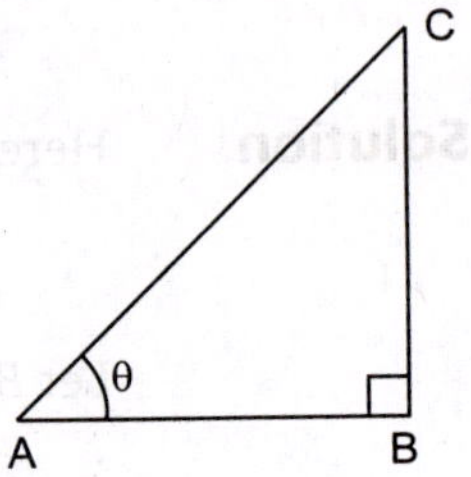


$$\sin\theta = \frac{\sqrt{3}}{2} = \frac{BC}{AC}$$

Let $BC = \sqrt{3}k$ and $AC = 2k$

From Pythagoras theorem,

$$AB^2 = AC^2 - BC^2 = (2k)^2 - (\sqrt{3}k)^2 = k^2 \Rightarrow AB = k$$

$$\therefore \quad \tan\theta = \frac{BC}{AB} = \frac{\sqrt{3}k}{k} = \sqrt{3}$$

Again, draw $\Delta PQR$ in which $\angle P = \phi$.

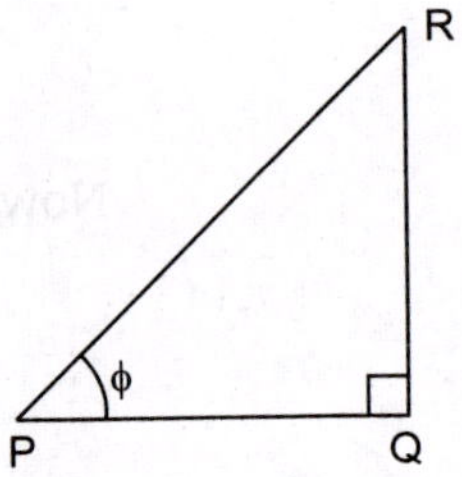


$$\sec\phi = \sqrt{2} = \frac{PR}{PQ}$$

Let $PR = \sqrt{2}\,t$ and $PQ = t$

From Pythagoras theorem,

$$QR^2 = PR^2 - PQ^2 = (\sqrt{2}\,t)^2 - t^2 = t^2$$

$$\Rightarrow \quad QR = t$$

$$\therefore \quad \tan\phi = \frac{QR}{PQ} = \frac{t}{t} = 1$$

Now, $$\frac{\tan\theta + \tan\phi}{1 - \tan\theta\tan\phi} = \frac{\sqrt{3}+1}{1 - \sqrt{3} \times 1} = \frac{(\sqrt{3}+1)^2}{(1-\sqrt{3})(1+\sqrt{3})} = \frac{3 + 1 + 2\sqrt{3}}{1-3} = \frac{4 + 2\sqrt{3}}{-2} = -(2+\sqrt{3})$$ **Ans.**

**Example 18.** In the adjoining figure, $\angle B = 90°$, $AC = 5$, $BC = 4$ and $\angle BAD = \theta$. If $D$ is the mid-point of $BC$, find:

(i) $\cot\theta$ (ii) $\sin\theta$ (iii) $\sec^2\theta - \tan^2\theta$

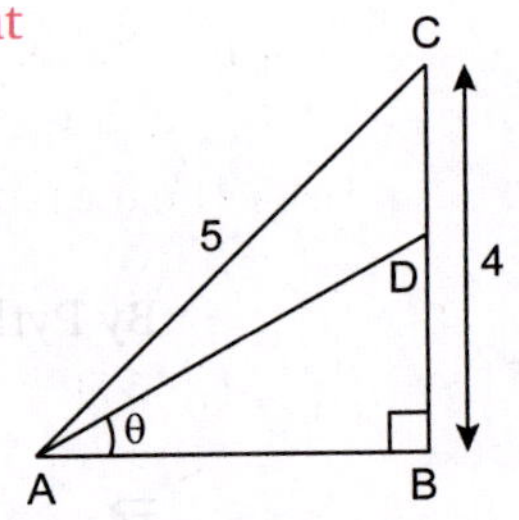


**Solution.** In $\Delta ABC$,

$$AC^2 = AB^2 + BC^2 \Rightarrow 5^2 = AB^2 + 4^2 \Rightarrow AB = 3$$

$D$ is the mid-point of $BC$.

$$\therefore \quad BD = \frac{BC}{2} = \frac{4}{2} = 2$$

In $\Delta ABD$,

$$AD^2 = AB^2 + BD^2 \Rightarrow 3^2 + 2^2 = 13 \Rightarrow AD = \sqrt{13}$$

(i) $\cot\theta = \dfrac{AB}{BD} = \dfrac{3}{2}$ **Ans.**

(ii) $\sin\theta = \dfrac{BD}{AD} = \dfrac{3}{\sqrt{13}}$ **Ans.**

(iii) $\sec^2\theta - \tan^2\theta = \left(\dfrac{AD}{AB}\right)^2 - \left(\dfrac{BD}{AB}\right)^2 = \left(\dfrac{\sqrt{13}}{3}\right)^2 - \left(\dfrac{2}{3}\right)^2 = \dfrac{13}{9} - \dfrac{4}{9} = \dfrac{9}{9} = 1$ **Ans.**

**Example 19.** If $\cos\theta + \sec\theta = 2$, find the value of $\cos^2\theta + \sec^2\theta$.

**Solution.** $\cos\theta + \sec\theta = 2 \Rightarrow (\cos\theta + \sec\theta)^2 = 2^2$

$\Rightarrow \cos^2\theta + \sec^2\theta + 2\cos\theta\ \sec\theta = 4 \Rightarrow \cos^2\theta + \sec^2\theta + 2\cos\theta \times \dfrac{1}{\cos\theta} = 4$

$\Rightarrow \cos^2\theta + \sec^2\theta + 2 = 4 \Rightarrow \cos^2\theta + \sec^2\theta = 4 - 2 = 2$ **Ans.**

**Example 20.** Prove that $\cot^2\theta - \dfrac{1}{\sin^2\theta} = -1$

**Solution.** L.H.S. $= \cot^2\theta - \dfrac{1}{\sin^2\theta} = \cot^2\theta - \operatorname{cosec}^2\theta$ $\left(\because \dfrac{1}{\sin\theta} = \operatorname{cosec}\theta\right)$

$= -(\operatorname{cosec}^2\theta - \cot^2\theta) = -1 = $ R.H.S.

## Exercise 17A

1. If $\sin\theta = \dfrac{1}{3}$, find the values of other $t$-ratios.

2. If $\sin\theta = \dfrac{1}{\sqrt{2}}$, find the values of other $t$-ratios.

3. If $\cos\theta = \dfrac{7}{25}$, find the values of other $t$-ratios.

4. If $\tan\theta = \dfrac{8}{15}$, find the values of other $t$-ratios.

5. Given that $\tan\theta = \dfrac{5}{12}$ and angle $\theta$ is an acute angle, find $\sin\theta$ and $\cos\theta$.

6. If $\sin\theta = \dfrac{3}{5}$ and $\theta$ is an acute angle, find (i) $\cos\theta$, (ii) $\tan\theta$.

7. In a right-angled triangle, it is given that $A$ is an acute angle and that $\tan A = \dfrac{3}{4}$. Without using tables, find the value of $\cos A$.

8. If $\sin\theta = \dfrac{6}{10}$, find without using table, the value of $(\cos\theta + \tan\theta)$.

9. Using the measurements given in fig.
   (a) Find the value of (i) $\sin\phi$, (ii) $\tan\theta$
   (b) Write an expression for $AD$ in terms of $\theta$.

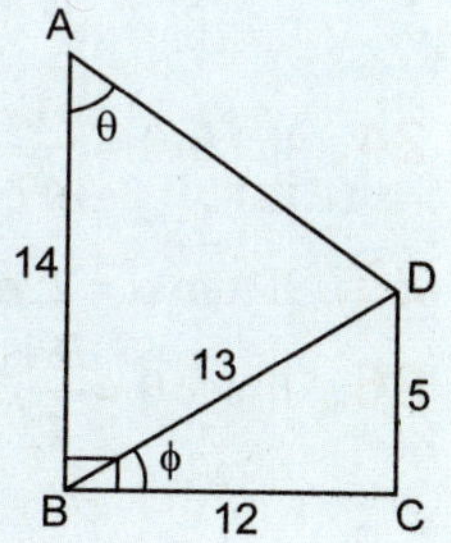

**10.** In the triangle given below [fig. (a)], calculate $\tan\theta$ if $\angle B = 90°$, $AB = 20$ cm and $AC = 40$ cm.

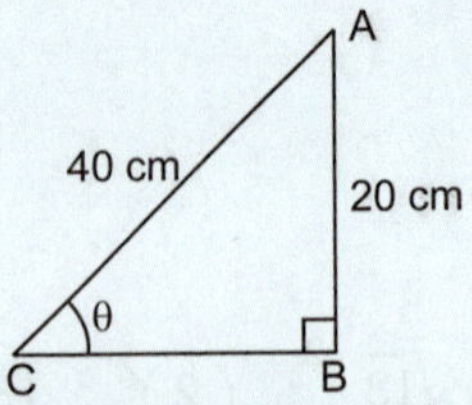


fig. (a)

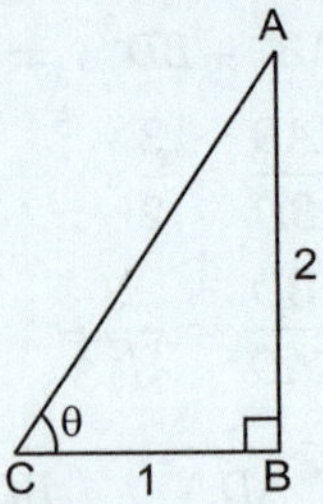


fig. (b)

**11.** *ABC* is a right-angled triangle, right-angled at *B*. Given that $\angle ACB = \theta$, side $AB = 2$ units and side $BC = 1$ unit, find the value of $\sin^2\theta + \tan^2\theta$. [fig. (b)]

**12.** In $\Delta ABC$, $AB = AC = 15$ cm, $BC = 18$ cm, find $\cos \angle ABC$.

**13.** Given $\sin\theta = \dfrac{p}{q}$, find $\cos\theta + \sin\theta$ in terms of *p* and *q*.

**14.** If $\tan\theta = \dfrac{4}{3}$, find without using tables, the value of $\sin\theta + \cos\theta$ (both $\sin\theta$ and $\cos\theta$ are positive).

**15.** In fig, $\Delta ABC$ is right-angled at *B*, $\Delta BSC$ is right-angled at *S*, and $\Delta BRS$ is right-angled at *R*, $AB = 18$ cm, $BC = 7.5$ cm, $RS = 5$ cm, $\angle BSR = x°$ and $\angle SAB = y°$. Find (i) $\tan x°$, (ii) $\sin y°$, (iii) $\cos y°$.

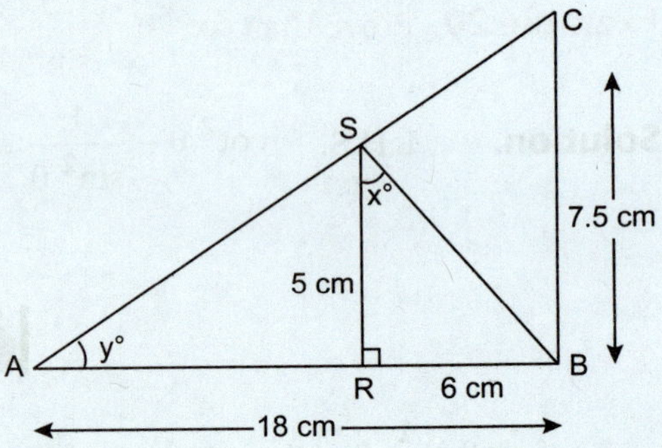


**16.** If $\tan\theta = \dfrac{p}{q}$, then prove that $\dfrac{p\sin\theta - q\cos\theta}{p\sin\theta + q\cos\theta} = \left(\dfrac{p^2 - q^2}{p^2 + q^2}\right)$.

**17.** If $\cot\theta = \dfrac{1}{\sqrt{3}}$, show that $\left(\dfrac{1-\cos^2\theta}{2-\sin^2\theta}\right) = \dfrac{3}{5}$.

**18.** If $\sec\theta = \dfrac{13}{5}$, show that $\dfrac{2\sin\theta - 3\cos\theta}{4\sin\theta - 9\cos\theta} = 3$.

**19.** If $5\tan\theta = 4$, show that $\dfrac{5\sin\theta - 3\cos\theta}{5\sin\theta + 2\cos\theta} = \dfrac{1}{6}$.

**20.** If $\cos\theta = \dfrac{12}{13}$, verify that $\sin\theta\,(1 - \tan\theta) = \dfrac{35}{156}$.

**21.** If $\sin\theta = \dfrac{3}{5}$, evaluate $\dfrac{\left(\cos\theta - \dfrac{1}{\tan\theta}\right)}{2\cot\theta}$.

**22.** If $\sec\theta = \dfrac{5}{4}$, evaluate $\dfrac{\sin\theta - 2\cos\theta}{\tan\theta - \cot\theta}$.

**23.** If $\tan\theta = \dfrac{4}{3}$, show that $\sqrt{\dfrac{1-\sin\theta}{1+\sin\theta}} = \dfrac{1}{3}$.

**24.** If $\tan\theta = \dfrac{1}{\sqrt{7}}$, show that $\dfrac{\operatorname{cosec}^2\theta - \sec^2\theta}{\operatorname{cosec}^2\theta + \sec^2\theta} = \dfrac{3}{4}$.

**25.** If $\tan\alpha = 2$, evaluate $\sin\alpha\sec\alpha + \tan^2\alpha - \operatorname{cosec}\alpha$.

**26.** If $\sec\theta = \dfrac{5}{4}$, verify that $\dfrac{\tan\theta}{1+\tan^2\theta} = \dfrac{\sin\theta}{\sec\theta}$.

27. Given $A$ is acute angle and $13 \sin A = 5$, evaluate without using tables: $\dfrac{5\sin A - 2\cos A}{\tan A}$.

28. If $5\cos A - 12\sin A = 0$, evaluate without using tables $\dfrac{\sin A + \cos A}{2\cos A - \sin A}$.

29. If $\theta$ is an acute angle and $\sin\theta = \cos\theta$, find the value of $2\tan^2\theta + \sin^2\theta - 1$.

30. If $\tan\theta + \cot\theta = 2$, prove that $\tan^2\theta + \cot^2\theta = 2$.

31. If $x = a\sin\theta + b\cos\theta$, $y = a\cos\theta - b\sin\theta$, prove that $x^2 + y^2 = a^2 + b^2$.

32. Prove that $\dfrac{1}{1+\tan^2 A} + \dfrac{1}{1+\cot^2 A} = 1$.

33. Prove that $\tan^2\theta - \dfrac{1}{\cos^2\theta} = -1$.

## Answers

1. $\cos\theta = \dfrac{2\sqrt{2}}{3}, \tan\theta = \dfrac{1}{2\sqrt{2}}, \text{cosec}\,\theta = 3, \sec\theta = \dfrac{3}{2\sqrt{2}}$ and $\cot\theta = 2\sqrt{2}$.

2. $\cos\theta = \dfrac{1}{\sqrt{2}}, \tan\theta = 1, \cot\theta = 1, \text{cosec}\,\theta = \sqrt{2}$ and $\sec\theta = \sqrt{2}$.

3. $\sin\theta = \dfrac{24}{25}, \tan\theta = \dfrac{24}{7}, \cot\theta = \dfrac{7}{24}, \text{cosec}\,\theta = \dfrac{25}{24}$ and $\sec\theta = \dfrac{25}{7}$.

4. $\sin\theta = \dfrac{8}{17}, \cos\theta = \dfrac{15}{17}, \text{cosec}\,\theta = \dfrac{17}{8}, \sec\theta = \dfrac{17}{15}$ and $\cot\theta = \dfrac{15}{8}$.

5. $\sin\theta = \dfrac{5}{13}, \cos\theta = \dfrac{12}{13}$.
6. (i) $\cos\theta = \dfrac{4}{5}$, (ii) $\tan\theta = \dfrac{3}{4}$.
7. $\dfrac{4}{5}$
8. $\dfrac{31}{20}$

9. (a) (i) $\dfrac{5}{13}$, (ii) $\dfrac{4}{3}$ (b) $\dfrac{9}{\cos\theta}$ or $\dfrac{12}{\sin\theta}$
10. $\dfrac{1}{\sqrt{3}}$
11. $\dfrac{24}{5}$
12. $\dfrac{3}{5}$

13. $\dfrac{p+\sqrt{q^2-p^2}}{q}$
14. $\dfrac{7}{5}$
15. (i) $\dfrac{6}{5}$, (ii) $\dfrac{5}{13}$ (iii) $\dfrac{12}{13}$
21. $-\dfrac{1}{5}$.
22. $\dfrac{12}{7}$

25. $\dfrac{12-\sqrt{5}}{2}$
27. $\dfrac{12}{65}$
28. $\dfrac{17}{19}$
29. $\dfrac{3}{2}$

# Exercise 17B

## Multiple Choice Questions

Choose the correct answer from the given four options in each of the following questions:

1. If $\sin\theta = \dfrac{5}{13}$, then $\cot\theta$ is equal to :

(a) $\dfrac{5}{12}$ (b) $\dfrac{12}{5}$ (c) $\dfrac{12}{13}$ (d) $\dfrac{13}{12}$

2. If $\sec\theta = \dfrac{17}{8}$, then $\tan\theta$ is equal to :

(a) $\dfrac{15}{8}$ (b) $\dfrac{8}{15}$ (c) $\dfrac{15}{17}$ (d) $\dfrac{17}{15}$

3. If $\tan\theta = \frac{3}{5}$, then $\cos\theta$ is equal to :

(a) $\frac{4}{3}$ (b) $\frac{3}{4}$ (c) $\frac{3}{\sqrt{34}}$ (d) $\frac{5}{\sqrt{34}}$

4. $\sqrt{\frac{1-\sin^2\theta}{1-\cos^2\theta}}$ is equal to :

(a) $\tan\theta$ (b) $\cot\theta$ (c) $\sec\theta$ (d) $\cos\theta$

5. If $\cot\theta = \frac{b}{a}$, then $\sec^2\theta - \tan^2\theta$ is equal to :

(a) 0 (b) 1 (c) –1 (d) $\frac{b}{\sqrt{a^2+b^2}}$

6. If $\sin\theta = \frac{a}{b}$, then $\tan\theta$ is equal to :

(a) $\frac{a}{\sqrt{b^2-a^2}}$ (b) $\frac{b}{\sqrt{b^2-a^2}}$ (c) $\frac{\sqrt{b^2-a^2}}{a}$ (d) $\frac{\sqrt{b^2-a^2}}{b}$

7. If $\sin\theta = 2\cos\theta$, then $\frac{3\sin\theta - \cos\theta}{3\sin\theta + \cos\theta}$ is equal to :

(a) 0 (b) $\frac{1}{2}$ (c) $\frac{2}{5}$ (d) $\frac{5}{7}$

8. $\cos\theta . \tan\theta$ is equal to :

(a) $\cot\theta$ (b) $\sin\theta$ (c) $\text{cosec}\,\theta$ (d) $\sec\theta$

9. If $\tan x + \cot x = 2$, then $\tan^2 x + \cot^2 x$ is equal to :

(a) 0 (b) 1 (c) 2 (d) 4

10. If $\text{cosec}\,\theta = \frac{5}{3}$, then $\sin^2 x + \cos^2 x + 1$ is equal to :

(a) 0 (b) $\frac{25}{9}$ (c) 2 (d) $\frac{9}{25}$

## Answers

| | | | | | | | | | |
|---|---|---|---|---|---|---|---|---|---|
| 1. (b) | 2. (a) | 3. (d) | 4. (b) | 5. (b) | 6. (a) | 7. (d) | 8. (b) | 9. (c) | 10. (c) |

## Valid Statements *Questions*

In the following questions, two statements (i) and (ii) are given. Choose the valid statement.

(a) Only (i) (b) Only (ii) (c) Both (i) and (ii) (d) Neither (i) nor (ii)

1. (i) In $\Delta ABC$, $\angle A = 90°$ and $\sin B = \frac{8}{17}$ then $\cos B = \frac{15}{17}$.

(ii) If $\sin\theta = \frac{1}{3}$, then $\cos\theta = \frac{2}{3}$.

2. (i) If $\cot\theta = \frac{a}{b}$, then $\tan\theta = \frac{b}{a}$.

(ii) $\sin\theta \cdot \cot\theta = \cos\theta$.

3. (i) If $\sin\theta + \text{cosec}\,\theta = 4$ then $\sin^2\theta + \text{cosec}^2\theta = 16$

(ii) $\sqrt{\dfrac{1-\cos^2\theta}{1-\sin^2\theta}} = \cot\theta$

4. (i) If $\tan\theta = \dfrac{3}{4}$, then $\cos\theta = \dfrac{3}{5}$

(ii) If $\sin\theta = 3\cos\theta$, then $\dfrac{\sin\theta - \cos\theta}{\sin\theta + \cos\theta} = \dfrac{1}{2}$

## *Answers*

**1.** (a) **2.** (c) **3.** (d) **4.** (b)

# SUMMARY *of the Chapter*

### Trigonometric Ratios:

1. $\sin\theta = \dfrac{\text{Perpendicular}}{\text{Hypotenuse}}$
2. $\cos\theta = \dfrac{\text{Base}}{\text{Hypotenuse}}$
3. $\tan\theta = \dfrac{\text{Perpendicular}}{\text{Base}}$
4. $\cot\theta = \dfrac{\text{Base}}{\text{Perpendicular}}$
5. $\sec\theta = \dfrac{\text{Hypotenuse}}{\text{Base}}$
6. $\text{cosec}\,\theta = \dfrac{\text{Hypotenuse}}{\text{Perpendicular}}$

### Reciprocal Relations:

1. $\sin\theta = \dfrac{1}{\text{cosec}\,\theta}$ and $\text{cosec}\,\theta = \dfrac{1}{\sin\theta}$
2. $\cos\theta = \dfrac{1}{\sec\theta}$ and $\sec\theta = \dfrac{1}{\cos\theta}$
3. $\tan\theta = \dfrac{1}{\cot\theta}$ and $\cot\theta = \dfrac{1}{\tan\theta}$

### Other Relations:

$$\tan\theta = \frac{\sin\theta}{\cos\theta} \text{ and } \cot\theta = \frac{\cos\theta}{\sin\theta}$$

# CHAPTER TEST

**1.** If $\tan\theta = \frac{1}{2}$, find the value of $\cot^2\theta + \sin^2\theta$.

**2.** If $\sec\theta = \frac{13}{5}$, find the value of

(a) $\sin\theta$ (b) $\tan\theta$
(c) $\text{cosec}^2\theta - \cot^2\theta$

**3.** If $\tan\theta = \frac{3}{5}$, find the value of $\frac{3\cos\theta - 5\sin\theta}{3\cos\theta + 5\sin\theta}$

**4.** In the adjoining figure, $\angle ACB = 90°$, $AB = 10$ cm, $AC = 8$ cm, $BD = 21$ cm, find

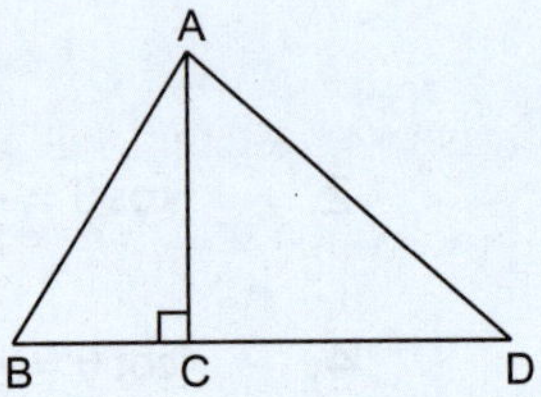


(a) $\sin B$

(b) $\sec D$

(c) $\cos^2 B + \cot^2 B$.

**5.** In $\Delta ABC$, $\angle B = 90°$ and $\cot A = 1$, find the value of $2\sin A\cos A$.

**6.** In the given figure, $\cos\theta = \frac{3}{5}$ and $\cos\phi = \frac{3}{5}$, find the length of $BC$.

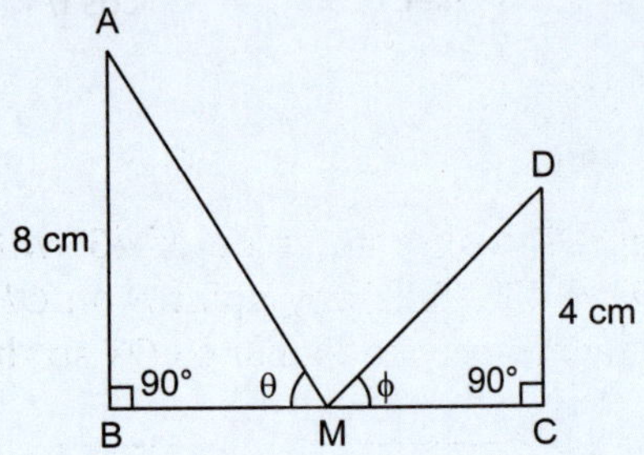


**7.** In the given figure, $C$ is the mid-point of $BD$, $\angle B = 90°$ and $\angle BAC = \phi$. If $BD = 2a$ and $AD = b$, find

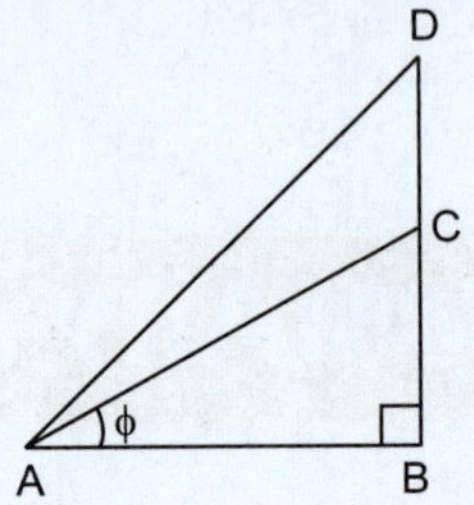


(a) $\tan\phi$ (b) $\sec\phi$
(c) $\text{cosec}\,\phi$

**8.** If $\tan B = \frac{5}{12}$, prove that $\tan^2 B - \sin^2 B = \sin^4 B \cdot \sec^2 B$.

**9.** In $\Delta ABC$, $\angle C = 90°$ and $\tan A = \frac{3}{5}$, prove that

$\sin A\cos B + \cos A\sin B = 1$

**10.** Prove that $(\sin A + \cos A)^2 + (\sin A - \cos A)^2 = 2$

## *Answers*

**1.** $\frac{21}{5}$ **2.** (a) $\frac{12}{13}$ (b) $\frac{12}{5}$ (c) 1

**3.** 0 **4.** (a) $\frac{4}{5}$ (b) $\frac{17}{15}$ (c) $\frac{369}{400}$

**5** 1 **6.** 9 cm

**7.** (a) $\frac{a}{\sqrt{b^2 - 4a^2}}$ (b) $\frac{\sqrt{b^2 - 3a^2}}{\sqrt{b^2 - 4a^2}}$ (c) $\frac{\sqrt{b^2 - 3a^2}}{a}$

Chapter

# 18 TRIGONOMETRIC RATIOS OF SOME STANDARD ANGLES AND COMPLEMENTARY ANGLES

## Syllabus

- Trigonometric Ratios: sine, cosine, tangent of an angle and their reciprocals.
- Trigonometric ratios of standard angles—0, 30, 45, 60, 90 degrees. Evaluation of an expression involving these ratios.
- Simple 2-D problems involving one right-angled triangle.
- Concept of trigonometric ratios of complementary angles and their direct application:
  - $\sin A = \cos (90 - A)$, $\cos A = \sin (90 - A)$
  - $\tan A = \cot (90 - A)$, $\cot A = \tan (90 - A)$
  - $\sec A = \operatorname{cosec} (90 - A)$, $\operatorname{cosec} A = \sec (90 - A)$

## INTRODUCTION

In this chapter, we shall find the trigonometric ratios of some standard angles 0°, 30 °, 45 °, 60° and 90°. We shall also discuss some 2-D problems involving in right angled triangle and also discuss the trigonometric ratios of complementary angles.

## Trigonometric Ratios of Standard Angles

### (i) Trigonometrical Ratios of Angle of 30°

Let the revolving line $OP$ starts from its initial position $OX$ and makes an angle $XOP = 30°$. Draw $PM$ perpendicular to $OX$ and extend it to meet $OQ$ at $Q$. Then $\Delta MOP$ and $\Delta MOQ$ are congruent and, therefore, $\angle P = \angle Q = 60°$.

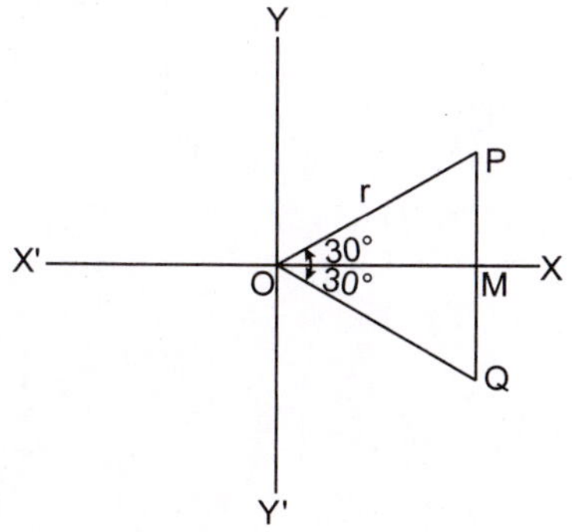


Hence, $\Delta POQ$ is an equilateral triangle.

$$\therefore \quad MP = \frac{1}{2} PQ = \frac{1}{2} OP = \frac{r}{2}, \text{ where } OP = r$$

From $\Delta OMP$, we have $OP^2 = OM^2 + MP^2$

$$\text{or} \quad OM^2 = OP^2 - MP^2 = r^2 - \frac{r^2}{4} = \frac{3r^2}{4}$$

$$\therefore \quad OM = \frac{\sqrt{3}}{2} r$$

(+ ve sign is taken as 30° lies in the first quadrant.)

$$\therefore \quad \sin 30° = \frac{MP}{OP} = \frac{r/2}{r} = \frac{1}{2},$$

$$\cos 30° = \frac{OM}{OP} = \frac{\sqrt{3}r}{2r} = \frac{\sqrt{3}}{2},$$

$$\tan 30° = \frac{MP}{OM} = \frac{r/2}{\sqrt{3}r/2} = \frac{1}{\sqrt{3}},$$

$$\cot 30° = \frac{OM}{MP} = \sqrt{3}, \quad \sec 30° = \frac{OP}{OM} = \frac{2}{\sqrt{3}}$$

$$\text{and} \quad \operatorname{cosec} 30° = \frac{OP}{MP} = 2.$$

### (ii) Trigonometric Ratios of Angle of 45°

Let the revolving line $OP$ makes an angle of 45° with the initial line $OX$ so that $\angle XOP = 45°$. Take any point $P$ on $OP$ in the final position. From $P$, draw $PM$ perpendicular to $OX$ so that $OM = MP = x$ (say)

$$\therefore \quad OP = \sqrt{(OM^2 + MP)^2} = \sqrt{(x^2 + x^2)} = x\sqrt{2}$$

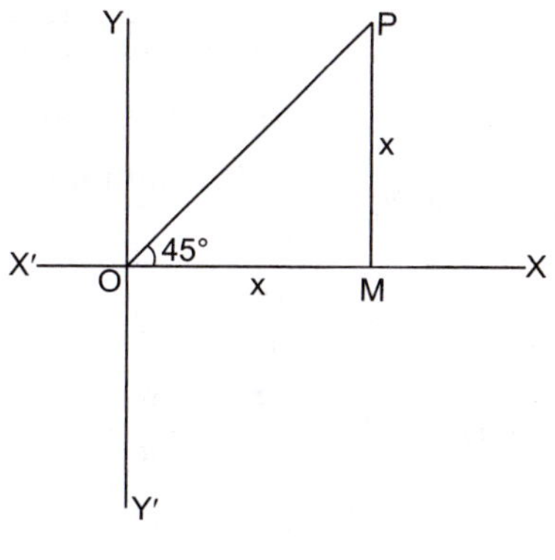

∴ From $\Delta POM$,

$$\sin 45° = \frac{PM}{OP} = \frac{x}{x\sqrt{2}} = \frac{1}{\sqrt{2}}, \ \cos 45° = \frac{OM}{OP} = \frac{x}{x\sqrt{2}} = \frac{1}{\sqrt{2}},$$

$$\tan 45° = \frac{PM}{OM} = \frac{x}{x} = 1,$$

$$\sec 45° = \frac{OP}{OM} = \sqrt{2}, \ \text{cosec } 45° = \frac{OP}{PM} = \sqrt{2},$$

$$\cot 45° = \frac{OM}{PM} = 1.$$

## (iii) Trigonometric Ratios of Angle of 60°

Let the revolving line $OP$ makes an angle of 60° with the initial line $OX$ so that $\angle XOP = 60°$. Take any point $P$ on $OP$ in the final position. From $P$ draw $PM$ perpendicular to $OX$. Then by geometry, we know that $OP = 2\ OM$, *i.e.*, $r = 2x$ and $MP = y = x\sqrt{3}$.

Hence, from $\Delta POM$

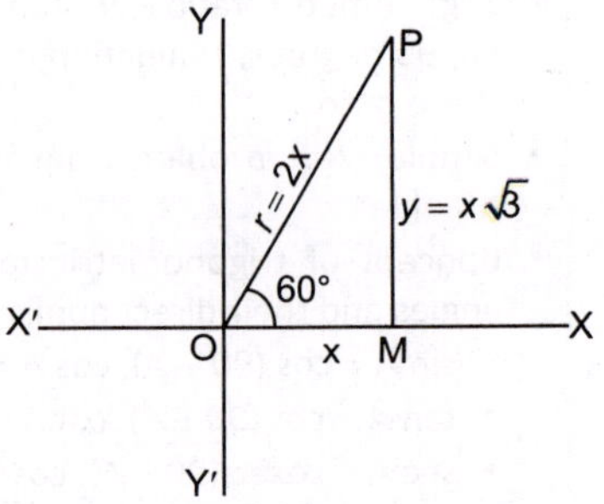


$$\sin 60° = \frac{PM}{OP} = \frac{x\sqrt{3}}{2x} = \frac{\sqrt{3}}{2},$$

$$\cos 60° = \frac{OM}{OP} = \frac{x}{r} = \frac{x}{2x} = \frac{1}{2},$$

$$\tan 60° = \frac{PM}{OM} = \frac{x\sqrt{3}}{x} = \sqrt{3},$$

$$\text{cosec } 60° = \frac{OP}{PM} = \frac{2}{\sqrt{3}}, \ \sec 60° = \frac{OP}{OM} = 2,$$

$$\cot 60° = \frac{OM}{PM} = \frac{1}{\sqrt{3}}.$$

## (iv) Trigonometric Ratios of Angle of 90°

Let the revolving line $OP$ starts from its initial position $OX$ and trace out an angle $\angle XOP = 90° - \phi$, where $\phi$ is negligible so that $\angle XOP$ is nearly equal to 90°. From $P$, draw $PM$ perpendicular to $XOX'$ so that distance $OM = 0$ and $PM = OP$ (nearly).

Now, from $\Delta OPM$,

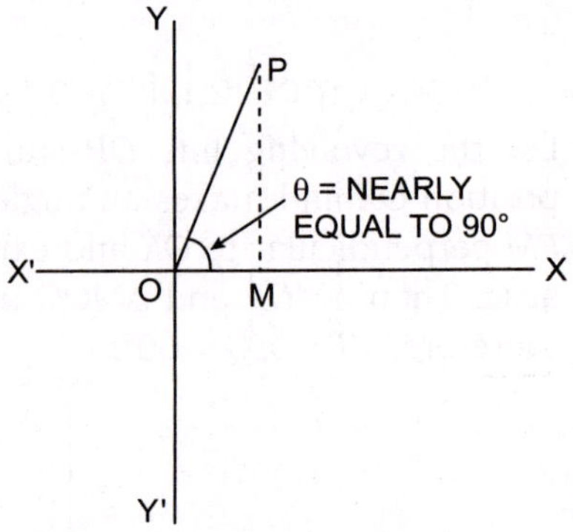


$$\sin 90° = \frac{PM}{OP} = \frac{OP}{OP} = 1, \quad \cos 90° = \frac{OM}{OP} = \frac{0}{OP} = 0,$$

$$\tan 90° = \frac{MP}{OM}$$

$$= \frac{OP}{\text{Infinitely samll quantity tending to zero}}$$

$$= \text{an infinitely large number} = \infty,$$

$$\cot 90° = \frac{OM}{MP} = \frac{\text{Infinitely small quantity tending to zero}}{MP} = 0,$$

$$\sec 90° = \frac{OP}{OM} = \infty,$$

$$\text{cosec } 90° = \frac{OP}{PM} = \frac{OP}{OP} = 1.$$

## (v) Trigonometric Ratios of Angle of 0°

Let the revolving line $OP$ starts from its initial position $OX$ and trace out $\angle XOP = \theta$, where $\theta$ is a very small angle tending to zero. From $P$ draw $PM$ perpendicular to $XOX'$ so that the distance $MP \to 0$ and $OP = OM$. Now,

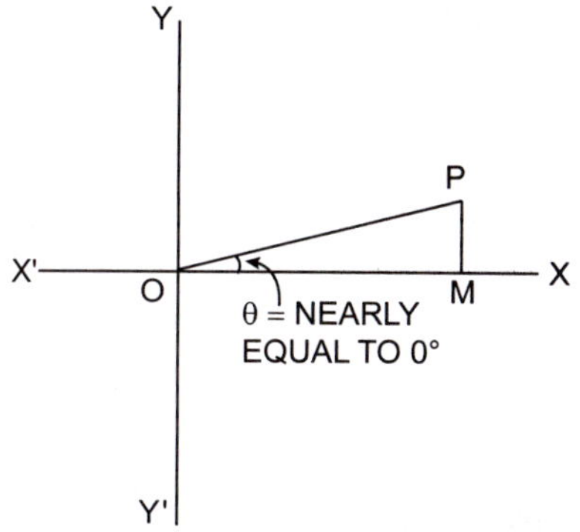


$$\sin 0^\circ = \frac{MP}{OP} = \frac{0}{OP} = 0,. \quad \cos 0^\circ = \frac{OM}{OP} = \frac{OM}{OP} = 1,$$

$$\tan 0^\circ = \frac{MP}{OM} = \frac{0}{OM} = 0,$$

$$\cot 0^\circ = \frac{OM}{MP} = \frac{1}{0} = \infty \text{ (in the limiting sense)},$$

$$\text{cosec } 0^\circ = \infty \text{ and } \sec 0^\circ = 1.$$

## Tabular Representation of *t*-Ratios of Standard Angles

The ratios of the angles 0°, 30°, 45°, 60° and 90° are very often used. They may be remembered very easily from a table which may be formed as follows:

| (i) | | 0° | 30° | 45° | 60° | 90° |
|---|---|---|---|---|---|---|
| (ii) | | 0 | 1 | 2 | 3 | 4 |
| (iii) | | $\frac{0}{4}$ | $\frac{1}{4}$ | $\frac{2}{4}$ | $\frac{3}{4}$ | $\frac{4}{4}$ |
| (iv) | | $\sqrt{\frac{0}{4}}$ | $\sqrt{\frac{1}{4}}$ | $\sqrt{\frac{2}{4}}$ | $\sqrt{\frac{3}{4}}$ | $\sqrt{\frac{4}{4}}$ |
| (v) | $\sin\theta$ | 0 | $\frac{1}{2}$ | $\frac{1}{\sqrt{2}}$ | $\frac{\sqrt{3}}{2}$ | 1 |
| (vi) | $\cos\theta$ | 1 | $\frac{\sqrt{3}}{2}$ | $\frac{1}{\sqrt{2}}$ | $\frac{1}{2}$ | 0 |
| (vii) | $\tan\theta$ | 0 | $\frac{1}{\sqrt{3}}$ | 1 | $\sqrt{3}$ | $\infty$ |
| (viii) | $\cot\theta$ | $\infty$ | $\sqrt{3}$ | 1 | $\frac{1}{\sqrt{3}}$ | 0 |
| (ix) | $\sec\theta$ | 1 | $\frac{2}{\sqrt{3}}$ | $\sqrt{2}$ | 2 | $\infty$ |
| (x) | $\text{cosec}\,\theta$ | $\infty$ | 2 | $\sqrt{2}$ | $\frac{2}{\sqrt{3}}$ | 1 |

(i) Standard angles 0°, 30°, 45°, 60°, 90° stated in order.
(ii) The numbers 0 to 4 written in the ascending order.
(iii) Each number has been divided by 4.
(iv) Square root has been taken of the fractions in the previous row.
(v) The simplified results of the previous row gives the values of $\sin\theta$.
(vi) The values of $\sin\theta$ given in the row (v) written in the reverse order give the values of $\cos\theta$.
(vii) The values of $\sin\theta$ in row (v) divided by $\cos\theta$ in row (vi) give the values of $\tan\theta$.
(viii) The reciprocals of the values of $\tan\theta$ given in the row (vii) give values of $\cot\theta$.
(ix) The reciprocals of the values of $\cos\theta$ given in the row (vi) give $\sec\theta$.
(x) The reciprocals of the values of $\sin\theta$ given in the row (v) give $\text{cosec}\,\theta$.

# Illustrative Examples

**Example 1.** Evaluate:

(i) $\sin 60° \cos 45° - \cos 60° \sin 45°$;

(ii) $2 \sin^2 30° \tan 60° - 3 \cos^2 60° \sec^2 30°$;

(iii) $\dfrac{5 \sin^2 30° + \cos^2 45° - 4 \tan^2 30°}{2 \sin 30° \cos 30° + \tan 45°}$.

**Solution.** (i) $\sin 60° \cos 45° - \cos 60° \sin 45° = \left(\dfrac{\sqrt{3}}{2} \times \dfrac{1}{\sqrt{2}} - \dfrac{1}{2} \times \dfrac{1}{\sqrt{2}}\right) = \dfrac{(\sqrt{3}-1)}{2\sqrt{2}}$ Ans.

(ii) $2 \sin^2 30° \tan 60° - 3 \cos^2 60° \sec^2 30° = 2 \times \left(\dfrac{1}{2}\right)^2 \times \sqrt{3} - 3 \times \left(\dfrac{1}{2}\right)^2 \times \left(\dfrac{2}{\sqrt{3}}\right)^2$

$= \left(\dfrac{2\sqrt{3}}{4} - 3 \times \dfrac{1}{4} \times \dfrac{4}{3}\right) = \left(\dfrac{\sqrt{3}}{2} - 1\right) = \dfrac{(\sqrt{3}-2)}{2}$ Ans.

(iii) $5 \sin^2 30° + \cos^2 45° - 4 \tan^2 30° = \left[5\left(\dfrac{1}{2}\right)^2 + \left(\dfrac{1}{\sqrt{2}}\right)^2 - 4 \times \left(\dfrac{1}{\sqrt{3}}\right)^2\right]$

$= \left(\dfrac{5}{4} + \dfrac{1}{2} - \dfrac{4}{3}\right) = \dfrac{5}{12}$

And, $2 \sin 30° \cos 30° + \tan 45° = \left(2 \times \dfrac{1}{2} \times \dfrac{\sqrt{3}}{2} + 1\right) = \dfrac{(\sqrt{3}+2)}{2}$

$\therefore \quad \dfrac{5 \sin^2 30° + \cos^2 45° - 4 \tan^2 30°}{2 \sin 30° \cos 30° + \tan 45°} = \dfrac{5}{12} \times \dfrac{2}{\sqrt{3}+2}$

$= \dfrac{5}{6(\sqrt{3}+2)}$ Ans.

**Example 2.** Verify each of the following :

(i) $\cos 60° \cos 30° - \sin 60° \sin 30° = \cos 90°$;

(ii) $\cos 60° = 1 - 2 \sin^2 30° = 2 \cos^2 30° - 1$

(iii) $\dfrac{\tan 60° - \tan 30°}{1 + \tan 60° \tan 30°} = \tan 30°$.

**Solution.** (i) $\cos 60° \cos 30° - \sin 60° \sin 30°$.

$= \left(\dfrac{1}{2} \times \dfrac{\sqrt{3}}{2} - \dfrac{\sqrt{3}}{2} \times \dfrac{1}{2}\right) = \left(\dfrac{\sqrt{3}}{4} - \dfrac{\sqrt{3}}{4}\right) = 0$

Also, $\cos 90° = 0$

$\therefore$ $\cos 60° \cos 30° - \sin 60° \sin 30° = \cos 90°$. Hence Proved.

(ii) $\cos 60° = \dfrac{1}{2}$;

$(1 - 2 \sin^2 30°) = \left[1 - 2 \times \left(\dfrac{1}{2}\right)^2\right] = \left[1 - 2 \times \dfrac{1}{4}\right] = \left(1 - \dfrac{1}{2}\right) = \dfrac{1}{2}$

And, $(2 \cos^2 30° - 1) = \left[2 \times \left(\dfrac{\sqrt{3}}{2}\right)^2 - 1\right] = \left(2 \times \dfrac{3}{4} - 1\right) = \left(\dfrac{3}{2} - 1\right) = \dfrac{1}{2}$

$\therefore$ $\cos 60° = (1 - 2 \sin^2 30°) = (2 \cos^2 30° - 1)$. Hence Proved.

(iii) $$\frac{\tan 60° - \tan 30°}{1 + \tan 60° \tan 30°} = \frac{\sqrt{3} - \frac{1}{\sqrt{3}}}{\left(1 + \sqrt{3} \times \frac{1}{\sqrt{3}}\right)} = \frac{\left(\frac{2}{\sqrt{3}}\right)}{2} = \frac{1}{\sqrt{3}}$$

And $$\tan 30° = \frac{1}{\sqrt{3}}$$

$\therefore$ $$\frac{\tan 60° - \tan 30°}{1 + \tan 60° \tan 30°} = \tan 30°$$ Hence Proved.

**Example 3.** Evaluate :

(i) $4 \cot^2 45° - \sec^2 60° + \sin^2 60° + \cos^2 90°$; (ii) $\frac{\sin 60°}{\cos^2 45°} - \cot 30° + 5 \cos 90°$;

(iii) $3 \cos^2 30° + \sec^2 30° + 2 \cos 0° + 3 \sin 90° - \tan^2 60°$

**Solution.** (i) $4 \cot^2 45° - \sec^2 60° + \sin^2 60° + \cos^2 90°$

$$= \left[4 \times (1)^2 - (2)^2 + \left(\frac{\sqrt{3}}{2}\right)^2 + (0)^2\right]$$

$$= \left(4 - 4 + \frac{3}{4} + 0\right) = \frac{3}{4}$$ Ans.

(ii) $$\frac{\sin 60°}{\cos^2 45°} - \cot 30° + 5 \cos 90° = \left[\frac{(\sqrt{3}/2)}{(1/\sqrt{2})^2} - \sqrt{3} + 5 \times 0\right]$$

$$= \left[\left(\frac{\sqrt{3}}{2} \times \frac{2}{1}\right) - \sqrt{3} + 0\right] = (\sqrt{3} - \sqrt{3}) = 0$$ Ans.

(iii) $3 \cos^2 30° + \sec^2 30° + 2 \cos 0° + 3 \sin 90° - \tan^2 60°$

$$= \left[3 \times \left(\frac{\sqrt{3}}{2}\right)^2 + \left(\frac{2}{\sqrt{3}}\right)^2 + (2 \times 1) + (3 \times 1) - \left(\sqrt{3}\right)^2\right]$$

$$= \left(3 \times \frac{3}{4} + \frac{4}{3} + 2 + 3 - 3\right) = \frac{67}{12}$$ Ans.

**Example 4.** If $2 \cos 3\theta - 1 = 0$ and $3\theta$ is an acute angle, find the value of $\theta$.

**Solution.** $2 \cos 3\theta - 1 = 0$

$\Rightarrow$ $\cos 3\theta = \frac{1}{2} = \cos 60°$ $\Rightarrow$ $3\theta = 60°$

$\Rightarrow$ $\theta = 20°$ Ans.

**Example 5.** If $\sqrt{3} \tan (2\theta - 10°) = 1$, and $(2\theta - 10°)$ is an acute angle, find the value of $\theta$.

**Solution.** $\sqrt{3} \tan (2\theta - 10°) = 1$, $\Rightarrow$ $\tan (2\theta - 10°) = \frac{1}{\sqrt{3}} = \tan 30°$

$\Rightarrow$ $2\theta - 10° = 30°$ $\Rightarrow$ $2\theta = 40°$

$\Rightarrow$ $\theta = 20°$ Ans.

**Example 6.** If $4 \sin^2 \theta - 3 = 0$ and $\theta$ is an acute angle, find the value of $\tan^2\theta + 2 \cos^2 \theta$.

**Solution.** $4 \sin^2 \theta - 3 = 0$

$\Rightarrow$ $\sin^2 \theta = \frac{3}{4}$ $\Rightarrow$ $\sin \theta = \frac{\sqrt{3}}{2}$ ($\because$ $\theta$ is acute angle; so $\sin \theta$ is positive)

$\Rightarrow$ $\sin \theta = \sin 60°$ $\Rightarrow$ $\theta = 60°$

Now, $\tan^2\theta + 2\cos^2\theta = \tan^2 60° + 2\cos^2 60°$

$$= (\sqrt{3})^2 + 2\left(\frac{1}{2}\right)^2$$

$$= 3 + \frac{1}{2} = \frac{7}{2}$$ Ans.

**Example 7.** If $\theta$ is an acute angle and $\sin\theta = \cos\theta$, find the value of $\sin^2\theta + \sin\theta\cos\theta + \cos^2\theta$.

**Solution.** $\sin\theta = \cos\theta$

$\Rightarrow \quad \frac{\sin\theta}{\cos\theta} = 1 \quad \Rightarrow \tan\theta = \tan 45° \Rightarrow \quad \theta = 45°$

Now, $\sin^2\theta + \sin\theta\cos\theta + \cos^2\theta = \sin^2 45° + \sin 45°\cos 45° + \cos^2 45°$

$$= \left(\frac{1}{\sqrt{2}}\right)^2 + \frac{1}{\sqrt{2}} \times \frac{1}{\sqrt{2}} + \left(\frac{1}{\sqrt{2}}\right)^2$$

$$= \frac{1}{2} + \frac{1}{2} + \frac{1}{2} = \frac{3}{2}$$ Ans.

**Example 8.** If $\frac{\cos\theta + \sin\theta}{\cos\theta - \sin\theta} = \frac{1+\sqrt{3}}{1-\sqrt{3}}$, find the value of $2\tan^2\theta + 3\cot^2\theta - \sec^2\theta$.

**Solution.** $\frac{\cos\theta + \sin\theta}{\cos\theta - \sin\theta} = \frac{1+\sqrt{3}}{1-\sqrt{3}}$

Using componendo and dividendo rule, we get,

$$\frac{(\cos\theta + \sin\theta) + (\cos\theta - \sin\theta)}{(\cos\theta + \sin\theta) - (\cos\theta - \sin\theta)} = \frac{(1+\sqrt{3}) + (1-\sqrt{3})}{(1+\sqrt{3}) - (1-\sqrt{3})}$$

$\Rightarrow \quad \frac{2\cos\theta}{2\sin\theta} = \frac{2}{2\sqrt{3}} \quad \Rightarrow \quad \cot\theta = \frac{1}{\sqrt{3}} = \cot 60° \quad \Rightarrow \quad \theta = 60°$

Now, $2\tan^2\theta + 3\cot^2\theta - \sec^2\theta$

$$= 2\tan^2 60° + 3\cot^2 60° - \sec^2 60°$$

$$= 2(\sqrt{3})^2 + 3\left(\frac{1}{\sqrt{3}}\right)^2 - (2)^2$$

$$= 6 + 1 - 4 = 3$$ Ans.

**Example 9.** Taking $A = 30°$; verify that :

(i) $\sin 2A = 2\sin A\cos A$; (ii) $\sin 3A = 3\sin A - 4\sin^3 A$;

(iii) $\sin A = \sqrt{\frac{1-\cos 2A}{2}}$; (iv) $\tan 2A = \frac{2\tan A}{1-\tan^2 A}$.

**Solution.** (i) When $A = 30°$, we have $2A = 60°$

$\therefore \quad \sin 2A = \sin 60° = \frac{\sqrt{3}}{2}$

And, $\quad 2\sin A\cos A = 2 \times \sin 30°\cos 30°$

$$= \left(2 \times \frac{1}{2} \times \frac{\sqrt{3}}{2}\right) = \frac{\sqrt{3}}{2}$$

$\therefore \quad \sin 2A = 2\sin A\cos A.$ Hence Proved.

(ii) When $A = 30°$, we have $3A = 90°$

$\therefore \quad \sin 3A = \sin 90° = 1$

And $\quad 3\sin A - 4\sin^3 A = 3\sin 30° - 4\sin^3 30°$

$$= \left[3 \times \frac{1}{2} - 4 \times \left(\frac{1}{2}\right)^3\right]$$

$$= \left(\frac{3}{2} - \frac{1}{2}\right) = 1$$

$\therefore$ $\sin 3A = 3 \sin A - 4 \sin^3 A.$ Hence Proved.

(iii) When $A = 30°$, we have $2A = 60°$

$\therefore$ $\sin A = \sin 30° = \frac{1}{2}$

And, $\frac{\sqrt{1 - \cos 2A}}{2} = \frac{\sqrt{1 - \cos 60°}}{2} = \sqrt{\left(\frac{1 - \frac{1}{2}}{2}\right)} = \sqrt{\left(\frac{1}{4}\right)} = \frac{1}{2}$

$\therefore$ $\sin A = \sqrt{\left(\frac{1 - \cos 2A}{2}\right)}$ Hence Proved.

(iv) When $A = 30°$, we have $2A = 60°$

$\therefore$ $\tan 2A = \tan 60° = \sqrt{3}$

And, $\frac{2 \tan A}{1 - \tan^2 A} = \frac{2 \tan 30°}{1 - \tan^2 30°}$

$$= \frac{\left(2 \times \frac{1}{\sqrt{3}}\right)}{\left[1 - \left(\frac{1}{\sqrt{3}}\right)^2\right]} = \frac{2/\sqrt{3}}{(1 - 1/3)} = \frac{2}{\sqrt{3}} \times \frac{3}{2} = \sqrt{3}$$

Hence, $\tan 2A = \frac{2 \tan A}{1 - \tan^2 A}$ Hence Proved.

**Example 10.** If $\sin(A + B) = 1$ and $\cos(A - B) = \frac{\sqrt{3}}{2}$, then find $A$ and $B$.

**Solution.** $\sin(A + B) = 1 \Rightarrow \sin(A + B) = \sin 90°$

$\therefore$ $A + B = 90°$ ...(*i*)

And, $\cos(A - B) = \frac{\sqrt{3}}{2}$

$\Rightarrow$ $\cos(A - B) = \cos 30°$

$\Rightarrow$ $A - B = 30°$ ...(*ii*)

Solving equations (*i*) and (*ii*), we get

$A = 60°$ and $B = 30°$ Ans.

**Example 11.** If $35° + x$ is an acute angle and $\cos(35° + x) = \sin 45°$, find the value of $x$.

**Solution.**

$$\cos(35° + x) = \sin 45°$$

$$= \frac{1}{\sqrt{2}}$$

$$= \cos 45°$$

$\Rightarrow$ $35° + x = 45°$

$\Rightarrow$ $x = 10°$ Ans.

**Example 12.** Solve : $\tan^2 (x - 5°) = 3$

**Solution.**
$$\tan^2 (x - 5°) = 3$$
$$\Rightarrow \tan (x - 5°) = \sqrt{3}$$
$$\Rightarrow \tan (x - 5°) = \tan 60°$$
$$\Rightarrow x - 5 = 60°$$
$$\Rightarrow x = 65°$$
Ans.

**Example 13.** If $(2 \sin \theta - \sqrt{3})(\tan \theta - 1) = 0$, find the value of $\theta$.

**Solution.**
$$(2 \sin \theta - \sqrt{3})(\tan \theta - 1) = 0$$
$$\Rightarrow 2 \sin \theta - \sqrt{3} = 0 \text{ or } \tan \theta - 1 = 0$$
$$\Rightarrow \sin \theta = \frac{\sqrt{3}}{2} \text{ or } \tan \theta = 1$$
$$\Rightarrow \sin \theta = \sin 60° \text{ or } \tan \theta = \tan 45°$$
$$\Rightarrow \theta = 60° \text{ or } \theta = 45°$$
Ans.

**Example 14.** If $A = 30°$, $B = 60°$, verify that $\sin (A + B) = \sin A \cos B + \cos A \sin B$

**Solution.**
$$\text{L.H.S.} = \sin (A + B)$$
$$= \sin (30° + 60°)$$
$$= \sin 90° = 1$$
$$\text{R.H.S.} = \sin A \cos B + \cos A \sin B$$
$$= \sin 30° \cos 60° + \cos 30° \sin 60°$$
$$= \frac{1}{2} \cdot \frac{1}{2} + \frac{\sqrt{3}}{2} \cdot \frac{\sqrt{3}}{2}$$
$$= \frac{1}{4} + \frac{3}{4} = 1$$
$$\therefore \quad \text{L.H.S.} = \text{R.H.S.}$$
Hence Verified.

## Exercise 18A

Find the value of each of the following expressions (Q. no. 1 to 6) :

1. $\sin 60° \cos 30° + \cos 60° \sin 30°$
2. $\cos 60° \cos 45° - \sin 60° \sin 45°$
3. $\sin 45° \cos 30° - \cos 45° \sin 30°$
4. $2 \sin^2 30° - 3 \cos^2 45° + \tan^2 60°$
5. $4 \cos^2 60° + 4 \sin^2 45° - \sin^2 30°$
6. (i) $7 \sin 30° \cos 60°$, (ii) $10 \tan 45°$
7. Prove that $\sin 60° = 2 \sin 30° \cos 30°$
8. Without using trigonometric tables find the value of $3 \sin^2 45° + 2 \cos^2 60°$.
9. If $0 \le x \le 90°$, state the numerical value of $x$ for which $\sin x° = \cos x°$.

Find the value of (Q. no. 10 to 14):

10. $\cos 90° + \cos^2 45° \sin 30° \tan 45°$
11. $\cos^2 45° + \sin^2 60° + \sin^2 30°$
12. $\sin^2 30° + \cos^2 60°$
13. $\dfrac{\sin^2 45° + \cos^2 45°}{\tan^2 60°}$
14. $\dfrac{\sin 30° - \sin 90° + 2 \cos 0°}{\tan 30° \times \tan 60°}$

**15.** Without using tables verify that

$$\cos 60° = \cos^2 30° - \sin^2 30°$$

**16.** Prove that

(i) $\cos^2 30° + \sin 30° + \tan^2 45° = 2\frac{1}{4}$ (ii) $4(\sin^4 30° + \cos^4 60°) - 3(\cos^2 45° - \sin^2 90°) = 2$

**17.** If $x = 30°$, without using tables, verify that : $\sin 2x = \frac{2\tan x}{1+\tan^2 x}$.

**18.** If $4\sin^2\theta - 1 = 0$ and angle $\theta$ is less than 90°, find the value of $\theta$ and hence the value of $\cos^2\theta + \tan^2\theta$.

**19.** Without using mathematical tables, evaluate,
$2\sqrt{2}\cos 45° \cos 60° + 2\sqrt{3}\sin 30° \tan 60° - \cos 0°$.

**20.** Without using tables find the value of
$\frac{4}{3}\tan^2 30° + \sin^2 60° - 3\cos^2 60° + \frac{3}{4}\tan^2 60° - 2\tan^2 45°$

**21.** If $\sin(A+B) = 1$ and $\cos(A-B) = 1$, find $A$ and $B$.

**22.** If $\sin(A-B) = \cos(A+B) = \frac{1}{2}$, find $A$ and $B$.

**23.** If $\tan(A-B) = \frac{1}{\sqrt{3}}$ and $\tan(A+B) = \sqrt{3}$, find $A$ and $B$.

**24.** Use the formula, $\cos\theta = \sqrt{\frac{1+\cos 2\theta}{2}}$, find the value of cos 30°, it being given that cos 60° = 1/2.

**25.** Find the value of $\theta$ from the following:

(i) $2\sin 2\theta = 1$ (ii) $\tan(\theta - 15°) = \frac{1}{\sqrt{3}}$ (iii) $\cos(2\theta - 50°) = \sin 60°$

**26.** If $A = 45°$, verify that

(i) $\sin 2A = 2\sin A\cos A$ (ii) $\cos 2A = 2\cos^2 A - 1$ (iii) $\sin A = \sqrt{\frac{1-\cos 2A}{2}}$

**27.** If $A = 60°$, $B = 30°$, verify that

(i) $\sin(A-B) = \sin A\cos B - \cos A\sin B$ (ii) $\tan(A-B) = \frac{\tan A - \tan B}{1+\tan A\tan B}$

## Answers

**1.** 1 **2.** $\frac{(\sqrt{2}-\sqrt{6})}{4}$ **3.** $\frac{(\sqrt{6}-\sqrt{2})}{4}$ **4.** 2 **5.** $\frac{11}{4}$ **6.** (i) $1\frac{3}{4}$ (ii) 10

**8.** 2 **9.** $x = 45°$ **10.** $\frac{1}{4}$ **11.** $1\frac{1}{2}$ **12.** $\frac{1}{2}$ **13.** $\frac{1}{3}$ **14.** 1.5

**18.** $30°, \frac{13}{12}$ **19.** 3 **20.** $\frac{25}{36}$ **21.** $A = 45°, B = 45°$ **22.** $A = 45°, B = 15°$

**23.** $A = 45°, B = 15°$ **24.** $(\sqrt{3}/2)$ **25.** (i) 15° (ii) 45° (iii) 40°.

## Application of Trigonometric Functions in 2-D Problems

A triangle contains 3 sides and 3 angles. If :

(i) two sides of a right angled.

(ii) one side and one angle of a right angled triangle are given then to determine the remaining sides and angles of triangle is called the solution of triangles.

# Illustrative Examples

**Example 1.** Find the value of $x$ from the following figures

(i)

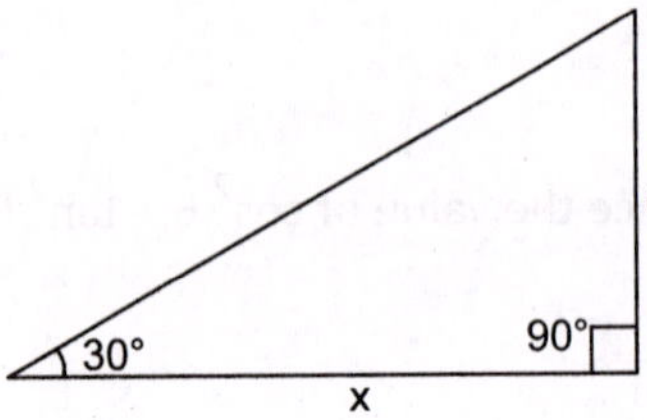


(ii)

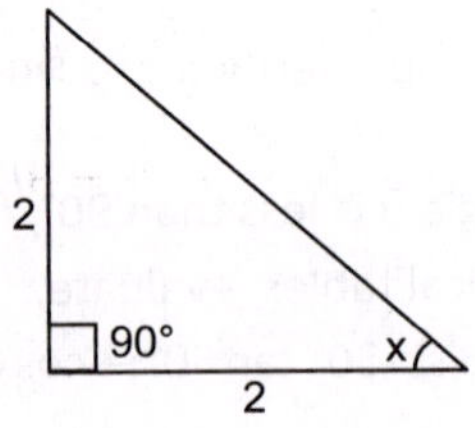


**Solution.** (i) Here

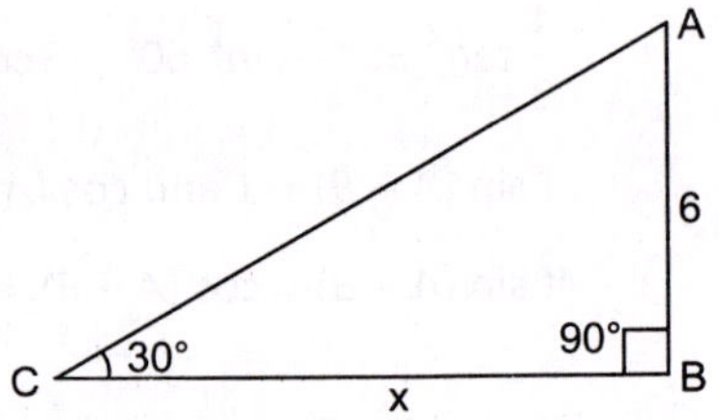


$$\tan 30° = \frac{AB}{BC}$$

$$\Rightarrow \quad \frac{1}{\sqrt{3}} = \frac{6}{x}$$

$$\Rightarrow \quad x = 6\sqrt{3}$$ **Ans.**

(ii) Here,

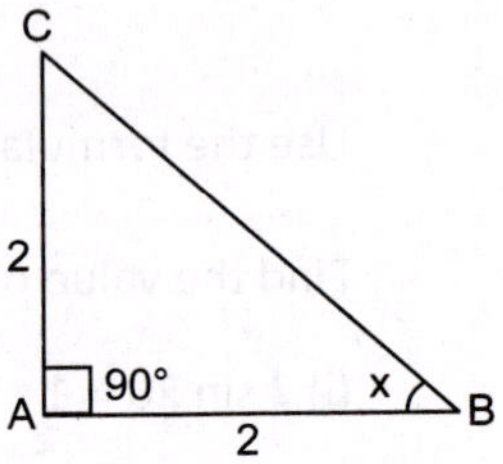


$$\tan x = \frac{AC}{AB} = \frac{2}{2} = 1$$

$$= \tan 45° \quad \Rightarrow \quad x = 45°$$ **Ans.**

**Example 2.** A ladder which is leaning against a wall, makes an angle 30° from the horizontal. The top of ladder reaches a window 15 m high on the wall. Find the distance of the foot of ladder from the wall.

**Solution.** Let $AC$ be the ladder which reaches to the window $C$ where

$BC = 15$ m and $\angle BAC = 30°$

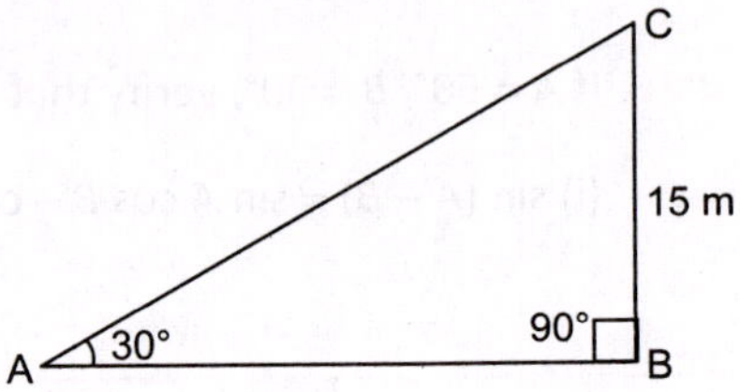


$$\therefore \quad \tan 30° = \frac{15}{AB} \quad \Rightarrow \quad \frac{1}{\sqrt{3}} = \frac{15}{AB}$$

$$\Rightarrow \quad AB = 15\sqrt{3}$$

$\therefore$ distance of foot of ladder from wall $= 15\sqrt{3}$ m **Ans.**

**Example 3.** A kite is flying at a height of 75 m from the ground. The string makes an angle 60° from the ground. Find the length of the string.

**Solution.** Let $A$ be the kite and $AB$ be the string.

Here, $\angle ABC = 60°$ and $AC = 75$ m

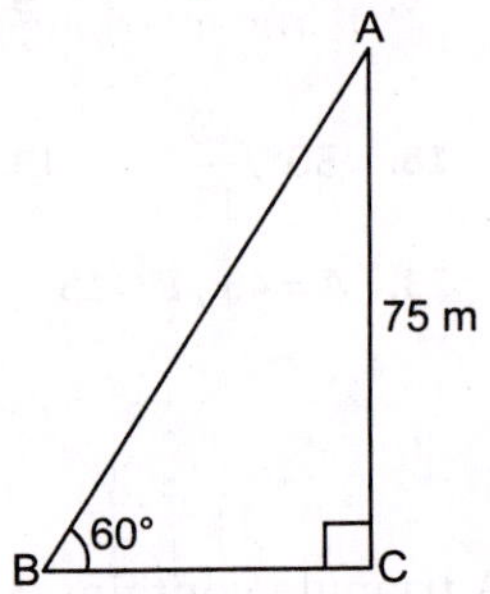


$$\therefore \quad \sin 60° = \frac{AC}{AB} \quad \Rightarrow \quad \frac{\sqrt{3}}{2} = \frac{75}{AB}$$

$$\Rightarrow \quad AB = \frac{150}{\sqrt{3}} = 50\sqrt{3}$$

$\therefore$ Length of string $= 50\sqrt{3}$ m **Ans.**

**Example 4.** A vertical tree 60 m high, is broken by the wind such that its top touches the ground and makes an angle of 30° from the ground. Find the height from which the tree is broken?

**Solution.** Let $BD$ be the vertical tree of height 60 m. It is broken from $C$ and part $CD$ takes the position $CA$.

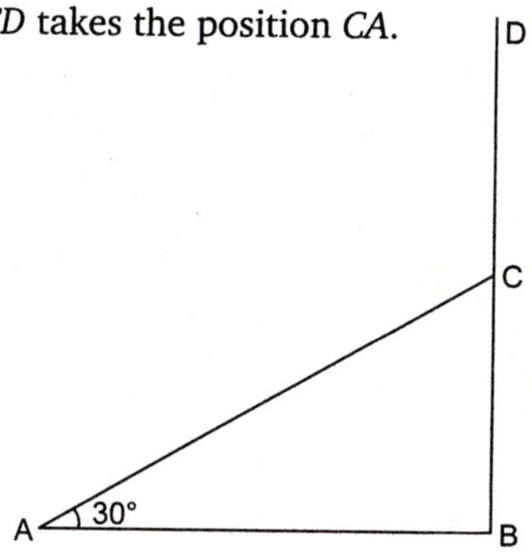


$\therefore$ $CD = CA$

Given $\angle BAC = 30°$

Let $BC = x$

$\therefore$ $AC = CD$

$= BD - BC$

$= 60 - x$

Now, $\sin 30° = \dfrac{BC}{AC} \Rightarrow \dfrac{1}{2} = \dfrac{x}{60 - x}$

$\Rightarrow$ $2x = 60 - x$

$\Rightarrow$ $3x = 60 \Rightarrow x = 20$

$\therefore$ Required height = 20 m

Ans.

## Exercise 18B

1. Find the value of $x$ from the following figures.

(i)

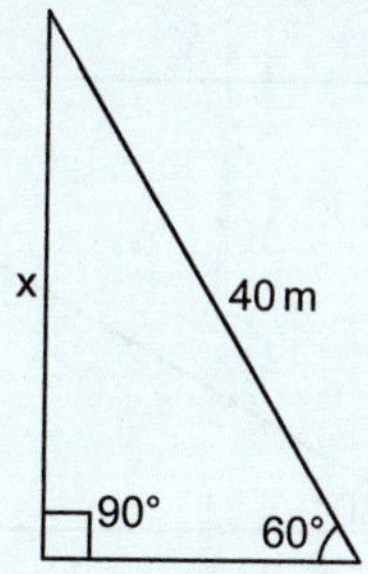


(ii)

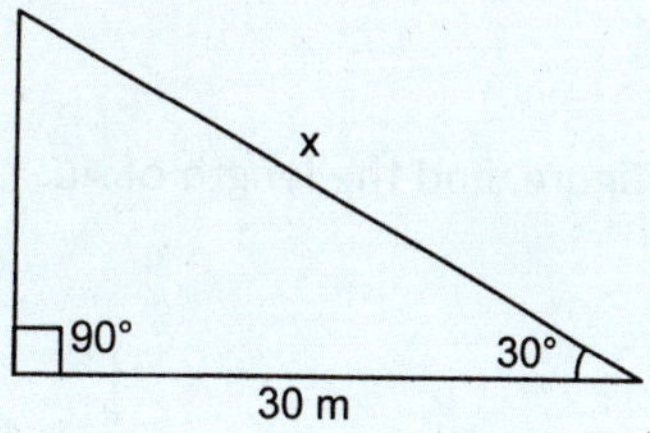


2. Find the value of θ from the following figures.

(i)

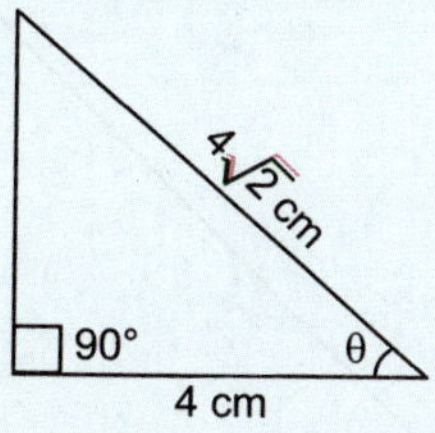


(ii)

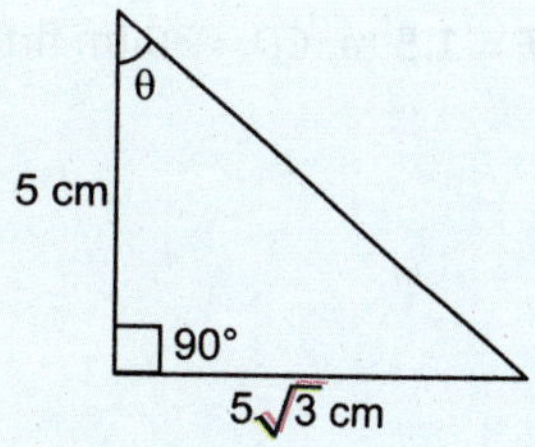


3. In $\Delta ABC$, $\angle B = 90°$, find $\angle A$ if :

(i) $BC$ is equal to $AB$. (ii) $AB$ is $\sqrt{3}$ times $BC$.

4. In the following figure, $CD = 20$ cm, find $AB$ and $BC$.

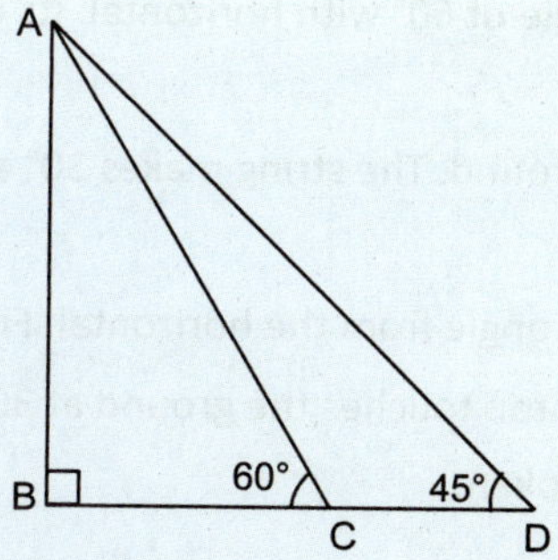

**5.** In the adjoining figure, $AB = 30$ cm, find $AD$ and $BC$.

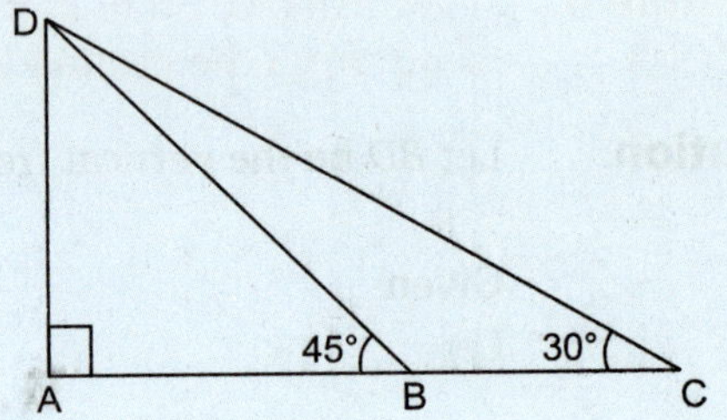


**6.** From the adjoining figure, find the value of $\theta$.

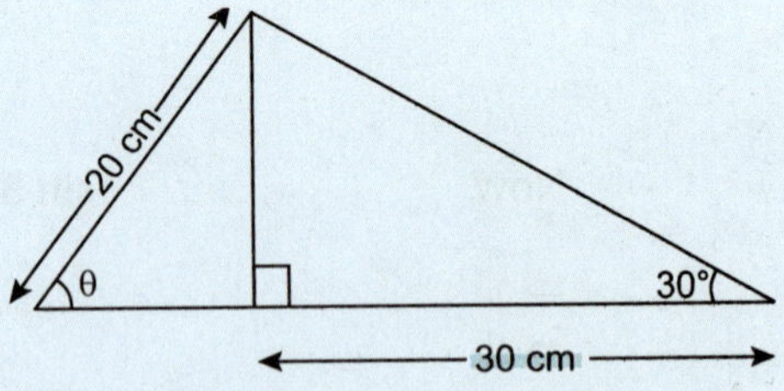


**7.** From the adjoining figure, find the length of $CD$.

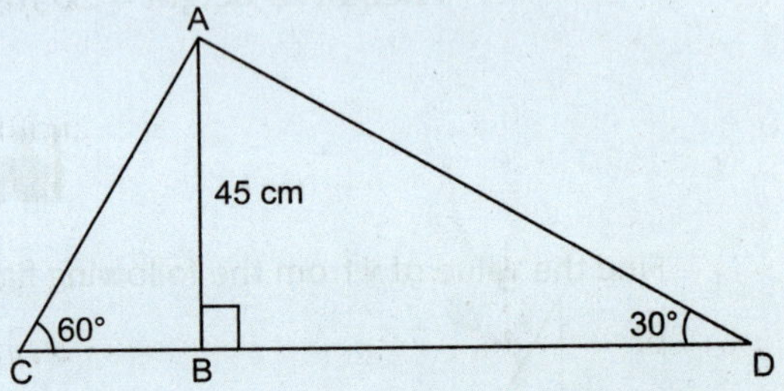


**8.** From the adjoining figure, find the length of $AC$.

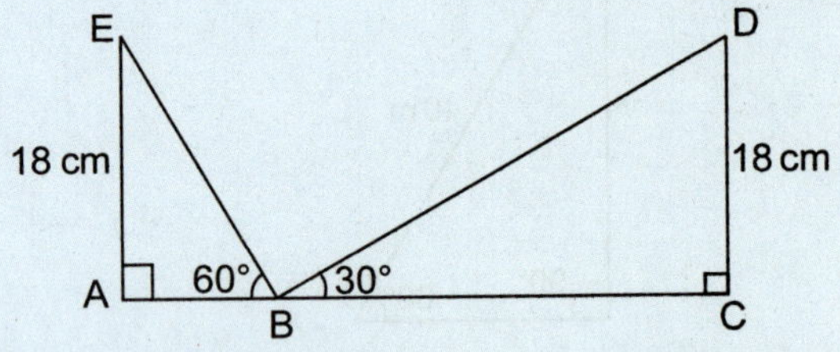


**9.** In the adjoining figure, $DE = 1.5$ m, $CD = 30$ m, find the length of $AC$.

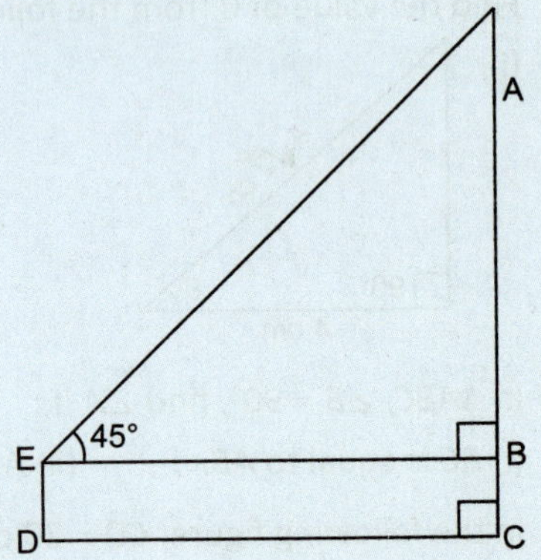


**10.** A ladder leaning against a wall makes an angle of 60° with horizontal. Its foot is 45 m away from the wall. Find the length of the ladder.

**11.** A kite is flying at a height of 30 m from the ground. The string makes 30° angle from the horizontal. Find the length of the string.

**12.** The string of a kite is 80 m long. It makes 45° angle from the horizontal. Find the height of the kite from the ground.

**13.** A vertical tree is broken by wind such that its top touches the ground at 30 m away from its foot and makes 30° angle from the ground. Find the height of tree before broken.

**14.** In the adjoining figure, $CD = 48$ cm, $\tan\theta = \frac{5}{12}$ and $\tan\phi = \frac{3}{4}$. Find the length of $AB$ and $BC$.

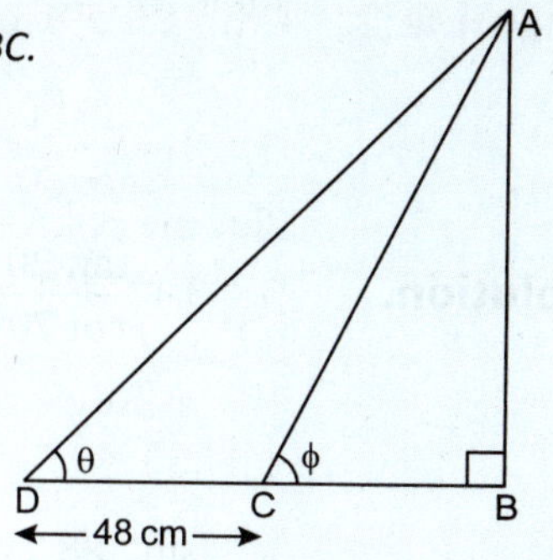


## *Answers*

**1.** (i) $20\sqrt{3}$ m (ii) $20\sqrt{3}$ m **2.** (i) 45° (ii) 60° **3.** (i) 45° (ii) 30° **4.** $AB = 10(3+\sqrt{3})$ cm, $BC = 10(\sqrt{3}+1)$ cm

**5.** $AD = 30$ cm, $BC = 30(\sqrt{3}-1)$ cm **6.** 60° **7.** $60\sqrt{3}$ cm **8.** $24\sqrt{3}$ cm **9.** 31.5 m **10.** 90 m

**11.** 60 m **12.** $40\sqrt{2}$ m **13.** $30\sqrt{3}$ m **14.** 45 cm, 60 cm

## Complementary Angles

Two angles are said to be complementary if their sum is 90°.

Let $\Delta ABC$ be a right angled triangle in which $\angle ABC = 90°$.

Let $\angle BAC = \theta$

Let $\angle ACB = 90° - \theta$

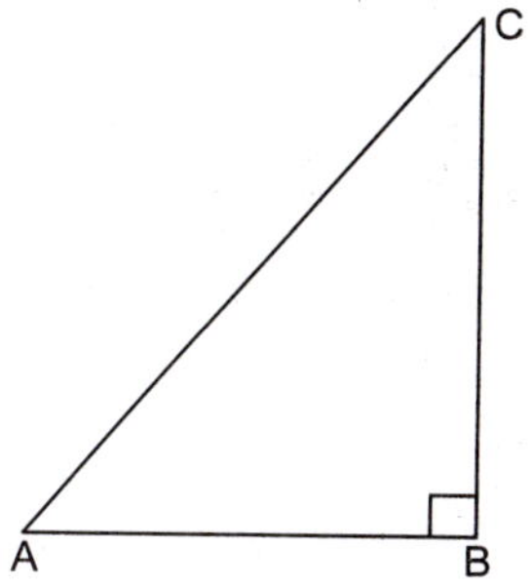


Now, $\sin\theta = \sin\angle BAC = \frac{BC}{AC}$

and $\cos(90° - \theta) = \cos\angle ACB = \frac{BC}{AC}$

$\therefore$ $\cos(90° - \theta) = \sin\theta$

Again $\cos\theta = \cos\angle BAC = \frac{AB}{AC}$

and $\sin(90° - \theta) = \sin\angle ACB = \frac{AB}{AC}$

$\therefore$ $\sin(90° - \theta) = \cos\theta$

Thus, we can find the following six results :

1. $\sin(90° - \theta) = \cos\theta$
2. $\cos(90° - \theta) = \sin\theta$
3. $\tan(90° - \theta) = \cot\theta$
4. $\cot(90° - \theta) = \tan\theta$
5. $\sec(90° - \theta) = \operatorname{cosec}\theta$
6. $\operatorname{cosec}(90° - \theta) = \sec\theta$

# Illustrative Examples

**Example 1.** Evaluate the following :

(i) $\frac{\sin 40°}{\cos 50°}$ (ii) $\sec 35° - \operatorname{cosec} 55°$

**Solution.** (i) $\frac{\sin 40°}{\cos 50°} = \frac{\sin 40°}{\cos(90° - 40°)} = \frac{\sin 40°}{\sin 40°}$. [$\because \cos(90° - \theta) = \sin\theta$]

$= 1$ Ans.

(ii) $\sec 35° - \operatorname{cosec} 55° = \sec(90° - 55°) - \operatorname{cosec} 55°$

$= \operatorname{cosec} 55° - \operatorname{cosec} 55°$ [$\because \sec(90° - \theta) = \operatorname{cosec}\theta$]

$= 0$ Ans.

**Example 2.** Evaluate the following :

(i) $3 + \dfrac{\tan 20°}{\cot 70°} + \tan^2 45°$ (ii) $\dfrac{\sin^2 28°}{\cos^2 62°} + \sec^2 45°$

**Solution.** (i) $3 + \dfrac{\tan 20°}{\cot 70°} + \tan^2 45° = 3 + \dfrac{\tan(90° - 70°)}{\cot 70°} + (1)^2$

$$= 4 + \frac{\cot 70°}{\cot 70°} = 4 + 1 = 5$$ Ans.

(ii) $\dfrac{\sin^2 28°}{\cos^2 62°} + \sec^2 45° = \dfrac{\sin^2 (90° - 62°)}{\cos^2 62°} + (\sqrt{2})^2$

$$= \frac{\cos^2 62°}{\cos^2 62°} + 2 = 1 + 2 = 3$$ Ans.

**Example 3.** Evaluate the following :

(i) $\cos 70° \operatorname{cosec} 20° + \sin 27° \sec 63°$ (ii) $2 \sin 18° \sec 72° + 5 \operatorname{cosec} 50° \cos 40°$

**Solution.** (i) $\cos 70° \operatorname{cosec} 20° + \sin 27° \sec 63°$

$$= \cos 70° \operatorname{cosec} (90° - 70°) + \sin 27° \sec (90° - 27°)$$

$$= \cos 70° \cdot \sec 70° + \sin 27° \cdot \operatorname{cosec} 27°$$

$$= \cos 70° \cdot \frac{1}{\cos 70°} + \sin 27° \cdot \frac{1}{\sin 27°}$$

$$= 1 + 1 = 2$$ Ans.

(ii) $2 \sin 18° \sec 72° + 5 \operatorname{cosec} 50° \cos 40°$

$$= 2 \sin 18° \cdot \sec (90° - 18°) + 5 \operatorname{cosec} (90° - 40°) \cdot \cos 40°$$

$$= 2 \sin 18° \cdot \operatorname{cosec} 18° + 5 \sec 40° \cdot \cos 40°$$

$$= 2 \sin 18° \cdot \frac{1}{\sin 18°} + 5 \cdot \frac{1}{\cos 40°} \cdot \cos 40°$$

$$= 2 + 5 = 7$$ Ans.

**Example 4.** Evaluate : $\cot 20° \cot 40° \cot 50° \cot 70°$

**Solution.** $\cot 20° \cot 40° \cot 50° \cot 70°$

$$= \cot 20° \cot 40° \cot (90° - 40°) \cot (90° - 20°)$$

$$= \cot 20° \cot 40° \tan 40° \tan 20°$$

$$= \frac{1}{\tan 20°} \cdot \frac{1}{\tan 40°} \cdot \tan 40° \cdot \tan 20°$$

$$= 1$$ Ans.

**Example 5.** Evaluate:

$2 \cos^2 0° + 4 \sin^2 45° \tan^2 60° + \sec 44° \sin 46° - \sin 90°$

**Solution.** $2 \cos^2 0° + 4 \sin^2 45° \tan^2 60° + \sec 44° \sin 46° - \sin 90°$

$$= 2(1)^2 + 4\left(\frac{1}{\sqrt{2}}\right)^2 (\sqrt{3})^2 + \sec (90° - 46°) \sin 46° - 1$$

$$= 2 + 6 + \operatorname{cosec} 46° \sin 46° - 1$$

$$= 7 + \frac{1}{\sin 46°} \sin 46° = 7 + 1 = 8$$ Ans.

**Example 6.** Evaluate : $\dfrac{\sin^2 10° + \sin^2 80°}{\cos^2 10° + \cos^2 80°}$

**Solution.** $\dfrac{\sin^2 10° + \sin^2 80°}{\cos^2 10° + \cos^2 80°} = \dfrac{\sin^2 10° + \sin^2(90° - 10°)}{\cos^2 10° + \cos^2(90° - 10°)}$

$= \dfrac{\sin^2 10° + \cos^2 10°}{\cos^2 10° + \sin^2 10°} = 1$ **Ans.**

**Example 7.** Evaluate : tan $(40°+ \theta)-$ cot $(50° - \theta)$

**Solution.** $\tan (40° + \theta) - \cot (50° - \theta)$

$= \tan [90° - (50 - \theta)] - \cot (50° - \theta)$

$= \cot (50° - \theta) - \cot (50° - \theta) = 0°$ **Ans.**

**Example 8.** Express sin 75° + cot 65° in terms of trigonometric ratios of angles between 0° and 45°.

**Solution.** $\sin 75° + \cot 65° = \sin (90° - 15°) + \cot (90° - 25°)$

$= \cos 15° + \tan 25°$ **Ans.**

**Example 9.** If $\sin A = \cos B$, prove that $A + B = 90°$.

**Solution.** $\sin A = \cos B \Rightarrow \sin A = \sin (90° - B) \Rightarrow A = 90° - B$

$\Rightarrow A + B = 90°$. **Hence Proved.**

**Example 10.** In $\Delta ABC$, prove that $\tan \dfrac{B+C}{2} = \cot \dfrac{A}{2}$.

**Solution.** In $\Delta ABC$,

$A + B + C = 180° \Rightarrow B + C = 180° - A$

$\Rightarrow \dfrac{B+C}{2} = 90° - \dfrac{A}{2} \Rightarrow \tan\left(\dfrac{B+C}{2}\right) = \tan\left(90° - \dfrac{A}{2}\right) = \cot \dfrac{A}{2}$ **Hence Proved.**

**Example 11.** If $\tan (3A + 10°) = \cot 5A$, and $3A + 10°$ and $5A$ are acute angles, find the value of $A$.

**Solution.** $\tan (3A + 10°) = \cot 5A$

$\Rightarrow \tan (3A + 10°) = \tan (90° - 5A) \Rightarrow 3A + 10° = 90° - 5A$

$\Rightarrow 8A = 80° \Rightarrow A = 10°$ **Ans.**

**Example 12.** If $\sin (2A - 15°) = \cos A$ and $2A - 15°$ and $A$ are acute angles, find the value of $A$.

**Solution.** $\sin (2A - 15°) = \cos A$

$\Rightarrow \sin (2A - 15°) = \sin (90° - A) \Rightarrow 2A - 15° = 90° - A$

$\Rightarrow 3A = 105° \Rightarrow A = 35°$ **Ans.**

**Example 13.** Prove that $\tan \theta + \tan (90° - \theta) = \sec \theta \sec (90° - \theta)$.

**Solution.** L.H.S. $= \tan \theta + \tan (90° - \theta)$

$= \tan \theta + \cot \theta$

$= \dfrac{\sin \theta}{\cos \theta} + \dfrac{\cos \theta}{\sin \theta} = \dfrac{\sin^2 \theta + \cos^2 \theta}{\cos \theta \sin \theta}$

$= \dfrac{1}{\cos \theta \sin \theta} = \sec \theta \operatorname{cosec} \theta$

$= \sec \theta \cdot \sec (90° - \theta) =$ R.H.S. **Hence Proved.**

**Example 14.** Simplify the following :

$$\frac{\operatorname{cosec}(90^\circ-\theta)\sin(90^\circ-\theta)\cot(90^\circ-\theta)}{\cos(90^\circ-\theta)\sec(90^\circ-\theta)\tan\theta}+\frac{\cot\theta}{\tan(90^\circ-\theta)}$$

**Solution.**

$$\frac{\operatorname{cosec}(90^\circ-\theta)\sin(90^\circ-\theta)\cot(90^\circ-\theta)}{\cos(90^\circ-\theta)\sec(90^\circ-\theta)\tan\theta}+\frac{\cot\theta}{\tan(90^\circ-\theta)}$$

$$=\frac{\sec\theta\cos\theta\tan\theta}{\sin\theta\operatorname{cosec}\theta\tan\theta}+\frac{\cot\theta}{\cot\theta}=\frac{\sec\theta\cdot\frac{1}{\sec\theta}}{\sin\theta\cdot\frac{1}{\sin\theta}}+1$$

$$=1+1=2$$

Ans.

## Exercise 18C

**1.** Evaluate the following :

(i) $\frac{\sin 32^\circ}{\cos 58^\circ}$ (ii) $\frac{\sec 48^\circ}{\operatorname{cosec} 42^\circ}$ (iii) $\frac{\tan 55^\circ}{\cot 35^\circ}$

**2.** Evaluate the following:

(i) $\sin 10^\circ-\cos 80^\circ$ (ii) $\tan 20^\circ-\cot 70^\circ$

**3.** Evaluate : $\sin 40^\circ \sin 50^\circ-\cos 40^\circ \cos 50^\circ$

**4.** Evaluate : $\tan 25^\circ \tan 65^\circ-\cot 25^\circ \cot 65^\circ$

**5.** Evaluate : $\left(\frac{\sin 18^\circ}{\cos 72^\circ}\right)^2+\left(\frac{\sec 32^\circ}{\operatorname{cosec} 58^\circ}\right)^2$

**6.** Evaluate : $4\cos 80^\circ \operatorname{cosec} 10^\circ+5\sin 59^\circ \sec 31^\circ$

**7.** Evaluate : $\tan 42^\circ \tan 25^\circ \tan 48^\circ \tan 65^\circ \tan 45^\circ$

**8.** Evaluate: $\frac{\sin 40^\circ}{\cos 50^\circ}+\frac{2\operatorname{cosec} 50^\circ}{\sec 40^\circ}-3\cos 50^\circ \operatorname{cosec} 40^\circ+1$

**9.** Evaluate : $\frac{\tan 70^\circ}{\cot 20^\circ}+\frac{\sin 38^\circ}{\cos 52^\circ}-4\sin^2 30^\circ$

**10.** Evaluate : $\frac{4\cos 57^\circ}{\sin 33^\circ}-\frac{\sqrt{3}\cdot\cos 38^\circ \operatorname{cosec} 52^\circ}{\tan 20^\circ \tan 60^\circ \tan 70^\circ}$

**11.** Express $\sin 65^\circ+\tan 57^\circ$ in terms of trigonometric ratios of angles between 0° and 45°.

**12.** Express $\cot 78^\circ+\sec 64^\circ$ in terms of trigonometric ratios of angles between 0° and 45°.

**13.** (i) If $\tan A=\cot B$, prove that $A+B=90^\circ$. (ii) If $\sec A=\operatorname{cosec} B$, prove that $A+B=90^\circ$.

**14.** In $\Delta ABC$, prove that

(i) $\sin\frac{A+B}{2}=\cos\frac{C}{2}$ (ii) $\sec\frac{C+A}{2}=\operatorname{cosec}\frac{B}{2}$

**15.** Find the value of $A$ if :

(i) $\sin 2A=\cos(A-6^\circ)$ where $2A$ and $(A-6^\circ)$ are acute angles.

(ii) $\sec 3A=\operatorname{cosec}(A-26^\circ)$ where $3A$ and $(A-26^\circ)$ are acute angles.

(iii) $\tan 4A=\cot(A-15^\circ)$ where $4A$ and $(A-15^\circ)$ are acute angles.

**16.** Prove that

(i) $\frac{\sin(90^\circ-\theta)}{\cos\theta}+\frac{\cos(90^\circ-\theta)}{\sin\theta}=2$

(ii) $\frac{\tan\theta}{\tan(90^\circ-\theta)}+\frac{\sin(90^\circ-\theta)}{\cos\theta}=\sec^2\theta$

(iii) $1-\frac{\sin(90^\circ-\theta)\sin\theta}{\tan\theta}=\sin^2\theta$

(iv) $\frac{\sin(90^\circ-\theta)}{\operatorname{cosec}(90^\circ-\theta)}+\frac{\cos(90^\circ-\theta)}{\sec(90^\circ-\theta)}=1$

### *Answers*

**1.** (i) 1 (ii) 1 (iii) 1 **2.** (i) 0 (ii) 0 **3.** 0 **4.** 0 **5.** 2 **6.** 9
**7.** 1 **8.** 0 **9.** 1 **10.** 3 **11.** $\cos 25^\circ+\cot 33^\circ$
**12.** $\tan 12^\circ+\operatorname{cosec} 26^\circ$ **15.** (i) 32° (ii) 29° (iii) 21°

# Exercise 18D

## Multiple Choice Questions

Choose the correct answer from the given four options in each of the following questions :

1. If $2\sin 2\theta = \sqrt{3}$ and $0° < 2\theta < 90°$, then $\theta$ is equal to :
   (a) 20° (b) 30° (c) 15° (d) 60°

2. The value of $\dfrac{1-\tan^2 45°}{1+\tan^2 45°}$ is :
   (a) 0 (b) 1 (c) 2 (d) $\dfrac{1}{2}$

3. The value of $\dfrac{3\tan 42°}{\cot 48° \tan 60°}$ is :
   (a) 9 (b) 1 (c) 3 (d) $\sqrt{3}$

4. In $\Delta ABC$, $\cos\dfrac{A+C}{2}$ is equal to :
   (a) 0 (b) 1 (c) $\cos\dfrac{B}{2}$ (d) $\sin\dfrac{B}{2}$

5. If $\sin\theta = \dfrac{1}{\sqrt{2}}$ and $\tan\phi = \dfrac{1}{\sqrt{3}}$ then $(2\theta + \phi)$ is equal to :
   (a) 75° (b) 90° (c) 120° (d) 150°

6. If $\sin(A+B) = 1$ and $\cos(A-B) = \dfrac{\sqrt{3}}{2}$ and $0° < A+B < 90°$, $A > B$ then $B$ is equal to :
   (a) 30° (b) 60° (c) 20° (d) 15°

7. If $\theta = 15°$ then $\dfrac{\sin 3\theta}{\cos 4\theta}$ is equal to :
   (a) $\sqrt{2}$ (b) 2 (c) $\sqrt{3}$ (d) 3

8. If $\sin\theta = \dfrac{1}{2}$ then $4\cos^3\theta - 3\cos\theta$ is equal to :
   (a) 1 (b) 7 (c) $-1$ (d) 0

9. The value of (sin 45°+ cos 45°) is :
   (a) $\dfrac{1}{2}$ (b) $\dfrac{1}{\sqrt{2}}$ (c) $\sqrt{2}$ (d) 2

10. The value of $\sec 42° \sin 48° + \operatorname{cosec} 35° \cos 55°$ is :
    (a) 3 (b) 0 (c) 1 (d) 2

### Answers

| | | | | | | | | | | | | | | | | | | | |
|---|---|---|---|---|---|---|---|---|---|---|---|---|---|---|---|---|---|---|---|
| **1.** | (b) | **2.** | (a) | **3.** | (d) | **4.** | (d) | **5.** | (c) | **6.** | (a) | **7.** | (a) | **8.** | (d) | **9.** | (c) | **10.** | (d) |

## Valid Statements Questions

In the following questions, two statements (i) and (ii) are given. Choose the valid statement.

(a) Only (i) (b) Only (ii) (c) Both (i) and (ii) (d) Neither (i) nor (ii)

1. (i) $\sin 60° \cdot \cos 60° = \dfrac{\sqrt{3}}{2}$
   (ii) $\sin x = \cos x$ then $x = 45°$

2. (i) $\tan 45° + \cot 45° = 2$
(ii) $\sin 20° - \cos 70° = 0$

3. (i) In $\Delta ABC$, $\sin\frac{A+B}{2} = \sin\frac{C}{2}$
(ii) If $\sin 2A = \cos(A-6°)$ and $2A$ and $(A-6°)$ are acute then $A = 35°$

4. (i) If $\theta = 15°$ then $\frac{\sin 3\theta}{\cos 4\theta} = \sqrt{2}$
(ii) $\cot 20° \cot 40° \cot 50° \cot 70° = 2$

## Answers

**1.** (b) **2.** (c) **3.** (d) **4.** (a)

# SUMMARY *of the Chapter*

- Trigonometric Ratios for angles 0°, 30°, 45°, 60° and 90° :

| Angle → / T-ratio ↓ | 0° | 30° | 45° | 60° | 90° |
|---|---|---|---|---|---|
| sin | 0 | $\frac{1}{2}$ | $\frac{1}{\sqrt{2}}$ | $\frac{\sqrt{3}}{2}$ | 1 |
| cos | 1 | $\frac{\sqrt{3}}{2}$ | $\frac{1}{\sqrt{2}}$ | $\frac{1}{2}$ | 0 |
| tan | 0 | $\frac{1}{\sqrt{3}}$ | 1 | $\sqrt{3}$ | $\infty$ (not defined) |
| cot | $\infty$ (not defined) | $\sqrt{3}$ | 1 | $\frac{1}{\sqrt{3}}$ | 0 |
| sec | 1 | $\frac{2}{\sqrt{3}}$ | $\sqrt{2}$ | 2 | $\infty$ (not defined) |
| cosec | $\infty$ (not defined) | 2 | $\sqrt{2}$ | $\frac{2}{\sqrt{3}}$ | 1 |

- $\sin\theta$ increases from 0 to 1 as $\theta$ increases from 0° to 90°.
- $\cos\theta$ decreases from 1 to 0 as $\theta$ increases from 0° to 90°.
- $\tan\theta$ increases from 0 to $\infty$ as $\theta$ increases from 0° to 90°.
- **Solution of Right Triangle.** To find the remaining sides and angles of a right angled triangle is called the solution of a right triangle when :
  (i) two sides of the triangle are given.
  (ii) one side and one acute angle are given.
- (i) $\sin(90° - \theta) = \cos\theta$
  (ii) $\cos(90° - \theta) = \sin\theta$
  (iii) $\tan(90° - \theta) = \cot\theta$
  (iv) $\text{cosec}(90° - \theta) = \sec\theta$
  (v) $\sec(90° - \theta) = \text{cosec}\,\theta$
  (vi) $\cot(90° - \theta) = \tan\theta$

# CHAPTER TEST

**1.** If $\sqrt{5}\tan 2\theta = \sqrt{15}$ and $0° < 2\theta < 90°$, find the value of $4\sin^2\theta + 3\cos^2\theta$.

**2.** Solve for $\theta$ : $2\sin^2\theta - 3\sin\theta + 1 = 0$.

**3.** If $\sin A = \dfrac{1}{3}$ and $A + B = 90°$, find the value of $\cos B$.

**4.** In $\Delta ABC$, prove that $\tan\dfrac{A+B}{2} = \cot\dfrac{C}{2}$.

**5.** If $\cos(A+B) = \sin(A-B) = \dfrac{1}{2}$, find the values of $A$ and $B$.

**6.** Evaluate : $\dfrac{3\cos 27°}{\sin 63°} + \dfrac{\tan 26°}{\cot 64°} + 2\sin 90°$

**7.** Prove that : $\dfrac{\cos(90°-\theta)\sec(90°-\theta)\tan\theta}{\operatorname{cosec}(90°-\theta)\sin(90°-\theta)\cot(90°-\theta)} + \dfrac{\sin(90°-\theta)}{\cos\theta} = 2$

**8.** Solve for $\theta$:
$\sin 4\theta = \cos 2\theta$ where $0° < 4\theta < 90°$

**9.** If $\tan(3\theta - 8°) = \cot 4\theta$ where $3\theta - 8°$ and $4\theta$ are acute, find the value of $\theta$.

**10.** In the adjoining figure $AC = 6$ cm. Find :

(a) $AB$

(b) $AD$

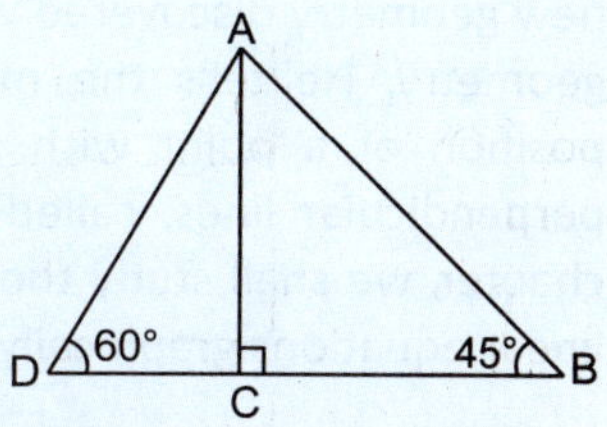


**11.** A ladder is placed against a vertical tower. If it makes an angle 60° with the horizontal ground and reaches upto a height of 48 m of the wall, find the length of the ladder.

**12.** From the adjoining figure, find :

(a) $AD$

(b) $AB$

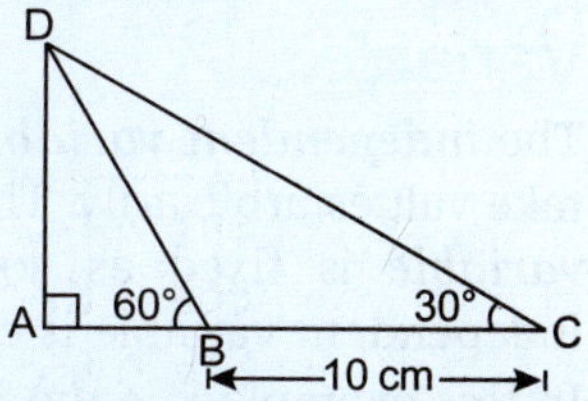


**13.** The perimeter of a rhombus is 36 cm and its one angle is 60°. Find the length of its diagonals.

**14.** The upper part of a tree broken over by wind, makes an angle of 60° with the ground and the horizontal distance from the root of the tree to the point where the top of tree touches the ground is 48 m. Find the height of the tree before broken.

## Answers

**1.** $\dfrac{13}{4}$ **2.** 30°, 90° **3.** $\dfrac{1}{3}$ **5.** $A = 45°$, $B = 15$ **6.** 6 **8.** 15° **9.** 14°

**10.** (a) $6\sqrt{2}$ cm (b) $4\sqrt{3}$ cm **11.** $32\sqrt{3}$ m **12.** (a) 8.66 cm (b) 5 cm **13.** 9 cm, $9\sqrt{3}$ cm

**14.** 179.136 m

UNIT VIII : CO-ORDINATE GEOMETRY

Chapter 19

# CO-ORDINATE GEOMETRY : AN INTRODUCTION

## Syllabus

Cartesian System, plotting of points in the plane for given co-ordinates, solving simultaneous linear equations in 2 variables graphically and finding the distance between two points using distance formula.

(a) Dependent and independent variables.

(b) Ordered pairs, co-ordinates of points and plotting them in the Cartesian plane.

(c) Solution of Simultaneous Linear Equations graphically.

(d) Distance formula.

## INTRODUCTION

In 1637, a French astrologer, Rene Decartes uses the algebra in the study of geometry and as a result, a new geometry discovered which is called co-ordinate geometry. He tells the method to determine the position of a point with respect to two mutually perpendicular lines, called co-ordinate axes. In this chapter, we shall study the solution of simultaneous linear equations graphically and distance formula.

## Independent and Dependent Variable

The ***independent variable*** is the variable that can take values arbitrarily. The value of the ***dependent variable*** is fixed as soon as the value of the independent variable is chosen, *e.g.*, $y = 3x + 5$.

In this example $x$ is the independent variable and $y$ is the dependent variable. As soon as the value of $x$ is chosen, the value of $y$ is determined. Now, if the value of $x$ is 2, $y$ becomes 11 and if $x$ is 3, the value of $y$ becomes 14.

Consider the linear equation $3x + 4y = 12$. Which contains two variables $x$ and $y$.

1. $$3x + 4y = 12$$
$$\Rightarrow \quad 4y = 12 - 3x$$
$$\Rightarrow \quad y = \frac{12 - 3x}{4}$$

Here, the variable $y$ is the subject of formula.

So, $y$ is called dependent variable and $x$ is called independent variable.

2. $$3x + 4y = 12$$
$$\Rightarrow \quad 3x = 12 - 4y$$
$$\Rightarrow \quad x = \frac{12 - 4y}{3}$$

Here, the variable $x$ is the subject of formula.

So, $x$ is called dependent variable and $y$ is called independent variable.

## Ordered Pair

When we want to depict the relationship between the independent variable $x$ and the dependent variable $y$ we use the notation of an ***ordered pair***, *e.g.*, $(x, y)$, where $x$ is the independent variable and $y$ is the dependent variable. The order of the variables is important, *e.g.*, $(x, y)$ is not the same as $(y, x)$.

In $(x, y)$, $x$ is in the first position, while in $(y, x)$, $x$ is in the second position. Hence, the order of the variables in an ordered pair is relevant and important.

In the ordered pair $(x, y)$, $x$ is called the ***first member*** (or, ***first component***) and $y$ is called the ***second member*** (or ***second component***).

## Equality of Ordered Pairs

Two ordered pairs $(p, q)$ and $(r, s)$ are said to be *equal*, which is written as $(p, q) = (r, s)$, if and only if $p = r$ and $q = s$.

## Rectangular Axes

In the adjoining figure, $X'OX$ and $Y'OY$ are two mutually intersecting lines which intersect each other at point $O$. $X'OX$ and $Y'OY$ are called rectangular oxes.

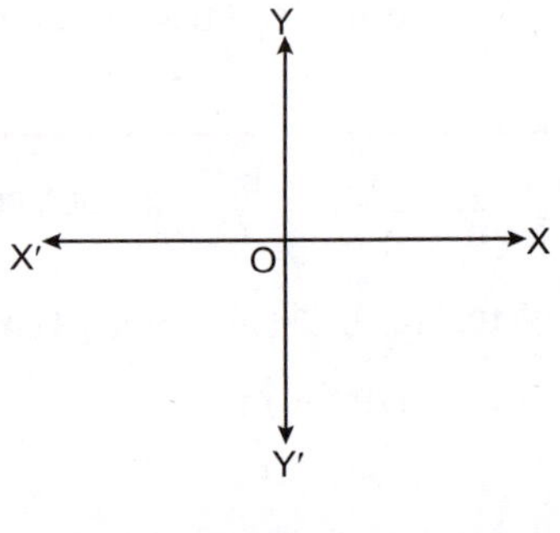


1. $X'OX$ is called $X$-axis.
2. $Y'OY$ is called $Y$-axis.
3. '$O$' is called the origin.

## Cartesian Co-ordinate System

To specify a point in space we require some frame of reference. One of the frames of reference is ***cartesian co-ordinate system***. In the cartesian co-ordinate system we choose mutually perpendicular lines as the frame of reference. These lines are called the ***axes*** of the co-ordinate system. The intersection point of the axes is called the ***origin***. Any point in the space can be specified by measuring its distance from the ***axes***. In a two dimensional space, we have two axes, the ***x-axis*** and the ***y-axis***, as shown in the adjoining figure. Any point in the two-dimensional space can be specified by providing the distance of the point from the two given axes. These distances are called the co-ordinates of the point, *e.g.*, $P = (2, 3)$. In our example, the point $P$ is 2 units away from the $y$-axis and 3 units away from the $x$-axis. So, the $x$-co-ordinate is 2 units and $y$-co-ordinate is 3 units. The $x$-co-ordinate is called the ***abscissa*** and the $y$-co-ordinate is called the ***ordinate***.

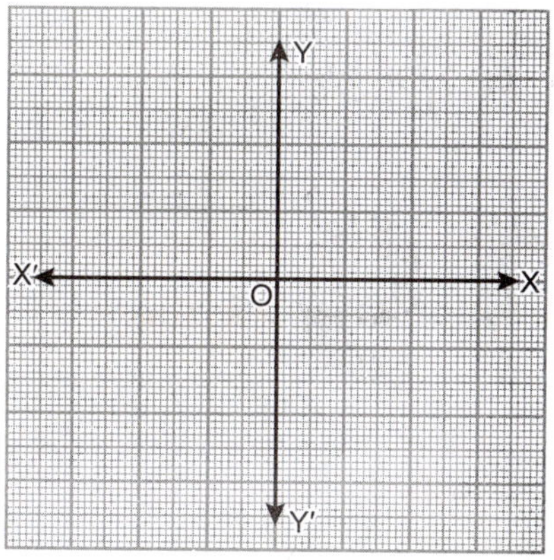


The point $P$ has co-ordinates (2, 3).

## Quadrant and Sign Convention

The adjoining figure contains two mutually perpendicular lines $X'OX$ and $Y'OY$ intersecting each other at $O$. These lines divide the cartesian plane into four equal parts, each of which is called a quadrant.

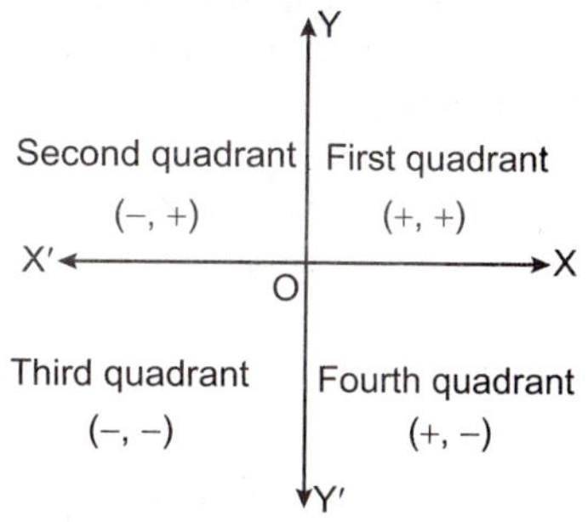


1. $XOY$ is called first quadrant.
2. $X'OY$ is called second quadrant.
3. $X'OY'$ is called third quadrant.
4. $XOY'$ is called fourth quadrant.
5. The right side of origin on $X$-axis is called positive $X$-axis.
6. The left side of origin on $X$-axis is called negative $X$-axis.
7. The upper side of origin on $Y$-axis is called positive $Y$-axis.
8. The lower side of origin on $Y$-axis is called negative $Y$-axis.

| Quadrant | Sign of a point |
|---|---|
| I | (+, +) |
| II | (–, +) |
| III | (–, –) |
| IV | (+, –) |

**NOTE**

(i) For each point on $X$-axis, ordinate = 0.
(ii) For each point on $Y$-axis, abscissa = 0.
(iii) Co-ordinates of origin = (0, 0).

## Illustrative Examples

**Example 1.** Express the equation $2x + 5y = 10$ in the form in which $y$ is dependent variable.

**Solution.** Given, $2x + 5y = 10$

$\Rightarrow$ $5y = 10 - 2x$

$\Rightarrow$ $y = \dfrac{10 - 2x}{5}$

Here, $y$ depends on $x$. Ans.

**Example 2.** Express the equation $5x - 7y = 18$ in the form in which $x$ is dependent variable.

**Solution.** Given, $5x - 7y = 18$

$\Rightarrow$ $5x = 18 + 7y \Rightarrow x = \dfrac{18 + 7y}{5}$

Here, $x$ is dependent variable. **Ans.**

**Example 3.** Point $P$ is on $X$-axis and is at a distance of 4 units from $Y$-axis to its left. Write the co-ordinates of point $P$.

**Solution.** $\because$ $P$ lies on $X$-axis.

$\therefore$ Its ordinate = 0

$P$ lies at 4 unit distance from $Y$-axis to its left.

$\therefore$ Co-ordinates of $P = (-4, 0)$ **Ans.**

**Example 4.** Point $M$ lies on $Y$-axis and is at a distance of 5 units from $X$-axis below it. Write the co-ordinates of $M$.

**Solution.** $\because$ $M$ lies on $Y$-axis.

$\therefore$ Its abscissa = 0

$M$ lies at 5 units distance from $X$-axis below it.

$\therefore$ Co-ordinates of $M = (0, -5)$ **Ans.**

**Example 5.** Find $X$ and $Y$ from the following :

(a) $(3x, 4y) = (12, -8)$ (b) $(x + 3, y - 2) = (0, 5)$ (c) $(x + y, x - y) = (7, -1)$

**Solution.** (a) $(3x, 4y) = (12, -8)$

$\Rightarrow$ $3x = 12$ and $4y = -8$

$\Rightarrow$ $x = 4$ and $y = -2$ **Ans.**

(b) $(x + 3, y - 2) = (0, 5)$

$\Rightarrow$ $x + 3 = 0$ and $y - 2 = 5$

$\Rightarrow$ $x = -3$ and $y = 7$ **Ans.**

(c) $(x + y, x - y) = (7, -1)$

$\Rightarrow$ $x + y = 7$ and $x - y = -1$

Solving, we get

$x = 3, y = 4$ **Ans.**

**Example 6.** If $(5, k - 3)$ lies on $X$-axis, find the value of $k$.

**Solution.** We know that, on $X$-axis

ordinate = 0

$\Rightarrow$ $k - 3 = 0$

$\Rightarrow$ $k = 3$ **Ans.**

**Example 7.** Plot the points $A$ (3, 4), $B$(2, –3), $C$(–3, –1), $D$(–2, 2), $E$(4, 0), $F$(0, 3) and $G$(0, –3) on the cartesian plane.

**Solution.** Draw two mutually perpendicular lines $X'OX$ and $Y'OY$ intersecting at '$O$'.

For point $A$(3, 4)

(a) Start from '$O$', on right side on $X$-axis upto 3 units.

(b) Now, from this position, move 4 units parallel to $Y$-axis along positive $Y$-axis and labelled it as point $A$ (3, 4).

Similarly plot the other given points. **Ans.**

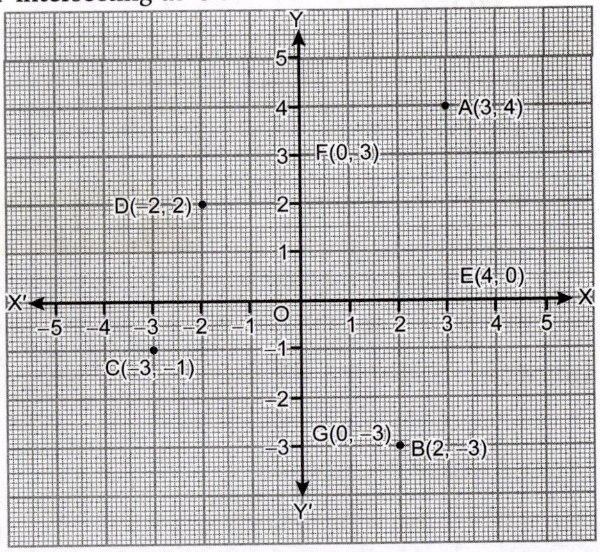

**Example 8.** $A(1, 1)$, $B(1, 4)$ and $C(4, 4)$ are the vertices of a square, Plot these points on a graph paper and use this graph to find the co-ordinates of the 4th vertex of the square.

**Solution.** Plot the points $A(1, 1)$, $B(1, 4)$ and $C(4, 4)$ on a graph paper. Join $AB$ and $BC$. Complete the square $ABCD$.

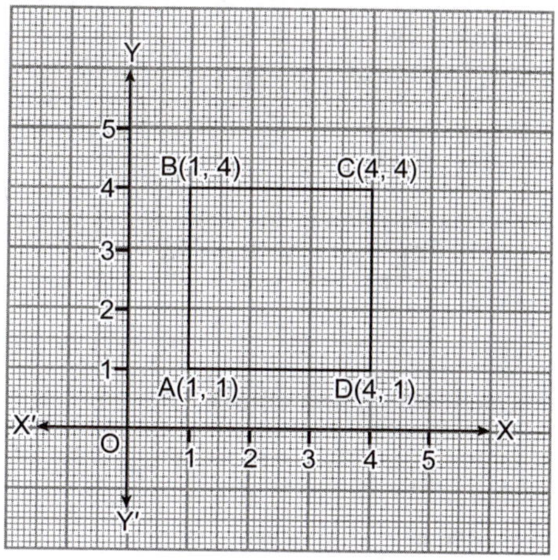


Read the co-ordinates of $D$

Co-ordinates of $D = (4, 1)$ **Ans.**

**Example 9.** Find the co-ordinates of a point whose abscissa is the solution of the equation $5 - 3x = -7$ and ordinate is the solution of the equation $5 - 2y = -5$.

**Solution.** Given first equation is

$$5 - 3x = -7$$
$$\Rightarrow \quad -3x = -7 - 5$$
$$\Rightarrow \quad -3x = -12$$
$$\Rightarrow \quad x = 4$$

and given second equation is

$$5 - 2y = -5$$
$$\Rightarrow \quad -2y = -5 - 5$$
$$\Rightarrow \quad -2y = -10$$
$$\Rightarrow \quad y = 5$$

$\therefore$ The co-ordinates of the point $= (4, 5)$ **Ans.**

**Example 10.** In the adjoining figure, an isosceles triangle $OAB$ is shown in which $OA = AB = 10$ units and $OB = 6$ units. Find the co-ordinates of its vertices.

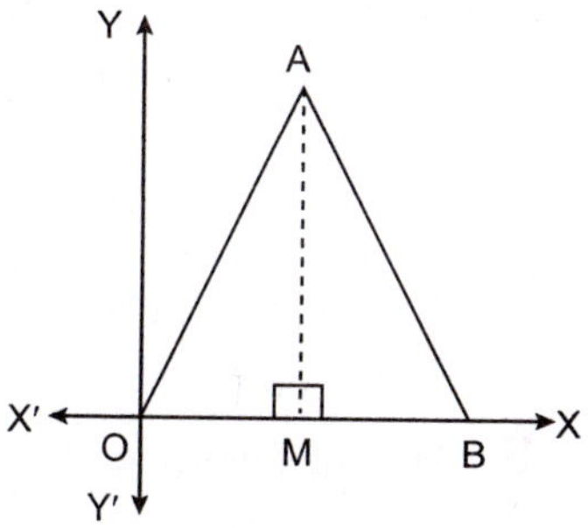


**Solution.** Draw $AM \perp OB$.

Then, $M$ is the mid-point of $OB$.

$$OM = \frac{1}{2} OB = \frac{1}{2} \times 6 = 3 \text{ units.}$$

In $\Delta AOM$,

$$AM^2 = OA^2 - OM^2$$
$$= 5^2 - 3^2 = 16$$
$$\Rightarrow \quad AM = 4$$

$\therefore$ Co-ordinates of $O = (0, 0)$ **Ans.**

Co-ordinates of $B = (6, 0)$ **Ans.**

Co-ordinates of $A = (OM, AM) = (3, 4)$ **Ans.**

## Exercise 19A

1. Express the following equations in the form in which $y$ is dependent variable.
   (a) $3x + 4y = 15$ (b) $6x - 5y = 7$
2. Express the following equations in the form in which $x$ is dependent variable.
   (a) $4x - 3y = 8$ (b) $3x + 7y = 12$
3. Find the values of $x$ and $y$ if :
   (a) $(3x, 5y) = (9, 10)$ (b) $(x + 3, 2y - 3) = (9, -9)$ (c) $(x + y, x - y) = (11, 3)$ (d) $(2x + y, x + 2y) = (5, 4)$
4. Plot the following points on the cartesian plane :
   (a) (3, 2) (b) (–4, 3) (c) (–3, –4) (d) (4, –3)
   (e) (2, 0) (f) (–3, 0) (g) (0, 4) (h) (0, –3)
5. Plot the following points on the cartesian plane whose :
   (a) abscissa is 5 and ordinate is 2
   (b) abscissa is –2 and ordinate is 3
   (c) abscissa is 3 and ordinate is twice of the abscissa
   (d) ordinate is 8 and abscissa is three-fourth of ordinate
6. In each of the following, find the co-ordinates of the point whose abscissa is the solution of first equation and the ordinate is the solution of the second equation :
   (a) $5x - 1 = 9$ and $3y + 1 = y - 5$ (b) $x + \frac{x}{2} = \frac{9}{2}$ and $2y + (y - 3) = 9$
   (c) $3x - (1 - x) = 9$ and $2y - 1 = 10 - \frac{5y}{3}$ (d) $\frac{13 - 3x}{2} = \frac{x + 3}{3}$ and $\frac{13 - 4y}{7} = \frac{6 - 3y}{4}$
7. From the following graph, find the co-ordinates of the point(s) satisfying the given condition.

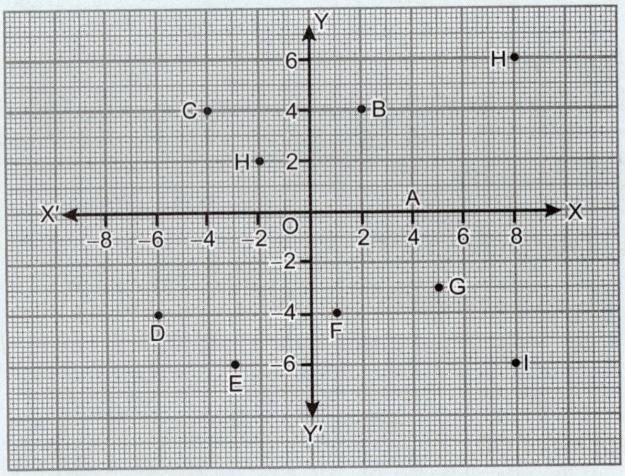


   (a) the abscissa is 4 (b) the ordinate is –4 (c) the ordinate is 6 (d) the abscissa is –3
   (e) the abscissa and ordinate are equal but opposite in sign.
   (f) the points whose abscissa are equal but ordinate are equal and opposite.
8. Plot the following points on the same graph paper and check whether they are collinear or not :
   (a) (–1, –1), (2, 2) and (3, 3) (b) (1, 2), (0, 0) and (–1, –2)
9. In each of the following cases, three vertices of a rectangle are given. Plot these points on a graph paper and find the co-ordinates of the fourth vertex :
   (a) $A(-1, 4)$, $B(4, 4)$, $C(4, -1)$ (b) $A(2, 0)$, $B(2, 3)$, $C(-4, 3)$
   (c) $A(5, 2)$, $B(5, 5)$, $C(1, 5)$

**10.** In each of the following cases, three vertices of a square *ABCD* are given. Plot these points on a graph paper and find the co-ordinates of the fourth vertex.

(a) $A(2, 1)$, $B(2, 5)$, $D(-2, 1)$ (b) $A(1, 1)$, $B(1, 4)$, $C(4, 4)$

**11.** The three vertices of a parallelogram *ABCD* are $A(-3, -4)$, $B(2, -2)$ and $C(2, 6)$. Plot these points on a graph paper and find the co-ordinates of the fourth vertex. Also find the area of the parallelogram.

**12.** Plot the points $A(2, 1)$, $B(2, -4)$, $C(-3, -4)$ and $D(-3, 1)$. What kind of quadrilateral is *ABCD*? Also find its area.

**13.** One vertex of a rectangle is at origin. Its two adjacent sides are along positive *x*-axis and along positive *y*-axis which are 4 units and 3 units respectively. Draw the rectangle on the graph paper and write the co-ordinates of its vertices.

**14.** Plot the point $M(4, -3)$. Draw the perpendiculars *MP* and *MQ* from *M* to *X*-axis and *Y*-axis respectively. Write the co-ordinates of *P* and *Q*.

## Answers

**1.** (a) $y = \dfrac{15 - 3x}{4}$, (b) $y = \dfrac{6x - 7}{5}$ **2.** (a) $x = \dfrac{8 + 3y}{4}$, (b) $x = \dfrac{12 - 7y}{3}$

**3.** (a) $x = 3, y = 2$, (b) $x = 6, y = -3$, (c) $x = 7, y = 4$, (d) $x = 2, y = 1$ **6.** (a) $(2, -3)$, (b) $(3, 4)$, (c) $(\frac{5}{2}, 3)$, (d) $(3, -2)$

**7.** (a) *A*, (b) *C*, (c) *H*, (d) *E*, (e) *C*, *H*, (f) *H*, *I* **8.** (a) yes, (b) yes **9.** (a) $(-1, -1)$, (b) $(-4, 0)$, (c) $(1, 2)$

**10.** (a) $(-2, 5)$, (b) $(4, 1)$ **11.** $(-3, 4)$, 40 square units **12.** square, 25 square units

**13.** $(0, 0)$, $(4, 0)$, $(4, 3)$, $(0, 3)$ **14.** $P(4, 0)$, $Q(0, -3)$

## Graph of $x = 0$, $y = 0$, $x = a$ and $y = b$

### 1. $x = 0$

We know that at *y*-axis, the value of *x* is always '0'. So *y*-axis represents the graph of the equation $x = 0$.

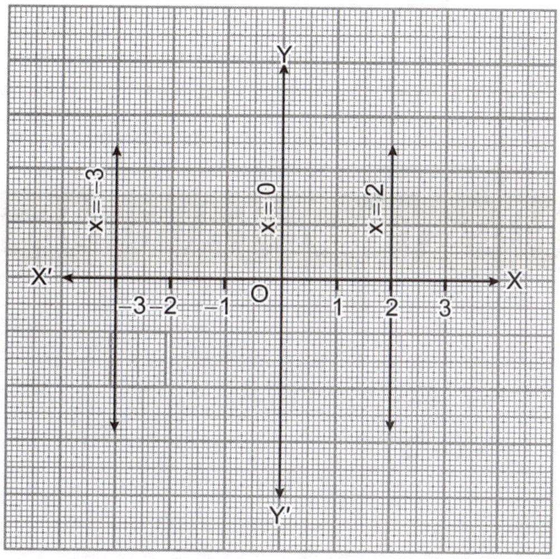


### 2. $x = a$

$x = a$ is the equation of a line parallel to *y*-axis at a distance of '*a*' units from *y*-axis, *e.g.*, $x = 2$ is a line parallel to *y*-axis at a distance of 2 units from it as shown in the graph. $x = -3$ is a line parallel to *y*-axis at a distance of 3 units from it on the left side of *y*-axis.

### 3. $y = 0$

We know that at $x$-axis, the value of $y$ is always '0', so $x$-axis represents the graph of the equation $y = 0$.

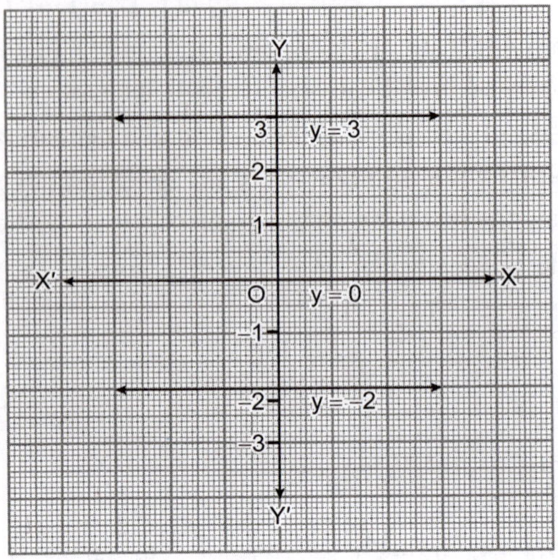


### 4. $y = b$

$y = b$ is the equation of a line parallel to $x$-axis at a distance of '$b$' units from $x$-axis, *e.g.*, $y = 3$ is a line parallel to $x$-axis at a distance of 3 units from it above $x$-axis. $y = -2$ is a line parallel to $x$-axis at a distance of 2 units from it below $x$-axis.

## Graph of a Linear Equation

When a linear equation in two variables is given then its graph is always a straight line.

To draw the graph of a linear equation :

(a) Choose three pairs of the values of two variables which satisfy the given equation.

(b) Plot these points on a graph paper.

(c) Join these points by a straight line.

It is the required graph of the given linear equation.

## Illustrative Examples

**Example 1.** Draw the graph of $y = x + 2$.

**Solution.** (i) The given equation is

$$y = x + 2$$

(ii) Value table :

| $x$ | 0 | 1 | 2 |
|---|---|---|---|
| $y$ | 2 | 3 | 4 |

(iii) Now, plot the points $A$ (0, 2), $B$ (1, 3), $C$ (2, 4) on the graph paper.

(iv) Join the points $A$, $B$ and $C$ and produce on either side. Line $ABC$ is the required graph.

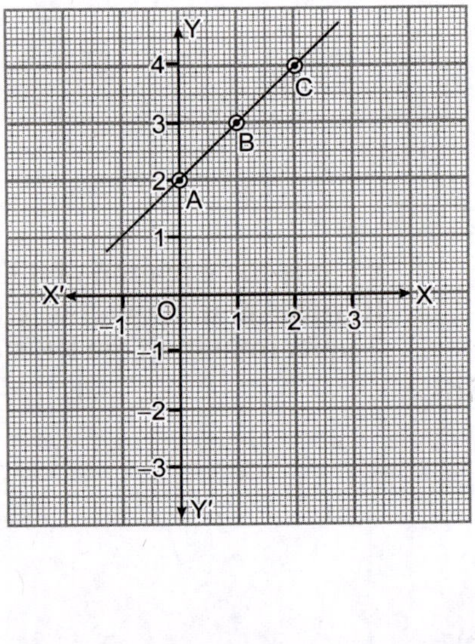

**Example 2.** Draw the graph of $y = -2x$.

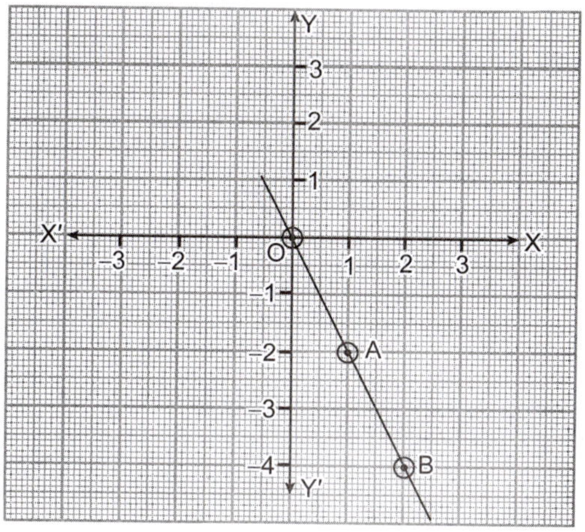


**Solution.** The given equation is $y = -2x$

The value table is :

| | | | |
|---|---|---|---|
| $x$ | 0 | 1 | 2 |
| $y$ | 0 | –2 | –4 |

These points are plotted on the graph paper as $O$, $A$ and $B$. Join $OAB$ and extend it.

Line $OAB$ is the required graph.

**Example 3.** Draw the graph of each of the following equations :

(i) $y = 2$, (ii) $y + 1 = 0$,

(iii) $x = 3$, (iv) $x + 2 = 0$.

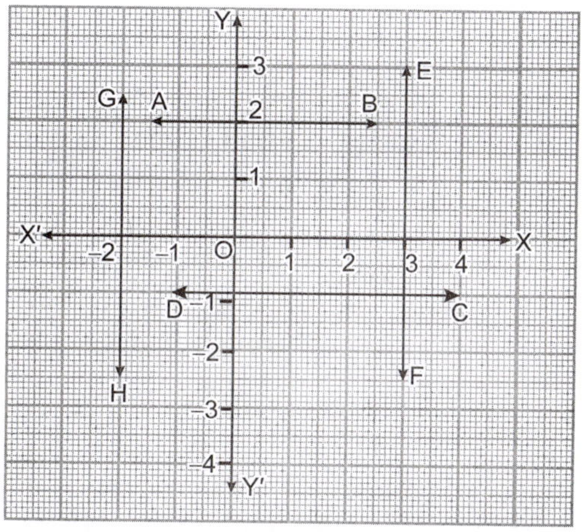


**Solution.**

(i) The graph of $y = 2$ is the straight line $AB$ which is parallel to $x$-axis at a distance of 2 units from it.

(ii) Since, $y + 1 = 0$, $y = -1$.

Hence, the graph is the straight line $CD$ which is parallel to $x$-axis at a distance of –1 unit.

(iii) The graph of $x = 3$ is the straight line $EF$ which is parallel to $y$-axis at a distance of 3 units from it.

(iv) Since $x + 2 = 0$, hence $x = -2$.

$\therefore$ The graph of $x + 2 = 0$ is the straight line $GH$.

**Example 4.** Draw the graph of $3x + 4y = 20$.

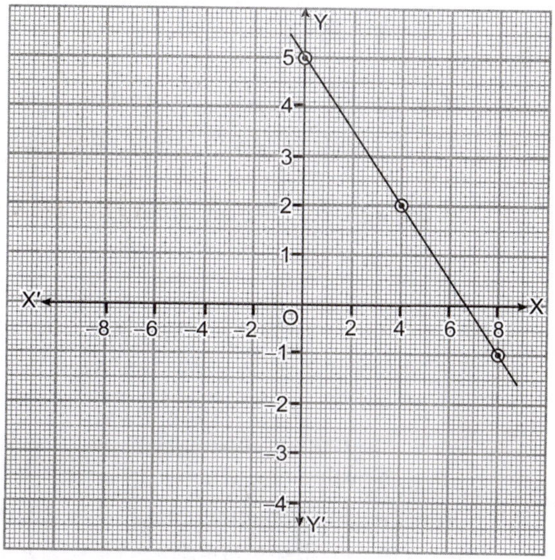


**Solution.** (i) The equation can be written as :

$$y = -\frac{3}{4}x + 5$$

(ii)

| | | | |
|---|---|---|---|
| $x$ | 0 | 4 | 8 |
| $y$ | 5 | 2 | –1 |

The graph is plotted in adjacent figure.

(iv) Join the points $A$, $B$ and $C$ and produce on either side.

Line $ABC$ is the required graph.

**Example 5.** Draw the graph of the equation $x + 2y = 4$. Use this graph to find :

(a) $x_1$, the value of $x$ when $y = 4$ (b) $y_1$, the value of $y$ when $x = -2$

**Solution.** Given equation is $x + 2y = 4$

$\Rightarrow$ $x = 4 - 2y$

Let $y = 0$ then $x = 4 - 2 \times 0 = 4$

Let $y = 1$ then $x = 4 - 2 \times 1 = 2$

Let $y = 2$ then $x = 4 - 2 \times 2 = 0$

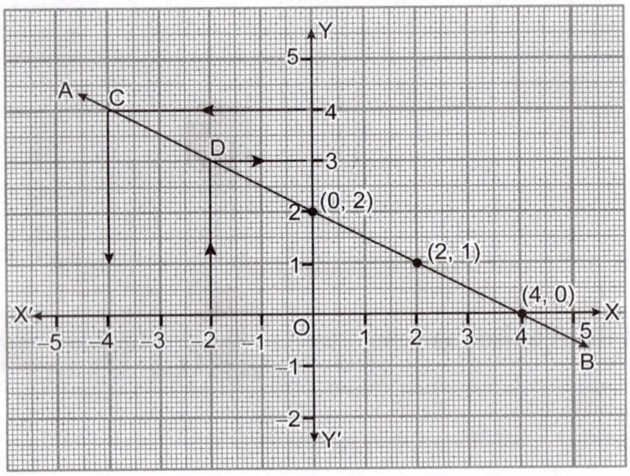


Table for values

| | | | |
|---|---|---|---|
| $x$ | 4 | 2 | 0 |
| $y$ | 0 | 1 | 2 |

Plot the points (4, 0), (2, 1) and (0, 2) on a graph paper and join them by a straight line $AB$.

(a) To find $x_1$ the value of $x$, when $y = 4$, through $y = 4$ draw a horizontal line which meets $AB$ at $C$.
Through $C$, draw a vertical line which meets $x$-axis at $x = -4$.
$\therefore$ At $y = 4$, $x = -4$ **Ans.**

(b) To find $y_1$, the value of $y$ when $x = -2$.
Through $x = -2$ draw a vertical line which meets $AB$ at $D$.
Through $D$, draw a horizontal line which meets $y$-axis at $y = 3$.
$\therefore$ At $x = -2$, $y = 3$ **Ans.**

## Exercise 19B

**1.** Draw the graph of the following lines :
(i) $x = 2$ (ii) $x + 3 = 0$ (iii) $2x - 7 = 0$
(iv) $y = 4$ (v) $y + 6 = 0$ (vi) $3y + 5 = 0$

**2.** Draw the graph of the following equations :
(i) $y = 2x$ (ii) $x = 3y$

**3.** Draw graphs for each equation given below :
(i) $2x - 5y = 10$ (ii) $\frac{1}{2}x + \frac{2}{3}y = 5$ (iii) $3x + 2y = 6$

In each case, find the co-ordinates of the points where the graph drawn meets the co-ordinate axes.

**4.** The graph of $3x + 2y = 12$ meets the $x$-axis at point $P$ and the $y$-axis at point $Q$. Use the graphical method, to find the co-ordinates of points $P$ and $Q$.

**5.** Draw the graph of equation $3x - 4y = 12$. Use the graph drawn to find :
(i) $y_1$, the value of $y$, when $x = 4$. (ii) $y_2$ , the value of $y$, when $x = 0$.

**6.** Draw the graph of equation $5x + 4y = 20$. Use the graph drawn to find :
(i) $x_1$, the value of $x$, when $y = 10$. (ii) $y_1$ , the value of $y$, when $x = 8$.

**7.** Draw the graph of the equations $x + y = 3$, $2x - y = 3$ and $x + 2y = 4$. Show that these three lines pass through the same point. Find the co-ordinates of this common point.

**8.** Draw the graph of the equations $x + 2y = 3$, $2x + y = 3$ and $x - y = 0$ . Show that these three lines pass through the same point. Find the co-ordinates of this common point.

**9.** Draw the graph of each pair or linear equations given below and then state whether the lines are parallel or perpendicular:
(i) $2x + y = 5$ and $2x + y = 7$ (ii) $x + 2y = 5$ and $2x - y = 0$

**10.** Draw the graph of the following equations and find their point of intersection.
(i) $x + y = 4$ and $3x - y = 8$ (ii) $x - 2y = 0$ and $2x + 3y = 7$

**11.** Draw the graph of $y = x + 2$ from $x = -3$ to $x = 2$.

**12.** Draw the graph of $y = 2x - 1$, $y = 2x + 1$ and $y = 2x$ from $x = 0$ to $x = 3$. On the same graph paper and check whether these lines are parallel to each other.

## Answers

**3.** (i) (5, 0), (0, –2 ), (ii) (10, 0), (0, $\frac{15}{2}$ ), (iii) (2, 0), (0, 3) **4.** $P(4, 0)$, $Q(0, 6)$ **5.** (i) $y_1 = 0$, (ii) $y_2 = -3$ **6.** (i) $x_1 = -4$, (ii) $y_1 = -5$
**7.** (2, 1) **8.** (1, 1) **9.** (i) parallel, (ii) perpendicular **10.** (i) (3, 1), (ii) (2, 1) **12.** parallel

## Graphical Solution of Simultaneous Linear Equations

### Steps :

(a) Draw the graphs of given simultaneous equations on the same graph paper.
(b) Find the co-ordinates of the point of intersection of the two lines.
(c) The co-ordinates of this point of intersection gives the solution of the given equations.

**NOTE**

1. If two equations have a unique solution, then the equations are called consistent and independent. In this case, the lines have only one common point.
2. If two equations have many common solutions, then the equations are called consistent and dependent. In this case, the two lines will coincide.
3. If two equations have no common solution, then the equations are called inconsistent. In this case, the two lines will be parallel.

## Illustrative Examples

**Example 1.** Solve the following equations graphically :

$$x + 2y = 5$$
$$3x - y = 1$$

**Solution.** Table for $x + 2y = 5$

| $x$ | 3 | 1 | –1 |
|---|---|---|---|
| $y$ | 1 | 2 | 3 |

Table for $3x - y = 1$

| $x$ | 1 | 2 | 0 |
|---|---|---|---|
| $y$ | 2 | 5 | –1 |

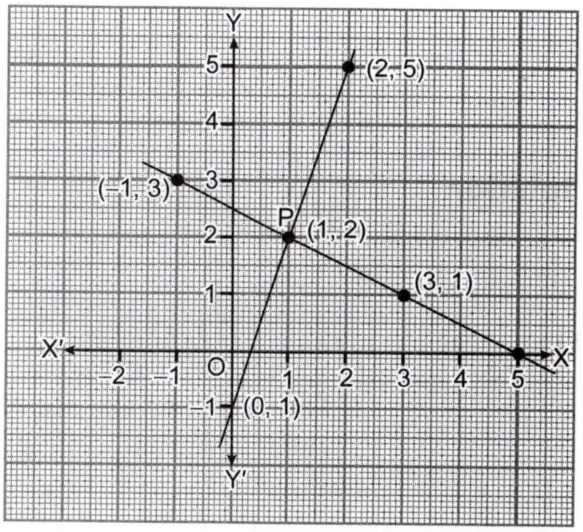


Draw the graph of each equation on the same graph paper.
Both the lines meet at point $P(1, 2)$

$\therefore$ Solution of given equations is

$x = 1, y = 2.$ Ans.

**Example 2.** Solve the following equations graphically :

$$x + 2y = 4$$
$$3x + y = 7$$

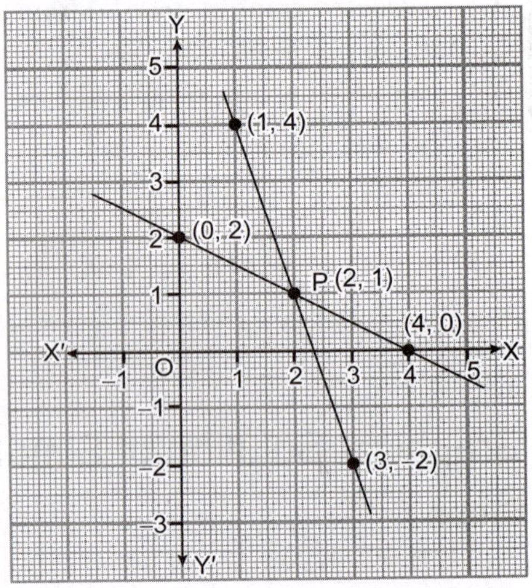


**Solution.** Table for $x + 2y = 4$

| | | | |
|---|---|---|---|
| $x$ | 0 | 2 | 4 |
| $y$ | 2 | 1 | 0 |

Table for $3x + y = 7$

| | | | |
|---|---|---|---|
| $x$ | 1 | 2 | 3 |
| $y$ | 4 | 1 | –2 |

Draw the graph of each equation on the same graph paper. Both the lines meet at point $P(2, 1)$

$\therefore$ Solution of given equations is

$$x = 2, y = 1.$$ Ans.

**Example 3.** Draw the graphs of the equations $5x - y = 5$ and $3x - y = 3$. Determine the co-ordinates of the vertices of the triangle formed by these lines and the $y$-axis.

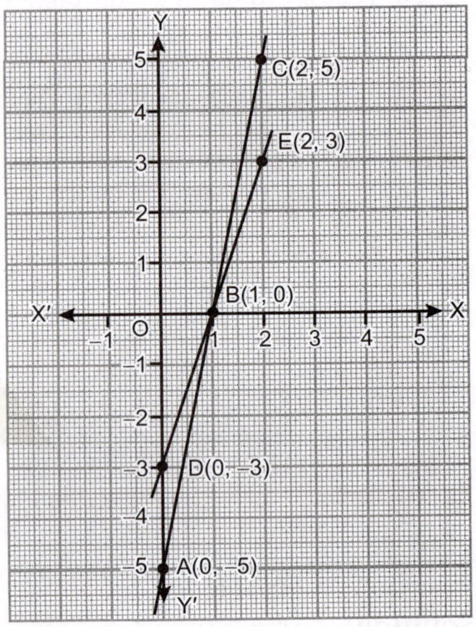


**Solution.** $5x - y = 5 \quad \Rightarrow y = 5x - 5$

| | | | |
|---|---|---|---|
| $x$ | 0 | 1 | 2 |
| $y$ | –5 | 0 | 5 |

Mark the points $A(0, -5)$, $B(1, 0)$ and $C(2, 5)$ and join them.

Again, $3x - y = 3 \quad \Rightarrow \quad y = 3x - 3$

| | | | |
|---|---|---|---|
| $x$ | 0 | 1 | 2 |
| $y$ | –3 | 0 | 3 |

Mark the points $D$ (0, –3), $B$ (1, 0) and $E$ (2, 3) and join them. The co-ordinates of the vertices of $\Delta BDA$ formed by two lines and $y$-axis are as follows :

$$B(1, 0), A(0, -5) \text{ and } D(0, -3)$$ Ans.

**Example 4.** Draw the graphs of the equations $x - y + 1 = 0$ and $3x + 2y - 12 = 0$. Determine the co-ordinates of the vertices of the triangle formed by these lines and the $x$-axis, and shade the triangular region. Also find the area of this triangle.

**Solution.** Pair of linear equations are

$$x - y + 1 = 0 \qquad ...(i)$$
$$\Rightarrow \quad y = x + 1$$

| | | | | |
|---|---|---|---|---|
| $x$ | 0 | 1 | –1 | 2 |
| $y$ | 1 | 2 | 0 | 3 |

$\therefore$ Points on this line are (0, 1), (1, 2), (–1, 0) and (2, 3). Mark these points on the graph paper and join them to form a straight line.

and $$3x + 2y - 12 = 0 \qquad ...(ii)$$
$$\Rightarrow \quad y = \frac{12 - 3x}{2}$$

| | | | | |
|---|---|---|---|---|
| $x$ | 0 | 4 | 2 | 1 |
| $y$ | 6 | 0 | 3 | 4.5 |

∴ Points on this line are (0, 6), (4, 0), (2, 3) and (1, 4.5). Mark these points on the same graph paper and join them to form another line which cuts the previous line at any point.

From the graph, we see that the two lines intersect each other at $D(2, 3)$.

So, $DCF$ is the required triangle whose vertices are $D(2, 3)$, $C(-1, 0)$ and $F(4, 0)$.

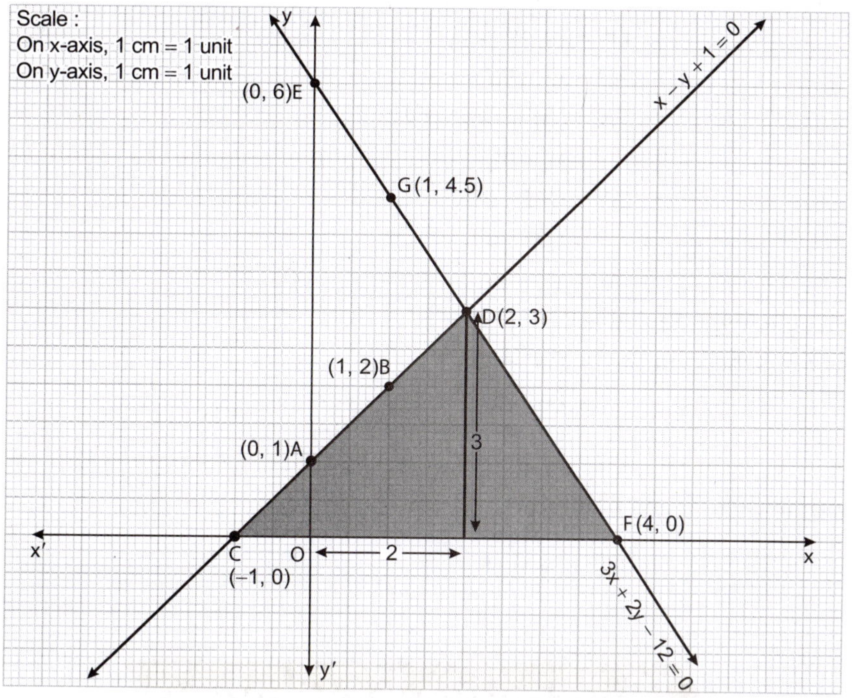


Also, Area $(\Delta DCF) = \frac{1}{2} \times \text{Base} \times \text{Altitude}$

$= \frac{1}{2} \times (4 + 1) \times 3$ square units

$= 7.5$ square units **Ans.**

## Exercise 19C

1. Solve graphically
   (i) $x + y = 4$, $3x + y = 6$ (ii) $x - 2y = 1$, $x + 2y = 5$ (iii) $x - y = 0$, $2x + y = 6$ (iv) $x + 3y = -2$, $2x - y = 3$
2. Use graph paper and take 2 cm = 1 unit on both axes.
   Draw the graphs of $x + y + 2 = 0$ and $3x - 2y + 1 = 0$. Write down the co-ordinates of the point of intersection of the lines.
3. Draw the graphs of the equations $x + 2y = 4$ and $3x - 2y = 4$. Find the area of triangle formed by the lines and $x$-axis.
4. Draw the graphs of the equations $x = -3$, $y = 2$ and $2x + 3y = 6$. Write down the vertices of the triangle formed by these lines.
5. A triangle is formed by the lines $x + 2y - 3 = 0$, $3x - 2y = -7$ and $y = -1$. Find the area of this triangle.
6. Draw the graphs of the equations $x - 5y + 14 = 0$, $2x - y + 1 = 0$ and $x - 2y + 8 = 0$. Write down the co-ordinates of the vertices of triangle formed.

### Answers

**1.** (i) (1, 3), (ii) (3, 1), (iii) (2, 2), (iv) (1, −1) **2.** (−1, −1) **3.** $\frac{4}{3}$ sq. unit

**4.** (−3, 2), (−3, 4), (0, 2) **5.** 12 sq. unit **6.** (−4, 2), (2, 5), (1, 3)

## Distance Between Two Given Points

Let $X'OX$ and $Y'OY$ be two mutually perpendicular axes. Let $P\ (x_1, y_1)$ and $Q\ (x_2, y_2)$ be two points in this cartesian plane. Draw $PL \perp OX$, $QM \perp OX$ and $PN \perp QM$.

It is clear from the figure that

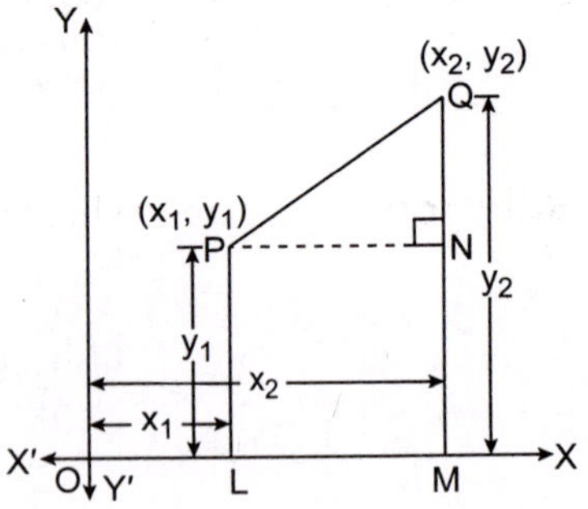


$$OL = x_1,\ PL = y_1$$

and $$OM = x_2,\ QM = y_2$$

Now, $$PN = LM = OM - OL$$
$$= x_2 - x_1$$

and $$QN = QM - MN$$
$$= QM - PL$$
$$= y_2 - y_1$$

$\Delta PQN$ is a right-angled triangle, right-angled at $N$.

$\therefore$ From Pythagoras theorem $PQ^2 = PN^2 + QN^2$
$$= (x_2 - x_1)^2 + (y_2 - y_1)^2$$

$\Rightarrow$ $$PQ = \sqrt{(x_2 - x_1)^2 + (y_2 - y_1)^2}$$

- The distance between origin $O(0, 0)$ and point $A(x_1, y_1)$ is
$$OP = \sqrt{x_1^2 + y_1^2}$$

## Illustrative Examples

**Example 1.** Find the distance between the following points :

(i) (3, 4) and (5, 2) (ii) (0, 2) and (4, – 1) (iii) ($a$, 2$a$) and (– $a$, – 2$a$) (iv) (4, – 3) and (– 6, 5)

**Solution.** (i) Distance between the points (3, 4) and (5, 2)

$$= \sqrt{(x_2 - x_1)^2 + (y_2 - y_1)^2} = \sqrt{(5-3)^2 + (2-4)^2}$$
$$= \sqrt{4+4} = \sqrt{8} = 2\sqrt{2} \text{ units}$$ **Ans.**

(ii) Distance between the points (0, 2) and (4, – 1)

$$= \sqrt{(x_2 - x_1)^2 + (y_2 - y_1)^2} = \sqrt{(4-0)^2 + (-1-2)^2}$$
$$= \sqrt{(4)^2 + (-3)^2} = \sqrt{16+9} = \sqrt{25} = 5 \text{ units}$$ **Ans.**

(iii) Distance between the points ($a$, 2$a$) and (– $a$, – 2$a$)

$$= \sqrt{(x_2 - x_1)^2 + (y_2 - y_1)^2} = \sqrt{(-a-a)^2 + (-2a-2a)^2}$$
$$= \sqrt{(-2a)^2 + (-4a)^2} = \sqrt{4a^2 + 16a^2} = \sqrt{20a^2} = 2\sqrt{5}\,a \text{ units}$$ **Ans.**

(iv) Distance between the points (4, – 3) and (– 6, 5)

$$= \sqrt{(x_2 - x_1)^2 + (y_2 - y_1)^2} = \sqrt{(-6-4)^2 + (5+3)^2}$$
$$= \sqrt{(-10)^2 + (8)^2} = \sqrt{100+64} = \sqrt{164} = 2\sqrt{41} \text{ units}$$ **Ans.**

**Example 2.** Find the distance between the points (5, 8) and (– 3, 2).

**Solution.** Distance between the points (5, 8) and (– 3, 2)

$$= \sqrt{(x_2 - x_1)^2 + (y_2 - y_1)^2} = \sqrt{(-3-5)^2 + (2-8)^2}$$

$$= \sqrt{(-8)^2 + (-6)^2} = \sqrt{64 + 36} = \sqrt{100} = 10 \text{ units}$$

Ans

**Example 3.** Find the distance between the points (2, 6) and (0, 9).

**Solution.** Distance between the points (2, 6) and (0, 9)

$$= \sqrt{(x_2 - x_1)^2 + (y_2 - y_1)^2} = \sqrt{(0-2)^2 + (9-6)^2}$$

$$= \sqrt{4 + 9} = \sqrt{13} \text{ units}$$

Ans.

**Example 4.** Find the distance of the point ($a \cos \theta, a \sin \theta$) from the origin.

**Solution.** Distance between the points ($a \cos \theta, a \sin \theta$) and origin (0, 0)

$$= \sqrt{(a \cos \theta - 0)^2 + (a \sin \theta - 0)^2}$$

$$= \sqrt{a^2 \cos^2 \theta + a^2 \sin^2 \theta} = \sqrt{a^2(\cos^2 \theta + \sin^2 \theta)}$$

$$= \sqrt{a^2} \qquad (\because \cos^2\theta + \sin^2\theta = 1)$$

$$= a \text{ units}$$

Ans.

**Example 5.** Find the distance of the point (3, 4) from the origin.

**Solution.** Distance of the point (3, 4) to the origin

$$= \sqrt{(3-0)^2 + (4-0)^2} = \sqrt{9+16} = \sqrt{25} = 5 \text{ units}$$

Ans.

**Example 6.** If the distance between the points ($x$, 2) and (6, 5) is 5 units, find the value of '$x$'.

**Solution.** Distance between the points ($x$, 2) and (6, 5)

$$= \sqrt{(6-x)^2 + (5-2)^2} = \sqrt{x^2 - 12x + 36 + 9} = \sqrt{x^2 - 12x + 45}$$

Given that,

$$\sqrt{x^2 - 12x + 45} = 5$$

$\Rightarrow \quad x^2 - 12x + 45 = 25$

$\Rightarrow \quad x^2 - 12x + 20 = 0$

$\Rightarrow \quad x^2 - 2x - 10x + 20 = 0$

$\Rightarrow \quad x(x-2) - 10(x-2) = 0$

$\Rightarrow \quad (x-2)(x-10) = 0$

$\Rightarrow \quad x - 2 = 0 \quad$ or $\quad x - 10 = 0$

$x = 2 \quad$ or $\quad x = 10$

Ans.

**Example 7.** If the distance between the points (–2, –5) and (–6, $y$) is 5 units, find the value of $y$.

**Solution.** Distance between the points (– 2, – 5) and (– 6, $y$)

$$= \sqrt{(-6+2)^2 + (y+5)^2} = \sqrt{16 + y^2 + 10y + 25}$$

$$= \sqrt{y^2 + 10y + 41}$$

Given that,

$$\sqrt{y^2 + 10y + 41} = 5$$

$\Rightarrow \quad y^2 + 10y + 41 = 25$

$\Rightarrow \quad y^2 + 10y + 16 = 0$

$\Rightarrow \quad y^2 + 2y + 8y + 16 = 0$

$\Rightarrow \quad y(y + 2) + 8(y + 2) = 0$

$\Rightarrow \quad (y + 2)(y + 8) = 0$

$\Rightarrow \quad y + 2 = 0 \quad \text{or} \quad y + 8 = 0$

$\Rightarrow \quad y = -2 \quad \text{or} \quad y = -8$ **Ans.**

**Example 8.** If the distances of $P(x, y)$ from $A(5, 1)$ and $B(-1, 5)$ are equal, then prove that : $3x = 2y$.

**Solution.** Since $P(x, y)$ is equidistant from $A(5, 1)$ and $B(-1, 5)$.

$\therefore \quad PA = PB$

$\Rightarrow \quad \sqrt{(x-5)^2 + (y-1)^2} = \sqrt{(x+1)^2 + (y-5)^2}$ (By using distance formula)

Squaring both sides, we get

$(x-5)^2 + (y-1)^2 = (x+1)^2 + (y-5)^2$

$\Rightarrow \quad x^2 - 10x + 25 + y^2 - 2y + 1 = x^2 + 2x + 1 + y^2 - 10y + 25$

$-10x - 2y + 26 = 2x - 10y + 26$

$\Rightarrow \quad -10x - 2x = -10y + 2y$

$\Rightarrow \quad 12x = 8y$

$\Rightarrow \quad 3x = 2y$ **Hence Proved.**

**Example 9.** Prove that the points $(5, -2)$, $(-4, 3)$ and $(10, 7)$ are the vertices of an isosceles right-angled triangle.

**Solution.** Let the points are $A(5, -2)$, $B(-4, 3)$ and $C(10, 7)$.

$\therefore \quad AB^2 = (-4-5)^2 + (3+2)^2 = (-9)^2 + (5)^2 = 81 + 25 = 106$

$BC^2 = (10+4)^2 + (7-3)^2 = (14)^2 + (4)^2 = 196 + 16 = 212$

$AC^2 = (10-5)^2 + (7+2)^2 = (5)^2 + (9)^2 = 25 + 81 = 106$

Therefore, $AB = AC = \sqrt{106}$

and $AB^2 + AC^2 = BC^2$

$\therefore$ $\Delta ABC$ is an isosceles right-angled triangle. **Hence Proved.**

**Example 10.** Prove that the points $(a, a)$, $(-a, -a)$ and $(-a\sqrt{3}, a\sqrt{3})$ are the vertices of an equilateral triangle.

**Solution.** Let the points are $A(a, a)$, $B(-a, -a)$ and $C(-a\sqrt{3}, a\sqrt{3})$.

$\therefore \quad AB = \sqrt{(-a-a)^2 + (-a-a)^2} = \sqrt{(-2a)^2 + (-2a)^2}$

$= \sqrt{4a^2 + 4a^2} = \sqrt{8a^2} = 2\sqrt{2}a$

$BC = \sqrt{(-a\sqrt{3} + a)^2 + (a\sqrt{3} + a)^2}$

$= \sqrt{3a^2 + a^2 - 2\sqrt{3}a^2 + 3a^2 + a^2 + 2\sqrt{3}a^2} = \sqrt{8a^2} = 2\sqrt{2}a$

and $\quad CA = \sqrt{(-a\sqrt{3} - a)^2 + (a\sqrt{3} - a)^2}$

$= \sqrt{3a^2 + a^2 + 2\sqrt{3}a^2 + 3a^2 + a^2 - 2\sqrt{3}a^2}$

$= \sqrt{8a^2} = 2\sqrt{2}a$

$\because \quad AB = BC = CA$

$\therefore$ $\Delta ABC$ is an equilateral triangle. **Hence Proved.**

**Example 11.** Prove that the points (4, 8), (7, 5), (1, –1) and (–2, 2) are the vertices of a parallelogram.

**Solution.** Let the points are $A(4, 8)$, $B(7, 5)$, $C(1, -1)$ and $D(-2, 2)$.

$\therefore \quad AB^2 = (7-4)^2 + (5-8)^2 = (3)^2 + (-3)^2 = 9 + 9 = 18$

$\Rightarrow \quad AB = 3\sqrt{2}$

$BC^2 = (1-7)^2 + (-1-5)^2 = (-6)^2 + (-6)^2 = 36 + 36 = 72$

$\Rightarrow \quad BC = 6\sqrt{2}$

$CD^2 = (-2-1)^2 + (2+1)^2 = (-3)^2 + (3)^2 = 9 + 9 = 18$

$\Rightarrow \quad CD = 3\sqrt{2}$

$DA^2 = (4+2)^2 + (8-2)^2 = 6^2 + 6^2 = 36 + 36 = 72$

$\Rightarrow \quad DA = 6\sqrt{2}$

$\because \quad AB = CD$ and $BC = DA$

$\therefore$ □ $ABCD$ is a parallelogram. Hence Proved.

**Example 12.** Prove that the points (2, – 1), (4, 1), (2, 3) and (0, 1) are the vertices of a square.

**Solution.** Let the points are $A(2, -1)$, $B(4, 1)$, $C(2, 3)$ and $D(0, 1)$.

$\therefore \quad AB^2 = (4-2)^2 + (1+1)^2 = 4 + 4 = 8$

$\Rightarrow \quad AB = \sqrt{8} = 2\sqrt{2}$

$BC^2 = (2-4)^2 + (3-1)^2 = (-2)^2 + (2)^2 = 4 + 4 = 8$

$\Rightarrow \quad BC = \sqrt{8} = 2\sqrt{2}$

$CD^2 = (0-2)^2 + (1-3)^2 = (-2)^2 + (-2)^2 = 4 + 4 = 8$

$\Rightarrow \quad CD = \sqrt{8} = 2\sqrt{2}$

$DA^2 = (2-0)^2 + (-1-1)^2 = (2)^2 + (-2)^2 = 4 + 4 = 8$

$\Rightarrow \quad DA = \sqrt{8} = 2\sqrt{2}$

$AC^2 = (2-2)^2 + (3+1)^2 = 0 + 16 = 16$

$\Rightarrow \quad AC = \sqrt{16} = 4$

and $\quad BD^2 = (0-4)^2 + (1-1)^2 = 16 + 0 = 16$

$\Rightarrow \quad BD = \sqrt{16} = 4$

Now, $\quad AB = BC = CD = DA$ and $AC = BD$

$\therefore$ □$ABCD$ is a square. Hence Proved.

**Example 13.** Show that the points $A(-3, 3)$, $B(7, -2)$ and $C(1, 1)$ are collinear.

**Solution.**

$$AB = \sqrt{(7+3)^2 + (-2-3)^2} = \sqrt{(10)^2 + (-5)^2}$$
$$= \sqrt{100 + 25} = \sqrt{125} = 5\sqrt{5}$$

$$BC = \sqrt{(1-7)^2 + (1+2)^2} = \sqrt{(-6)^2 + (3)^2}$$
$$= \sqrt{36 + 9} = \sqrt{45} = 3\sqrt{5}$$

and
$$AC = \sqrt{(1+3)^2 + (1-3)^2} = \sqrt{(4)^2 + (-2)^2}$$
$$= \sqrt{16 + 4} = \sqrt{20} = 2\sqrt{5}$$

Now, $\quad AC + BC = 2\sqrt{5} + 3\sqrt{5} = 5\sqrt{5} = AB$

$\therefore$ Points $A$, $B$ and $C$ are collinear. Hence Proved.

**Example 14.** Show that the points (9, – 2), (– 5, 12) and (– 7, 10) lie on that circle whose centre is the point (1, 4).

**Solution.** Let the given points are $A$ (9, – 2), $B$ (– 5, 12) and $C$ (– 7, 10).

If point '$O$' is (1, 4), then

$$OA = \sqrt{(1-9)^2 + (4+2)^2} = \sqrt{(-8)^2 + (6)^2}$$
$$= \sqrt{64 + 36} = \sqrt{100} = 10$$
$$OB = \sqrt{(1+5)^2 + (4-12)^2} = \sqrt{(6)^2 + (-8)^2}$$
$$= \sqrt{36 + 64} = \sqrt{100} = 10$$

and
$$OC = \sqrt{(1+7)^2 + (4-10)^2} = \sqrt{(8)^2 + (-6)^2}$$
$$= \sqrt{64 + 36} = \sqrt{100} = 10$$

$\therefore$ $OA = OB = OC$

$\Rightarrow$ Point '$O$' is equidistant from the points $A$, $B$ and $C$.

$\Rightarrow$ Point (1, 4) is the centre of that circle at which the points (9, –2), (– 5, 12) and (– 7, 10) lie.

Hence Proved.

**Example 15.** In the given figure, $\Delta ABC$ is an equilateral triangle of side 3 units. Find the co-ordinates of the other two vertices.

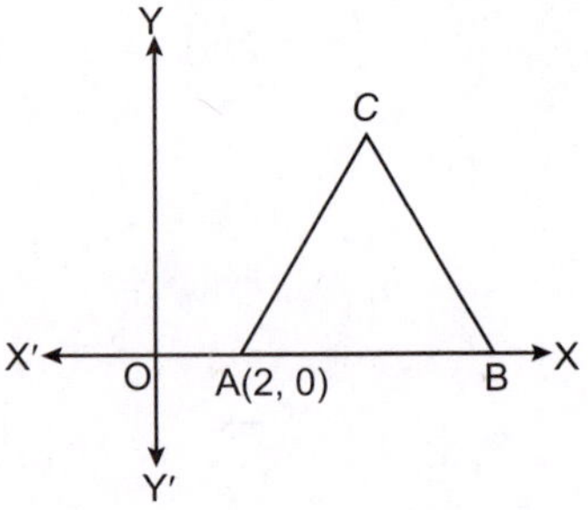


**Solution.** Since $B$ is at a distance of 3 units from $A$ on $X$-axis in the positive direction. So, $B$ will be 5 units away from the origin.

So, $B \equiv (5, 0)$

Let $M$ be the mid-point of $AB$

$\therefore$ $$AM = \frac{1}{2} AB = \frac{3}{2} \text{ units}$$

Also $AC = 3$ units

$\therefore$ In right $\Delta CMA$, by Pythagoras theorem

$$CM^2 = AC^2 - AM^2$$
$$= 9 - \frac{9}{4} = \frac{27}{4}$$

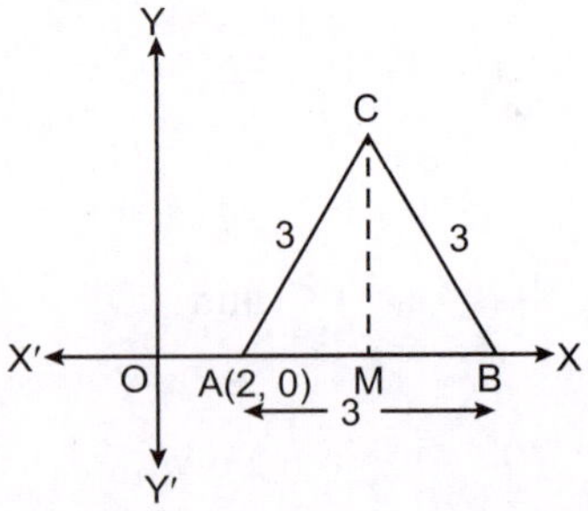


$\therefore$ $$CM = \sqrt{\frac{27}{4}} = \frac{3\sqrt{3}}{2}$$

So, the co-ordinates of $C$ are $(OM, MC)$

$\Rightarrow$ $C \equiv (OA + AM, MC)$.

$\Rightarrow$ $$C \equiv \left(2 + \frac{3}{2}, \frac{3\sqrt{3}}{2}\right) \equiv \left(\frac{7}{2}, \frac{3\sqrt{3}}{2}\right)$$ Ans.

**Example 16.** A cyclic quadrilateral is drawn such that three of its consecutive vertices are (0, 4), (0, 0) and (2, 0). Find the longest distance between any two vertices of this quadrilateral.

**Solution.** On plotting the points on the graph paper, we see that 3 points $A$, $O$, $B$ form a right-angled triangle.

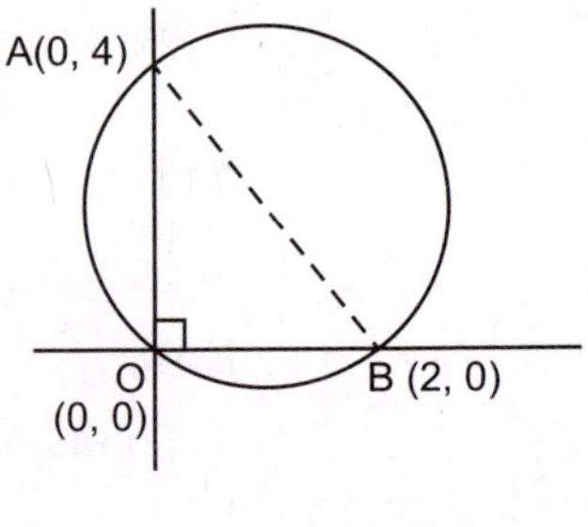


$\therefore$ $AB$ is the diameter and we know that diameter is the longest chord of a circle. ($\because$ Angle in a semi-circle is right angle)

$\therefore$ Longest distance between any two vertices

$$= \text{Diameter } AB$$
$$= \sqrt{(2-0)^2 + (0-4)^2} = \sqrt{4 + 16} = 2\sqrt{5} \text{ units}$$ Ans.

**Example 17.** The co-ordinates of two vertices of an equilateral triangle are (0, 0) and $(3, \sqrt{3})$. Find the co-ordinates of the third vertex of the triangle.

**Solution.** Let the $\Delta ABC$ is an equilateral triangle in which the co-ordinates of points $B$ and $C$ are (0, 0) and $(3, \sqrt{3})$ respectively.

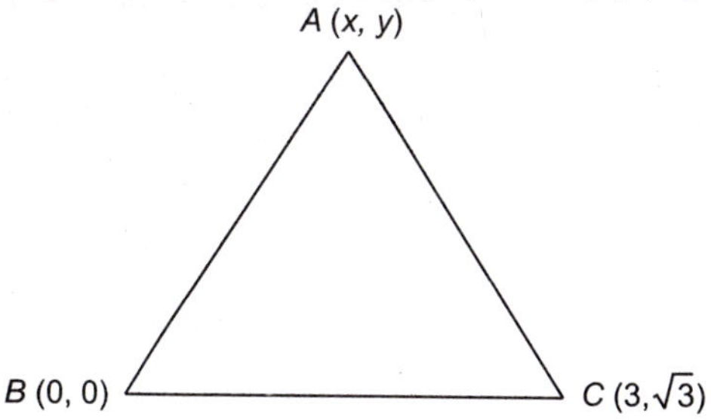


Let the co-ordinates of third vertex $A$ be $(x, y)$.
In equilateral $\Delta ABC$

$$AB = AC = BC$$
$$\Rightarrow \quad AB^2 = AC^2 = BC^2$$
$$\therefore \quad AB^2 = AC^2$$
$$\Rightarrow \quad (x-0)^2 + (y-0)^2 = (x-3)^2 + (y-\sqrt{3})^2$$
$$\Rightarrow \quad x^2 + y^2 = x^2 - 6x + 9 + y^2 - 2\sqrt{3}y + 3$$
$$\Rightarrow \quad 6x + 2\sqrt{3}y = 12$$
$$\Rightarrow \quad 3x + \sqrt{3}y = 6$$
$$\Rightarrow \quad \sqrt{3}\,x + y = 2\sqrt{3} \quad \Rightarrow \quad y = 2\sqrt{3} - \sqrt{3}x \qquad \ldots (i)$$

and

$$AB^2 = BC^2$$
$$\Rightarrow \quad (x-0)^2 + (y-0)^2 = (3-0)^2 + (\sqrt{3}-0)^2$$
$$\Rightarrow \quad x^2 + y^2 = 9 + 3$$
$$\Rightarrow \quad x^2 + (2\sqrt{3} - \sqrt{3}x)^2 = 12 \qquad \text{[From eq. } (i)]$$
$$\Rightarrow \quad x^2 + 12 + 3x^2 - 12x = 12$$
$$\Rightarrow \quad 4x^2 - 12x = 0$$
$$\Rightarrow \quad 4x(x-3) = 0$$
$$\Rightarrow \quad x = 0 \quad \text{or} \quad x - 3 = 0$$
$$\Rightarrow \quad x = 0 \quad \text{or} \quad x = 3$$

Put these values in eq. *(i)*

$$x = 0, \text{ then } y = 2\sqrt{3} - 0 = 2\sqrt{3}$$
$$x = 3, \text{ then } y = 2\sqrt{3} - 3\sqrt{3} = -\sqrt{3}$$

$\therefore$ Co-ordinates of third vertex = $(0, 2\sqrt{3})$ or $(3, -\sqrt{3})$

Ans.

**Example 18.** What point on the $X$-axis is equidistant from (7, 6) and (–3, 4)?

**Solution.** We know that $y$-co-ordinate of a point on $X$-axis is always 0. So, let a point on $X$-axis be $P(x, 0)$ and let two given points be $A(7, 6)$ and $B(-3, 4)$.
According to the condition,

$$PA = PB$$
$$\Rightarrow \quad \sqrt{(x-7)^2 + (0-6)^2} = \sqrt{(x+3)^2 + (0-4)^2}$$

Squaring both sides, we have

$$x^2 - 14x + 49 + 36 = x^2 + 6x + 9 + 16$$
$$\Rightarrow \quad 20x = 60$$
$$\Rightarrow \quad x = 3$$

$\therefore$ Required point is (3, 0)

Ans.

**Example 19.** Find the equation of the set of all points equidistant from the point (4, 2) and the $X$-axis.

**Solution.** Let the point, which is equidistant from $A(4, 2)$ and the $X$-axis be $P(x, y)$. Since, $P(x, y)$ is equidistant from $X$-axis, therefore this distance will be perpendicular to the $X$-axis.

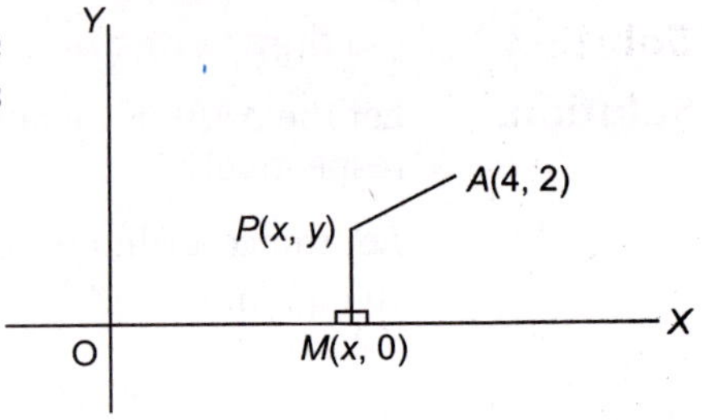


So, the foot of perpendicular from $P$ on $X$-axis will be $M(x, 0)$.
Now, according to the problem,

$$PA = PM$$

$$\Rightarrow \quad \sqrt{(x-4)^2 + (y-2)^2} = \sqrt{(x-x)^2 + (y-0)^2}$$

Squaring on both sides, we have

$$x^2 - 8x + 16 + y^2 - 4y + 4 = y^2$$

$$\Rightarrow \quad x^2 - 8x - 4y + 20 = 0$$

which is the required equation (locus). **Ans.**

**Remark**

Any equation in $x$ and $y$ is called the 'Locus' of a point $(x, y)$. Actually, locus is the path (curve) created by a point under given conditions. Every point on this curve will satisfy the given conditions. So, don't afraid with the word 'Locus'. It is nothing but any equation in $x$ and $y$ or any figure on the plane.

**Example 20.** Find the equation of the set of points such that the sum of its distances from (0, 3) and (0, –3) is 8.

**Solution.** Let $P(x, y)$ be any general point and let $A \equiv (0, 3)$ and $B \equiv (0, -3)$ such that

$$PA + PB = 8.$$

$$\Rightarrow \quad \sqrt{(x-0)^2 + (y-3)^2} + \sqrt{(x-0)^2 + (y+3)^2} = 8$$

$$\Rightarrow \quad \sqrt{x^2 + y^2 - 6y + 9} = 8 - \sqrt{x^2 + y^2 + 6y + 9}$$

Squaring both sides, we have

$$\Rightarrow \quad x^2 + y^2 - 6y + 9 = 64 + x^2 + y^2 + 6y + 9 - 16\sqrt{x^2 + y^2 + 6y + 9}$$

$$\Rightarrow \quad 12y + 64 = 16\sqrt{x^2 + y^2 + 6y + 9}$$

$$\Rightarrow \quad 3y + 16 = 4\sqrt{x^2 + y^2 + 6y + 9}$$

Squaring again, we have

$$\therefore \quad 9y^2 + 256 + 96y = 16(x^2 + y^2 + 6y + 9)$$

$$\Rightarrow \quad 16x^2 + 7y^2 = 112$$

$$\text{or} \quad \frac{x^2}{7} + \frac{y^2}{9} = 1$$

which is the required equation. **Ans.**

**Example 21.** Find the equation of the set of all points which are twice as far from (3, 2) as from (1, 1).

**Solution.** Let $P(x, y)$ be a point and let $A \equiv (3, 2)$ and $B \equiv (1, 1)$ be two other points on the plane, such that

$$PA = 2PB$$

$$\Rightarrow \quad \sqrt{(x-3)^2 + (y-2)^2} = 2\sqrt{(x-1)^2 + (y-1)^2}$$

Squaring both sides, we have

$$x^2 - 6x + 9 + y^2 - 4y + 4 = 4(x^2 - 2x + 1 + y^2 - 2y + 1)$$

$$\Rightarrow \quad 3x^2 + 3y^2 - 2x - 4y - 5 = 0$$

which is the required equation. **Ans.**

**Example 22.** Find a point on the line $3x - y + 3 = 0$, which is twice as far from (3, 2) as from (1, 1).

**Solution.** Let $P(x, 3x + 3)$ be a point on $3x - y + 3 = 0$ (as this satisfies the given equation) which is twice as far from $A(3, 2)$ as from $B(1, 1)$.

So, $$PA = 2PB$$

$$\Rightarrow \quad \sqrt{(x-3)^2 + (3x+1)^2} = 2\sqrt{(x-1)^2 + (3x+2)^2}$$

Squaring both sides, we have

$$x^2 - 6x + 9 + 9x^2 + 6x + 1 = 4(x^2 - 2x + 1 + 9x^2 + 12x + 4)$$

$$\Rightarrow \quad 30x^2 + 40x + 10 = 0 \quad \Rightarrow \quad 3x^2 + 4x + 1 = 0$$

$$\Rightarrow \quad 3x + 1)\ (x + 1) = 0$$

$$\therefore \quad x = -1 \quad \text{or} \quad x = -\frac{1}{3}$$

When $x = -1 \Rightarrow y = 3(-1) + 3 = 0$ | when $x = -\frac{1}{3} \Rightarrow y = 3\left(-\frac{1}{3}\right) + 3 = 2$

So, required points are $(-1, 0)$ and $\left(-\frac{1}{3}, 2\right)$. **Ans.**

**Example 23.** Show that $\Delta ABC$, where $A(-2, 0)$, $B(2, 0)$, $C(0, 2)$ and $\Delta PQR$ where $P(-4, 0)$, $Q(4, 0)$ and $R(0, 4)$ are similar triangles.

**Solution.** We have, $A \equiv (-2, 0)$, $B \equiv (2, 0)$ and $C \equiv (0, 2)$

$\therefore$ Length of sides of $\Delta ABC$ are,

$$AB = \sqrt{(2+2)^2 + (0-0)^2} = 4 \quad \ldots(i)$$

$$BC = \sqrt{(0-2)^2 + (2-0)^2} = 2\sqrt{2} \quad \ldots(ii)$$

$$CA = \sqrt{(0+2)^2 + (2-0)^2} = 2\sqrt{2} \quad \ldots(iii)$$

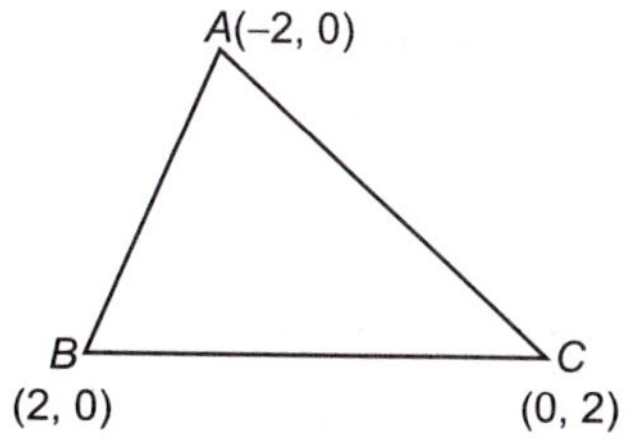


Also, it is given that

$$P \equiv (-4, 0),\ Q \equiv (4, 0) \text{ and } R \equiv (0, 4)$$

$\therefore$ Length of sides of $\Delta PQR$ are

$$PQ = \sqrt{(4+4)^2 + (0-0)^2} = 8 \quad \ldots(iv)$$

$$QR = \sqrt{(0-4)^2 + (4-0)^2} = 4\sqrt{2} \quad \ldots(v)$$

$$PR = \sqrt{(0+4)^2 + (4-0)^2} = 4\sqrt{2} \quad \ldots(vi)$$

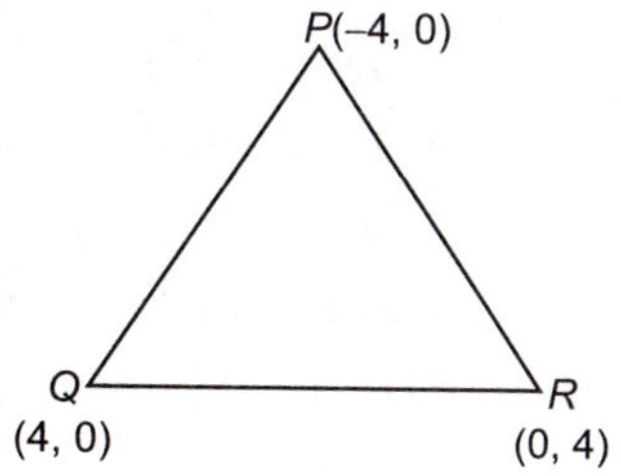


Here, $$\frac{AB}{PQ} = \frac{4}{8} = \frac{1}{2} \quad \text{[From (i) and (iv)]}$$

$$\frac{BC}{QR} = \frac{2\sqrt{2}}{4\sqrt{2}} = \frac{1}{2} \quad \text{[From (ii) and (v)]}$$

and $$\frac{AC}{PR} = \frac{2\sqrt{2}}{4\sqrt{2}} = \frac{1}{2} \quad \text{[From (iii) and (vi)]}$$

Since $$\frac{AB}{PQ} = \frac{BC}{QR} = \frac{AC}{PR} \quad \left(\text{Each equals } \frac{1}{2}\right)$$

$$\therefore \quad \Delta ABC \sim \Delta PQR$$

($\because$ Corresponding sides are proportional)

**Hence Proved.**

# Exercise 19D

1. Find the distance between the following points :
   (i) $A(-6, 4)$ and $B(2, -2)$ (ii) $A(-5, -1)$ and $B(0, 4)$ (iii) $A(4, -1)$ and $B(7, 3)$
   (iv) $A(3, 4)$ and $B(5, 2)$ (v) $A(4, 5)$ and $B(-2, 5)$ (vi) $A(3, -4)$ and $B(7, 0)$
2. Find the distance of the following points from origin :
   (i) (3, –4) (ii) (–8, –6) (iii) (5, 12) (iv) (7, 24)
3. Find the distance between the points $(a, b)$ and $(-b, a)$.
4. Find the distance between the points $(2a, 3a)$ and $(6a, 6a)$.
5. Find the distance between origin and the point $(a, -b)$.
6. If the distance between the points (6, 0) and $(0, y)$ is 10 units, find the value of $y$.
7. If the distance between the points $(3, x)$ and (–2, –6) is 13 units, then find the value of $x$.
8. Prove that the distance between the origin and the point (–6, –8) is twice the distance between the points (4, 0) and (0, 3).
9. Find the co-ordinates of a point whose abscissa is 10 and its distance from the point (2, –3) is 10 units.
10. Prove that the following points are the vertices of a right-angled triangle :
    (i) $A(-2, 2)$, $B(13, 11)$ and $C(10, 14)$ (ii) $A(-1, -6)$, $B(-9, -10)$ and $C(-7, 6)$
11. Prove that the following point are the vertices of an isosceles right-angled triangle :
    (i) $A(-8, -9)$, $B(0, -3)$ and $C(-6, 5)$ (ii) $A(0, -3)$, $B(2, -1)$, and $C(-2, -1)$
12. Prove that the points $A(1, 1)$, $B(-1, -1)$ and $C(\sqrt{3}, -\sqrt{3})$ are the vertices of an equilateral triangle.
13. Prove that the points (–1, –2), (–2, –5), (– 4, – 6) and (– 3, –3) are the vertices of a parallelogram.
14. Prove that the points (– 4, –3), (–3, 2), (2, 3) and (1, –2) are the vertices of a rhombus.
15. Show that the following points are the vertices of a rectangle :
    (i) $A(4, 2)$, $B(0, -4)$, $C(-3, -2)$, $D(1, 4)$ (ii) $A(1, -1)$, $B(-2, 2)$, $C(4, 8)$, $D(7, 5)$
16. Show that the points $A(2, 1)$, $B(0, 3)$, $C(-2, 1)$ and $D(0, -1)$ are the vertices of a square.
17. Show that the points (1, 1), (2, 3) and (5, 9) are collinear.
18. Show that the points (0, 0), (5, 3) and (10, 6) are collinear.
19. Show that the points (–3, 2), (2, –3) and $(1, 2\sqrt{3})$ lie on the circumference of that circle, whose centre is origin.
20. If the point $(x, y)$ is equidistant from the points $(a + b, b - a)$ and $(a - b, a + b)$, then prove that $bx = ay$.
21. If (1, 1) and (1, 8) are the opposite vertices of a square, then find the co-ordinates of remaining two vertices.

## Answers

**1.** (i) 10 units, (ii) $5\sqrt{2}$ units, (iii) 5 units, (iv) $2\sqrt{2}$ units, (v) 6 units, (vi) $4\sqrt{2}$ units, **2.** (i) 5 units, (ii) 10 units, (iii) 13 units, (iv) 25 units
**3.** $\sqrt{2(a^2 + b^2)}$ units **4.** $5a$ units **5.** $\sqrt{a^2 + b^2}$ **6.** $\pm 8$ **7.** 6, – 18
**9.** (10, 3) or (10, – 9) **21.** $\left(-\frac{5}{2}, \frac{9}{2}\right), \left(\frac{9}{2}, \frac{9}{2}\right)$

# Exercise 19E

## Multiple Choice Questions

Choose the correct answer from the given four options in each of the following questions:

1. The distance of the point (12, –5) from origin is:
   (a) 5 units (b) 12 units (c) 13 units (d) 17 units
2. Point (4, –3) lies in quadrant:
   (a) I (b) II (c) III (d) IV
3. The distance of point (4, –6) from $X$-axis is:
   (a) –6 (b) 6 (c) –4 (d) 4
4. The vertices of a triangle are (0, 0), (6, 0) and (0, 8). Its perimeter is:
   (a) 24 units (b) 20 units (c) 16 units (d) 14 units
5. If point (2, $k$) lies on the line $3x + 5y = 17$, then the value of $k$ is:
   (a) $\frac{5}{11}$ (b) $\frac{11}{5}$ (c) $\frac{3}{11}$ (d) $\frac{11}{3}$
6. The distance between the points (3, 0) and (0, –3) is:
   (a) 3 units (b) 6 units (c) 0 (d) $3\sqrt{2}$ units
7. The pair of equations $x = 3$ and $y = 4$ graphically represent lines which are:
   (a) coincident (b) parallel
   (c) intersecting at point (4, 3) (d) intersecting at point (3, 4)
8. The distance between the points (4, 0) and (–4, 0) is:
   (a) 4 units (b) $4\sqrt{2}$ units (c) 8 units (d) 0
9. The points (–3, 0), (3, 0) and (0, 4) are the vertices of:
   (a) a right triangle (b) a scalene triangle
   (c) an isosceles triangle (d) an equilateral triangle
10. Point (0, –3) lies:
    (a) on $X$-axis (b) on $Y$-axis (c) in I quadrant (d) in IV quadrant
11. Which of the following points lie on the graph of the equation $2x + y = 4$?
    (a) (1, 2) (b) (0, 2) (c) (4, 0) (d) (–2, 4)
12. Points (3, 1), (6, 4) and (8, 6) are:
    (a) collinear (b) vertices of an equilateral triangle
    (c) vertices of a right triangle (d) vertices of an isosceles triangle

### Answers

| | | | | | | |
|---|---|---|---|---|---|---|
| **1.** (c) | **2.** (d) | **3.** (b) | **4.** (a) | **5.** (b) | **6.** (d) | **7.** (d) |
| **8.** (c) | **9.** (c) | **10.** (b) | **11.** (a) | **12.** (a) | | |

# SUMMARY *of the Chapter*

- Dependent and Independent Variables : In a given formula, the subject of the formula is called dependent variable and the other variable is called independent variable.
- Ordered Pair : A pair of two numbers listed in a specific order within a bracket (), is called an ordered pair.
- Rectangular Axes : If $X'OX$ and $Y'OY$ are two mutually perpendicular lines, intersecting each other at '$O$' then these lines are called the rectangular axis.
  - $X'OX$ is called the $x$-axis.
  - $Y'OY$ is called the $y$-axis.
  - '$O$' is called the origin.
- Cartesian Co-ordinate System : The $x$-axis, $y$-axis and origin together is called cartesian system.
- Co-ordinate of a Point : The co-ordinates of a point are $(a, b)$ where '$a$' is the perpendicular distance form this point to $y$-axis and '$b$' is the perpendicular distance of this point to $x$-axis.
- Quadrant and Sign Convention: $X'OX$ and $Y'OY$ divide the cartesian plane into 4 equal parts, each part is called a quadrant.

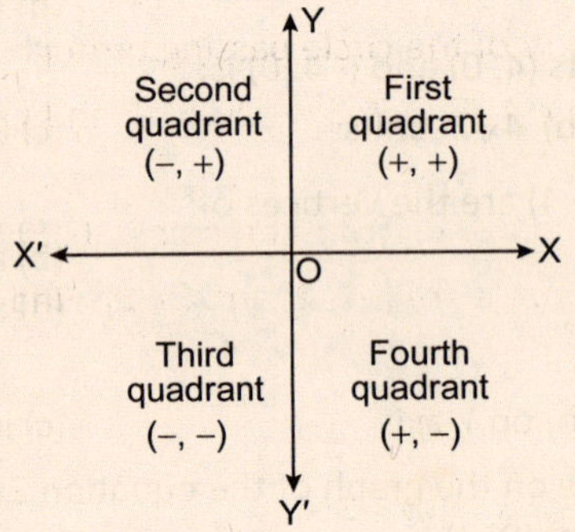


| Quadrant | Sign of a point $(x, y)$ |
|---|---|
| I | (+, +) |
| II | (–, +) |
| III | (–, –) |
| IV | (+, –) |

  - Co-ordinates of origin = (0, 0)
  - For each point on $x$-axis, ordinate = 0
  - For each point on $y$-axis, abscissa = 0
- Distance between Two Points : Distance between two points $(x_1, y_1)$ and $(x_2, y_2)$ is $\sqrt{(x_2 - x_1)^2 + (y_2 - y_1)^2}$.

# CHAPTER TEST

1. In which quadrant the following points lie?
   (a) (5, –3) (b) (1, 4) (c) (–3, –2) (d) (–2, 1)
2. Draw the graph of $2y + 3x = 6$.
3. Solve graphically : $x + 2y = 5$
   $2x + y = 4$
4. Draw the graph of the equation $2x - 3y = 6$, from the graph, find:
   (a) the value of $y$ when $x = -3$
   (b) the value of $x$ when $y = -2$
5. $A(4, -3)$, $B(4, 3)$ and $D(10, -3)$ are the vertices of a square $ABCD$. Use graph
   (a) find the co-ordinates of $C$.
   (b) find the co-ordinates of the point of intersection of the diagonals.
6. Prove that (0, 3), (4, 6) and (3, –1) are the vertices of a right-angled triangle.
7. Find the co-ordinates of the centre of the circle passing through the three points (5, 1), (–3, –7) and (7, –1).
8. A triangle is formed by the lines $x + 2y = 3$, $3x - 2y = -7$ and $y = -1$. Find graphically, the co-ordinates of the vertices of triangle.
9. Find a point on $y$-axis which is equidistant from the points (6, 5) and (–4, 3).
10. The two opposite vertices of a square are (–1, 2) and (3, 2). Find the co-ordinates of the other two vertices.

## *Answers*

**1.** (a) IV, (b) I, (c) III, (d) II
**3.** $x = 1$, $y = 2$
**4.** (a) $y = -4$, (b) $x = 0$
**5.** (a) (10, 3), (b) (7, 0)
**7.** (2, –4)
**8.** (–1, 2), (–3, –1), (5, –1)
**9.** (0, 9)
**10.** (1, 0), (1, 4)

NOTES